Y0-BPT-302

SEVENTH EDITION

beginning ALGEBRA WITH APPLICATIONS

with Math Study Skills Workbook
by Paul D. Nolting, Ph.D.

SPECIAL EDITION FOR PALOMAR COLLEGE

RICHARD N. AUFMANN
Palomar College, California

VERNON C. BARKER
Palomar College, California

JOANNE S. LOCKWOOD
New Hampshire Community Technical College, New Hampshire

Houghton Mifflin Company
Boston New York

BEGINNING ALGEBRA, WITH APPLICATIONS, SEVENTH EDITION
By Richard N. Aufmann, Vernon C. Barker, and Joanne S. Lockwood
Copyright © 2008 by Houghton Mifflin Company. All rights reserved.

Publisher: Richard Stratton
Senior Sponsoring Editor: Lynn Cox
Senior Marketing Manager: Katherine Greig
Marketing Associate: Naveen Hariprasad
Associate Editor: Noel Kamm
Editorial Assistant: Laura Ricci
Senior Project Editor: Nancy Blodget
Editorial Assistant: Sarah Driver
Art and Design Manager: Gary Crespo
Photo Editor: Marcy Kagan
Composition Buyer: Chuck Dutton

Photo credits are listed on page 664, immediately following the Appendix.

MATH STUDY SKILLS WORKBOOK, THIRD EDITION
By Paul D. Nolting
Copyright © 2008 by Houghton Mifflin Company. All rights reserved.

Publisher: Richard Stratton
Senior Sponsoring Editor: Lynn Cox
Associate Editor: Noel Kamm
Editorial Assistant: Laura Ricci
Associate Project Editor: Susan Miscio
Editorial Assistant: Joanna Carter
Associate Manufacturing Manager: Brian Pieragostini/Susan Brooks
Senior Marketing Manager: Katherine Greig
Marketing Associate: Naveen Hariprasad

Photo credits: p. 7, Digital Vision/Getty; p. 13, Jacobs Stock Photography/Photodisc/Getty; p. 31, PNC/Photodisc/Getty; p. 51, Stockbyte/Getty; p. 65, Rubberball/Getty; p. 85, Image Source/Getty; p. 105, © Royalty-Free/CORBIS

EDUSPACE STUDENT REGISTRATION AND ENROLLMENT GUIDE
Copyright © 2007 by Houghton Mifflin Company. All rights reserved.

"Houghton Mifflin Company," its colophon, and "Eduspace" are registered trademarks of the Houghton Mifflin Company.
Blackboard and the Blackboard logo are registered trademarks of Blackboard. Copyright © 2003. Other trademarks are the property of their respective owners.

Custom Publishing Editor: Luis Rosas
Custom Publishing Production Manager: Christina Battista
Project Coordinator: Jen Feltri

Cover Design:Althea Chen
Cover Image: PhotoDisc

This book contains select works from existing Houghton Mifflin Company resources and was produced by Houghton Mifflin Custom Publishing for collegiate use. As such, those adopting and/or contributing to this work are responsible for editorial content, accuracy, continuity and completeness.

Compilation copyright © 2008 by Houghton Mifflin Company. All rights reserved.

No part of this work may be reproduced or transmitted in any form or by any means, electronic or mechanical, including photocopying and recording, or by any information storage or retrieval system without the prior written permission of Houghton Mifflin Company unless such copying is expressly permitted by federal copyright law. Address inquiries to College Permissions, Houghton Mifflin Company, 222 Berkeley Street, Boston, MA 02116-3764.

Printed in the United States of America.

ISBN-13: 978-0-618-96923-4
ISBN-10: 0-618-96923-3
1023634

1 2 3 4 5 6 7 8 9 – AB – 09 08 07

Houghton Mifflin
Custom Publishing

222 Berkeley Street • Boston, MA 02116

Address all correspondence and order information to the above address.

EDUSPACE®

Houghton Mifflin's Online Learning Tool
Powered by Blackboard™

Student Registration and Enrollment Guide

Your personal account information

Use the registration code below to create your personal Eduspace account

HM76E16WKM49X

***Note if you have purchased a used textbook, the access code above may have already been activated. Please go to http://college.hmco.com to find out more about purchasing a new access code.*

Registering and Enrolling in a Course

Note you must have an email account to register

1. Go to the Eduspace website **http://www.eduspace.com** and choose to **Register**. If you are already registered and have an Eduspace username, log into Eduspace and skip to step 4.
2. Follow the on-screen directions to fill in the required fields and then click **Create Account**.
3. Before you can enroll in a course, you must log in to Eduspace. Enter the username and password you just chose when registering in the field provided and click **Login**.
4. Select this button to enroll 

5. Select "Student (Enroll into Course)"
6. Enter your ***course code*** in the space below (you can get this number from your professor)

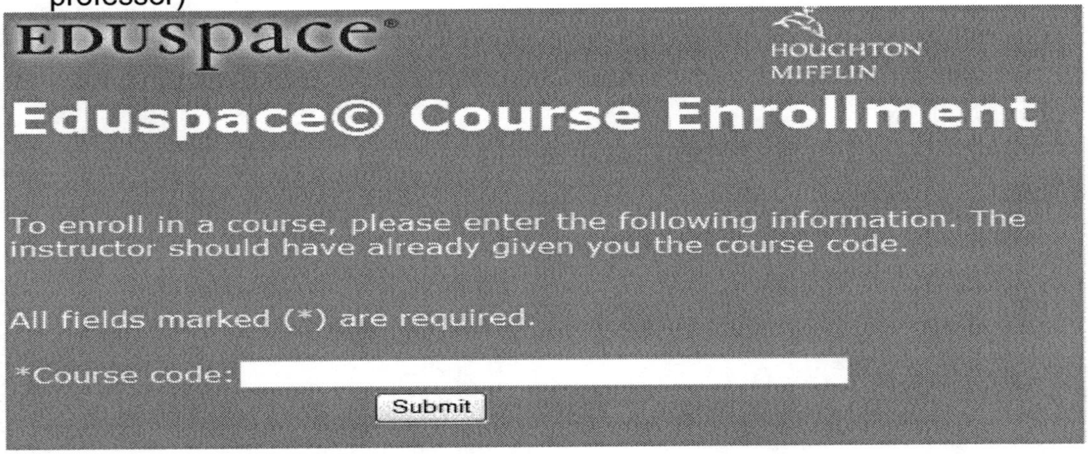

7. Eduspace enrolls you in the course as a student. Close the enrollment window and click the Courses tab to see the course listed under "Courses in which you are enrolled".
8. Click the name of the course to enter the course.

For More Information on Using Eduspace

Eduspace contains a wealth of functionality – for your online course, homework, and gradebook functions – beyond what is covered in this guide.

To learn more:

- Access our Online Guide to Getting Started with Eduspace after logging into Eduspace and from the My Eduspace tab clicking the guide link in the How Do I?
- Click the Help button at the top of any screen for comprehensive information on all Eduspace features.
- Get quick answers to using specific features of Eduspace or answers to questions you may have by contacting Eduspace Technical Support at **800-732-3223**.

Location

Main Campus E2

Mathematics Learning Center

Monday — Thursday
9:00 am — 8:00 pm

Friday
9:00 am — 3:00 pm

We have the following items available for check out and use in the Math Center:

1. Scientific Calculators
2. A few graphing calculators
3. Rulers, Protractors, and 1 compass
4. Books on Reserve
5. Software on Reserve
6. Some instructors may leave study guides, quiz keys or exam keys at the Front Desk for checkout. Please check with your instructor.
7. Study guides for the Backup Placement Test.
8. There is a stapler and pencil sharpener available for student use.

HOUGHTON MIFFLIN

Math Study Help Available

- **Text Specific DVD's hosted by Dana Mosley, covering most text content**
- **HM3 Tutorials—CDs**
- **HM eduSpace—online tutorial**

All students enrolled in a math class at Palomar College are eligible for ***free tutoring in the Math Center.***

http://math.palomar.edu/mlc/

Contents

Preface

The seventh edition of *Beginning Algebra with Applications* provides mathematically sound and comprehensive coverage of the topics considered essential in a first-year algebra course. The text has been designed not only to meet the needs of the traditional college student, but also to serve the needs of returning students whose mathematical proficiency may have declined during years away from formal education.

In this new edition of *Beginning Algebra with Applications,* we have continued to integrate some of the approaches suggested by AMATYC. Each chapter opens by illustrating and referencing a mathematical application within the chapter. At the end of each section there are "Applying Concepts" exercises that include writing, synthesis, critical thinking, and challenge problems. At the end of each chapter there is a "Focus on Problem Solving" section that introduces students to various problem-solving strategies. This is followed by "Projects & Group Activities," which can be used for cooperative learning activities.

NEW! Changes to the Content in This Edition

Chapter 1 has been expanded and reorganized. The title is now "Prealgebra Review" to reflect the content and intent.

In response to user requests, in Section 3 of Chapter 1, the presentation of operations on fractions has been changed from presenting addition and subtraction of rational numbers first, followed by multiplication and division, to presenting multiplication and division of rational numbers first, followed by addition and subtraction. A new section, "Concepts from Geometry," has been added at the end of the chapter to provide students with a review of angle measurement and the perimeter and area of plane geometric figures.

Chapter 11 now includes a section on complex numbers. Section 11.4 presents simplifying complex numbers, operations on complex numbers, and solving quadratic equations with complex number solutions.

NEW! Changes to Exercises in This Edition

Two new types of exercises have been added to this edition of the text: Interactive Exercises and Think About It Exercises.

The Interactive Exercises test students' understanding of the basic concepts presented in a lesson. Included when appropriate, these exercises generally appear at the beginning of an objective's exercise set and provide students with guided practice on some of the objective's underlying principles. Sometimes they test students' knowledge of the terms associated with a topic, but more often they are fill-in-the-blank exercises in which students are given part of a solution to a problem and are asked to complete the missing portions. These exercises act as stepping stones to the remaining exercises for the objective. We are confident that these Interactive Exercises will lead to greater student success in mastering the essential skills.

The Think About It Exercises are conceptual in nature. They generally appear near the end of an objective's exercise set and ask the students to think about the objective's concepts, make generalizations, and apply them to more abstract problems. Their focus is on mental mathematics, not calculation or computation, and they are meant to help students synthesize concepts. We are confident that their use will lead to a deeper conceptual understanding of the course content.

Throughout the text, data problems have been updated to reflect current data and trends. These application problems will demonstrate to students the variety of problems in real life that require mathematical analysis. Instructors will find that many of these problems lead to interesting class discussions.

NEW! Enhancements to the Instructional Media Package

HM Testing™ (powered by Diploma®) is a new computerized testing platform that provides instructors with a wide array of algorithmic test items, improved functionality, ease of use, and gradebook functions. HM Testing offers all the tools needed to create, author, deliver, and customize multiple types of tests—including authoring and editing algorithmic questions.

Eduspace®, Houghton Mifflin's Online Learning Tool (powered by Blackboard®), is a web-based learning system that provides instructors and students with powerful course management tools and text-specific content to support all of their online teaching and learning needs. Resources such as HM Assess, algorithmic automatically graded homework exercises, video explanations, an online multimedia eBook, live online tutoring with SMARTHINKING®, and additional study materials all come ready-to-use. Instructors can choose to use the content as is, modify it, or even add their own content.

HM Assess™ is a new diagnostic assessment tool that tests core concepts in mathematics and provides students with access to individual study paths for self-remediation. These paths are carefully designed to offer self-study options and to appeal to a variety of learning styles through review of the concepts, interactive lessons, similar examples, and additional practice exercises. Both course assessments and chapter assessments are available.

Students using Eduspace with HM Assess can:

- Assess their core competencies and remediate themselves via individual study paths.
- Review and reinforce concepts with algorithmically generated exercises.
- View video tutorials.
- Access, complete, and submit homework online.

Acknowledgments

We would like to especially thank users of the previous edition for their helpful suggestions to improve the text. Also, we sincerely appreciate the suggestions and the time and effort of the following people who reviewed this manuscript and/or its previous edition in preparation for the seventh edition.

Joe Archuleta, *Imperial Valley College, Imperial, CA*
Kevin Argo, *Halifax Community College, Weldon, NC*
Don K. Brown, *Georgia Southern University, Statesboro, GA*
Kai S. Chuang, *New Mexico State University, Carlsbad, NM*
Wil Clarke, *La Sierra University, Riverside, CA*
Andres Delgado, *Orange County Community College, Middletown, NY*
Sudhir Goel, *Valdosta State University, Valdosta, GA*

Anne Haney
Kenneth S. Hirschel, *Orange County Community College, Middletown, NY*
Kathryn Lavelle, *Westchester Community College, Valhalla, NY*
Yash Manchanda, *Saddleback Community College, Mission Viejo, CA*
Roger Martin, *Louisiana State University, Shreveport, LA*
Terri Seiver, *San Jacinto College, Pasadena, TX*
Gail Ulager, *Robert Morris College, Moon Township, PA*
Tom Wheeler, *Georgia Southwestern State University, Americus, GA*
Jean Wilberg, *SUNY Morrisville College, Morrisville, NY*
Michael D. Young, *Pitt Community College, Winterville, NC*

STUDENT SUCCESS

Beginning Algebra with Applications is designed to foster student success through an integrated text and media program.

AIM for Success

Welcome to *Beginning Algebra with Applications*. As you begin this course, we know two important facts: (1) We want you to succeed. (2) You want to succeed. To do that requires an effort from each of us. For the next few pages, we are going to show you what is required of you to achieve that success and how you can use the features of this text to be successful.

Motivation One of the most important keys to success is motivation. We can try to motivate you by offering interesting or important ways mathematics can benefit you. But, in the end, the motivation must come from you. On the first day of class, it is easy to be motivated. Eight weeks into the term, it is harder to keep that motivation.

To stay motivated, there must be outcomes from this course that are worth your time, money, and energy. List some reasons you are taking this course. Do not make a mental list—actually write them out.

Take Note
Motivation alone will not lead to success. For instance, suppose a person who cannot swim is placed in a boat, taken out to the middle of a lake, and then thrown overboard. That person has a lot of motivation but there is a high likelihood the person will drown without some help. Motivation gives us the desire to learn but is not the same as learning.

Although we hope that one of the reasons you listed was an interest in mathematics, we know that many of you are taking this course because it is required to graduate, it is a prerequisite for a course you must take, or because it is required for your major. Although you may not agree that this course is necessary, it is! If you are motivated to graduate or complete the requirements for your major, then use that motivation to succeed in this course. Do not become distracted from your goal to complete your education!

Commitment To be successful, you must make a committment to succeed. This means devoting time to math so that you achieve a better understanding of the subject.

List some activities (sports, hobbies, talents such as dance, art, or music) that you enjoy and at which you would like to become better.

ACTIVITY	TIME SPENT	TIME WISHED SPENT

Thinking about these activities, put the number of hours that you spend each week practicing these activities next to the activity. Next to that number, indicate the number of hours per week you would like to spend on these activities.

Whether you listed surfing or sailing, aerobics or restoring cars, or any other activity you enjoy, note how many hours a week you spend doing it. To succeed in math, you must be willing to commit the same amount of time. Success requires some sacrifice.

The "I Can't Do Math" Syndrome There may be things you cannot do, such as lift a two-ton boulder. You can, however, do math. It is much easier than lifting the two-ton boulder. When

xxv

page xxv

AIM for Success

This preface helps students develop the study skills necessary to achieve success in college mathematics.

It also provides students with an explanation of how to effectively use the features of the text.

AIM for Success can be used as a lesson on the first day of class or as a student project. A lesson plan, with accompanying PowerPoint slides, is available for instructors on the Online Teaching Center.

Objective-Based Approach

All lessons, exercise sets, tests, and supplements are organized around a carefully constructed hierarchy of objectives. This organization serves as a framework for a complete learning system, allowing students to remediate their learning independently at any point in the process.

Each chapter's objectives are listed on the chapter opener page, which serves as a road-map to student learning.

CHAPTER

5 **Linear Equations and Inequalities**

OBJECTIVES

5.1
1 Graph points in a rectangular coordinate system
2 Scatter diagrams
3 Average rate of change

5.2
1 Determine solutions of linear equations in two variables
2 Graph equations of the form $y = mx + b$
3 Graph equations of the form $Ax + By = C$

5.3
1 Find the slope of a straight line
2 Graph a line using the slope and y-intercept

5.4
1 Find the equation of a line using the equation $y = mx + b$
2 Find the equation of a line using the point-slope formula
3 Find the equation of a line given two points

5.5
1 Introduction to functions
2 Graphs of linear functions

5.6
1 Graph inequalities in two variables

DVD SSM Online Study Center

Need help? For online student resources, such as section quizzes, visit the Online Study Center at college.hmco.com/pic/aufmannBAWA7e.

Millions of people live and work in New York City every day, making it one of the busiest places on Earth. The U.S. Bureau of the Census records how many people live in a particular city each year and keeps track of how populations grow and change. By comparing the population over the years, we are able to determine the rate of change in the population and then use that rate to predict populations in the future. Average rate of change, which is discussed in **Section 5.1, Exercise 71, on page 297,** provides projections of the population of the United States for every five years from 2005 to 2030.

page 246

A numbered objective describes the topic of each lesson.

5.3 **Slopes of Straight Lines**

OBJECTIVE 1 **Find the slope of a straight line**

page 276

All exercise sets correspond directly to objectives.

5.3 Exercises

1 Find the slope of a straight line

1. Explain how to find the slope of a line when you know two points on the line.

2. What is the difference between a line that has zero slope and a line whose slope is undefined?

page 283

Answers to the Prep Tests, Chapter Review Exercises, Chapter Tests, and Cumulative Review Exercises refer students back to the original objectives for further study.

Answers to Chapter 5 Selected Exercises

PREP TEST

1. -3 [1.4.2]	**2.** -1 [2.1.1]	**3.** $-3x + 12$ [2.2.4]	**4.** -2 [3.2.1]
6. -2 [3.2.1]	**7.** 13 [2.1.1]	**8.** $\frac{3}{4}x - 4$ [2.2.4]	**9.** **a, b, c** [3.3.1]

page A14

Prep Test

1. Simplify: $\dfrac{5-(-7)}{4-8}$

2. Evaluate $\dfrac{a-b}{c-d}$ when $a = 3$, $b = -2$, $c = -3$, and $d = 2$.

3. Simplify: $-3(x - 4)$

4. Solve: $3x + 6 = 0$

5. Solve $4x + 5y = 20$ when $y = 0$.

6. Solve $3x - 7y = 11$ when $x = -1$.

7. Given $y = -4x + 5$, find the value of y when $x = -2$.

8. Simplify: $\frac{1}{4}(3x - 16)$

9. Which of the following are solutions of the inequality $-4 < x + 3$?
a. 0 **b.** -3 **c.** 5 **d.** -7 **e.** -10

page 247

Assessment and Review

Prep Tests assess students' mastery of prerequisite skills for the upcoming chapter.

The Answers found at the back of the book refer them to the appropriate section objective for review.

Chapter 5 Summary

Key Words

A **rectangular coordinate system** is formed by two number lines, one horizontal and one vertical, that intersect at the zero point of each line. The number lines that make up a rectangular coordinate system are called the **coordinate axes,** or simply the **axes.** The **origin** is the point of intersection of the two coordinate axes. Generally, the horizontal axis is labeled the ***x*-axis,** and the vertical axis is labeled the ***y*-axis.** A rectangular coordinate system divides the plane determined by the axes into four regions called **quadrants.** [5.1.1, pp. 247]

Examples

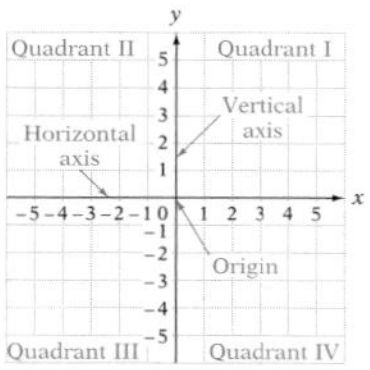

page 316

The **end-of-chapter material** includes:

Chapter Summary

Chapter Review Exercises

Chapter Test

These resources help students prepare for tests.

Cumulative Review Exercises

1. Simplify: $12 - 18 \div 3 \cdot (-2)^2$

2. Evaluate $\dfrac{a-b}{a^2-c}$ when $a = -2$, $b = 3$, and $c = -4$.

3. Simplify: $4(2 - 3x) - 5(x - 4)$

4. Solve: $2x - \dfrac{2}{3} = \dfrac{7}{3}$

page 325

Cumulative Review Exercises help students maintain skills learned in previous chapters.

Online Assessment and Remediation

Eduspace® (powered by Blackboard®), Houghton Mifflin's text-specific online learning system, now includes **HM Assess™.** This diagnostic assessment tool tests core concepts and provides students with access to *individual study paths* for self-remediation.

Students using HM Assess can:

- Assess their core competencies and remediate themselves based on their individual learning style.
- Review and reinforce concepts with algorithmically generated exercises.
- View video tutorials.
- Take practice quizzes.

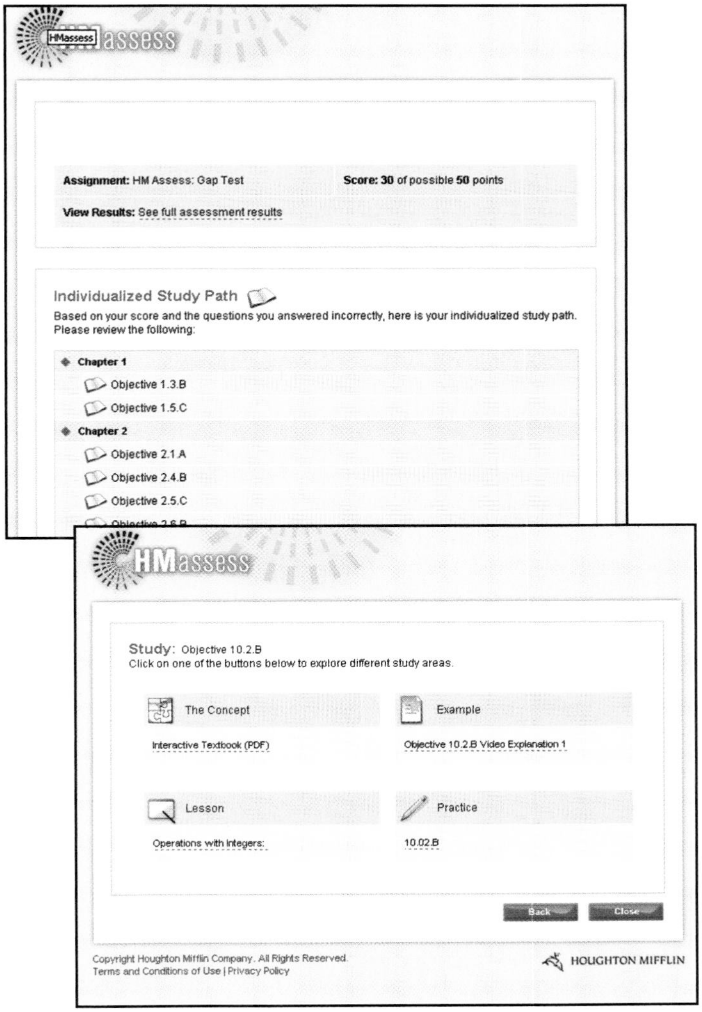

Online Practice Problems

Step-by-step guided solutions and fully worked similar examples in **Eduspace**® provide further opportunities for students to actively develop their skills and understanding of the topics.

Live, Online Tutoring

SMARTHINKING® live, online tutoring provides guidance for students as they work through problems without ever giving them the answers.

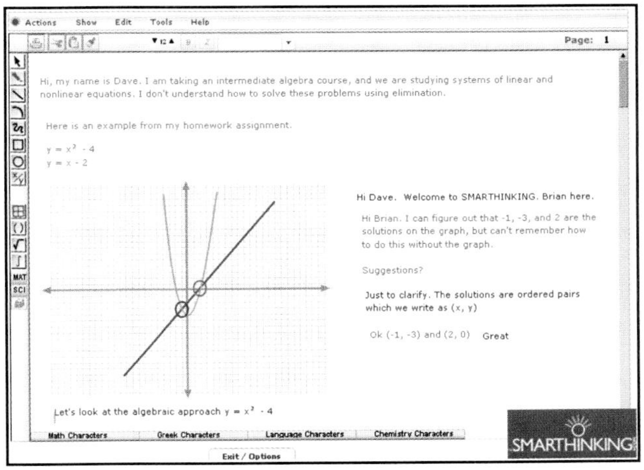

Online Self Tests

Online Study Center **ACE Self Tests** on the student **Online Study Center** let students practice chapter tests to help them prepare for exams.

AUFMANN INTERACTIVE METHOD (AIM)

Beginning Algebra with Applications uses an interactive style that engages students in trying new skills and reinforcing learning through structured exercises.

EXAMPLE 1 Multiply: $(2xy)(3x^2y)$

Solution $(2xy)(3x^2y)$

$= (2 \cdot 3)(x \cdot x^2)(y \cdot y)$

- **Use the Commutative and Associative Properties of Multiplication to rearrange and group factors.**

$= 6x^{1+2}y^{1+1}$

- **Multiply variables with the same base by adding the exponents.**

$= 6x^3y^2$

PROBLEM 1 Multiply: $(3x^2)(6x^3)$

Solution See page S16.

EXAMPLE 2 Multiply: $(2x^2y)(-5xy^4)$

Solution $(2x^2y)(-5xy^4)$

$= [2(-5)](x^2 \cdot x)(y \cdot y^4)$

- **Use the Properties of Multiplication to rearrange and group factors.**

$= -10x^3y^5$

- **Multiply variables with the same base by adding the exponents.**

PROBLEM 2 Multiply: $(-3xy^2)(-4x^2y^3)$

Solution See page S16.

page 375

An Interactive Approach

- Each section of the text is divided into objectives, and every objective contains one or more sets of matched-pair examples. The first example in each set is worked out.
- The second example, called "Problem," is for the student to work. By solving this problem, the student actively practices concepts as they are presented in the text.

SECTION 7.2

Problem 1

$(3x^2)(6x^3) = (3 \cdot 6)(x^2 \cdot x^3) = 18x^5$

Problem 2

$(-3xy^2)(-4x^2y^3)$
$= [(-3)(-4)](x \cdot x^2)(y^2 \cdot y^3)$
$= 12x^3y^5$

page S16

- *Complete worked-out* solutions to these Problems appear at the back of the book for students to check their work.

NEW! Interactive Exercises

Placed at the beginning of an objective's exercise set (when appropriate), these exercises provide guided practice and test students' understanding of the underlying concepts in a lesson. They also act as stepping-stones to the remaining exercises for the objective.

1 Multiply monomials

1. Explain how to multiply two exponential expressions with the same base. Provide an example.

2. Use the Rule for Multiplying Exponential Expressions to multiply: $(x^7)(x^2) = x^{\underline{?} + \underline{?}} = \underline{\quad ? \quad}$.

3. Multiply: $(5a^6b)(2a^5b^3)$

$(5a^6b)(2a^5b^3)$

$= (5 \cdot \underline{\quad ? \quad})(a^6 \cdot \underline{\quad ? \quad})(b \cdot \underline{\quad ? \quad})$

- **Use the Commutative and Associative Properties of Multiplication to rearrange and group factors.**

$= (\underline{\quad ? \quad})(a^{\underline{?} + \underline{?}})(b^{\underline{?} + \underline{?}})$

- **Multiply variables with the same base by __?__ the exponents.**

$= 10a^{\underline{?}}b^{\underline{?}}$

- **Simplify.**

page 377

CONCEPTUAL UNDERSTANDING

Beginning Algebra with Applications helps students understand the course concepts through the textbook exposition and feature set.

EXAMPLE 2 Is -4 a solution of $4 + 5x = x^2 - 2x$?

Solution

$$\begin{array}{c|c} 4 + 5x = & x^2 - 2x \\ \hline 4 + 5(-4) & (-4)^2 - 2(-4) \\ 4 + (-20) & 16 - (-8) \end{array}$$

$$-16 \neq 24$$

No, -4 is not a solution of the equation $4 + 5x = x^2 - 2x$.

- **Replace the variable by the given number, -4.**
- **Evaluate the numerical expressions using the Order of Operations Agreement.**
- **Compare the results. If the results are equal, the given number is a solution. If the results are not equal, the given number is not a solution.**

PROBLEM 2 Is 5 a solution of $10x - x^2 = 3x - 10$?

Solution See page S5.

OBJECTIVE 2 **Solve equations of the form $x + a = b$**

To **solve an equation** means to find a solution of the equation. The simplest equation to solve is an equation of the form **variable = constant,** because the constant is the solution.

If $x = 5$, then 5 is the solution of the equation because $5 = 5$ is a true equation.

Take Note

Think of an equation as a balance scale. If the weights added to each side of the equation are not the same, the pans no longer balance.

The solution of the equation shown at the right is 7. $\quad x + 2 = 9 \quad 7 + 2 = 9$

Note that if 4 is added to each side of the equation, the solution is still 7. $\quad x + 2 + 4 = 9 + 4$, $x + 6 = 13 \quad 7 + 6 = 13$

If -5 is added to each side of the equation, the solution is still 7. $\quad x + 2 + (-5) = 9 + (-5)$, $x - 3 = 4 \quad 7 - 3 = 4$

This illustrates the Addition Property of Equations.

Addition Property of Equations

The same number or variable term can be added to each side of an equation without changing the solution of the equation.

This property is used in solving equations. Note the effect of adding, to each side of the equation $x + 2 = 9$, the opposite of the constant term 2. After each side of the equation is simplified, the equation is in the form variable = constant. The solution is the constant.

$$\begin{aligned} x + 2 &= 9 \\ x + 2 + (-2) &= 9 + (-2) \\ x + 0 &= 7 \\ x &= 7 \end{aligned}$$

variable = constant

The solution is 7.

page 107

Features in the Exposition

- Key terms, in bold, emphasize important vocabulary.
- Margin notes titled Take Note amplify the concept under discussion or alert students to points requiring special attention.
- Key concepts are presented in orange boxes in order to highlight them and provide for easy reference.

In solving an equation, the goal is to rewrite the given equation in the form variable = constant. The Addition Property of Equations can be used to rewrite an equation in this form. The Addition Property of Equations is used to remove a term from one side of an equation by adding the opposite of that term to each side of the equation.

EXAMPLE 3 Solve and check: $y - 6 = 9$

Solution

$$\begin{aligned} y - 6 &= 9 \\ y - 6 + 6 &= 9 + 6 \\ y + 0 &= 15 \\ y &= 15 \end{aligned}$$

- **The goal is to rewrite the equation in the form *variable = constant*.**
- **Add 6 to each side of the equation (the Addition Property of Equations).**
- **Simplify using the Inverse Property of Addition.**
- **Simplify using the Addition Property of Zero. Now the equation is in the form *variable = constant*.**

Check

$$\begin{array}{c|c} y - 6 = & 9 \\ \hline 15 - 6 & 9 \end{array}$$

$$9 = 9$$

- **This is a true equation. The solution checks.**

The solution is 15.

- **Write the solution.**

PROBLEM 3 Solve and check: $x - \frac{1}{3} = -\frac{3}{4}$

Solution See page S5.

page 108

- Important points are now highlighted, to help students recognize what is most important and to study more effectively.

CONCEPTUAL UNDERSTANDING (*continued*)

Beginning Algebra with Applications helps students understand the course concepts through the textbook exposition and feature set.

Features in the Exercise Sets

3.1 Concept Review

Determine whether the statement is always true, sometimes true, or never true.

1. Both sides of an equation can be multiplied by the same number without changing the solution of the equation.
2. Both sides of an equation can be divided by the same number without changing the solution of the equation.
3. For an equation of the form $ax = b, a \neq 0$, multiplying both sides of the equation by the reciprocal of a will result in an equation of the form $x = constant$.
4. Use the Multiplication Property of Equations to remove a term from one side of an equation.

page 118

- **Concept Review** exercises appear at the beginning of each exercise set and are designed to test a student's understanding of the topic.

31. Without solving the equation $x + \frac{13}{15} = -\frac{21}{43}$, determine whether x is less than or greater than $-\frac{21}{43}$. Explain your answer.

32. Without solving the equation $x - \frac{11}{16} = \frac{19}{24}$, determine whether x is less than or greater than $\frac{19}{24}$. Explain your answer.

page 119

- **NEW! Think About It Exercises** are conceptual in nature. They ask the students to think about the objective's concepts, make generalizations, and apply them to more abstract problems. The focus is on mental mathematics, and they are designed to help students synthesize concepts.

2 Solve equations of the form $x + a = b$

27. How is the Addition Property of Equations used to solve an equation?

28. Explain why the goal in solving an equation is to write the equation in the form *variable* = *constant*.

page 119

- **Writing Exercises** require students to verbalize concepts, which is a crucial step in learning them.

3.1 Applying Concepts

Solve.

226. $\frac{2m + m}{5} = -9$

227. $\frac{3y - 8y}{7} = 15$

228. $\frac{1}{\frac{1}{x}} = 5$

229. $\frac{1}{\frac{1}{x}} + 8 = -19$

230. $\frac{4}{\frac{3}{b}} = 8$

231. $\frac{5}{\frac{7}{a}} - \frac{3}{\frac{7}{a}} = 6$

232. Solve for x: $x \div 28 = 1481$ remainder 25

233. Geometry Find the value of x in the diagram shown at the right.

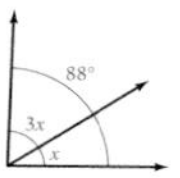

234. Consumerism Your bill for dinner, including a 7.25% sales tax, was $92.74. You want to leave a 15% tip on the cost of the dinner before the sales tax. Find the amount of the tip to the nearest dollar.

235. Consumerism The total cost for a dinner was $97.52. This included a 15% tip calculated on the cost of the dinner after a 6% sales tax. Find the cost of dinner before the tip and tax.

page 128

- **Applying Concepts** are more challenging problems involving multiple concepts that require interpretation, analysis, and critical thinking. They are designed to help students to apply and internalize concepts.

PROBLEM SOLVING

Beginning Algebra with Applications emphasizes applications, problem solving, and critical thinking.

58. Education One method used to "curve" the grades on an exam is to use the formula $R = 10\sqrt{O}$, where R is the revised score and O is the original score. Use this formula to find the original score on an exam that has a revised score of 75. Round to the nearest whole number.

59. Physics A formula used in the study of shallow-water wave motion is $C = \sqrt{32H}$, where C is the wave velocity in feet per second and H is the depth in feet. Use this formula to find the depth of the water when the wave velocity is 20 ft/s.

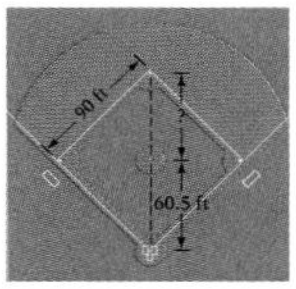

60. Sports The infield of a baseball diamond is a square. The distance between successive bases is 90 ft. The pitcher's mound is on the diagonal between home plate and second base at a distance of 60.5 ft from home plate. Is the pitcher's mound more or less than halfway between home plate and second base?

61. Sports The infield of a softball diamond is a square. The distance between successive bases is 60 ft. The pitcher's mound is on the diagonal between home plate and second base at a distance of 46 ft from home plate. Is the pitcher's mound more or less than halfway between home plate and second base?

page 571

Integrated Real-Life Applications

Wherever appropriate, the last objective of a section presents applications that require students to use problem-solving strategies, along with the skills covered in that section, to solve practical problems. This carefully integrated applied approach generates student awareness of the value of algebra as a real-life tool. Applications are taken from many disciplines and are emphasized through sourced data.

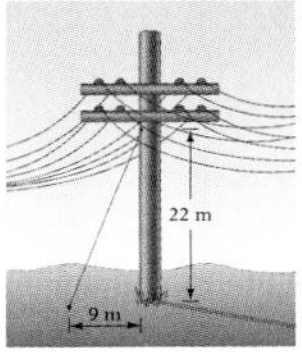

EXAMPLE 4 A guy wire is attached to a point 22 m above the ground on a telephone pole that is perpendicular to the ground. The wire is anchored to the ground at a point 9 m from the base of the pole. Find the length of the guy wire. Round to the nearest hundredth.

Strategy To find the length of the guy wire, use the Pythagorean Theorem. One leg is the distance from the bottom of the wire to the base of the telephone pole. The other leg is the distance from the top of the wire to the base of the telephone pole. The guy wire is the hypotenuse. Solve the Pythagorean Theorem for the hypotenuse.

Solution

$c = \sqrt{a^2 + b^2}$

$c = \sqrt{(22)^2 + (9)^2}$

$c = \sqrt{484 + 81}$

$c = \sqrt{565}$

$c \approx 23.77$

The guy wire has a length of 23.77 m.

PROBLEM 4 A ladder 12 ft long is resting against a building. How high on the building will the ladder reach when the bottom of the ladder is 5 ft from the building? Round to the nearest hundredth.

Solution See page S25.

EXAMPLE 5 How far would a submarine periscope have to be above the water for the lookout to locate a ship 5 mi away? The equation for the distance in miles that the lookout can see is $d = \sqrt{1.5h}$, where h is the height in feet above the surface of the water. Round to the nearest hundredth.

Strategy To find the height above water, replace d in the equation with the given value. Then solve for h.

Solution

$d = \sqrt{1.5h}$

$5 = \sqrt{1.5h}$

$5^2 = \left(\sqrt{1.5h}\right)^2$

$25 = 1.5h$

$\frac{25}{1.5} = h$

$16.67 \approx h$

The periscope must be 16.67 ft above the water.

PROBLEM 5 Find the length of a pendulum that makes one swing in 1.5 s. The equation for the time of one swing is $T = 2\pi\sqrt{\frac{L}{32}}$, where T is the time in seconds and L is the length in feet. Round to the nearest hundredth.

Solution See page S25.

page 567

Problem-Solving Strategies

A carefully developed approach to problem solving emphasizes the importance of *strategy* when solving problems.

- Students are encouraged to develop their own strategies as part of their solutions to problems.
- Model strategies are always presented as guides for students to follow as they attempt the parallel Problems that accompany each numbered Example.

Problem 5

Strategy To find the length of the pendulum, replace T in the equation with the given value and solve for L.

Solution

$T = 2\pi\sqrt{\frac{L}{32}}$

$1.5 = 2\pi\sqrt{\frac{L}{32}}$

$\frac{1.5}{2\pi} = \sqrt{\frac{L}{32}}$

$\left(\frac{1.5}{2\pi}\right)^2 = \left(\sqrt{\frac{L}{32}}\right)^2$

$\left(\frac{1.5}{2\pi}\right)^2 = \frac{L}{32}$

$32\left(\frac{1.5}{2\pi}\right)^2 = L$ • **Use the π key on your calculator.**

$1.82 \approx L$

The length of the pendulum is 1.82 ft.

page S25

81. Geometry A circular fountain is being designed for a triangular plaza in a cultural center. The fountain is placed so that each side of the triangle touches the fountain as shown in the diagram at the right. Find the area of the fountain. The formula for the radius of the circle is given by

$$r = \sqrt{\frac{(s-a)(s-b)(s-c)}{s}}$$

where $s = \frac{1}{2}(a+b+c)$ and a, b, and c are the lengths of the sides of the triangle. Round to the nearest hundredth.

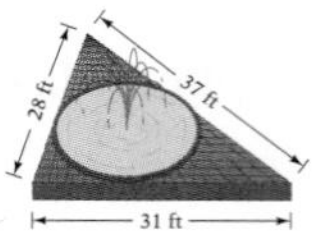

82. Can the Pythagorean Theorem be used to find the length of side c of the triangle at the right? If so, determine c. If not, explain why the theorem cannot be used.

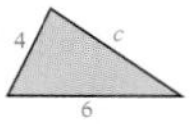

83. What is a Pythagorean triple? Provide at least three examples of Pythagorean triples.

84. Complete the statement using the symbol $<$, $=$, or $>$. Explain how you determined which symbol to use.

a. For an acute triangle with side c the longest side, $a^2 + b^2$______ c^2.
b. For a right triangle with side c the longest side, $a^2 + b^2$______ c^2.
c. For an obtuse triangle with side c the longest side, $a^2 + b^2$______ c^2.

Focus on Problem Solving

Deductive Reasoning Deductive reasoning uses a rule or statement of fact to reach a conclusion. In the section Equations Containing Fractions in the "Rational Expressions" chapter, we established the rule that if two angles of one triangle are equal to two angles of another triangle, then the two triangles are similar. Thus any time we establish this fact about two triangles, we know that the triangles are similar. Two examples of deductive reasoning follow.

Given that ΔΔΔ = ◊◊◊◊ and ◊◊◊◊ = ÓÓ, then ΔΔΔΔΔΔ is equivalent to how many Ós?

Because 3 Δs = 4 ◊s and 4 ◊s = 2 Ós, 3 Δs = 2 Ós.

6 Δs is twice 3 Δs. We need to find twice 2 Ós, which is 4 Ós.

Therefore, ΔΔΔΔΔΔ = ÓÓÓÓ.

Lomax, Parish, Thorpe, and Wong are neighbors. Each drives a different type of vehicle: a compact car, a sedan, a sports car, or a station wagon. From the

page 573

Focus on Problem Solving

Students are introduced to various successful problem-solving strategies within the end-of-chapter material. Strategies include:

- drawing a diagram,
- applying solutions to other problems,
- working backwards,
- inductive reasoning,
- and trial and error.

NEW! Think About It Exercises

These exercises focus on concepts, not on calculation or computation, and will help develop students' critical thinking skills.

41. Without actually solving the equations, identify which equation has no solution.

a. $-\sqrt{2x-5} = -3$ **b.** $\sqrt{2x} - 5 = -3$ **c.** $\sqrt{2x-5} = -3$

42. How many times will the Property of Squaring Both Sides of an Equation be used in the solving of each equation? Do not solve.

a. $\sqrt{x-3} = \sqrt{4x-7}$ **b.** $\sqrt{x-6} = \sqrt{x} - 3$

page 569

Additional Resources—Get More Value from Your Textbook!

Instructor Resources

Instructor's Annotated Edition (IAE) The Instructor's Annotated Edition is ideal for seasoned instructors, teaching assistants, or adjuncts. Reduced student pages leave room in the margin of the IAE for extensive instructor support materials at point-of-use.

Online Teaching Center This web site offers instructors prep tests and chapter tests, instructor's solutions, quick quizzes, AIM for Success Practice Sheets, topic sequences, and more.

HM Testing™ (Powered by Diploma®) "Testing the way you want it" HM Testing offers all the tools needed to create, author/edit algorithmic questions, customize and deliver multiple types of tests.

Student Resources

Student Solutions Manual Contains complete solutions to all odd-numbered exercises, and all of the solutions to the end-of-chapter material.

Math Study Skills Workbook, Third Edition, by Paul Nolting Helps students identify their strengths, weaknesses, and personal learning styles in math. Nolting offers study tips, proven test-taking strategies, a homework system, and recommendations for reducing anxiety and improving grades.

Online Study Center This free web site gives students access to ACE practice tests, glossary flashcards, chapter summaries, and other study resources.

DVD **Instructional DVDs** Hosted by Dana Mosely, these text-specific DVDs cover all sections of the text and provide explanations of key concepts, examples, exercises, and applications in a lecture-based format. DVDs are now closed-captioned for the hearing-impaired.

Eduspace® (powered by Blackboard®) Eduspace is a web-based learning system that provides instructors with powerful course management tools and students with text-specific content to support all of their online teaching and learning needs. In addition to new, enhanced algorithms, Eduspace now includes:

HM Assess™ Houghton Mifflin's new diagnostic tool tests core concepts and provides students with individual study paths for self-remediation. Instructors can use HM Assess to quickly gauge which students are in jeopardy and identify which concepts to spend extra time reviewing.

Visit **www.eduspace.com** for more information.

SMARTHINKING® Live, Online Tutoring SMARTHINKING provides an easy-to-use and effective online, text-specific tutoring service. A dynamic **Whiteboard** and a **Graphing Calculator** function enable students and e-structors to collaborate easily.

Online Course Content for Blackboard®, WebCT®, and eCollege® Deliver program- or text-specific Houghton Mifflin content online using your institution's local course management system. Houghton Mifflin offers homework, tutorials, videos, and other resources formatted for Blackboard, WebCT, eCollege, and other course management systems. Add to an existing online course or create a new one by selecting from a wide range of powerful learning and instructional materials.

For more information, visit **college.hmco.com/pic/aufmannBAWA7e** or contact your Houghton Mifflin sales representative.

AIM for Success

Welcome to *Beginning Algebra with Applications*. As you begin this course, we know two important facts: (1) We want you to succeed. (2) You want to succeed. To do that requires an effort from each of us. For the next few pages, we are going to show you what is required of you to achieve that success and how you can use the features of this text to be successful.

Motivation

One of the most important keys to success is motivation. We can try to motivate you by offering interesting or important ways mathematics can benefit you. But, in the end, the motivation must come from you. On the first day of class, it is easy to be motivated. Eight weeks into the term, it is harder to keep that motivation.

To stay motivated, there must be outcomes from this course that are worth your time, money, and energy. List some reasons you are taking this course. Do not make a mental list—actually write them out.

Take Note

Motivation alone will not lead to success. For instance, suppose a person who cannot swim is placed in a boat, taken out to the middle of a lake, and then thrown overboard. That person has a lot of motivation but there is a high likelihood the person will drown without some help. Motivation gives us the desire to learn but is not the same as learning.

____

____

____

Although we hope that one of the reasons you listed was an interest in mathematics, we know that many of you are taking this course because it is required to graduate, it is a prerequisite for a course you must take, or it is required for your major. Although you may not agree that this course is necessary, it is! If you are motivated to graduate or complete the requirements for your major, then use that motivation to succeed in this course. Do not become distracted from your goal to complete your education!

Commitment

To be successful, you must make a commitment to succeed. This means devoting time to math so that you achieve a better understanding of the subject.

List some activities (sports, hobbies, talents such as dance, art, or music) that you enjoy and at which you would like to become better.

ACTIVITY	***TIME SPENT***	***TIME WISHED SPENT***

Thinking about these activities, put the number of hours that you spend each week practicing these activities next to the activity. Next to that number, indicate the number of hours per week you would like to spend on these activities.

Whether you listed surfing or sailing, aerobics or restoring cars, or any other activity you enjoy, note how many hours a week you spend doing it. To succeed in math, you must be willing to commit the same amount of time. Success requires some sacrifice.

The "I Can't Do Math" Syndrome

There may be things you cannot do, such as lift a two-ton boulder. You can, however, do math. It is much easier than lifting the two-ton boulder. When you first learned the activities you listed above, you probably could not do them well. With practice, you got better. With practice, you will be better at math. Stay focused, motivated, and committed to success.

It is difficult for us to emphasize how important it is to overcome the "I Can't Do Math Syndrome." If you listen to interviews of very successful athletes after a particularly bad performance, you will note that they focus on the positive aspect of what they did, not the negative. Sports psychologists encourage athletes to always be positive—to have a "Can Do" attitude. Develop this attitude toward math.

Strategies for Success

Textbook Reconnaissance Right now, do a 15-minute "textbook reconnaissance" of this book. Here's how:

First, read the table of contents. Do it in three minutes or less. Next, look through the entire book, page by page. Move quickly. Scan titles, look at pictures, notice diagrams.

A textbook reconnaissance shows you where a course is going. It gives you the big picture. That's useful because brains work best when going from the general to the specific. Getting the big picture before you start makes details easier to recall and understand later on.

Your textbook reconnaissance will work even better if, as you scan, you look for ideas or topics that are interesting to you. List three facts, topics, or problems that you found interesting during your textbook reconnaissance.

____

____

____

The idea behind this technique is simple: It's easier to work at learning material if you know it's going to be useful to you.

Not all the topics in this book will be "interesting" to you. But that is true of any subject. Surfers find that on some days the waves are better than others, musicians find some music more appealing than other music, computer gamers find some computer games more interesting than others, and car enthusiasts find some cars more exciting than others. Some car enthusiasts would rather have a completely restored 1957 Chevrolet than a new Ferrari.

Know the Course Requirements To do your best in this course, you must know exactly what your instructor requires. Course requirements may be stated in a *syllabus*, which is a printed outline of the main topics of the course, or they may be presented orally. When they are listed in a syllabus or on other printed pages, keep them in a safe place. When they are presented orally, make sure to take complete notes. In either case, it is important that you understand them completely and follow them exactly. Be sure you know the answer to the following questions.

1. What is your instructor's name?
2. Where is your instructor's office?
3. At what times does your instructor hold office hours?
4. Besides the textbook, what other materials does your instructor require?
5. What is your instructor's attendance policy?
6. If you must be absent from a class meeting, what should you do before returning to class? What should you do when you return to class?
7. What is the instructor's policy regarding collection or grading of homework assignments?

8. What options are available if you are having difficulty with an assignment? Is there a math tutoring center?
9. Is there a math lab at your school? Where is it located? What hours is it open?
10. What is the instructor's policy if you miss a quiz?
11. What is the instructor's policy if you miss an exam?
12. Where can you get help when studying for an exam?

Remember: Your instructor wants to see you succeed. If you need help, ask! Do not fall behind. If you are running a race and fall behind by 100 yards, you may be able to catch up but it will require more effort than had you not fallen behind.

Take Note

Besides time management, there must be realistic ideas of how much time is available. There are very few people who can *successfully* work full-time and go to school full-time. If you work 40 hours a week, take 15 units, spend the recommended study time given at the right, and sleep 8 hours a day, you will use over 80% of the available hours in a week. That leaves less than 20% of the hours in a week for family, friends, eating, recreation, and other activities.

Time Management We know that there are demands on your time. Family, work, friends, and entertainment all compete for your time. We do not want to see you receive poor job evaluations because you are studying math. However, it is also true that we do not want to see you receive poor math test scores because you devoted too much time to work. When several competing and important tasks require your time and energy, the only way to manage the stress of being successful at both is to manage your time efficiently.

Instructors often advise students to spend twice the amount of time outside of class studying as they spend in the classroom. Time management is important if you are to accomplish this goal and succeed in school. The following activity is intended to help you structure your time more efficiently.

List the name of each course you are taking this term, the number of class hours each course meets, and the number of hours you should spend studying each subject outside of class. Then fill in a weekly schedule like the one below. Begin by writing in the hours spent in your classes, the hours spent at work (if you have a job), and any other commitments that are not flexible with respect to the time that you do them. Then begin to write down commitments that are more flexible, including hours spent studying. Remember to reserve time for activities such as meals and exercise. You should also schedule free time.

	Monday	Tuesday	Wednesday	Thursday	Friday	Saturday	Sunday
7–8 a.m.							
8–9 a.m.							
9–10 a.m.							
10–11 a.m.							
11–12 p.m.							
12–1 p.m.							
1–2 p.m.							
2–3 p.m.							
3–4 p.m.							
4–5 p.m.							
5–6 p.m.							
6–7 p.m.							
7–8 p.m.							
8–9 p.m.							
9–10 p.m.							
10–11 p.m.							
11–12 a.m.							

We know that many of you must work. If that is the case, realize that working 10 hours a week at a part-time job is equivalent to taking a three-unit class. If you must work, consider letting your education progress at a slower rate to allow you to be successful at both work and school. There is no rule that says you must finish school in a certain time frame.

Schedule Study Time As we encouraged you to do by filling out the time management form above, schedule a certain time to study. You should think of this time the way you would the time for work or class—that is, reasons for missing study time should be as compelling as reasons for missing work or class. "I just didn't feel like it" is not a good reason to miss your scheduled study time.

Although this may seem like an obvious exercise, list a few reasons you might want to study.

____

____

____

Of course we have no way of knowing the reasons you listed, but from our experience one reason given quite frequently is "To pass the course." There is nothing wrong with that reason. If that is the most important reason for you to study, then use it to stay focused.

One method of keeping to a study schedule is to form a ***study group.*** Look for people who are committed to learning, who pay attention in class, and who are punctual. Ask them to join your group. Choose people with similar educational goals but different methods of learning. You can gain insight from seeing the material from a new perspective. Limit groups to four or five people; larger groups are unwieldy.

There are many ways to conduct a study group. Begin with the following suggestions and see what works best for your group.

1. Test each other by asking questions. Each group member might bring two or three sample test questions to each meeting.
2. Practice teaching each other. Many of us who are teachers learned a lot about our subject when we had to explain it to someone else.
3. Compare class notes. You might ask other students about material in your notes that is difficult for you to understand.
4. Brainstorm test questions.
5. Set an agenda for each meeting. Set approximate time limits for each agenda item and determine a quitting time.

And finally, probably the most important aspect of studying is that it should be done in relatively small chunks. If you can only study three hours a week for this course (probably not enough for most people), do it in blocks of one hour on three separate days, preferably after class. Three hours of studying on a Sunday is not as productive as three hours of paced study.

Text Features That Promote Success

There are 11 chapters in this text. Each chapter is divided into sections, and each section is subdivided into learning objectives. Each learning objective is labeled with a number from 1 to 5.

Preparing for a Chapter Before you begin a new chapter, you should take some time to review previously learned skills. There are two ways to do this. The first is to complete the ***Cumulative Review,*** which occurs after every chapter (except Chapter 1). For instance, turn to page 163. The questions in this review are taken from the previous chapters. The answers for all these exercises can be found on page A10. Turn to those pages now and locate the answers for the Chapter 3 Cumulative Review. After the answer to the first exercise, which is 6, you will see the objective reference [1.2.2]. This means that this question was taken from Chapter 1, Section 2, Objective 2. If you missed this question, you should return to that objective and restudy the material.

A second way of preparing for a new chapter is to complete the ***Prep Test.*** This test focuses on the particular skills that will be required for the new chapter. Turn to page 106 to see a Prep Test. The answers for the Prep Test are the first set of answers in the answer section for a chapter. Turn to page A7 to see the answers for the Chapter 3 Prep Test. Note that an objective reference is given for each question. If you answer a question incorrectly, restudy the objective from which the question was taken.

Before the class meeting in which your professor begins a new section, you should read each objective statement for that section. Next, browse through the objective material, being sure to note each word in bold type. These words indicate important concepts that you must know in order to learn the material. Do not worry about trying to understand all the material. Your professor is there to assist you with that endeavor. The purpose of browsing through the material is so that your brain will be prepared to accept and organize the new information when it is presented to you.

Turn to page 2. Write down the title of the first objective in Section 1.1. Under the title of the objective, write down the words in the objective that are in bold print. It is not necessary for you to understand the meaning of these words. You are in this class to learn their meaning.

______________ ______________ ______________ ______________

______________ ______________ ______________ ______________

______________ ______________ ______________ ______________

______________ ______________ ______________ ______________

______________ ______________ ______________ ______________

Math Is Not a Spectator Sport To learn mathematics you must be an active participant. Listening and watching your professor do mathematics is not enough. Mathematics requires that you interact with the lesson you are studying. If you filled in the blanks above, you were being interactive. There are other ways this textbook has been designed to help you be an active learner.

$y + \frac{1}{2} = \frac{5}{4}$

$y + \frac{1}{2} - \frac{1}{2} = \frac{5}{4} - \frac{1}{2}$

$y + 0 = \frac{5}{4} - \frac{2}{4}$

$y = \frac{3}{4}$

The solution is $\frac{3}{4}$.

Instructional Examples Blue lines indicate an instructional example that usually has explanatory remarks to the left of the solution. These examples are used for two purposes. The first is to provide additional examples of important concepts. Secondly, these examples examine important techniques or principles that are often used in the solution of other types of problems.

Solve: $y + \frac{1}{2} = \frac{5}{4}$

The goal is to rewrite the equation in the form *variable* = *constant*.

$y + \frac{1}{2} = \frac{5}{4}$

Add the opposite of the constant term $\frac{1}{2}$ to each side of the equation. This is equivalent to subtracting $\frac{1}{2}$ from each side of the equation.

$y + \frac{1}{2} - \frac{1}{2} = \frac{5}{4} - \frac{1}{2}$

$y + 0 = \frac{5}{4} - \frac{2}{4}$

$y = \frac{3}{4}$

The solution $\frac{3}{4}$ checks.

The solution is $\frac{3}{4}$.

page 108

When you complete the example, get a clean sheet of paper. Write down the problem and then try to complete the solution without referring to your notes or the book. When you can do that, move on to the next part of the objective.

Leaf through the book now and write down the page numbers of two other occurrences of an instructional example.

Example/Problem Pairs One of the key instructional features of this text is Example/Problem pairs. Note that each Example is completely worked out and the "Problem" following the example is not. Study the worked-out example carefully by working through each step. Then work the Problem. If you get stuck, refer to the page number following the Problem which directs you to the page on which the Problem is solved—a complete worked-out solution is provided. Try to use the given solution to get a hint for the step you are stuck on. Then try to complete your solution.

EXAMPLE 4 Solve: $\frac{1}{2} = x + \frac{2}{3}$

Solution

$\frac{1}{2} = x + \frac{2}{3}$

$\frac{1}{2} - \frac{2}{3} = x + \frac{2}{3} - \frac{2}{3}$ • **Subtract $\frac{2}{3}$ from each side of the equation.**

$-\frac{1}{6} = x$ • **Simplify each side of the equation.**

The solution is $-\frac{1}{6}$.

PROBLEM 4 Solve: $-8 = 5 + x$

Solution See page S5.

Problem 4:

$-8 = 5 + x$

$-8 - 5 = 5 - 5 + x$

$-13 = x$

The solution is −13.

page 109

When you have completed your solution, check your work against the solution we provided. (Turn to page S5 to see the solution of Problem 4.) Be aware that frequently there is more than one way to solve a problem. Your answer, however, should be the same as the given answer. If you have any question as to whether your method will "always work," check with your instructor or with someone in the math center.

Browse through the textbook and write down the page numbers where two other Example/Problem pairs occur.

Remember: Be an active participant in your learning process. When you are sitting in class watching and listening to an explanation, you may think that you understand. However, until you actually try to do it, you will have no confirmation of the new knowledge or skill. Most of us have had the experience of sitting in class thinking we knew how to do something only to get home and realize that we didn't.

Take Note

There is a strong connection between reading and being a successful student in math or in any other subject. If you have difficulty reading, consider taking a reading course. Reading is much like other skills. There are certain things you can learn that will make you a better reader.

Word Problems Word problems are difficult because we must read the problem, determine the quantity we must find, think of a method to do that, and then actually solve the problem. In short, we must formulate a *strategy* to solve the problem and then devise a *solution*.

Note in the Example/Problem pair below that both a strategy and a solution are provided for the word problem. The strategy is a written description of how we will solve the problem. In the corresponding Problem, you are asked to formulate a strategy. Do not skip this step, and be sure to write it out.

Problem 11:

Strategy:

To find the percent of questions answers correctly, solve the basic percent equation using $B = 80$ and $A = 72$.

Solution:

$$PB = A$$
$$P(80) = 72$$
$$80P = 72$$
$$\frac{80P}{80} = \frac{72}{80}$$
$$P = 0.9$$

90% of the questions were answered correctly.

EXAMPLE 11 During a recent year, nearly 1.2 million dogs or litters were registered with the American Kennel Club. The most popular breed was the Labrador retriever, with 172,841 registered. What percent of the registrations were Labrador retrievers? Round to the nearest tenth of a percent. (*Source:* American Kennel Club)

Strategy To find the percent, solve the basic percent equation using $B = 1.2$ million $= 1{,}200{,}000$ and $A = 172{,}841$. The percent is unknown.

Solution

$$PB = A$$
$$P(1{,}200{,}000) = 172{,}841$$
$$\frac{P(1{,}200{,}000)}{1{,}200{,}000} = \frac{172{,}841}{1{,}200{,}000}$$
$$P \approx 0.144$$
$$P \approx 14.4\%$$

Approximately 14.4% of the registrations were Labrador retrievers.

PROBLEM 11 A student correctly answered 72 of the 80 questions on an exam. What percent of the questions were answered correctly?

Solution See page S6.

page 115

Take Note

If a rule has more than one part, be sure to make a notation to that effect.

Rule Boxes Pay special attention to rules placed in boxes. These rules give you the reasons certain types of problems are solved the way they are. When you see a rule, try to rewrite the rule in your own words.

Multiplying each side of an equation by the same number (NOT 0) will not change the solution.

Multiplication Property of Equations

Each side of an equation can be multiplied by the same nonzero number without changing the solution of the equation.

page 109

Find and write down two page numbers on which there are rule boxes.

Chapter Exercises When you have completed studying an objective, do the exercises in the exercise set that correspond with that objective. The exercises are labeled with the same number as the objective. Math is a subject that needs to be learned in small sections and practiced continually in order to be mastered. Doing all of the exercises in each exercise set will help you master the problem-solving techniques necessary for success. As you work through the exercises for an objective, check your answers to the odd-numbered exercises with those in the back of the book.

Preparing for a Test There are important features of this text that can be used to prepare for a test.

- Chapter Summary
- Chapter Review Exercises
- Chapter Test

After completing a chapter, read the Chapter Summary. (See page 157 for the Chapter 3 Summary.) This summary highlights the important topics covered in the chapter. The page number following each topic refers you to the page in the text on which you can find more information about the concept.

Following the Chapter Summary are Chapter Review Exercises (see page 159) and a Chapter Test (see page 161). Doing the review exercises is an important way of testing your understanding of the chapter. The answer to each review exercise is given at the back of the book, along with its objective reference. After checking your answers, restudy any objective from which a question you missed was taken. It may be helpful to retry some of the exercises for that objective to reinforce your problem-solving techniques.

The Chapter Test should be used to prepare for an exam. We suggest that you try the Chapter Test a few days before your actual exam. Take the test in a quiet place and try to complete the test in the same amount of time you will be allowed for your exam. When taking the Chapter Test, practice the strategies of successful test takers: (1) scan the entire test to get a feel for the questions; (2) read the directions carefully; (3) work the problems that are easiest for you first; and perhaps most importantly, (4) try to stay calm.

When you have completed the Chapter Test, check your answers. If you missed a question, review the material in that objective and rework some of the exercises from that objective. This will strengthen your ability to perform the skills in that objective.

Your career goal goes here. →

Is it difficult to be successful? YES! Successful music groups, artists, professional athletes, chefs, and ____________ have to work very hard to achieve their goals. They focus on their goals and ignore distractions. The things we ask you to do to achieve success take time and commitment. We are confident that if you follow our suggestions, you will succeed.

CHAPTER

1 Prealgebra Review

OBJECTIVES

1.1
1. Order relations
2. Opposites and absolute value

1.2
1. Add integers
2. Subtract integers
3. Multiply integers
4. Divide integers
5. Application problems

1.3
1. Write rational numbers as decimals
2. Multiply and divide rational numbers
3. Add and subtract rational numbers
4. Convert among percents, fractions, and decimals

1.4
1. Exponential expressions
2. The Order of Operations Agreement

1.5
1. Measures of angles
2. Perimeter problems
3. Area problems

DVD SSM *Online Study Center*

Need help? For online student resources, such as section quizzes, visit the Online Study Center at college.hmco.com/pic/aufmannBAWA7e.

How do investment bankers know which shares of stock to buy or sell? They decide based on each stock's price and whether it is likely to increase or decrease over time. Positive or negative numbers are used to express the amount of change in the price of a share of stock. Stock market analysts calculate the moving average of a stock, which averages the changes in a stock's price over several days. The moving average is used every day to discover trends in the movement of the price and to create investment strategies. **Exercises 156 and 157 on page 22** involve calculating moving averages for different stocks.

Prep Test

1. What is 127.1649 rounded to the nearest hundredth?

2. Add: 49,147 + 596

3. Subtract: 5004 − 487

4. Multiply: 407 × 28

5. Divide: 456 ÷ 19

6. What is the smallest number into which both 8 and 12 divide evenly?

7. What is the greatest number that divides evenly into both 16 and 20?

8. Without using 1, write 21 as a product of two whole numbers.

9. Represent the shaded portion of the figure as a fraction.

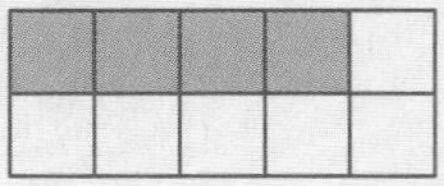

1.1 Introduction to Integers

OBJECTIVE 1 Order relations

It seems to be a human characteristic to group similar items. For instance, a botanist places plants with similar characteristics in groups called species. Nutritionists classify foods according to food groups; for example, pasta, crackers, and rice are among the foods in the bread group.

Mathematicians place objects with similar properties in groups called sets. A **set** is a collection of objects. The objects in a set are called **elements** of the set.

The **roster method** of writing sets encloses a list of the elements in braces. The set of sections within an orchestra is written {brass, percussion, strings, woodwinds}.

When the elements of a set are listed, each element is listed only once. For instance, if the list of numbers 1, 2, 3, 2, 3 were placed in a set, the set would be {1, 2, 3}.

The numbers that we use to count objects, such as the number of students in a classroom or the number of people living in an apartment house, are the natural numbers.

Natural numbers = {1, 2, 3, 4, 5, 6, 7, 8, 9, 10, . . .}

The three dots mean that the list of natural numbers continues on and on and that there is no largest natural number.

Point of Interest

The Alexandrian astronomer Ptolemy began using omicron, o, *the first letter of the Greek word that means "nothing," as the symbol for zero in* A.D. *150. It was not until the 13th century, however, that Fibonacci introduced 0 to the Western world as a placeholder so that we could distinguish, for example, 45 from 405.*

The natural numbers do not include zero. The number zero is used for describing data such as the number of people who have run a two-minute mile and the number of college students at Providence College who are under the age of 10. The set of whole numbers includes the natural numbers and zero.

Whole numbers = {0, 1, 2, 3, 4, 5, 6, 7, . . .}

The whole numbers do not provide all the numbers that are useful in applications. For instance, a meteorologist also needs numbers below zero.

Integers = {. . . , −5, −4, −3, −2, −1, 0, 1, 2, 3, 4, 5, . . .}

Each integer can be shown on a number line. The integers to the left of zero on the number line are called **negative integers.** The integers to the right of zero are called **positive integers** or natural numbers. Zero is neither a positive nor a negative integer.

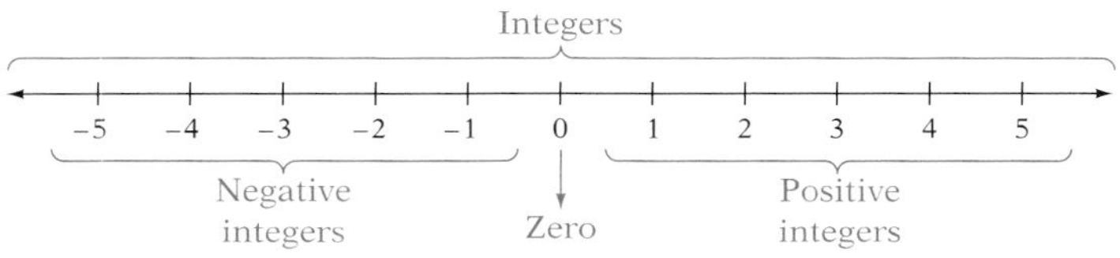

The **graph of an integer** is shown by placing a heavy dot on the number line directly above the number. The graphs of −3 and 4 are shown on the number line below.

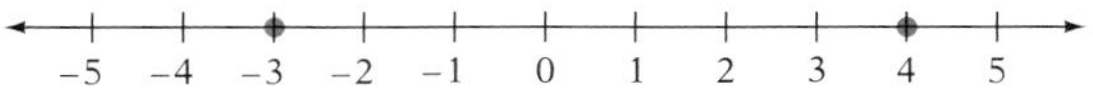

Consider the following sentences.

The quarterback threw the football, and the receiver caught *it*.

A student purchased a computer and used *it* to write English and history papers.

In the first sentence, *it* is used to mean the football; in the second sentence, *it* means the computer. In language, the word *it* can stand for many different objects. Similarly, in mathematics, a letter of the alphabet can be used to stand for a number. Such a letter is called a **variable.** Variables are used in the following definition of inequality symbols.

Definition of Inequality Symbols

If a and b are two numbers and a is to the left of b on the number line, then a **is less than** b. This is written $\boldsymbol{a < b}$.

If a and b are two numbers and a is to the right of b on the number line, then a **is greater than** b. This is written $\boldsymbol{a > b}$.

> **Point of Interest**
>
> *The symbols for "is less than" and "is greater than" were introduced by Thomas Harriot around 1630. Before that, ⊏ and ⊐ were used for < and >, respectively.*

Negative 4 is less than negative 1.

$-4 < -1$

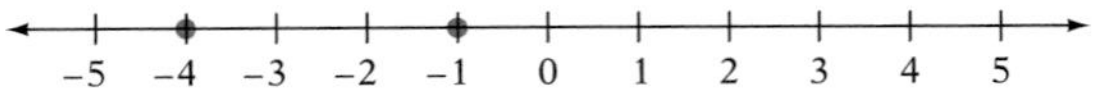

5 is greater than 0.

$5 > 0$

There are also inequality symbols for **is less than or equal to** (≤) and **is greater than or equal to** (≥).

$7 \le 15$ 7 is less than or equal to 15. This is true because $7 < 15$.

$6 \le 6$ 6 is less than or equal to 6. This is true because $6 = 6$.

EXAMPLE 1 Use the roster method to write the set of negative integers greater than or equal to -6.

Solution $A = \{-6, -5, -4, -3, -2, -1\}$ • **A set is designated by a capital letter.**

PROBLEM 1 Use the roster method to write the set of positive integers less than 5.

Solution See page S1.

EXAMPLE 2 Given $A = \{-6, -2, 0\}$, which elements of set A are less than or equal to -2?

Solution $-6 < -2$ • **Find the order relation between each element of set *A* and −2.**

$-2 = -2$

$0 > -2$

The elements -6 and -2 are less than or equal to -2.

PROBLEM 2 Given $B = \{-5, -1, 5\}$, which elements of set B are greater than -1?

Solution See page S1.

OBJECTIVE 2 Opposites and absolute value

Two numbers that are the same distance from zero on the number line but are on opposite sides of zero are **opposite numbers** or **opposites.** The opposite of a number is also called its **additive inverse.**

The opposite of 5 is -5.

The opposite of -5 is 5.

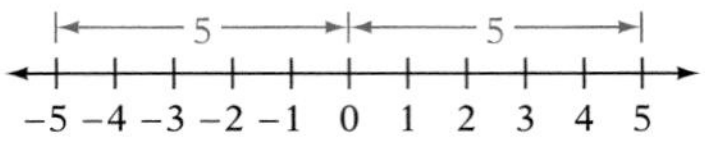

The negative sign can be read "the opposite of."

$-(2) = -2$ The opposite of 2 is -2.

$-(-2) = 2$ The opposite of -2 is 2.

EXAMPLE 3 Find the opposite number. **A.** 6 **B.** -51

Solution **A.** -6 **B.** 51

PROBLEM 3 Find the opposite number. **A.** -9 **B.** 62

Solution See page S1.

The **absolute value** of a number is its distance from zero on the number line. Therefore, the absolute value of a number is a positive number or zero. The symbol for absolute value is two vertical bars, | |.

The distance from 0 to 3 is 3. Therefore, the absolute value of 3 is 3.

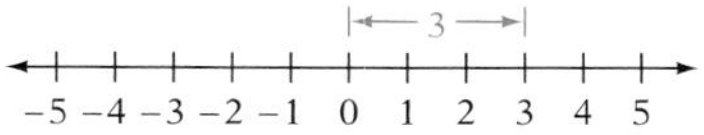

$$|3| = 3$$

The distance from 0 to -3 is 3. Therefore, the absolute value of -3 is 3.

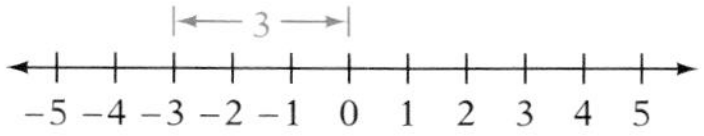

$$|-3| = 3$$

Point of Interest

The definition of absolute value given in the box is written in what is called rhetorical style. That is, it is written without the use of variables. This is how all mathematics was written prior to the Renaissance. During that period, from the 14th to the 16th century, the idea of expressing a variable symbolically was developed. In terms of that symbolism, the definition of absolute value is

$$|x| = \begin{cases} x, & x > 0 \\ 0, & x = 0 \\ -x, & x < 0 \end{cases}$$

Absolute Value

The absolute value of a positive number is the number itself. The absolute value of zero is zero. The absolute value of a negative number is the opposite of the negative number.

EXAMPLE 4 Evaluate. **A.** $|-4|$ **B.** $-|-10|$

Solution **A.** $|-4| = 4$

B. $-|-10| = -10$

- **The absolute value sign does not affect the negative sign in front of the absolute value sign. You can read $-|-10|$ as "the opposite of the absolute value of negative 10."**

PROBLEM 4 Evaluate. **A.** $|-5|$ **B.** $-|-9|$

Solution See page S1.

1.1 Concept Review

Determine whether the statement is always true, sometimes true, or never true.

1. The absolute value of a number is positive.

2. The absolute value of a number is negative.

3. If x is an integer, then $|x| < -3$.

4. If x is an integer, then $|x| > -2$.

5. The opposite of a number is a positive number.

6. The set of positive integers is {0, 1, 2, 3, 4, . . .}.

7. If a is an integer, then $a \le a$.

8. If a and b are integers and $a > b$, then $a \ge b$.

9. If x is a negative integer, then $|x| = -x$.

10. Suppose a and b are integers and $a < b$. Then $|a| < |b|$.

1.1 Exercises

1 Order relations

1. How do the whole numbers differ from the natural numbers?

2. Explain the difference between the symbols $<$ and $\le$.

3. Another name for the set of positive integers is the set of __?__ numbers.

4. The inequality $-5 < -1$ is read "negative five __?__ negative one."

5. The inequality $0 \ge -4$ is read "zero __?__ negative four."

6. Which number is greater, -10 or -3?

Place the correct symbol, $<$ or $>$, between the two numbers.

7. $-2 \quad -5$

8. $-6 \quad -1$

9. $-16 \quad 1$

10. $-2 \quad 13$

11. $3 \quad -7$

12. $5 \quad -6$

13. $0 \quad -3$

14. $8 \quad 0$

15. $-42 \quad 27$

16. $-36 \quad 49$

17. $21 \quad -34$

18. $53 \quad -46$

19. $-27 \quad -39$

20. $-51 \quad -20$

21. $-131 \quad 101$

22. $127 \quad -150$

23. A number n is to the right of the number 5 on the number line. Which of the following is true?
a. n is positive. **b.** n is negative. **c.** n is 0.
d. n can be positive, negative, or 0.

24. A number n is to the left of the number 5 on the number line. Which of the following is true?
a. n is positive. **b.** n is negative. **c.** n is 0.
d. n can be positive, negative, or 0.

25. Do the inequalities $6 \geq 1$ and $1 \leq 6$ express the same order relation?

26. Use the "≤" inequality symbol to rewrite the order relation expressed by the inequality $-2 \geq -5$.

Use the roster method to write the set.

27. the natural numbers less than 9

28. the natural numbers less than or equal to 6

29. the positive integers less than or equal to 8

30. the positive integers less than 4

31. the negative integers greater than -7

32. the negative integers greater than or equal to -5

Solve.

33. Given $A = \{-7, 0, 2, 5\}$, which elements of set A are greater than 2?

34. Given $B = \{-8, 0, 7, 15\}$, which elements of set B are greater than 7?

35. Given $D = \{-23, -18, -8, 0\}$, which elements of set D are less than -8?

36. Given $C = \{-33, -24, -10, 0\}$, which elements of set C are less than -10?

37. Given $E = \{-35, -13, 21, 37\}$, which elements of set E are greater than -10?

38. Given $F = \{-27, -14, 14, 27\}$, which elements of set F are greater than -15?

39. Given $B = \{-52, -46, 0, 39, 58\}$, which elements of set B are less than or equal to 0?

40. Given $A = \{-12, -9, 0, 12, 34\}$, which elements of set A are greater than or equal to 0?

41. Given $C = \{-23, -17, 0, 4, 29\}$, which elements of set C are greater than or equal to -17?

42. Given $D = \{-31, -12, 0, 11, 45\}$, which elements of set D are less than or equal to -12?

43. Given that set A is the positive integers less than 10, which elements of set A are greater than or equal to 5?

44. Given that set B is the positive integers less than or equal to 12, which elements of set B are greater than 6?

45. Given that set D is the negative integers greater than or equal to -10, which elements of set D are less than -4?

46. Given that set C is the negative integers greater than -8, which elements of set C are less than or equal to -3?

2 Opposites and absolute value

47. What is the additive inverse of a number?

48. What is the absolute value of a number?

49. The opposite of a negative number is a ____?____ number.

50. The additive inverse of 7 is ___?___.

51. The equation $|-5| = 5$ is read "the ___?___ of negative five is five."

52. Write the statement "the opposite of negative nine is nine" in symbols.

Find the opposite number.

53. 22

54. 45

55. -31

56. -88

57. -168

58. -97

59. 630

60. 450

Evaluate.

61. $-(-18)$

62. $-(-30)$

63. $-(49)$

64. $-(67)$

65. $|16|$

66. $|19|$

67. $|-12|$

68. $|-22|$

69. $-|29|$

70. $-|20|$

71. $-|-14|$

72. $-|-18|$

73. $-|0|$

74. $|-30|$

75. $-|34|$

76. $-|-45|$

Solve.

77. Given $A = \{-8, -5, -2, 1, 3\}$, find
a. the opposite of each element of set A.
b. the absolute value of each element of set A.

78. Given $B = \{-11, -7, -3, 1, 5\}$, find
a. the opposite of each element of set B.
b. the absolute value of each element of set B.

79. True or false? The absolute value of a negative number n is greater than n.

80. A number n is positive. In order to make the statement $|n|$ ___?___ n a true statement, which symbol must replace the question mark?
a. $>$ **b.** $<$ **c.** $\leq$ **d.** $=$

Place the correct symbol, $<$ or $>$, between the two numbers.

81. $|-83| \quad |58|$

82. $|22| \quad |-19|$

83. $|43| \quad |-52|$

84. $|-71| \quad |-92|$

85. $|-68| \quad |-42|$

86. $|12| \quad |-31|$

87. $|-45| \quad |-61|$

88. $|-28| \quad |43|$

1.1 Applying Concepts

Write the given numbers in order from least to greatest.

89. $|-5|, 6, -|-8|, -19$

90. $-4, |-15|, -|-7|, 0$

91. $-(-3), -22, |-25|, |-14|$

92. $-|-26|, -(-8), |-17|, -(5)$

Meteorology A meteorologist may report a wind-chill temperature. This is the equivalent temperature, including the effects of wind and temperature, that a person would feel in calm air conditions. The table below gives the wind-chill temperature for various wind speeds and temperatures. For instance, when the temperature is 5°F and the wind is blowing at 15 mph, the wind-chill temperature is −13°F. Use this table for Exercises 93 and 94.

Wind Chill Factors															
Wind Speed (in mph)	Thermometer Reading (in degrees Fahrenheit)														
	25	20	15	10	5	0	−5	−10	−15	−20	−25	−30	−35	−40	−45
5	19	13	7	1	−5	−11	−16	−22	−28	−34	−40	−46	−52	−57	−63
10	15	9	3	−4	−10	−16	−22	−28	−35	−41	−47	−53	−59	−66	−72
15	13	6	0	−7	−13	−19	−26	−32	−39	−45	−51	−58	−64	−71	−77
20	11	4	−2	−9	−15	−22	−29	−35	−42	−48	−55	−61	−68	−74	−81
25	9	3	−4	−11	−17	−24	−31	−37	−44	−51	−58	−64	−71	−78	−84
30	8	1	−5	−12	−19	−26	−33	−39	−46	−53	−60	−67	−73	−80	−87
35	7	0	−7	−14	−21	−27	−34	−41	−48	−55	−62	−69	−76	−82	−89
40	6	−1	−8	−15	−22	−29	−36	−43	−50	−57	−64	−71	−78	−84	−91
45	5	−2	−9	−16	−23	−30	−37	−44	−51	−58	−65	−72	−79	−86	−93

93. Which of the following weather conditions feels colder?

a. a temperature of 5°F with a 20 mph wind or a temperature of 10°F with a 15 mph wind

b. a temperature of −25°F with a 10 mph wind or a temperature of −15°F with a 20 mph wind

94. Which of the following weather conditions feels warmer?

a. a temperature of 5°F with a 25 mph wind or a temperature of 10°F with a 10 mph wind

b. a temperature of −5°F with a 10 mph wind or a temperature of −15°F with a 5 mph wind

Complete.

95. On the number line, the two points that are four units from 0 are ________ and ________.

96. On the number line, the two points that are six units from 0 are ________ and ________.

97. On the number line, the two points that are seven units from 4 are ________ and ________.

98. On the number line, the two points that are five units from −3 are ________ and ________.

99. If a is a positive number, then $-a$ is a ________ number.

100. If a is a negative number, then $-a$ is a ________ number.

101. An integer that is its own opposite is ______.

102. True or False. If $a \geq 0$, then $|a| = a$.

103. True or False. If $a \leq 0$, then $|a| = -a$.

104. Give examples of some games that use negative integers in the scoring.

105. Give some examples of English words that are used as variables.

106. Write an essay describing your interpretation of the data presented in the table at the right.

The Twenty-First Century: An Easier Ladder to Climb
Number of 30- to 34-year-olds competing for jobs

	1992	*1999*	*2005*
Men	10.3 million	9.2 million	8.5 million
Women	8.3 million	7.9 million	7.8 million
Total	18.6 million	17.1 million	16.3 million

1.2 Operations with Integers

OBJECTIVE 1 Add integers

A number can be represented anywhere along the number line by an arrow. A positive number is represented by an arrow pointing to the right, and a negative number is represented by an arrow pointing to the left. The size of the number is represented by the length of the arrow.

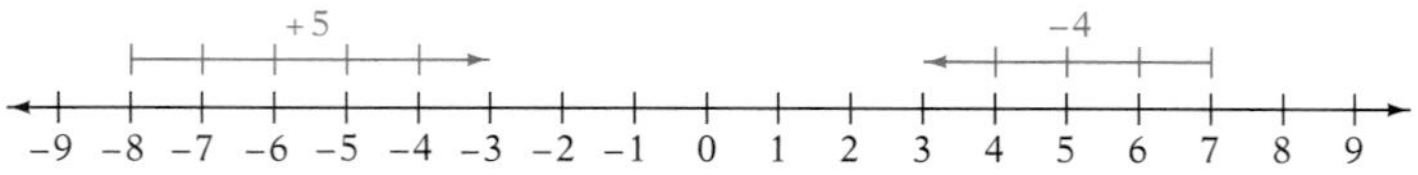

Addition is the process of finding the total of two numbers. The numbers being added are called **addends.** The total is called the **sum.** Addition of integers can be shown on the number line. To add integers, find the point on the number line corresponding to the first addend. At that point, draw an arrow representing the second addend. The sum is the number directly below the tip of the arrow.

$4 + 2 = 6$

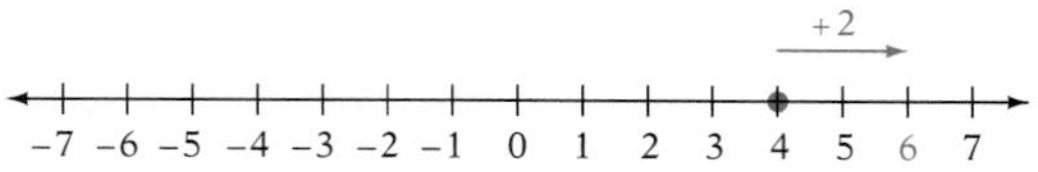

$-4 + (-2) = -6$

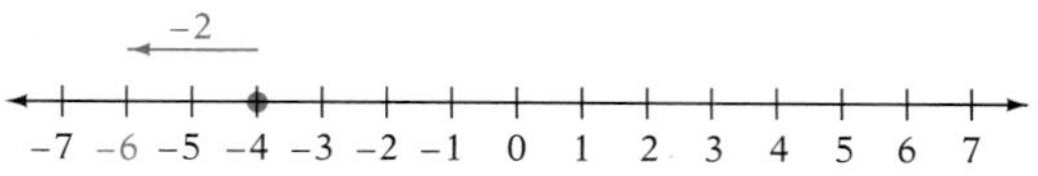

$-4 + 2 = -2$

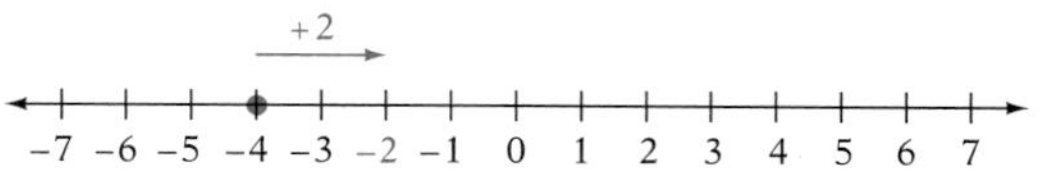

$4 + (-2) = 2$

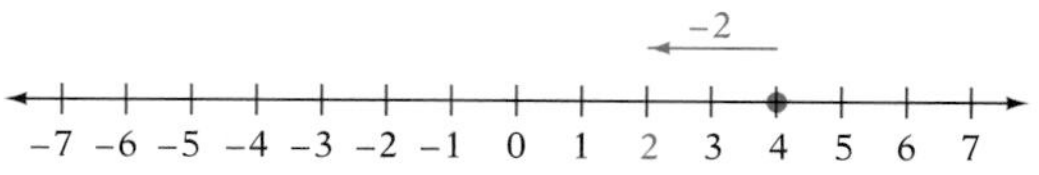

The pattern for addition shown on the preceding number lines is summarized in the following rules for adding integers.

Addition of Integers

Integers with the same sign
To add two numbers with the same sign, add the absolute values of the numbers. Then attach the sign of the addends.

$2 + 8 = 10$

$-2 + (-8) = -10$

Integers with different signs
To add two numbers with different signs, find the absolute value of each number. Then subtract the smaller of these absolute values from the larger one. Attach the sign of the number with the larger absolute value.

$-2 + 8 = 6$

$2 + (-8) = -6$

EXAMPLE 1 Add. **A.** $162 + (-247)$ **B.** $-14 + (-47)$
C. $-4 + (-6) + (-8) + 9$

Solution **A.** $162 + (-247) = -85$

- **The signs are different. Subtract the absolute values of the numbers (247 − 162). Attach the sign of the number with the larger absolute value.**

B. $-14 + (-47) = -61$

- **The signs are the same. Add the absolute values of the numbers (14 + 47). Attach the sign of the addends.**

C. $-4 + (-6) + (-8) + 9$
$= -10 + (-8) + 9$
$= -18 + 9$
$= -9$

- **To add more than two numbers, add the first two numbers. Then add the sum to the third number. Continue until all the numbers have been added.**

PROBLEM 1 Add.

A. $-162 + 98$ **B.** $-154 + (-37)$ **C.** $-36 + 17 + (-21)$

Solution See page S1.

OBJECTIVE 2 Subtract integers

Subtraction is the process of finding the difference between two numbers. Subtraction of an integer is defined as addition of the opposite integer.

Subtract 8 − 3 by using addition of the opposite.

Subtraction → Addition of the Opposite

$$8 - (+3) = 8 + (-3) = 5$$

(+3) and (−3): Opposites

To subtract one integer from another, add the opposite of the second integer to the first integer.

first number	−	second number	=	first number	+	the opposite of the second number		
40	−	60	=	40	+	(−60)	=	−20
−40	−	60	=	−40	+	(−60)	=	−100
−40	−	(−60)	=	−40	+	60	=	20
40	−	(−60)	=	40	+	60	=	100

EXAMPLE 2 Subtract: $-12 - 8$

Solution $-12 - 8 = -12 + (-8)$ • **Rewrite subtraction as addition of the opposite.**

$= -20$ • **Add.**

PROBLEM 2 Subtract: $-8 - 14$

Solution See page S1.

When subtraction occurs several times in a problem, rewrite each subtraction as addition of the opposite. Then add.

EXAMPLE 3 Subtract: $-8 - 30 - (-12) - 7 - (-14)$

Solution $-8 - 30 - (-12) - 7 - (-14)$

$= -8 + (-30) + 12 + (-7) + 14$ • **Rewrite each subtraction as addition of the opposite.**

$= -38 + 12 + (-7) + 14$ • **Add the first two numbers. Then add the sum to the third number. Continue until all the numbers have been added.**

$= -26 + (-7) + 14$

$= -33 + 14$

$= -19$

PROBLEM 3 Subtract: $4 - (-3) - 12 - (-7) - 20$

Solution See page S1.

OBJECTIVE 3

Multiply integers

Point of Interest

The cross × was first used as a symbol for multiplication in 1631 in a book titled The Key to Mathematics. *In that same year, another book,* Practice of the Analytical Art, *advocated the use of a dot to indicate multiplication.*

Multiplication is the process of finding the product of two numbers.

Several different symbols are used to indicate multiplication. The numbers being multiplied are called **factors;** for instance, 3 and 2 are factors in each of the examples at the right. The result is called the **product.** Note that when parentheses are used and there is no arithmetic operation symbol, the operation is multiplication.

$3 \times 2 = 6$
$3 \cdot 2 = 6$
$(3)(2) = 6$
$3(2) = 6$
$(3)2 = 6$

When 5 is multiplied by a sequence of decreasing integers, each product decreases by 5.

$$(5)(3) = 15$$
$$(5)(2) = 10$$
$$(5)(1) = 5$$
$$(5)(0) = 0$$

The pattern developed can be continued so that 5 is multiplied by a sequence of negative numbers. The resulting products must be negative in order to maintain the pattern of decreasing by 5.

$$(5)(-1) = -5$$
$$(5)(-2) = -10$$
$$(5)(-3) = -15$$
$$(5)(-4) = -20$$

This illustrates that the product of a positive number and a negative number is negative.

When −5 is multiplied by a sequence of decreasing integers, each product increases by 5.

$$(-5)(3) = -15$$
$$(-5)(2) = -10$$
$$(-5)(1) = -5$$
$$(-5)(0) = 0$$

The pattern developed can be continued so that −5 is multiplied by a sequence of negative numbers. The resulting products must be positive in order to maintain the pattern of increasing by 5.

$$(-5)(-1) = 5$$
$$(-5)(-2) = 10$$
$$(-5)(-3) = 15$$
$$(-5)(-4) = 20$$

This illustrates that the product of two negative numbers is positive.

This pattern for multiplication is summarized in the following rules for multiplying integers.

Multiplication of Integers

Integers with the same sign
To multiply two numbers with the same sign, multiply the absolute values of the numbers. The product is positive.

$$4 \cdot 8 = 32$$
$$(-4)(-8) = 32$$

Integers with different signs
To multiply two numbers with different signs, multiply the absolute values of the numbers. The product is negative.

$$-4 \cdot 8 = -32$$
$$(4)(-8) = -32$$

EXAMPLE 4 Multiply. **A.** $-42 \cdot 62$ **B.** $2(-3)(-5)(-7)$

Solution **A.** $-42 \cdot 62$
$= -2604$

• **The signs are different. The product is negative.**

B. $2(-3)(-5)(-7)$
$= -6(-5)(-7)$
$= 30(-7)$
$= -210$

• **To multiply more than two numbers, multiply the first two numbers. Then multiply the product by the third number. Continue until all the numbers have been multiplied.**

PROBLEM 4 Multiply. **A.** $-38 \cdot 51$ **B.** $-7(-8)(9)(-2)$

Solution See page S1.

OBJECTIVE 4 Divide integers

For every division problem there is a related multiplication problem.

$$\text{Division: } \frac{8}{2} = 4 \qquad \text{Related multiplication: } 4 \cdot 2 = 8$$

This fact can be used to illustrate the rules for dividing signed numbers.

The quotient of two numbers with the same sign is positive.

$\frac{12}{3} = 4$ because $4 \cdot 3 = 12$.

$\frac{-12}{-3} = 4$ because $4(-3) = -12$.

The quotient of two numbers with different signs is negative.

$\frac{12}{-3} = -4$ because $-4(-3) = 12$.

$\frac{-12}{3} = -4$ because $-4 \cdot 3 = -12$.

Division of Integers

Integers with the same sign
To divide two numbers with the same sign, divide the absolute values of the numbers. The quotient is positive.

Integers with different signs
To divide two numbers with different signs, divide the absolute values of the numbers. The quotient is negative.

Note that $\frac{-12}{3} = -4$, $\frac{12}{-3} = -4$, and $-\frac{12}{3} = -4$. This suggests the following rule.

If a and b are two integers, and $b \neq 0$, then $\frac{a}{-b} = \frac{-a}{b} = -\frac{a}{b}$.

Read $b \neq 0$ as "b is not equal to 0." The reason why the denominator must not be equal to 0 is explained in the following discussion of zero and one in division.

Zero and One in Division

Zero divided by any number other than zero is zero.	$\frac{0}{a} = 0, a \neq 0$	because $0 \cdot a = 0$.
Division by zero is not defined.	$\frac{4}{0} = ?$	$? \times 0 = 4$ There is no number whose product with zero is 4.
Any number other than zero divided by itself is 1.	$\frac{a}{a} = 1, a \neq 0$	because $1 \cdot a = a$.
Any number divided by 1 is the number.	$\frac{a}{1} = a$	because $a \cdot 1 = a$.

EXAMPLE 5 Divide. **A.** $(-120) \div (-8)$ **B.** $\frac{95}{-5}$ **C.** $-\frac{-81}{3}$

Solution **A.** $(-120) \div (-8) = 15$

B. $\frac{95}{-5} = -19$

C. $-\frac{-81}{3} = -(-27) = 27$

PROBLEM 5 Divide. **A.** $(-135) \div (-9)$ **B.** $\frac{84}{-6}$ **C.** $-\frac{36}{-12}$

Solution See page S1.

OBJECTIVE 5 Application problems

In many courses, your course grade depends on the *average* of all your test scores. You compute the average by calculating the sum of all your test scores and then dividing that result by the number of tests. Statisticians call this average an **arithmetic mean.** Besides its application to finding the average of your test scores, the arithmetic mean is used in many other situations.

Stock market analysts calculate the **moving average** of a stock. This is the arithmetic mean of the changes in the value of a stock for a given number of days. To illustrate the procedure, we will calculate the 5-day moving average of a stock. In actual practice, a stock market analyst may use 15 days, 30 days, or some other number.

The table below shows the amount of increase or decrease, in cents, in the closing price of a stock for a 10-day period.

Day 1	*Day 2*	*Day 3*	*Day 4*	*Day 5*	*Day 6*	*Day 7*	*Day 8*	*Day 9*	*Day 10*
+50	−175	+225	0	−275	−75	−50	+50	−475	−50

To calculate the 5-day moving average of this stock, determine the average of the stock for days 1 through 5, days 2 through 6, days 3 through 7, and so on.

Days 1–5	*Days 2–6*	*Days 3–7*	*Days 4–8*	*Days 5–9*	*Days 6–10*
+50	−175	+225	0	−275	−75
−175	+225	0	−275	−75	−50
+225	0	−275	−75	−50	+50
0	−275	−75	−50	+50	−475
−275	−75	−50	+50	−475	−50
Sum = −175	Sum = −300	Sum = −175	Sum = −350	Sum = −825	Sum = −600
$= \frac{-175}{5}$	$= \frac{-300}{5}$	$= \frac{-175}{5}$	$= \frac{-350}{5}$	$= \frac{-825}{5}$	$= \frac{-600}{5}$
Average = −35	Average = −60	Average = −35	Average = −70	Average = −165	Average = −120

The 5-day moving average is the list of means: −35, −60, −35, −70, −165, and −120. If the numbers in the list tend to increase, the price of the stock is showing an upward trend; if they decrease, the price of the stock is showing a downward trend. For the stock shown here, the price of the stock is showing a downward trend. These trends help analysts determine whether to recommend a stock.

EXAMPLE 6 The daily low temperatures, in degrees Celsius, during one week were recorded as follows: $-8°$, $2°$, $0°$, $-7°$, $1°$, $6°$, $-1°$. Find the average daily low temperature for the week.

Strategy To find the average daily low temperature:

- ▶ Add the seven temperature readings.
- ▶ Divide the sum by 7.

Solution

$$\begin{aligned} &-8 + 2 + 0 + (-7) + 1 + 6 + (-1) \\ &= -6 + 0 + (-7) + 1 + 6 + (-1) \\ &= -6 + (-7) + 1 + 6 + (-1) \\ &= -13 + 1 + 6 + (-1) \\ &= -12 + 6 + (-1) \\ &= -6 + (-1) \\ &= -7 \end{aligned}$$

$$-7 \div 7 = -1$$

The average daily low temperature was $-1°C$.

PROBLEM 6 The daily high temperatures, in degrees Celsius, during one week were recorded as follows: $-5°$, $-6°$, $3°$, $0°$, $-4°$, $-7°$, $-2°$. Find the average daily high temperature for the week.

Solution See page S1.

1.2 Concept Review

Determine whether the statement is always true, sometimes true, or never true.

1. The sum of two integers is larger than either of the integers being added.

2. The sum of two nonzero integers with the same sign is positive.

3. The quotient of two integers with different signs is negative.

4. To find the opposite of a number, multiply the number by -1.

5. To find the opposite of an integer, divide the integer by -1.

6. To perform the subtraction $a - b$, add the opposite of a to b.

7. $4(-8) = -4$

8. If x and y are two integers and $y = 0$, then $\frac{x}{y} = 0$.

9. If x and y are two different integers, then $x - y = y - x$.

10. If x is an integer and $4x = 0$, then $x = 0$.

1.2 Exercises

1 Add integers

1. Explain how to add two integers with the same sign.

2. Explain how to add two integers with different signs.

3. In the addition equation $8 + (-3) = 5$, the addends are __?__ and __?__, and the sum is __?__.

4. Use the diagram at the right to complete this addition equation: __?__ + __?__ = __?__.

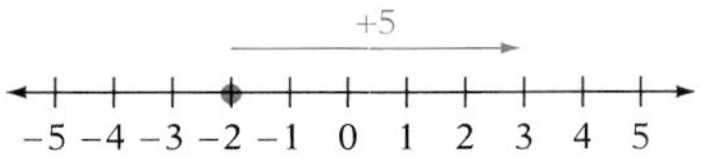

Add.

5. $-3 + (-8)$

6. $-12 + (-1)$

7. $-4 + (-5)$

8. $-12 + (-12)$

9. $6 + (-9)$

10. $4 + (-9)$

11. $-6 + 7$

12. $-12 + 6$

13. $2 + (-3) + (-4)$

14. $7 + (-2) + (-8)$

15. $-3 + (-12) + (-15)$

16. $9 + (-6) + (-16)$

17. $-17 + (-3) + 29$

18. $13 + 62 + (-38)$

19. $-3 + (-8) + 12$

20. $-27 + (-42) + (-18)$

21. $13 + (-22) + 4 + (-5)$

22. $-14 + (-3) + 7 + (-6)$

23. $-22 + 10 + 2 + (-18)$

24. $-6 + (-8) + 13 + (-4)$

25. $-126 + (-247) + (-358) + 339$

26. $-651 + (-239) + 524 + 487$

Complete Exercises 27 and 28 without actually finding the sums.

27. Is the sum $812 + (-537)$ positive or negative?

28. Is the sum of -57 and -31 positive or negative?

2 Subtract integers

29. Explain the meaning of the words *minus* and *negative*.

30. Explain how to rewrite $6 - (-9)$ as addition of the opposite.

31. $-10 - 4 = -10 + \underline{\quad ? \quad}$ • **Rewrite subtraction as addition of the opposite.**
$= \underline{\quad ? \quad}$ • **Add.**

32. $8 - (-5) = 8 + \underline{\quad ? \quad}$ • **Rewrite subtraction as addition of the opposite.**
$= \underline{\quad ? \quad}$ • **Add.**

Subtract.

33. $16 - 8$

34. $12 - 3$

35. $7 - 14$

36. $7 - (-2)$

37. $3 - (-4)$

38. $-6 - (-3)$

39. $-4 - (-2)$

40. $6 - (-12)$

41. $-12 - 16$

42. $-4 - 3 - 2$

43. $4 - 5 - 12$

44. $12 - (-7) - 8$

45. $-12 - (-3) - (-15)$

46. $4 - 12 - (-8)$

47. $13 - 7 - 15$

48. $-6 + 19 - (-31)$

49. $-30 - (-65) - 29 - 4$

50. $42 - (-82) - 65 - 7$

51. $-16 - 47 - 63 - 12$

52. $42 - (-30) - 65 - (-11)$

53. $-47 - (-67) - 13 - 15$

54. $-18 - 49 - (-84) - 27$

Complete Exercises 55 and 56 without actually finding the difference.

55. Is the difference $-25 - 52$ positive or negative?

56. Is the difference 8 minus -5 positive or negative?

3 Multiply integers

57. Explain how to multiply two integers with the same sign.

58. Explain how to multiply two integers with different signs.

59. Name the operation in each expression. Justify your answer.
a. $8(-7)$ **b.** $8 - 7$ **c.** $8 - (-7)$ **d.** $-xy$ **e.** $x(-y)$ **f.** $-x - y$

60. Name the operation in each expression. Justify your answer.
a. $(4)(-6)$ **b.** $4 - (6)$ **c.** $4 - (-6)$ **d.** $-ab$ **e.** $a(-b)$ **f.** $-a - b$

61. In the equation $(-10)(7) = -70$, the factors are $\underline{\quad ? \quad}$ and $\underline{\quad ? \quad}$, and the product is $\underline{\quad ? \quad}$.

62. In the equation $15(-3) = -45$, the 15 and -3 are called the $\underline{\quad ? \quad}$, and -45 is called the $\underline{\quad ? \quad}$.

63. For the product $(-4)(-12)$, the signs of the factors are the same. The sign of the product is __?__. The product is __?__.

64. For the product $(10)(-10)$, the signs of the factors are different. The sign of the product is __?__. The product is __?__.

Multiply.

65. $14 \cdot 3$

66. $62 \cdot 9$

67. $5(-4)$

68. $4(-7)$

69. $-8(2)$

70. $-9(3)$

71. $(-5)(-5)$

72. $(-3)(-6)$

73. $(-7)(0)$

74. $-32 \cdot 4$

75. $-24 \cdot 3$

76. $19(-7)$

77. $6(-17)$

78. $-8(-26)$

79. $-4(-35)$

80. $-5(23)$

81. $5 \cdot 7(-2)$

82. $8(-6)(-1)$

83. $(-9)(-9)(2)$

84. $-8(-7)(-4)$

85. $-5(8)(-3)$

86. $(-6)(5)(7)$

87. $-1(4)(-9)$

88. $6(-3)(-2)$

89. $4(-4) \cdot 6(-2)$

90. $-5 \cdot 9(-7) \cdot 3$

91. $-9(4) \cdot 3(1)$

92. $8(8)(-5)(-4)$

93. $-6(-5)(12)(0)$

94. $7(9) \cdot 10(-1)$

95. Is the product of three negative integers positive or negative?

96. Is the product of four positive numbers and three negative numbers positive or negative?

4 Divide integers

97. Write the division expression $\frac{-15}{3}$ using the division symbol: __?__ $\div$ __?__.

98. Write the division expression $8 \div (-4)$ as a fraction: $\frac{?}{?}$. The quotient is __?__.

Write the related multiplication problem.

99. $\frac{-36}{-12} = 3$

100. $\frac{28}{-7} = -4$

101. $\frac{-55}{11} = -5$

102. $\frac{-20}{-10} = 2$

Divide.

103. $12 \div (-6)$

104. $18 \div (-3)$

105. $(-72) \div (-9)$

106. $(-64) \div (-8)$

107. $0 \div (-6)$

108. $-49 \div 0$

109. $45 \div (-5)$

110. $-24 \div 4$

111. $-36 \div 4$

112. $-56 \div 7$

113. $-81 \div (-9)$

114. $-40 \div (-5)$

115. $72 \div (-3)$

116. $44 \div (-4)$

117. $-60 \div 5$

118. $144 \div 9$

119. $78 \div (-6)$

120. $84 \div (-7)$

121. $-72 \div 4$

122. $-80 \div 5$

123. $-114 \div (-6)$

124. $-128 \div 4$

125. $-130 \div (-5)$

126. $(-280) \div 8$

127. $-132 \div (-12)$

128. $-156 \div (-13)$

129. $-182 \div 14$

130. $-144 \div 12$

131. $143 \div 11$

132. $168 \div 14$

Complete Exercises 133 and 134 without using a calculator.

133. State whether the quotient $-\frac{520}{-13}$ is positive or negative.

134. State whether each quotient is positive, negative, zero, or undefined.
a. $-61 \div 0$ **b.** $0 \div 85$ **c.** $-172 \div (-4)$ **d.** $-96 \div 4$

5 Application problems

135. At 2:00 P.M. the temperature was 85°F. By 10:00 P.M. the temperature had dropped by 20°F. Which expression can be used to find the temperature, in degrees Fahrenheit, at 10:00 P.M.?
a. $85 + 20$ **b.** $85 - 20$ **c.** $20 - 85$ **d.** $85 \div 20$

136. After three tests, a student's test average was 82. After the fourth test, the student's test average was 84. Was the student's grade on the fourth test higher or lower than 82?

137. **Temperature** Find the temperature after a rise of 9°C from −6°C.

138. **Temperature** Find the temperature after a rise of 7°C from −18°C.

139. **Temperature** The high temperature for the day was 10°C. The low temperature was −4°C. Find the difference between the high and low temperatures for the day.

140. **Temperature** The low temperature for the day was −2°C. The high temperature was 11°C. Find the difference between the high and low temperatures for the day.

141. **Chemistry** The temperature at which mercury boils is 360°C. Mercury freezes at −39°C. Find the difference between the temperature at which mercury boils and the temperature at which it freezes.

142. **Chemistry** The temperature at which radon boils is −62°C. Radon freezes at −71°C. Find the difference between the temperature at which radon boils and the temperature at which it freezes.

Geography The elevation, or height, of places on Earth is measured in relation to sea level, or the average level of the ocean's surface. The following table shows height above sea level as a positive number and depth below sea level as a negative number. (*Source: Information Please Almanac*)

Continent	*Highest Elevation (in meters)*		*Lowest Elevation (in meters)*	
Africa	Mt. Kilimanjaro	5895	Qattara Depression	−133
Asia	Mt. Everest	8844	Dead Sea	−400
Europe	Mt. Elbrus	5634	Caspian Sea	−28
North America	Mt. McKinley	6194	Death Valley	−86
South America	Mt. Aconcagua	6960	Salinas Grandes	−40

Mt. Aconcagua

143. Use the table to find the difference in elevation between Mt. Elbrus and the Caspian Sea.

144. Use the table to find the difference in elevation between Mt. Aconcagua and Salinas Grandes.

145. Use the table to find the difference in elevation between Mt. Kilimanjaro and the Qattara Depression.

146. Use the table to find the difference in elevation between Mt. McKinley and Death Valley.

147. Use the table to find the difference in elevation between Mt. Everest and the Dead Sea.

148. **Temperature** The daily low temperatures, in degrees Celsius, during one week were recorded as follows: 4°, −5°, 8°, 0°, −9°, −11°, −8°. Find the average daily low temperature for the week.

149. **Temperature** The daily high temperatures, in degrees Celsius, during one week were recorded as follows: −8°, −9°, 6°, 7°, −2°, −14°, −1°. Find the average daily high temperature for the week.

150. **Temperature** On January 22, 1943, the temperature at Spearfish, South Dakota, rose from −4°F to 45°F in two minutes. How many degrees did the temperature rise during those two minutes?

151. **Temperature** In a 24-hour period in January of 1916, the temperature in Browning, Montana, dropped from 44°F to −56°F. How many degrees did the temperature drop during that time?

Aviation The table at the right shows the average temperatures at different cruising altitudes for airplanes. Use the table for Exercises 152 and 153.

Cruising Altitude	*Average Temperature*
12,000 ft	16°F
20,000 ft	−12°F
30,000 ft	−48°F
40,000 ft	−70°F
50,000 ft	−70°F

152. What is the difference between the average temperature at 12,000 ft and the average temperature at 40,000 ft?

153. How much colder is the average temperature at 30,000 ft than at 20,000 ft?

154. **Education** To discourage random guessing on a multiple-choice exam, a professor assigns 5 points for a correct answer, −2 points for an incorrect answer, and 0 points for leaving the question blank. What is the score for a student who had 20 correct answers, had 13 incorrect answers, and left 7 questions blank?

155. **Education** To discourage random guessing on a multiple-choice exam, a professor assigns 7 points for a correct answer, −3 points for an incorrect answer, and −1 point for leaving the question blank. What is the score for a student who had 17 correct answers, had 8 incorrect answers, and left 2 questions blank?

156. **The Stock Market** The value of a share of eBay stock on November 15, 2005, was $43.05. The table below shows the amount of increase or decrease, to the nearest 10 cents, from the November 15 closing price of the stock for a 10-day period. Calculate the 5-day moving average for this stock.

Day 1	*Day 2*	*Day 3*	*Day 4*	*Day 5*	*Day 6*	*Day 7*	*Day 8*	*Day 9*	*Day 10*
−50	+130	+90	+150	+60	−10	+10	−130	−90	+30

157. **The Stock Market** The value of a share of Disney stock on November 15, 2005, was $26.06. The table below shows the amount of increase or decrease, to the nearest 10 cents, from the November 15 closing price of the stock for a 10-day period. Calculate the 5-day moving average for this stock.

Day 1	*Day 2*	*Day 3*	*Day 4*	*Day 5*	*Day 6*	*Day 7*	*Day 8*	*Day 9*	*Day 10*
−20	+10	−80	−20	−10	+10	0	+10	0	+20

1.2 Applying Concepts

Simplify.

158. $|-7 + 12|$

159. $|13 - (-4)|$

160. $|-13 - (-2)|$

161. $|18 - 21|$

Assuming the pattern is continued, find the next three numbers in the pattern.

162. $-7, -11, -15, -19, \ldots$

163. $16, 11, 6, 1, \ldots$

164. $7, -14, 28, -56, \ldots$

165. $1024, -256, 64, \ldots$

Solve.

166. 32,844 is divisible by 3. By rearranging the digits, find the largest possible number that is still divisible by 3.

167. 4563 is not divisible by 4. By rearranging the digits, find the largest possible number that is divisible by 4.

168. How many three-digit numbers of the form 8__4 are divisible by 3?

In each exercise, determine which statement is false.

169. **a.** $|3 + 4| = |3| + |4|$ **b.** $|3 - 4| = |3| - |4|$ **c.** $|4 + 3| = |4| + |3|$ **d.** $|4 - 3| = |4| - |3|$

170. **a.** $|5 + 2| = |5| + |2|$ **b.** $|5 - 2| = |5| - |2|$ **c.** $|2 + 5| = |2| + |5|$ **d.** $|2 - 5| = |2| - |5|$

Determine which statement is true for all real numbers.

171. **a.** $|x + y| \le |x| + |y|$ **b.** $|x + y| = |x| + |y|$ **c.** $|x + y| \ge |x| + |y|$

172. **a.** $||x| - |y|| \le |x| - |y|$ **b.** $||x| - |y|| = |x| - |y|$ **c.** $||x| - |y|| \ge |x| - |y|$

173. Is the difference between two integers always smaller than either one of the numbers in the difference? If not, give an example for which the difference between two integers is greater than either integer.

174. If $-4x$ equals a positive integer, is x a positive or a negative integer? Explain your answer.

175. Explain why division by zero is not allowed.

1.3 Rational Numbers

OBJECTIVE 1 Write rational numbers as decimals

Point of Interest

As early as A.D. 630, the Hindu mathematician Brahmagupta wrote a fraction as one number over another separated by a space. The Arab mathematician al Hassar (around A.D. 1050) was the first to show a fraction with the horizontal bar separating the numerator and denominator.

A **rational number** is the quotient of two integers. Therefore, a rational number is a number that can be written in the form $\frac{a}{b}$, where a and b are integers, and b is not zero. A rational number written in this way is commonly called a **fraction.**

$\frac{a}{b}$ ← a: an integer; b: a nonzero integer

$\left.\frac{2}{3}, \frac{-4}{9}, \frac{18}{-5}, \frac{4}{1}\right\}$ Rational numbers

Because an integer can be written as the quotient of the integer and 1, every integer is a rational number.

$5 = \frac{5}{1} \qquad -3 = \frac{-3}{1}$

A number written in **decimal notation** is also a rational number.

three-tenths $0.3 = \frac{3}{10}$

thirty-five hundredths $0.35 = \frac{35}{100}$

negative four-tenths $-0.4 = -\frac{4}{10}$

A rational number written as a fraction can be written in decimal notation.

Take Note

The fraction bar can be read "divided by."

$\frac{5}{8} = 5 \div 8$

Take Note

Dividing the numerator by the denominator results in a remainder of 0. The decimal 0.625 is a terminating decimal.

EXAMPLE 1 Write $\frac{5}{8}$ as a decimal.

Solution

$$\begin{array}{r} 0.625 \\ 8\overline{)5.000} \\ \underline{-4\,8} \\ 20 \\ \underline{-16} \\ 40 \\ \underline{-40} \\ 0 \end{array}$$

0.625 ← This is called a **terminating decimal.**

0 ← The remainder is zero.

$\frac{5}{8} = 0.625$

PROBLEM 1 Write $\frac{4}{25}$ as a decimal.

Solution See page S1.

EXAMPLE 2 Write $\frac{4}{11}$ as a decimal.

Solution

$$\begin{array}{r} 0.3636\ldots \\ 11\overline{)4.0000} \\ \underline{-33} \\ 70 \\ \underline{-66} \\ 40 \\ \underline{-33} \\ 70 \\ \underline{-66} \\ 4 \end{array}$$

← This is called a **repeating decimal.**

← The remainder is never zero.

$\frac{4}{11} = 0.\overline{36}$ ← The bar over the digits 3 and 6 is used to show that these digits repeat.

Take Note

No matter how far we carry out the division, the remainder is never zero. The decimal $0.\overline{36}$ is a repeating decimal.

PROBLEM 2 Write $\frac{4}{9}$ as a decimal. Place a bar over the repeating digits of the decimal.

Solution See page S1.

Rational numbers can be written as fractions, such as $-\frac{6}{7}$ or $\frac{8}{3}$, where the numerator and denominator are integers. But every rational number also can be written as a repeating decimal (such as 0.25767676 . . .) or a terminating decimal (such as 1.73). This was illustrated in Examples 1 and 2.

Numbers that cannot be written either as a repeating decimal or as a terminating decimal are called **irrational numbers.** For example, 2.45445444544445... is an irrational number. Two other examples are $\sqrt{2}$ and π.

$$\sqrt{2} = 1.414213562\ldots \qquad \pi = 3.141592654\ldots$$

The three dots mean that the digits continue on and on without ever repeating or terminating. Although we cannot write a decimal that is exactly equal to $\sqrt{2}$ or to π, we can give approximations of these numbers. The symbol $\approx$ is read "is approximately equal to." Shown below are $\sqrt{2}$ rounded to the nearest thousandth and π rounded to the nearest hundredth.

$$\sqrt{2} \approx 1.414 \qquad \pi \approx 3.14$$

The rational numbers and the irrational numbers taken together are called the **real numbers.**

OBJECTIVE 2 Multiply and divide rational numbers

The sign rules for multiplying and dividing integers apply to multiplication and division of rational numbers.

The product of two fractions is the product of the numerators divided by the product of the denominators.

EXAMPLE 3 Multiply: $\frac{3}{8} \cdot \frac{12}{17}$

Solution

$$\frac{3}{8} \cdot \frac{12}{17} = \frac{3 \cdot 12}{8 \cdot 17}$$

- **Multiply the numerators. Multiply the denominators.**

$$= \frac{3 \cdot \overset{1}{\cancel{2}} \cdot \overset{1}{\cancel{2}} \cdot 3}{2 \cdot \underset{1}{\cancel{2}} \cdot \underset{1}{\cancel{2}} \cdot 17}$$

- **Write the prime factorization of each factor. Divide by the common factors.**

$$= \frac{9}{34}$$

- **Multiply the numbers remaining in the numerator. Multiply the numbers remaining in the denominator.**

PROBLEM 3 Multiply: $-\frac{7}{12} \cdot \frac{9}{14}$

Solution See page S1.

The **reciprocal** of a fraction is the fraction with the numerator and denominator interchanged. For instance, the reciprocal of $\frac{2}{3}$ is $\frac{3}{2}$, and the reciprocal of $-\frac{5}{4}$ is $-\frac{4}{5}$. To divide fractions, multiply the dividend by the reciprocal of the divisor.

Take Note

The method for dividing fractions is sometimes stated "To divide fractions, invert the divisor and multiply." Inverting the divisor means writing its reciprocal.

EXAMPLE 4 Divide: $\frac{3}{10} \div \left(-\frac{18}{25}\right)$

Solution

$$\frac{3}{10} \div \left(-\frac{18}{25}\right) = -\left(\frac{3}{10} \div \frac{18}{25}\right)$$

- **The signs are different. The quotient is negative.**

$$= -\left(\frac{3}{10} \cdot \frac{25}{18}\right)$$

- **Change division to multiplication. Invert the divisor.**

$$= -\left(\frac{3 \cdot 25}{10 \cdot 18}\right)$$

- **Multiply the numerators. Multiply the denominators.**

$$= -\left(\frac{\overset{1}{\cancel{3}} \cdot \overset{1}{\cancel{5}} \cdot 5}{2 \cdot \underset{1}{\cancel{5}} \cdot 2 \cdot \underset{1}{\cancel{3}} \cdot 3}\right)$$

$$= -\frac{5}{12}$$

PROBLEM 4 Divide: $-\frac{3}{8} \div \left(-\frac{5}{12}\right)$

Solution See page S1.

To multiply decimals, multiply as in the multiplication of whole numbers. Write the decimal point in the product so that the number of decimal places in the product equals the sum of the decimal places in the factors.

EXAMPLE 5 Multiply: $(-6.89)(0.00035)$

Solution

$$\begin{array}{rl} 6.89 & \text{2 decimal places} \\ \times\, 0.00035 & \text{5 decimal places} \\ \hline 3445 & \\ 2067 & \\ \hline 0.0024115 & \text{7 decimal places} \end{array}$$

• **Multiply the absolute values.**

$(-6.89)(0.00035) = -0.0024115$

• **The signs are different. The product is negative.**

PROBLEM 5 Multiply: $(-5.44)(3.8)$

Solution See page S2.

To divide decimals, move the decimal point in the divisor to make it a whole number. Move the decimal point in the dividend the same number of places to the right. Place the decimal point in the quotient directly over the decimal point in the dividend. Then divide as in the division of whole numbers.

EXAMPLE 6 Divide: $1.32 \div 0.27$. Round to the nearest tenth.

Solution $0.27.\overline{)1.32.}$

• **Move the decimal point two places to the right in the divisor and in the dividend. Place the decimal point in the quotient.**

$$\begin{array}{r} 4.88 \approx 4.9 \\ 27.\overline{)132.00} \\ -108 \\ \hline 24\ 0 \\ -21\ 6 \\ \hline 2\ 40 \\ -2\ 16 \\ \hline 24 \end{array}$$

• **The symbol $\approx$ is used to indicate that the quotient is an approximate value that has been rounded off.**

PROBLEM 6 Divide $-0.394 \div 1.7$. Round to the nearest hundredth.

Solution See page S2.

Take Note

Moving the decimal point in the numerator and denominator is the same as multiplying the numerator and the denominator by the same number. For the problem at the right, we have

$$1.32 \div 0.27 = \frac{1.32}{0.27} = \frac{1.32}{0.27} \cdot \frac{100}{100} = \frac{132}{27}$$

OBJECTIVE 3 Add and subtract rational numbers

The sign rules for adding integers apply to addition of rational numbers.

To add or subtract rational numbers written as fractions, first rewrite the fractions as equivalent fractions with a common denominator. The common denominator is the **least common multiple (LCM)** of the denominators. The LCM of the denominators is also called the **lowest common denominator (LCD).**

EXAMPLE 7 Add: $-\frac{5}{6} + \frac{3}{10}$

Solution Prime factorization of 6 and 10:

• **Find the LCM of the denominators 6 and 10.**

$6 = 2 \cdot 3 \qquad 10 = 2 \cdot 5$

$\text{LCM} = 2 \cdot 3 \cdot 5 = 30$

Take Note

You can find the LCM by multiplying the denominators and then dividing by the greatest *common factor* of the two denominators. In the case of 6 and 10, $6 \cdot 10 = 60$. Now divide by 2, the greatest common factor of 6 and 10.

$$60 \div 2 = 30$$

Alternatively, you can use as the common denominator the product of the denominators, which in this case is 60. Write each fraction with a denominator of 60. Add the fractions. Then simplify the sum.

$$-\frac{5}{6} + \frac{3}{10} = -\frac{50}{60} + \frac{18}{60} = \frac{-50 + 18}{60} = \frac{-32}{60} = -\frac{8}{15}$$

$$-\frac{5}{6} + \frac{3}{10} = -\frac{25}{30} + \frac{9}{30}$$

• **Rewrite the fractions as equivalent fractions, using the LCM of the denominators as the common denominator.**

$$= \frac{-25 + 9}{30}$$

• **Add the numerators, and place the sum over the common denominator.**

$$= \frac{-16}{30}$$

$$= -\frac{8}{15}$$

• **Write the answer in simplest form.**

PROBLEM 7 Subtract: $\frac{5}{9} - \frac{11}{12}$

Solution See page S2.

EXAMPLE 8 Simplify: $-\frac{3}{4} + \frac{1}{6} - \frac{5}{8}$

Solution

$$-\frac{3}{4} + \frac{1}{6} - \frac{5}{8} = -\frac{18}{24} + \frac{4}{24} - \frac{15}{24}$$

• **The LCM of 4, 6, and 8 is 24.**

$$= \frac{-18}{24} + \frac{4}{24} + \frac{-15}{24}$$

$$= \frac{-18 + 4 + (-15)}{24}$$

$$= \frac{-29}{24}$$

$$= -\frac{29}{24}$$

PROBLEM 8 Simplify: $-\frac{7}{8} - \frac{5}{6} + \frac{1}{2}$

Solution See page S2.

To add or subtract decimals, write the numbers so that the decimal points are in a vertical line. Then proceed as in the addition or subtraction of integers. Write the decimal point in the answer directly below the decimal points in the problem.

EXAMPLE 9 Add: $14.02 + 137.6 + 9.852$

Solution

```
   14.02
  137.6
+   9.852
  -------
  161.472
```

• **Write the decimals so that the decimal points are in a vertical line.**

• **Write the decimal point in the sum directly below the decimal points in the problem.**

PROBLEM 9 Add: $3.097 + 4.9 + 3.09$

Solution See page S2.

EXAMPLE 10 Add: $-114.039 + 84.76$

Solution

$$\begin{array}{r} 114.039 \\ -\ 84.76 \\ \hline 29.279 \end{array}$$

• **The signs are different. Subtract the absolute value of the number with the smaller absolute value from the absolute value of the number with the larger absolute value.**

$-114.039 + 84.76$
$= -29.279$

• **Attach the sign of the number with the larger absolute value.**

PROBLEM 10 Subtract: $16.127 - 67.91$

Solution See page S2.

OBJECTIVE 4 Convert among percents, fractions, and decimals

"A population growth rate of 3%," "a manufacturer's discount of 25%," and "an 8% increase in pay" are typical examples of the many ways in which percent is used in applied problems. **Percent** means "parts of 100." Thus 27% means 27 parts of 100.

In applied problems involving a percent, it is usually necessary either to rewrite the percent as a fraction or a decimal, or to rewrite a fraction or a decimal as a percent.

To write 27% as a fraction, remove the percent sign and multiply by $\frac{1}{100}$.

$$27\% = 27\left(\frac{1}{100}\right) = \frac{27}{100}$$

To write a percent as a decimal, remove the percent sign and multiply by 0.01.

To write 33% as a decimal, remove the percent sign and multiply by 0.01.

$$33\% = 33(0.01) = 0.33$$

Move the decimal point two places to the left. Then remove the percent sign.

Write 100% as a decimal.

$$100\% = 100(0.01) = 1$$

EXAMPLE 11 Write 130% as a fraction and as a decimal.

Solution $130\% = 130\left(\frac{1}{100}\right) = \frac{130}{100} = 1\frac{3}{10}$

• **To write a percent as a fraction, remove the percent sign and multiply by $\frac{1}{100}$.**

$130\% = 130(0.01) = 1.30$

• **To write a percent as a decimal, remove the percent sign and multiply by 0.01.**

PROBLEM 11 Write 125% as a fraction and as a decimal.

Solution See page S2.

EXAMPLE 12 Write $33\frac{1}{3}\%$ as a fraction.

Solution $33\frac{1}{3}\% = 33\frac{1}{3}\left(\frac{1}{100}\right) = \frac{100}{3}\left(\frac{1}{100}\right)$
$= \frac{1}{3}$

- **Write the mixed number $33\frac{1}{3}$ as the improper fraction $\frac{100}{3}$.**

PROBLEM 12 Write $16\frac{2}{3}\%$ as a fraction.

Solution See page S2.

EXAMPLE 13 Write 0.25% as a decimal.

Solution $0.25\% = 0.25(0.01) = 0.0025$

- **Remove the percent sign and multiply by 0.01.**

PROBLEM 13 Write 6.08% as a decimal.

Solution See page S2.

A fraction or decimal can be written as a percent by multiplying by 100%. Recall that 100% = 1, and multiplying a number by 1 does not change the number.

To write $\frac{5}{8}$ as a percent, multiply by 100%.

$$\frac{5}{8} = \frac{5}{8}(100\%) = \frac{500}{8}\% = 62.5\% \text{ or } 62\frac{1}{2}\%$$

To write 0.82 as a percent, multiply by 100%.

$$0.82 = 0.82(100\%) = 82\%$$

Move the decimal point two places to the right. Then write the percent sign.

EXAMPLE 14 Write as a percent. **A.** 0.027 **B.** 1.34

Solution **A.** $0.027 = 0.027(100\%) = 2.7\%$

B. $1.34 = 1.34(100\%) = 134\%$

- **To write a decimal as a percent, multiply by 100%.**

PROBLEM 14 Write as a percent. **A.** 0.043 **B.** 2.57

Solution See page S2.

EXAMPLE 15 Write $\frac{5}{6}$ as a percent. Round to the nearest tenth of a percent.

Solution $\frac{5}{6} = \frac{5}{6}(100\%) = \frac{500}{6}\% \approx 83.3\%$

- **To write a fraction as a percent, multiply by 100%.**

PROBLEM 15 Write $\frac{5}{9}$ as a percent. Round to the nearest tenth of a percent.

Solution See page S2.

EXAMPLE 16 Write $\frac{7}{16}$ as a percent. Write the remainder in fractional form.

Solution $\frac{7}{16} = \frac{7}{16}(100\%) = \frac{700}{16}\% = 43\frac{3}{4}\%$ • **Multiply the fraction by 100%.**

PROBLEM 16 Write $\frac{9}{16}$ as a percent. Write the remainder in fractional form.

Solution See page S2.

1.3 Concept Review

Determine whether the statement is always true, sometimes true, or never true.

1. To multiply two fractions, you must first rewrite the fractions as equivalent fractions with a common denominator.
2. The number $\frac{\pi}{3}$ is an example of a rational number.
3. A rational number can be written as a terminating decimal.
4. The number 2.585585558... is an example of a repeating decimal.
5. An irrational number is a real number.
6. 37%, 0.37, and $\frac{37}{100}$ are three numbers that have the same value.
7. To write a decimal as a percent, multiply the decimal by $\frac{1}{100}$.
8. If a, b, c, and d are natural numbers, then $\frac{a}{b} + \frac{c}{d} = \frac{a+c}{b+d}$.
9. −12 is an example of a number that is both an integer and a rational number.
10. $\frac{7}{9}$ is an example of a number that is both a rational number and an irrational number.

1.3 Exercises

1 Write rational numbers as decimals

1. To write $\frac{2}{3}$ as a decimal, divide ___?___ by ___?___. The quotient is 0.6666..., which is a ___?___ decimal.
2. A number such as 0.747447444474444..., whose decimal representation neither ends nor repeats, is an example of an ___?___ number.

Write as a decimal. Place a bar over the repeating digits of a repeating decimal.

3. $\frac{1}{3}$ **4.** $\frac{2}{3}$ **5.** $\frac{1}{4}$ **6.** $\frac{3}{4}$ **7.** $\frac{2}{5}$

8. $\frac{4}{5}$ **9.** $\frac{1}{6}$ **10.** $\frac{5}{6}$ **11.** $\frac{1}{8}$ **12.** $\frac{7}{8}$

13. $\frac{2}{9}$ **14.** $\frac{8}{9}$ **15.** $\frac{5}{11}$ **16.** $\frac{10}{11}$ **17.** $\frac{7}{12}$

18. $\frac{11}{12}$ **19.** $\frac{4}{15}$ **20.** $\frac{8}{15}$ **21.** $\frac{7}{16}$ **22.** $\frac{15}{16}$

23. $\frac{6}{25}$ **24.** $\frac{14}{25}$ **25.** $\frac{9}{40}$ **26.** $\frac{21}{40}$ **27.** $\frac{15}{22}$

28. $\frac{19}{22}$ **29.** $\frac{11}{24}$ **30.** $\frac{19}{24}$ **31.** $\frac{5}{33}$ **32.** $\frac{25}{33}$

33. To write $\frac{a}{b}$ as a decimal, we divide a by b (b is not zero). After finding the quotient to ten decimal places, we still have a nonzero remainder and no repeating pattern of digits. Can you conclude that $\frac{a}{b}$ is an irrational number?

34. Is $\frac{\sqrt{2}}{2}$ a rational or an irrational number?

2 Multiply and divide rational numbers

35. The product of 1.762 and −8.4 will have __?__ decimal places.

36. The reciprocal of $\frac{4}{9}$ is __?__. To find the quotient $-\frac{2}{3} \div \frac{4}{9}$, find the product $-\frac{2}{3} \cdot$ __?__. The quotient $-\frac{2}{3} \div \frac{4}{9}$ is __?__.

Simplify.

37. $\frac{1}{2}\left(-\frac{3}{4}\right)$ **38.** $-\frac{2}{9}\left(-\frac{3}{14}\right)$ **39.** $\left(-\frac{3}{8}\right)\left(-\frac{4}{15}\right)$

40. $\frac{5}{8}\left(-\frac{7}{12}\right)\frac{16}{25}$

41. $\left(\frac{1}{2}\right)\left(-\frac{3}{4}\right)\left(-\frac{5}{8}\right)$

42. $\left(\frac{5}{12}\right)\left(-\frac{8}{15}\right)\left(-\frac{1}{3}\right)$

43. $\frac{3}{8} \div \frac{1}{4}$

44. $\frac{5}{6} \div \left(-\frac{3}{4}\right)$

45. $-\frac{5}{12} \div \frac{15}{32}$

46. $\frac{1}{8} \div \left(-\frac{5}{12}\right)$

47. $-\frac{4}{9} \div \left(-\frac{2}{3}\right)$

48. $-\frac{6}{11} \div \frac{4}{9}$

49. $(1.2)(3.47)$

50. $(-0.8)(6.2)$

51. $(-1.89)(-2.3)$

52. $(6.9)(-4.2)$

53. $(1.06)(-3.8)$

54. $(-2.7)(-3.5)$

55. $(1.2)(-0.5)(3.7)$

56. $(-2.4)(6.1)(0.9)$

57. $(-0.8)(3.006)(-5.1)$

Complete Exercises 58 and 59 without actually finding the products and quotients.

58. State whether each product or quotient is positive or negative.

a. $\left(-\frac{11}{12}\right)\left(-\frac{5}{4}\right)\left(-\frac{1}{2}\right)$ **b.** $-1.572 \div -8.4$

59. State whether each product or quotient is greater than one or less than one.

a. $\frac{11}{13} \cdot \frac{50}{51}$ **b.** $8.713 \div 7.2$

Simplify. Round to the nearest hundredth.

60. $-24.7 \div 0.09$

61. $-1.27 \div (-1.7)$

62. $9.07 \div (-3.5)$

63. $-354.2086 \div 0.1719$

64. $-2658.3109 \div (-0.0473)$

65. $(-3.92) \div (-45.008)$

3 Add and subtract rational numbers

66. The least common multiple of the denominators of the fractions $\frac{5}{8}$, $-\frac{1}{6}$, and $\frac{2}{9}$ is ___?___.

67. Write the fraction $\frac{3}{14}$ as an equivalent fraction with the denominator 28: $\frac{3}{14} = \frac{?}{28}$.

Simplify.

68. $\frac{3}{8} + \frac{5}{8}$

69. $-\frac{1}{4} + \frac{3}{4}$

70. $\frac{7}{8} - \frac{3}{8}$

71. $-\frac{5}{6} - \frac{1}{6}$

72. $-\frac{5}{12} - \frac{3}{8}$

73. $-\frac{5}{6} - \frac{5}{9}$

74. $-\frac{6}{13} + \frac{17}{26}$

75. $-\frac{7}{12} + \frac{5}{8}$

76. $-\frac{5}{8} - \left(-\frac{11}{12}\right)$

77. $\frac{1}{3} + \frac{5}{6} - \frac{2}{9}$

78. $\frac{1}{2} - \frac{2}{3} + \frac{1}{6}$

79. $-\frac{3}{8} - \frac{5}{12} - \frac{3}{16}$

80. $-\frac{5}{16} + \frac{3}{4} - \frac{7}{8}$

81. $\frac{1}{2} - \frac{3}{8} - \left(-\frac{1}{4}\right)$

82. $\frac{3}{4} - \left(-\frac{7}{12}\right) - \frac{7}{8}$

83. $\frac{1}{3} - \frac{1}{4} - \frac{1}{5}$

84. $\frac{2}{3} - \frac{1}{2} + \frac{5}{6}$

85. $\frac{5}{16} + \frac{1}{8} - \frac{1}{2}$

86. $\frac{5}{8} - \left(-\frac{5}{12}\right) + \frac{1}{3}$

87. $\frac{1}{8} - \frac{11}{12} + \frac{1}{2}$

88. $-\frac{7}{9} + \frac{14}{15} + \frac{8}{21}$

89. $1.09 + 6.2$

90. $-32.1 - 6.7$

91. $5.13 - 8.179$

92. $-13.092 + 6.9$

93. $2.54 - 3.6$

94. $5.43 + 7.925$

95. $-16.92 - 6.925$

96. $-3.87 + 8.546$

97. $6.9027 - 17.692$

98. $2.09 - 6.72 - 5.4$

99. $16.4 + 3.09 - 7.93$

100. $-18.39 + 4.9 - 23.7$

101. $19 - (-3.72) - 82.75$

102. $-3.07 - (-2.97) - 17.4$

103. $-3.09 - 4.6 - 27.3$

104. $317.09 - 46.902 + 583.0714$

105. $71.0235 - 86.0974 + 254.309$

Complete Exercises 106 and 107 without actually finding the sums and differences.

106. State whether each sum or difference is positive or negative.

a. $\frac{1}{5} - \frac{1}{2}$ **b.** $-21.765 + 15.1$ **c.** $0.837 + (-0.24)$ **d.** $-\frac{3}{4} + \frac{9}{10}$

107. Estimate each sum to the nearest integer.

a. $\frac{7}{8} + \frac{4}{5}$ **b.** $\frac{1}{3} + \left(-\frac{1}{2}\right)$ **c.** $-0.125 + 1.25$ **d.** $-1.3 + 0.2$

4 Convert among percents, fractions, and decimals

108. **a.** Explain how to convert a fraction to a percent.
b. Explain how to convert a percent to a fraction.

109. **a.** Explain how to convert a decimal to a percent.
b. Explain how to convert a percent to a decimal.

110. Explain why multiplying a number by 100% does not change the value of the number.

111. To write 80% as a fraction, remove the percent sign and multiply by ___?___: 80% = 80 · ___?___ = ___?___.

112. To write 68% as a decimal, remove the percent sign and multiply by ___?___: 68% = 68 · ___?___ = ___?___.

113. To write $\frac{3}{10}$ as a percent, multiply by ___?___: $\frac{3}{10} = \frac{3}{10} \cdot$ ___?___ = ___?___.

114. To write 1.25 as a percent, multiply by ___?___: 1.25 = 1.25 · ___?___ = ___?___.

Write as a fraction and as a decimal.

115. 75% **116.** 40% **117.** 50% **118.** 10%

119. 64% **120.** 88% **121.** 175% **122.** 160%

123. 19% **124.** 87% **125.** 5% **126.** 2%

127. 450% **128.** 380% **129.** 8% **130.** 4%

Write as a fraction.

131. $11\frac{1}{9}\%$ **132.** $37\frac{1}{2}\%$ **133.** $31\frac{1}{4}\%$ **134.** $66\frac{2}{3}\%$

135. $\frac{1}{2}\%$ **136.** $5\frac{3}{4}\%$ **137.** $6\frac{1}{4}\%$ **138.** $83\frac{1}{3}\%$

Write as a decimal.

139. 7.3% **140.** 9.1% **141.** 15.8% **142.** 0.3%

143. 9.15% **144.** 121.2% **145.** 18.23% **146.** 0.15%

Write as a percent.

147. 0.15 **148.** 0.37 **149.** 0.05 **150.** 0.02

151. 0.175 **152.** 0.125 **153.** 1.15 **154.** 2.142

155. 0.008 **156.** 0.004 **157.** 0.065 **158.** 0.083

Write as a percent. Round to the nearest tenth of a percent.

159. $\frac{27}{50}$ **160.** $\frac{83}{100}$ **161.** $\frac{1}{3}$ **162.** $\frac{3}{8}$

163. $\frac{4}{9}$ **164.** $\frac{9}{20}$ **165.** $2\frac{1}{2}$ **166.** $1\frac{2}{7}$

Write as a percent. Write the remainder in fractional form.

167. $\frac{3}{8}$ **168.** $\frac{3}{16}$ **169.** $\frac{5}{14}$ **170.** $\frac{4}{7}$

171. $1\frac{1}{4}$ **172.** $2\frac{5}{8}$ **173.** $1\frac{5}{9}$ **174.** $1\frac{13}{16}$

Complete Exercises 175 and 176 without actually finding the percents.

175. Does $\frac{4}{3}$ represent a number greater than 100% or less than 100%?

176. Does 0.055 represent a number greater than 1% or less than 1%?

Employment The graph at the right shows the responses to a survey that asked respondents, "How did you find your most recent job?" Use the graph for Exercises 177 to 179.

177. What fraction of the respondents found their most recent jobs on the Internet?

178. What fraction of the respondents found their most recent jobs through a referral?

179. Did more or less than one-quarter of the respondents find their most recent jobs through a newspaper ad?

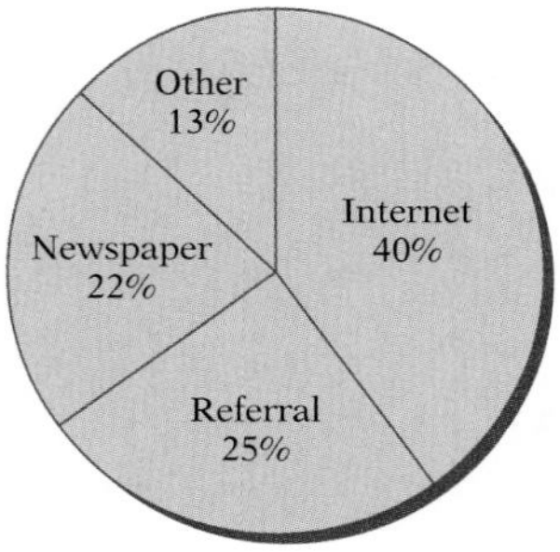

How Did You Find Your Most Recent Job?

1.3 Applying Concepts

Classify each of the following numbers as a natural number, an integer, a positive integer, a negative integer, a rational number, an irrational number, or a real number. List all that apply.

180. -1 **181.** 28

182. $-\frac{9}{34}$

183. -7.707

184. $5.2\overline{6}$

185. $0.171771777\ldots$

Solve.

186. Find the average of $\frac{5}{8}$ and $\frac{3}{4}$.

187. **The Postal Service** Postage for first-class mail is \$.39 for the first ounce or fraction of an ounce and \$.24 for each additional ounce or fraction of an ounce. Find the cost of mailing, by first-class mail, a letter that weighs $4\frac{1}{2}$ oz.

Government The table at the right shows the surplus or deficit, in billions of dollars, for the federal budget for selected years from 1945 through 2000. A negative sign (−) indicates a deficit. Use this table for Exercises 188 to 193. (*Source:* U.S. Office of Management and Budget)

Year	*Federal Budget Surplus or Deficit (in billions of dollars)*
1945	−47.553
1950	−3.119
1955	−2.993
1960	0.301
1965	−1.411
1970	−2.842
1975	−53.242
1980	−73.835
1985	−212.334
1990	−221.194
1995	−163.899
1996	−107.450
1997	−21.940
1998	69.246
1999	79.263
2000	117.305

188. In which year listed was the deficit greatest?

189. Find the difference between the deficits in the years 1980 and 1985.

190. Calculate the difference between the surplus in 1960 and the deficit in 1955.

191. How many times greater was the deficit in 1985 than in 1975? Round to the nearest whole number.

192. What was the average deficit per quarter, in millions of dollars, for the year 1970?

193. Find the average surplus or deficit for the years 1995 through 2000. Round to the nearest million.

194. Use a calculator to determine the decimal representations of $\frac{17}{99}$, $\frac{45}{99}$, and $\frac{73}{99}$. Make a conjecture as to the decimal representation of $\frac{83}{99}$. Does your conjecture work for $\frac{33}{99}$? What about $\frac{1}{99}$?

195. If the same positive integer is added to both the numerator and the denominator of $\frac{2}{5}$, is the new fraction less than, equal to, or greater than $\frac{2}{5}$?

196. A magic square is one in which the numbers in every row, column, and diagonal sum to the same number. Complete the magic square at the right.

$\frac{2}{3}$		
	$\frac{1}{6}$	$\frac{5}{6}$
		$-\frac{1}{3}$

197. Let x represent the price of a car. If the sales tax is 6% of the price, express the total of the price of the car and the sales tax in terms of x.

198. Let x represent the price of a suit. If the suit is on sale at a discount rate of 30%, express the price of the suit after the discount in terms of x.

199. The price of a pen was 60¢. During a storewide sale, the price was reduced to a different whole number of cents, and the entire stock was sold for $54.59. Find the price of the pen during the sale.

200. Find three natural numbers a, b, and c such that $\frac{1}{a} + \frac{1}{b} + \frac{1}{c}$ is a natural number.

201. If a and b are rational numbers and $a < b$, is it always possible to find a rational number c such that $a < c < b$? If not, explain why. If so, show how to find one.

202. In your own words, define **a.** a rational number, **b.** an irrational number, and **c.** a real number.

203. Explain why you "invert and multiply" when dividing a fraction by a fraction.

204. Explain why you need a common denominator when adding two fractions and why you don't need a common denominator when multiplying two fractions.

1.4 Exponents and the Order of Operations Agreement

OBJECTIVE 1 Exponential expressions

Point of Interest

René Descartes (1596–1650) was the first mathematician to use exponential notation extensively as it is used today. However, for some unknown reason, he always used xx for x^2.

Repeated multiplication of the same factor can be written using an exponent.

$$2 \cdot 2 \cdot 2 \cdot 2 \cdot 2 = 2^5 \quad (\text{2 is the base, 5 is the exponent}) \qquad a \cdot a \cdot a \cdot a = a^4 \quad (a \text{ is the base, 4 is the exponent})$$

The **exponent** indicates how many times the factor, called the **base,** occurs in the multiplication. The multiplication $2 \cdot 2 \cdot 2 \cdot 2 \cdot 2$ is in **factored form.** The exponential expression 2^5 is in **exponential form.**

2^1 is read "the first power of two" or just "two." → Usually the exponent 1 is not written.

2^2 is read "the second power of two" or "two squared."

2^3 is read "the third power of two" or "two cubed."

2^4 is read "the fourth power of two."

2^5 is read "the fifth power of two."

a^5 is read "the fifth power of a."

There is a geometric interpretation of the first three natural-number powers.

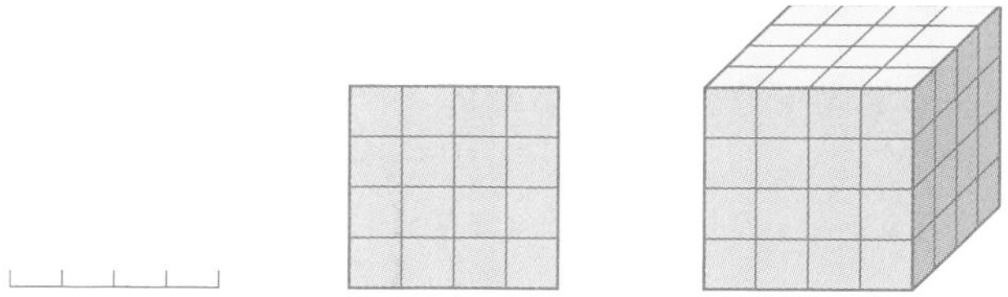

$4^1 = 4$
Length: 4 ft

$4^2 = 16$
Area: 16 ft^2

$4^3 = 64$
Volume: 64 ft^3

To evaluate an exponential expression, write each factor as many times as indicated by the exponent. Then multiply.

$$3^5 = 3 \cdot 3 \cdot 3 \cdot 3 \cdot 3 = 243$$
$$2^3 \cdot 3^2 = (2 \cdot 2 \cdot 2) \cdot (3 \cdot 3) = 8 \cdot 9 = 72$$

Take Note

The -4 is squared only when the negative sign is *inside* the parentheses. In $(-4)^2$, we are squaring -4; in -4^2, we are finding the opposite of 4^2.

EXAMPLE 1 Evaluate $(-4)^2$ and -4^2.

Solution $(-4)^2 = (-4)(-4) = 16$

$-4^2 = -(4 \cdot 4) = -16$

PROBLEM 1 Evaluate $(-5)^3$ and -5^3.

Solution See page S2.

Take Note

The product of an even number of negative factors is positive. The product of an odd number of negative factors is negative.

EXAMPLE 2 Evaluate $(-2)^4$ and $(-2)^5$.

Solution

$$\begin{aligned}(-2)^4 &= (-2)(-2)(-2)(-2)\\ &= 4(-2)(-2)\\ &= -8(-2)\\ &= 16\end{aligned}$$

$$\begin{aligned}(-2)^5 &= (-2)(-2)(-2)(-2)(-2)\\ &= 4(-2)(-2)(-2)\\ &= -8(-2)(-2)\\ &= 16(-2)\\ &= -32\end{aligned}$$

PROBLEM 2 Evaluate $(-3)^3$ and $(-3)^4$.

Solution See page S2.

EXAMPLE 3 Evaluate $(-3)^2 \cdot 2^3$ and $\left(-\frac{2}{3}\right)^3$.

Solution $(-3)^2 \cdot 2^3 = (-3)(-3) \cdot (2)(2)(2) = 9 \cdot 8 = 72$

$$\left(-\frac{2}{3}\right)^3 = \left(-\frac{2}{3}\right)\left(-\frac{2}{3}\right)\left(-\frac{2}{3}\right) = -\frac{2 \cdot 2 \cdot 2}{3 \cdot 3 \cdot 3} = -\frac{8}{27}$$

PROBLEM 3 Evaluate $(3^3)(-2)^3$ and $\left(-\frac{2}{5}\right)^2$.

Solution See page S2.

OBJECTIVE 2 The Order of Operations Agreement

Evaluate $2 + 3 \cdot 5$.

There are two arithmetic operations, addition and multiplication, in this problem. The operations could be performed in different orders.

Add first.	$\underbrace{2 + 3} \cdot 5$	Multiply first.	$2 + \underbrace{3 \cdot 5}$
Then multiply.	$\underbrace{5 \cdot 5}_{25}$	Then add.	$\underbrace{2 + 15}_{17}$

In order to prevent there being more than one answer to the same problem, an Order of Operations Agreement has been established.

The Order of Operations Agreement

Step 1 Perform operations inside grouping symbols. **Grouping symbols** include parentheses ( ), brackets [ ], absolute value symbols | |, and the fraction bar.

Step 2 Simplify exponential expressions.

Step 3 Do multiplication and division as they occur from left to right.

Step 4 Do addition and subtraction as they occur from left to right.

EXAMPLE 4 Simplify: $12 - 24(8 - 5) \div 2^2$

Solution $12 - 24(8 - 5) \div 2^2$

$= 12 - 24(3) \div 2^2$ • **Perform operations inside grouping symbols.**

$= 12 - 24(3) \div 4$ • **Simplify exponential expressions.**

$= 12 - 72 \div 4$ • **Do multiplication and division as they occur from left to right.**

$= 12 - 18$

$= -6$ • **Do addition and subtraction as they occur from left to right.**

PROBLEM 4 Simplify: $36 \div (8 - 5)^2 - (-3)^2 \cdot 2$

Solution See page S2.

One or more of the steps shown in Example 4 may not be needed to simplify an expression. In that case, proceed to the next step in the Order of Operations Agreement.

EXAMPLE 5 Simplify: $\frac{4+8}{2+1} - |3-1| + 2$

Solution $\frac{4+8}{2+1} - |3-1| + 2$

$= \frac{12}{3} - |2| + 2$ — **• Perform operations inside grouping symbols (above and below the fraction bar and inside the absolute value symbols).**

$= \frac{12}{3} - 2 + 2$ — **• Find the absolute value of 2.**

$= 4 - 2 + 2$ — **• Do multiplication and division as they occur from left to right.**

$= 2 + 2$ — **• Do addition and subtraction as they occur from left to right.**

$= 4$

PROBLEM 5 Simplify: $27 \div 3^2 + (-3)^2 \cdot 4$

Solution See page S2.

When an expression has grouping symbols inside grouping symbols, first perform the operations inside the *inner* grouping symbols by following Steps 2, 3, and 4 of the Order of Operations Agreement. Then perform the operations inside the *outer* grouping symbols by following Steps 2, 3, and 4 in sequence.

EXAMPLE 6 Simplify: $6 \div [4 - (6 - 8)] + 2^2$

Solution $6 \div [4 - (6 - 8)] + 2^2$

$= 6 \div [4 - (-2)] + 2^2$ — **• Perform operations inside inner grouping symbols.**

$= 6 \div 6 + 2^2$ — **• Perform operations inside outer grouping symbols.**

$= 6 \div 6 + 4$ — **• Simplify exponential expressions.**

$= 1 + 4$ — **• Do multiplication and division.**

$= 5$ — **• Do addition and subtraction.**

PROBLEM 6 Simplify: $4 - 3[4 - 2(6 - 3)] \div 2$

Solution See page S2.

1.4 Concept Review

Determine whether the statement is always true, sometimes true, or never true.

1. $(-5)^2$, -5^2, and $-(5)^2$ all represent the same number.

2. By the Order of Operations Agreement, addition is performed before division.

3. In the expression 3^8, 8 is the base.

4. The expression 9^4 is in exponential form.

5. To evaluate the expression $6 + 7 \cdot 10$ means to determine what one number it is equal to.

6. When using the Order of Operations Agreement, we consider the absolute value symbol a grouping symbol.

7. Using the Order of Operations Agreement, it is possible to get more than one correct answer to a problem.

8. The Order of Operations Agreement is used for natural numbers, integers, rational numbers, and real numbers.

9. The expression $(2^3)^2$ equals $2^{(3^2)}$.

10. Suppose a and b are positive integers. Then $a^b = b^a$.

1.4 Exercises

1 Exponential expressions

1. In the expression $(-5)^2$, -5 is called the ___?___ and 2 is called the ___?___. To evaluate $(-5)^2$, find the product (___?___)(___?___) = ___?___.

2. The exponential expression 4^3 is read "the ___?___ power of ___?___" or "four ___?___." To evaluate 4^3, find the product (___?___)(___?___)(___?___) = ___?___.

Evaluate.

3. 6^2

4. 7^4

5. -7^2

6. -4^3

7. $(-3)^2$

8. $(-2)^3$

9. $(-3)^4$

10. $(-5)^3$

11. $\left(\frac{1}{2}\right)^2$

12. $\left(-\frac{3}{4}\right)^3$

13. $(0.3)^2$

14. $(1.5)^3$

15. $\left(\frac{2}{3}\right)^2 \cdot 3^3$

16. $\left(-\frac{1}{2}\right)^3 \cdot 8$

17. $(0.3)^3 \cdot 2^3$

18. $(0.5)^2 \cdot 3^3$

19. $(-3) \cdot 2^2$

20. $(-5) \cdot 3^4$

21. $(-2) \cdot (-2)^3$

22. $(-2) \cdot (-2)^2$

23. $2^3 \cdot 3^3 \cdot (-4)$

24. $(-3)^3 \cdot 5^2 \cdot 10$

25. $(-7) \cdot 4^2 \cdot 3^2$

26. $(-2) \cdot 2^3 \cdot (-3)^2$

27. $\left(\frac{2}{3}\right)^2 \cdot \frac{1}{4} \cdot 3^3$

28. $\left(\frac{3}{4}\right)^2 \cdot (-4) \cdot 2^3$

29. $8^2 \cdot (-3)^5 \cdot 5$

Complete Exercises 30 and 31 without actually finding the products.

30. Is the fifth power of negative eighteen positive or negative?

31. Is the product $-(3^2)(-5^3)$ positive or negative?

2 The Order of Operations Agreement

32. Why do we need an Order of Operations Agreement?

33. Describe each step in the Order of Operations Agreement.

34. Simplify: $2(3^3)$

$2(3^3) = 2(\underline{\ \ ?\ \ })$	• **Simplify exponential expressions.**
$= \underline{\ \ ?\ \ }$	• **Do multiplication and division.**

35. Simplify: $3 - 5(6 - 8)^2$

$3 - 5(6 - 8)^2 = 3 - 5(\underline{\ \ ?\ \ })^2$	• **Perform operations inside grouping symbols.**
$= 3 - 5(\underline{\ \ ?\ \ })$	• **Simplify exponential expressions.**
$= 3 - \underline{\ \ ?\ \ }$	• **Do multiplication and division.**
$= \underline{\ \ ?\ \ }$	• **Do addition and subtraction.**

Simplify by using the Order of Operations Agreement.

36. $4 - 8 \div 2$

37. $2^2 \cdot 3 - 3$

38. $2(3 - 4) - (-3)^2$

39. $16 - 32 \div 2^3$

40. $24 - 18 \div 3 + 2$

41. $8 - (-3)^2 - (-2)$

42. $16 + 15 \div (-5) - 2$

43. $14 - 2^2 - |4 - 7|$

44. $3 - 2[8 - (3 - 2)]$

45. $-2^2 + 4[16 \div (3 - 5)]$

46. $6 + \dfrac{16 - 4}{2^2 + 2} - 2$

47. $24 \div \dfrac{3^2}{8 - 5} - (-5)$

48. $96 \div 2[12 + (6 - 2)] - 3^3$

49. $4 \cdot [16 - (7 - 1)] \div 10$

50. $16 \div 2 - 4^2 - (-3)^2$

51. $18 \div |9 - 2^3| + (-3)$

52. $16 - 3(8 - 3)^2 \div 5$

53. $4(-8) \div [2(7 - 3)^2]$

54. $\dfrac{(-10) + (-2)}{6^2 - 30} \div |2 - 4|$

55. $16 - 4 \cdot \dfrac{3^3 - 7}{2^3 + 2} - (-2)^2$

56. $0.3(1.7 - 4.8) + (1.2)^2$

57. $(1.65 - 1.05)^2 \div 0.4 + 0.8$

58. $\dfrac{3}{8} \div \left|\dfrac{5}{6} + \dfrac{2}{3}\right|$

59. $\left(\dfrac{3}{4}\right)^2 - \left(\dfrac{1}{2}\right)^3 \div \dfrac{3}{5}$

60. Which expression is equivalent to $9 - 2^2(1 - 5)$?
a. $7^2(-4)$ **b.** $5(-4)$ **c.** $9 - 4(-4)$ **d.** $9 + 4(-4)$

61. Which expression is equivalent to $15 + 15 \div 3 - 4^2$?
a. $30 \div 3 - 16$ **b.** $15 + 5 - 16$ **c.** $15 + 5 + 16$ **d.** $15 + 15 \div (-1)^2$

1.4 Applying Concepts

62. Using the Order of Operations Agreement, describe how to simplify Exercise 52.

Place the correct symbol, $<$ or $>$, between the two numbers.

63. $(0.9)^3 \quad 1^5$ **64.** $(-3)^3 \quad (-2)^5$ **65.** $(-1.1)^2 \quad (0.9)^2$

Simplify.

66. $1^2 + 2^2 + 3^2 + 4^2$ **67.** $1^3 + 2^3 + 3^3 + 4^3$

68. $(-1)^3 + (-2)^3 + (-3)^3 + (-4)^3$ **69.** $(-2)^2 + (-4)^2 + (-6)^2 + (-8)^2$

Solve.

70. Find a rational number, r, that satisfies the condition.
a. $r^2 < r$ **b.** $r^2 = r$ **c.** $r^2 > r$

71. **Computers** A computer can do 6,000,000 additions in 1 s. To the nearest second, how many seconds will it take the computer to do 10^8 additions?

72. The sum of two natural numbers is 41. Each of the two numbers is the square of a natural number. Find the two numbers.

Determine the ones digit when the expression is evaluated.

73. 34^{202} **74.** 23^{502} **75.** 27^{622}

76. Prepare a report on the Kelvin scale. Include in your report an explanation of how to convert between the Kelvin scale and the Celsius scale.

1.5 Concepts from Geometry

OBJECTIVE 1 Measures of angles

The word *geometry* comes from the Greek words for "earth" (*geo*) and "measure." The original purpose of geometry was to measure land. Today, geometry is used in many disciplines, such as physics, biology, geology, architecture, art, and astronomy.

Here are some basic geometric concepts.

A **plane** is a flat surface such as a table top that extends indefinitely. Figures that lie entirely in a plane are called **plane figures.**

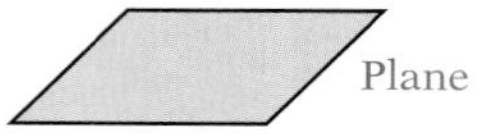

Space extends in all directions. Objects in space, such as a baseball, house, or a tree, are called **solids.**

A **line** extends indefinitely in two directions in a plane. A line has no width.

A **ray** starts at a point and extends indefinitely in one direction. By placing a point on the ray at the right, we can name the ray *AB*.

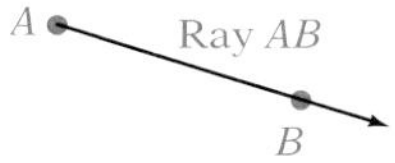

A **line segment** is part of a line and has two endpoints. The line segment *AB* is designated by its two endpoints.

Lines in a plane can be parallel or intersect. **Parallel lines** never meet. The distance between parallel lines in a plane is always the same. We write $p \parallel q$ to indicate line p is parallel to line q. **Intersecting lines** cross at a point in the plane.

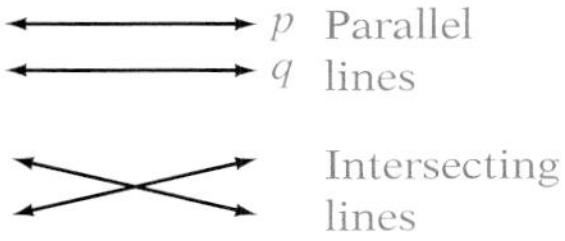

Take Note

When three letters are used to name an angle, the vertex is always the middle letter. We could also refer to the angle at the right as $\angle CAB$.

An **angle** is formed when two rays start from the same point. Rays *AB* and *AC* start from the same point *A*. The point at which the rays meet is called the **vertex** of the angle. The symbol $\angle$ is read "angle" and is used to name an angle. We can refer to the angle at the right as $\angle A$, $\angle BAC$, or $\angle x$.

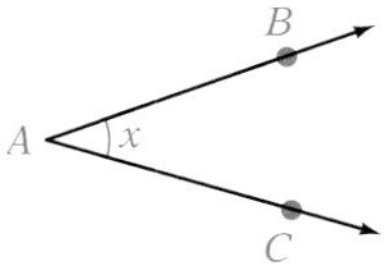

Point of Interest

The Babylonians chose 360° for the measure of one full rotation, probably because they knew there were 365 days in a year and the closest number to 365 with many divisors was 360.

An angle can be measured in **degrees.** The symbol for degree is °. A ray rotated 1 revolution about its beginning point creates an angle of 360°.

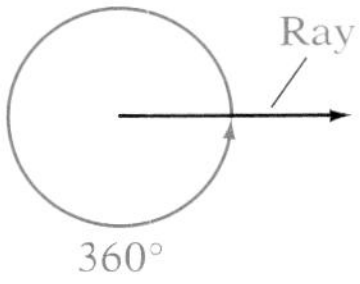

The measure of an angle is symbolized by $m\angle$. For instance, $m\angle C = 40°$. Read this as "the measure of angle *C* is 40°."

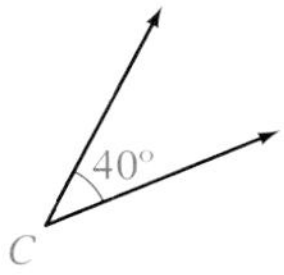

$\frac{1}{4}$ of a revolution is $\frac{1}{4}$ of 360°, or 90°. A 90° angle is called a **right angle.** The symbol ⊾ is used to represent a right angle. **Perpendicular lines** are intersecting lines that form right angles. We write $p \perp q$ to indicate line p is perpendicular to line q.

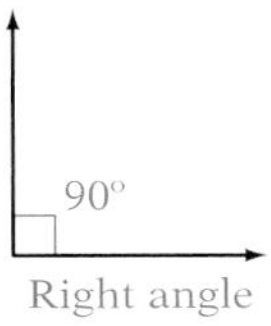

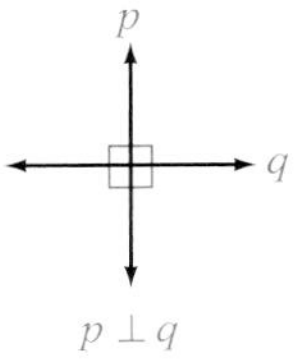

Complementary angles are two angles whose sum is 90°.

$$m\angle A + m\angle B = 35° + 55° = 90°$$

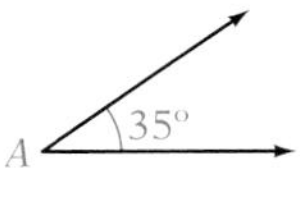

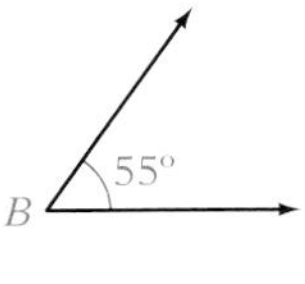

$\angle A$ and $\angle B$ are complementary angles.

$\frac{1}{2}$ of a revolution is $\frac{1}{2}$ of 360°, or 180°. A 180° angle is called a **straight angle.**

Straight angle

Supplementary angles are two angles whose sum is 180°.

$m\angle A + m\angle B = 123° + 57° = 180°$

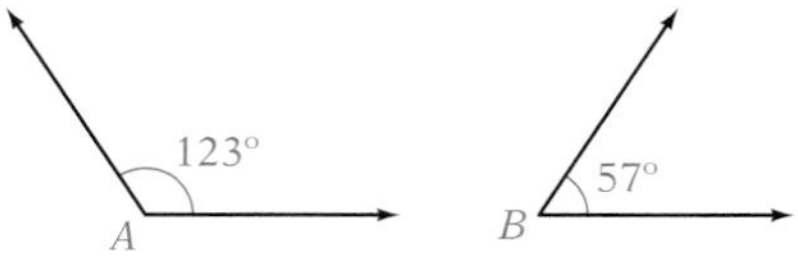

$\angle A$ and $\angle B$ are supplementary angles.

EXAMPLE 1 Find the complement of 39°.

Solution To find the complement of 39°, subtract 39° from 90°.

$90° - 39° = 51°$

51° is the complement of 39°.

PROBLEM 1 Find the complement of 87°.

Solution See page S3.

EXAMPLE 2 Find the supplement of 122°.

Solution To find the supplement of 122°, subtract 122° from 180°.

$180° - 122° = 58°$

58° is the complement of 122°.

PROBLEM 2 Find the supplement of 87°.

Solution See page S3.

EXAMPLE 3 For the figure at the right, find $m\angle AOB$.

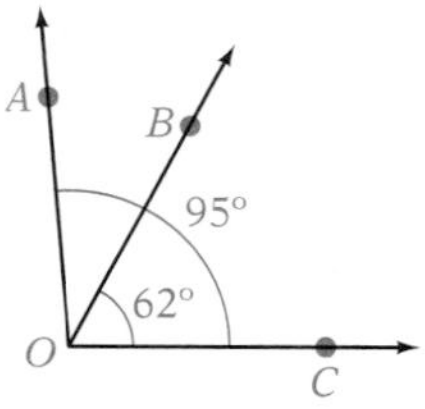

Solution $m\angle AOB$ is the difference between $m\angle AOC$ and $m\angle BOC$.

$m\angle AOB = 95° - 62° = 33°$

$m\angle AOB = 33°$

PROBLEM 3 For the figure at the right, find $m\angle x$.

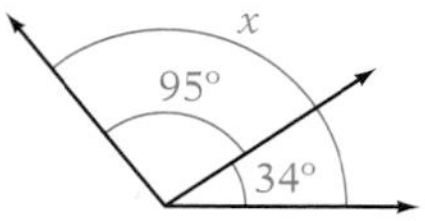

Solution See page S3.

OBJECTIVE 2 Perimeter problems

Perimeter is the distance around a plane figure. Perimeter is used in buying fencing for a yard, wood for the frame of a painting, and rain gutters around a house. The perimeter of a plane figure is the sum of the lengths of the sides of the figure. Formulas for four common geometric figures are given below.

A **triangle** is a three-sided plane figure.

Perimeter = side 1 + side 2 + side 3

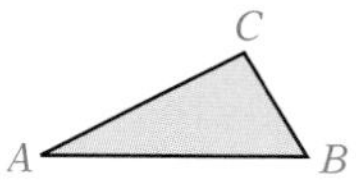

An **isosceles triangle** has two sides of the same length. An **equilateral triangle** has all three sides the same length.

A **parallelogram** is a four-sided plane figure with opposite sides parallel.

A **rectangle** is a parallelogram that has four right angles.

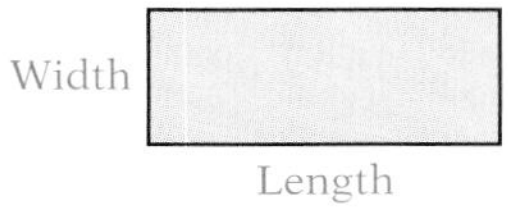

Perimeter = 2 · length + 2 · width

A **square** is a rectangle with four equal sides.

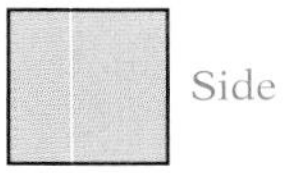

Perimeter = 4 · side

A **circle** is a plane figure in which all points are the same distance from point O, the **center of the circle.** The **diameter** of a circle is a line segment across the circle passing through the center. AB is a diameter of the circle at the right. The **radius** of a circle is a line segment from the center of the circle to a point on the circle. OC is a radius of the circle at the right. The perimeter of a circle is called its **circumference.**

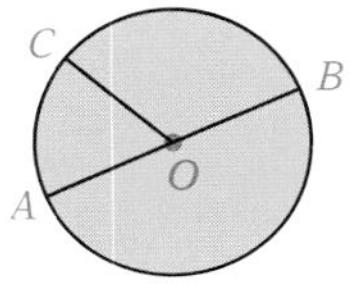

Diameter = 2 · radius or **Radius = $\frac{1}{2}$ · diameter**

Circumference = 2 · π · radius or **Circumference = π · diameter,**

where $\pi \approx 3.14$ or $\frac{22}{7}$.

The diameter of a circle is 25 cm. Find the radius of the circle.

$$\text{Radius} = \frac{1}{2} \cdot \text{diameter}$$
$$= \frac{1}{2} \cdot 25 = 12.5$$

The radius is 12.5 cm.

EXAMPLE 4 Find the perimeter of a rectangle with a width of 6 ft and a length of 18 feet.

Solution

$$\text{Perimeter} = 2 \cdot \text{length} + 2 \cdot \text{width}$$
$$= 2 \cdot 18 \text{ ft} + 2 \cdot 6 \text{ ft}$$
$$= 36 \text{ ft} + 12 \text{ ft} = 48 \text{ ft}$$

PROBLEM 4 Find the perimeter of a square that has a side of length 4.2 m.

Solution See page S3.

EXAMPLE 5 Find the circumference of a circle with a radius of 23 cm. Use 3.14 for π.

Solution
$$\begin{aligned}\text{Circumference} &= 2 \cdot \pi \cdot \text{radius}\\ &\approx 2 \cdot 3.14 \cdot 23 \text{ cm}\\ &= 144.44 \text{ cm}\end{aligned}$$

PROBLEM 5 Find the circumference of a circle with a diameter of 5 in. Use 3.14 for π.

Solution See page S3.

EXAMPLE 6 A chain-link fence costs \$4.37 per foot. How much will it cost to fence a rectangular playground that is 108 ft wide and 195 ft long?

Strategy To find the cost of the fence:

- ▶ Find the perimeter of the playground.
- ▶ Multiply the perimeter by the per-foot cost of the fencing.

Solution
$$\begin{aligned}\text{Perimeter} &= 2 \cdot \text{length} + 2 \cdot \text{width}\\ &= 2 \cdot 195 \text{ ft} + 2 \cdot 108 \text{ ft}\\ &= 390 \text{ ft} + 216 \text{ ft} = 606 \text{ ft}\end{aligned}$$

$$\text{Cost} = 606 \times \$4.37 = \$2648.22$$

The cost is \$2648.22.

PROBLEM 6 A metal strip is being installed around a circular table that has a diameter of 36 in. If the per-foot cost of the metal strip is \$3.21, find the cost for the metal strip. Use 3.14 for π. Round to the nearest cent.

Solution See page S3.

OBJECTIVE 3 Area problems

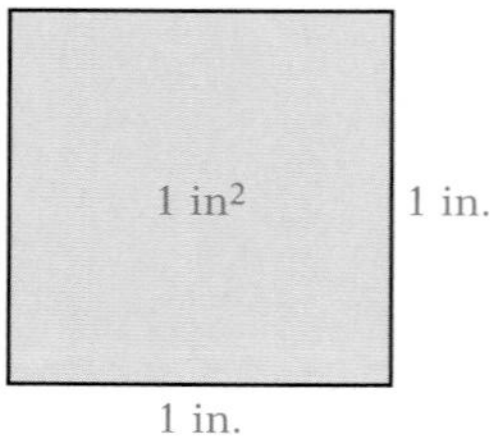

Area is a measure of the amount of surface in a region. Area is used to describe the size of a rug, a farm, a house, or a national park.

Area is measured in square units.

A square that is 1 in. on each side has an area of 1 square inch, which is written 1 in^2.

A square that is 1 cm on each side has an area of 1 square centimeter, which is written 1 cm^2.

Areas of common geometric figures are given by the following formulas.

Rectangle

$$\begin{aligned}\text{Area} &= \text{length} \cdot \text{width}\\ &= 3 \text{ cm} \cdot 2 \text{ cm}\\ &= 6 \text{ cm}^2\end{aligned}$$

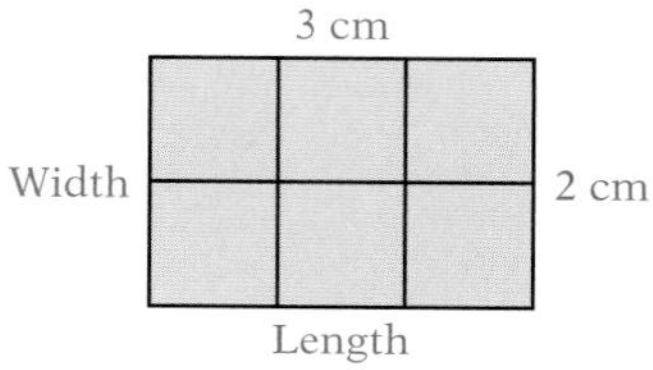

Square

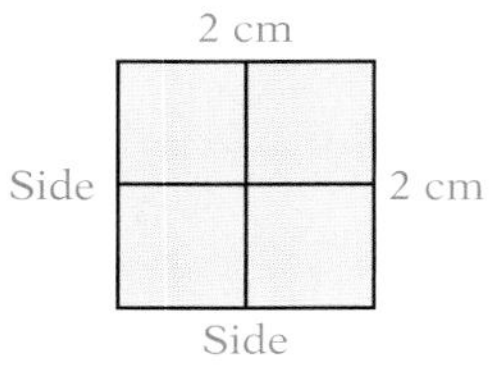

$$\begin{aligned}\textbf{Area} &= \textbf{side} \cdot \textbf{side}\\ &= 2\text{ cm} \cdot 2\text{ cm}\\ &= 4\text{ cm}^2\end{aligned}$$

Parallelogram

The **base of a parallelogram** is one of the parallel sides. The **height of a parallelogram** is the distance between the base and the opposite parallel side. It is perpendicular to the base.

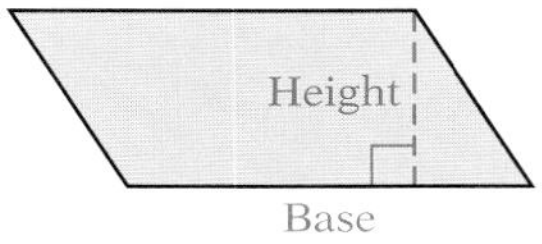

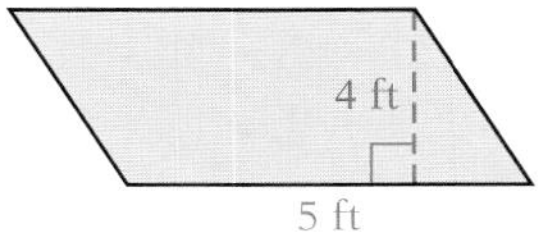

$$\begin{aligned}\textbf{Area} &= \textbf{base} \cdot \textbf{height}\\ &= 5\text{ ft} \cdot 4\text{ ft}\\ &= 20\text{ ft}^2\end{aligned}$$

Circle

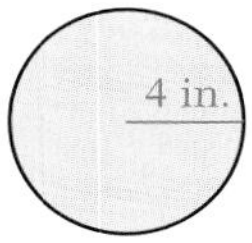

$$\begin{aligned}\textbf{Area} &= \pi(\textbf{radius})^2\\ &\approx 3.14(4\text{ in.})^2 = 50.24\text{ in}^2\end{aligned}$$

Triangle

For the triangle at the right, the **base of the triangle** is AB; the **height of the triangle** is CD. Note that the height is perpendicular to the base.

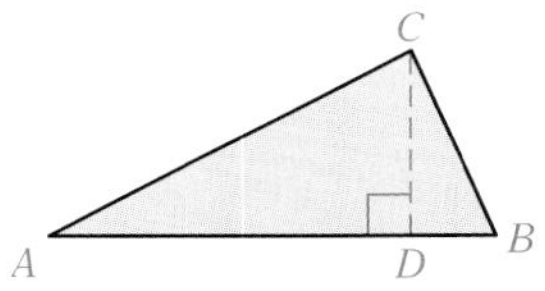

$$\begin{aligned}\textbf{Area} &= \frac{1}{2} \cdot \textbf{base} \cdot \textbf{height}\\ &= \frac{1}{2} \cdot 5\text{ in.} \cdot 4\text{ in.} = 10\text{ in}^2\end{aligned}$$

Take Note

The height of a triangle is always perpendicular to the base. Sometimes it is necessary to extend the base so that a perpendicular line segment can be drawn. The extension is *not* part of the base.

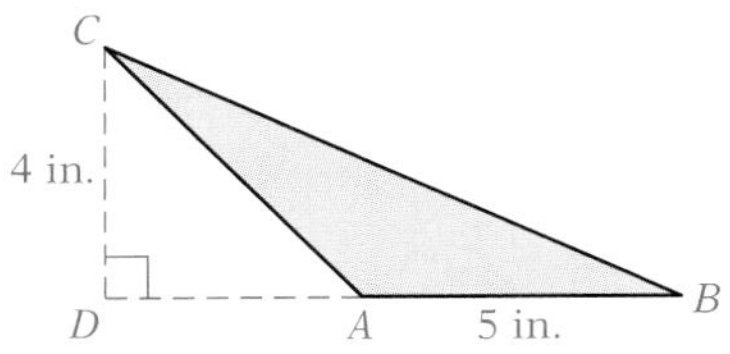

EXAMPLE 7 Find the area of a rectangle whose length is 8 in. and whose width is 6 in.

Solution Area = length × width
$= 8\text{ in.} \times 6\text{ in.} = 48\text{ in}^2$

PROBLEM 7 Find the area of a triangle whose base is 5 ft and whose height is 3 ft.

Solution See page S3.

EXAMPLE 8 Find the area of a circle whose diameter is 5 cm. Use 3.14 for π.

Solution $\text{Radius} = \frac{1}{2} \cdot \text{diameter}$

$= \frac{1}{2} \cdot 5 \text{ cm} = 2.5 \text{ cm}$

$\text{Area} = \pi \cdot (\text{radius})^2$

$\approx 3.14(2.5 \text{ cm})^2 = 19.625 \text{ cm}^2$

PROBLEM 8 Find the area of a circle whose radius is 6 in. Use 3.14 for π.

Solution See page S3.

EXAMPLE 9 Find the area of the parallelogram shown at the right.

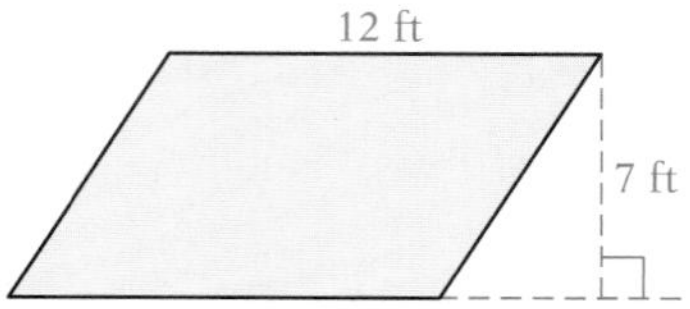

Solution $\text{Area} = \text{base} \cdot \text{height}$

$= 12 \text{ ft} \times 7 \text{ ft} = 84 \text{ ft}^2$

PROBLEM 9 Find the area of the parallelogram shown at the right.

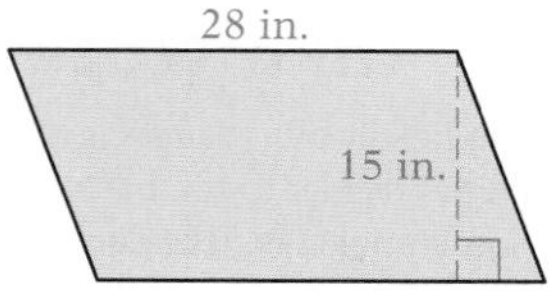

Solution See page S3.

EXAMPLE 10 To conserve water during a drought, a city's water department is offering homeowners a rebate on their water bill of \$1.27 per square foot of lawn that is removed from a yard and replaced with drought-resistant plants. What rebate would a homeowner receive who replaced a rectangular lawn area that is 15 ft wide and 25 ft long?

Strategy To find the amount of the rebate:

- ▶ Find the area of the replaced lawn.
- ▶ Multiply the area by the per-square-foot rebate.

Solution $\text{Area} = \text{length} \times \text{width}$

$= 25 \text{ ft} \times 15 \text{ ft} = 375 \text{ ft}^2$

$\text{Rebate} = 375 \times \$1.27 = \$476.25$

The rebate is \$476.25.

PROBLEM 10 An interior designer is choosing between two hallway rugs. A nylon rug costs \$1.25 per square foot, and a wool rug costs \$1.93 per square foot. If the dimensions of the carpet are to be 4 ft by 15 ft, how much more expensive than the nylon rug will the wool rug be?

Solution See page S3.

1.5 Concept Review

Determine whether the statement is always true, sometimes true, or never true.

1. A ray is designated by its two endpoints.
2. Perpendicular lines form four 90° angles.
3. The sum of the measures of two straight angles is 360°.
4. Every square is a parallelogram.
5. Perimeter is measured in square units.
6. A parallelogram has a base and a height.

1.5 Exercises

1 Measures of angles

1. If $\angle A$ and $\angle B$ are complementary angles, then $m\angle A + m\angle B = \underline{\quad ? \quad}$.
2. If $\angle C$ and $\angle D$ are supplementary angles, then $m\angle C + m\angle D = \underline{\quad ? \quad}$.
3. If $\angle E$ is a right angle, then $m\angle E = \underline{\quad ? \quad}$.
4. If $\angle F$ is a straight angle, then $m\angle F = \underline{\quad ? \quad}$.
5. When the time is 3 o'clock on an analog clock, is the measure of the smaller angle between the hands of the clock more than or less than 120°?
6. In one hour, the hour hand on an analog clock travels through how many degrees?
7. Find the complement of a 62° angle.
8. Find the complement of a 13° angle.
9. Find the supplement of a 48° angle.
10. Find the supplement of a 106° angle.

11. Find the complement of a 7° angle.

12. Find the complement of a 76° angle.

13. Find the supplement of an 89° angle.

14. Find the supplement of a 21° angle.

15. Angle *AOB* is a straight angle. Find $m\angle AOC$.

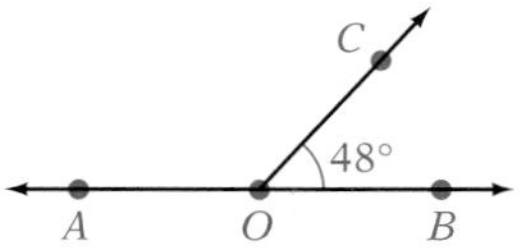

16. Angle *AOB* is a straight angle. Find $m\angle COB$.

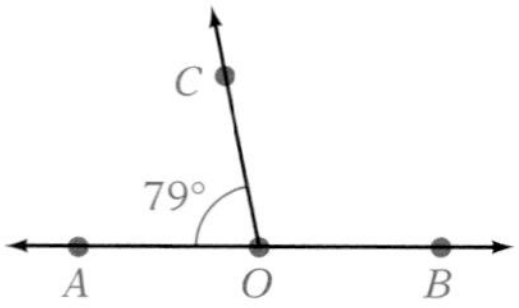

17. Find $m\angle x$.

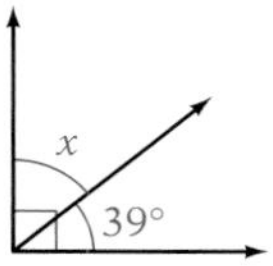

18. Find $m\angle x$.

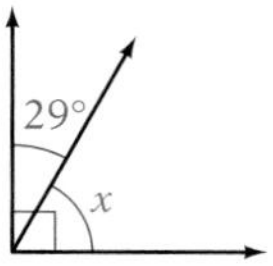

19. Find $m\angle AOB$.

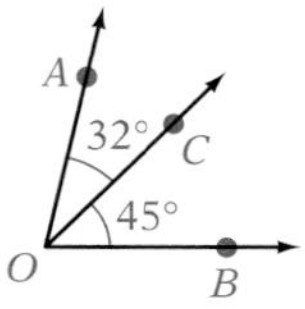

20. Find $m\angle AOB$.

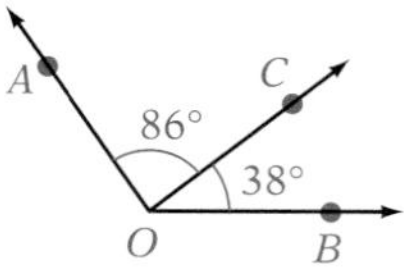

21. Find $m\angle AOC$.

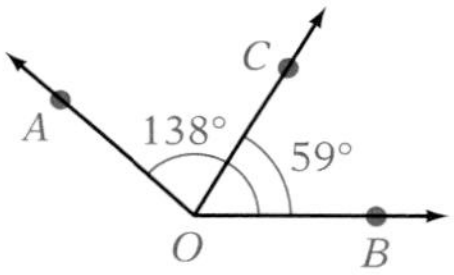

22. Find $m\angle AOC$.

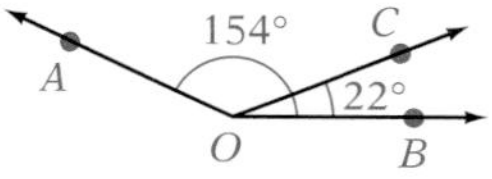

23. Find $m\angle A$.

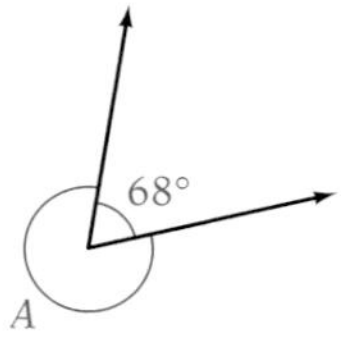

24. Find $m\angle A$.

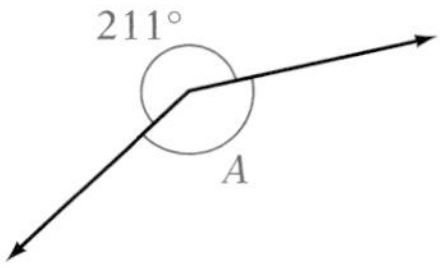

2 Perimeter problems

25. A plane figure that has three sides is called a ___?___.

26. The name of a parallelogram in which all angles are the same measure is a ___?___.

27. Find the perimeter of a triangle with sides 2.51 cm, 4.08 cm, and 3.12 cm.

28. Find the perimeter of a triangle with sides 4 ft 5 in., 5 ft 3 in., and 6 ft 11 in.

29. Find the perimeter of a rectangle whose length is 4 ft 8 in. and whose width is 2 ft 5 in.

30. Find the perimeter of a rectangle whose dimensions are 5 m by 8 m.

31. Find the perimeter of a square whose side is 13 in.

32. Find the perimeter of a square whose side is 34 cm.

33. Find the circumference of a circle whose radius is 21 cm. Use 3.14 for π.

34. Find the circumference of a circle whose radius is 3.4 m. Use 3.14 for π.

35. Find the circumference of a circle whose diameter is 1.2 m. Use 3.14 for π.

36. Find the circumference of a circle whose diameter is 15 in. Use 3.14 for π.

37. **Art** The wood framing for an art canvas costs \$4.81 per foot. How much would the wood framing cost for a rectangular picture that measures 3 ft by 5 ft?

38. **Ceramics** A decorative mosaic tile is being installed on the border of a square wall behind a stove. If one side of the square measures 5 ft and the cost of installing the mosaic tile is \$4.86 per foot, find the cost to install the decorative border.

39. **Sewing** To prevent fraying, a binding is attached to the outside of a circular rug whose radius is 3 ft. If the binding costs \$1.05 per foot, find the cost of the binding. Use 3.14 for π.

40. **Landscaping** A drip irrigation system is installed around a circular flower garden that is 4 ft in diameter. If the irrigation system costs \$2.46 per foot, find the cost to place the irrigation system around the flower garden. Use 3.14 for π.

41. In the pattern at the right, the length of one side of a square is 1 unit. If the pattern were to be continued, what would the perimeter of the eighth figure in the pattern be?

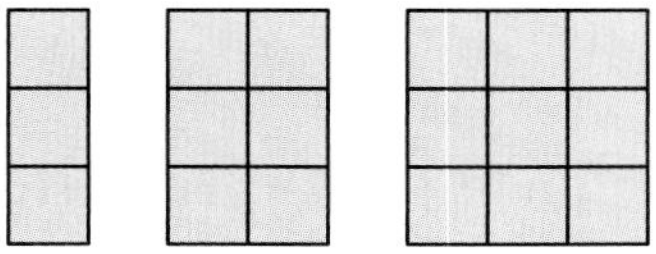

42. Which has the greater perimeter, a square whose side is 1 ft or a rectangle that has a length of 2 in. and a width of 1 in.?

3 Area problems

43. The formula for the area of a rectangle is Area = length · ____?____.

44. The formula for the area of a parallelogram is Area = base · ____?____.

45. Find the area of a rectangle that measures 4 ft by 8 ft.

46. Find the area of a rectangle that measures 3.4 cm by 5.6 cm.

47. Find the area of a parallelogram whose height is 14 cm and whose base is 27 cm.

48. Find the area of a parallelogram whose height is 7 ft and whose base is 18 ft.

49. Find the area of a circle whose radius is 4 in. Use 3.14 for π.

50. Find the area of a circle whose radius is 8.2 m. Use 3.14 for π.

51. Find the area of a square whose side measures 4.1 m.

52. Find the area of a square whose side measures 5 yd.

53. Find the area of a triangle whose height is 7 cm and whose base is 15 cm.

54. Find the area of a triangle whose height is 8 in. and whose base is 13 in.

55. Find the area of a circle whose diameter is 17 in. Use 3.14 for π.

56. Find the area of a circle whose diameter is 3.6 m. Use 3.14 for π.

57. **Landscaping** A landscape architect recommends 0.1 gallon of water per day for each square foot of lawn. How many gallons of water should be used per day on a rectangular lawn area that is 33 ft by 42 ft?

58. **Interior Design** One side of a square room measures 18 ft. How many square yards of carpet are necessary to carpet the room? *Hint*: $1 \text{ yd}^2 = 9 \text{ ft}^2$.

59. **Carpentry** A circular, inlaid-wood design for a dining table cost \$35 per square foot to build. If the radius of the design is 15 in., find the cost to build the design. Use 3.14 for π. Round to the nearest dollar. *Hint*: $144 \text{ in}^2 = 1 \text{ ft}^2$.

60. **Interior Design** A circular stained glass window cost \$48 per square foot to build. If the diameter of the window is 4 ft, find the cost to build the window. Round to the nearest dollar.

61. **Construction** The cost of plastering the walls of a rectangular room that is 18 ft long, 14 ft wide, and 8 ft high is \$2.56 per square foot. If 125 ft^2 is not plastered because of doors and windows, find the cost to plaster the room.

62. **Interior Design** A room is 12 ft long, 9 ft wide, and 9 ft high. Two adjacent walls of the rooms are going to be wallpapered using wallpaper that costs \$15.25 per square yard. What is the cost to wallpaper the two walls? *Hint*: $1 \text{ yd}^2 = 9 \text{ ft}^2$.

63. If both the length and the width of a rectangle are doubled, how many times larger is the area of the resulting rectangle?

64. A rectangle has a perimeter of 20 units. What dimensions will result in a rectangle with the greatest possible area? Consider only whole-number dimensions.

1.5 Applying Concepts

65. Find the perimeter and area of the figure. Use 3.14 for π.

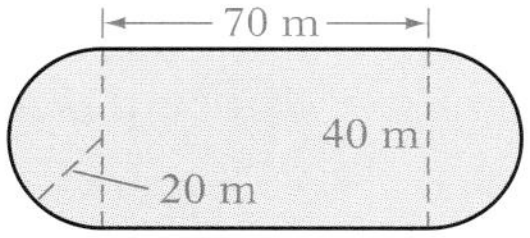

66. Find the perimeter and area of the figure.

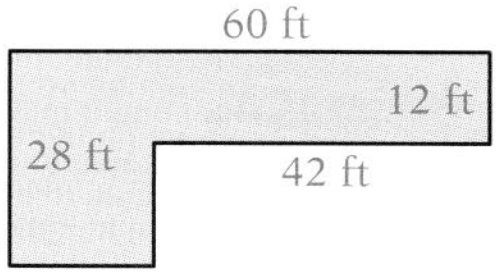

67. Find the outside perimeter and area of the shaded portion of the figure.

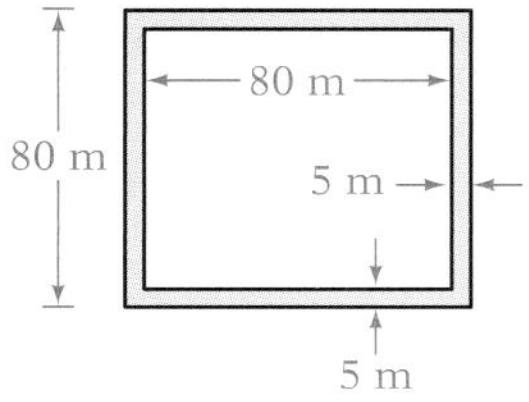

68. Find the area of the shaded portion of the figure.

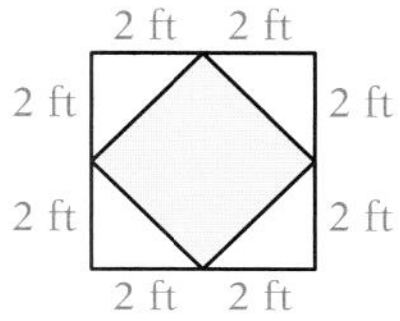

69. A trapezoid is a four-sided plane figure with two parallel sides. The area of a trapezoid is given by Area $= \frac{1}{2} \cdot$ height(base 1 + base 2). See the figure at the right.

a. Find the area of a trapezoid for which base 1 is 5 in., base 2 is 8 in., and the height is 6 in.

b. Find the area of the trapezoid shown at the right.

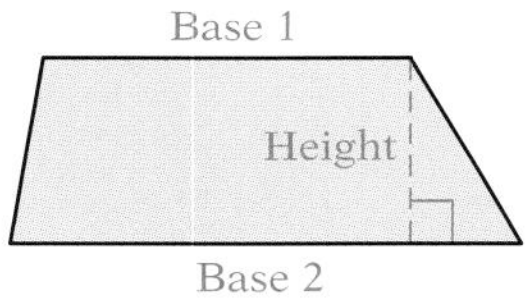

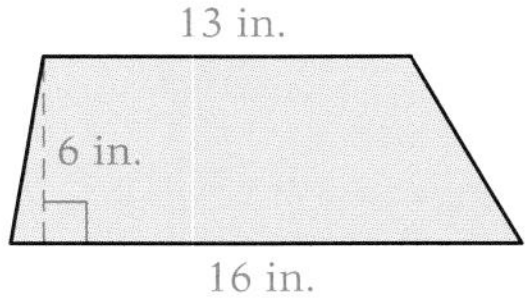

70.  Draw parallelogram *ABCD* or one similar to it and then cut it out. Cut along the dotted line to form the shaded triangle. Slide the triangle so that the slanted side corresponds to the slanted side of the parallelogram as shown. Explain how this demonstrates that the area of a parallelogram is the product of the base and the height.

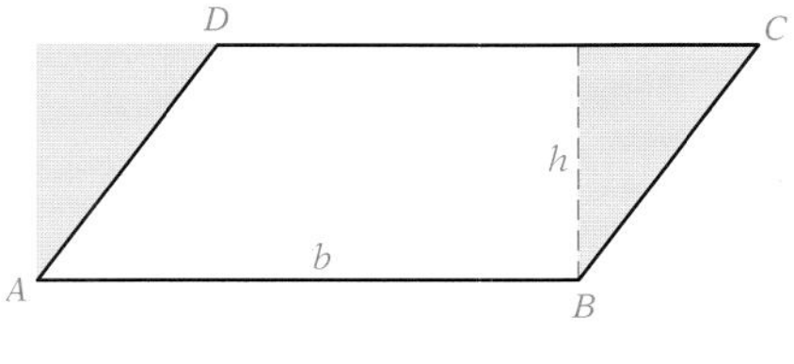

Focus on Problem Solving

Inductive Reasoning

Suppose you take 9 credit hours each semester. The total number of credit hours you have taken at the end of each semester can be described in a list of numbers.

$$9, 18, 27, 36, 45, 54, 63, \ldots$$

The list of numbers that indicates the total credit hours is an ordered list of numbers, called a **sequence.** Each number in a sequence is called a **term** of the sequence. The list is ordered because the position of a number in the list indicates the semester in which that number of credit hours has been taken. For example, the 7th term of the sequence is 63, and a total of 63 credit hours have been taken after the 7th semester.

Assuming the pattern is continued, find the next three numbers in the pattern

$$-6, -10, -14, -18, \ldots$$

This list of numbers is a sequence. The first step in solving this problem is to observe the pattern in the list of numbers. In this case, each number in the list is 4 less than the previous number. The next three numbers are $-22, -26, -30$.

This process of discovering the pattern in a list of numbers is inductive reasoning. **Inductive reasoning** involves making generalizations from specific examples; in other words, we reach a conclusion by making observations about particular facts or cases.

Try the following exercises. Each exercise requires inductive reasoning.

Name the next two terms in the sequence.

1. 1, 3, 5, 7, 1, 3, 5, 7, 1, . . .

2. 1, 4, 2, 5, 3, 6, 4, . . .

3. 1, 2, 4, 7, 11, 16, . . .

4. A, B, C, G, H, I, M, . . .

Draw the next shape in the sequence.

5.

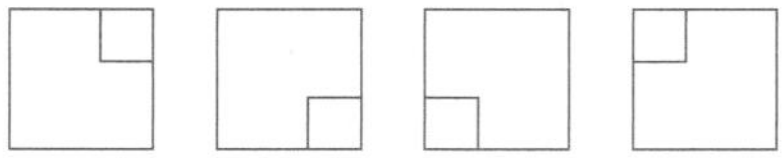

6.

Solve.

7. Convert $\frac{1}{11}, \frac{2}{11}, \frac{3}{11}, \frac{4}{11}$, and $\frac{5}{11}$ to decimals. Then use the pattern you observe to convert $\frac{6}{11}, \frac{7}{11}$, and $\frac{9}{11}$ to decimals.

8. Convert $\frac{1}{33}, \frac{2}{33}, \frac{4}{33}, \frac{5}{33}$, and $\frac{7}{33}$ to decimals. Then use the pattern you observe to convert $\frac{8}{33}, \frac{13}{33}$, and $\frac{19}{33}$ to decimals.

Projects & Group Activities

Calculators Does your calculator use the Order of Operations Agreement? To find out, try this problem:

$$2 + 4 \cdot 7$$

If your answer is 30, then the calculator uses the Order of Operations Agreement. If your answer is 42, it does not use that agreement.

Even if your calculator does not use the Order of Operations Agreement, you can still correctly evaluate numerical expressions. The parentheses keys, $\boxed{(}$ and $\boxed{)}$, are used for this purpose.

Remember that $2 + 4 \cdot 7$ means $2 + (4 \cdot 7)$ because the multiplication must be completed before the addition. To evaluate this expression, enter the following:

Enter:	2	$\boxed{+}$	$\boxed{(}$	4	$\boxed{\times}$	7	$\boxed{)}$	$\boxed{=}$
Display:	2	2	$\boxed{(}$	4	4	7	28	30

When using your calculator to evaluate numerical expressions, insert parentheses around multiplications or divisions. This has the effect of forcing the calculator to do the operations in the order you want rather than in the order the calculator wants.

Evaluate.

1. $3 \cdot (15 - 2 \cdot 3) - 36 \div 3$ **2.** $4 \cdot 2^2 - (12 + 24 \div 6) - 5$

3. $16 \div 4 \cdot 3 + (3 \cdot 4 - 5) + 2$ **4.** $15 \cdot 3 \div 9 + (2 \cdot 6 - 3) + 4$

Using your calculator to simplify numerical expressions sometimes requires use of the $\boxed{+/-}$ key or, on some calculators, the negative key, which is frequently shown as $\boxed{(-)}$. These keys change the sign of the number currently in the display. To enter -4:

- For those calculators with $\boxed{+/-}$, press 4 and then $\boxed{+/-}$.
- For those calculators with $\boxed{(-)}$, press $\boxed{(-)}$ and then 4.

Here are the keystrokes for evaluating the expression $3(-4) - (-5)$.

Calculators with $\boxed{+/-}$ key: 3 $\boxed{\times}$ 4 $\boxed{+/-}$ $-$ 5 $\boxed{+/-}$ $\boxed{=}$

Calculators with $\boxed{(-)}$ key: 3 $\boxed{\times}$ $\boxed{(-)}$ 4 $\boxed{-}$ $\boxed{(-)}$ 5 $\boxed{=}$

This example illustrates that calculators make a distinction between negative and minus. To perform the operation $3 - (-3)$, you cannot enter 3 $\boxed{-}$ $\boxed{-}$ 3. This would result in 0, which is not the correct answer. You must enter

3 $\boxed{-}$ 3 $\boxed{+/-}$ $\boxed{=}$ or 3 $\boxed{-}$ $\boxed{(-)}$ 3 $\boxed{=}$

Use a calculator to evaluate each of the following expressions.

5. $-16 \div 2$ **6.** $3(-8)$ **7.** $47 - (-9)$

8. $-50 - (-14)$ **9.** $4 - (-3)^2$ **10.** $-8 + (-6)^2 - 7$

Chapter 1 Summary

Key Words	Examples
A **set** is a collection of objects. The objects in the set are called the **elements** of the set. The **roster method** of writing sets encloses a list of the elements in braces. [1.1.1, p. 2]*	The set of even natural numbers less than 10 is written $A = \{2, 4, 6, 8\}$. The elements in this set are the numbers 2, 4, 6, and 8.
The set of **natural numbers** is $\{1, 2, 3, 4, 5, 6, 7, \ldots\}$. The set of **integers** is $\{\ldots, -4, -3, -2, -1, 0, 1, 2, 3, 4, \ldots\}$. [1.1.1, pp. 2–3]	
A number a **is less than** another number b, written $a < b$, if a is to the left of b on the number line. A number a **is greater than** another number b, written $a > b$, if a is to the right of b on the number line. The symbol $\leq$ means **is less than or equal to.** The symbol $\geq$ means **is greater than or equal to.** [1.1.1, pp. 3–4]	$-9 < 7$ $4 > -5$
Two numbers that are the same distance from zero on the number line but on opposite sides of zero are **opposite numbers,** or **opposites.** The opposite of a number is also called its **additive inverse.** [1.1.2, p. 4]	5 and -5 are opposites.
The **absolute value** of a number is its distance from zero on the number line. The absolute value of a number is positive or zero. [1.1.2, p. 5]	$\lvert -12 \rvert = 12$ $-\lvert 7 \rvert = -7$
A **rational number** is a number that can be written in the form $\frac{a}{b}$, where a and b are integers and $b \neq 0$. A rational number written in this form is commonly called a **fraction.** [1.3.1, p. 24]	$\frac{3}{8}, \frac{-9}{11}$, and $\frac{4}{1}$ are rational numbers.
An **irrational number** is a number that has a decimal representation that never terminates or repeats. [1.3.1, p. 25]	π, $\sqrt{2}$, and 2.171171117111117... are irrational numbers.
The rational numbers and the irrational numbers taken together are called the **real numbers.** [1.3.1, p. 25]	$\frac{3}{8}, \frac{-9}{11}, \frac{4}{1}, \pi, \sqrt{2}$, and 2.171171117111117... are real numbers.
Percent means "parts of 100." [1.3.4, p. 29]	63% means 63 of 100 equal parts.
An expression of the form a^n is in **exponential form,** where a is the **base** and n is the **exponent.** [1.4.1, p. 38]	6^3 is an exponential expression in which 6 is the base and 3 is the exponent.

*The numbers in brackets refer to the objective where the Key Word or Essential Rule or Procedure is first introduced. For example, the reference [1.1.1] stands for Chapter 1, Section 1, Objective 1. This notation will be used in all Chapter Summaries throughout the text.

A **plane** is a flat surface that extends indefinitely. A **line** extends indefinitely in two directions in a plane. A **ray** starts at a point and extends indefinitely in one direction. A **line segment** is part of a line and has two endpoints. [1.5.1, pp. 44–45]

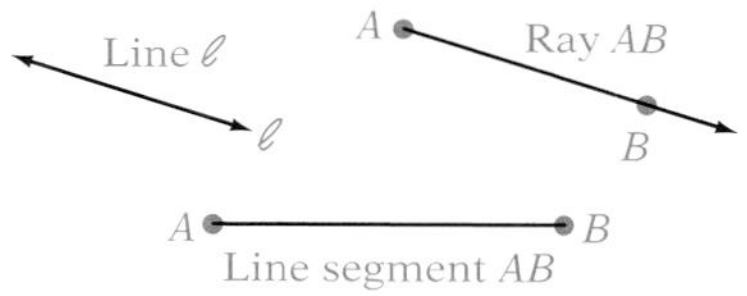

Lines in a plane can be parallel or intersect. **Parallel lines** never meet. The distance between parallel lines in a plane is always the same. **Intersecting lines** cross at a point in the plane. [1.5.1, p. 45]

An **angle** is formed when two rays start from the same point. The point at which the rays meet is called the **vertex** of the angle. An angle can be measured in **degrees.** The measure of an angle is symbolized by $m\angle$. [1.5.1, p. 45]

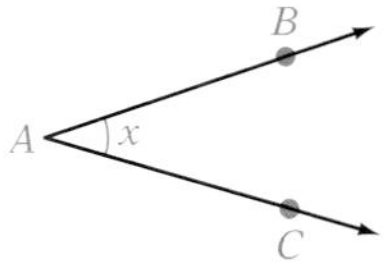

This angle can be named $\angle A$, $\angle BAC$, $\angle CAB$, or $\angle x$.

A **right angle** has a measure of 90°. **Perpendicular lines** are intersecting lines that form right angles. **Complementary angles** are two angles whose sum is 90°. A **straight angle** has a measure of 180°. **Supplementary angles** are two angles whose sum is 180°. [1.5.1, pp. 45–46]

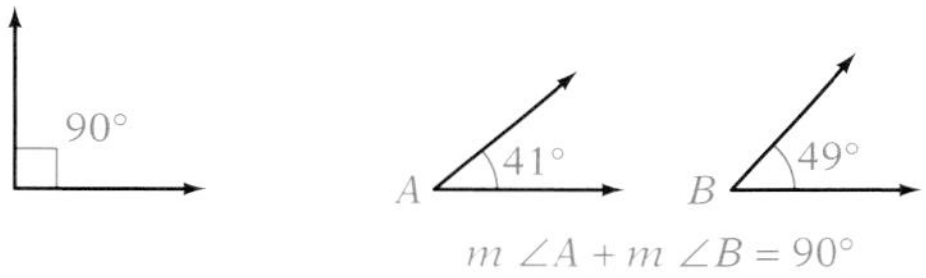

$\angle A$ and $\angle B$ are complementary angles.

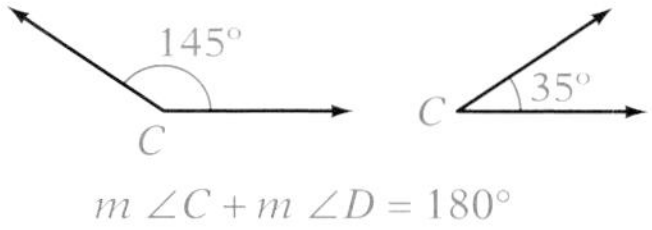

$\angle C$ and $\angle D$ are supplementary angles.

A **circle** is a plane figure in which all points are the same distance from point O, the **center** of the circle. The **diameter** of a circle is a line segment across the circle passing through the center. The **radius** of a circle is a line segment from the center of the circle to a point on the circle. The perimeter of a circle is called its **circumference**. [1.5.2, p. 47]

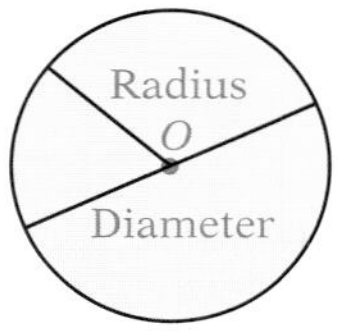

Essential Rules and Procedures

To add two integers with the same sign, add the absolute values of the numbers. Then attach the sign of the addends. [1.2.1, p. 11]

$9 + 3 = 12$
$-9 + (-3) = -12$

To add two integers with different signs, find the absolute value of each number. Then subtract the smaller of these absolute values from the larger one. Attach the sign of the number with the greater absolute value. [1.2.1, p. 11]

$9 + (-3) = 6$
$-9 + 3 = -6$

To subtract one integer from another, add the opposite of the second integer to the first integer. [1.2.2, pp. 11–12]	$6 - 11 = 6 + (-11) = -5$ $-2 - (-8) = -2 + 8 = 6$
To multiply two integers with the same sign, multiply the absolute values of the numbers. The product is positive. [1.2.3, p. 13]	$3(5) = 15$ $(-3)(-5) = 15$
To multiply two integers with different signs, multiply the absolute values of the numbers. The product is negative. [1.2.3, p. 13]	$-3(5) = -15$ $3(-5) = -15$
To divide two integers with the same sign, divide the absolute values of the numbers. The quotient is positive. [1.2.4, p. 14]	$14 \div 2 = 7$ $-14 \div (-2) = 7$
To divide two integers with different signs, divide the absolute values of the numbers. The quotient is negative. [1.2.4, p. 14]	$14 \div (-2) = -7$ $-14 \div 2 = -7$
Zero and One in Division [1.2.4, p. 14] $\frac{0}{a} = 0, a \neq 0$ Division by zero is undefined. $\frac{a}{a} = 1, a \neq 0$ $\frac{a}{1} = a$	$\frac{0}{3} = 0$ $\frac{9}{0}$ is undefined. $\frac{-2}{-2} = 1$ $\frac{-6}{1} = -6$
To convert a percent to a decimal, remove the percent sign and multiply by 0.01. [1.3.4, p. 29]	$85\% = 85(0.01) = 0.85$
To convert a percent to a fraction, remove the percent sign and multiply by $\frac{1}{100}$. [1.3.4, p. 29]	$25\% = 25 \cdot \frac{1}{100} = \frac{25}{100} = \frac{1}{4}$
To convert a decimal or a fraction to a percent, multiply by 100%. [1.3.4, p. 30]	$0.5 = 0.5(100\%) = 50\%$ $\frac{3}{8} = \frac{3}{8} \cdot 100\% = \frac{300}{8}\% = 37.5\%$
Order of Operations Agreement [1.4.2, p. 40] **Step 1** Perform operations inside grouping symbols. **Step 2** Simplify exponential expressions. **Step 3** Do multiplication and division as they occur from left to right. **Step 4** Do addition and subtraction as they occur from left to right.	$16 \div (-2)^3 + (7 - 12)$ $= 16 \div (-2)^3 + (-5)$ $= 16 \div (-8) + (-5)$ $= -2 + (-5)$ $= -7$
Diameter $= 2 \cdot$ radius [1.5.2, p. 47] **Radius** $= \frac{1}{2} \cdot$ diameter	Find the diameter of a circle whose radius is 10 in. Diameter $= 2 \cdot$ radius $= 2(10 \text{ in.}) = 20$ in.

Perimeter is the distance around a plane figure. [1.5.2, pp. 46–47]

Triangle:	Perimeter = side 1 + side 2 + side 3
Rectangle:	Perimeter = 2 · length + 2 · width
Square:	Perimeter = 4 · side
Circle:	Circumference = 2 · π · radius
	Circumference = π · diameter

Find the perimeter of a rectangle whose width is 12 m and whose length is 15 m.

Perimeter = 2 · 15 m + 2 · 12 m = 54 m

Find the circumference of a circle whose radius is 3 in. Use 3.14 for π.

Circumference = 2 · π · 3 in. ≈ 18.84 in.

Area is a measure of the amount of surface in a region. [1.5.3, pp. 48–49]

Triangle:	Area = $\frac{1}{2}$ · base · height
Rectangle:	Area = length · width
Square:	Area = side · side
Parallelogram:	Area = base · height
Circle:	Area = $\pi(\text{radius})^2$

Find the area of a triangle whose base is 13 m and whose height is 11 m.

Area = $\frac{1}{2}$ · 13 m · 11 m = 71.5 m^2

Find the area of a circle whose radius is 9 cm.

Area = $\pi \cdot (9\text{ cm})^2 \approx 254.34\text{ cm}^2$

Chapter 1 Review Exercises

1. Use the roster method to write the set of natural numbers less than 7.

2. Write $\frac{5}{8}$ as a percent.

3. Evaluate: $-|-4|$

4. Subtract: $16 - (-30) - 42$

5. Find the area of a triangle whose base is 4 cm and whose height is 9 cm.

6. Write $\frac{7}{9}$ as a decimal. Place a bar over the repeating digits of the decimal.

7. Simplify: $(6.02)(-0.89)$

8. Simplify: $\dfrac{-10 + 2}{2 + (-4)} \div 2 + 6$

9. Find the opposite of -4 .

10. Subtract: $16 - 30$

11. Write 0.672 as a percent.

12. Write $79\frac{1}{2}\%$ as a fraction.

13. Divide: $-72 \div 8$

14. Write $\frac{17}{20}$ as a decimal.

15. Divide: $\dfrac{5}{12} \div \left(-\dfrac{5}{6}\right)$

16. Simplify: $3^2 - 4 + 20 \div 5$

17. Find $m\angle AOB$ for the figure at the right.

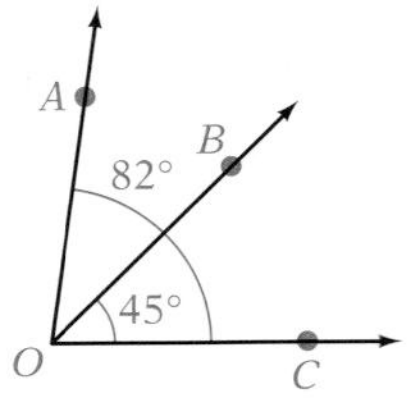

18. Add: $-22 + 14 + (-8)$

19. Multiply: $(-5)(-6)(3)$

20. Subtract: $6.039 - 12.92$

21. Given $A = \{-5, -3, 0\}$, which elements of set A are less than or equal to -3?

22. Write 7% as a decimal.

23. Evaluate: $\frac{3}{4} \cdot (4)^2$

24. Place the correct symbol, < or >, between the two numbers.

$$-2 \quad -40$$

25. Add: $13 + (-16)$

26. Find the complement of a 56° angle.

27. Add: $-\frac{2}{5} + \frac{7}{15}$

28. Evaluate: $(-3^3) \cdot 2^2$

29. Write $2\frac{7}{9}$ as a percent. Round to the nearest tenth of a percent.

30. Write 240% as a decimal.

31. Find the supplement of a 28° angle.

32. Divide: $96 \div (-12)$

33. Find the area of a circle whose diameter is 6 m. Use 3.14 for π.

34. Simplify: $2^3 \div 4 - 2(2 - 7)$

35. Evaluate: $|-3|$

36. Write $2\frac{8}{9}$ as a percent. Write the remainder in fractional form.

37. Given $C = \{-12, -8, -1, 7\}$, find

a. the opposite of each element of set C.
b. the absolute value of each element of set C.

38. Write $\frac{7}{11}$ as a decimal. Place a bar over the repeating digits of the decimal.

39. Divide: $0.2654 \div (-0.023)$
Round to the nearest tenth.

40. Simplify: $(7 - 2)^2 - 5 - 3 \cdot 4$

41. Add: $-12 + 8 + (-4)$

42. Add: $-\frac{5}{8} + \frac{1}{6}$

43. Given $D = \{-24, -17, -9, 0, 4\}$, which elements of set D are greater than -19?

44. Write 0.002 as a percent.

45. Evaluate: $-4^2 \cdot \left(\frac{1}{2}\right)^2$

46. Add: $-1.329 + 4.89$

47. Evaluate: $-|17|$

48. Subtract: $-5 - 22 - (-13) - 19 - (-6)$

49. Multiply: $\left(\frac{1}{3}\right)\left(-\frac{4}{5}\right)\left(\frac{3}{8}\right)$

50. Place the correct symbol, < or >, between the two numbers.

$-43 \quad -34$

51. Find the perimeter of a rectangle whose length is 12 in. and whose width is 10 in.

52. Evaluate $(-2)^3 \cdot 4^2$.

53. Write 0.075 as a percent.

54. Write $\frac{19}{35}$ as a percent. Write the remainder in fractional form.

55. Add: $14 + (-18) + 6 + (-20)$

56. Multiply: $-4(-8)(12)(0)$

57. Simplify: $2^3 - 7 + 16 \div (-3 + 5)$

58. Simplify: $\frac{3}{4} + \frac{1}{2} - \frac{3}{8}$

59. Divide: $-128 \div (-8)$

60. Place the correct symbol, < or >, between the two numbers.

$-57 \quad 28$

61. Evaluate: $\left(-\frac{1}{3}\right)^3 \cdot 9^2$

62. Add: $-7 + (-3) + (-12) + 16$

63. Multiply: $5(-2)(10)(-3)$

64. Use the roster method to write the set of negative integers greater than -4.

65. **Landscaping** A landscape company is proposing to replace a rectangular flower bed that measures 8 ft by 12 ft with sod that costs $2.51 per square foot. Find the cost to replace the flower bed with the sod.

66. **Temperature** Find the temperature after a rise of 14°C from −6°C.

67. **Temperature** The daily low temperatures, in degrees Celsius, for a three-day period were recorded as follows: −8°, 7°, −5°. Find the average low temperature for the three-day period.

68. **Temperature** Use the table to find the difference between the record high temperature and the record low temperature for January in Bismarck, North Dakota.

Bismarck, North Dakota

	Jan	*Feb*	*Mar*	*Apr*	*May*	*Jun*	*Jul*	*Aug*	*Sep*	*Oct*	*Nov*	*Dec*
Record High	62°F (1981)	69°F (1992)	80°F (1967)	93°F (1992)	96°F (1980)	107°F (1988)	109°F (1973)	107°F (1973)	105°F (1959)	95°F (1963)	75°F (1978)	65°F (1979)
Record Low	−44°F (1950)	−43°F (1994)	−28°F (1995)	−12°F (1975)	15°F (1967)	30°F (1969)	35°F (1971)	33°F (1988)	11°F (1974)	−10°F (1991)	−30°F (1985)	−40°F (1983)

Source: www.weather.com

69. **Temperature** Find the temperature after a rise of 7°C from −13°C.

70. **Temperature** The temperature on the surface of the planet Venus is 480°C. The temperature on the surface of the planet Pluto is −234°C. Find the difference between the surface temperatures on Venus and Pluto.

Chapter 1 Test

1. Write 55% as a fraction.

2. Given $B = \{-8, -6, -4, -2\}$, which elements of set B are less than −5?

3. Find $m\angle x$ for the figure at the right.

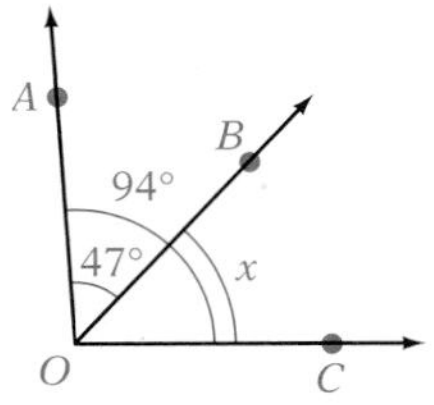

4. Write $\frac{3}{20}$ as a decimal.

5. Multiply: $\frac{3}{4}\left(-\frac{2}{21}\right)$

6. Divide: $-75 \div 5$

7. Evaluate: $\left(-\frac{2}{3}\right)^3 \cdot 3^2$

8. Add: $-7 + (-3) + 12$

9. Use the roster method to write the set of positive integers less than or equal to 6.

10. Write 1.59 as a percent.

11. Evaluate: $|-29|$

12. Place the correct symbol, < or >, between the two numbers.

$$-47 \quad -68$$

13. Subtract: $-\frac{4}{9} - \frac{5}{6}$

14. Find the area of a parallelogram whose base is 10 cm and whose height is 9 cm.

15. Simplify: $8 + \frac{12 - 4}{3^2 - 1} - 6$

16. Divide: $-\frac{5}{8} \div \left(-\frac{3}{4}\right)$

17. Write $\frac{3}{13}$ as a percent. Round to the nearest tenth of a percent.

18. Write 6.2% as a decimal.

19. Subtract: $13 - (-5) - 4$

20. Write $\frac{13}{30}$ as a decimal. Place a bar over the repeating digits of the decimal.

21. Multiply: $(-0.9)(2.7)$

22. Find the complement of a 28° angle.

23. Evaluate: $2^2 \cdot (-4)^2 \cdot 10$

24. Evaluate: $-|-34|$

25. Find the circumference of a circle whose diameter is 27 in. Use 3.14 for π.

26. Given $A = \{-17, -6, 5, 9\}$, find

a. the opposite of each element of set A.
b. the absolute value of each element of set A.

27. Write $\frac{16}{23}$ as a percent. Write the remainder in fractional form.

28. Add: $-18.354 + 6.97$

29. Multiply: $-4(8)(-5)$

30. Simplify: $9(-4) \div [2(8 - 5)^2]$

31. **Temperature** Find the temperature after a rise of 12°C from −8°C.

32. **Temperature** Use the table to find the average of the record low temperatures in Fairbanks, Alaska, for the first four months of the year.

Fairbanks, Alaska

	Jan	*Feb*	*Mar*	*Apr*	*May*	*Jun*	*Jul*	*Aug*	*Sep*	*Oct*	*Nov*	*Dec*
Record High	50°F (1981)	47°F (1987)	56°F (1994)	74°F (1960)	89°F (1960)	96°F (1969)	94°F (1975)	93°F (1994)	84°F (1957)	65°F (1969)	49°F (1997)	44°F (1985)
Record Low	−61°F (1969)	−58°F (1993)	−49°F (1956)	−24°F (1986)	−1°F (1964)	30°F (1950)	35°F (1959)	27°F (1987)	3°F (1992)	−27°F (1975)	−46°F (1990)	−62°F (1961)

Source: www.weather.com

33. **Recreation** The recreation department for a city is enclosing a rectangular playground that measures 150 ft by 200 ft with new fencing that costs \$6.52 per foot. Find the cost of the new fencing.

CHAPTER

2 Variable Expressions

OBJECTIVES

2.1
1 Evaluate variable expressions

2.2
1 The Properties of the Real Numbers
2 Simplify variable expressions using the Properties of Addition
3 Simplify variable expressions using the Properties of Multiplication
4 Simplify variable expressions using the Distributive Property
5 Simplify general variable expressions

2.3
1 Translate a verbal expression into a variable expression
2 Translate a verbal expression into a variable expression and then simplify the resulting expression
3 Translate application problems

With the rise of online catalogs and Internet stores, shoppers are turning to their computers to make purchases. A recent survey by Consumer Internet Barometer found that approximately 25 percent of people who had purchased a product online were extremely satisfied with their experience. In **Exercise 114 on page 95,** you are asked to use variables to express the number of people who were extremely satisfied with their online purchase in terms of the number of online buyers. This is called a variable expression.

Online Study Center DVD SSM

Need help? For online student resources, such as section quizzes, visit the Online Study Center at college.hmco.com/pic/aufmannBAWA7e.

Prep Test

1. Subtract: $-12 - (-15)$
2. Divide: $-36 \div (-9)$
3. Add: $-\frac{3}{4} + \frac{5}{6}$
4. What is the reciprocal of $-\frac{9}{4}$?
5. Divide: $\left(-\frac{3}{4}\right) \div \left(-\frac{5}{2}\right)$
6. Evaluate: -2^4
7. Evaluate: $\left(\frac{2}{3}\right)^3$
8. Evaluate: $3 \cdot 4^2$
9. Evaluate: $7 - 2 \cdot 3$
10. Evaluate: $5 - 7(3 - 2^2)$

2.1 Evaluating Variable Expressions

OBJECTIVE 1 Evaluate variable expressions

Point of Interest

Historical manuscripts indicate that mathematics is at least 4000 years old. Yet it was only 400 years ago that mathematicians started using variables to stand for numbers. The idea that a letter can stand for some number was a critical turning point in mathematics.

Often we discuss a quantity without knowing its exact value, such as the price of gold next month, the cost of a new automobile next year, or the tuition for next semester. In algebra, a letter of the alphabet is used to stand for a quantity that is unknown or one that can change, or *vary*. The letter is called a **variable.** An expression that contains one or more variables is called a **variable expression.**

A variable expression is shown at the right. The expression can be rewritten by writing subtraction as the addition of the opposite.

$$3x^2 - 5y + 2xy - x - 7$$

$$3x^2 + (-5y) + 2xy + (-x) + (-7)$$

Note that the expression has five addends. The **terms** of a variable expression are the addends of the expression. The expression has five terms.

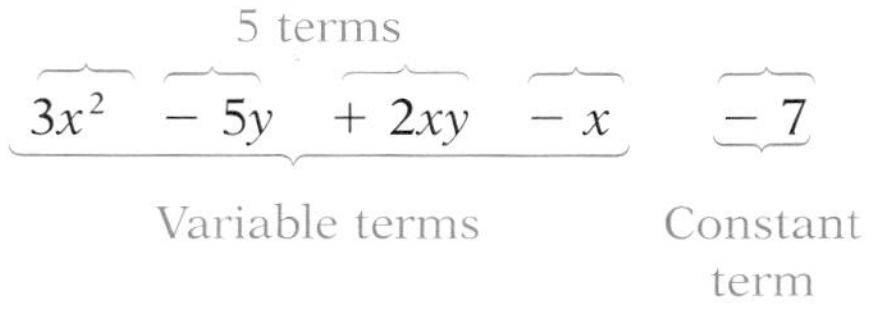

The terms $3x^2$, $-5y$, $2xy$, and $-x$ are **variable terms.**

The term -7 is a **constant term,** or simply a **constant.**

Each variable term is composed of a **numerical coefficient** and a **variable part** (the variable or variables and their exponents).

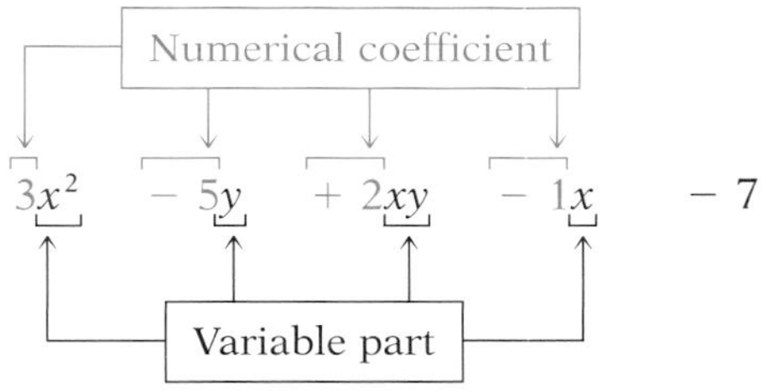

When the numerical coefficient is 1 or -1, the 1 is usually not written ($x = 1x$ and $-x = -1x$).

EXAMPLE 1 Name the variable terms of the expression $2a^2 - 5a + 7$.

Solution $2a^2, -5a$

PROBLEM 1 Name the constant term of the expression $6n^2 + 3n - 4$.

Solution See page S3.

Variable expressions occur naturally in science. In a physics lab, a student may discover that a weight of 1 pound will stretch a spring $\frac{1}{2}$ inch. A weight of 2 pounds will stretch the spring 1 inch. By experimenting, the student can discover that the distance the spring will stretch is found by multiplying the weight, in pounds, by $\frac{1}{2}$. By letting W represent the number of pounds attached to the spring, we can represent the distance, in inches, that the spring stretches by the variable expression $\frac{1}{2}W$.

With a weight of W pounds, the spring will stretch $\frac{1}{2} \cdot W = \frac{1}{2}W$ inches.

With a weight of 10 pounds, the spring will stretch $\frac{1}{2} \cdot 10 = 5$ inches.

With a weight of 3 pounds, the spring will stretch $\frac{1}{2} \cdot 3 = 1\frac{1}{2}$ inches.

Replacing the variable or variables in a variable expression with numbers and then simplifying the resulting numerical expression is called **evaluating the variable expression.**

EXAMPLE 2 Evaluate $ab - b^2$ when $a = 2$ and $b = -3$.

Solution $ab - b^2$

$2(-3) - (-3)^2$ • **Replace each variable in the expression with the number it represents.**

$= 2(-3) - 9$ • **Use the Order of Operations Agreement to simplify the resulting numerical expression.**

$= -6 - 9$

$= -15$

PROBLEM 2 Evaluate $2xy + y^2$ when $x = -4$ and $y = 2$.

Solution See page S3.

EXAMPLE 3 Evaluate $\frac{a^2 - b^2}{a - b}$ when $a = 3$ and $b = -4$.

Solution $\frac{a^2 - b^2}{a - b}$

$\frac{(3)^2 - (-4)^2}{3 - (-4)}$ • **Replace each variable in the expression with the number it represents.**

$= \frac{9 - 16}{3 - (-4)}$ • **Use the Order of Operations Agreement to simplify the resulting numerical expression.**

$= \frac{-7}{7}$

$= -1$

PROBLEM 3 Evaluate $\frac{a^2 + b^2}{a + b}$ when $a = 5$ and $b = -3$.

Solution See page S3.

EXAMPLE 4 Evaluate $x^2 - 3(x - y) - z^2$ when $x = 2$, $y = -1$, and $z = 3$.

Solution $x^2 - 3(x - y) - z^2$

$(2)^2 - 3[2 - (-1)] - (3)^2$
- **Replace each variable in the expression with the number it represents.**

$= (2)^2 - 3(3) - (3)^2$
- **Use the Order of Operations Agreement to simplify the resulting numerical expression.**

$= 4 - 3(3) - 9$

$= 4 - 9 - 9$

$= -5 - 9$

$= -14$

PROBLEM 4 Evaluate $x^3 - 2(x + y) + z^2$ when $x = 2$, $y = -4$, and $z = -3$.

Solution See page S3.

EXAMPLE 5 The diameter of the base of a right circular cylinder is 5 cm. The height of the cylinder is 8.5 cm. Find the volume of the cylinder. Round to the nearest tenth.

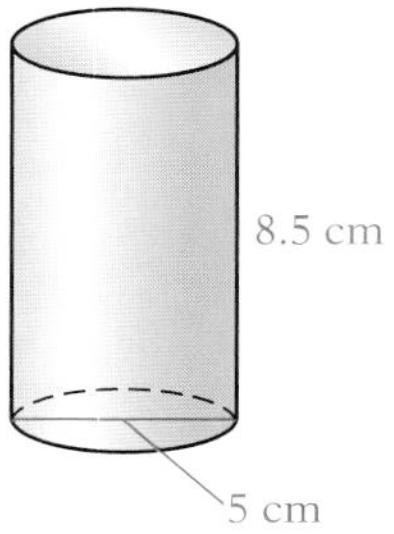

Solution $V = \pi r^2 h$
- **Use the formula for the volume of a right circular cylinder.**

$V = \pi(2.5)^2(8.5)$
- $r = \frac{1}{2}d = \frac{1}{2}(5) = 2.5$

$V = \pi(6.25)(8.5)$
- **Use the π key on your calculator to enter the value of π.**

$V \approx 166.9$

The volume is approximately 166.9 cm^3.

PROBLEM 5 The diameter of the base of a right circular cone is 9 cm. The height of the cone is 9.5 cm. Find the volume of the cone. Round to the nearest tenth.

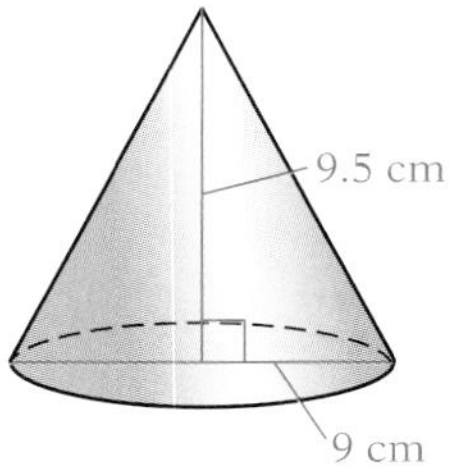

Solution See page S3.

Take Note

For your reference, geometric formulas are printed at the back of this textbook.

A graphing calculator can be used to evaluate variable expressions. When the value of each variable is stored in the calculator's memory and a variable expression is then entered on the calculator, the calculator evaluates that variable expression for the values of the variables stored in its memory. See the Appendix for a description of keystroking procedures.

2.1 Concept Review

Determine whether the statement is always true, sometimes true, or never true.

1. The expression $3x^2$ is a variable expression.

2. In the expression $8y^3 - 4y$, the terms are $8y^3$ and $4y$.

3. For the expression x^5, the value of x is 1.

4. For the expression $6a + 7b$, 7 is a constant term.

5. The Order of Operations Agreement is used in evaluating a variable expression.

6. The result of evaluating a variable expression is a single number.

2.1 Exercises

1 Evaluate variable expressions

1. To identify the terms of the variable expression $3x^2 - 4x - 7$, first write subtraction as addition of the opposite: $3x^2 + (\underline{\ ?\ }) + (\underline{\ ?\ })$. The terms of $3x^2 - 4x - 7$ are $\underline{\ ?\ }$, $\underline{\ ?\ }$, and $\underline{\ ?\ }$.

2. Evaluate $mn^2 - m$ when $m = -2$ and $n = 5$.

$mn^2 - m = (-2)(5)^2 - (-2)$	• **Replace *m* with $\underline{\ ?\ }$ and *n* with $\underline{\ ?\ }$.**
$= (-2)(\underline{\ ?\ }) - (-2)$	• **Simplify the exponential expression.**
$= \underline{\ ?\ } - (-2)$	• **Multiply.**
$= -50 + \underline{\ ?\ }$	• **Write subtraction as addition of the opposite.**
$= \underline{\ ?\ }$.	• **Add.**

Name the terms of the variable expression. Then underline the constant term.

3. $2x^2 + 5x - 8$ **4.** $-3n^2 - 4n + 7$ **5.** $6 - a^4$

Name the variable terms of the expression. Then underline the variable part of each term.

6. $9b^2 - 4ab + a^2$ **7.** $7x^2y + 6xy^2 + 10$ **8.** $5 - 8n - 3n^2$

Name the coefficients of the variable terms.

9. $x^2 - 9x + 2$ **10.** $12a^2 - 8ab - b^2$ **11.** $n^3 - 4n^2 - n + 9$

12. What is the meaning of the phrase "evaluate a variable expression"?

13. What is the difference between the meaning of "the value of the variable" and the meaning of "the value of the variable expression"?

Evaluate the variable expression when $a = 2$, $b = 3$, and $c = -4$.

14. $3a + 2b$ **15.** $a - 2c$ **16.** $-a^2$

17. $2c^2$ **18.** $-3a + 4b$ **19.** $3b - 3c$

20. $b^2 - 3$ **21.** $-3c + 4$ **22.** $16 \div (2c)$

23. $6b \div (-a)$ **24.** $bc \div (2a)$ **25.** $-2ab \div c$

26. $a^2 - b^2$ **27.** $b^2 - c^2$ **28.** $(a + b)^2$

29. $a^2 + b^2$ **30.** $2a - (c + a)^2$ **31.** $(b - a)^2 + 4c$

32. $b^2 - \dfrac{ac}{8}$ **33.** $\dfrac{5ab}{6} - 3cb$ **34.** $(b - 2a)^2 + bc$

Evaluate the variable expression when $a = -2$, $b = 4$, $c = -1$, and $d = 3$.

35. $\dfrac{b + c}{d}$ **36.** $\dfrac{d - b}{c}$ **37.** $\dfrac{2d + b}{-a}$

38. $\dfrac{b + 2d}{b}$ **39.** $\dfrac{b - d}{c - a}$ **40.** $\dfrac{2c - d}{-ad}$

41. $(b + d)^2 - 4a$ **42.** $(d - a)^2 - 3c$ **43.** $(d - a)^2 \div 5$

44. $(b - c)^2 \div 5$ **45.** $b^2 - 2b + 4$ **46.** $a^2 - 5a - 6$

47. $\dfrac{bd}{a} \div c$ **48.** $\dfrac{2ac}{b} \div (-c)$ **49.** $2(b + c) - 2a$

50. $3(b - a) - bc$ **51.** $\dfrac{b - 2a}{bc^2 - d}$ **52.** $\dfrac{b^2 - a}{ad + 3c}$

53. $\frac{1}{3}d^2 - \frac{3}{8}b^2$

54. $\frac{5}{8}a^4 - c^2$

55. $\frac{-4bc}{2a - b}$

56. $\frac{abc}{b - d}$

57. $a^3 - 3a^2 + a$

58. $d^3 - 3d - 9$

59. $-\frac{3}{4}b + \frac{1}{2}(ac + bd)$

60. $-\frac{2}{3}d - \frac{1}{5}(bd - ac)$

61. $(b - a)^2 - (d - c)^2$

62. $(b + c)^2 + (a + d)^2$

63. $4ac + (2a)^2$

64. $3dc - (4c)^2$

Evaluate the variable expression when $a = 2.7$, $b = -1.6$, and $c = -0.8$.

65. $c^2 - ab$

66. $(a + b)^2 - c$

67. $\frac{b^3}{c} - 4a$

Complete Exercises 68 and 69 without a calculator.

68. If $\frac{b + c}{abc}$ is evaluated when $a = -25$, $b = 67$, and $c = -82$, will the result be positive or negative?

69. A sphere has a radius of 2 cm.

a. Can the exact volume of the sphere be V cm^3, where V is a whole number?

b. Can the exact volume of the sphere be V cm^2, where V is an irrational number?

Solve. Round to the nearest tenth.

70. Geometry Find the volume of a sphere that has a radius of 8.5 cm.

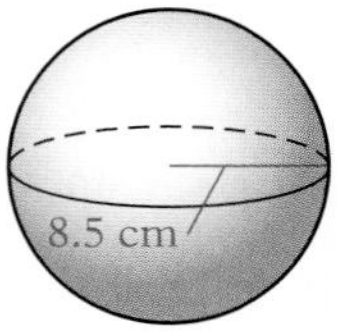

71. Geometry Find the volume of a right circular cylinder that has a radius of 1.25 in. and a height of 5.25 in.

72. Geometry The radius of the base of a right circular cylinder is 3.75 ft. The height of the cylinder is 9.5 ft. Find the surface area of the cylinder.

73. Geometry The length of one base of a trapezoid is 17.5 cm, and the length of the other base is 10.25 cm. The height is 6.75 cm. What is the area of the trapezoid?

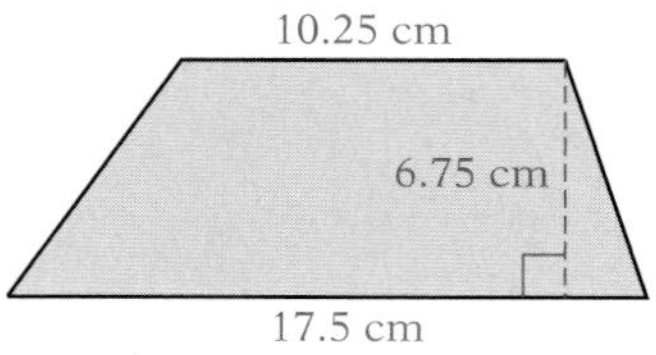

74. Geometry A right circular cone has a height of 2.75 in. The diameter of the base is 1 in. Find the volume of the cone.

75. Geometry A right circular cylinder has a height of 12.6 m. The diameter of the base is 7 m. Find the volume of the cylinder.

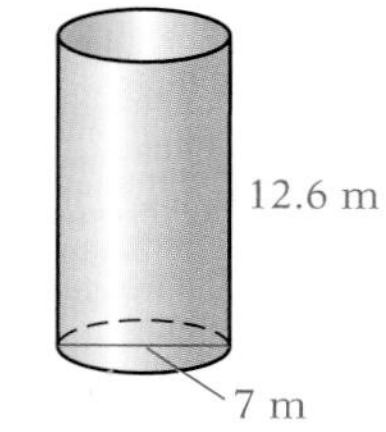

76. The value of z is the value of $a^2 - 2a$ when $a = -3$. Find the value of z^2.

77. The value of a is the value of $3x^2 - 4x - 5$ when $x = -2$. Find the value of $3a - 4$.

78. The value of c is the value of $a^2 + b^2$ when $a = 2$ and $b = -2$. Find the value of $c^2 - 4$.

79. The value of d is the value of $3w^2 - 2v$ when $w = -1$ and $v = 3$. Find the value of $d^2 - 4d$.

2.1 Applying Concepts

Evaluate the variable expression when $a = -2$ and $b = -3$.

80. $|2a + 3b|$

81. $|-4ab|$

82. $|5a - b|$

Evaluate the variable expression when $a = \frac{2}{3}$ and $b = -\frac{3}{2}$.

83. $\frac{1}{3}a^5b^6$

84. $\frac{(2ab)^3}{2a^3b^3}$

85. $|5ab - 8a^2b^2|$

Evaluate the following expressions for $x = 2$, $y = 3$, and $z = -2$.

86. $3^x - x^3$

87. $2^y - y^2$

88. z^y

89. z^x

90. $x^x - y^y$

91. $y^{(x^2)}$

92. For each of the following, determine the first natural number x, greater than 2, for which the second expression is larger than the first. On the basis of your answers, make a conjecture that appears to be true about the expressions x^n and n^x, where $n = 3, 4, 5, 6, 7, \ldots$ and x is a natural number greater than 2.

a. x^3, 3^x

b. x^4, 4^x

c. x^5, 5^x

d. x^6, 6^x

2.2 Simplifying Variable Expressions

OBJECTIVE 1 The Properties of the Real Numbers

The Properties of the Real Numbers describe the way operations on numbers can be performed. Here are some of the Properties of the Real Numbers and an example of each.

The Commutative Property of Addition

If a and b are real numbers, then $a + b = b + a$.

Two terms can be added in either order; the sum is the same.

$$4 + 3 = 7 \quad \text{and} \quad 3 + 4 = 7$$

The Commutative Property of Multiplication

If a and b are real numbers, then $a \cdot b = b \cdot a$.

Two factors can be multiplied in either order; the product is the same.

$$(5)(-2) = -10 \quad \text{and} \quad (-2)(5) = -10$$

The Associative Property of Addition

If a, b, and c are real numbers, then $(a + b) + c = a + (b + c)$.

When three or more terms are added, the terms can be grouped (with parentheses, for example) in any order; the sum is the same.

$$2 + (3 + 4) = 2 + 7 = 9 \quad \text{and} \quad (2 + 3) + 4 = 5 + 4 = 9$$

The Associative Property of Multiplication

If a, b, and c are real numbers, then $(a \cdot b) \cdot c = a \cdot (b \cdot c)$.

When three or more factors are multiplied, the factors can be grouped in any order; the product is the same.

$$(2 \cdot 3) \cdot 4 = 6 \cdot 4 = 24 \quad \text{and} \quad 2 \cdot (3 \cdot 4) = 2 \cdot 12 = 24$$

The Addition Property of Zero

If a is a real number, then $a + 0 = 0 + a = a$.

The sum of a term and zero is the term.

$$4 + 0 = 4 \qquad 0 + 4 = 4$$

The Multiplication Property of Zero

If a is a real number, then $a \cdot 0 = 0 \cdot a = 0$.

The product of a term and zero is zero.

$$(5)(0) = 0 \qquad (0)(5) = 0$$

The Multiplication Property of One

If a is a real number, then $a \cdot 1 = 1 \cdot a = a$.

The product of a term and 1 is the term.

$$6 \cdot 1 = 6 \qquad 1 \cdot 6 = 6$$

The Inverse Property of Addition

If a is a real number, then $a + (-a) = (-a) + a = 0$.

The sum of a number and its opposite is zero.
The opposite of a number is called its **additive inverse.**

$$8 + (-8) = 0 \qquad (-8) + 8 = 0$$

The Inverse Property of Multiplication

If a is a real number, and $a \neq 0$, then $a \cdot \frac{1}{a} = \frac{1}{a} \cdot a = 1$.

The product of a number and its reciprocal is 1.

$\frac{1}{a}$ is the **reciprocal** of a. $\frac{1}{a}$ is also called the **multiplicative inverse** of a.

$$7 \cdot \frac{1}{7} = 1 \qquad \frac{1}{7} \cdot 7 = 1$$

The Distributive Property

If a, b, and c are real numbers, then $a(b + c) = ab + ac$ or $(b + c)a = ba + ca$.

By the Distributive Property, the term outside the parentheses is multiplied by each term inside the parentheses.

$$2(3 + 4) = 2 \cdot 3 + 2 \cdot 4 \qquad (4 + 5)2 = 4 \cdot 2 + 5 \cdot 2$$
$$2 \cdot 7 = 6 + 8 \qquad 9 \cdot 2 = 8 + 10$$
$$14 = 14 \qquad 18 = 18$$

EXAMPLE 1 Complete the statement by using the Commutative Property of Multiplication.

$(6)(5) = (?)(6)$

Solution $(6)(5) = (5)(6)$ • **The Commutative Property of Multiplication states that $a \cdot b = b \cdot a$.**

PROBLEM 1 Complete the statement by using the Inverse Property of Addition.

$7 + ? = 0$

Solution See page S4.

EXAMPLE 2 Identify the property that justifies the statement.

$2(8 + 5) = 16 + 10$

Solution The Distributive Property • **The Distributive Property states that $a(b + c) = ab + ac$.**

PROBLEM 2 Identify the property that justifies the statement.

$5 + (13 + 7) = (5 + 13) + 7$

Solution See page S4.

OBJECTIVE 2 Simplify variable expressions using the Properties of Addition

Like terms of a variable expression are terms with the same variable part. (Because $x^2 = x \cdot x$, x^2 and x are not like terms.)

Constant terms are like terms. 4 and 9 are like terms.

like terms

$$3x + 4 - 7x + 9 - x^2$$

like terms

To **combine like terms,** use the Distributive Property $ba + ca = (b + c)a$ to add the coefficients.

$$2x + 3x = (2 + 3)x$$
$$= 5x$$

EXAMPLE 3 Simplify. **A.** $-2y + 3y$ **B.** $5x - 11x$

Solution **A.** $-2y + 3y$

$= (-2 + 3)y$ • **Use the Distributive Property $ba + ca = (b + c)a$.**

$= 1y$ • **Add the coefficients.**

$= y$ • **Use the Multiplication Property of One.**

B. $5x - 11x$

$= [5 + (-11)]x$ • **Use the Distributive Property** ***ba + ca = (b + c)a*.**

$= -6x$ • **Add the coefficients.**

PROBLEM 3 Simplify. **A.** $9x + 6x$ **B.** $-4y - 7y$

Solution See page S4.

In simplifying more complicated expressions, use the Properties of Addition.

The Commutative Property of Addition can be used when adding two like terms. The terms can be added in either order. The sum is the same.

$$2x + (-4x) = -4x + 2x$$
$$[2 + (-4)]x = (-4 + 2)x$$
$$-2x = -2x$$

The Associative Property of Addition is used when adding three or more terms. The terms can be grouped in any order. The sum is the same.

$$3x + 5x + 9x = (3x + 5x) + 9x = 3x + (5x + 9x)$$
$$8x + 9x = 3x + 14x$$
$$17x = 17x$$

By the Addition Property of Zero, the sum of a term and zero is the term.

$$5x + 0 = 0 + 5x = 5x$$

By the Inverse Property of Addition, the sum of a term and its additive inverse is zero.

$$7x + (-7x) = -7x + 7x = 0$$

EXAMPLE 4 Simplify. **A.** $8x + 3y - 8x$ **B.** $4x^2 + 5x - 6x^2 - 2x$

Solution **A.** $8x + 3y - 8x$

$= 3y + 8x - 8x$ • **Use the Commutative Property of Addition to rearrange the terms.**

$= 3y + (8x - 8x)$ • **Use the Associative Property of Addition to group like terms.**

$= 3y + 0$ • **Use the Inverse Property of Addition.**

$= 3y$ • **Use the Addition Property of Zero.**

B. $4x^2 + 5x - 6x^2 - 2x$

$= 4x^2 - 6x^2 + 5x - 2x$ • **Use the Commutative Property of Addition to rearrange the terms.**

$= (4x^2 - 6x^2) + (5x - 2x)$ • **Use the Associative Property of Addition to group like terms.**

$= -2x^2 + 3x$ • **Combine like terms.**

PROBLEM 4 Simplify. **A.** $3a - 2b + 5a$ **B.** $x^2 - 7 + 9x^2 - 14$

Solution See page S4.

OBJECTIVE 3 Simplify variable expressions using the Properties of Multiplication

The Properties of Multiplication are used in simplifying variable expressions.

The Associative Property is used when multiplying three or more factors. $2(3x) = (2 \cdot 3)x = 6x$

The Commutative Property can be used to change the order in which factors are multiplied. $(3x) \cdot 2 = 2 \cdot (3x) = 6x$

By the Multiplication Property of One, the product of a term and 1 is the term. $(8x)(1) = (1)(8x) = 8x$

By the Inverse Property of Multiplication, the product of a term and its reciprocal is 1. $5x \cdot \frac{1}{5x} = \frac{1}{5x} \cdot 5x = 1, x \neq 0$

EXAMPLE 5 Simplify. **A.** $2(-x)$ **B.** $\frac{3}{2}\left(\frac{2x}{3}\right)$ **C.** $(16x)2$

Solution

A. $2(-x) = 2(-1 \cdot x)$ • $-x = -1x = -1 \cdot x$

$= [2 \cdot (-1)]x$ • **Use the Associative Property of Multiplication to group factors.**

$= -2x$ • **Multiply.**

B. $\frac{3}{2}\left(\frac{2x}{3}\right) = \frac{3}{2}\left(\frac{2}{3}x\right)$ • **Note that** $\frac{2x}{3} = \frac{2}{3} \cdot \frac{x}{1} = \frac{2}{3}x$.

$= \left(\frac{3}{2} \cdot \frac{2}{3}\right)x$ • **Use the Associative Property of Multiplication to group factors.**

$= 1x$ • **Use the Inverse Property of Multiplication.**

$= x$ • **Use the Multiplication Property of One.**

C. $(16x)2 = 2(16x)$ • **Use the Commutative Property of Multiplication to rearrange factors.**

$= (2 \cdot 16)x$ • **Use the Associative Property of Multiplication to group factors.**

$= 32x$ • **Multiply.**

PROBLEM 5 Simplify. **A.** $-7(-2a)$ **B.** $-\frac{5}{6}(-30y^2)$ **C.** $(-5x)(-2)$

Solution See page S4.

OBJECTIVE 4 Simplify variable expressions using the Distributive Property

The Distributive Property is used to remove parentheses from a variable expression.

$$3(2x - 5) = 3(2x) - 3(5) = 6x - 15$$

An extension of the Distributive Property is used when an expression contains more than two terms.

$$4(x^2 + 6x - 1)$$
$$= 4(x^2) + 4(6x) - 4(1)$$
$$= 4x^2 + 24x - 4$$

EXAMPLE 6 Simplify. **A.** $-3(5 + x)$ **B.** $-(2x - 4)$ **C.** $(2y - 6)2$ **D.** $5(3x + 7y - z)$

Solution

A. $-3(5 + x)$
$= -3(5) + (-3)x$ • **Use the Distributive Property.**
$= -15 - 3x$ • **Multiply.**

B. $-(2x - 4)$
$= \quad (2x - 4)$ • **Just as $-x = -1x$, $-(2x - 4) = \quad (2x - 4)$.**
$= -1(2x) - (-1)(4)$ • **Use the Distributive Property.**
$= -2x + 4$ • ***Note:* When a negative sign immediately precedes the parentheses, remove the parentheses and change the sign of each term inside the parentheses.**

C. $(2y - 6)2$
$= (2y)(2) - (6)(2)$ • **Use the Distributive Property $(b + c)a = ba + ca$.**
$= 4y - 12$

D. $5(3x + 7y - z)$
$= 5(3x) + 5(7y) - 5(z)$ • **Use the Distributive Property.**
$= 15x + 35y - 5z$

PROBLEM 6 Simplify. **A.** $7(4 + 2y)$ **B.** $-(5x - 12)$ **C.** $(3a - 1)5$ **D.** $-3(6a^2 - 8a + 9)$

Solution See page S4.

OBJECTIVE 5 Simplify general variable expressions

When simplifying variable expressions, use the Distributive Property to remove parentheses and brackets used as grouping symbols.

EXAMPLE 7 Simplify: $4(x - y) - 2(-3x + 6y)$

Solution $4(x - y) - 2(-3x + 6y)$
$= 4x - 4y + 6x - 12y$ • **Use the Distributive Property to remove parentheses.**
$= 10x - 16y$ • **Combine like terms.**

PROBLEM 7 Simplify: $7(x - 2y) - 3(-x - 2y)$

Solution See page S4.

EXAMPLE 8 Simplify: $2x - 3[2x - 3(x + 7)]$

Solution $2x - 3[2x - 3(x + 7)]$

$= 2x - 3[2x - 3x - 21]$ • **Use the Distributive Property to remove the inner grouping symbols.**

$= 2x - 3[-x - 21]$ • **Combine like terms inside the grouping symbols.**

$= 2x + 3x + 63$ • **Use the Distributive Property to remove the brackets.**

$= 5x + 63$ • **Combine like terms.**

PROBLEM 8 Simplify: $3y - 2[x - 4(2 - 3y)]$

Solution See page S4.

2.2 Concept Review

Determine whether the statement is always true, sometimes true, or never true.

1. The Associative Property of Addition states that two terms can be added in either order and the sum will be the same.
2. When three numbers are multiplied, the numbers can be grouped in any order and the product will be the same.
3. The Multiplication Property of One states that multiplying a number by one does not change the number.
4. The sum of a number and its additive inverse is zero.
5. The product of a number and its multiplicative inverse is one.
6. The terms x and x^2 are like terms because both have a coefficient of 1.
7. $3(x + 4) = 3x + 4$ is an example of the correct application of the Distributive Property.
8. To add like terms, add the coefficients; the variable part remains unchanged.

2.2 Exercises

1 The Properties of the Real Numbers

1. The fact that two terms can be added in either order is called the ___?___ Property of Addition.
2. The fact that three or more factors can be multiplied by grouping them in any order is called the ___?___ Property of Multiplication.

3. The Inverse Property of Multiplication tells us that the product of a number and its ___?___ is one.

4. The Inverse Property of Addition tells us that the sum of a number and its ___?___ is zero.

Use the given property to complete the statement.

5. The Commutative Property of Multiplication
$2 \cdot 5 = 5 \cdot ?$

6. The Commutative Property of Addition
$9 + 17 = ? + 9$

7. The Associative Property of Multiplication
$(4 \cdot 5) \cdot 6 = 4 \cdot (? \cdot 6)$

8. The Associative Property of Addition
$(4 + 5) + 6 = ? + (5 + 6)$

9. The Distributive Property
$2(4 + 3) = 8 + ?$

10. The Addition Property of Zero
$? + 0 = -7$

11. The Inverse Property of Addition
$8 + ? = 0$

12. The Inverse Property of Multiplication
$\frac{1}{-5}(-5) = ?$

13. The Multiplication Property of One
$? \cdot 1 = -4$

14. The Multiplication Property of Zero
$12 \cdot ? = 0$

Identify the property that justifies the statement.

15. $-7 + 7 = 0$

16. $(-8)\left(-\frac{1}{8}\right) = 1$

17. $23 + 19 = 19 + 23$

18. $-21 + 0 = -21$

19. $2 + (6 + 14) = (2 + 6) + 14$

20. $(-3 + 9)8 = -24 + 72$

21. $3 \cdot 5 = 5 \cdot 3$

22. $-32(0) = 0$

23. $(4 \cdot 3) \cdot 5 = 4 \cdot (3 \cdot 5)$

24. $\frac{1}{4}(1) = \frac{1}{4}$

2 Simplify variable expressions using the Properties of Addition

25. What are *like terms*? Give an example of two like terms. Give an example of two terms that are not like terms.

26. Explain the meaning of the phrase "simplify a variable expression."

27. Which of the following are like terms?
$3x, 3x^2, 5x, 5xy$

28. Which of the following are like terms?
$-7a, -7b, -4a, -7a^2$

29. Simplify $5a - 8a$ by combining like terms.

$5a - 8a = 5a + \underline{\ ?\ }$ • **Write subtraction as addition of the opposite.**

$= [5 + (-8)]a$ • **Use the _?_ Property $ba + ca = (b + c)a$.**

$= \underline{\ ?\ }\ a$ • **Add the coefficients.**

30. Simplify $6xy - 6x + 7xy$ by combining like terms.

$6xy - 6x + 7xy = 6xy + 7xy - 6x$ • **Use the _?_ Property of Addition to rearrange the terms.**

$= (6 + 7)(\underline{\ ?\ }) - 6x$ • **Use the Distributive Property $ba + ca = (b + c)a$.**

$= \underline{\ ?\ } - 6x$ • **Add the coefficients.**

Simplify.

31. $6x + 8x$ **32.** $12x + 13x$ **33.** $9a - 4a$ **34.** $12a - 3a$

35. $4y - 10y$ **36.** $8y - 6y$ **37.** $-3b - 7$ **38.** $-12y - 3$

39. $-12a + 17a$ **40.** $-3a + 12a$ **41.** $5ab - 7ab$ **42.** $9ab - 3ab$

43. $-12xy + 17xy$ **44.** $-15xy + 3xy$ **45.** $-3ab + 3ab$ **46.** $-7ab + 7ab$

47. $-\frac{1}{2}x - \frac{1}{3}x$ **48.** $-\frac{2}{5}y + \frac{3}{10}y$ **49.** $\frac{3}{8}x^2 - \frac{5}{12}x^2$ **50.** $\frac{2}{3}y^2 - \frac{4}{9}y^2$

51. $3x + 5x + 3x$ **52.** $8x + 5x + 7x$ **53.** $5a - 3a + 5a$ **54.** $10a - 17a + 3a$

55. $-5x^2 - 12x^2 + 3x^2$ **56.** $-y^2 - 8y^2 + 7y^2$ **57.** $7x - 8x + 3y$

58. $8y - 10x + 8x$ **59.** $7x - 3y + 10x$ **60.** $8y + 8x - 8y$

61. $3a - 7b - 5a + b$ **62.** $-5b + 7a - 7b + 12a$ **63.** $3x - 8y - 10x + 4x$

64. $3y - 12x - 7y + 2y$ **65.** $x^2 - 7x - 5x^2 + 5x$ **66.** $3x^2 + 5x - 10x^2 - 10x$

67. State whether the given number will be positive, negative, or zero after the variable expression $15a^2 - 12a + 7 - 21a^2 + 29a - 7$ is simplified.
a. the coefficient of a^2 **b.** the coefficient of a **c.** the constant term

68. Which expressions are equivalent to $-10x - 10y - 10y - 10x$?
a. 0 **b.** $-20y$ **c.** $-20x$ **d.** $-20x - 20y$ **e.** $-20y - 20x$

3 Simplify variable expressions using the Properties of Multiplication

69. Simplify: $4(-12x)$

$4(-12x) = [4(-12)]x$ • **Use the _?_ Property of Multiplication to group factors.**

$= \underline{\ ?\ }$ • **Multiply.**

70. Simplify: $\left(\frac{1}{2}a^2\right)\left(-\frac{3}{2}\right)$

$\left(\frac{1}{2}a^2\right)\left(-\frac{3}{2}\right) = (\underline{\ ?\ })\left(\frac{1}{2}a^2\right)$ • **Use the Commutative Property of Mulitplication to rearrange factors.**

$= \left(-\frac{3}{2} \cdot \underline{\ ?\ }\right)a^2$ • **Use the Associative Property of Multiplication to group factors.**

$= \underline{\ ?\ }\ a^2$ • **Multiply.**

Simplify.

71. $4(3x)$

72. $12(5x)$

73. $-3(7a)$

74. $-2(5a)$

75. $-2(-3y)$

76. $-5(-6y)$

77. $(4x)2$

78. $(6x)12$

79. $(3a)(-2)$

80. $(7a)(-4)$

81. $(-3b)(-4)$

82. $(-12b)(-9)$

83. $-5(3x^2)$

84. $-8(7x^2)$

85. $\frac{1}{3}(3x^2)$

86. $\frac{1}{5}(5a)$

87. $\frac{1}{8}(8x)$

88. $-\frac{1}{4}(-4a)$

89. $-\frac{1}{7}(-7n)$

90. $\left(\frac{3x}{4}\right)\left(\frac{4}{3}\right)$

91. $\frac{12x}{5}\left(\frac{5}{12}\right)$

92. $(-6y)\left(-\frac{1}{6}\right)$

93. $(-10n)\left(-\frac{1}{10}\right)$

94. $\frac{1}{3}(9x)$

95. $\frac{1}{7}(14x)$

96. $-\frac{1}{5}(10x)$

97. $-\frac{1}{8}(16x)$

98. $-\frac{2}{3}(12a^2)$

99. $-\frac{5}{8}(24a^2)$

100. $-\frac{1}{2}(-16y)$

101. $-\frac{3}{4}(-8y)$

102. $(16y)\left(\frac{1}{4}\right)$

103. $(33y)\left(\frac{1}{11}\right)$

104. $(-6x)\left(\frac{1}{3}\right)$

105. $(-10x)\left(\frac{1}{5}\right)$

106. $(-8a)\left(-\frac{3}{4}\right)$

107. After $\frac{2}{7}x^2$ is multiplied by a proper fraction, is the coefficient of x^2 greater than one or less than one?

108. After $-152m$ is multiplied by a whole number, is the coefficient of m greater than zero or less than zero?

4 Simplify variable expressions using the Distributive Property

109. Simplify: $-8(3x - 2)$

$-8(3x - 2) = (-8)(3x) - (-8)(2)$ • **Use the ___?___ Property.**

$= \underline{\ ?\ }\ x + \underline{\ ?\ }$ • **Multiply.**

110. Simplify: $(7a - 3)(-2)$

$(7a - 3)(-2) = (7a)(\underline{\ ?\ }) - 3(\underline{\ ?\ })$ • **Use the Distributive Property.**

$= \underline{\ ?\ } + \underline{\ ?\ }$ • **Multiply.**

Simplify.

111. $-(x + 2)$

112. $-(x + 7)$

113. $2(4x - 3)$

114. $5(2x - 7)$

115. $-2(a + 7)$

116. $-5(a + 16)$

117. $-3(2y - 8)$

118. $-5(3y - 7)$

119. $(5 - 3b)7$

120. $(10 - 7b)2$

121. $-3(3 - 5x)$

122. $-5(7 - 10x)$

123. $3(5x^2 + 2x)$

124. $6(3x^2 + 2x)$

125. $-2(-y + 9)$

126. $-5(-2x + 7)$

127. $(-3x - 6)5$

128. $(-2x + 7)7$

129. $2(-3x^2 - 14)$

130. $5(-6x^2 - 3)$

131. $-3(2y^2 - 7)$

132. $-8(3y^2 - 12)$

133. $-(6a^2 - 7b^2)$

134. $3(x^2 + 2x - 6)$

135. $4(x^2 - 3x + 5)$

136. $-2(y^2 - 2y + 4)$

137. $-3(y^2 - 3y - 7)$

138. $2(-a^2 - 2a + 3)$

139. $4(-3a^2 - 5a + 7)$

140. $-5(-2x^2 - 3x + 7)$

141. $-3(-4x^2 + 3x - 4)$

142. $3(2x^2 + xy - 3y^2)$

143. $5(2x^2 - 4xy - y^2)$

144. $-(3a^2 + 5a - 4)$

145. $-(8b^2 - 6b + 9)$

146. After the expression $17x - 31$ is multiplied by a negative integer, is the constant term positive or negative?

147. The expression $5x - 8xy + 7y$ is multiplied by a positive integer. How many variable terms does the resulting expression have?

5 Simplify general variable expressions

148. When simplifying $4(3a - 7) + 2(a - 3)$, the first step is to use the Distributive Property to remove parentheses:
$4(3a - 7) + 2(a - 3) = (\underline{\ ?\ })a - \underline{\ ?\ } + (\underline{\ ?\ })a - \underline{\ ?\ }$

149. When simplifying $12m - (m - 3)$, the first step is to remove the parentheses and change the sign of each term inside the parentheses:
$12m - \underline{\ ?\ } + \underline{\ ?\ }$

Simplify.

150. $4x - 2(3x + 8)$

151. $6a - (5a + 7)$

152. $9 - 3(4y + 6)$

153. $10 - (11x - 3)$

154. $5n - (7 - 2n)$

155. $8 - (12 + 4y)$

156. $3(x + 2) - 5(x - 7)$

157. $2(x - 4) - 4(x + 2)$

158. $12(y - 2) + 3(7 - 3y)$

159. $6(2y - 7) - 3(3 - 2y)$

160. $3(a - b) - 4(a + b)$

161. $2(a + 2b) - (a - 3b)$

162. $4[x - 2(x - 3)]$

163. $2[x + 2(x + 7)]$

164. $-2[3x + 2(4 - x)]$

165. $-5[2x + 3(5 - x)]$

166. $-3[2x - (x + 7)]$

167. $-2[3x - (5x - 2)]$

168. $2x - 3[x - 2(4 - x)]$

169. $-7x + 3[x - 7(3 - 2x)]$

170. $-5x - 2[2x - 4(x + 7)] - 6$

171. $4a - 2[2b - (b - 2a)] + 3b$

172. $2x + 3(x - 2y) + 5(3x - 7y)$

173. $5y - 2(y - 3x) + 2(7x - y)$

174. Which expression is equivalent to $12 - 7(y - 9)$?
a. $5(y - 9)$ **b.** $12 - 7y - 63$
c. $12 - 7y + 63$ **d.** $12 - 7y - 9$

175. Which expression is equivalent to $7[3b + 5(b - 6)]$?
a. $7[3b + 5b - 6)]$ **b.** $7[3b + 5b - 30)]$
c. $7[3b + 5b + 6)]$ **d.** $7[8b - 6]$

2.2 Applying Concepts

Simplify.

176. $C - 0.7C$

177. $\frac{1}{3}(3x + y) - \frac{2}{3}(6x - y)$

178. $-\frac{1}{4}[2x + 2(y - 6y)]$

Complete.

179. A number that has no reciprocal is ______ .

180. A number that is its own reciprocal is ______ .

181. The additive inverse of $a - b$ is ______.

182. Determine whether the statement is true or false. If the statement is false, give an example that illustrates that it is false.
a. Division is a commutative operation.
b. Division is an associative operation.
c. Subtraction is an associative operation.
d. Subtraction is a commutative operation.
e. Addition is a commutative operation.

183. Define an operation $\otimes$ as $a \otimes b = (a \cdot b) - (a + b)$.
For example, $7 \otimes 5 = (7 \cdot 5) - (7 + 5) = 35 - 12 = 23$.
a. Is $\otimes$ a commutative operation? Support your answer.
b. Is $\otimes$ an associative operation? Support your answer.

184. Give examples of two operations that occur in everyday experience and are not commutative (for example, putting on socks and then shoes).

185. In your own words, explain the Distributive Property.

2.3 Translating Verbal Expressions into Variable Expressions

OBJECTIVE 1 Translate a verbal expression into a variable expression

One of the major skills required in applied mathematics is the ability to translate a verbal expression into a variable expression. This requires recognizing the verbal phrases that translate into mathematical operations. Here is a partial list of the phrases used to indicate the different mathematical operations.

Point of Interest

The way in which expressions are symbolized has changed over time. Here are some expressions as they may have appeared in the early 16th century.

R p. 9 *for* $x + 9$. *The symbol* **R** *was used for a variable to the first power. The symbol* **p.** *was used for plus.*

R m. 3 *for* $x - 3$. *Again, the symbol* **R** *was used for the variable. The symbol* **m.** *was used for minus.*

The square of a variable was designated by **Q** *and the cube was designated by* **C.** *The expression* $x^3 + x^2$ *was written* **C p. Q.**

Addition	added to	6 added to y	$y + 6$
	more than	8 more than x	$x + 8$
	the sum of	the sum of x and z	$x + z$
	increased by	t increased by 9	$t + 9$
	the total of	the total of 5 and y	$5 + y$
	plus	b plus 17	$b + 17$
Subtraction	minus	x minus 2	$x - 2$
	less than	7 less than t	$t - 7$
	less	7 less t	$7 - t$
	subtracted from	5 subtracted from d	$d - 5$
	decreased by	m decreased by 3	$m - 3$
	the difference between	the difference between y and 4	$y - 4$
Multiplication	times	10 times t	$10t$
	of	one-half of x	$\frac{1}{2}x$
	the product of	the product of y and z	yz
	multiplied by	y multiplied by 11	$11y$
	twice	twice n	$2n$
Division	divided by	x divided by 12	$\frac{x}{12}$
	the quotient of	the quotient of y and z	$\frac{y}{z}$
	the ratio of	the ratio of t to 9	$\frac{t}{9}$
Power	the square of	the square of x	x^2
	the cube of	the cube of a	a^3

Translating a phrase that contains the word *sum*, *difference*, *product*, or *quotient* can sometimes cause a problem. In the examples at the right, note where the operation symbol is placed.

the *sum* of *x and y*	$x + y$
the *difference* between *x and y*	$x - y$
the *product* of *x and y*	$x \cdot y$
the *quotient* of *x and y*	$\frac{x}{y}$

EXAMPLE 1 Translate into a variable expression.

A. the total of five times b and c

B. the quotient of eight less than n and fourteen

C. thirteen more than the sum of seven and the square of x

Solution

A. the total of five times b and c

- **Identify words that indicate mathematical operations.**

$5b + c$

- **Use the operations to write the variable expression.**

B. the quotient of eight less than n and fourteen

- **Identify words that indicate mathematical operations.**

$\frac{n - 8}{14}$

- **Use the operations to write the variable expression.**

C. thirteen more than the sum of seven and the square of x

$(7 + x^2) + 13$

PROBLEM 1 Translate into a variable expression.

A. eighteen less than the cube of x

B. y decreased by the sum of z and nine

C. the difference between the square of q and the sum of r and t

Solution See page S4.

In most applications that involve translating phrases into variable expressions, the variable to be used is not given. To translate these phrases, a variable must be assigned to an unknown quantity before the variable expression can be written.

EXAMPLE 2 Translate "a number multiplied by the total of six and the cube of the number" into a variable expression.

Solution

the unknown number: n

- **Assign a variable to one of the unknown quantities.**

the cube of the number: n^3

the total of six and the cube of the number: $6 + n^3$

- **Use the assigned variable to write an expression for any other unknown quantity.**

$n(6 + n^3)$

- **Use the assigned variable to write the variable expression.**

Take Note

The expression $n(6 + n^3)$ must have parentheses. If we write $n \cdot 6 + n^3$, then by the Order of Operations Agreement, only the 6 is multiplied by n, but we want n to be multiplied by the *total* of 6 and n^3.

PROBLEM 2 Translate "a number added to the product of five and the square of the number" into a variable expression.

Solution See page S4.

EXAMPLE 3 Translate "the quotient of twice a number and the difference between the number and twenty" into a variable expression.

Solution the unknown number: n

twice the number: $2n$

the difference between the number and twenty: $n - 20$

$$\frac{2n}{n - 20}$$

PROBLEM 3 Translate "the product of three and the sum of seven and twice a number" into a variable expression.

Solution See page S4.

OBJECTIVE 2 Translate a verbal expression into a variable expression and then simplify the resulting expression

After translating a verbal expression into a variable expression, simplify the variable expression by using the Properties of the Real Numbers.

EXAMPLE 4 Translate and simplify "the total of four times an unknown number and twice the difference between the number and eight."

Solution the unknown number: n — **• Assign a variable to one of the unknown quantities.**

four times the unknown number: $4n$

twice the difference between the number and eight: $2(n - 8)$ — **• Use the assigned variable to write an expression for any other unknown quantity.**

$4n + 2(n - 8)$ — **• Use the assigned variable to write the variable expression.**

$= 4n + 2n - 16$ — **• Simplify the variable expression.**

$= 6n - 16$

PROBLEM 4 Translate and simplify "a number minus the difference between twice the number and seventeen."

Solution See page S4.

EXAMPLE 5 Translate and simplify "the difference between five-eighths of a number and two-thirds of the same number."

Solution the unknown number: n — **• Assign a variable to one of the unknown quantities.**

five-eighths of the number: $\frac{5}{8}n$ — **• Use the assigned variable to write an expression for any other unknown quantity.**

two-thirds of the number: $\frac{2}{3}n$

$\frac{5}{8}n - \frac{2}{3}n$ • **Use the assigned variable to write the variable expression.**

$= \frac{15}{24}n - \frac{16}{24}n$ • **Simplify the variable expression.**

$= -\frac{1}{24}n$

PROBLEM 5 Translate and simplify "the sum of three-fourths of a number and one-fifth of the same number."

Solution See page S4.

OBJECTIVE 3 Translate application problems

Many of the applications of mathematics require that you identify an unknown quantity, assign a variable to that quantity, and then attempt to express another unknown quantity in terms of that variable.

Suppose we know that the sum of two numbers is 10 and that one of the two numbers is 4. We can find the other number by subtracting 4 from 10.

one number: 4
other number: $10 - 4 = 6$
The two numbers are 4 and 6.

Now suppose we know that the sum of two numbers is 10, we don't know either number, and we want to express *both* numbers in terms of the *same* variable.

Let one number be x. Again, we can find the other number by subtracting x from 10.

one number: x
other number: $10 - x$
The two numbers are x and $10 - x$.

Note that the sum of x and $10 - x$ is 10. $x + (10 - x) = x + 10 - x = 10$

EXAMPLE 6 The length of a swimming pool is 20 ft longer than the width. Express the length of the pool in terms of the width.

Solution the width of the pool: W • **Assign a variable to the width of the pool.**

the length is 20 more than the width: $W + 20$ • **Express the length of the pool in terms of *W*.**

Take Note

Any variable can be used. For example, if the width is y, then the length is $y + 20$.

PROBLEM 6 An older computer takes twice as long to process a set of data as does a newer model. Express the amount of time it takes the older computer to process the data in terms of the amount of time it takes the newer model.

Solution See page S4.

EXAMPLE 7 An investor divided \$5000 between two accounts, one a mutual fund and the other a money market fund. Use one variable to express the amounts invested in each account.

Solution the amount invested in the mutual fund: x • **Assign a variable to the amount invested in one account.**

the amount invested in the money market fund: $5000 - x$ • **Express the amount invested in the other account in terms of *x*.**

Take Note

It is also correct to assign the variable to the amount in the money market fund. Then the amount in the mutual fund is $5000 - x$.

PROBLEM 7 A guitar string 6 ft long was cut into two pieces. Use one variable to express the lengths of the two pieces.

Solution See page S4.

2.3 Concept Review

Determine whether the statement is always true, sometimes true, or never true.

1. "Five less than n" can be translated as "$5 - n$."
2. A variable expression contains an equals sign.
3. If the sum of two numbers is 12 and one of the two numbers is x, then the other number can be expressed as $x - 12$.
4. The words *total* and *times* both indicate multiplication.
5. The words *quotient* and *ratio* both indicate division.
6. The expressions $7y - 8$ and $(7y) - 8$ are equivalent.
7. The phrase "five times the sum of x and y" and the phrase "the sum of five times x and y" yield the same variable expression.

2.3 Exercises

1 Translate a verbal expression into a variable expression

For each phrase, identify the words that indicate mathematical operations.

1. the sum of seven and three times m
2. twelve less than the quotient of x and negative two
3. the total of ten and fifteen divided by a number
4. twenty subtracted from the product of eight and the cube of a number

Translate into a variable expression.

5. d less than nineteen
6. the sum of six and c
7. r decreased by twelve
8. w increased by fifty-five
9. a multiplied by twenty-eight
10. y added to sixteen

11. five times the difference between n and seven

12. thirty less than the square of b

13. y less the product of three and y

14. the sum of four-fifths of m and eighteen

15. the product of negative six and b

16. nine increased by the quotient of t and five

17. four divided by the difference between p and six

18. the product of seven and the total of r and eight

19. the quotient of nine less than x and twice x

20. the product of a and the sum of a and thirteen

21. twenty-one less than the product of s and negative four

22. fourteen more than one-half of the square of z

23. the ratio of eight more than d to d

24. the total of nine times the cube of m and the square of m

25. three-eighths of the sum of t and fifteen

26. s decreased by the quotient of s and two

27. w increased by the quotient of seven and w

28. the difference between the square of c and the total of c and fourteen

29. d increased by the difference between sixteen times d and three

30. the product of eight and the total of b and five

31. a number divided by nineteen

32. thirteen less a number

33. forty more than a number

34. three-sevenths of a number

35. the square of the difference between a number and ninety

36. the quotient of twice a number and five

37. the sum of four-ninths of a number and twenty

38. eight subtracted from the product of fifteen and a number

39. the product of a number and ten more than the number

40. six less than the total of a number and the cube of the number

41. fourteen added to the product of seven and a number

42. the quotient of three and the total of four and a number

43. the quotient of twelve and the sum of a number and two

44. eleven plus one-half of a number

45. the ratio of two and the sum of a number and one

46. a number multiplied by the difference between twice the number and nine

47. the difference between sixty and the quotient of a number and fifty

48. the product of nine less than a number and the number

49. the sum of the square of a number and three times the number

50. the quotient of seven more than twice a number and the number

51. the sum of three more than a number and the cube of the number

52. a number decreased by the difference between the cube of the number and ten

53. a number decreased by one-fourth of the square of the number

54. four less than the product of seven and the square of a number

55. a number decreased by the quotient of seven and the number

56. eighty decreased by the product of thirteen and a number

57. the cube of a number decreased by the product of twelve and the number

58. the quotient of five and the sum of a number and nineteen

59. Which of the following phrases translate(s) into the variable expression $25n^2 - 9$?
a. the difference between nine and the product of twenty-five and the square of a number
b. nine subtracted from the square of twenty-five and a number
c. nine less than the product of twenty-five and the square of a number

60. Which of the following phrases translate(s) into the variable expression $32 - \frac{a}{7}$?
a. the difference between thirty-two and the quotient of a number and seven
b. thirty-two decreased by the quotient of a number and seven
c. thirty-two minus the ratio of a number to seven

2 Translate a verbal expression into a variable expression and then simplify the resulting expression

61. The phrase "the total of one-half of a number and three-fourths of the number" can be translated as $(\underline{\quad ? \quad})n + (\underline{\quad ? \quad})n$. This expression simplifies to $\underline{\quad ? \quad}$.

62. The phrase "the difference between twelve times a number and fifteen times the number" can be translated as $(\underline{\quad ? \quad})n - (\underline{\quad ? \quad})n$. This expression simplifies to $\underline{\quad ? \quad}$.

Translate into a variable expression. Then simplify the expression.

63. a number increased by the total of the number and ten

64. a number added to the product of five and the number

65. a number decreased by the difference between nine and the number

66. eight more than the sum of a number and eleven

67. the difference between one-fifth of a number and three-eighths of the number

68. a number minus the sum of the number and fourteen

69. four more than the total of a number and nine

70. the sum of one-eighth of a number and one-twelfth of the number

71. twice the sum of three times a number and forty

72. the sum of a number divided by two and the number

73. seven times the product of five and a number

74. sixteen multiplied by one-fourth of a number

75. the total of seventeen times a number and twice the number

76. the difference between nine times a number and twice the number

77. a number plus the product of the number and twelve

78. nineteen more than the difference between a number and five

79. three times the sum of the square of a number and four

80. a number subtracted from the product of the number and seven

81. three-fourths of the sum of sixteen times a number and four

82. the difference between fourteen times a number and the product of the number and seven

83. sixteen decreased by the sum of a number and nine

84. eleven subtracted from the difference between eight and a number

85. five more than the quotient of four times a number and two

86. twenty minus the sum of four-ninths of a number and three

87. six times the total of a number and eight

88. four times the sum of a number and twenty

89. seven minus the sum of a number and two

90. three less than the sum of a number and ten

91. one-third of the sum of a number and six times the number

92. twice the quotient of four times a number and eight

93. the total of eight increased by the cube of a number and twice the cube of the number

94. the sum of five more than the square of a number and twice the square of the number

95. twelve more than a number added to the difference between the number and six

96. a number plus four added to the difference between three and twice the number

97. the sum of a number and nine added to the difference between the number and twenty

98. seven increased by a number added to twice the difference between the number and two

99. fourteen plus the product of three less than a number and ten

100. a number plus the product of the number minus five and seven

3 Translate application problems

101. The sum of two numbers is 25. To express both numbers in terms of the same variable, let x be one number. Then the other number is ___?___.

102. The length of a rectangle is five times the width. To express the length and the width in terms of the same variable, let W be the width. Then the length is ___?___.

103. The width of a rectangle is one-half the length. To express the length and the width in terms of the same variable, let L be the length. Then the width is ___?___.

104. An electrician's bill is $75 for materials and $50 an hour for labor. To express the total amount of the bill in terms of the number of hours of labor, let h be the number of hours of labor. Then the cost of the labor is ___?___, so the total amount for the materials and labor is ___?___.

Write a variable expression.

105. The sum of two numbers is 18. Express the two numbers in terms of the same variable.

106. The sum of two numbers is 20. Express the two numbers in terms of the same variable.

107. **Genetics** The human genome contains 11,000 more genes than the roundworm genome. Express the number of genes in the human genome in terms of the number of genes in the roundworm genome. (*Source:* Celera, USA TODAY research)

108. **Noise Level** The noise level of an ambulance siren is 10 decibels louder than that of a car horn. Express the noise level of an ambulance siren in terms of the noise level of a car horn. (*Source:* League for the Hard of Hearing)

109. **Space Exploration** A survey in *USA Today* reported that almost three-fourths of Americans think that money should be spent on exploration of Mars. Express the number of Americans who think that money should be spent on exploration of Mars in terms of the total number of Americans.

110. **Biology** According to the American Podiatric Medical Association, the bones in your foot account for one-fourth of all bones in your body. Express the number of bones in your foot in terms of the number of bones in your body.

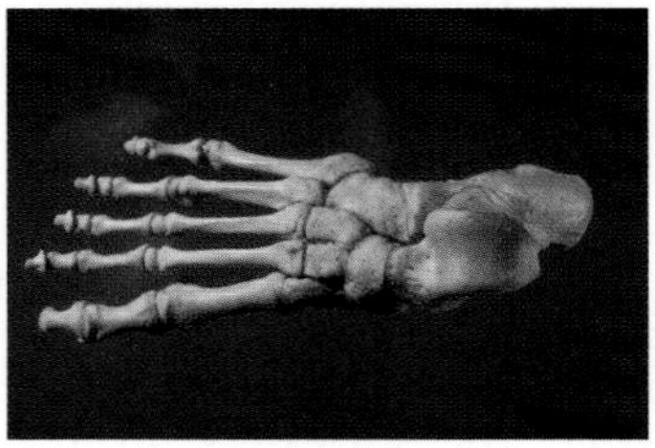

111. **Sports** In football, the number of points awarded for a touchdown is three times the number of points awarded for a safety. Express the number of points awarded for a touchdown in terms of the number of points awarded for a safety.

112. WEB Cost of Living A cost-of-living calculator at **homefair.com** shows that a person living in Manhattan would need twice the salary of a person living in Miami. Express the salary needed to live in Manhattan in terms of the salary needed to live in Miami.

113. Astronomy The diameter of Saturn's moon Rhea is 253 miles more than the diameter of Saturn's moon Dione. Express the diameter of Rhea in terms of the diameter of Dione. (*Source:* NASA)

114. Online Sales A recent survey conducted by Consumer Internet Barometer found that approximately 25% of those people who purchased a product online were extremely satisfied with their experience. Express the number of people who were extremely satisfied with their online purchases in terms of the number of people surveyed.

115. Agriculture In a recent year, Alabama produced one-half the number of pounds of pecans that Texas produced in the same year. Express the amount of pecans produced in Alabama in terms of the amount produced in Texas. (*Source:* National Agricultural Statistics Service)

116. Taxes According to the Internal Revenue Service, it takes about one-fifth the time to fill out Schedule B (interest and dividends) than it does to complete Schedule A (itemized deductions). Express the amount of time it takes to fill out Schedule B in terms of the time it takes to fill out Schedule A.

117. Demography According to the U.S. Bureau of the Census, the world population in the year 2050 is expected to be twice the world population in 1980. Express the expected world population in 2050 in terms of the world population in 1980.

118. Geometry The length of a rectangle is 5 m more than twice the width. Express the length of the rectangle in terms of the width.

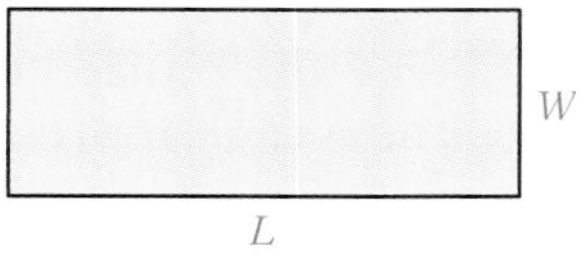

119. Geometry In a triangle, the measure of the smallest angle is 10 degrees less than one-half the measure of the largest angle. Express the measure of the smallest angle in terms of the measure of the largest angle.

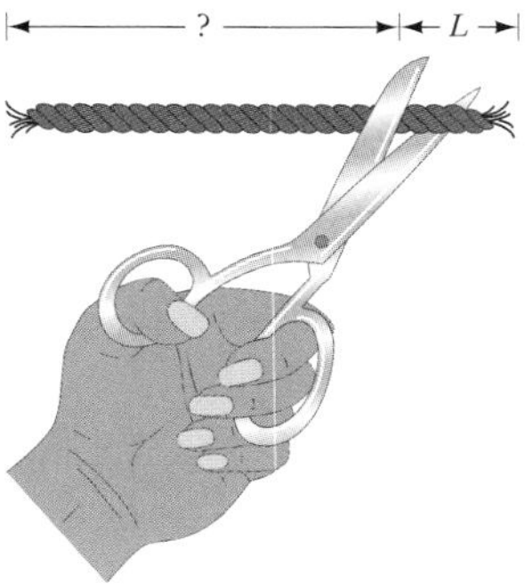

120. Sports A halyard 12 ft long is cut into two pieces. Use the same variable to express the lengths of the two pieces.

121. Coins A coin bank contains thirty-five coins in nickels and dimes. Use the same variable to express the number of nickels and the number of dimes in the coin bank.

122. Travel Two cars are traveling in opposite directions and at different rates. Two hours later the cars are 200 mi apart. Express the distance traveled by the faster car in terms of the distance traveled by the slower car.

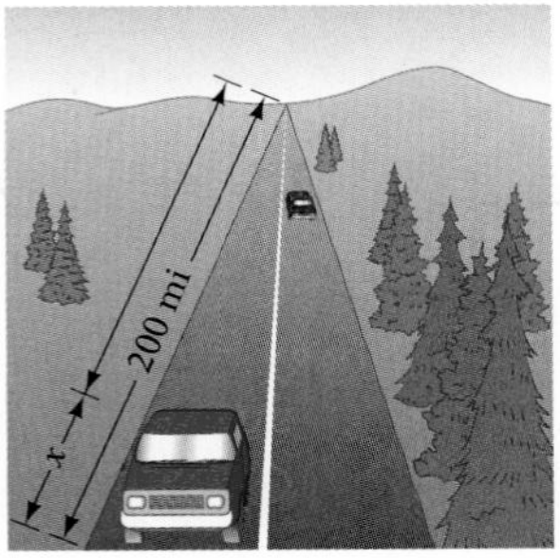

123. Wages An employee is paid \$720 per week plus \$27 for each hour of overtime worked. Express the employee's weekly pay in terms of the number of hours of overtime worked.

124. Billing An auto repair bill is \$138 for parts and \$45 for each hour of labor. Express the amount of the repair bill in terms of the number of hours of labor.

125. Consumerism The cost of a cellular phone service is \$19.95 per month plus \$.08 per minute for phone calls. Express the monthly cost of the phone service in terms of the number of minutes of phone calls.

2.3 Applying Concepts

126. Chemistry The chemical formula for glucose (sugar) is $C_6H_{12}O_6$. This formula means that there are twelve hydrogen atoms, six carbon atoms, and six oxygen atoms in each molecule of glucose. If x represents the number of atoms of oxygen in a pound of sugar, express the number of hydrogen atoms in the pound of sugar in terms of x.

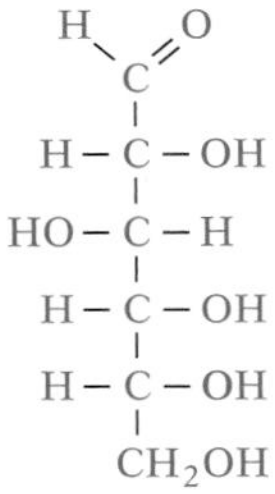

127. Metalwork A wire whose length is given as x inches is bent into a square. Express the length of a side of the square in terms of x.

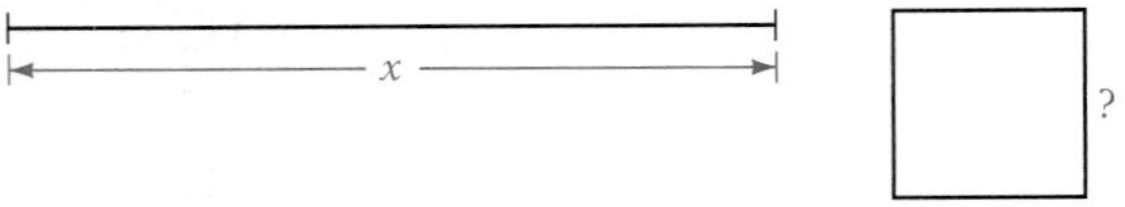

128. Pulleys A block-and-tackle system is designed so that pulling one end of a rope five feet will move a weight on the other end a distance of three feet. If x represents the distance the rope is pulled, express the distance the weight moves in terms of x.

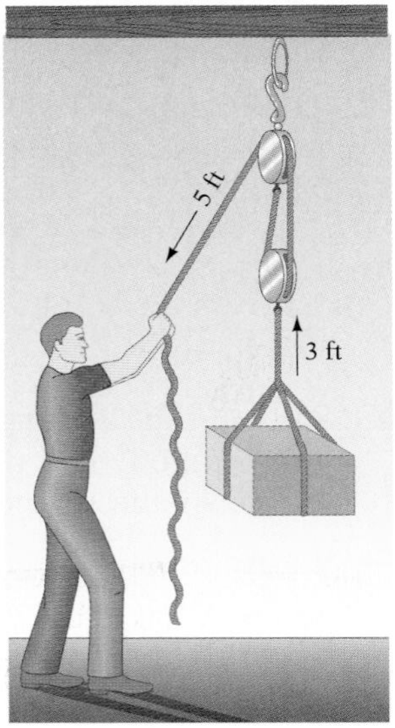

129. Translate the expressions $5x + 8$ and $5(x + 8)$ into phrases.

130. In your own words, explain how variables are used.

131. Explain the similarities and differences between the expressions "the difference between x and 5" and "5 less than x."

Focus on Problem Solving

From Concrete to Abstract

In your study of algebra, you will find that the problems are less concrete than those you studied in arithmetic. Problems that are concrete provide information pertaining to a specific instance. Algebra is more abstract. Abstract problems are theoretical; they are stated without reference to a specific instance. Let's look at an example of an abstract problem.

How many minutes are there in h hours?

A strategy that can be used to solve this problem is to begin by substituting a number for the variable.

How many minutes are there in 5 hours?

You know that there are 60 minutes in 1 hour. To find the number of minutes in 5 hours, multiply 5 by 60.

$60 \cdot 5 = 300$ There are 300 minutes in 5 hours.

Use the same procedure to find the number of minutes in h hours: multiply h by 60.

$60 \cdot h = 60h$ There are $60h$ minutes in h hours.

This problem might be taken a step further:

If you walk one mile in x minutes, how far can you walk in h hours?

Consider the same problem using numbers in place of the variables.

If you walk one mile in 20 minutes, how far can you walk in 3 hours?

To solve this problem, you need to calculate the number of minutes in 3 hours (multiply 3 by 60), and divide the result by the number of minutes it takes to walk one mile (20 minutes).

$\frac{60 \cdot 3}{20} = \frac{180}{20} = 9$ If you walk one mile in 20 minutes, you can walk 9 miles in 3 hours.

Use the same procedure to solve the related abstract problem. Calculate the number of minutes in h hours (multiply h by 60), and divide the result by the number of minutes it takes to walk one mile (x minutes).

$\frac{60 \cdot h}{x} = \frac{60h}{x}$ If you walk one mile in x minutes, you can walk $\frac{60h}{x}$ miles in h hours.

At the heart of the study of algebra is the use of variables. It is the variables in the problems above that make them abstract. But it is variables that allow us to generalize situations and state rules about mathematics.

Try each of the following problems.

1. How many hours are there in d days?
2. You earn d dollars an hour. What are your wages for working h hours?

3. If p is the price of one share of stock, how many shares can you purchase with d dollars?

4. A company pays a television station d dollars to air a commercial lasting s seconds. What is the cost per second?

5. After every v videotape rentals, you are entitled to one free rental. You have rented t tapes, where $t < v$. How many more do you need to rent before you are entitled to a free rental?

6. Your car gets g miles per gallon. How many gallons of gasoline does your car consume traveling t miles?

7. If you drink j ounces of juice each day, how many days will q quarts of the juice last?

8. A TV station has m minutes of commercials each hour. How many ads lasting s seconds each can be sold for each hour of programming?

9. A factory worker can assemble p products in m minutes. How many products can the factory worker assemble in h hours?

10. If one candy bar costs n nickels, how many candy bars can be purchased with q quarters?

Projects & Group Activities

Investigation into Operations with Even and Odd Integers

An **even integer** is an integer that is divisible by 2. For example, 6, −12, and 480 are even integers. An **odd integer** is an integer that is not evenly divisible by 2. For example, 3, −25, and 971 are odd integers.

Complete each statement with the word *even* or *odd*.

1. If k is an odd integer, then $k + 1$ is an ______ integer.
2. If k is an odd integer, then $k - 2$ is an ______ integer.
3. If n is an integer, then $2n$ is an ______ integer.
4. If m and n are even integers, then $m - n$ is an ______ integer.
5. If m and n are even integers, then mn is an ______ integer.
6. If m and n are odd integers, then $m + n$ is an ______ integer.
7. If m and n are odd integers, then $m - n$ is an ______ integer.
8. If m and n are odd integers, then mn is an ______ integer.
9. If m is an even integer and n is an odd integer, then $m - n$ is an ______ integer.
10. If m is an even integer and n is an odd integer, then $m + n$ is an ______ integer.

Chapter 2 Summary

Key Words

A **variable** is a letter that is used to stand for a quantity that is unknown or that can change. A **variable expression** is an expression that contains one or more variables. [2.1.1, p. 67]

Examples: $5x - 4y + 7z$ is a variable expression. It contains the variables x, y, and z.

The **terms of a variable expression** are the addends of the expression. Each term is a **variable term** or a **constant term.** [2.1.1, p. 67]

The expression $4a^2 - 6b^3 + 7$ has three terms: $4a^2$, $-6b^3$, and 7. Of these, $4a^2$ and $-6b^3$ are variable terms. 7 is a constant term.

A variable term is composed of a **numerical coefficient** and a **variable part.** [2.1.1, p. 67]

For the expression $8p^4r$, 8 is the coefficient and p^4r is the variable part.

Replacing the variables in a variable expression with numbers and then simplifying the numerical expression is called **evaluating the variable expression.** [2.1.1, p. 68]

To evaluate $a^2 - 2b$ when $a = -3$ and $b = -5$, simplify the expression $(-3)^2 - 2(-5)$.

Like terms of a variable expression are the terms with the same variable part. [2.2.2, p. 76]

For the expression $2st - 3t + 9s - 11st$, the terms $2st$ and $-11st$ are like terms.

The **additive inverse** of a number is the opposite of the number [2.2.1, p. 75]

The additive inverse of 8 is −8. The additive inverse of −15 is 15.

The **multiplicative inverse** of a number is the reciprocal of the number. [2.2.1, p. 75]

The multiplicative inverse of $\frac{3}{8}$ is $\frac{8}{3}$.

Essential Rules and Procedures

The Commutative Property of Addition
If a and b are real numbers, then $a + b = b + a$. [2.2.1, p. 74]

$5 + 2 = 7$ and $2 + 5 = 7$

The Commutative Property of Multiplication
If a and b are real numbers, then $ab = ba$. [2.2.1, p. 74]

$6(-3) = -18$ and $-3(6) = -18$

The Associative Property of Addition
If a, b, and c are real numbers, then $(a + b) + c = a + (b + c)$. [2.2.1, p. 74]

$-1 + (4 + 7) = -1 + 11 = 10$
$(-1 + 4) + 7 = 3 + 7 = 10$

The Associative Property of Multiplication
If a, b, and c are real numbers, then $(ab)c = a(bc)$. [2.2.1, p. 74]

$(-2 \cdot 5) \cdot 3 = -10 \cdot 3 = -30$
$-2 \cdot (5 \cdot 3) = -2 \cdot 15 = -30$

The Addition Property of Zero If a is a real number, then $a + 0 = 0 + a = a$. [2.2.1, p. 74]	$9 + 0 = 9$ $\quad 0 + 9 = 9$
The Multiplication Property of Zero If a is a real number, then $a \cdot 0 = 0 \cdot a = 0$. [2.2.1, p. 75]	$-8(0) = 0$ $\quad 0(-8) = 0$
The Multiplication Property of One If a is a real number, then $1 \cdot a = a \cdot 1 = a$. [2.2.1, p. 75]	$7 \cdot 1 = 7$ $\quad 1 \cdot 7 = 7$
The Inverse Property of Addition If a is a real number, then $a + (-a) = (-a) + a = 0$. [2.2.1, p. 75]	$4 + (-4) = 0$ $\quad -4 + 4 = 0$
The Inverse Property of Multiplication If a is a real number and $a \neq 0$, then $a \cdot \frac{1}{a} = \frac{1}{a} \cdot a = 1$. [2.2.1, p. 75]	$6 \cdot \frac{1}{6} = 1$ $\quad \frac{1}{6} \cdot 6 = 1$
The Distributive Property If a, b, and c are real numbers, then $a(b + c) = ab + ac$. [2.2.1, p. 75]	$5(2 + 3) = 5 \cdot 2 + 5 \cdot 3$ $= 10 + 15$ $= 25$

Chapter 2 Review Exercises

1. Simplify: $-7y^2 + 6y^2 - (-2y^2)$

2. Simplify: $(12x)\left(\frac{1}{4}\right)$

3. Simplify: $\frac{2}{3}(-15a)$

4. Simplify: $-2(2x - 4)$

5. Simplify: $5(2x + 4) - 3(x - 6)$

6. Evaluate $a^2 - 3b$ when $a = 2$ and $b = -4$.

7. Complete the statement by using the Inverse Property of Addition.
$-9 + ? = 0$

8. Simplify: $-4(-9y)$

9. Simplify: $-2(-3y + 9)$

10. Simplify: $3[2x - 3(x - 2y)] + 3y$

11. Simplify: $-4(2x^2 - 3y^2)$

12. Simplify: $3x - 5x + 7x$

13. Evaluate $b^2 - 3ab$ when $a = 3$ and $b = -2$.

14. Simplify: $\frac{1}{5}(10x)$

15. Simplify: $5(3 - 7b)$

16. Simplify: $2x + 3[4 - (3x - 7)]$

17. Identify the property that justifies the statement.
$-4(3) = 3(-4)$

18. Simplify: $3(8 - 2x)$

19. Simplify: $-2x^2 - (-3x^2) + 4x^2$

20. Simplify: $-3x - 2(2x - 7)$

21. Simplify: $-3(3y^2 - 3y - 7)$

22. Simplify: $-2[x - 2(x - y)] + 5y$

23. Evaluate $\dfrac{-2ab}{2b - a}$ when $a = -4$ and $b = 6$.

24. Simplify: $(-3)(-12y)$

25. Simplify: $4(3x - 2) - 7(x + 5)$

26. Simplify: $(16x)\left(\dfrac{1}{8}\right)$

27. Simplify: $-3(2x^2 - 7y^2)$

28. Evaluate $3(a - c) - 2ab$ when $a = 2$, $b = 3$, and $c = -4$.

29. Simplify: $2x - 3(x - 2)$

30. Simplify: $2a - (-3b) - 7a - 5b$

31. Simplify: $-5(2x^2 - 3x + 6)$

32. Simplify: $3x - 7y - 12x$

33. Simplify: $\dfrac{1}{2}(12a)$

34. Simplify: $2x + 3[x - 2(4 - 2x)]$

35. Simplify: $3x + (-12y) - 5x - (-7y)$

36. Simplify: $\left(-\dfrac{5}{6}\right)(-36b)$

37. Complete the statement by using the Distributive Property.
$(6 + 3)7 = 42 + ?$

38. Simplify: $4x^2 + 9x - 6x^2 - 5x$

39. Simplify: $-\dfrac{3}{8}(16x^2)$

40. Simplify: $-3[2x - (7x - 9)]$

41. Simplify: $-(8a^2 - 3b^2)$

42. Identify the property that justifies the statement. $-32(0) = 0$

43. Translate "*b* decreased by the product of seven and *b*" into a variable expression.

44. Translate "the sum of a number and twice the square of the number" into a variable expression.

45. Translate "three less than the quotient of six and a number" into a variable expression.

46. Translate "ten divided by the difference between *y* and two" into a variable expression.

47. Translate and simplify "eight times the quotient of twice a number and sixteen."

48. Translate and simplify "the product of four and the sum of two and five times a number."

49. **Geometry** The length of the base of a triangle is 15 in. more than the height of the triangle. Express the length of the base of the triangle in terms of the height of the triangle.

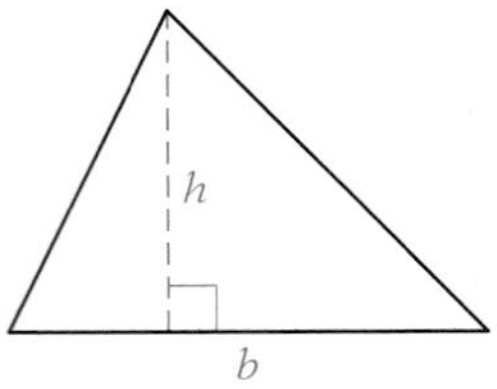

50. **Mixtures** A coffee merchant made 20 lb of a blend of coffee using only mocha java beans and espresso beans. Use the same variable to express the amounts of mocha java beans and espresso beans in the coffee blend.

Chapter 2 Test

1. Simplify: $(9y)4$

2. Simplify: $7x + 5y - 3x - 8y$

3. Simplify: $8n - (6 - 2n)$

4. Evaluate $3ab - (2a)^2$ when $a = -2$ and $b = -3$.

5. Identify the property that justifies the statement.
$\frac{3}{8}(1) = \frac{3}{8}$

6. Simplify: $-4(-x + 10)$

7. Simplify: $\frac{2}{3}x^2 - \frac{7}{12}x^2$

8. Simplify: $(-10x)\left(-\frac{2}{5}\right)$

9. Simplify: $(-4y^2 + 8)6$

10. Complete the statement by using the Inverse Property of Addition.
$-19 + ? = 0$

11. Evaluate $\frac{-3ab}{2a + b}$ when $a = -1$ and $b = 4$.

12. Simplify: $5(x + y) - 8(x - y)$

13. Simplify: $6b - 9b + 4b$

14. Simplify: $13(6a)$

15. Simplify: $3(x^2 - 5x + 4)$

16. Evaluate $4(b - a) + bc$ when $a = 2$, $b = -3$, and $c = 4$.

17. Simplify: $6x - 3(y - 7x) + 2(5x - y)$

18. Translate "the quotient of eight more than n and seventeen" into a variable expression.

19. Translate "the difference between the sum of a and b and the square of b" into a variable expression.

20. Translate "the sum of the square of a number and the product of the number and eleven" into a variable expression.

21. Translate and simplify "twenty times the sum of a number and nine."

22. Translate and simplify "two more than a number added to the difference between the number and three."

23. Translate and simplify "a number minus the product of one-fourth and twice the number."

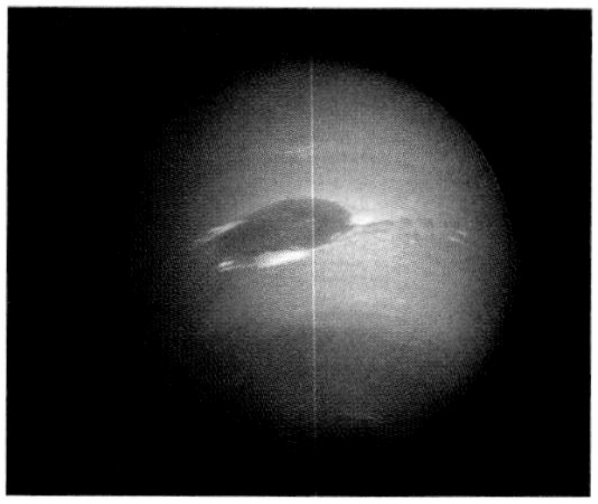

24. Astronomy The distance from Neptune to the sun is thirty times the distance from Earth to the sun. Express the distance from Neptune to the sun in terms of the distance from Earth to the sun.

25. Carpentry A nine-foot board is cut into two pieces of different lengths. Use the same variable to express the lengths of the two pieces.

Cumulative Review Exercises

1. Add: $-4 + 7 + (-10)$

2. Subtract: $-16 - (-25) - 4$

3. Multiply: $(-2)(3)(-4)$

4. Divide: $(-60) \div 12$

5. Write $1\frac{1}{4}$ as a decimal.

6. Write 60% as a fraction and as a decimal.

7. Use the roster method to write the set of negative integers greater than or equal to -4.

8. Write $\frac{2}{25}$ as a percent.

9. Subtract: $\frac{7}{12} - \frac{11}{16} - \left(-\frac{1}{3}\right)$

10. Divide: $\frac{5}{12} \div \left(\frac{3}{2}\right)$

11. Multiply: $\left(-\frac{9}{16}\right)\left(\frac{8}{27}\right)\left(-\frac{3}{2}\right)$

12. Simplify: $-3^2 \cdot \left(-\frac{2}{3}\right)^3$

13. Simplify: $-2^5 \div (3 - 5)^2 - (-3)$

14. Simplify: $\left(-\frac{3}{4}\right)^2 - \left(\frac{3}{8} - \frac{11}{12}\right)$

15. Evaluate $a - 3b^2$ when $a = 4$ and $b = -2$.

16. Simplify: $-2x^2 - (-3x^2) + 4x^2$

17. Simplify: $8a - 12b - 9a$

18. Simplify: $\frac{1}{3}(9a)$

19. Simplify: $\left(-\frac{5}{8}\right)(-32b)$

20. Simplify: $5(4 - 2x)$

21. Simplify: $-3(-2y + 7)$

22. Simplify: $-2(3x^2 - 4y^2)$

23. Simplify: $-4(2y^2 - 5y - 8)$

24. Simplify: $-4x - 3(2x - 5)$

25. Simplify: $3(4x - 1) - 7(x + 2)$

26. Simplify: $3x + 2[x - 4(2 - x)]$

27. Simplify: $3[4x - 2(x - 4y)] + 5y$

28. Translate "the difference between six and the product of a number and twelve" into a variable expression.

29. Translate and simplify "the total of five and the difference between a number and seven."

30. **Internet Connections** The speed of a Digital Subscriber Line (DSL) Internet connection is ten times faster than that of a dial-up connection. Express the speed of the DSL connection in terms of the speed of the dial-up connection.

CHAPTER

3 Solving Equations and Inequalities

OBJECTIVES

3.1
1 Determine whether a given number is a solution of an equation
2 Solve equations of the form $x + a = b$
3 Solve equations of the form $ax = b$
4 Application problems: uniform motion
5 Applications of percent

3.2
1 Solve equations of the form $ax + b = c$
2 Solve equations of the form $ax + b = cx + d$
3 Solve equations containing parentheses
4 Application problems

3.3
1 Solve inequalities using the Addition Property of Inequalities
2 Solve inequalities using the Multiplication Property of Inequalities
3 Solve general inequalities

In what year will these children enter high school? When will these children be eligible to collect Social Security or to retire? How many others will retire that same year? Demographers ask these questions when studying population groups to make projections for the future. These projections are used by organizations such as college administrators and managers of retirement communities. The **Focus on Problem Solving on pages 155–156** provides an example of how demography can be used to plan as far as 50 years into the future.

DVD SSM *Online Study Center*

Need help? For online student resources, such as section quizzes, visit the Online Study Center at college.hmco.com/pic/aufmannBAWA7e.

Prep Test

1. Subtract: $8 - 12$
2. Multiply: $-\frac{3}{4}\left(-\frac{4}{3}\right)$
3. Multiply: $-\frac{5}{8}(16)$
4. Write 90% as a decimal.
5. Write 0.75 as a percent.
6. Evaluate $3x^2 - 4x - 1$ when $x = -4$.
7. Simplify: $3x - 5 + 7x$
8. Simplify: $8x - 9 - 8x$
9. Simplify: $6x - 3(6 - x)$

3.1 Introduction to Equations

OBJECTIVE 1 Determine whether a given number is a solution of an equation

Point of Interest

One of the most famous equations ever stated is $E = mc^2$. This equation, stated by Albert Einstein, shows that there is a relationship between mass m and energy E.

An **equation** expresses the equality of two mathematical expressions. The expressions can be either numerical or variable expressions.

$$\left.\begin{array}{l} 9 + 3 = 12 \\ 3x - 2 = 10 \\ y^2 + 4 = 2y - 1 \\ z = 2 \end{array}\right\} \text{Equations}$$

The equation at the right is true if the variable is replaced by 5.

$x + 8 = 13$

$5 + 8 = 13$ A true equation

The equation $x + 8 = 13$ is false if the variable is replaced by 7.

$7 + 8 = 13$ A false equation

A **solution** of an equation is a number that, when substituted for the variable, results in a true equation. 5 is a solution of the equation $x + 8 = 13$. 7 is not a solution of the equation $x + 8 = 13$.

EXAMPLE 1 Is -3 a solution of the equation $4x + 16 = x^2 - 5$?

Solution

$$\begin{array}{c|c} \multicolumn{2}{c}{4x + 16 = x^2 - 5} \\ \hline 4(-3) + 16 & (-3)^2 - 5 \\ -12 + 16 & 9 - 5 \\ & \end{array}$$

$$4 = 4$$

- **Replace the variable by the given number, -3.**
- **Evaluate the numerical expressions using the Order of Operations Agreement.**
- **Compare the results. If the results are equal, the given number is a solution. If the results are not equal, the given number is not a solution.**

Yes, -3 is a solution of the equation $4x + 16 = x^2 - 5$.

PROBLEM 1 Is $\frac{1}{4}$ a solution of $5 - 4x = 8x + 2$?

Solution See page S5.

EXAMPLE 2 Is −4 a solution of $4 + 5x = x^2 - 2x$?

Solution

$4 + 5x$	$= x^2 - 2x$
$4 + 5(-4)$	$(-4)^2 - 2(-4)$
$4 + (-20)$	$16 - (-8)$

$$-16 \neq 24$$

No, −4 is not a solution of the equation $4 + 5x = x^2 - 2x$.

- **Replace the variable by the given number, −4.**
- **Evaluate the numerical expressions using the Order of Operations Agreement.**
- **Compare the results. If the results are equal, the given number is a solution. If the results are not equal, the given number is not a solution.**

PROBLEM 2 Is 5 a solution of $10x - x^2 = 3x - 10$?

Solution See page S5.

OBJECTIVE 2 Solve equations of the form $x + a = b$

To **solve an equation** means to find a solution of the equation. The simplest equation to solve is an equation of the form **variable = constant,** because the constant is the solution.

If $x = 5$, then 5 is the solution of the equation because $5 = 5$ is a true equation.

Take Note

Think of an equation as a balance scale. If the weights added to each side of the equation are not the same, the pans no longer balance.

The solution of the equation shown at the right is 7.

$$x + 2 = 9 \qquad 7 + 2 = 9$$

Note that if 4 is added to each side of the equation, the solution is still 7.

$$x + 2 + 4 = 9 + 4$$
$$x + 6 = 13 \qquad 7 + 6 = 13$$

If −5 is added to each side of the equation, the solution is still 7.

$$x + 2 + (-5) = 9 + (-5)$$
$$x - 3 = 4 \qquad 7 - 3 = 4$$

This illustrates the Addition Property of Equations.

Addition Property of Equations

The same number or variable term can be added to each side of an equation without changing the solution of the equation.

This property is used in solving equations. Note the effect of adding, to each side of the equation $x + 2 = 9$, the opposite of the constant term 2. After each side of the equation is simplified, the equation is in the form variable = constant. The solution is the constant.

$$x + 2 = 9$$
$$x + 2 + (-2) = 9 + (-2)$$
$$x + 0 = 7$$
$$x = 7$$

variable = constant

The solution is 7.

In solving an equation, the goal is to rewrite the given equation in the form variable = constant. The Addition Property of Equations can be used to rewrite an equation in this form. The Addition Property of Equations is used to remove a term from one side of an equation by adding the opposite of that term to each side of the equation.

EXAMPLE 3 Solve and check: $y - 6 = 9$

Solution

$y - 6 = 9$	• **The goal is to rewrite the equation in the form *variable = constant*.**
$y - 6 + 6 = 9 + 6$	• **Add 6 to each side of the equation (the Addition Property of Equations).**
$y + 0 = 15$	• **Simplify using the Inverse Property of Addition.**
$y = 15$	• **Simplify using the Addition Property of Zero. Now the equation is in the form *variable = constant*.**

Check

$y - 6 = 9$	
$15 - 6$	9

$9 = 9$ • **This is a true equation. The solution checks.**

The solution is 15. • **Write the solution.**

PROBLEM 3 Solve and check: $x - \frac{1}{3} = -\frac{3}{4}$

Solution See page S5.

Because subtraction is defined in terms of addition, the Addition Property of Equations makes it possible to subtract the same number from each side of an equation without changing the solution of the equation.

Solve: $y + \frac{1}{2} = \frac{5}{4}$

The goal is to rewrite the equation in the form *variable = constant*.

$$y + \frac{1}{2} = \frac{5}{4}$$

Add the opposite of the constant term $\frac{1}{2}$ to each side of the equation. This is equivalent to subtracting $\frac{1}{2}$ from each side of the equation.

$$y + \frac{1}{2} - \frac{1}{2} = \frac{5}{4} - \frac{1}{2}$$

$$y + 0 = \frac{5}{4} - \frac{2}{4}$$

$$y = \frac{3}{4}$$

The solution $\frac{3}{4}$ checks. The solution is $\frac{3}{4}$.

EXAMPLE 4 Solve: $\frac{1}{2} = x + \frac{2}{3}$

Solution

$$\frac{1}{2} = x + \frac{2}{3}$$

$$\frac{1}{2} - \frac{2}{3} = x + \frac{2}{3} - \frac{2}{3}$$ • Subtract $\frac{2}{3}$ from each side of the equation.

$$-\frac{1}{6} = x$$ • Simplify each side of the equation.

The solution is $-\frac{1}{6}$.

PROBLEM 4 Solve: $-8 = 5 + x$

Solution See page S5.

Note from the solution to Example 4 that an equation can be rewritten in the form *constant* = *variable*. Whether the equation is written in the form *variable* = *constant* or in the form *constant* = *variable*, the solution is the constant.

OBJECTIVE 3 Solve equations of the form *ax* = *b*

The solution of the equation shown at the right is 3. $2x = 6$ $\quad 2 \cdot 3 = 6$

Note that if each side of the equation is multiplied by 5, the solution is still 3.

$$5 \cdot 2x = 5 \cdot 6$$
$$10x = 30 \qquad 10 \cdot 3 = 30$$

If each side is multiplied by −4, the solution is still 3.

$$(-4) \cdot 2x = (-4) \cdot 6$$
$$-8x = -24 \qquad -8 \cdot 3 = -24$$

This illustrates the Multiplication Property of Equations.

Multiplication Property of Equations

Each side of an equation can be multiplied by the same nonzero number without changing the solution of the equation.

This property is used in solving equations. Note the effect of multiplying each side of the equation $2x = 6$ by the reciprocal of the coefficient 2. After each side of the equation is simplified, the equation is in the form variable = constant. The solution is the constant.

$$2x = 6$$
$$\frac{1}{2} \cdot 2x = \frac{1}{2} \cdot 6$$
$$1x = 3$$
$$x = 3$$

variable = constant

The solution is 3.

In solving an equation, the goal is to rewrite the given equation in the form variable = constant. The Multiplication Property of Equations can be used to rewrite an equation in this form. The Multiplication Property of Equations is used to remove a coefficient from a variable term in an equation by multiplying each side of the equation by the reciprocal of the coefficient.

EXAMPLE 5 Solve: $\frac{3x}{4} = -9$

Solution

$\frac{3x}{4} = -9$ • $\frac{3x}{4} = \frac{3}{4}x$

$\frac{4}{3} \cdot \frac{3}{4}x = \frac{4}{3}(-9)$ • **Multiply each side of the equation by the reciprocal of the coefficient $\frac{3}{4}$ (the Multiplication Property of Equations).**

$1x = -12$ • **Simplify using the Inverse Property of Multiplication.**

$x = -12$ • **Simplify using the Multiplication Property of One. Now the equation is in the form *variable = constant.***

The solution is -12. • **Write the solution.**

PROBLEM 5 Solve: $-\frac{2x}{5} = 6$

Solution See page S5.

Because division is defined in terms of multiplication, the Multiplication Property of Equations makes it possible to divide each side of an equation by the same number without changing the solution of the equation.

Solve: $8x = 16$

The goal is to rewrite the equation in the form *variable = constant*. $8x = 16$

Multiply each side of the equation by the reciprocal of 8. This is equivalent to dividing each side by 8.

$$\frac{8x}{8} = \frac{16}{8}$$
$$x = 2$$

The solution 2 checks. The solution is 2.

When using the Multiplication Property of Equations to solve an equation, multiply each side of the equation by the reciprocal of the coefficient when the coefficient is a fraction. Divide each side of the equation by the coefficient when the coefficient is an integer or a decimal.

EXAMPLE 6 Solve and check: $4x = 6$

Solution

$4x = 6$

$\frac{4x}{4} = \frac{6}{4}$ • **Divide each side of the equation by 4, the coefficient of *x*.**

$x = \frac{3}{2}$ • **Simplify each side of the equation.**

Check
$$\begin{array}{c|c} 4x & 6 \\ \hline 4\left(\frac{3}{2}\right) & 6 \end{array}$$
$$6 = 6$$ • **This is a true equation. The solution checks.**

The solution is $\frac{3}{2}$.

PROBLEM 6 Solve and check: $6x = 10$

Solution See page S5.

Before using one of the Properties of Equations, check to see whether one or both sides of the equation can be simplified. In Example 7, like terms appear on the left side of the equation. The first step in solving this equation is to combine the like terms so that there is only one variable term on the left side of the equation.

EXAMPLE 7 Solve: $5x - 9x = 12$

Solution
$$5x - 9x = 12$$
$$-4x = 12$$ • **Combine like terms.**
$$\frac{-4x}{-4} = \frac{12}{-4}$$ • **Divide each side of the equation by -4.**
$$x = -3$$

The solution is -3.

PROBLEM 7 Solve: $4x - 8x = 16$

Solution See page S5.

OBJECTIVE 4

Application problems: uniform motion

Any object that travels at a constant speed in a straight line is said to be in *uniform motion*. **Uniform motion** means that the speed and direction of an object do not change. For instance, a car traveling at a constant speed of 45 mph on a straight road is in uniform motion.

Take Note

A car traveling in a *circle* at a constant speed of 45 mph is *not* in uniform motion because the direction of the car is always changing.

The solution of a uniform motion problem is based on the equation $d = rt$, where d is the distance traveled, r is the rate of travel, and t is the time spent traveling. Suppose a car travels at 50 mph for 3 h. Because the rate (50 mph) and the time (3 h) are known, we can find the distance traveled by solving the equation $d = rt$ for d.

$$d = rt$$
$$d = 50(3)$$ • $r = 50, t = 3$
$$d = 150$$

The car travels a distance of 150 mi.

A jogger runs 3 mi in 45 min. What is the rate of the jogger in miles per hour?

Because the answer must be in miles per *hour* and the time is given in *minutes*, convert 45 min to hours.

$$45 \text{ min} = \frac{3}{4} \text{ h}$$

To find the rate of the jogger, solve the equation $d = rt$ for r using $d = 3$ and $t = \frac{3}{4}$.

$$d = rt$$
$$3 = r\left(\frac{3}{4}\right)$$
$$3 = \frac{3}{4}r$$
$$\left(\frac{4}{3}\right)3 = \left(\frac{4}{3}\right)\frac{3}{4}r$$
$$4 = r$$

The rate of the jogger is 4 mph.

If two objects are moving in opposite directions, then the rate at which the distance between them is increasing is the sum of the speeds of the two objects. For instance, in the diagram at the right, two cars start from the same point and travel in opposite directions. The distance between them is changing at the rate of 70 mph.

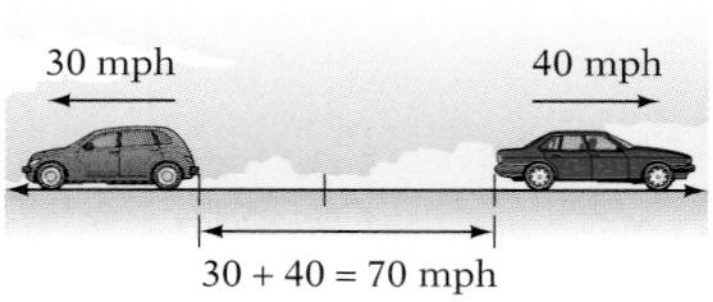

Similarly, if two objects are moving toward each other, the distance between them is decreasing at a rate that is equal to the sum of the speeds. The rate at which the two planes at the right are approaching one another is 800 mph.

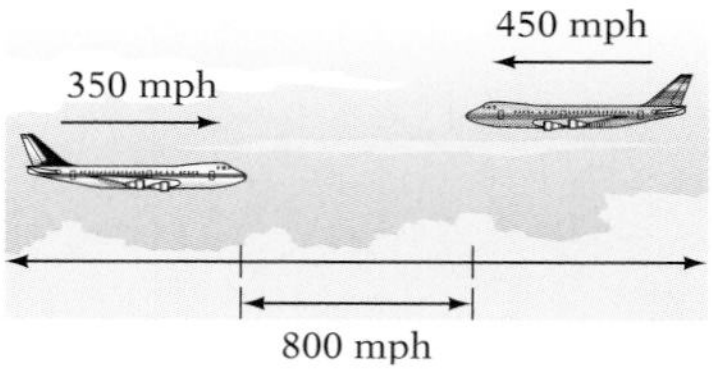

EXAMPLE 8 Two cars start from the same point and move in opposite directions. The car moving west is traveling 45 mph, and the car moving east is traveling 60 mph. In how many hours will the cars be 210 mi apart?

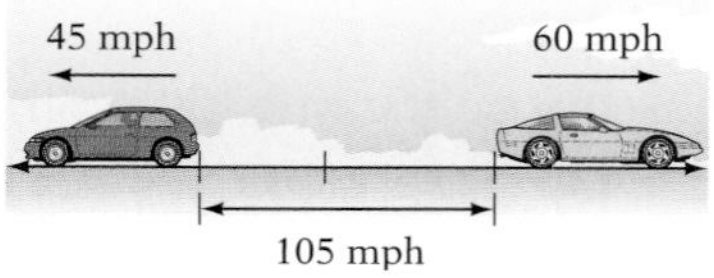

Strategy The distance is 210 mi. Therefore, $d = 210$. The cars are moving in opposite directions, so the rate at which the distance between them is changing is the sum of the rates of the two cars. The rate is 45 mph + 60 mph = 105 mph. Therefore, $r = 105$. To find the time, solve the equation $d = rt$ for t.

Solution

$$d = rt$$
$$210 = 105t \qquad \bullet\ d = 210, r = 105$$
$$\frac{210}{105} = \frac{105t}{105}$$
$$2 = t$$

In 2 h, the cars will be 210 mi apart.

PROBLEM 8 Two cyclists start at the same time at opposite ends of an 80-mile course. One cyclist is traveling 18 mph, and the second cyclist is traveling 14 mph. How long after they begin will they meet?

Solution See page S5.

If a motorboat is on a river that is flowing at a rate of 4 mph, the boat will float down the river at a speed of 4 mph even though the motor is not on. Now suppose the motor is turned on and the power adjusted so that the boat will travel at 10 mph without the aid of the current. Then, if the boat is moving *with* the current, its effective speed is the speed of the boat using power plus the speed of the current: 10 mph + 4 mph = 14 mph. However, if the boat is moving in the opposite direction of the current, the current slows the boat down, and the effective speed of the boat is the speed of the boat using power minus the speed of the current: 10 mph − 4 mph = 6 mph.

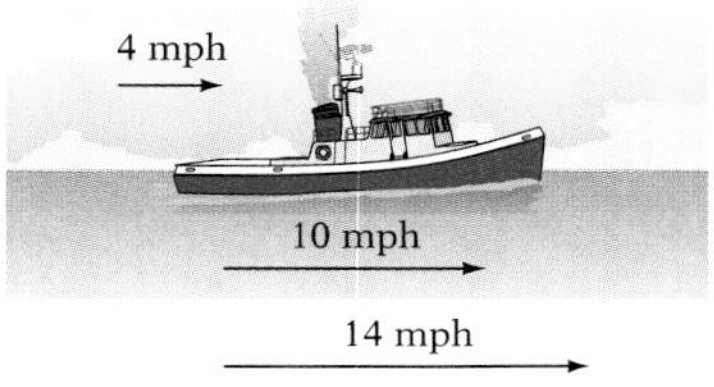

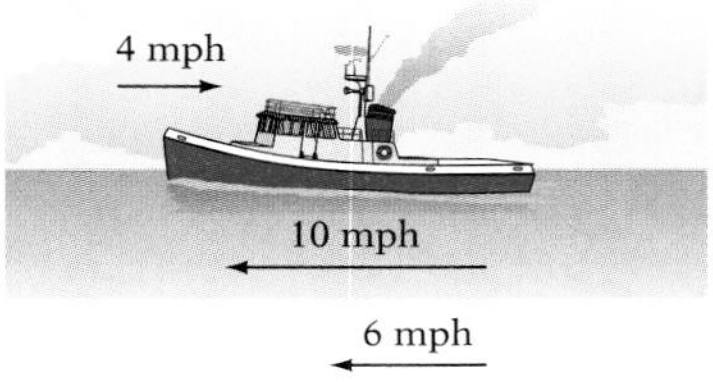

There are other situations in which these concepts may be applied.

Take Note

"ft/s" is an abbreviation for "feet per second."

EXAMPLE 9 An airline passenger is walking between two airline terminals and decides to get on a moving sidewalk that is 150 ft long. If the passenger walks at a rate of 7 ft/s and the moving sidewalk moves at a rate of 9 ft/s, how long, in seconds, will it take the passenger to walk from one end of the moving sidewalk to the other?

Strategy The distance is 150 ft. Therefore, $d = 150$. The passenger is traveling at 7 ft/s and the moving sidewalk is traveling at 9 ft/s. The rate of the passenger is the sum of the two rates, or 16 ft/s. Therefore, $r = 16$. To find the time, solve the equation $d = rt$ for t.

Solution

$$d = rt$$
$$150 = 16t \qquad \bullet\ d = 150, r = 16$$
$$\frac{150}{16} = \frac{16t}{16}$$
$$9.375 = t$$

It will take the passenger 9.375 s to travel the length of the moving sidewalk.

PROBLEM 9 A plane that can normally travel at 250 mph in calm air is flying into a headwind of 25 mph. How far can the plane fly in 3 h?

Solution See page S5.

OBJECTIVE 5 Applications of percent

The solution of a problem that involves a percent requires solving the basic percent equation.

The Basic Percent Equation

$$\text{Percent} \cdot \text{base} = \text{amount}$$
$$P \cdot B = A$$

To translate a problem involving a percent into an equation, remember that the word *of* translates into "multiply" and the word *is* translates into "=." The base usually follows the word *of*.

20% of what number is 30?

Given: $P = 20\% = 0.20$
$A = 30$
Unknown: Base

$$PB = A$$
$$(0.20)B = 30$$
$$\frac{0.20B}{0.20} = \frac{30}{0.20}$$
$$B = 150$$

The number is 150.

What percent of 40 is 30?

Given: $B = 40$
$A = 30$
Unknown: Percent

$$PB = A$$
$$P(40) = 30$$
$$40P = 30$$
$$\frac{40P}{40} = \frac{30}{40}$$
$$P = \frac{3}{4}$$

We must write the fraction as a percent in order to answer the question.

$$P = 75\%$$

30 is 75% of 40.

Find 25% of 200.

Given: $P = 25\% = 0.25$
$B = 200$
Unknown: Amount

$$PB = A$$
$$0.25(200) = A$$
$$50 = A$$

25% of 200 is 50.

In most cases, we write a percent as a decimal before solving the basic percent equation. However, some percents are more easily written as a fraction. For example,

$$33\frac{1}{3}\% = \frac{1}{3} \qquad 66\frac{2}{3}\% = \frac{2}{3} \qquad 16\frac{2}{3}\% = \frac{1}{6} \qquad 83\frac{1}{3}\% = \frac{5}{6}$$

EXAMPLE 10 12 is $33\frac{1}{3}\%$ of what number?

Solution

$$PB = A \qquad \bullet\ 33\frac{1}{3}\% = \frac{1}{3}$$
$$\frac{1}{3}B = 12$$
$$3 \cdot \frac{1}{3}B = 3 \cdot 12$$
$$B = 36$$

The number is 36.

PROBLEM 10 27 is what percent of 60?

Solution See page S6.

EXAMPLE 11 During a recent year, nearly 1.2 million dogs or litters were registered with the American Kennel Club. The most popular breed was the Labrador retriever, with 172,841 registered. What percent of the registrations were Labrador retrievers? Round to the nearest tenth of a percent. (*Source:* American Kennel Club)

Strategy To find the percent, solve the basic percent equation using $B = 1.2$ million $= 1{,}200{,}000$ and $A = 172{,}841$. The percent is unknown.

Solution

$$PB = A$$
$$P(1{,}200{,}000) = 172{,}841$$
$$\frac{P(1{,}200{,}000)}{1{,}200{,}000} = \frac{172{,}841}{1{,}200{,}000}$$
$$P \approx 0.144$$
$$P \approx 14.4\%$$

Approximately 14.4% of the registrations were Labrador retrievers.

Point of Interest

As noted at the right, 172,841 of the dogs or litters registered were Labrador retrievers. Listed below are the next most popular breeds and their registrations.
Golden retrievers: 66,300
German shepherds: 57,660
Dachshunds: 54,773
Beagles: 52,026

PROBLEM 11 A student correctly answered 72 of the 80 questions on an exam. What percent of the questions were answered correctly?

Solution See page S6.

EXAMPLE 12 According to the Centers for Disease Control and Prevention, 30.8% of the adult population of Kentucky smokes. How many adults in Kentucky smoke? Use a figure of 3,000,000 for the number of adults in Kentucky.

Strategy To find the number of adults who smoke, solve the basic percent equation using $B = 3{,}000{,}000$ and $P = 30.8\% = 0.308$. The amount is unknown.

Solution

$$PB = A$$
$$0.308(3{,}000{,}000) = A$$
$$924{,}000 = A$$

Approximately 924,000 adults in Kentucky smoke.

PROBLEM 12 The price of a digital camcorder is \$895. A 6% sales tax is added to the price. How much is the sales tax?

Solution See page S6.

The simple interest that an investment earns is given by the equation

$$I = Prt$$

where I is the simple interest, P is the principal, or amount invested, r is the simple interest rate, and t is the time.

Take Note

$18 \text{ months} = \frac{18}{12} \text{ years}$
$= 1.5 \text{ years}$

A \$1500 investment has an annual simple interest rate of 7%. Find the simple interest earned on the investment after 18 months.

The time is given in months, but the interest rate is an annual rate. Therefore, we must convert 18 months to years.

18 months = 1.5 years

To find the interest earned, solve the equation $I = Prt$ for I using $P = 1500$, $r = 0.07$, and $t = 1.5$.

$I = Prt$
$I = 1500(0.07)(1.5)$
$I = 157.5$

The interest earned is \$157.50.

EXAMPLE 13 In April, Marshall Wardell was charged \$8.72 in interest on an unpaid credit card balance of \$545. Find the annual interest rate for this credit card.

Strategy The interest is \$8.72. Therefore, $I = 8.72$. The unpaid balance is \$545. This is the principal on which interest is calculated. Therefore, $P = 545$. The time is 1 month. Because the *annual* interest rate must be found and the time is given as 1 month, write 1 month as $\frac{1}{12}$ year. Therefore, $t = \frac{1}{12}$. To find the interest rate, solve the equation $I = Prt$ for r.

Solution

$$I = Prt$$

$$8.72 = 545r\left(\frac{1}{12}\right) \qquad \bullet\ I = 8.72,\ P = 545,\ t = \frac{1}{12}$$

$$8.72 = \frac{545}{12}r$$

$$\frac{12}{545}(8.72) = \frac{12}{545}\left(\frac{545}{12}r\right)$$

$$0.192 = r$$

The annual interest rate is 19.2%.

Take Note

Municipal bonds are frequently sold by government agencies to pay for roads, aqueducts, and other essential public needs. An investor who purchases one of these bonds is paid interest on the cost of the bond for a certain number of years. When that time period expires, the cost of the bond is returned to the investor.

PROBLEM 13 Clarissa Adams purchased a \$1000 municipal bond that earns an annual simple interest rate of 6.4%. How much must she deposit into a bank account that earns 8% annual simple interest so that the interest earned from each account after one year is the same?

Solution See page S6.

The amount of a substance in a solution can be given as a percent of the total solution. For instance, if a certain fruit juice drink is advertised as containing 27% cranberry juice, then 27% of the contents of the bottle must be cranberry juice.

Solving problems involving mixtures is based on the percent mixture equation

$$\boldsymbol{Q = Ar}$$

where Q is the quantity of a substance in the solution, A is the amount of the solution, and r is the percent concentration of the substance.

Point of Interest

In the jewelry industry, the amount of gold in a piece of jewelry is measured in karats. *Pure gold is 24 karats. A necklace that is 18 karats is*

$\frac{18}{24} = 0.75 = 75\%$ *gold.*

The formula for a perfume requires that the concentration of jasmine be 1.2% of the total amount of perfume. How many ounces of jasmine are in a 2-ounce bottle of this perfume?

The amount of perfume is 2 oz. Therefore, $A = 2$. The percent concentration is 1.2%, so $r = 0.012$. To find the number of ounces of jasmine, solve the equation $Q = Ar$ for Q.

$$Q = Ar$$
$$Q = 2(0.012)$$
$$Q = 0.024$$

The bottle contains 0.024 oz of jasmine.

EXAMPLE 14 To make a certain color of blue, 4 oz of cyan must be contained in 1 gal of paint. What is the percent concentration of cyan in the paint?

Strategy The amount of cyan is given in ounces and the amount of paint is given in gallons; we must convert ounces to gallons or gallons to ounces. For this problem, we will convert gallons to ounces: 1 gal = 128 oz.

Solution To find the percent concentration of cyan, solve the equation $Q = Ar$ for r using $Q = 4$ and $A = 128$.

$$Q = Ar$$
$$4 = 128r$$
$$\frac{4}{128} = \frac{128r}{128}$$
$$0.03125 = r$$

The percent concentration of cyan is 3.125%.

PROBLEM 14 The concentration of sugar in Choco-Pops cereal is 25%. If a bowl of this cereal contains 2 oz of sugar, how many ounces of cereal are in the bowl?

Solution See page S6.

3.1 Concept Review

Determine whether the statement is always true, sometimes true, or never true.

1. Both sides of an equation can be multiplied by the same number without changing the solution of the equation.

2. Both sides of an equation can be divided by the same number without changing the solution of the equation.

3. For an equation of the form $ax = b, a \neq 0$, multiplying both sides of the equation by the reciprocal of a will result in an equation of the form $x = constant$.

4. Use the Multiplication Property of Equations to remove a term from one side of an equation.

5. Adding a negative 3 to each side of an equation yields the same result as subtracting 3 from each side of the equation.

6. In the basic percent equation, the amount follows the word *of*.

7. An equation contains an equals sign.

3.1 Exercises

1 Determine whether a given number is a solution of an equation

1. Complete the sentence using the word *expression* or the word *equation*.
a. $8x = 4x + 10$ is an ___?___. **b.** $8x - 4x + 10$ is an ___?___.

2. Determine whether -3 is a solution of the equation $9 - 5x = -3 - 9x$.

$9 - 5x$	$= -3 - 9x$	
$9 - 5(-3)$	$-3 - 9(-3)$	• **Replace the variable by the given number, ___?___.**
$9 +$ ___?___	$-3 +$ ___?___	• **Evaluate the numerical expressions.**
___?___	___?___	• **Compare the results.**

The results are ___?___; therefore, -3 is a solution of the equation $9 - 5x = -3 - 9x$.

3. Is 4 a solution of $2x = 8$?

4. Is 3 a solution of $y + 4 = 7$?

5. Is -1 a solution of $2b - 1 = 3$?

6. Is -2 a solution of $3a - 4 = 10$?

7. Is 1 a solution of $4 - 2m = 3$?

8. Is 2 a solution of $7 - 3n = 2$?

9. Is 5 a solution of $2x + 5 = 3x$?

10. Is 4 a solution of $3y - 4 = 2y$?

11. Is 0 a solution of $4a + 5 = 3a + 5$?

12. Is 0 a solution of $4 - 3b = 4 - 5b$?

13. Is -2 a solution of $4 - 2n = n + 10$?

14. Is -3 a solution of $5 - m = 2 - 2m$?

15. Is 3 a solution of $z^2 + 1 = 4 + 3z$?

16. Is 2 a solution of $2x^2 - 1 = 4x - 1$?

17. Is -1 a solution of $y^2 - 1 = 4y + 3$?

18. Is -2 a solution of $m^2 - 4 = m + 3$?

19. Is 4 a solution of $x(x + 1) = x^2 + 5$?

20. Is 3 a solution of $2a(a - 1) = 3a + 3$?

21. Is $-\frac{1}{4}$ a solution of $8t + 1 = -1$?

22. Is $\frac{1}{2}$ a solution of $4y + 1 = 3$?

23. Is $\frac{2}{5}$ a solution of $5m + 1 = 10m - 3$?

24. Is $\frac{3}{4}$ a solution of $8x - 1 = 12x + 3$?

25. Is 2.1 a solution of $x^2 - 4x = x + 1.89$?

26. Is 1.5 a solution of $c^2 - 3c = 4c - 8.25$?

2 Solve equations of the form $x + a = b$

27. How is the Addition Property of Equations used to solve an equation?

28. Explain why the goal in solving an equation is to write the equation in the form *variable* = *constant*.

29. To solve the equation $p - 30 = 57$, use the Addition Property of Equations to add ___?___ to each side of the equation. The solution is ___?___.

30. To solve the equation $18 + n = 25$, ___?___ 18 from each side of the equation. The solution is ___?___.

31. Without solving the equation $x + \frac{13}{15} = -\frac{21}{43}$, determine whether x is less than or greater than $-\frac{21}{43}$. Explain your answer.

32. Without solving the equation $x - \frac{11}{16} = \frac{19}{24}$, determine whether x is less than or greater than $\frac{19}{24}$. Explain your answer.

Solve and check.

33. $x + 5 = 7$

34. $y + 3 = 9$

35. $b - 4 = 11$

36. $z - 6 = 10$

37. $2 + a = 8$

38. $5 + x = 12$

39. $m + 9 = 3$

40. $t + 12 = 10$

41. $n - 5 = -2$

42. $x - 6 = -5$

43. $b + 7 = 7$

44. $y - 5 = -5$

45. $a - 3 = -5$

46. $x - 6 = -3$

47. $z + 9 = 2$

48. $n + 11 = 1$

49. $10 + m = 3$

50. $8 + x = 5$

51. $9 + x = -3$

52. $10 + y = -4$

53. $b - 5 = -3$

54. $t - 6 = -4$

55. $2 = x + 7$

56. $-8 = n + 1$

57. $4 = m - 11$

58. $-6 = y - 5$

59. $12 = 3 + w$

60. $-9 = 5 + x$

61. $4 = -10 + b$

62. $-7 = -2 + x$

63. $m + \frac{2}{3} = -\frac{1}{3}$

64. $c + \frac{3}{4} = -\frac{1}{4}$

65. $x - \frac{1}{2} = \frac{1}{2}$

66. $x - \frac{2}{5} = \frac{3}{5}$

67. $\frac{5}{8} + y = \frac{1}{8}$

68. $\frac{4}{9} + a = -\frac{2}{9}$

69. $m + \frac{1}{2} = -\frac{1}{4}$

70. $b + \frac{1}{6} = -\frac{1}{3}$

71. $x + \frac{2}{3} = \frac{3}{4}$

72. $n + \frac{2}{5} = \frac{2}{3}$

73. $-\frac{5}{6} = x - \frac{1}{4}$

74. $-\frac{1}{4} = c - \frac{2}{3}$

75. $-\frac{1}{21} = m + \frac{2}{3}$

76. $\frac{5}{9} = b - \frac{1}{3}$

77. $\frac{5}{12} = n + \frac{3}{4}$

78. $d + 1.3619 = 2.0148$

79. $w + 2.932 = 4.801$

80. $-0.813 + x = -1.096$

81. $-1.926 + t = -1.042$

3 Solve equations of the form $ax = b$

82. How is the Multiplication Property of Equations used to solve an equation?

83. Why, when the Multiplication Property of Equations is used, must the number that multiplies each side of the equation not be zero?

84. To solve the equation $\frac{2}{3}w = -18$, use the Multiplication Property of Equations to multiply each side of the equation by ___?___. The solution is ___?___.

85. To solve the equation $56 = 8n$, ___?___ each side of the equation by 8. The solution is ___?___.

86. Without solving the equation $-\frac{15}{41}x = -\frac{23}{25}$, determine whether x is less than or greater than zero. Explain your answer.

87. Without solving the equation $\frac{5}{28}x = -\frac{3}{44}$, determine whether x is less than or greater than zero. Explain your answer.

Solve and check.

88. $5x = 15$

89. $4y = 28$

90. $3b = -12$

91. $2a = -14$

92. $-3x = 6$

93. $-5m = 20$

94. $-3x = -27$

95. $-6n = -30$

96. $20 = 4c$

97. $18 = 2t$

98. $-32 = 8w$

99. $-56 = 7x$

100. $8d = 0$

101. $-5x = 0$

102. $36 = 9z$

103. $35 = -5x$

104. $-64 = 8a$

105. $-32 = -4y$

106. $-42 = 6t$

107. $-12m = -144$

108. $\frac{x}{3} = 2$

109. $\frac{x}{4} = 3$

110. $-\frac{y}{2} = 5$

111. $-\frac{b}{3} = 6$

112. $\frac{n}{7} = -4$

113. $\frac{t}{6} = -3$

114. $\frac{2}{5}x = 12$

115. $-\frac{4}{3}c = -8$

116. $\frac{5}{6}y = -20$

117. $-\frac{2}{3}d = 8$

118. $-\frac{3}{5}m = 12$

119. $-\frac{3}{4}x = -24$

120. $\frac{2n}{3} = 2$

121. $\frac{5x}{6} = -10$

122. $\frac{-3z}{8} = 9$

123. $\frac{-4x}{5} = -12$

124. $-6 = -\frac{2}{3}y$

125. $-15 = -\frac{3}{5}x$

126. $\frac{2}{9} = \frac{2}{3}y$

127. $-\frac{6}{7} = -\frac{3}{4}b$

128. $-\frac{2}{5}m = -\frac{6}{7}$

129. $5x + 2x = 14$

130. $3n + 2n = 20$

131. $7d - 4d = 9$

132. $10y - 3y = 21$

133. $2x - 5x = 9$

134. $\frac{x}{1.4} = 3.2$

135. $\frac{z}{2.9} = -7.8$

136. $3.4a = 7.004$

137. $2.3m = 2.415$

138. $-3.7x = 7.77$

139. $-1.6m = 5.44$

140. In the equation $15x = y$, y is a positive integer. Is the value of x a negative number?

141. In the equation $-6x = y$, y is a negative integer. Is the value of x a negative number?

142. In the equation $-\frac{1}{4}x = y$, y is a positive integer. Is the value of x a negative number?

4 Application problems: uniform motion

143. In the formula $d = rt$, d represents ___?___, r represents ___?___, and t represents ___?___.

144. A car that travels 10 mi in 30 min is traveling at a rate of ___?___ miles per hour.

145. Maria and Nathan start hiking at the same time. Maria hikes at 3 mph and Nathan hikes at 2.5 mph. After t hours, Maria has hiked ___?___ miles and Nathan has hiked ___?___ miles.

146. A plane flies at a rate of 325 mph in calm air. The wind is blowing at 30 mph. Flying with the wind, the plane travels ___?___ mph. Flying against the wind, the plane travels ___?___ mph.

147. Joe and John live 2 mi apart. They leave their houses at the same time and walk toward each other until they meet. Joe walks faster than John does.

a. Is the distance walked by Joe less than, equal to, or greater than the distance walked by John?

b. Is the time spent walking by Joe less than, equal to, or greater than the time spent walking by John?

c. What is the total distance traveled by both Joe and John?

148. Morgan and Emma ride their bikes from Morgan's house to the store. Morgan begins biking 5 min before Emma begins. Emma bikes faster than Morgan and catches up with her just as they reach the store.

a. Is the distance biked by Emma less than, equal to, or greater than the distance biked by Morgan?

b. Is the time spent biking by Emma less than, equal to, or greater than the time spent biking by Morgan?

149. A train travels at 45 mph for 3 h and then increases its speed to 55 mph for 2 more hours. How far does the train travel in the 5-hour period?

150. As part of a training program for the Boston Marathon, a runner wants to build endurance by running at a rate of 9 mph for 20 min. How far will the runner travel in that time period?

151. It takes a hospital dietician 40 min to drive from home to the hospital, a distance of 20 mi. What is the dietician's average rate of speed?

152. Marcella leaves home at 9:00 A.M. and drives to school, arriving at 9:45 A.M. If the distance between home and school is 27 mi, what is Marcella's average rate of speed?

153. The Ride for Health Bicycle Club has chosen a 36-mile course for this Saturday's ride. If the riders plan on averaging 12 mph while they are riding and they have a 1-hour lunch break planned, how long will it take them to complete the trip?

154. Palmer's average running speed is 3 kilometers per hour faster than his walking speed. If Palmer can run around a 30-kilometer course in 2 h, how many hours would it take for Palmer to walk the same course?

155. A shopping mall has a moving sidewalk that takes shoppers from the shopping area to the parking garage, a distance of 250 ft. If your normal walking rate is 5 ft/s and the moving sidewalk is traveling at 3 ft/s, how many seconds would it take you to walk on the moving sidewalk from the parking garage to the shopping area?

156. K&B River Tours offers a river trip that takes passengers from the K&B dock to a small island that is 24 mi away. The passengers spend 1 h at the island and then return to the K&B dock. If the speed of the boat is 10 mph in calm water and the rate of the current is 2 mph, how long does the trip last?

157. Two joggers start at the same time from opposite ends of an 8-mile jogging trail and begin running toward each other. One jogger is running at a rate of 5 mph, and the other jogger is running at a rate of 7 mph. How long, in minutes, after they start will the two joggers meet?

158. Two cyclists start from the same point at the same time and move in opposite directions. One cyclist is traveling at 8 mph, and the other cyclist is traveling at 9 mph. After 30 min, how far apart are the two cyclists?

159. Petra, who can paddle her canoe at a rate of 10 mph in calm water, is paddling her canoe on a river whose current is 2 mph. How long will it take her to travel 4 mi upstream against the current?

160. At 8:00 A.M., a train leaves a station and travels at a rate of 45 mph. At 9:00 A.M., a second train leaves the same station on the same track and travels in the direction of the first train at a speed of 60 mph. At 10:00 A.M., how far apart are the two trains?

5 Applications of percent

161. Employee A had an annual salary of $52,000, Employee B had an annual salary of $58,000, and Employee C had an annual salary of $56,000 before each employee was given a 5% raise. Which of the three employees now has the highest annual salary? Explain how you arrived at your answer.

162. Each of three employees earned an annual salary of $65,000 before Employee A was given a 3% raise, Employee B was given a 6% raise, and Employee C was given a 4.5% raise. Which of the three employees now has the highest annual salary? Explain how you arrived at your answer.

Solve.

163. 12 is what percent of 50?

164. What percent of 125 is 50?

165. Find 18% of 40.

166. What is 25% of 60?

167. 12% of what is 48?

168. 45% of what is 9?

169. What is $33\frac{1}{3}\%$ of 27?

170. Find $16\frac{2}{3}\%$ of 30.

171. What percent of 12 is 3?

172. 10 is what percent of 15?

173. 60% of what is 3?

174. 75% of what is 6?

175. 12 is what percent of 6?

176. 20 is what percent of 16?

177. $5\frac{1}{4}\%$ of what is 21?

178. $37\frac{1}{2}\%$ of what is 15?

179. Find 15.4% of 50.

180. What is 18.5% of 46?

181. 1 is 0.5% of what?

182. 3 is 1.5% of what?

183. $\frac{3}{4}\%$ of what is 3?

184. $\frac{1}{2}\%$ of what is 3?

185. Find 125% of 16.

186. What is 250% of 12?

187. 16.4 is what percent of 20.4? Round to the nearest percent.

188. Find 18.3% of 625. Round to the nearest tenth.

189. Without solving an equation, determine whether 40% of 80 is less than, equal to, or greater than 80% of 40.

190. Without solving an equation, determine whether $\frac{1}{4}\%$ of 80 is less than, equal to, or greater than 25% of 80.

Complete Exercises 191 to 193 by replacing the question marks with the correct number from the problem situation or with the word *unknown*.

191. **Problem Situation:** It rained on 24 of the 30 days of June. What percent of the days in June were rainy days?
Using the formula $PB = A$, $P =$ ___?___, $B =$ ___?___, and $A =$ ___?___.

192. **Problem Situation:** \$7000 invested in a simple interest account earns \$420 of interest in 2 years. What is the annual simple interest rate?
Using the formula $I = Prt$, $I =$ ___?___, $P =$ ___?___, $r =$ ___?___, and $t =$ ___?___.

193. **Problem Situation:** The label on a 32-ounce bottle of lemonade states that it contains 10% real lemon juice. How many ounces of real lemon juice are in the bottle?
Using the formula $Q = Ar$, $Q =$ ___?___, $A =$ ___?___, and $r =$ ___?___.

194. **a.** Convert 30 months to years. **b.** Convert 3 months to years.
c. Convert 9 months to years. **d.** Convert 15 months to years.

195. **Stadiums** The Arthur Ashe Tennis Stadium in New York has a seating capacity of 22,500 people. Of these seats, 1.11% are wheelchair-accessible seats. How many seats in the stadium are reserved for wheelchair accessibility? Round to the nearest whole number.

196. Education The graph at the right shows the sources of revenue in a recent year for public schools in the United States. The total revenue was \$419.8 billion dollars. How many billion dollars more did public schools receive from the state than from the federal government? Round to the nearest billion dollars. (*Source*: Census Bureau)

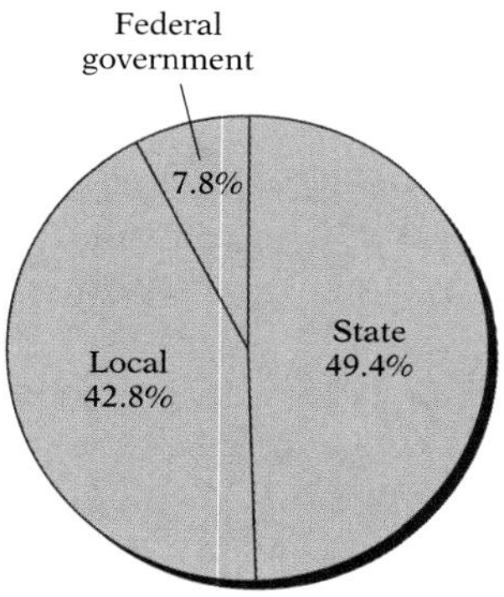

Sources of Revenue for Public Schools

197. Natural Resources On average, a person uses 13.2 gal of water per day for showering. This is 17.8% of the total amount of water used per person per day in the average single-family home. Find the total amount of water used per person per day in the average single-family home. Round to the nearest whole number. (*Source:* American Water Works Association)

198. Business During a recent year, 276 billion product coupons were issued by manufacturers. Shoppers redeemed 4.8 billion of these coupons. What percent of the coupons issued were redeemed by customers? Round to the nearest tenth of a percent. (*Source:* NCH NuWorld Consumer Behavior Study, America Coupon Council)

199. Travel According to the annual Summer Vacation Survey conducted by Myvesta, a nonprofit consumer education organization, the average summer vacation costs \$2252. If \$1850 of this amount is charged on a credit card, what percent of the vacation cost is charged? Round to the nearest tenth of a percent.

200. The Internet A recent survey by Internetworldstats.com found that there were 973 million people worldwide who had access to the Internet. What percent of the world's population had access to the Internet? Use a figure of 6.4 billion people for the world population. Round to the nearest tenth of a percent.

201. The Internet The graph at the right shows the responses to a Yahoo! survey that asked people how many hours per week they typically spend online. How many people were surveyed?

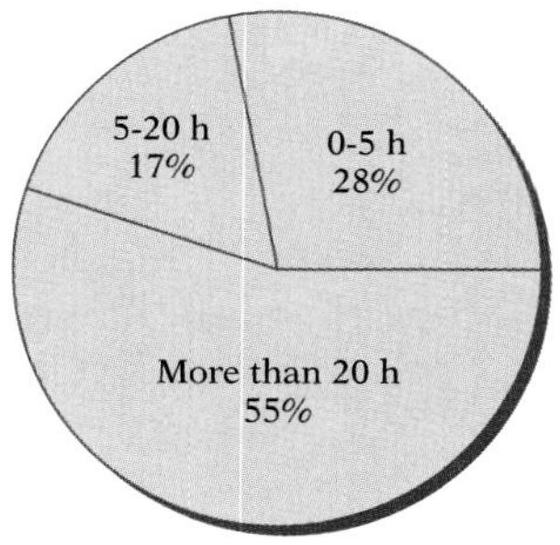

Hours per Week Spent Online

202. Food Industry Of the 63,800 pizzerias in the United States, 2750 are in New York. What percent of the pizzerias in the United States are in New York? Round to the nearest tenth of a percent. (*Source*: USA TODAY, February 22, 2005)

203. Safety Recently, the National Safety Council collected data on the leading causes of accidental death. The findings revealed that for people age 20, 30 died from a fall, 47 from fire, 200 from drowning, and 1950 from motor vehicle accidents. What percent of the accidental deaths were not attributed to motor vehicle accidents? Round to the nearest percent.

204. Health According to *Health* magazine, the average American has increased his or her daily consumption of calories from 18 years ago by 11.6%. If the average daily consumption was 1970 calories 18 years ago, what is the average daily consumption today? Round to the nearest whole number.

205. **Energy** The Energy Information Administration reports that if every U.S. household switched 4 h of lighting per day from incandescent bulbs to compact fluorescent bulbs, we would save 31.7 billion kilowatt-hours of electricity a year, or 33% of the total electricity used for home lighting. What is the total electricity used for home lighting in this country? Round to the nearest tenth of a billion.

206. **The Federal Government** To override a presidential veto, at least $66\frac{2}{3}\%$ of the Senate must vote to override the veto. There are 100 senators in the Senate. What is the minimum number of votes needed to override a veto?

207. **Advertising** Suppose that 125 million people saw a particular 30-second commercial for a soft drink during Super Bowl XL and that the cost for the commercial was approximately \$2.5 million.

a. If the soft drink manufacturer makes a profit of \$.08 on each can sold, what percent of the people watching the commercial would have to buy one can of the soft drink for the company to recover the cost of the commercial?

b. What percent of the people watching the commercial would have to purchase one six-pack of the soft drink for the company to recover the cost of the commercial? Round to the nearest tenth of a percent.

208. **Recreation** The graph at the right shows participation in All-American Soap Box Derbies. (*Source*: All-American Soap Box Derby) Round answers to the nearest tenth of a percent.

a. What percent of the participants in 2000 were male?

b. What percent of the participants in 2004 were female?

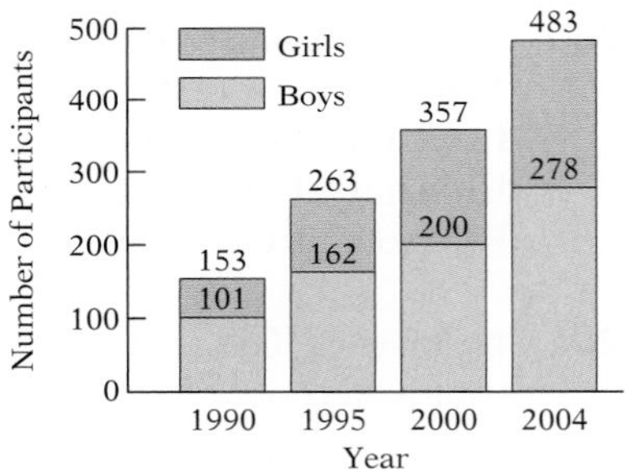

Participation in Soap Box Derbies

209. **Consumerism** A 16-horsepower lawn tractor with automatic transmission sells for \$1579.99. This is 11% more than the price of the same lawn tractor with a standard transmission. What is the price of the less expensive model? Round to the nearest cent.

210. **Investment** If Miranda Perry invests \$2500 in an account that earns an 8% annual simple interest rate, how much interest will Miranda have earned after 9 months?

211. **Investment** Kachina Caron invests \$1200 in a simple interest account and earns \$72 in 8 months. What is the annual simple interest rate?

212. **Investment** How much money must Andrea invest for two years in an account that earns an annual simple interest rate of 8% if she wants to earn \$300 from the investment?

213. **Investment** Sal Boxer divided a gift of \$3000 into two different accounts. He placed \$1000 in one account that earned an annual simple interest rate of 7.5%. The remaining money was placed in an account that earned an annual simple interest rate of 8.25%. How much interest did Sal earn from the two accounts after one year?

214. **Investment** If Americo invests \$2500 at an 8% annual simple interest rate and Octavia invests \$3000 at a 7% annual simple interest rate, which of the two will earn the greater amount of interest in one year?

215. **Investment** Makana invested \$900 in an account that earned an annual simple interest rate that was 1% higher than the rate her friend Marlys earned on her investment. If Marlys earned \$51 after one year from an investment of \$850, how much did Makana earn after one year?

216. **Investment** A \$2000 investment at an annual simple interest rate of 6% earned as much interest after one year as another investment in an account that earned 8% annual simple interest. How much was invested at 8%?

217. **Investment** An investor places \$1000 in an account that earns 9% annual simple interest and \$1000 in an account that earns 6% annual simple interest. If each investment is left in the account for the same period of time, is the interest rate on the combined investment less than 6%, between 6% and 9%, or greater than 9%?

218. **Mixture Problem** The concentration of platinum in a necklace is 15%. The necklace weighs 12 g. Find the amount of platinum in the necklace.

219. **Mixture Problem** A 250-milliliter solution of a fabric dye contains 5 ml of hydrogen peroxide. What is the percent concentration of the hydrogen peroxide?

220. **Mixture Problem** A carpet is made of a blend of wool and other fibers. If the concentration of wool in the carpet is 75% and the carpet weighs 175 lb, how much wool is in the carpet?

221. **Mixture Problem** Apple Dan's 32-ounce apple-flavored fruit drink contains 8 oz of apple juice. Forty ounces of a generic brand of apple-flavored fruit drink contains 9 oz of apple juice. Which of the two brands has the greater concentration of apple juice?

222. **Mixture Problem** Bakers use simple syrup in many of their recipes. Simple syrup is made by combining 500 g of sugar with 500 g of water and mixing it well until the sugar dissolves. What is the percent concentration of sugar in simple syrup?

223. **Mixture Problem** A pharmacist has 50 g of a topical cream that contains 75% glycerin. How many grams of the cream are not glycerin?

224. **Mixture Problem** A chemist has 100 ml of a solution that is 9% acetic acid. If the chemist adds 50 ml of pure water to this solution, what is the percent concentration of the resulting mixture?

225. **Mixture Problem** A 500-gram salt and water solution contains 50 g of salt. This mixture is left in the open air and 100 g of water evaporates from the solution. What is the percent concentration of salt in the remaining solution?

3.1 Applying Concepts

Solve.

226. $\dfrac{2m + m}{5} = -9$

227. $\dfrac{3y - 8y}{7} = 15$

228. $\dfrac{1}{\frac{1}{x}} = 5$

229. $\dfrac{1}{\frac{1}{x}} + 8 = -19$

230. $\dfrac{4}{\frac{3}{b}} = 8$

231. $\dfrac{5}{\frac{7}{a}} - \dfrac{3}{\frac{7}{a}} = 6$

232. Solve for x: $x \div 28 = 1481$ remainder 25

233. **Geometry** Find the value of x in the diagram shown at the right.

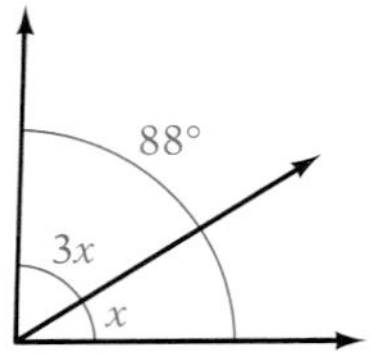

234. **Consumerism** Your bill for dinner, including a 7.25% sales tax, was \$92.74. You want to leave a 15% tip on the cost of the dinner before the sales tax. Find the amount of the tip to the nearest dollar.

235. **Consumerism** The total cost for a dinner was \$97.52. This included a 15% tip calculated on the cost of the dinner after a 6% sales tax. Find the cost of dinner before the tip and tax.

236. **Business** A retailer decides to increase the original price of each item in the store by 10%. After the price increase, the retailer notices a significant drop in sales and so decides to reduce the current price of each item in the store by 10%. Are the prices back to the original prices? If not, are the prices lower or higher than the original prices?

237. If a quantity increases by 100%, how many times its original value is the new value?

238. Make up an equation of the form $x + a = b$ that has 2 as a solution.

239. Make up an equation of the form $ax = b$ that has -2 as a solution.

240. **Monthly Mortgage Payments** Suppose you have a \$100,000 30-year mortgage. What is the difference between the monthly payment if the interest rate on your loan is 7.75% and the monthly payment if the interest rate is 7.25%? (*Hint:* You will need to discuss the question with an agent at a bank that provides mortgage services, discuss the question with a real estate agent, or find and use the formula for determining the monthly payment on a mortgage.)

241. The following problem does not contain enough information: "How many hours does it take to fly from Los Angeles to New York?" What additional information do we need in order to answer the question?

3.2 General Equations

OBJECTIVE 1 Solve equations of the form $ax + b = c$

In solving an equation of the form $ax + b = c$, the goal is to rewrite the equation in the form *variable* = *constant*. This requires applying both the Addition and the Multiplication Properties of Equations.

Solve: $\frac{2}{5}x - 3 = -7$

$$\frac{2}{5}x - 3 = -7$$

Add 3 to each side of the equation.

$$\frac{2}{5}x - 3 + 3 = -7 + 3$$

Simplify.

$$\frac{2}{5}x = -4$$

Multiply each side of the equation by the reciprocal of the coefficient $\frac{2}{5}$.

$$\frac{5}{2} \cdot \frac{2}{5}x = \frac{5}{2}(-4)$$

Simplify. Now the equation is in the form *variable* = *constant*.

$$x = -10$$

Check

$$\begin{array}{r|l} \frac{2}{5}x - 3 & = -7 \\ \hline \frac{2}{5}(-10) - 3 & -7 \\ -4 - 3 & -7 \\ -7 & = -7 \end{array}$$

Write the solution.

The solution is -10.

EXAMPLE 1 Solve: $3x - 7 = -5$

Solution

$$3x - 7 = -5$$

$$3x - 7 + 7 = -5 + 7$$

- **Add 7 to each side of the equation.**

$$3x = 2$$

- **Simplify.**

$$\frac{3x}{3} = \frac{2}{3}$$

- **Divide each side of the equation by 3.**

$$x = \frac{2}{3}$$

- **Simplify. Now the equation is in the form *variable* = *constant*.**

The solution is $\frac{2}{3}$.

- **Write the solution.**

PROBLEM 1 Solve: $5x + 7 = 10$

Solution See page S6.

EXAMPLE 2 Solve: $5 = 9 - 2x$

Solution

$$5 = 9 - 2x$$

$$5 - 9 = 9 - 9 - 2x$$ • Subtract 9 from each side of the equation.

$$-4 = -2x$$ • Simplify.

$$\frac{-4}{-2} = \frac{-2x}{-2}$$ • Divide each side of the equation by -2.

$$2 = x$$ • Simplify.

The solution is 2. • Write the solution.

PROBLEM 2 Solve: $11 = 11 + 3x$

Solution See page S6.

Note in Example 4 in the Introduction to Equations section that the original equation, $\frac{1}{2} = x + \frac{2}{3}$, contained fractions with denominators of 2 and 3. The least common multiple of 2 and 3 is 6. The least common multiple has the property that both 2 and 3 will divide evenly into it. Therefore, if both sides of the equation are multiplied by 6, both of the denominators will divide evenly into 6. The result is an equation that does not contain any fractions. Multiplying an equation that contains fractions by the LCM of the denominators is called **clearing denominators.** It is an alternative method of solving an equation that contains fractions.

Solve: $\frac{1}{2} = x + \frac{2}{3}$

$$\frac{1}{2} = x + \frac{2}{3}$$

Multiply both sides of the equation by 6, the LCM of the denominators.

$$6\left(\frac{1}{2}\right) = 6\left(x + \frac{2}{3}\right)$$

Simplify each side of the equation. Use the Distributive Property on the right side of the equation.

$$3 = 6(x) + 6\left(\frac{2}{3}\right)$$

Note that multiplying both sides of the equation by the LCM of the denominators eliminated the fractions.

$$3 = 6x + 4$$

Solve the resulting equation.

$$3 - 4 = 6x + 4 - 4$$

$$-1 = 6x$$

$$\frac{-1}{6} = \frac{6x}{6}$$

$$-\frac{1}{6} = x$$

The solution is $-\frac{1}{6}$.

EXAMPLE 3 Solve: $\frac{2}{3} + \frac{1}{4}x = -\frac{1}{3}$

Solution

$$\frac{2}{3} + \frac{1}{4}x = -\frac{1}{3}$$

- **The equation contains fractions. Find the LCM of the denominators.**

$$12\left(\frac{2}{3} + \frac{1}{4}x\right) = 12\left(-\frac{1}{3}\right)$$

- **The LCM of 3 and 4 is 12. Multiply each side of the equation by 12.**

$$12\left(\frac{2}{3}\right) + 12\left(\frac{1}{4}x\right) = -4$$

- **Use the Distributive Property to multiply the left side of the equation by 12.**

$$8 + 3x = -4$$

- **The equation now contains no fractions.**

$$8 - 8 + 3x = -4 - 8$$
$$3x = -12$$
$$\frac{3x}{3} = \frac{-12}{3}$$
$$x = -4$$

The solution is -4.

PROBLEM 3 Solve: $\frac{5}{2} - \frac{2}{3}x = \frac{1}{2}$

Solution See page S6.

OBJECTIVE 2 Solve equations of the form $ax + b = cx + d$

In solving an equation of the form $ax + b = cx + d$, the goal is to rewrite the equation in the form *variable* = *constant*. Begin by rewriting the equation so that there is only one variable term in the equation. Then rewrite the equation so that there is only one constant term.

Solve: $4x - 5 = 6x + 11$

$$4x - 5 = 6x + 11$$

Subtract $6x$ from each side of the equation.

$$4x - 6x - 5 = 6x - 6x + 11$$

Simplify. Now there is only one variable term in the equation.

$$-2x - 5 = 11$$

Add 5 to each side of the equation.

$$-2x - 5 + 5 = 11 + 5$$

Simplify. Now there is only one constant term in the equation.

$$-2x = 16$$

Divide each side of the equation by -2.

$$\frac{-2x}{-2} = \frac{16}{-2}$$

Simplify. Now the equation is in the form *variable* = *constant*.

$$x = -8$$

Check

$$\begin{array}{r|l} 4x - 5 = & 6x + 11 \\ \hline 4(-8) - 5 & 6(-8) + 11 \\ -32 - 5 & -48 + 11 \\ -37 = & -37 \end{array}$$

Write the solution. The solution is -8.

Take Note

As shown below, we could have rewritten the equation in the form *constant* = *variable* by subtracting $4x$ from each side, adding 7 to each side, and then dividing each side by 4.

$$4x - 3 = 8x - 7$$
$$-3 = 4x - 7$$
$$4 = 4x$$
$$1 = x$$

The solution is 1.

EXAMPLE 4 Solve: $4x - 3 = 8x - 7$

Solution

$$4x - 3 = 8x - 7$$

$$4x - 8x - 3 = 8x - 8x - 7$$
- **Subtract $8x$ from each side of the equation.**

$$-4x - 3 = -7$$
- **Simplify. Now there is only one variable term in the equation.**

$$-4x - 3 + 3 = -7 + 3$$
- **Add 3 to each side of the equation.**

$$-4x = -4$$
- **Simplify. Now there is only one constant term in the equation.**

$$\frac{-4x}{-4} = \frac{-4}{-4}$$
- **Divide each side of the equation by -4.**

$$x = 1$$
- **Simplify. Now the equation is in the form *variable* = *constant*.**

The solution is 1.
- **Write the solution.**

PROBLEM 4 Solve: $5x + 4 = 6 + 10x$

Solution See page S7.

OBJECTIVE 3 Solve equations containing parentheses

When an equation contains parentheses, one of the steps in solving the equation requires the use of the Distributive Property. The Distributive Property is used to remove parentheses from a variable expression. $a(b + c) = ab + ac$

Solve: $4 + 5(2x - 3) = 3(4x - 1)$

$$4 + 5(2x - 3) = 3(4x - 1)$$

Use the Distributive Property to remove parentheses.
$$4 + 10x - 15 = 12x - 3$$

Simplify.
$$10x - 11 = 12x - 3$$

Subtract $12x$ from each side of the equation.
$$10x - 12x - 11 = 12x - 12x - 3$$

Simplify. Now there is only one variable term in the equation.
$$-2x - 11 = -3$$

Add 11 to each side of the equation.
$$-2x - 11 + 11 = -3 + 11$$

Simplify. Now there is only one constant term in the equation.	$-2x = 8$
Divide each side of the equation by -2.	$\dfrac{-2x}{-2} = \dfrac{8}{-2}$
Simplify. Now the equation is in the form *variable* = *constant*.	$x = -4$

Check $4 + 5(2x - 3) = 3(4x - 1)$

$4 + 5[2(-4) - 3]$	$3[4(-4) - 1]$
$4 + 5(-8 - 3)$	$3(-16 - 1)$
$4 + 5(-11)$	$3(-17)$
$4 - 55$	-51

$$-51 = -51$$

Write the solution. The solution is -4.

In Chapter 2, we discussed the use of a graphing calculator to evaluate variable expressions. The same procedure can be used to check the solution of an equation. Consider the example above. After we divide both sides of the equation by -2, the solution appears to be -4. To check this solution, store the value of x, -4, in the calculator. Evaluate the expression on the left side of the original equation: $4 + 5(2x - 3)$. The result is -51. Now evaluate the expression on the right side of the original equation: $3(4x - 1)$. The result is -51. Because the results are equal, the solution -4 checks. See the Appendix for a description of keystroking procedures.

EXAMPLE 5 Solve: $3x - 4(2 - x) = 3(x - 2) - 4$

Solution

$$3x - 4(2 - x) = 3(x - 2) - 4$$

$$3x - 8 + 4x = 3x - 6 - 4$$

• **Use the Distributive Property to remove parentheses.**

$$7x - 8 = 3x - 10$$

• **Simplify.**

$$7x - 3x - 8 = 3x - 3x - 10$$

• **Subtract $3x$ from each side of the equation.**

$$4x - 8 = -10$$

$$4x - 8 + 8 = -10 + 8$$

• **Add 8 to each side of the equation.**

$$4x = -2$$

$$\frac{4x}{4} = \frac{-2}{4}$$

• **Divide each side of the equation by 4.**

$$x = -\frac{1}{2}$$

• **The equation is in the form *variable* = *constant*.**

The solution is $-\frac{1}{2}$.

PROBLEM 5 Solve: $5x - 4(3 - 2x) = 2(3x - 2) + 6$

Solution See page S7.

EXAMPLE 6 Solve: $3[2 - 4(2x - 1)] = 4x - 10$

Solution

$$3[2 - 4(2x - 1)] = 4x - 10$$

$$3[2 - 8x + 4] = 4x - 10$$

- Use the Distributive Property to remove the parentheses.

$$3[6 - 8x] = 4x - 10$$

- Simplify inside the brackets.

$$18 - 24x = 4x - 10$$

- Use the Distributive Property to remove the brackets.

$$18 - 24x - 4x = 4x - 4x - 10$$

- Subtract $4x$ from each side of the equation.

$$18 - 28x = -10$$

$$18 - 18 - 28x = -10 - 18$$

- Subtract 18 from each side of the equation.

$$-28x = -28$$

$$\frac{-28x}{-28} = \frac{-28}{-28}$$

- Divide each side of the equation by -28.

$$x = 1$$

The solution is 1.

PROBLEM 6 Solve: $-2[3x - 5(2x - 3)] = 3x - 8$

Solution See page S7.

OBJECTIVE 4 Application problems

EXAMPLE 7 A company uses the equation $V = C - 6000t$ to determine the depreciated value V, after t years, of a milling machine that originally cost C dollars. If a milling machine originally cost \$50,000, in how many years will the depreciated value of the machine be \$38,000?

Strategy To find the number of years, replace C with 50,000 and V with 38,000 in the given equation, and solve for t.

Solution

$$V = C - 6000t$$

$$38{,}000 = 50{,}000 - 6000t$$

$$38{,}000 - 50{,}000 = 50{,}000 - 50{,}000 - 6000t$$

$$-12{,}000 = -6000t$$

$$\frac{-12{,}000}{-6000} = \frac{-6000t}{-6000}$$

$$2 = t$$

The depreciated value of the machine will be \$38,000 in 2 years.

PROBLEM 7 The value V of an investment of \$7500 at an annual simple interest rate of 6% is given by the equation $V = 450t + 7500$, where t is the amount of time, in years, that the money is invested. In how many years will the value of a \$7500 investment be \$10,200?

Solution See page S7.

Take Note

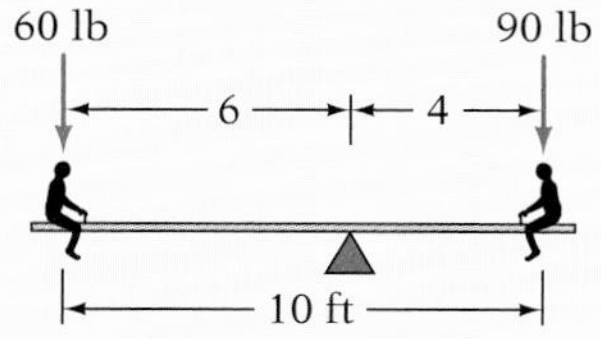

This system balances because

$$F_1x = F_2(d - x)$$
$$60(6) = 90(10 - 6)$$
$$60(6) = 90(4)$$
$$360 = 360$$

A lever system is shown below. It consists of a lever, or bar; a fulcrum; and two forces, F_1 and F_2. The distance d represents the length of the lever, x represents the distance from F_1 to the fulcrum, and $d - x$ represents the distance from F_2 to the fulcrum.

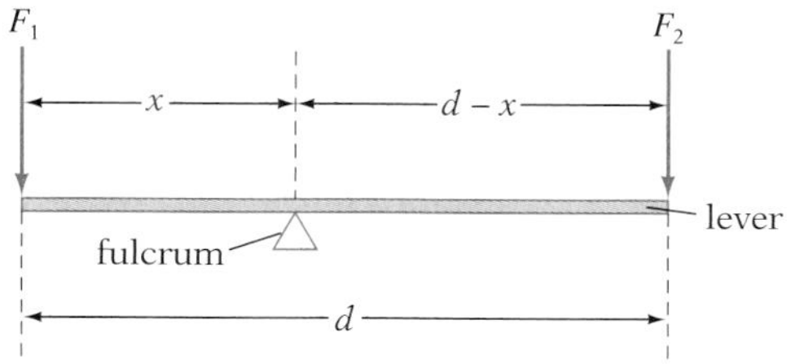

A principle of physics states that when the lever system balances,

$$\boldsymbol{F_1x = F_2(d - x)}$$

EXAMPLE 8 A lever is 10 ft long. A force of 100 lb is applied to one end of the lever, and a force of 400 lb is applied to the other end. When the system balances, how far is the fulcrum from the 100-pound force?

Strategy Draw a diagram of the situation.

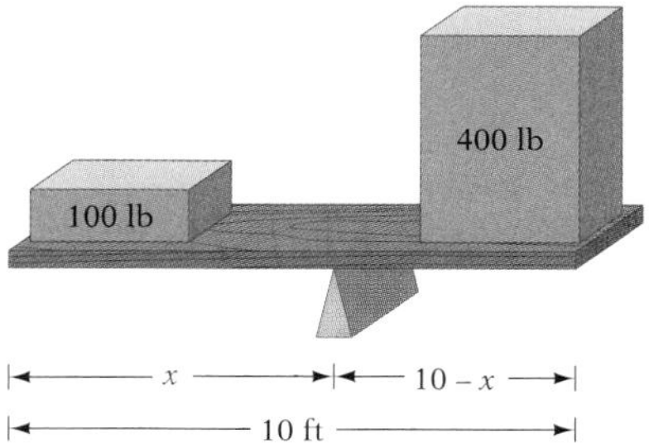

The lever is 10 ft long, so $d = 10$. One force is 100 lb, so $F_1 = 100$. The other force is 400 lb, so $F_2 = 400$. To find the distance of the fulcrum from the 100-pound force, replace the variables F_1, F_2, and d in the lever-system equation with the given values, and solve for x.

Solution

$$\begin{aligned}
F_1x &= F_2(d - x)\\
100x &= 400(10 - x)\\
100x &= 4000 - 400x\\
100x + 400x &= 4000 - 400x + 400x\\
500x &= 4000\\
\frac{500x}{500} &= \frac{4000}{500}\\
x &= 8
\end{aligned}$$

The fulcrum is 8 ft from the 100-pound force.

PROBLEM 8 A lever is 14 ft long. At a distance of 6 ft from the fulcrum, a force of 40 lb is applied. How large a force must be applied to the other end of the lever so that the system will balance?

Solution See page S7.

3.2 Concept Review

Determine whether the statement is always true, sometimes true, or never true.

1. The same variable term can be added to both sides of an equation without changing the solution of the equation.

2. The same variable term can be subtracted from both sides of an equation without changing the solution of the equation.

3. An equation of the form $ax + b = c$ cannot be solved if a is a negative number.

4. The solution of the equation $\frac{x}{3} = 0$ is 0.

5. The solution of the equation $\frac{x}{0} = 3$ is 0.

6. In solving an equation of the form $ax + b = cx + d$, the goal is to rewrite the equation in the form *variable* = *constant*.

7. In solving an equation of the form $ax + b = cx + d$, subtracting cx from each side of the equation results in an equation with only one variable term in it.

3.2 Exercises

1 Solve equations of the form $ax + b = c$

1. The first step in solving the equation $5 + 8x = 29$ is to subtract __?__ from each side of the equation. The second step is to divide each side of the equation by __?__.

2. To clear denominators from the equation $\frac{x}{9} + 2 = \frac{1}{6}$, multiply each side of the equation by __?__, the least common multiple of the denominators 9 and 6.

Complete Exercises 3 and 4 without actually finding the solutions.

3. Is the solution of the equation $15x + 73 = -347$ positive or negative?

4. Is the solution of the equation $17 = 25 - 40a$ positive or negative?

Solve and check.

5. $3x + 1 = 10$ **6.** $4y + 3 = 11$ **7.** $2a - 5 = 7$ **8.** $5m - 6 = 9$

9. $5 = 4x + 9$ **10.** $2 = 5b + 12$ **11.** $13 = 9 + 4z$ **12.** $7 - c = 9$

13. $2 - x = 11$ **14.** $4 - 3w = -2$ **15.** $5 - 6x = -13$ **16.** $8 - 3t = 2$

17. $-5d + 3 = -12$ **18.** $-8x - 3 = -19$ **19.** $-7n - 4 = -25$ **20.** $-12x + 30 = -6$

21. $-13 = -11y + 9$ **22.** $2 = 7 - 5a$ **23.** $3 = 11 - 4n$ **24.** $-35 = -6b + 1$

25. $-8x + 3 = -29$ **26.** $-3m - 21 = 0$ **27.** $7x - 3 = 3$ **28.** $8y + 3 = 7$

29. $6a + 5 = 9$ **30.** $3m + 4 = 11$ **31.** $11 = 15 + 4n$ **32.** $4 = 2 - 3c$

33. $9 - 4x = 6$ **34.** $7 - 8z = 0$ **35.** $1 - 3x = 0$ **36.** $6y - 5 = -7$

37. $8b - 3 = -9$ **38.** $5 - 6m = 2$ **39.** $7 - 9a = 4$ **40.** $9 = -12c + 5$

41. $10 = -18x + 7$ **42.** $2y + \frac{1}{3} = \frac{7}{3}$ **43.** $3x - \frac{5}{6} = \frac{13}{6}$ **44.** $5y + \frac{3}{7} = \frac{3}{7}$

45. $9x + \frac{4}{5} = \frac{4}{5}$ **46.** $4 = 7 - 2w$ **47.** $7 = 9 - 5a$ **48.** $-6y + 5 = 13$

49. $-4x + 3 = 9$ **50.** $\frac{1}{2}a - 3 = 1$ **51.** $\frac{1}{3}m - 1 = 5$ **52.** $\frac{2}{5}y + 4 = 6$

53. $\frac{3}{4}n + 7 = 13$ **54.** $-\frac{2}{3}x + 1 = 7$ **55.** $-\frac{3}{8}b + 4 = 10$ **56.** $\frac{x}{4} - 6 = 1$

57. $\frac{y}{5} - 2 = 3$ **58.** $\frac{2x}{3} - 1 = 5$ **59.** $\frac{3c}{7} - 1 = 8$ **60.** $4 - \frac{3}{4}z = -2$

61. $3 - \frac{4}{5}w = -9$ **62.** $5 + \frac{2}{3}y = 3$ **63.** $17 + \frac{5}{8}x = 7$ **64.** $17 = 7 - \frac{5}{6}t$

65. $\frac{2}{3} = y - \frac{1}{2}$ **66.** $\frac{3}{4} = \frac{1}{12}x + 2$ **67.** $\frac{3}{8} = \frac{5}{12} - \frac{1}{3}b$ **68.** $\frac{2}{3} = \frac{3}{4} - \frac{1}{2}y$

69. $7 = \frac{2x}{5} + 4$ **70.** $5 - \frac{4c}{7} = 8$ **71.** $7 - \frac{5}{9}y = 9$

72. $6a + 3 + 2a = 11$

73. $5y + 9 + 2y = 23$

74. $7x - 4 - 2x = 6$

75. $11z - 3 - 7z = 9$

76. $2x - 6x + 1 = 9$

77. $b - 8b + 1 = -6$

78. $-1 = 5m + 7 - m$

79. $8 = 4n - 6 + 3n$

80. $0.15y + 0.025 = -0.074$

81. $1.2x - 3.44 = 1.3$

82. $3.5 = 3.5 + 0.076x$

83. $-6.5 = 4.3y - 3.06$

Solve.

84. If $2x - 3 = 7$, evaluate $3x + 4$.

85. If $3x + 5 = -4$, evaluate $2x - 5$.

86. If $4 - 5x = -1$, evaluate $x^2 - 3x + 1$.

87. If $2 - 3x = 11$, evaluate $x^2 + 2x - 3$.

2 Solve equations of the form *ax* + *b* = *cx* + *d*

88. To solve the equation $7x - 4 = 2x + 6$, we subtract $2x$ from each side of the equation and add 4 to each side of the equation. The resulting equation is __?__ = __?__. The solution of the equation is __?__.

89. To solve $\frac{1}{6}x - 7 = \frac{3}{4}x$, begin by clearing denominators:

$(\underline{\ ?\ })\left(\frac{1}{6}x - 7\right) = (\underline{\ ?\ })\left(\frac{3}{4}x\right)$	**• Multiply each side of the equation by the LCM of the denominators, 6 and 4.**
$12\left(\frac{1}{6}x\right) - (12)(7) = 9x$	**• Use the __?__ Property on the left side of the equation. Simplify the right side.**
$\underline{\ ?\ }\ x - \underline{\ ?\ } = 9x$	**• Simplify.**
$2x - \underline{\ ?\ } - 84 = 9x - \underline{\ ?\ }$	**• Subtract 2*x* from each side of the equation.**
$-84 = \underline{\ ?\ }\ x$	**• Simplify.**
$-\frac{84}{7} = \frac{7x}{7}$	**• __?__ each side of the equation by __?__.**
$\underline{\ ?\ } = x$	**• Simplify.**

Complete Exercises 90 and 91 without actually finding the solutions.

90. Describe the step that will allow you to rewrite the equation $2x - 3 = 7x + 12$ so that it has one variable term with a positive coefficient.

91. If you rewrite the equation $8 - y = y + 6$ so that it has one variable term on the left side of the equation, what will be the coefficient of the variable?

Solve and check.

92. $8x + 5 = 4x + 13$

93. $6y + 2 = y + 17$

94. $7m + 4 = 6m + 7$

95. $11n + 3 = 10n + 11$

96. $5x - 4 = 2x + 5$

97. $9a - 10 = 3a + 2$

98. $12y - 4 = 9y - 7$

99. $13b - 1 = 4b - 19$

100. $15x - 2 = 4x - 13$

101. $7a - 5 = 2a - 20$

102. $3x + 1 = 11 - 2x$

103. $n - 2 = 6 - 3n$

104. $2x - 3 = -11 - 2x$

105. $4y - 2 = -16 - 3y$

106. $2b + 3 = 5b + 12$

107. $m + 4 = 3m + 8$

108. $4x - 7 = 5x + 1$

109. $6d - 2 = 7d + 5$

110. $4y - 8 = y - 8$

111. $5a + 7 = 2a + 7$

112. $6 - 5x = 8 - 3x$

113. $10 - 4n = 16 - n$

114. $2x - 4 = 6x$

115. $2b - 10 = 7b$

116. $8m = 3m + 20$

117. $9y = 5y + 16$

118. $-x - 4 = -3x - 16$

119. $8 - 4x = 18 - 5x$

120. $6 - 10a = 8 - 9a$

121. $5 - 7m = 2 - 6m$

122. $8b + 5 = 5b + 7$

123. $6y - 1 = 2y + 2$

124. $7x - 8 = x - 3$

125. $10x - 3 = 3x - 1$

126. $5n + 3 = 2n + 1$

127. $8a - 2 = 4a - 5$

128. $\frac{1}{5}d = \frac{1}{2}d + 3$

129. $\frac{3}{4}x = \frac{1}{12}x + 2$

130. $\frac{2}{3}a = \frac{1}{5}a + 7$

131. $\frac{4}{5}c - 7 = \frac{1}{10}c$

132. $\frac{1}{2}y = 10 - \frac{1}{3}y$

133. $\frac{2}{3}b = 2 - \frac{5}{6}b$

134. $8.7y = 3.9y + 9.6$

135. $4.5x - 5.4 = 2.7x$

136. $5.6x = 7.2x - 6.4$

Solve.

137. If $5x = 3x - 8$, evaluate $4x + 2$.

138. If $7x + 3 = 5x - 7$, evaluate $3x - 2$.

139. If $2 - 6a = 5 - 3a$, evaluate $4a^2 - 2a + 1$.

140. If $1 - 5c = 4 - 4c$, evaluate $3c^2 - 4c + 2$.

3 Solve equations containing parentheses

141. Use the Distributive Property to remove the parentheses from the equation $4x + 3(x + 6) = 74$: $4x +$ __?__ $+$ __?__ $= 74$.

142. Use the Distributive Property to remove the parentheses from the equation $9x - 5(4 - x) = 2(x + 2)$:
$9x -$ __?__ $+$ __?__ $=$ __?__ $+$ __?__.

143. In each of the following equations, y is the same positive integer. For which equations will x have the same solution?

a. $5 - 2(x - 1) = y$ **b.** $3(x - 1) = y$
c. $5 - 2x + 2 = y$ **d.** $5 - 2x + 1 = y$

144. In solving the equation $9 - (8 - x) = 5x - 1$, how many times will you use the Distributive Property to remove parentheses?

Solve and check.

145. $5x + 2(x + 1) = 23$

146. $6y + 2(2y + 3) = 16$

147. $9n - 3(2n - 1) = 15$

148. $12x - 2(4x - 6) = 28$

149. $7a - (3a - 4) = 12$

150. $9m - 4(2m - 3) = 11$

151. $5(3 - 2y) + 4y = 3$

152. $4(1 - 3x) + 7x = 9$

153. $10x + 1 = 2(3x + 5) - 1$

154. $5y - 3 = 7 + 4(y - 2)$

155. $4 - 3a = 7 - 2(2a + 5)$

156. $9 - 5x = 12 - (6x + 7)$

157. $3y - 7 = 5(2y - 3) + 4$

158. $2a - 5 = 4(3a + 1) - 2$

159. $5 - (9 - 6x) = 2x - 2$

160. $7 - (5 - 8x) = 4x + 3$

161. $3[2 - 4(y - 1)] = 3(2y + 8)$

162. $5[2 - (2x - 4)] = 2(5 - 3x)$

163. $3a + 2[2 + 3(a - 1)] = 2(3a + 4)$

164. $5 + 3[1 + 2(2x - 3)] = 6(x + 5)$

165. $-2[4 - (3b + 2)] = 5 - 2(3b + 6)$

166. $-4[x - 2(2x - 3)] + 1 = 2x - 3$

167. $0.3x - 2(1.6x) - 8 = 3(1.9x - 4.1)$

168. $0.56 - 0.4(2.1y + 3) = 0.2(2y + 6.1)$

Solve.

169. If $4 - 3a = 7 - 2(2a + 5)$, evaluate $a^2 + 7a$.

170. If $9 - 5x = 12 - (6x + 7)$, evaluate $x^2 - 3x - 2$.

171. If $2z - 5 = 3(4z + 5)$, evaluate $\frac{z^2}{z - 2}$.

172. If $3n - 7 = 5(2n + 7)$, evaluate $\frac{n^2}{2n - 6}$.

4 Application problems

Physics Black ice is an ice covering on roads that is especially difficult to see and therefore extremely dangerous for motorists. The distance that a car traveling 30 mph will slide after its brakes are applied is related to the outside temperature by the formula $C = \frac{1}{4}D - 45$, where C is the Celsius temperature and D is the distance in feet that the car will slide.

173. Determine the distance a car will slide on black ice when the outside temperature is -3°C.

174. Determine the distance a car will slide on black ice when the outside temperature is -11°C.

Physics The pressure at a certain depth in the ocean can be approximated by the equation $P = \frac{1}{2}D + 15$, where P is the pressure in pounds per square inch and D is the depth in feet.

175. Find the depth of a diver when the pressure on the diver is 35 lb/in^2.

176. Find the depth of a diver when the pressure on the diver is 45 lb/in^2.

Physics The distance s, in feet, that an object will fall in t seconds is given by $s = 16t^2 + vt$, where v is the initial downward velocity of the object in feet per second.

177. Find the initial velocity of an object that falls 80 ft in 2 s.

178. Find the initial velocity of an object that falls 144 ft in 3 s.

Forensic Science Forensic scientists have determined that the equation $H = 2.9L + 78.1$ can be used to approximate the height H, in centimeters, of an adult on the basis of the length L, in centimeters, of its humerus (the bone extending from the shoulder to the elbow).

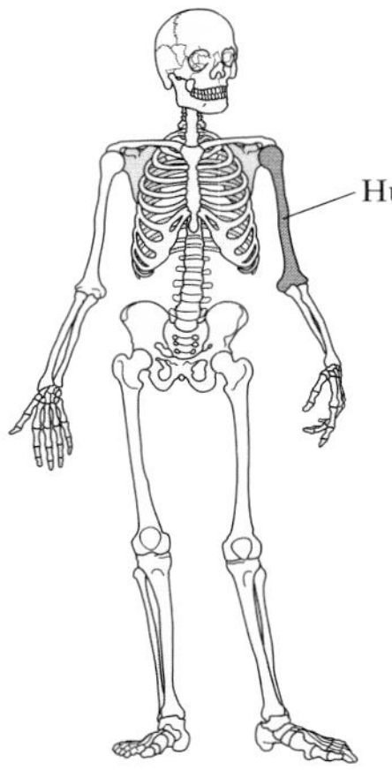

179. Use this formula to approximate the height of an adult whose humerus measures 36 cm.

180. According to this formula, what is the length of the humerus of an adult whose height is 168 cm?

Business The fare, F, to be charged a customer by a taxi company is calculated using the formula $F = 1.50 + 0.95(m - 1)$, where m is the number of miles traveled.

181. A customer is charged \$6.25. How many miles was the passenger driven?

182. A passenger is charged \$9.10. Find the number of miles the customer was driven.

Employment A person's accurate typing speed can be approximated by the equation $S = \frac{W - 5e}{10}$, where S is the accurate typing speed in words per minute, W is the number of words typed in ten minutes, and e is the number of errors made.

183. After taking a 10-minute typing test, a job candidate was told that he had an accurate speed of 35 words per minute. He had typed a total of 390 words. How many errors did he make?

184. A job applicant took a 10-minute typing test and was told that she had an accurate speed of 37 words per minute. If she had typed a total of 400 words, how many errors did she make?

Business A telephone company estimates that the number N of phone calls made per day between two cities of populations P_1 and P_2 that are d miles apart is given by the equation $N = \frac{2.51P_1P_2}{d^2}$.

185. Estimate the population P_2, given that P_1 is 48,000, the number of phone calls is 1,100,000, and the distance between the cities is 75 mi. Round to the nearest thousand.

186. Estimate the population P_1, given that P_2 is 125,000, the number of phone calls is 2,500,000, and the distance between the cities is 50 mi. Round to the nearest thousand.

Business To determine the break-even point, or the number of units that must be sold so that no profit or loss occurs, an economist uses the equation $Px = Cx + F$, where P is the selling price per unit, x is the number of units sold, C is the cost to make each unit, and F is the fixed cost.

187. An economist has determined that the selling price per unit for a television is \$250. The cost to make one television is \$165, and the fixed cost is \$29,750. Find the break-even point.

188. A manufacturing engineer determines that the cost per unit for a compact disc is \$3.35 and that the fixed cost is \$6180. The selling price for the compact disc is \$8.50. Find the break-even point.

Lever Systems Use the lever-system equation $F_1x = F_2(d - x)$.

189. In the lever-system equation $F_1x = F_2(d - x)$, what does x represent? What does d represent? What does $d - x$ represent?

190. Two children sit on a seesaw that is 12 ft long. One child weighs 85 lb, and the other child weighs 65 lb. If x is the distance of the 65-pound child from the fulcrum when the seesaw balances, state the value of each of the other variables in the lever-system formula $F_1x = F_2(d - x)$: $F_1 =$ ___?___, $F_2 =$ ___?___, and $d =$ ___?___.

For Exercises 191 to 193, use the following information: Two people sit on a seesaw that is 8 ft long. The seesaw balances when the fulcrum is 3 ft from one of the people.

191. How far is the fulcrum from the other person?

192. Which person is heavier, the person who is 3 ft from the fulcrum or the other person?

193. If the two people switch places, will the seesaw still balance?

194. Suppose an 80-pound child is sitting at one end of a 7-foot seesaw, and a 60-pound child is sitting at the other end. The 80-pound child is 3 ft from the fulcrum. Use the lever-system equation to explain why the seesaw balances.

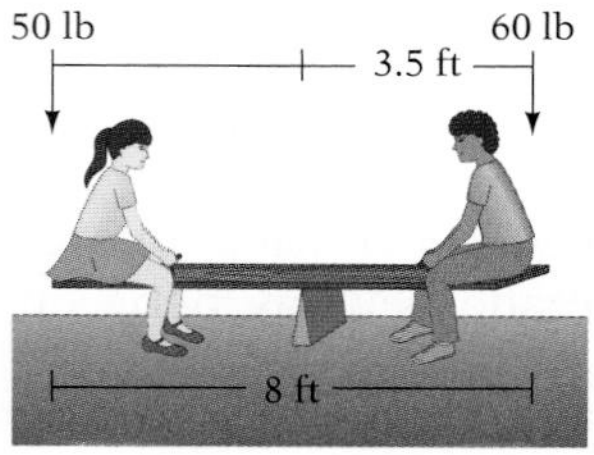

195. Two children are sitting 8 ft apart on a seesaw. One child weighs 60 lb and the second child weighs 50 lb. The fulcrum is 3.5 ft from the child weighing 60 lb. Is the seesaw balanced?

196. An adult and a child are on a seesaw that is 14 ft long. The adult weighs 175 lb and the child weighs 70 lb. How many feet from the child must the fulcrum be placed so that the seesaw balances?

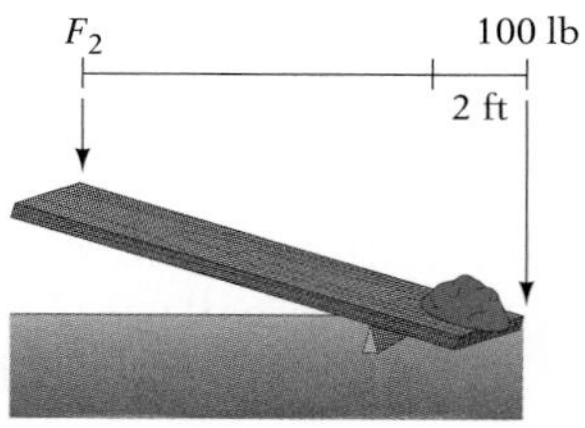

197. A lever 10 ft long is used to balance a 100-pound rock. The fulcrum is placed 2 ft from the rock. What force must be applied to the other end of the lever to balance the rock?

198. A 50-pound weight is applied to the left end of a seesaw that is 10 ft long. The fulcrum is 4 ft from the 50-pound weight. A weight of 30 lb is applied to the right end of the seesaw. Is the 30-pound weight adequate to balance the seesaw?

199. In preparation for a stunt, two acrobats are standing on a plank that is 18 ft long. One acrobat weighs 128 lb, and the second acrobat weighs 160 lb. How far from the 128-pound acrobat must the fulcrum be placed so that the acrobats are balanced on the plank?

200. A screwdriver 9 in. long is used as a lever to open a can of paint. The tip of the screwdriver is placed under the lip of the lid with the fulcrum 0.15 in. from the lip. A force of 30 lb is applied to the other end of the screwdriver. Find the force on the lip of the lid.

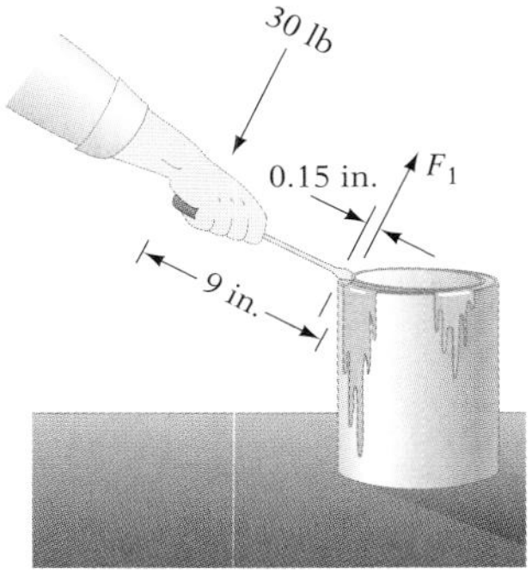

3.2 Applying Concepts

Solve. If the equation has no solution, write "No solution."

201. $3(2x - 1) - (6x - 4) = -9$

202. $\frac{1}{5}(25 - 10b) + 4 = \frac{1}{3}(9b - 15) - 6$

203. $3[4(w + 2) - (w + 1)] = 5(2 + w)$

204. $\frac{2(5x - 6) - 3(x - 4)}{7} = x + 2$

205. Solve for x: $32{,}166 \div x = 518$ remainder 50

206. One-half of a certain number equals two-thirds of the same number. Find the number.

207. Write an equation of the form $ax + b = cx + d$ that has 4 as a solution.

208. Does the sentence "Solve $3x - 4(x - 1)$" make sense? Why or why not?

209. The equation $x = x + 1$ has no solution, whereas the solution of the equation $2x + 1 = 1$ is zero. Is there a difference between no solution and a solution of zero? Explain your answer.

3.3 Inequalities

OBJECTIVE 1 Solve inequalities using the Addition Property of Inequalities

An expression that contains the symbol $>$, $<$, $\geq$, or $\leq$ is called an **inequality.** An inequality expresses the relative order of two mathematical expressions. The expressions can be either numerical or variable expressions.

$$\left.\begin{array}{l} 4 > 2 \\ 3x \leq 7 \\ x^2 - 2x > y + 4 \end{array}\right\} \text{Inequalities}$$

The **solution set of an inequality** is a set of numbers, each element of which, when substituted for the variable, results in a true inequality. The solution set of an inequality can be graphed on the number line.

The graph of the solution set of $x > 1$ is shown at the right. The solution set is the real numbers greater than 1. The parenthesis on the graph indicates that 1 is not included in the solution set.

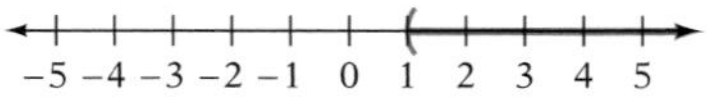

The graph of the solution set of $x \geq 1$ is shown at the right. The bracket at 1 indicates that 1 is included in the solution set.

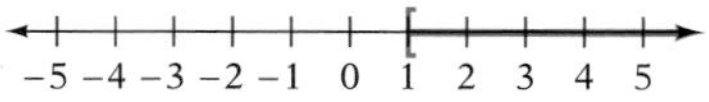

The graph of the solution set of $x < -1$ is shown at the right. The numbers less than -1 are to the left of -1 on the number line.

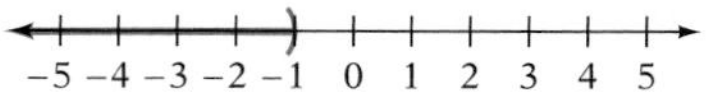

EXAMPLE 1 Graph: $x < 3$

Solution

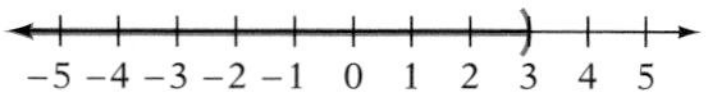

- **The solution set is the numbers less than 3.**

PROBLEM 1 Graph: $x > -2$

Solution See page S7.

The inequality at the right is true if the variable is replaced by 7, 9.3, or $\frac{15}{2}$.

$$x + 3 > 8$$

$$\left.\begin{array}{r} 7 + 3 > 8 \\ 9.3 + 3 > 8 \\ \frac{15}{2} + 3 > 8 \end{array}\right\} \text{True inequalities}$$

The inequality $x + 3 > 8$ is false if the variable is replaced by 4, 1.5, or $-\frac{1}{2}$.

$$\left.\begin{array}{r} 4 + 3 > 8 \\ 1.5 + 3 > 8 \\ -\frac{1}{2} + 3 > 8 \end{array}\right\} \text{False inequalities}$$

There are many values of the variable x that will make the inequality $x + 3 > 8$ true. The solution set of $x + 3 > 8$ is any number greater than 5.

The graph of the solution set of $x + 3 > 8$ is shown at the right.

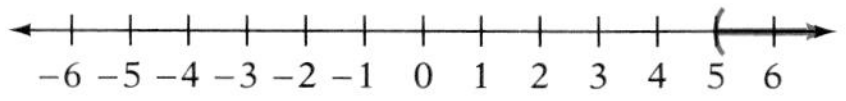

In solving an inequality, the goal is to rewrite the given inequality in the form *variable* > *constant* or *variable* < *constant*. The Addition Property of Inequalities is used to rewrite an inequality in this form.

Addition Property of Inequalities

The same number can be added to each side of an inequality without changing the solution set of the inequality.

If $a > b$, then $a + c > b + c$.

If $a < b$, then $a + c < b + c$.

The Addition Property of Inequalities also holds true for an inequality containing the symbol $\geq$ or $\leq$.

The Addition Property of Inequalities is used when, in order to rewrite an inequality in the form *variable* > *constant* or *variable* < *constant*, a term must be removed from one side of the inequality. Add the opposite of the term to each side of the inequality.

Because subtraction is defined in terms of addition, the Addition Property of Inequalities makes it possible to subtract the same number from each side of an inequality without changing the solution set of the inequality.

Solve: $x + 4 < 5$

$$x + 4 < 5$$

Subtract 4 from each side of the inequality.

$$x + 4 - 4 < 5 - 4$$

Simplify.

$$x < 1$$

The graph of the solution set of $x + 4 < 5$ is shown at the right.

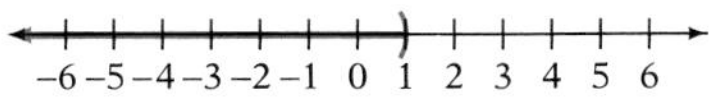

Solve: $5x - 6 \leq 4x - 4$

$$5x - 6 \leq 4x - 4$$

Subtract $4x$ from each side of the inequality.

$$5x - 4x - 6 \leq 4x - 4x - 4$$

Simplify.

$$x - 6 \leq -4$$

Add 6 to each side of the inequality.

$$x - 6 + 6 \leq -4 + 6$$

Simplify.

$$x \leq 2$$

EXAMPLE 2 Solve and graph the solution set of $x + 5 > 3$.

Solution

$$x + 5 > 3$$
$$x + 5 - 5 > 3 - 5 \quad \text{• Subtract 5 from each side of the inequality.}$$
$$x > -2$$

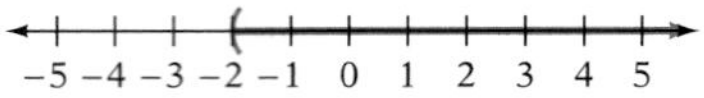

PROBLEM 2 Solve and graph the solution set of $x + 2 < -2$.

Solution See page S7.

EXAMPLE 3 Solve: $7x - 14 \le 6x - 16$

Solution

$$7x - 14 \le 6x - 16$$
$$7x - 6x - 14 \le 6x - 6x - 16 \quad \text{• Subtract } 6x \text{ from each side of the inequality.}$$
$$x - 14 \le -16$$
$$x - 14 + 14 \le -16 + 14 \quad \text{• Add 14 to each side of the inequality.}$$
$$x \le -2$$

PROBLEM 3 Solve: $5x + 3 > 4x + 5$

Solution See page S7.

OBJECTIVE 2 Solve inequalities using the Multiplication Property of Inequalities

In solving an inequality, the goal is to rewrite the given inequality in the form *variable* > *constant* or *variable* < *constant*. The Multiplication Property of Inequalities is used when, in order to rewrite an inequality in this form, a coefficient must be removed from one side of the inequality.

Take Note

$c > 0$ means c is a positive number.

The inequality symbols are not changed.

Multiplication Property of Inequalities—Rule 1

Each side of an inequality can be multiplied by the same positive number without changing the solution set of the inequality.

If $a > b$ and $c > 0$, then $ac > bc$. If $a < b$ and $c > 0$, then $ac < bc$.

$$5 > 4 \quad \text{• A true inequality}$$
$$5(2) > 4(2) \quad \text{• Multiply by } \textit{positive } 2.$$
$$10 > 8 \quad \text{• A true inequality}$$

Take Note

$c < 0$ means c is a negative number.

The inequality symbol is reversed in each case.

Multiplication Property of Inequalities—Rule 2

If each side of an inequality is multiplied by the same negative number and the inequality symbol is reversed, then the solution set of the inequality is not changed.

If $a > b$ and $c < 0$, then $ac < bc$. If $a < b$ and $c < 0$, then $ac > bc$.

$6 < 9$	• **A true inequality**
$6(-3) > 9(-3)$	• **Multiply by *negative* 3 and reverse the inequality symbol.**
$-18 > -27$	• **A true inequality**

The Multiplication Property of Inequalities also holds true for an inequality containing the symbol $\geq$ or $\leq$.

Solve: $-\frac{3}{2}x \leq 6$

Multiply each side of the inequality by the reciprocal of the coefficient $-\frac{3}{2}$. Because $-\frac{2}{3}$ is a negative number, the inequality symbol must be reversed.

$$-\frac{3}{2}x \leq 6$$

$$-\frac{2}{3}\left(-\frac{3}{2}x\right) \geq -\frac{2}{3}(6)$$

Simplify.

$$x \geq -4$$

The graph of the solution set of $-\frac{3}{2}x \leq 6$ is shown at the right.

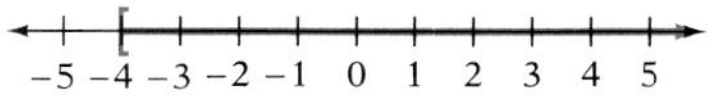

> **Take Note**
>
> Any time an inequality is multiplied or divided by a negative number, the inequality symbol must be reversed. Compare these two examples:
>
> $2x < -4$, $\frac{2x}{2} < \frac{-4}{2}$, $x < -2$ — Divide each side by *positive* 2. The inequality symbol is *not* reversed.
>
> $-2x < 4$, $\frac{-2x}{-2} > \frac{4}{-2}$, $x > -2$ — Divide each side by *negative* 2. The inequality symbol *is* reversed.

Recall that division is defined in terms of multiplication. Therefore, the Multiplication Property of Inequalities allows each side of an inequality to be divided by the same number. When each side of an inequality is divided by a positive number, the inequality symbol remains the same. When each side of an inequality is divided by a negative number, the inequality symbol must be reversed.

Solve: $-5x > 8$

$$-5x > 8$$

Divide each side of the inequality by -5. Because -5 is a negative number, the inequality symbol must be reversed.

$$\frac{-5x}{-5} < \frac{8}{-5}$$

Simplify.

$$x < -\frac{8}{5}$$

EXAMPLE 4 Solve and graph the solution set of $7x < -14$.

Solution

$7x < -14$

$\frac{7x}{7} < \frac{-14}{7}$ • **Divide each side of the inequality by 7. Because 7 is a *positive* number, do not change the inequality symbol.**

$x < -2$

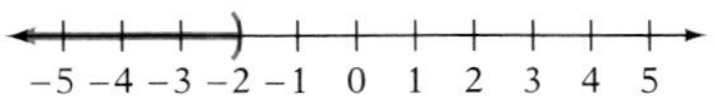

PROBLEM 4 Solve and graph the solution set of $3x < 9$.

Solution See page S7.

EXAMPLE 5 Solve: $-\frac{5}{8}x \le \frac{5}{12}$

Solution

$$-\frac{5}{8}x \le \frac{5}{12}$$

$$-\frac{8}{5}\left(-\frac{5}{8}x\right) \ge -\frac{8}{5}\left(\frac{5}{12}\right)$$

$$x \ge -\frac{2}{3}$$

- **Multiply each side of the inequality by the reciprocal of $-\frac{5}{8}$. $-\frac{8}{5}$ is a negative number. Reverse the inequality symbol.**

PROBLEM 5 Solve: $-\frac{3}{4}x \ge 18$

Solution See page S7.

OBJECTIVE 3 Solve general inequalities

In solving an inequality, it is often necessary to apply both the Addition and the Multiplication Properties of Inequalities.

Take Note

Solving these inequalities is similar to solving the equations in Section 3.2 *except* that when you multiply or divide the inequality by a negative number, you must reverse the inequality symbol.

Solve: $3x - 2 < 5x + 4$

$$3x - 2 < 5x + 4$$

Subtract $5x$ from each side of the inequality. Simplify.

$$3x - 5x - 2 < 5x - 5x + 4$$
$$-2x - 2 < 4$$

Add 2 to each side of the inequality. Simplify.

$$-2x - 2 + 2 < 4 + 2$$
$$-2x < 6$$

Divide each side of the inequality by -2. Because -2 is a negative number, the inequality symbol must be reversed. Simplify.

$$\frac{-2x}{-2} > \frac{6}{-2}$$
$$x > -3$$

EXAMPLE 6 Solve: $7x - 3 \le 3x + 17$

Solution

$$7x - 3 \le 3x + 17$$
$$7x - 3x - 3 \le 3x - 3x + 17$$
$$4x - 3 \le 17$$
$$4x - 3 + 3 \le 17 + 3$$
$$4x \le 20$$
$$\frac{4x}{4} \le \frac{20}{4}$$
$$x \le 5$$

- **Subtract $3x$ from each side of the inequality.**
- **Add 3 to each side of the inequality.**
- **Divide each side of the inequality by 4.**

PROBLEM 6 Solve: $5 - 4x > 9 - 8x$

Solution See page S8.

When an inequality contains parentheses, one of the steps in solving the inequality requires the use of the Distributive Property.

Solve: $-2(x - 7) > 3 - 4(2x - 3)$

$$-2(x - 7) > 3 - 4(2x - 3)$$

Use the Distributive Property to remove parentheses. Simplify.

$$-2x + 14 > 3 - 8x + 12$$
$$-2x + 14 > 15 - 8x$$

Add $8x$ to each side of the inequality. Simplify.

$$-2x + 8x + 14 > 15 - 8x + 8x$$
$$6x + 14 > 15$$

Subtract 14 from each side of the inequality. Simplify.

$$6x + 14 - 14 > 15 - 14$$
$$6x > 1$$

Divide each side of the inequality by 6.

$$\frac{6x}{6} > \frac{1}{6}$$

Simplify.

$$x > \frac{1}{6}$$

EXAMPLE 7 Solve: $3(3 - 2x) \geq -5x - 2(3 - x)$

Solution

$$3(3 - 2x) \geq -5x - 2(3 - x)$$
$$9 - 6x \geq -5x - 6 + 2x$$
- **Use the Distributive Property.**

$$9 - 6x \geq -3x - 6$$
$$9 - 6x + 3x \geq -3x + 3x - 6$$
- **Add $3x$ to each side of the inequality.**

$$9 - 3x \geq -6$$
$$9 - 9 - 3x \geq -6 - 9$$
- **Subtract 9 from each side of the inequality.**

$$-3x \geq -15$$
$$\frac{-3x}{-3} \leq \frac{-15}{-3}$$
- **Divide each side of the inequality by -3. Reverse the inequality symbol.**

$$x \leq 5$$

PROBLEM 7 Solve: $8 - 4(3x + 5) \leq 6(x - 8)$

Solution See page S8.

3.3 Concept Review

Determine whether the statement is always true, sometimes true, or never true.

1. The same variable term can be added to both sides of an inequality without changing the solution set of the inequality.

2. The same variable term can be subtracted from both sides of an inequality without changing the solution set of the inequality.

3. Both sides of an inequality can be multiplied by the same number without changing the solution set of the inequality.

4. Both sides of an inequality can be divided by the same number without changing the solution set of the inequality.

5. Suppose $a > 0$ and $b < 0$. Then $ab > 0$.

6. Suppose $a < 0$. Then $a^2 > 0$.

7. Suppose $a > 0$ and $b < 0$. Then $a^2 > b$.

8. Suppose $a > b$. Then $-a > -b$.

9. Suppose $a < b$. Then $ac < bc$.

10. Suppose $a \neq 0$, $b \neq 0$, and $a > b$. Then $\frac{1}{a} > \frac{1}{b}$.

3.3 Exercises

1 Solve inequalities using the Addition Property of Inequalities

Complete Exercises 1 and 2 by replacing the question mark in the first statement with "includes" or "does not include." Replace the question mark in the second statement with the correct inequality symbol: $>$, $<$, $\geq$, or $\leq$.

1. The graph of the solution set shown at the right __?__ the number -2. In the graph of the solution set of the inequality, x __?__ -2.

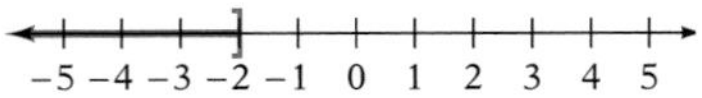

2. The graph of the solution set shown at the right __?__ the number -3. In the graph of the solution set of the inequality, x __?__ -3.

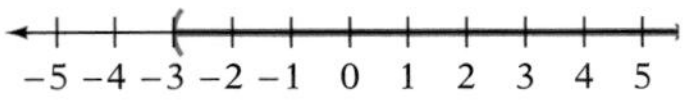

Graph.

3. $x > 2$

4. $x \geq -1$

5. $x \leq 0$

6. $x < 4$

7. Which numbers are solutions of the inequality $x + 7 \leq -3$?
a. -17 **b.** 8 **c.** -10 **d.** 0

8. Which numbers are solutions of the inequality $x - 5 < -6$?
a. 1 **b.** -1 **c.** 12 **d.** -5

Solve and graph the solution set.

9. $x + 1 < 3$

10. $y + 2 < 2$

11. $x - 5 > -2$

12. $x - 3 > -2$

13. $n + 4 \geq 7$

14. $x + 5 \geq 3$

15. $x - 6 \leq -10$

16. $y - 8 \leq -11$

17. $5 + x \geq 4$

18. $-2 + n \geq 0$

For Exercises 19 to 22, state whether the solution set of an inequality in the given form contains only negative numbers, only positive numbers, or both negative and positive numbers.

19. $x + n < a$, where n and a are both positive and $n > a$

20. $x + n > a$, where n and a are both positive and $n < a$

21. $x - n > -a$, where n and a are both positive and $n > a$

22. $x - n > -a$, where n and a are both positive and $n < a$

Solve.

23. $y - 3 \geq -12$

24. $x + 8 \geq -14$

25. $3x - 5 < 2x + 7$

26. $5x + 4 < 4x - 10$

27. $8x - 7 \geq 7x - 2$

28. $3n - 9 \geq 2n - 8$

29. $2x + 4 < x - 7$

30. $9x + 7 < 8x - 7$

31. $4x - 8 \leq 2 + 3x$

32. $5b - 9 < 3 + 4b$

33. $6x + 4 \geq 5x - 2$

34. $7x - 3 \geq 6x - 2$

35. $2x - 12 > x - 10$

36. $3x + 9 > 2x + 7$

37. $d + \frac{1}{2} < \frac{1}{3}$

38. $x - \frac{3}{8} < \frac{5}{6}$

39. $x + \frac{5}{8} \geq -\frac{2}{3}$

40. $y + \frac{5}{12} \geq -\frac{3}{4}$

41. $2x - \frac{1}{2} < x + \frac{3}{4}$

42. $6x - \frac{1}{3} \leq 5x - \frac{1}{2}$

43. $3x + \frac{5}{8} > 2x + \frac{5}{6}$

44. $4b - \frac{7}{12} \geq 3b - \frac{9}{16}$

45. $x + 5.8 \leq 4.6$

46. $n - 3.82 \leq 3.95$

47. $x - 0.23 \leq 0.47$

48. $3.8x < 2.8x - 3.8$

49. $1.2x < 0.2x - 7.3$

2 Solve inequalities using the Multiplication Property of Inequalities

50. Which numbers are solutions of the inequality $5x > 15$?
a. 6 **b.** −4 **c.** 3 **d.** 5

51. Which numbers are solutions of the inequality $-4x \leq 12$?
a. 0 **b.** 3 **c.** −3 **d.** −4

Complete Exercises 52 and 53 by replacing the question mark with "remains the same" or "is reversed."

52. The inequality $x + 4 > -8$ can be solved by subtracting 4 from each side of the inequality. The inequality symbol ___?___.

53. The inequality $-4x > 8$ can be solved by dividing each side of the inequality by -4. The inequality symbol ___?___.

Solve and graph the solution set.

54. $3x < 12$

55. $8x \leq -24$

56. $5y \geq 15$

57. $24x > -48$

58. $16x \leq 16$

59. $3x > 0$

60. $-8x > 8$

61. $-2n \leq -8$

62. $-6b > 24$

63. $-4x < 8$

Solve.

64. $-5y \geq 20$

65. $3x < 5$

66. $7x > 2$

67. $-8x \leq -40$

68. $-6x \leq -40$

69. $10x > -25$

70. $-3x \geq \frac{6}{7}$

71. $-5x \geq \frac{10}{3}$

72. $\frac{5}{6}n < 15$

73. $\frac{2}{3}x < -12$

74. $\frac{5}{6}x < -20$

75. $-\frac{3}{8}x < 6$

76. $\frac{3}{4}x < 12$

77. $\frac{2}{3}y \geq 4$

78. $\frac{5}{8}x \geq 10$

79. $-\frac{2}{3}x \leq 4$

80. $-\frac{3}{7}x \leq 6$

81. $-\frac{2}{11}b \geq -6$

82. $-\frac{4}{7}x \geq -12$

83. $\frac{2}{3}n < \frac{1}{2}$

84. $\frac{3}{5}x > \frac{7}{10}$

85. $-\frac{2}{3}x \geq \frac{4}{7}$

86. $-\frac{3}{8}x \geq \frac{9}{14}$

87. $-\frac{3}{4}y \geq -\frac{5}{8}$

88. $-\frac{8}{9}x \geq -\frac{16}{27}$

89. $\frac{2}{3}x \leq \frac{9}{14}$

90. $\frac{7}{12}x \leq \frac{9}{14}$

91. $-\frac{3}{5}y < \frac{9}{10}$

92. $-\frac{5}{12}y < \frac{1}{6}$

93. $-0.27x < 0.135$

94. $-0.63x < 4.41$

95. $8.4y \geq -6.72$

96. $3.7y \geq -1.48$

97. $1.5x \le 6.30$

98. $2.3x \le 5.29$

99. $-3.9x \ge -19.5$

100. $0.035x < -0.0735$

101. $0.07x < -0.378$

102. $-11.7x \le 4.68$

Complete Exercises 103 and 104 without actually solving the inequalities or using a calcualtor.

103. A number n is a solution of the inequality $-0.8157n < 7.304$. Which of the following must be true?
a. n is positive. **b.** n is negative. **c.** n is 0.
d. n can be positive, negative, or 0.

104. A number n is a solution of the inequality $-917n \ge -10{,}512$. Which of the following must be true?
a. n is positive. **b.** n is negative. **c.** n is 0.
d. n can be positive, negative, or 0.

3 Solve general inequalities

105. In your own words, state the Addition Property of Inequalities and the Multiplication Property of Inequalities.

106. What differentiates solving linear equations from solving linear inequalities?

107. Solve: $9 - 5x \ge -2x$

$9 - 5x \ge -2x$	
$9 - 5x + \underline{\ ?\ } \ge -2x + \underline{\ ?\ }$	• **Add $2x$ to each side of the inequality.**
$9 - \underline{\ ?\ } \ge \underline{\ ?\ }$	• **Simplify.**
$9 - 9 - 3x \ge 0 - 9$	• **Subtract __?__ from each side of the inequality.**
$\underline{\ ?\ } \ge \underline{\ ?\ }$	• **Simplify.**
$\dfrac{-3x}{?} \ \underline{\ ?\ } \ \dfrac{-9}{?}$	• **Divide each side of the inequality by -3. Reverse the inequality symbol.**
$x \le \underline{\ ?\ }$	• **Simplify.**

108. The first step of solving the inequality $8(3x - 1) < 11x + 5$ is to use the __?__ Property to __?__.

Solve.

109. $4x - 8 < 2x$

110. $7x - 4 < 3x$

111. $2x - 8 > 4x$

112. $3y + 2 > 7y$

113. $8 - 3x \le 5x$

114. $10 - 3x \le 7x$

115. $3x + 2 \ge 5x - 8$

116. $2n - 9 \ge 5n + 4$

117. $5x - 2 < 3x - 2$

118. $8x - 9 > 3x - 9$

119. $0.1(180 + x) > x$

120. $x > 0.2(50 + x)$

121. $0.15x + 55 > 0.10x + 80$

122. $-3.6b + 16 < 2.8b + 25.6$

123. $2(3x - 1) > 3x + 4$

124. $5(2x + 7) > -4x - 7$

125. $3(2x - 5) \ge 8x - 5$

126. $5x - 8 \ge 7x - 9$

127. $2(2y - 5) \le 3(5 - 2y)$

128. $2(5x - 8) \le 7(x - 3)$

129. $5(2 - x) > 3(2x - 5)$

130. $4(3d - 1) > 3(2 - 5d)$

131. $5(x - 2) > 9x - 3(2x - 4)$

132. $3x - 2(3x - 5) > 4(2x - 1)$

133. $4 - 3(3 - n) \le 3(2 - 5n)$

134. $15 - 5(3 - 2x) \le 4(x - 3)$

135. $2x - 3(x - 4) \ge 4 - 2(x - 7)$

136. $4 + 2(3 - 2y) \le 4(3y - 5) - 6y$

137. $\frac{1}{2}(9x - 10) \le -\frac{1}{3}(12 - 6x)$

138. $\frac{1}{4}(8 - 12d) < \frac{2}{5}(10d + 15)$

139. $\frac{2}{3}(9t - 15) + 4 < 6 + \frac{3}{4}(4 - 12t)$

140. $\frac{3}{8}(16 - 8c) - 9 \ge \frac{3}{5}(10c - 15) + 7$

141. $3[4(n - 2) - (1 - n)] > 5(n - 4)$

142. $2(m + 7) \le 4[3(m - 2) - 5(1 + m)]$

143. What number is a solution of $3x - 4 \ge 5$ but not a solution of $3x - 4 > 5$?

144. What number is a solution of $8 - 2(x + 6) \le 4$ but not a solution of $8 - 2(x + 6) < 4$?

145. Which inequalities are equivalent to the inequality $-7x - 2 > -4x + 1$?

a. $-3 > -11x$ **b.** $3x > 3$ **c.** $-3 > 3x$ **d.** $3x < -3$

146. Which inequalities are equivalent to the inequality $10 - 7(x - 4) \ge 3$?

a. $-7x + 38 \ge 3$ **b.** $3x - 12 \ge 3$ **c.** $35 \ge 7x$ **d.** $-18 - 7x \ge 3$

3.3 Applying Concepts

Use the roster method to list the set of positive integers that are solutions of the inequality.

147. $7 - 2b \le 15 - 5b$

148. $13 - 8a \ge 2 - 6a$

149. $2(2c - 3) < 5(6 - c)$

150. $-6(2 - d) \ge 4(4d - 9)$

Use the roster method to list the set of integers that are common to the solution sets of the two inequalities.

151. $5x - 12 \le x + 8$
$3x - 4 \ge 2 + x$

152. $6x - 5 > 9x - 2$
$5x - 6 < 8x + 9$

153. $4(x - 2) \le 3x + 5$
$7(x - 3) \ge 5x - 1$

154. $3(x + 2) < 2(x + 4)$
$4(x + 5) > 3(x + 6)$

Graph.

155. $|x| < 3$

156. $|x| < 4$

157. $|x| > 2$

158. $|x| > 1$

Focus on Problem Solving

Analyzing Data

Demography is the statistical study of human populations. Many groups are interested in the size of certain segments of the population and projections of population growth. For example, public school administrators want estimates of the number of school-age children who will be living in their district 10 years from now.

The U.S. government provides estimates of the future population of the United States. You can find these projections at the Census Bureau website at **www.census.gov.** The table below contains data from this website.

	Age	Under 5	5-17	18-24	25-34	35-44	45-54	55-64	65 and older
2010	Male	10,272	26,639	15,388	19,286	19,449	21,706	16,973	16,966
	Female	9,827	25,363	14,774	19,565	19,993	22,455	18,457	22,749
2050	Male	13,748	35,227	18,734	25,034	24,550	22,340	21,127	36,289
	Female	13,165	33,608	18,069	25,425	25,039	23,106	22,517	45,710

Population Projections of the United States, by Age and Sex (in thousands)

For the following exercises, round all percents to the nearest hundredth of a percent.

1. Which of the age groups listed are of interest to public school officials?
2. Which age group is of interest to retirement home administrators?
3. Which age groups are of concern to accountants determining future benefits to be paid out by the Social Security Administration?
4. Which age group is of interest to manufacturers of disposable diapers?
5. Which age groups are of primary concern to college and university admissions officers?
6. In which age groups do males outnumber females? In which do females outnumber males?
7. What percent of the projected population aged 65 and older in the year 2010 is female? Does this percent decrease for the projected population in 2050? If so, by how much?
8. Find the difference between the percent of the population that will be under 18 in 2010 and the percent that will be under 18 in 2050.

9. Assume that the work force consists of people aged 25 to 64. Find the decrease in the percent of the population represented by that age group from 2010 to 2050.

10. Find the increase in the percent of the population represented by those aged 65 and older from 2010 to 2050.

11. Why are the sizes of the current work force and the population aged 65 and older of concern to the Social Security Administration?

12. Describe any patterns you see in the table.

13. Calculate a statistic based on the data in the table and explain why it would be of interest to an institution (such as a school system) or a manufacturer of consumer goods (such as a baby food manufacturer).

Projects & Group Activities

The Consumer Price Index

WEB

The consumer price index (CPI) is a percent that is written without the percent sign. For instance, a CPI of 160.1 means 160.1%. This number means that an item that cost \$100 between 1982 and 1984 (the base years) would cost \$160.10 today. Determining the cost is an application of the basic percent equation.

$$PB = A$$

$$(\text{CPI})(\text{cost in base year}) = \text{cost today}$$

$$1.601(100) = 160.1$$ • **160.1% = 1.601**

The table below gives the CPI for various products in October 2005. If you have Internet access, you can obtain current data for the items below plus other items not on this list by visiting the website of the Bureau of Labor Statistics at **www.bls.gov.**

Product	*CPI*
All items	199.2
Food and beverages	192.5
Housing	198.4
Clothes	122.7
Transportation	184.0
Medical Care	326.2
Energy	204.3
Education: Tuition	454.7

1. Of the items listed, are there any items that cost more than twice as much in 2005 as they cost during the base years? If so, which ones?

2. Of the items listed, are there any items that cost more than one-and-one-half times as much in 2005 as they cost during the base years, but less than twice as much as they cost during the base years? If so, which ones?

3. If the average cost for tuition for one semester at a public college was \$4000 in the base years, what was the average cost for tuition for one semester at a public college in 2005?

4. If a new car cost \$30,000 in 2005, what would a comparable new car have cost during the base years? Use the transportation category.

5. If rent for an urban apartment in 2005 was \$3000, what was the rent for the same apartment during the base years?

6. The CPI for all items in the summer of 1970 was 39.0. What salary in 2005 would have had the same purchasing power as a salary of \$10,000 in 1970?

Chapter 3 Summary

Key Words	*Examples*
An **equation** expresses the equality of two mathematical expressions. [3.1.1, p. 106]	$5(3x - 2) = 4x + 7$ is an equation.
A **solution of an equation** is a number that, when substituted for the variable, results in a true equation. [3.1.1, p. 106]	1 is the solution of the equation $6x - 4 = 2$ because $6(1) - 4 = 2$ is a true equation.
To **solve** an equation means to find a solution of the equation. The goal is to rewrite the equation in the form **variable = constant,** because the constant is the solution. [3.1.2, p. 107]	The equation $x = -9$ is in the form *variable* = *constant*. The constant, -9, is the solution of the equation.
An **inequality** is an expression that contains the symbol $<$, $>$, $\leq$, or $\geq$. [3.3.1, p. 144]	$8x - 1 \geq 5x + 23$ is an inequality.
The **solution set of an inequality** is a set of numbers, each element of which, when substituted for the variable, results in a true inequality. [3.3.1, p. 144]	The solution set of $8x - 1 \geq 5x + 23$ is $x \geq 8$ because every number greater than or equal to 8, when substituted for the variable, results in a true inequality.

Essential Rules and Procedures

The Addition Property of Equations
The same number or variable term can be added to each side of an equation without changing the solution of the equation. [3.1.2, p. 107]

$$\begin{aligned} x + 12 &= -19 \\ x + 12 - 12 &= -19 - 12 \\ x &= -31 \end{aligned}$$

The Multiplication Property of Equations
Each side of an equation can be multiplied by the same nonzero number without changing the solution of the equation. [3.1.3, p. 109]

$$\begin{aligned} -6x &= 24 \\ \frac{-6x}{-6} &= \frac{24}{-6} \\ x &= -4 \end{aligned}$$

To solve an equation of the form $ax + b = c$ or an equation of the form $ax + b = cx + d$, use both the Addition and the Multiplication Properties of Equations. [3.2.1 and 3.2.2, pp. 129, 131]

$$\begin{aligned} 7x - 4 &= 3x + 16 \\ 7x - 3x - 4 &= 3x - 3x + 16 \\ 4x - 4 &= 16 \\ 4x - 4 + 4 &= 16 + 4 \\ 4x &= 20 \\ \frac{4x}{4} &= \frac{20}{4} \\ x &= 5 \end{aligned}$$

To solve an equation containing parentheses, use the Distributive Property to remove parentheses. [3.2.3, p. 132]

$$\begin{aligned} 3(2x - 1) &= 15 \\ 6x - 3 &= 15 \\ 6x - 3 + 3 &= 15 + 3 \\ 6x &= 18 \\ \frac{6x}{6} &= \frac{18}{6} \\ x &= 3 \end{aligned}$$

The Addition Property of Inequalities
The same number or variable term can be added to each side of an inequality without changing the solution set of the inequality.

If $a > b$, then $a + c > b + c$.
If $a < b$, then $a + c < b + c$. [3.3.1, p. 145]

$$\begin{aligned} x - 9 &\le 14 \\ x - 9 + 9 &\le 14 + 9 \\ x &\le 23 \end{aligned}$$

The Multiplication Property of Inequalities

Rule 1 Each side of an inequality can be multiplied by the same **positive number** without changing the solution set of the inequality.
If $a > b$ and $c > 0$, then $ac > bc$.
If $a < b$ and $c > 0$, then $ac < bc$.

$$\begin{aligned} 7x &< -21 \\ \frac{7x}{7} &< \frac{-21}{7} \\ x &< -3 \end{aligned}$$

Rule 2 If each side of an inequality is multiplied by the same **negative number** and the inequality symbol is reversed, then the solution set of the inequality is not changed.
If $a > b$ and $c < 0$, then $ac < bc$.
If $a < b$ and $c < 0$, then $ac > bc$. [3.3.2, p. 146]

$$\begin{aligned} -7x &\ge 21 \\ \frac{-7x}{-7} &\le \frac{21}{-7} \\ x &\le -3 \end{aligned}$$

The Basic Percent Equation
Percent · base = amount
$P \cdot B = A$
[3.1.5, p. 114]

40% of what number is 16?

$$\begin{aligned} PB &= A \\ 0.40B &= 16 \\ \frac{0.40B}{0.40} &= \frac{16}{0.40} \\ B &= 40 \end{aligned}$$

The number is 40.

Uniform Motion Equation
Distance = rate · time
$d = rt$
[3.1.4, p. 111]

A car travels 200 mi in 4 h. Find the rate of speed.

$$d = rt$$
$$200 = r \cdot 4$$
$$50 = r$$

The rate of speed is 50 mph.

Simple Interest Equation
Simple interest = principal · simple interest rate · time
$I = prt$
[3.1.5, p. 116]

A \$5000 investment earns an annual simple interest rate of 4%. Find the interest earned in 6 months.

$$I = prt$$
$$I = 5000(0.04)(0.5)$$
$$I = 100$$

The interest earned is \$100.

Percent Mixture Equation
Quantity of a substance in a solution
= amount of the solution · percent concentration of the substance
$Q = Ar$
[3.1.5, p. 117]

An 8-ounce bottle of cough syrup is 2% alcohol. Find the amount of alcohol in the cough syrup.

$$Q = Ar$$
$$Q = 8(0.02)$$
$$Q = 0.16$$

The syrup contains 0.16 oz alcohol.

Lever-System Equation
$F_1x = F_2(d - x)$, where F_1 and F_2 are two forces, d is the length of the lever, x is the distance from F_1 to the fulcrum, and $d - x$ is the distance from F_2 to the fulcrum [3.2.4, p. 135]

A 30-pound child is sitting at one end of an 8-foot seesaw, 5 ft from the fulcrum. A 50-pound child is sitting at the other end. The seesaw balances.

$$F_1x = F_2(d - x)$$
$$30(5) = 50(8 - 5)$$
$$30(5) = 50(3)$$
$$150 = 150$$

Chapter 3 Review Exercises

1. Is 3 a solution of $5x - 2 = 4x + 5$?

2. Solve: $x - 4 = 16$

3. Solve: $8x = -56$

4. Solve: $5x - 6 = 29$

5. Solve: $5x + 3 = 10x - 17$

6. Solve: $3(5x + 2) + 2 = 10x + 5[x - (3x - 1)]$

7. What is 81% of 500?

8. 18 is 72% of what number?

9. 27 is what percent of 40?

10. Graph: $x \le -2$

11. Solve and graph the solution set of $x - 3 > -1$.

12. Solve and graph the solution set of $3x > -12$.

13. Solve: $3x + 4 \geq -8$

14. Solve: $7x - 2(x + 3) \geq x + 10$

15. Is 2 a solution of $x^2 + 4x + 1 = 3x + 7$?

16. Solve: $4.6 = 2.1 + x$

17. Solve: $\frac{x}{7} = -7$

18. Solve: $14 + 6x = 17$

19. Solve: $12y - 1 = 3y + 2$

20. Solve: $x + 5(3x - 20) = 10(x - 4)$

21. What is $66\frac{2}{3}\%$ of 24?

22. 60 is 48% of what number?

23. 0.5 is what percent of 3?

24. Solve and graph the solution set of $2 + x < -2$.

25. Solve and graph the solution set of $5x \leq -10$.

26. Solve: $6x + 3(2x - 1) = -27$

27. Solve: $a - \frac{1}{6} = \frac{2}{3}$

28. Solve: $\frac{3}{5}a = 12$

29. Solve: $32 = 9x - 4 - 3x$

30. Solve: $-4[x + 3(x - 5)] = 3(8x + 20)$

31. Solve: $4x - 12 < x + 24$

32. What is $\frac{1}{2}\%$ of 3000?

33. Solve: $3x + 7 + 4x = 42$

34. Solve: $5x - 6 > 19$

35. 8 is what percent of 200?

36. Solve: $6x - 9 < 4x + 3(x + 3)$

37. Solve: $5 - 4(x + 9) > 11(12x - 9)$

38. **Geometry** Find the measure of the third angle of a triangle if the first angle is 20° and the second angle is 50°. Use the equation $A + B + C = 180°$, where A, B, and C are the measures of the angles of a triangle.

39. **Lever Systems** A lever is 12 ft long. At a distance of 2 ft from the fulcrum, a force of 120 lb is applied. How large a force must be applied to the other end of the lever so that the system will balance? Use the lever-system equation $F_1x = F_2(d - x)$.

40. **Geometry** Use the equation $P = 2L + 2W$, where P is the perimeter of a rectangle, L is its length, and W is its width, to find the width of a rectangle that has a perimeter of 49 ft and a length of 18.5 ft.

41. **Discounts** Find the discount on a 26-inch, 21-speed dual-index grip-shifting bicycle if the sale price is \$128 and the regular price is \$159.99. Use the equation $S = R - D$, where S is the sale price, R is the regular price, and D is the discount.

42. **Conservation** In Central America and Mexico, 1184 plants and animals are at risk of extinction. This represents approximately 10.7% of all the species at risk of extinction on Earth. Approximately how many plants and animals are at risk of extinction on Earth? (*Source:* World Conservation Union)

43. **Physics** The pressure at a certain depth in the ocean can be approximated by the equation $P = 15 + \frac{1}{2}D$, where P is the pressure in pounds per square inch and D is the depth in feet. Use this equation to find the depth when the pressure is 55 lb/in^2.

44. **Lever Systems** A lever is 8 ft long. A force of 25 lb is applied to one end of the lever, and a force of 15 lb is applied to the other end. Find the location of the fulcrum when the system balances. Use the lever-system equation $F_1x = F_2(d - x)$.

45. **Geometry** Find the length of a rectangle when the perimeter is 84 ft and the width is 18 ft. Use the equation $P = 2L + 2W$, where P is the perimeter of a rectangle, L is the length, and W is the width.

46. **Uniform Motion Problem** A motorboat that can travel 15 mph in calm water is traveling with the current of a river that is moving at 5 mph. How long will it take the motorboat to travel 30 mi?

47. **Investments** Cathy Serano would like to earn \$125 per year from two investments. She has found one investment that will pay her \$75 per year. How much must she invest in an account that earns an annual simple interest rate of 8% to reach her goal?

48. **Mixture Problem** A 150-milliliter acid solution contains 9 ml of hydrochloric acid. What is the percent concentration of hydrochloric acid?

Chapter 3 Test

1. Solve: $\frac{3}{4}x = -9$

2. Solve: $6 - 5x = 5x + 11$

3. Solve: $3x - 5 = -14$

4. Is -2 a solution of $x^2 - 3x = 2x - 6$?

5. Solve: $x + \frac{1}{2} = \frac{5}{8}$

6. Solve: $5x - 2(4x - 3) = 6x + 9$

7. Solve: $7 - 4x = -13$

8. Solve: $11 - 4x = 2x + 8$

9. Solve: $x - 3 = -8$

10. Solve: $3x - 2 = 5x + 8$

11. Solve: $-\frac{3}{8}x = 5$

12. Solve: $6x - 3(2 - 3x) = 4(2x - 7)$

13. Solve: $6 - 2(5x - 8) = 3x - 4$

14. Solve: $9 - 3(2x - 5) = 12 + 5x$

15. Solve: $3(2x - 5) = 8x - 9$

16. 20 is what percent of 16?

17. 30% of what is 12?

18. Graph: $x > -2$

19. Solve and graph the solution set of $-2 + x \leq -3$.

20. Solve and graph the solution set of $\frac{3}{8}x > -\frac{3}{4}$.

21. Solve: $x + \frac{1}{3} > \frac{5}{6}$

22. Solve: $3(x - 7) \geq 5x - 12$

23. Solve: $-\frac{3}{8}x \leq 6$

24. Solve: $4x - 2(3 - 5x) \leq 6x + 10$

25. Solve: $3(2x - 5) \geq 8x - 9$

26. Solve: $15 - 3(5x - 7) < 2(7 - 2x)$

27. Solve: $-6x + 16 = -2x$

28. 20 is $83\frac{1}{3}\%$ of what number?

29. Solve and graph the solution set of $\frac{2}{3}x \geq 2$.

30. Is 5 a solution of $x^2 + 2x + 1 = (x + 1)^2$?

31. **Space Travel** A person's weight on the moon is $16\frac{2}{3}\%$ of the person's weight on Earth. If an astronaut weighs 180 lb on Earth, how much would the astronaut weigh on the moon?

32. **Chemistry** A chemist mixes 100 g of water at 80°C with 50 g of water at 20°C. Use the equation $m_1 \cdot (T_1 - T) = m_2 \cdot (T - T_2)$ to find the final temperature of the water after mixing. In this equation, m_1 is the quantity of water at the hotter temperature, T_1 is the temperature of the hotter water, m_2 is the quantity of water at the cooler temperature, T_2 is the temperature of the cooler water, and T is the final temperature of the water after mixing.

33. **Manufacturing** A financial manager has determined that the cost per unit for a calculator is \$15 and that the fixed costs per month are \$2000. Find the number of calculators produced during a month in which the total cost was \$5000. Use the equation $T = U \cdot N + F$, where T is the total cost, U is the cost per unit, N is the number of units produced, and F is the fixed cost.

34. **Uniform Motion Problem** Two hikers start at the same time from opposite ends of a 15-mile course. One hiker is walking at a rate of 3.5 mph, and the second hiker is walking at a rate of 4 mph. How long after they begin will they meet?

35. **Investments** Victor Jameson has invested \$750 in a simple interest account that has an annual interest rate of 6.2%. How much must he invest in a second account that earns 5% simple interest so that the interest earned on the second account is the same as that earned on the first account?

36. **Mixture Problem** An 8-ounce glass of chocolate milk contains 2 oz of chocolate syrup. Find the percent concentration of chocolate syrup in the chocolate milk.

Cumulative Review Exercises

1. Subtract: $-6 - (-20) - 8$

2. Multiply: $(-2)(-6)(-4)$

3. Subtract: $-\frac{5}{6} - \left(-\frac{7}{16}\right)$

4. Divide: $-2\frac{1}{3} \div 1\frac{1}{6}$

5. Simplify: $-4^2 \cdot \left(-\frac{3}{2}\right)^3$

6. Simplify: $25 - 3 \cdot \frac{(5-2)^2}{2^3+1} - (-2)$

7. Evaluate $3(a - c) - 2ab$ when $a = 2$, $b = 3$, and $c = -4$.

8. Simplify: $3x - 8x + (-12x)$

9. Simplify: $2a - (-3b) - 7a - 5b$

10. Simplify: $(16x)\left(\frac{1}{8}\right)$

11. Simplify: $-4(-9y)$

12. Simplify: $-2(-x^2 - 3x + 2)$

13. Simplify: $-2(x - 3) + 2(4 - x)$

14. Simplify: $-3[2x - 4(x - 3)] + 2$

15. Use the roster method to write the set of negative integers greater than -8.

16. Write $\frac{7}{8}$ as a percent. Write the remainder in fractional form.

17. Write 342% as a decimal.

18. Write $62\frac{1}{2}\%$ as a fraction.

19. Is -3 a solution of $x^2 + 6x + 9 = x + 3$?

20. Solve: $x - 4 = -9$

21. Solve: $\frac{3}{5}x = -15$

22. Solve: $13 - 9x = -14$

23. Solve: $5x - 8 = 12x + 13$

24. Solve: $8x - 3(4x - 5) = -2x - 11$

25. Solve: $-\frac{3}{4}x > \frac{2}{3}$

26. Solve: $5x - 4 \geq 4x + 8$

27. Solve: $3x + 17 < 5x - 1$

28. Translate "the difference between eight and the quotient of a number and twelve" into a variable expression.

29. Translate and simplify "the sum of a number and two more than the number."

30. **Dollar Bills** A club treasurer has some five-dollar bills and some ten-dollar bills. The treasurer has a total of 35 bills. Use one variable to express the number of each denomination of bill.

31. **Fishing** A fishing wire 3 ft long is cut into two pieces, one shorter than the other. Express the length of the shorter piece in terms of the length of the longer piece.

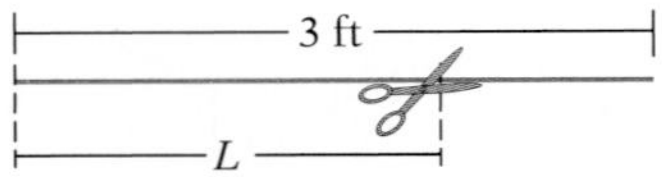

32. **Taxes** A computer programmer receives a weekly wage of \$650, and \$110.50 is deducted for income tax. Find the percent of the computer programmer's salary deducted for income tax.

33. **Foot Racing** The world record time for a 1-mile race can be approximated by the equation $t = 17.08 - 0.0067y$, where t is the time in minutes and y is the year of the race. Use this equation to predict the year in which the first "4-minute mile" was run. (The actual year was 1954.) Round to the nearest whole number.

34. **Chemistry** A chemist mixes 300 g of water at 75°C with 100 g of water at 15°C. Use the equation $m_1 \cdot (T_1 - T) = m_2 \cdot (T - T_2)$ to find the final temperature of the water. In this equation, m_1 is the quantity of water at the hotter temperature, T_1 is the temperature of the hotter water, m_2 is the quantity of water at the cooler temperature, T_2 is the temperature of the cooler water, and T is the final temperature of the water after mixing.

35. **Lever Systems** A lever is 25 ft long. At a distance of 12 ft from the fulcrum, a force of 26 lb is applied. How large a force must be applied to the other end of the lever so that the system will balance? Use the lever system equation $F_1x = F_2(d - x)$.

CHAPTER

4 Solving Equations and Inequalities: Applications

OBJECTIVES

How do TV stations know which of their programs receive the best ratings? Most stations use data from Nielsen Media Research, which surveys television viewers to determine the number of people watching particular TV shows. The larger the audience, the greater the number of points the show receives. Programs with the highest ratings can demand higher fees from companies who pay to have their commercials aired during the show. The **Projects & Group Activities on pages 235 and 236** describe the meaning of Nielsen rating points and their relationship to market share.

DVD SSM *Online Study Center*

Need help? For online student resources, such as section quizzes, visit the Online Study Center at college.hmco.com/pic/aufmannBAWA7e.

Prep Test

1. Simplify: $R - 0.35R$
2. Simplify: $0.08x + 0.05(400 - x)$
3. Simplify: $n + (n + 2) + (n + 4)$
4. Translate into a variable expression: "The difference between five and twice a number."
5. Write 0.4 as a percent.
6. Solve: $25x + 10(9 - x) = 120$
7. Solve: $36 = 48 - 48r$
8. Solve: $4(2x - 5) < 12$
9. A snack mixture weighs 20 oz and contains nuts and pretzels. Let n represent the number of ounces of nuts in the mixture. Express the number of ounces of pretzels in the mixture in terms of n.

4.1 Translating Sentences into Equations

OBJECTIVE 1 Translate a sentence into an equation and solve

An equation states that two mathematical expressions are equal. Therefore, to translate a sentence into an equation requires recognizing the words or phrases that mean "equals." Some of these phrases that mean "equals" are *is*, *is equal to*, *amounts to*, and *represents*.

Once the sentence is translated into an equation, the equation can be solved by rewriting the equation in the form *variable* = *constant*.

EXAMPLE 1 Translate "two times the sum of a number and eight equals the sum of four times the number and six" into an equation and solve.

Solution the unknown number: n • **Assign a variable to the unknown quantity.**

two times the sum of a number and eight	equals	the sum of four times the number and six

• **Find two verbal expressions for the same value.**

$$2(n + 8) = 4n + 6$$

• **Write a mathematical expression for each verbal expression. Write the equals sign.**

• **Solve the equation.**

$$2n + 16 = 4n + 6$$
$$2n - 4n + 16 = 4n - 4n + 6$$
$$-2n + 16 = 6$$
$$-2n + 16 - 16 = 6 - 16$$
$$-2n = -10$$
$$\frac{-2n}{-2} = \frac{-10}{-2}$$
$$n = 5$$

The number is 5.

PROBLEM 1 Translate "nine less than twice a number is five times the sum of the number and twelve" into an equation and solve.

Solution See page S8.

OBJECTIVE 2 Application problems

EXAMPLE 2 The temperature of the sun on the Kelvin scale is 6500 K. This is 4740° less than the temperature on the Fahrenheit scale. Find the Fahrenheit temperature.

Strategy To find the Fahrenheit temperature, write and solve an equation using F to represent the Fahrenheit temperature.

Solution

6500	is	4740° less than the Fahrenheit temperature

$$6500 = F - 4740$$
$$6500 + 4740 = F - 4740 + 4740$$
$$11{,}240 = F$$

The temperature of the sun is 11,240°F.

PROBLEM 2 A molecule of octane gas has eight carbon atoms. This represents twice the number of carbon atoms in a butane gas molecule. Find the number of carbon atoms in a butane gas molecule.

Solution See page S8.

EXAMPLE 3 A board 10 ft long is cut into two pieces. Three times the length of the shorter piece is twice the length of the longer piece. Find the length of each piece.

> **Take Note**
>
> We could also let x represent the length of the longer piece and let $10 - x$ represent the length of the shorter piece. Then our equation would be
>
> $$3(10 - x) = 2x$$
>
> Show that this equation results in the same solutions.

Strategy Draw a diagram. To find the length of each piece, write and solve an equation using x to represent the length of the shorter piece and $10 - x$ to represent the length of the longer piece.

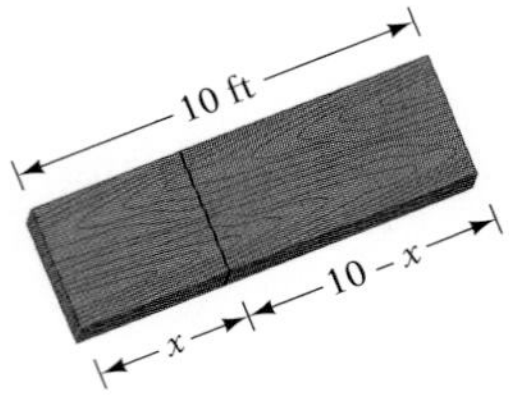

Solution

three times the length of the shorter piece	is	twice the length of the longer piece

$$\begin{aligned} 3x &= 2(10 - x) \\ 3x &= 20 - 2x \\ 3x + 2x &= 20 - 2x + 2x \\ 5x &= 20 \\ \frac{5x}{5} &= \frac{20}{5} \\ x &= 4 \\ 10 - x &= 10 - 4 = 6 \end{aligned}$$

- **The length of the shorter piece is 4 ft.**
- **Substitute the value of x into the variable expression for the longer piece and evaluate.**

The length of the shorter piece is 4 ft. The length of the longer piece is 6 ft.

PROBLEM 3 A company manufactures 160 bicycles per day. Four times the number of 3-speed bicycles made each day equals 30 less than the number of 10-speed bicycles made each day. Find the number of 10-speed bicycles manufactured each day.

Solution See page S8.

4.1 Concept Review

Determine whether the statement is always true, sometimes true, or never true.

1. When two expressions represent the same value, we say that the expressions are equal to each other.

2. Both "four less than a number" and "the difference between four and a number" are translated as "$4 - n$."

3. When translating a sentence into an equation, we can use any variable to represent an unknown number.

4. When translating a sentence into an equation, translate the word *is* as "=."

5. If a rope 19 inches long is cut into two pieces and one of the pieces has length x inches, then the length of the other piece can be expressed as $(x - 19)$ inches.

6. In addition to a number, the answer to an application problem must have a unit, such as meters, dollars, minutes, or miles per hour.

4.1 Exercises

1 Translate a sentence into an equation and solve

1. When we translate a sentence into an equation, the word *is* translates into the __?__ sign.

2. The sum of two numbers is twelve. If n represents one of the numbers, then the other number is represented by __?__.

Translate into an equation and solve.

3. The difference between a number and fifteen is seven. Find the number.

4. The sum of five and a number is three. Find the number.

5. The product of seven and a number is negative twenty-one. Find the number.

6. The quotient of a number and four is two. Find the number.

7. Four less than three times a number is five. Find the number.

8. The difference between five and twice a number is one. Find the number.

9. Four times the sum of twice a number and three is twelve. Find the number.

10. Twenty-one is three times the difference between four times a number and five. Find the number.

11. Twelve is six times the difference between a number and three. Find the number.

12. The difference between six times a number and four times the number is negative fourteen. Find the number.

13. Twenty-two is two less than six times a number. Find the number.

14. Negative fifteen is three more than twice a number. Find the number.

15. Seven more than four times a number is three more than two times the number. Find the number.

16. The difference between three times a number and four is five times the number. Find the number.

17. Eight less than five times a number is four more than eight times the number. Find the number.

18. The sum of a number and six is four less than six times the number. Find the number.

19. Twice the difference between a number and twenty-five is three times the number. Find the number.

20. Four times a number is three times the difference between thirty-five and the number. Find the number.

21. The sum of two numbers is twenty. Three times the smaller is equal to two times the larger. Find the two numbers.

22. The sum of two numbers is fifteen. One less than three times the smaller is equal to the larger. Find the two numbers.

23. The sum of two numbers is eighteen. The total of three times the smaller and twice the larger is forty-four. Find the two numbers.

24. The sum of two numbers is two. The difference between eight and twice the smaller number is two less than four times the larger. Find the two numbers.

25. The sum of two numbers is fourteen. One number is ten more than the other number. Write two different equations that can be used to find the numbers by first writing an equation in which n represents "the larger number" and then writing an equation in which n represents "the smaller number."

26. The sum of two numbers is seven. Twice one number is four less than the other number. Which of the following equations does *not* represent this situation?

a. $2n = 7 - n - 4$ **b.** $2(7 - x) = x - 4$
c. $2x + 4 = 7 - x$ **d.** $2n - 4 = 7 - n$

2 Application problems

27. The number of calories in a cup of low-fat milk is two-thirds the number of calories in a cup of whole milk. In this situation, let n represent the number of calories in a cup of ____?____ milk, and let $\frac{2}{3}n$ represent the number of calories in a cup of ____?____ milk.

28. A cup of low-fat milk has 100 calories. Use the information in Exercise 27 to write an equation that can be used to find the number of calories in a cup of whole milk: __?__ = __?__.

Write an equation and solve.

29. Depreciation As a result of depreciation, the value of a car is now $9600. This is three-fifths of its original value. Find the original value of the car.

30. Structures The length of the Royal Gorge Bridge in Colorado is 320 m. This is one-fourth the length of the Golden Gate Bridge. Find the length of the Golden Gate Bridge.

The Golden Gate Bridge

31. Nutrition One slice of cheese pizza contains 290 calories. A medium-size orange has one-fifth that number of calories. How many calories are in a medium-size orange?

32. History John D. Rockefeller died in 1937. At the time of his death, Rockefeller had accumulated a wealth of $1,400 million, which was equal to one-sixty-fifth of the gross national product of the United States at that time. What was the U.S. gross national product in 1937? (*Source: The Wealthy 100: A Ranking of the Richest Americans, Past and Present*)

John D. Rockefeller

33. Agriculture A soil supplement that weighs 18 lb contains iron, potassium, and a mulch. There is fifteen times as much mulch as iron and twice as much potassium as iron. Find the amount of mulch in the soil supplement.

34. Commissions A real estate agent sold two homes and received commissions totaling $6000. The agent's commission on one home was one and one-half times the commission on the second home. Find the agent's commission on each home.

35. Safety Loudness, or the intensity of sound, is measured in decibels. The sound level of a television is about 70 decibels, which is considered a safe hearing level. A food blender runs at 20 decibels higher than a TV, and a jet engine's decibel reading is 40 less than twice that of a blender. At this level, exposure can cause hearing loss. Find the intensity of the sound of a jet engine.

Point of Interest

The low-frequency pulses or whistles made by blue whales have been measured at up to 188 decibels, making them the loudest sounds produced by a living organism.

36. Education A university employs a total of 600 teaching assistants and research assistants. There are three times as many teaching assistants as research assistants. Find the number of research assistants employed by the university.

37. Consumerism The purchase price of a new big-screen TV, including finance charges, was $3276. A down payment of $450 was made. The remainder was paid in 24 equal monthly installments. Find the monthly payment.

38. **Consumerism** The purchase price of a new computer system, including finance charges, was \$6350. A down payment of \$350 was made. The remainder was paid in 24 equal monthly installments. Find the monthly payment.

39. **Geometry** Greek architects considered a rectangle whose length was approximately 1.6 times its width to be the most visually appealing. Find the length and width of a rectangle constructed in this manner if the sum of the length and width is 130 ft.

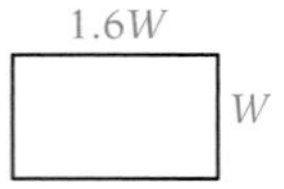

40. **Geography** Greenland, the largest island in the world, is 21 times larger than Iceland. The combined area of Greenland and Iceland is 880,000 mi^2. Find the area of Greenland.

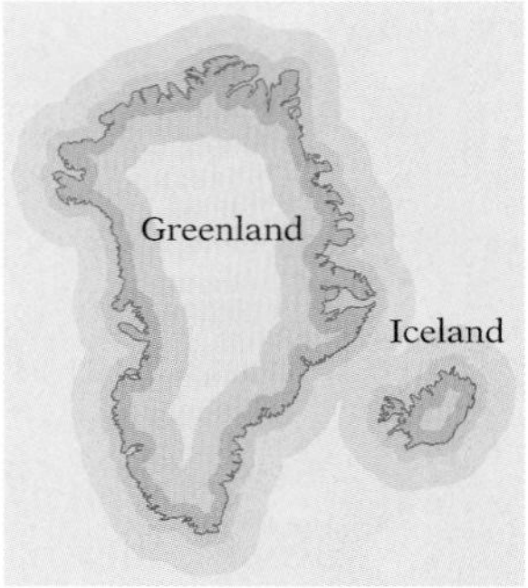

41. **Consumerism** The cost to replace a water pump in a sports car was \$600. This included \$375 for the water pump and \$45 per hour for labor. How many hours of labor were required to replace the water pump?

42. **Utilities** The cost of electricity in a certain city is \$.08 for each of the first 300 kWh (kilowatt-hours) and \$.13 for each kWh over 300 kWh. Find the number of kilowatt-hours used by a family that receives a \$51.95 electric bill.

43. **Consumerism** The fee charged by a ticketing agency for a concert is \$5.50 plus \$37.50 for each ticket purchased. If your total charge for tickets is \$343, how many tickets are you purchasing?

44. **Carpentry** A carpenter is building a wood door frame. The height of the frame is 1 ft less than three times the width. What is the width of the largest door frame that can be constructed from a board 19 ft long? (*Hint:* A door frame consists of only three sides; there is no frame below a door.)

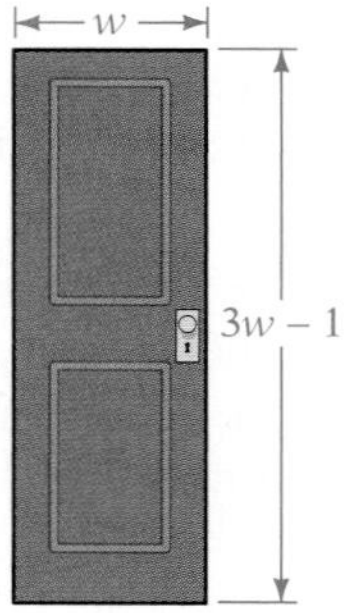

45. **Construction** The length of a rectangular cement patio is 3 ft less than three times the width. The sum of the length and width of the patio is 21 ft. Find the length of the patio.

46. **Carpentry** A 20-foot board is cut into two pieces. Twice the length of the shorter piece is 4 ft more than the length of the longer piece. Find the length of the shorter piece.

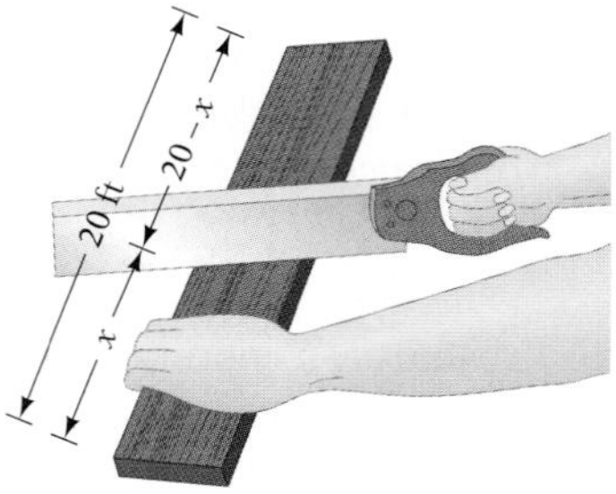

47. **Labor Unions** A union charges monthly dues of \$4.00 plus \$.15 for each hour worked during the month. A union member's dues for March were \$29.20. How many hours did the union member work during the month of March?

48. **Business** The cellular phone service for a business executive is \$35 per month plus \$.40 per minute of phone use. In a month when the executive's cellular phone bill was \$99.80, how many minutes did the executive use the phone?

49. Business A technical information hotline charges a customer $9.00 plus $.50 per minute to answer questions about software. How many minutes did a customer who received a bill for $14.50 use this service?

50. Metalwork A wire 12 ft long is cut into two pieces. Each piece is bent into the shape of a square. The perimeter of the larger square is twice the perimeter of the smaller square. Find the perimeter of the larger square.

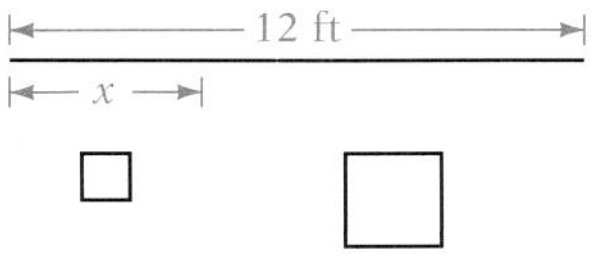

4.1 Applying Concepts

51. The amount of liquid in a container triples every minute. The container becomes completely filled at 3:40 P.M. What fractional part of the container is filled at 3:39 P.M.?

52. Travel A cyclist traveling at a constant speed completes $\frac{3}{5}$ of a trip in $1\frac{1}{2}$ h. In how many additional hours will the cyclist complete the entire trip?

53. Postage The rate for first-class mail is $.39 for the first ounce and $.24 for each additional ounce or fraction of an ounce. If the cost to mail a package first class is $3.27, how much does the package weigh?

54. Wages Four employees are paid at four consecutive levels on a wage scale. The difference between any two consecutive levels is $320 per month. The average of the four employees' monthly wages is $3880. What is the monthly wage of the highest-paid employee?

55. Coins A coin bank contains nickels, dimes, and quarters. There are 14 nickels in the bank, $\frac{1}{6}$ of the coins are dimes, and $\frac{3}{5}$ of the coins are quarters. How many coins are in the coin bank?

56. Business During one day at an office, one-half of the amount of money in the petty cash drawer was used in the morning, and one-third of the remaining money was used in the afternoon, leaving $5 in the petty cash drawer at the end of the day. How much money was in the petty cash drawer at the start of the day?

57. A formula is an equation that relates variables in a known way. Find two examples of formulas that are used in your college major. Explain what each of the variables represents.

4.2 Integer, Coin, and Stamp Problems

OBJECTIVE 1 Consecutive integer problems

Recall that the integers are the numbers . . . , −4, −3, −2, −1, 0, 1, 2, 3, 4, ...

An **even integer** is an integer that is divisible by 2. Examples of even integers are −8, 0, and 22.

An **odd integer** is an integer that is not divisible by 2. Examples of odd integers are −17, 1, and 39.

Consecutive integers are integers that follow one another in order. Examples of consecutive integers are shown at the right. (Assume the variable n represents an integer.)

11, 12, 13
−8, −7, −6
$n, n + 1, n + 2$

Examples of **consecutive even integers** are shown at the right. (Assume the variable n represents an even integer.)

24, 26, 28
−10, −8, −6
$n, n + 2, n + 4$

Examples of **consecutive odd integers** are shown at the right. (Assume the variable n represents an odd integer.)

19, 21, 23,
−1, 1, 3
$n, n + 2, n + 4$

Solve: The sum of three consecutive odd integers is 51. Find the integers.

STRATEGY for solving a consecutive integer problem

▶ Let a variable represent one of the integers. Express each of the other integers in terms of that variable. Remember that consecutive integers differ by 1. Consecutive even or consecutive odd integers differ by 2.

First odd integer: n
Second odd integer: $n + 2$
Third odd integer: $n + 4$

▶ Determine the relationship among the integers.

The sum of the three odd integers is 51.

$$n + (n + 2) + (n + 4) = 51$$
$$3n + 6 = 51$$
$$3n = 45$$
$$n = 15$$

$n + 2 = 15 + 2 = 17$
$n + 4 = 15 + 4 = 19$

• **Substitute the value of n into the variable expressions for the second and third integers.**

The three consecutive odd integers are 15, 17, and 19.

EXAMPLE 1 Find three consecutive even integers such that three times the second integer is six more than the sum of the first and third integers.

Strategy
- ▶ First even integer: n
  Second even integer: $n + 2$
  Third even integer: $n + 4$
- ▶ Three times the second integer equals six more than the sum of the first and third integers.

Solution

$$3(n + 2) = n + (n + 4) + 6$$
$$3n + 6 = 2n + 10$$
$$n + 6 = 10$$
$$n = 4$$

• **The first even integer is 4.**

$$n + 2 = 4 + 2 = 6$$
$$n + 4 = 4 + 4 = 8$$

• **Substitute the value of n into the variable expressions for the second and third integers.**

The three consecutive even integers are 4, 6, and 8.

PROBLEM 1 Find three consecutive integers whose sum is −12.

Solution See page S8.

OBJECTIVE 2 Coin and stamp problems

$3 \cdot 25 = 75$ cents

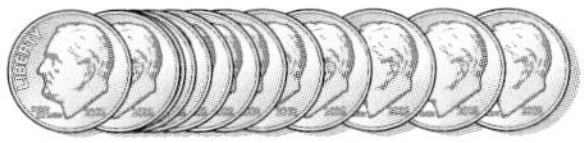

$d \cdot 10 = 10d$ cents

In solving problems that deal with coins or stamps of different values, it is necessary to represent the values of the coins or stamps in the same unit of money. Frequently, the unit of money is cents.

The value of 3 quarters in cents is $3 \cdot 25$ or 75 cents.
The value of 4 nickels in cents is $4 \cdot 5$ or 20 cents.
The value of d dimes in cents is $d \cdot 10$ or $10d$ cents.

Solve: A coin bank contains $1.20 in dimes and quarters. In all, there are nine coins in the bank. Find the number of quarters in the bank.

STRATEGY for solving a coin problem

▶ For each denomination of coin, write a numerical or variable expression for the number of coins, the value of the coin in cents, and the total value of the coins in cents. The results can be recorded in a table.

Take Note

Use the information given in the problem to fill in the number and value columns of the table. Fill in the total value column by multiplying the two expressions you wrote in each row.

The total number of coins is 9.

Number of quarters: x
Number of dimes: $9 - x$

Coin	Number of coins	$\cdot$	Value of coin in cents	$=$	Total value in cents
Quarter	x	$\cdot$	25	$=$	$25x$
Dime	$9 - x$	$\cdot$	10	$=$	$10(9 - x)$

▶ Determine the relationship between the total values of the different coins. Use the fact that the sum of the total values of the different denominations of coins is equal to the total value of all the coins.

The sum of the total values of the different denominations of coins is equal to the total value of all the coins (120 cents).

$$25x + 10(9 - x) = 120$$
$$25x + 90 - 10x = 120$$
$$15x + 90 = 120$$
$$15x = 30$$
$$x = 2$$

• **The total value of the quarters plus the total value of the dimes equals the amount of money in the bank.**

There are 2 quarters in the bank.

EXAMPLE 2 A collection of stamps consists of 3¢ stamps and 8¢ stamps. The number of 8¢ stamps is five more than three times the number of 3¢ stamps. The total value of all the stamps is \$1.75. Find the number of each type of stamp in the collection.

Strategy ▶ Number of 3¢ stamps: x
Number of 8¢ stamps: $3x + 5$

Stamp	Number	Value	Total value
3¢	x	3	$3x$
8¢	$3x + 5$	8	$8(3x + 5)$

▶ The sum of the total values of the different types of stamps equals the total value of all the stamps (175 cents).

Solution

$$3x + 8(3x + 5) = 175$$
$$3x + 24x + 40 = 175$$
$$27x + 40 = 175$$
$$27x = 135$$
$$x = 5$$

• **The total value of the 3¢ stamps plus the total value of the 8¢ stamps equals the total value of all the stamps.**

$$3x + 5 = 3(5) + 5$$
$$= 15 + 5 = 20$$

• **Find the number of 8¢ stamps.**

There are five 3¢ stamps and twenty 8¢ stamps in the collection.

PROBLEM 2 A coin bank contains nickels, dimes, and quarters. There are five times as many nickels as dimes and six more quarters than dimes. The total value of all the coins is \$6.30. Find the number of each kind of coin in the bank.

Solution See page S8.

4.2 Concept Review

Determine whether the statement is always true, sometimes true, or never true.

1. An even integer is a multiple of 2.

2. When $10d$ is used to represent the value of d dimes, 10 is written as the coefficient of d because it is the number of cents in one dime.

3. Given the consecutive odd integers -5 and -3, the next consecutive odd integer is -1.

4. If the first of three consecutive odd integers is n, then the second and third consecutive odd integers are represented as $n + 1$ and $n + 3$.

5. You have a total of 20 coins in nickels and dimes. If n represents the number of nickels you have, then $n - 20$ represents the number of dimes you have.

6. You have a total of seven coins in dimes and quarters. The total value of the coins is \$1.15. If d represents the number of dimes you have, then $10d + 25(7 - d) = 1.15$.

4.2 Exercises

1 Consecutive integer problems

1. Integers that follow one another in order are called ___?___ integers.

2. Two consecutive integers differ by ___?___. Two consecutive even integers differ by ___?___. Two consecutive odd integers differ by ___?___.

3. Explain how to represent three consecutive integers using only one variable.

4. Explain why both consecutive even integers and consecutive odd integers are represented algebraically as $n, n + 2, n + 4, \ldots$.

5. The sum of three consecutive integers is 54. Find the integers.

6. The sum of three consecutive integers is 75. Find the integers.

7. The sum of three consecutive even integers is 84. Find the integers.

8. The sum of three consecutive even integers is 48. Find the integers.

9. The sum of three consecutive odd integers is 57. Find the integers.

10. The sum of three consecutive odd integers is 81. Find the integers.

11. Find two consecutive even integers such that five times the first integer is equal to four times the second integer.

12. Find two consecutive even integers such that six times the first integer equals three times the second integer.

13. Nine times the first of two consecutive odd integers equals seven times the second. Find the integers.

14. Five times the first of two consecutive odd integers is three times the second. Find the integers.

15. Find three consecutive integers whose sum is negative twenty-four.

16. Find three consecutive even integers whose sum is negative twelve.

17. Three times the smallest of three consecutive even integers is two more than twice the largest. Find the integers.

18. Twice the smallest of three consecutive odd integers is five more than the largest. Find the integers.

19. Find three consecutive odd integers such that three times the middle integer is six more than the sum of the first and third integers.

20. Find three consecutive odd integers such that four times the middle integer is equal to two less than the sum of the first and third integers.

21. Which of the following could *not* be used to represent three consecutive even integers?

a. $n + 2, n + 4, n + 6$ **b.** $n, n + 4, n + 6$
c. $n + 1, n + 3, n + 5$ **d.** $n - 2, n, n + 2$

22. If n is an odd integer, which expression represents the third consecutive odd integer after n?

a. $n + 6$ **b.** $n + 4$ **c.** $n + 3$ **d.** $n + 2$

2 Coin and stamp problems

23. Explain how to represent the total value of x nickels using the equation

Number of coins · Value of the coin in cents = Total value in cents

24. Suppose a coin purse contains only dimes and quarters. In the context of this situation, explain the meaning of the statement "The sum of the total values of the different denominations of coins is equal to the total value of all the coins."

25. A bank contains 32 coins in nickels and dimes. Let n represent the number of nickels. Complete the following table.

Coin	Number of coins	$\cdot$	Value of the coin in cents	=	Total value of the coins in cents
Nickel	n	$\cdot$	?	=	?
Dime	?	$\cdot$	?	=	?

26. The total value of the 32 coins in Exercise 25 is \$2.70. The total value of the coins in cents is ___?___. Use this information and the information in the table in Exercise 25 to write an equation that can be solved to find the number of nickels in the bank: ___?___ + ___?___ = ___?___.

27. **a.** How many pennies are in d dollars?
b. How many nickels are in d dollars?
c. How many quarters are in d dollars?

28. **a.** How many cents are n 39¢ stamps worth?
b. How many dollars are n 39¢ stamps worth?

29. A bank contains 27 coins in dimes and quarters. The coins have a total value of \$4.95. Find the number of dimes and quarters in the bank.

30. A coin purse contains 18 coins in nickels and dimes. The coins have a total value of \$1.15. Find the number of nickels and dimes in the coin purse.

31. A business executive bought 40 stamps for \$14.40. The purchase included 39¢ stamps and 24¢ stamps. How many of each type of stamp were bought?

32. A postal clerk sold some 34¢ stamps and some 23¢ stamps. Altogether, 15 stamps were sold for a total cost of \$4.44. How many of each type of stamp were sold?

33. A drawer contains 29¢ stamps and 3¢ stamps. The number of 29¢ stamps is four less than three times the number of 3¢ stamps. The total value of all the stamps is \$1.54. How many 29¢ stamps are in the drawer?

34. The total value of the dimes and quarters in a bank is \$6.05. There are six more quarters than dimes. Find the number of each type of coin in the bank.

35. A child's piggy bank contains 44 coins in quarters and dimes. The coins have a total value of \$8.60. Find the number of quarters in the bank.

36. A coin bank contains nickels and dimes. The number of dimes is 10 less than twice the number of nickels. The total value of all the coins is \$2.75. Find the number of each type of coin in the bank.

37. A total of 26 bills are in a cash box. Some of the bills are one-dollar bills, and the rest are five-dollar bills. The total amount of cash in the box is \$50. Find the number of each type of bill in the cash box.

38. A bank teller cashed a check for \$200 using twenty-dollar bills and ten-dollar bills. In all, 12 bills were handed to the customer. Find the number of twenty-dollar bills and the number of ten-dollar bills.

39. A coin bank contains pennies, nickels, and dimes. There are six times as many nickels as pennies and four times as many dimes as pennies. The total amount of money in the bank is \$7.81. Find the number of pennies in the bank.

40. A coin bank contains pennies, nickels, and quarters. There are seven times as many nickels as pennies and three times as many quarters as pennies. The total amount of money in the bank is \$5.55. Find the number of pennies in the bank.

41. A collection of stamps consists of 22¢ stamps and 40¢ stamps. The number of 22¢ stamps is three more than four times the number of 40¢ stamps. The total value of the stamps is \$8.34. Find the number of 22¢ stamps in the collection.

42. A collection of stamps consists of 2¢ stamps, 8¢ stamps, and 14¢ stamps. The number of 2¢ stamps is five more than twice the number of 8¢ stamps. The number of 14¢ stamps is three times the number of 8¢ stamps. The total value of the stamps is \$2.26. Find the number of each type of stamp in the collection.

43. A collection of stamps consists of 3¢ stamps, 7¢ stamps, and 12¢ stamps. The number of 3¢ stamps is five less than the number of 7¢ stamps. The number of 12¢ stamps is one-half the number of 7¢ stamps. The total value of all the stamps is \$2.73. Find the number of each type of stamp in the collection.

44. A collection of stamps consists of 2¢ stamps, 5¢ stamps, and 7¢ stamps. There are nine more 2¢ stamps than 5¢ stamps and twice as many 7¢ stamps as 5¢ stamps. The total value of the stamps is \$1.44. Find the number of each type of stamp in the collection.

45. A collection of stamps consists of 6¢ stamps, 8¢ stamps, and 15¢ stamps. The number of 6¢ stamps is three times the number of 8¢ stamps. There are six more 15¢ stamps than there are 6¢ stamps. The total value of all the stamps is \$5.16. Find the number of each type of stamp.

46. A child's piggy bank contains nickels, dimes, and quarters. There are twice as many nickels as dimes and four more quarters than nickels. The total value of all the coins is \$9.40. Find the number of each type of coin.

4.2 Applying Concepts

47. Find four consecutive even integers whose sum is −36.

48. Find four consecutive odd integers whose sum is −48.

49. A coin bank contains only dimes and quarters. The number of quarters in the bank is two less than twice the number of dimes. There are 34 coins in the bank. How much money is in the bank?

50. A postal clerk sold twenty stamps to a customer. The number of 39¢ stamps purchased was two more than twice the number of 24¢ stamps purchased. If the customer bought only 39¢ stamps and 24¢ stamps, how much money did the clerk collect from the customer?

51. Find three consecutive odd integers such that the sum of the first and third integers is twice the second integer.

52. Find four consecutive integers such that the sum of the first and fourth integers equals the sum of the second and third integers.

4.3 Geometry Problems

OBJECTIVE 1 Perimeter problems

Recall that the **perimeter** of a plane geometric figure is a measure of the distance around the figure. Perimeter is used, for example, in buying fencing for a lawn and in determining how much baseboard is needed for a room.

The perimeter of a triangle is the sum of the lengths of the three sides. Therefore, if a, b, and c represent the lengths of the sides of a triangle, the perimeter, P, of the triangle is given by $\boldsymbol{P = a + b + c}$.

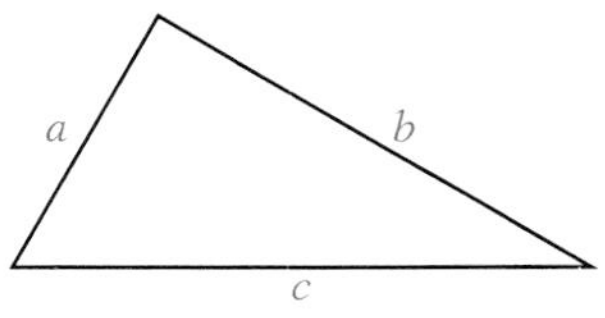

$P = a + b + c$

Two special types of triangles are shown below. An **isosceles triangle** has two sides of equal length. The three sides of an **equilateral triangle** are of equal length.

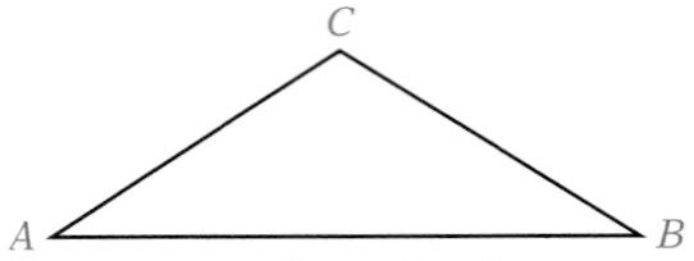

Isosceles triangle

$AC = BC$
$\angle A = \angle B$

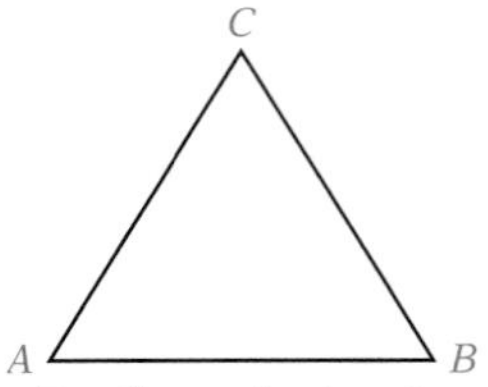

Equilateral triangle

$AB = AC = BC$
$\angle A = \angle B = \angle C$

Point of Interest

Leonardo da Vinci painted the Mona Lisa on a rectangular canvas whose height was approximately 1.6 times its width. Rectangles with these proportions, called **golden rectangles,** *were used extensively in Renaissance art.*

The perimeter of a rectangle is the sum of the lengths of the four sides. Let L represent the length and W represent the width of a rectangle. Then the perimeter, P, of the rectangle is given by $P = L + W + L + W$. Combine like terms and the formula is $\boldsymbol{P = 2L + 2W}$.

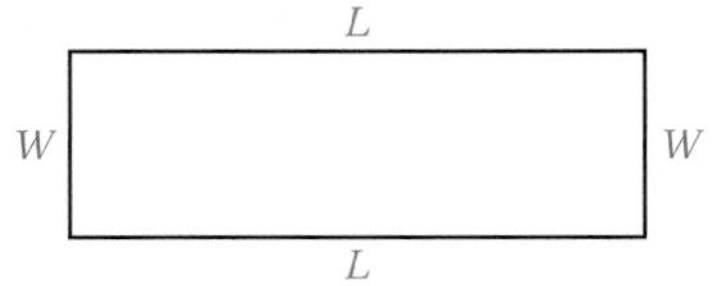

$P = 2L + 2W$

A square is a rectangle in which each side has the same length. Let s represent the length of each side of a square. Then the perimeter, P, of the square is given by $P = s + s + s + s$. Combine like terms and the formula is $\boldsymbol{P = 4s}$.

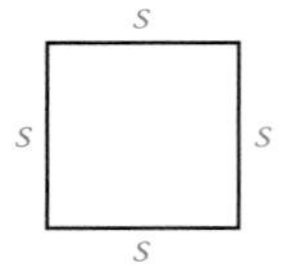

$P = 4s$

Formulas for Perimeters of Geometric Figures

Perimeter of a triangle:	$P = a + b + c$
Perimeter of a rectangle:	$P = 2L + 2W$
Perimeter of a square:	$P = 4s$

The perimeter of a rectangle is 26 ft. The length of the rectangle is 1 ft more than twice the width. Find the width and length of the rectangle.

Strategy

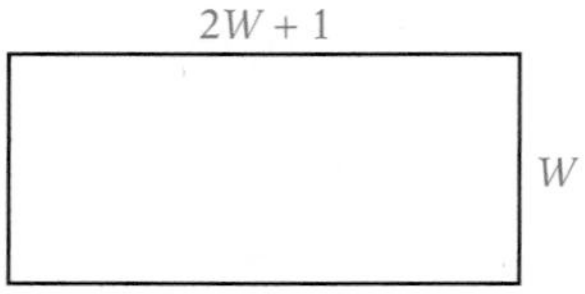

Let a variable represent the width. — Width: W
Represent the length in terms of that variable. — Length: $2W + 1$
Use the formula for the perimeter of a rectangle.

Solution

$$P = 2L + 2W$$

$P = 26$. Substitute $2W + 1$ for L.

$$26 = 2(2W + 1) + 2W$$

Use the Distributive Property.	$26 = 4W + 2 + 2W$
Combine like terms.	$26 = 6W + 2$
Subtract 2 from each side of the equation.	$24 = 6W$
Divide each side of the equation by 6.	$4 = W$
Find the length of the rectangle by substituting 4 for W in $2W + 1$.	$L = 2W + 1$ $= 2(4) + 1 = 8 + 1 = 9$

The width is 4 ft. The length is 9 ft.

EXAMPLE 1 The perimeter of an isosceles triangle is 25 ft. The length of the third side is 2 ft less than the length of one of the equal sides. Find the measures of the three sides of the triangle.

Strategy

- Each equal side: x
  The third side: $x - 2$
- Use the equation for the perimeter of a triangle.

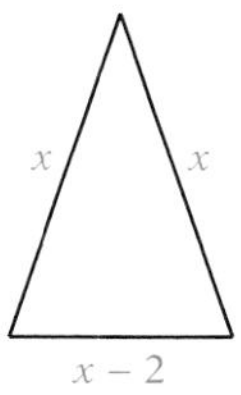

Solution

$$P = a + b + c$$

$$25 = x + x + (x - 2)$$
$$25 = 3x - 2$$
$$27 = 3x$$
$$9 = x$$

$x - 2 = 9 - 2 = 7$ • **Substitute the value of x into the variable expression for the length of the third side.**

Each of the equal sides measures 9 ft.
The third side measures 7 ft.

PROBLEM 1 A carpenter is designing a square patio with a perimeter of 52 ft. What is the length of each side?

Solution See page S9.

OBJECTIVE 2 Problems involving angles formed by intersecting lines

Recall that a unit used to measure angles is the **degree.** The symbol for degree is °. ∠ is the symbol for angle.

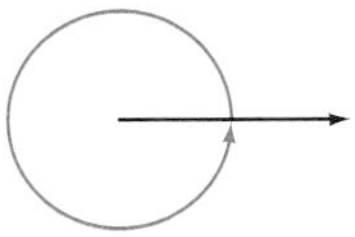

360°

One complete revolution is 360°. It is likely that the Babylonians chose 360° for a circle because they knew that there are 365 days in one year, and 360 is the closest number to 365 that is divisible by many numbers.

A 90° angle is called a **right angle.** The symbol ∟ represents a right angle. Angle C (∠C) is a right angle.

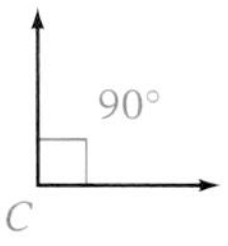

A 180° angle is called a **straight angle.** The angle at the right is a straight angle.

An **acute angle** is an angle whose measure is between 0° and 90°. $\angle A$ at the right is an acute angle.

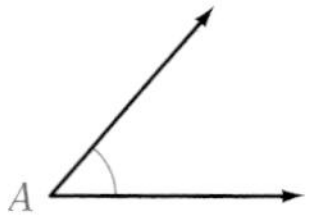

An **obtuse angle** is an angle whose measure is between 90° and 180°. $\angle B$ at the right is an obtuse angle.

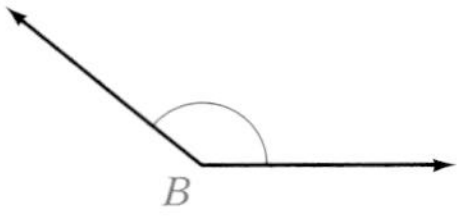

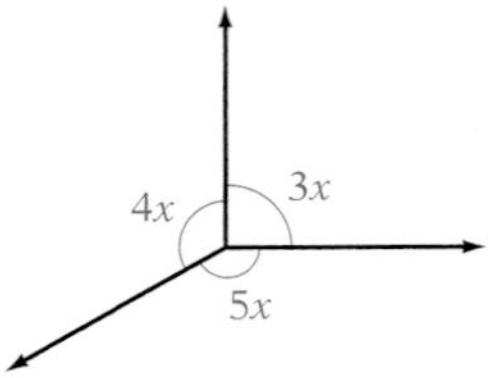

Given the diagram at the left, find x.

Strategy The sum of the measures of the three angles is 360°. To find x, write an equation and solve for x.

Solution

$$3x + 4x + 5x = 360^\circ$$
$$12x = 360^\circ$$
$$x = 30^\circ$$

The measure of x is 30°.

Complementary angles are two angles whose measures have the sum 90°.

$\angle D + \angle E = 70^\circ + 20^\circ = 90^\circ$

$\angle D$ and $\angle E$ are complementary angles.

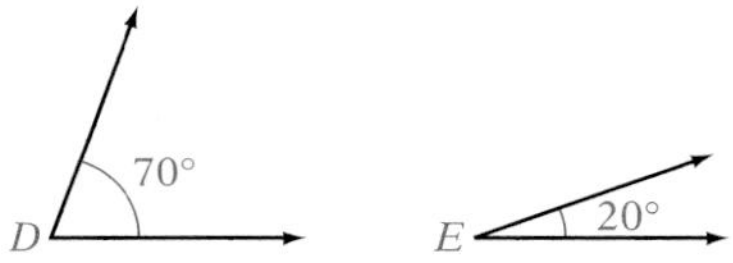

Supplementary angles are two angles whose measures have the sum 180°.

$\angle F + \angle G = 130^\circ + 50^\circ = 180^\circ$

$\angle F$ and $\angle G$ are supplementary angles.

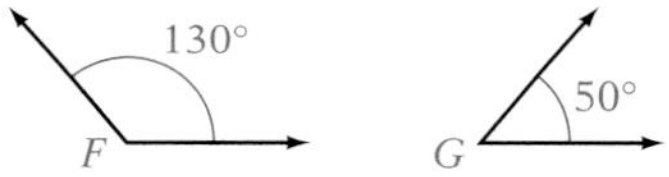

EXAMPLE 2 Find the complement of a 39° angle.

Strategy To find the complement, let x represent the complement of a 39° angle. Use the fact that complementary angles are two angles whose sum is 90° to write an equation. Solve for x.

Solution

$$39^\circ + x = 90^\circ$$
$$x = 51^\circ$$

• **Subtract 39 from each side of the equation.**

The complement of a 39° angle is a 51° angle.

PROBLEM 2 Find the supplement of a 107° angle.

Solution See page S9.

Parallel lines never meet. The distance between them is always the same. The symbol ∥ means "is parallel to." In the figure at the right, $\ell_1 \parallel \ell_2$.

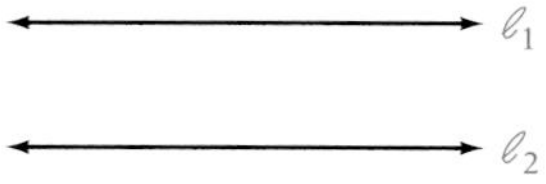

Perpendicular lines are intersecting lines that form right angles. The symbol $\perp$ means "is perpendicular to." In the figure at the right, $p \perp q$.

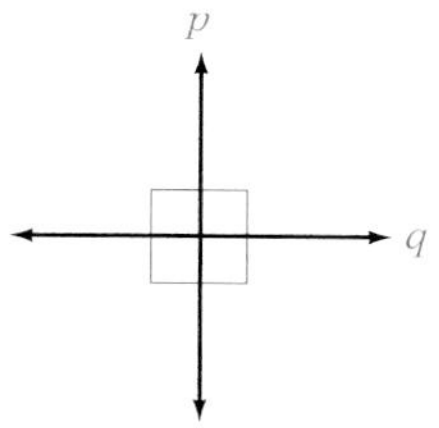

Four angles are formed by the intersection of two lines. If the two lines are perpendicular, then each of the four angles is a right angle. If the two lines are not perpendicular, then two of the angles formed are acute angles and two of the angles formed are obtuse angles. The two acute angles are always opposite each other, and the two obtuse angles are always opposite each other.

In the figure at the right, $\angle w$ and $\angle y$ are acute angles, and $\angle x$ and $\angle z$ are obtuse angles.

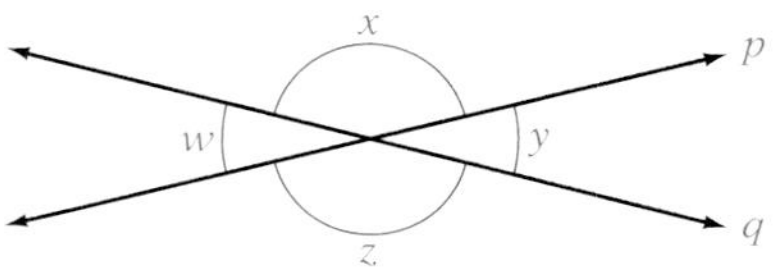

Two angles that are on opposite sides of the intersection of two lines are called **vertical angles.** Vertical angles have the same measure. $\angle w$ and $\angle y$ are vertical angles. $\angle x$ and $\angle z$ are vertical angles.

Vertical angles have the same measure.

$$\angle w = \angle y$$
$$\angle x = \angle z$$

Two angles that share a common side are called **adjacent angles.** For the figure shown above, $\angle x$ and $\angle y$ are adjacent angles, as are $\angle y$ and $\angle z$, $\angle z$ and $\angle w$, and $\angle w$ and $\angle x$. Adjacent angles of intersecting lines are supplementary angles.

Adjacent angles of intersecting lines are supplementary angles.

$$\angle x + \angle y = 180^\circ$$
$$\angle y + \angle z = 180^\circ$$
$$\angle z + \angle w = 180^\circ$$
$$\angle w + \angle x = 180^\circ$$

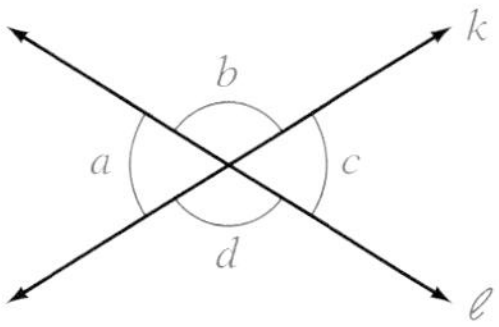

In the diagram at the left, $\angle b = 115^\circ$. Find the measures of angles a, c, and d.

$\angle a$ is supplementary to $\angle b$ because $\angle a$ and $\angle b$ are adjacent angles of intersecting lines.

$$\angle a + \angle b = 180^\circ$$
$$\angle a + 115^\circ = 180^\circ$$
$$\angle a = 65^\circ$$

$\angle c = \angle a$ because $\angle c$ and $\angle a$ are vertical angles. $\quad \angle c = 65^\circ$

$\angle d = \angle b$ because $\angle d$ and $\angle b$ are vertical angles. $\quad \angle d = 115^\circ$

EXAMPLE 3 Find x.

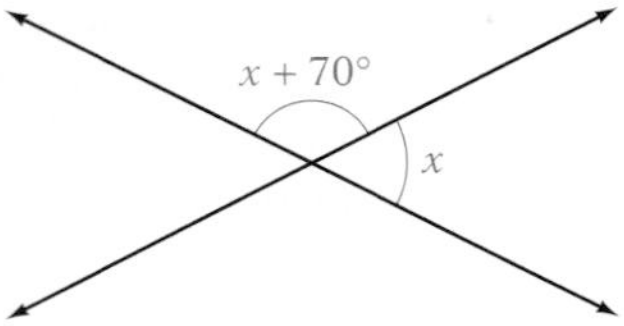

Strategy The angles labeled are adjacent angles of intersecting lines and are therefore supplementary angles. To find x, write an equation and solve for x.

Solution

$$x + (x + 70°) = 180°$$
$$2x + 70° = 180°$$
$$2x = 110°$$
$$x = 55°$$

PROBLEM 3 Find x.

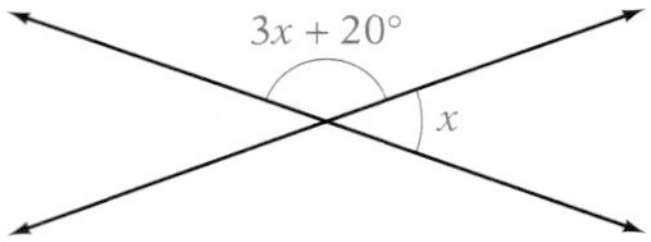

Solution See page S9.

A line that intersects two other lines at different points is called a **transversal.** If the lines cut by a transversal t are parallel lines and the transversal is not perpendicular to the parallel lines, all four acute angles have the same measure and all four obtuse angles have the same measure. In the figure at the right,

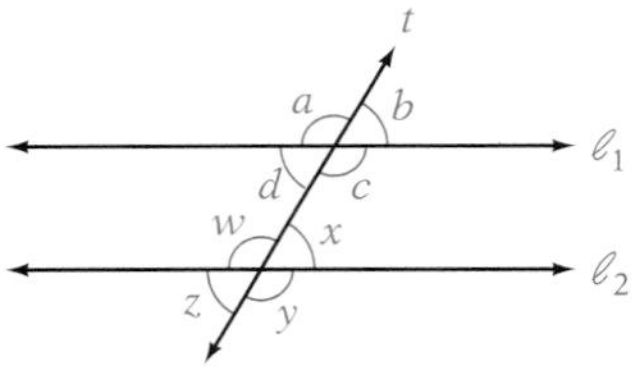

$$\angle b = \angle d = \angle x = \angle z$$
$$\angle a = \angle c = \angle w = \angle y$$

Alternate interior angles are two nonadjacent angles that are on opposite sides of the transversal and between the lines. In the figure above, $\angle c$ and $\angle w$ are alternate interior angles, and $\angle d$ and $\angle x$ are alternate interior angles. Alternate interior angles have the same measure.

Alternate interior angles have the same measure.

$$\angle c = \angle w$$
$$\angle d = \angle x$$

Alternate exterior angles are two nonadjacent angles that are on opposite sides of the transversal and outside the parallel lines. In the figure above, $\angle a$ and $\angle y$ are alternate exterior angles, and $\angle b$ and $\angle z$ are alternate exterior angles. Alternate exterior angles have the same measure.

Alternate exterior angles have the same measure.

$$\angle a = \angle y$$
$$\angle b = \angle z$$

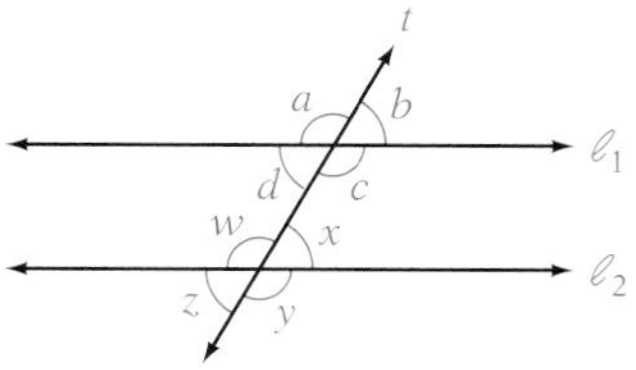

Corresponding angles are two angles that are on the same side of the transversal and are both acute angles or are both obtuse angles. In the figure at the left, the following pairs of angles are corresponding angles: $\angle a$ and $\angle w$, $\angle d$ and $\angle z$, $\angle b$ and $\angle x$, and $\angle c$ and $\angle y$. Corresponding angles have the same measure.

Corresponding angles have the same measure.

$\angle a = \angle w$
$\angle d = \angle z$
$\angle b = \angle x$
$\angle c = \angle y$

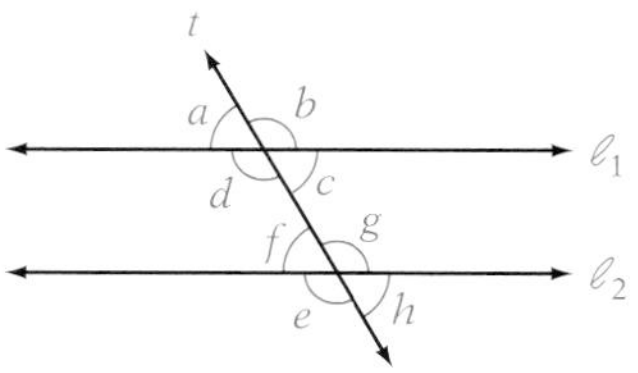

In the diagram at the left, $\ell_1 \| \ell_2$ and $\angle f = 58°$. Find the measures of $\angle a$, $\angle c$, and $\angle d$.

$\angle a$ and $\angle f$ are corresponding angles. $\angle a = \angle f = 58°$

$\angle c$ and $\angle f$ are alternate interior angles. $\angle c = \angle f = 58°$

$\angle d$ is supplementary to $\angle a$.

$$\angle d + \angle a = 180°$$
$$\angle d + 58° = 180°$$
$$\angle d = 122°$$

EXAMPLE 4 Given $\ell_1 \| \ell_2$, find x.

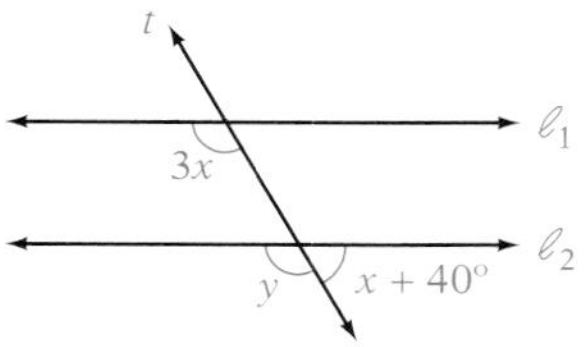

Strategy $3x = y$ because corresponding angles have the same measure. $y + (x + 40°) = 180°$ because adjacent angles of intersecting lines are supplementary angles.

Substitute $3x$ for y and solve for x.

Solution

$$y + (x + 40°) = 180°$$
$$3x + (x + 40°) = 180°$$
$$4x + 40° = 180°$$
$$4x = 140°$$
$$x = 35°$$

PROBLEM 4 Given $\ell_1 \| \ell_2$, find x.

Solution See page S9.

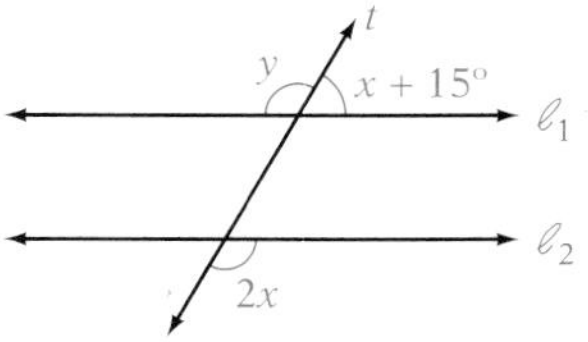

OBJECTIVE 3 Problems involving the angles of a triangle

If the lines cut by a transversal are not parallel lines, the three lines will intersect at three points. In the figure at the right, the transversal t intersects lines p and q. The three lines intersect at points A, B, and C. The geometric figure formed by line segments AB, BC, and AC is a **triangle.**

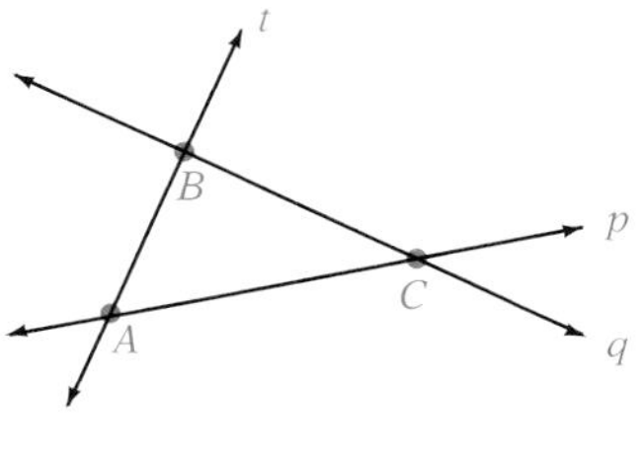

The angles within the region enclosed by the triangle are called **interior angles.** In the figure at the right, angles a, b, and c are interior angles. The sum of the measures of the interior angles is 180°.

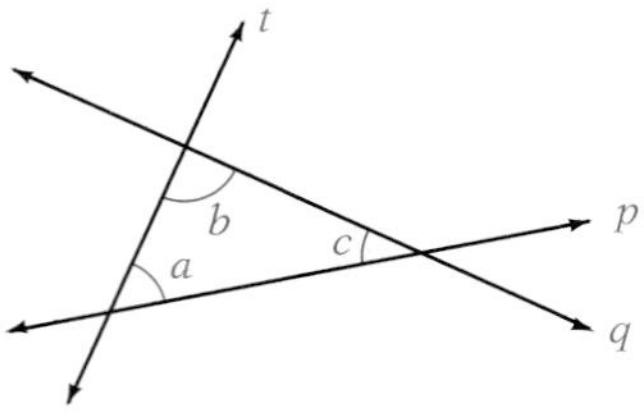

$\angle a + \angle b + \angle c = 180°$

The Sum of the Measures of the Interior Angles of a Triangle

The sum of the measures of the interior angles of a triangle is 180°.

An angle adjacent to an interior angle is an **exterior angle.** In the figure at the right, angles m and n are exterior angles for angle a. The sum of the measures of an interior and an exterior angle is 180°.

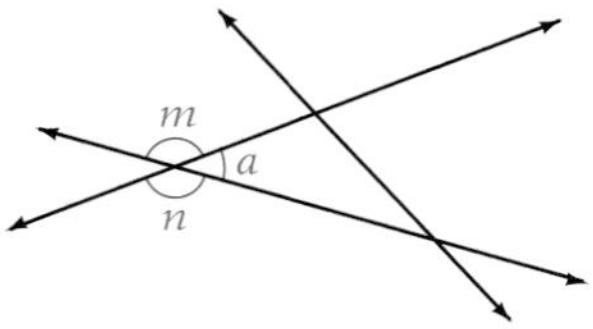

$\angle a + \angle m = 180°$
$\angle a + \angle n = 180°$

Given that $\angle c = 40°$ and $\angle e = 60°$, find the measure of $\angle d$.

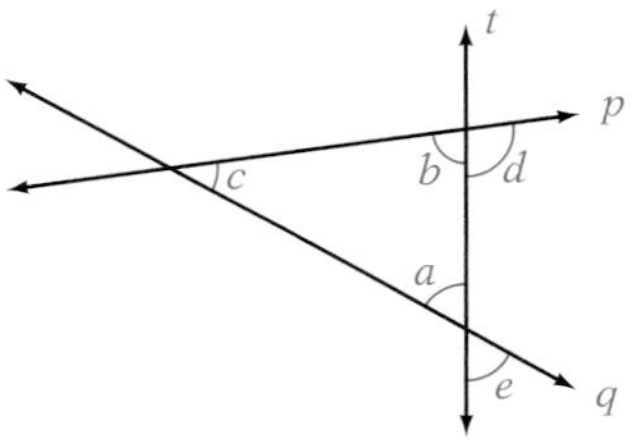

$\angle a$ and $\angle e$ are vertical angles. $\angle a = \angle e = 60°$

The sum of the interior angles is 180°.

$\angle c + \angle a + \angle b = 180°$
$40° + 60° + \angle b = 180°$
$100° + \angle b = 180°$
$\angle b = 80°$

$\angle b$ and $\angle d$ are supplementary angles.

$\angle b + \angle d = 180°$
$80° + \angle d = 180°$
$\angle d = 100°$

EXAMPLE 5 Given that $\angle a = 45°$ and $\angle x = 100°$, find the measures of angles b, c, and y.

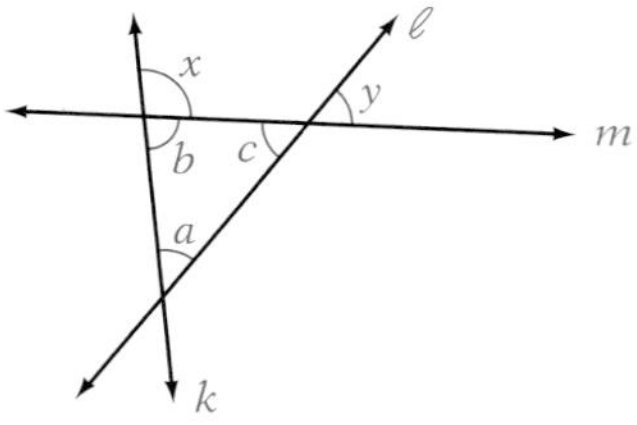

Strategy

- To find the measure of $\angle b$, use the fact that $\angle b$ and $\angle x$ are supplementary angles.
- To find the measure of $\angle c$, use the fact that the sum of the measures of the interior angles of a triangle is $180°$.
- To find the measure of $\angle y$, use the fact that $\angle c$ and $\angle y$ are vertical angles.

Solution

$$\angle b + \angle x = 180°$$
$$\angle b + 100° = 180°$$
$$\angle b = 80°$$

$$\angle a + \angle b + \angle c = 180°$$
$$45° + 80° + \angle c = 180°$$
$$125° + \angle c = 180°$$
$$\angle c = 55°$$

$$\angle y = \angle c = 55°$$

PROBLEM 5 Given that $\angle y = 55°$, find the measures of angles a, b, and d.

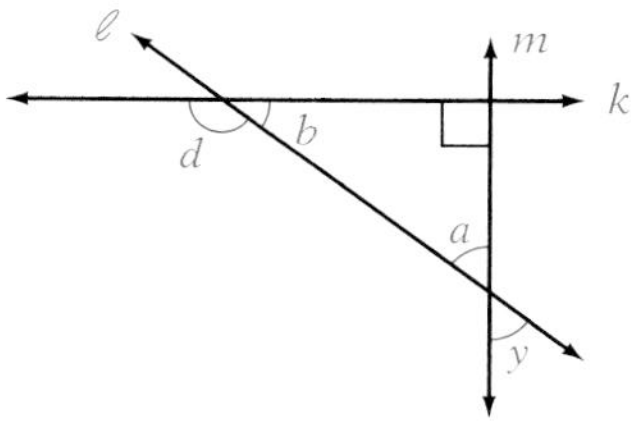

Solution See page S9.

EXAMPLE 6 Two angles of a triangle measure $43°$ and $86°$. Find the measure of the third angle.

Strategy To find the measure of the third angle, use the fact that the sum of the measures of the interior angles of a triangle is $180°$. Write an equation using x to represent the measure of the third angle. Solve the equation for x.

Solution

$$x + 43° + 86° = 180°$$
$$x + 129° = 180°$$
$$x = 51°$$

The measure of the third angle is $51°$.

PROBLEM 6 One angle of a triangle is a right angle, and one angle measures $27°$. Find the measure of the third angle.

Solution See page S9.

4.3 Concept Review

Determine whether the statement is always true, sometimes true, or never true.

1. The formula for the perimeter of a rectangle is $P = 2L + 2W$, where L represents the length and W represents the width of a rectangle.

2. In the formula for the perimeter of a triangle, $P = a + b + c$, the variables a, b, and c represent the measures of the three angles of a triangle.

3. If two angles of a triangle measure 52° and 73°, then the third angle of the triangle measures 55°.

4. An isosceles triangle has two sides of equal measure and two angles of equal measure.

5. The perimeter of a geometric figure is a measure of the area of the figure.

6. In a right triangle, the sum of the measures of the two acute angles is 90°.

4.3 Exercises

1 Perimeter problems

1. What is the difference between an isosceles triangle and an equilateral triangle?

2. Which of the following units can be used to measure perimeter?
a. feet
b. square miles
c. meters
d. ounces
e. cubic inches
f. centimeters

3. The length of the third side of an isosceles triangle is three units less than twice the length of one of the equal sides. If x is the length of one of the equal sides, an expression for the length of the third side is ___?___ .

4. The width of a rectangle is 25% of the length of the rectangle.
a. If L is the length of the rectangle, then the width of the rectangle is ___?___.
b. Write an expression for the perimeter of the rectangle: 2(___?___) + 2(___?___).
c. Simplify the expression you wrote for the perimeter of the rectangle: ___?___.

5. True or false? The formula for the perimeter of a rectangle can be written as $P = 2(L + W)$.

6.  The perimeter of an isosceles triangle is 54 ft. Let s be the length of one of the two equal sides. Is it possible for s to be 30 ft?

7. In an isosceles triangle, the third side is 50% of the length of one of the equal sides. Find the length of each side when the perimeter is 125 ft.

8. In an isosceles triangle, the length of one of the equal sides is three times the length of the third side. The perimeter is 21 m. Find the length of each side.

9. The perimeter of a rectangle is 42 m. The length of the rectangle is 3 m less than twice the width. Find the length and width of the rectangle.

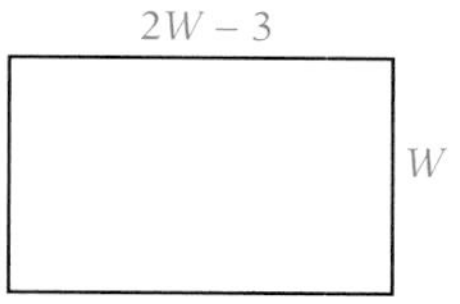

10. The width of a rectangle is 25% of the length. The perimeter is 250 cm. Find the length and width of the rectangle.

11. The perimeter of a rectangle is 120 ft. The length of the rectangle is twice the width. Find the length and width of the rectangle.

12. The perimeter of a rectangle is 50 m. The width of the rectangle is 5 m less than the length. Find the length and width of the rectangle.

13. The perimeter of a triangle is 110 cm. One side is twice the second side. The third side is 30 cm more than the second side. Find the length of each side.

14. The perimeter of a triangle is 33 ft. One side of the triangle is 1 ft longer than the second side. The third side is 2 ft longer than the second side. Find the length of each side.

15. The width of the rectangular foundation of a building is 30% of the length. The perimeter of the foundation is 338 ft. Find the length and width of the foundation.

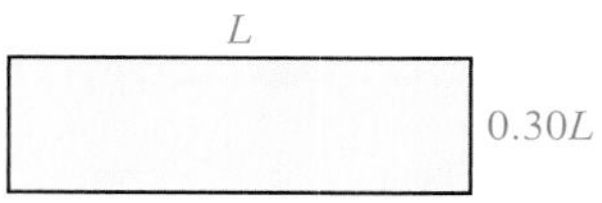

16. The perimeter of a rectangular playground is 440 ft. If the width is 100 ft, what is the length of the playground?

17. A rectangular vegetable garden has a perimeter of 64 ft. The length of the garden is 20 ft. What is the width of the garden?

18. Each of two sides of a triangular banner measures 18 in. If the perimeter of the banner is 46 in., what is the length of the third side of the banner?

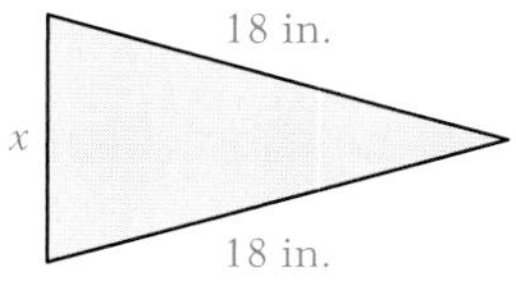

19. The perimeter of a square picture frame is 48 in. Find the length of each side of the frame.

20. A square rug has a perimeter of 32 ft. Find the length of each side of the rug.

2 Problems involving angles formed by intersecting lines

21. Name the number of degrees in each of the following.
   a. a right angle
   b. a straight angle
   c. one complete revolution
   d. an acute angle
   e. an obtuse angle
   f. complementary angles
   g. supplementary angles

22. Determine whether enough information is given to solve the problem.
   a. Find the sum of the measures of the two acute angles in a right triangle.
   b. Find the measures of the two acute angles in a right triangle.

23. Let x be the complement of a 53° angle. Then $x + 53 =$ __?__, so $x =$ __?__. The complement of a 53° angle is a __?__ angle.

24. Find x.

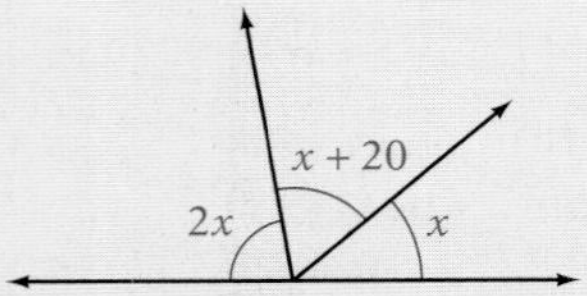

$x + x + 20 + 2x =$ __?__ • **A straight angle measures 180°.**

(__?__)$x + 20 = 180$ • **Combine like terms.**

$4x =$ __?__ • **Subtract 20 from each side of the equation.**

$x =$ __?__ • **Divide each side of the equation by 4.**

25. Find the complement of a 28° angle.

26. Find the complement of a 46° angle.

27. Find the supplement of a 73° angle.

28. Find the supplement of a 119° angle.

Find the measure of $\angle x$.

29.

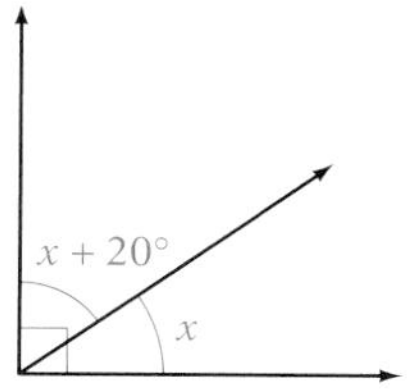

30.

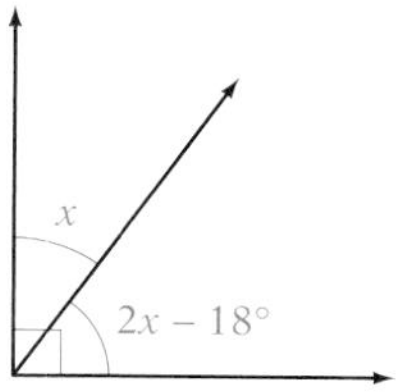

31.

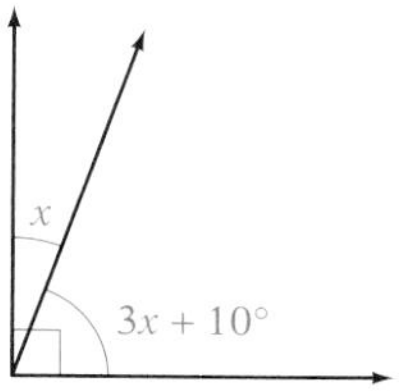

Find the measure of $\angle a$.

32.

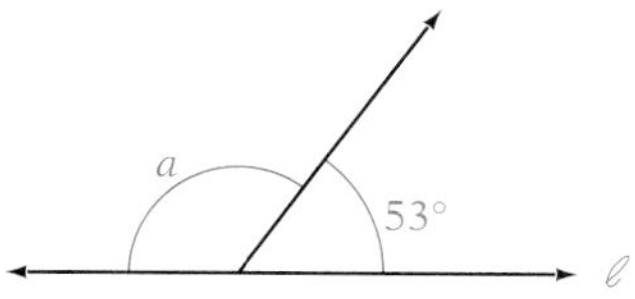

33.

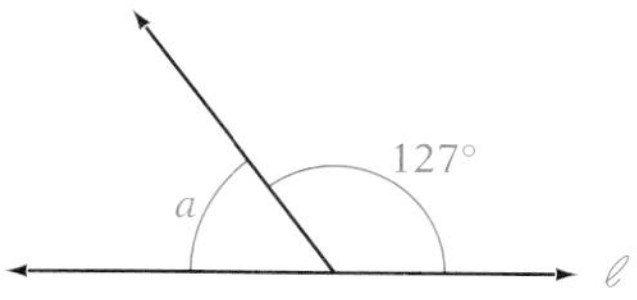

34.

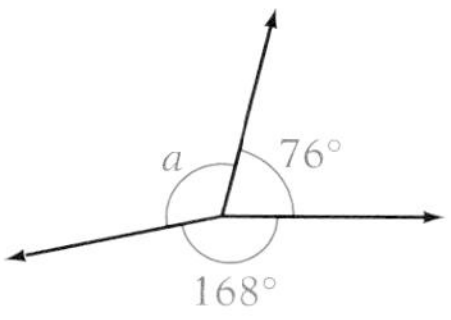

35.

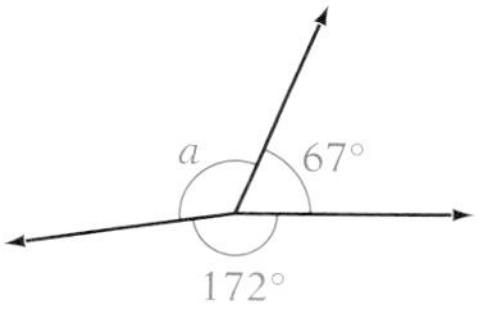

Find x.

36.

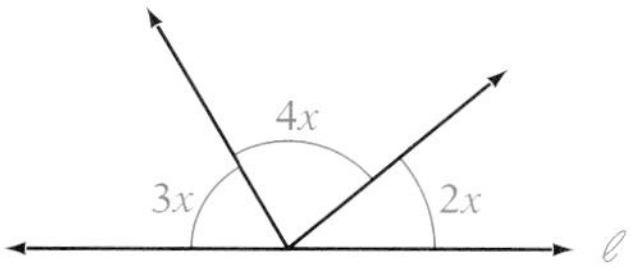

37.

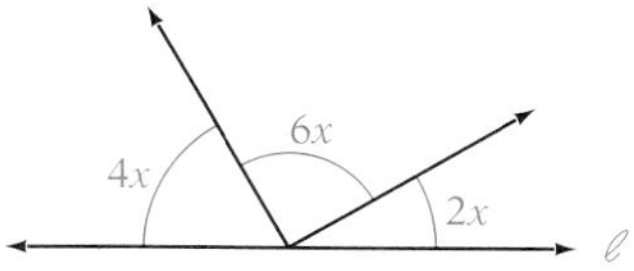

38.

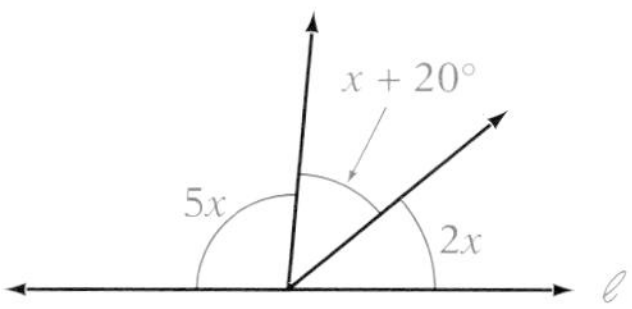

39.

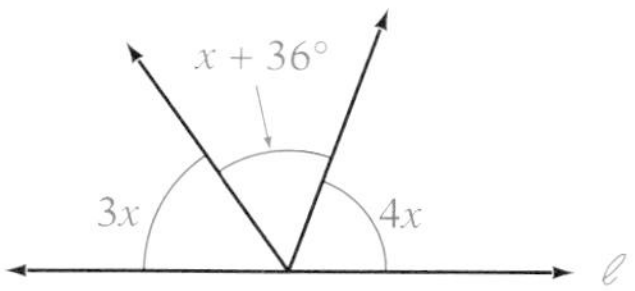

40.

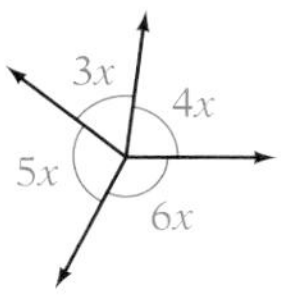

41.

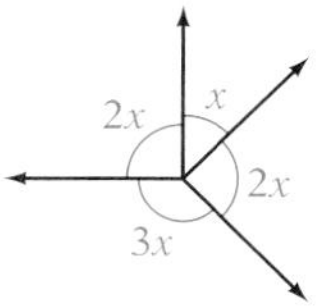

Find the measure of $\angle x$.

42.

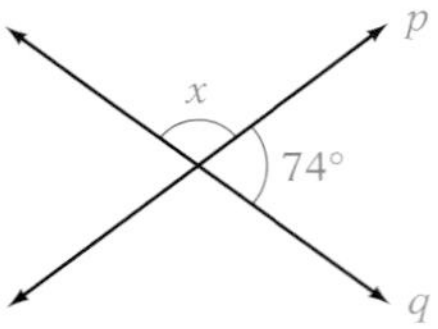

43.

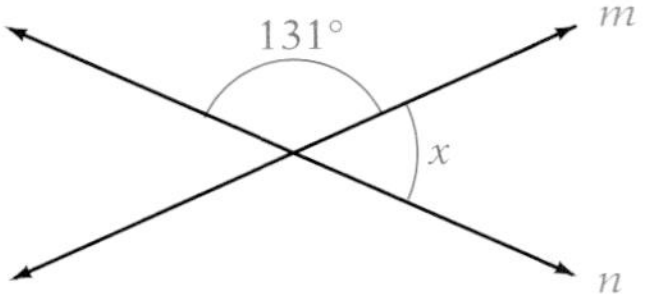

Find x.

44.

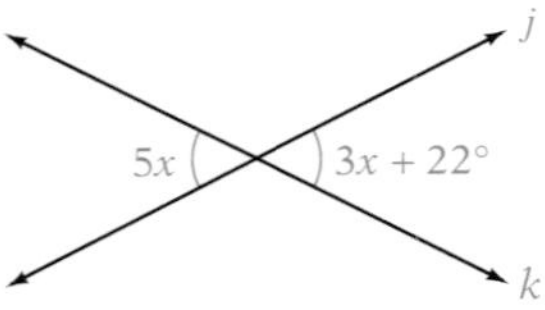

45.

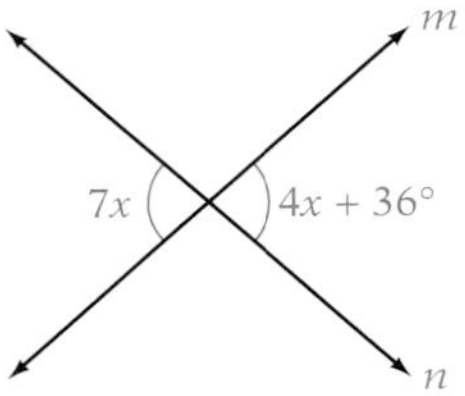

For Exercises 46 to 49, use the following diagram, in which $\ell_1 \parallel \ell_2$.

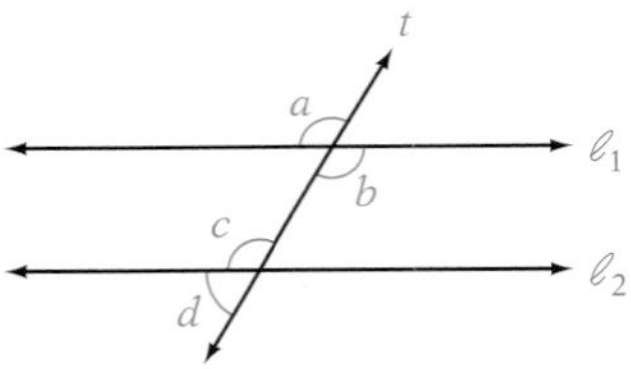

46. True or false? $\angle a$ and $\angle b$ have the same measure even if ℓ_1 and ℓ_2 are not parallel.

47. True or false? $\angle a$ and $\angle c$ have the same measure even if ℓ_1 and ℓ_2 are not parallel.

48. True or false? $\angle c$ and $\angle d$ are supplementary only if ℓ_1 and ℓ_2 are parallel.

49. True or false? $\angle c$ and $\angle d$ have the same measure only if t and ℓ_2 are perpendicular.

Given that $\ell_1 \parallel \ell_2$, find the measures of angles a and b.

50.

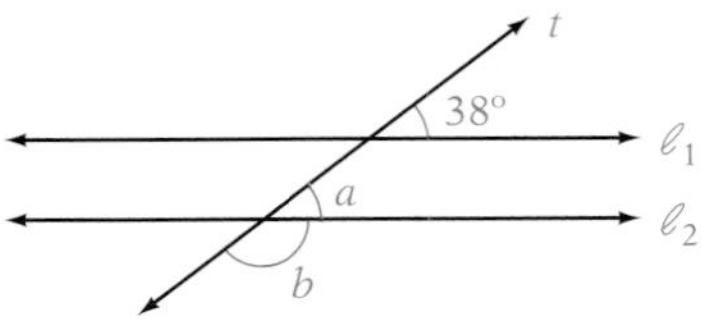

51.

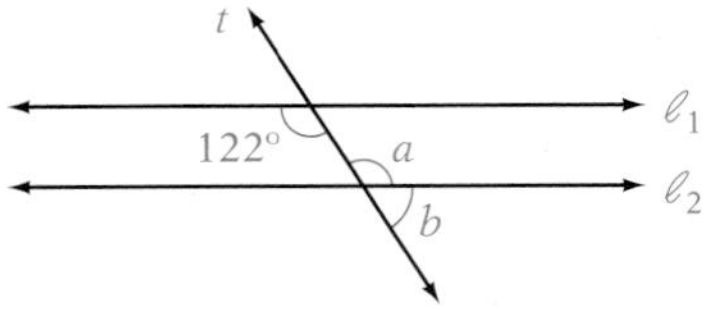

52.

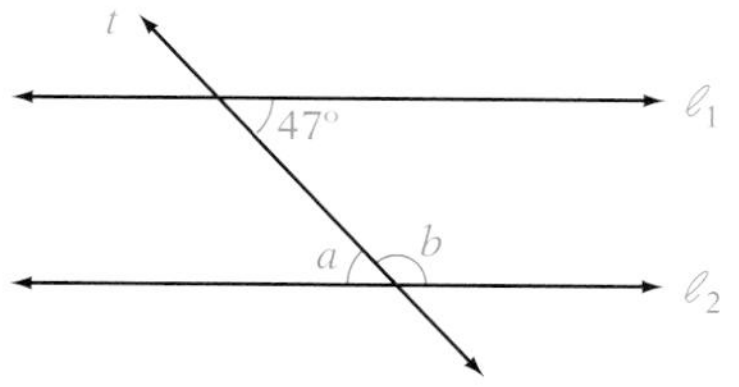

53.

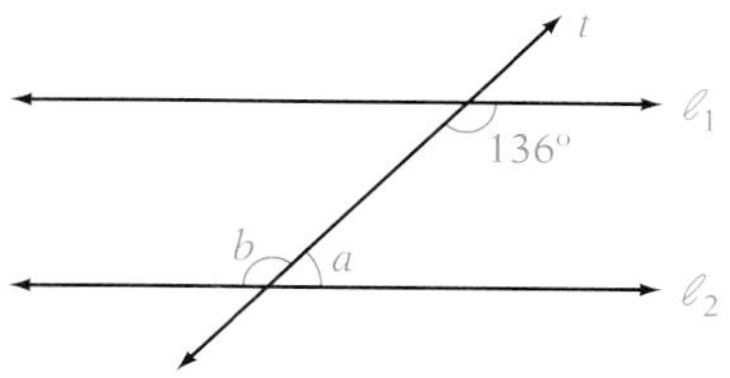

Given that $\ell_1 \| \ell_2$, find x.

54.

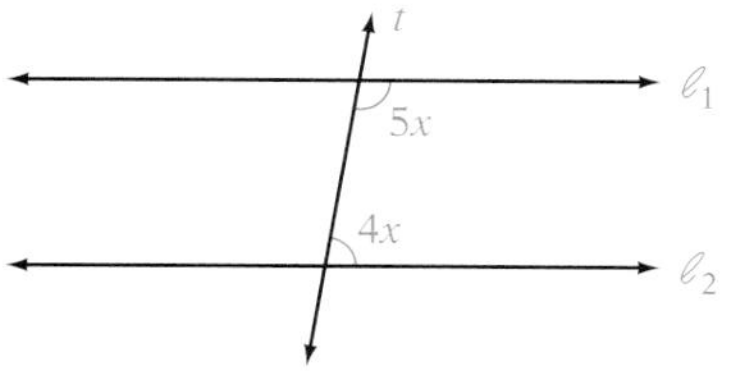

55.

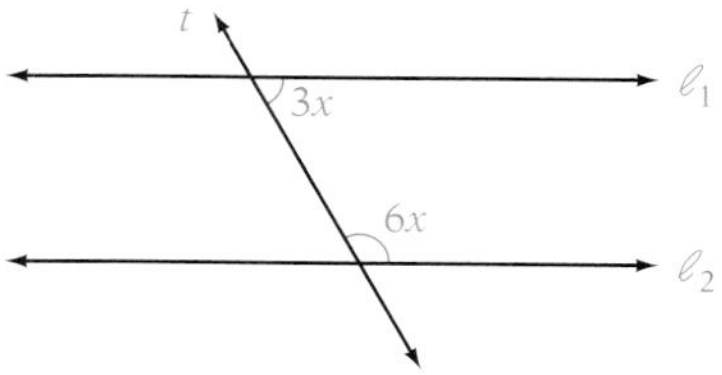

56.

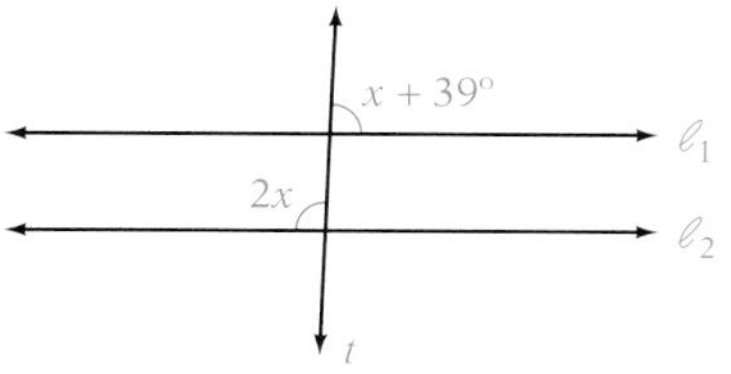

57.

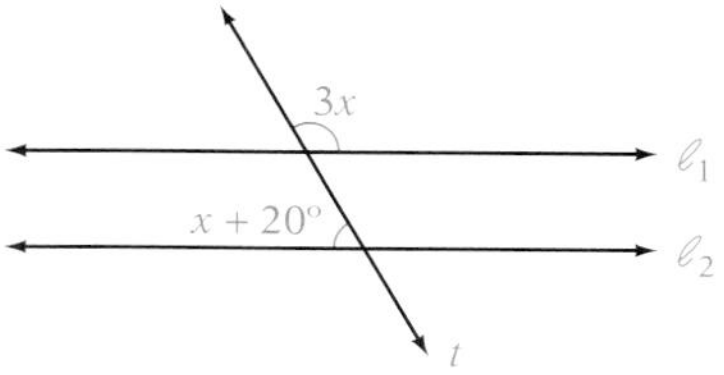

58. Given that $\angle a = 51°$, find the measure of $\angle b$.

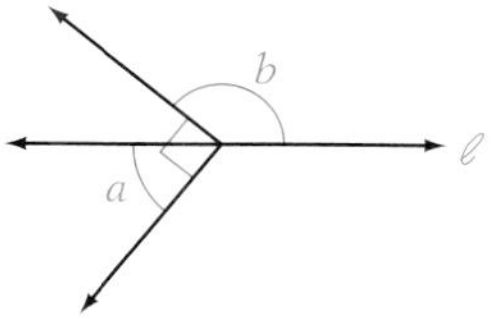

59. Given that $\angle a = 38°$, find the measure of $\angle b$.

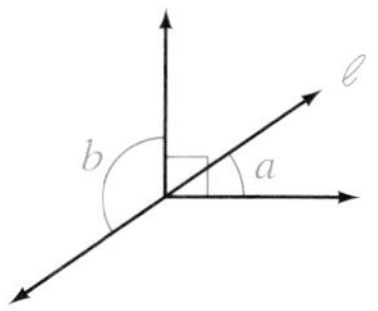

3 Problems involving the angles of a triangle

60. The three angles within the region enclosed by a triangle are called the triangle's ___?___ angles. An angle adjacent to one of these angles is an ___?___ angle of the triangle.

61. Given that $\angle x = 50°$ and $\angle c = 85°$, find the measure of $\angle a$.

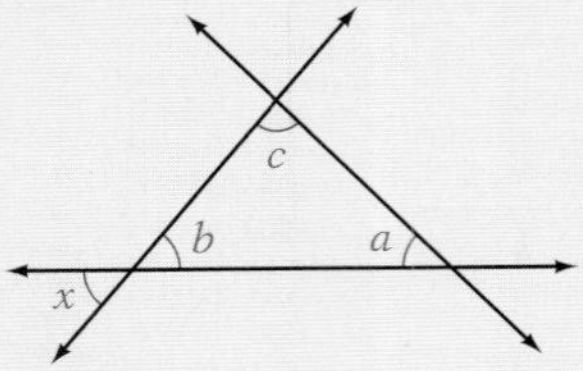

$\angle b = \angle x = 50°$ — • ___?___ **angles have the same measure.**

$\angle b + \angle c + \angle a =$ ___?___ — • **The sum of the measures of the interior angles of a triangle is 180°.**

___?___ + ___?___ $+ \angle a = 180°$ — • **Replace $\angle b$ with 50° and $\angle c$ with 85°.**

___?___ $+ \angle a = 180°$ — • **Add.**

$\angle a =$ ___?___ — • **Subtract 135° from each side of the equation.**

62. Given that $\angle a = 95°$ and $\angle b = 70°$, find the measures of angles x and y.

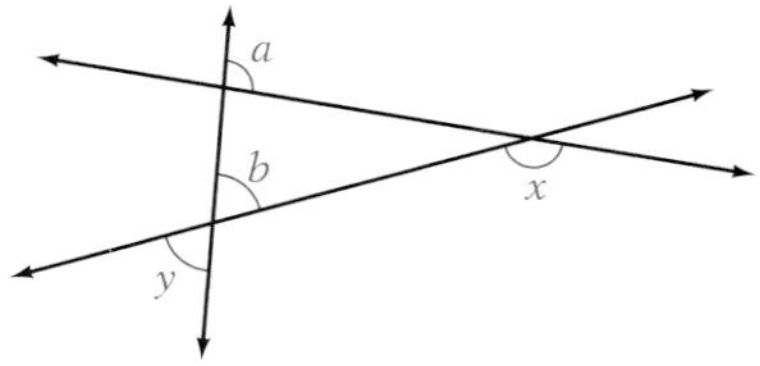

63. Given that $\angle a = 35°$ and $\angle b = 55°$, find the measures of angles x and y.

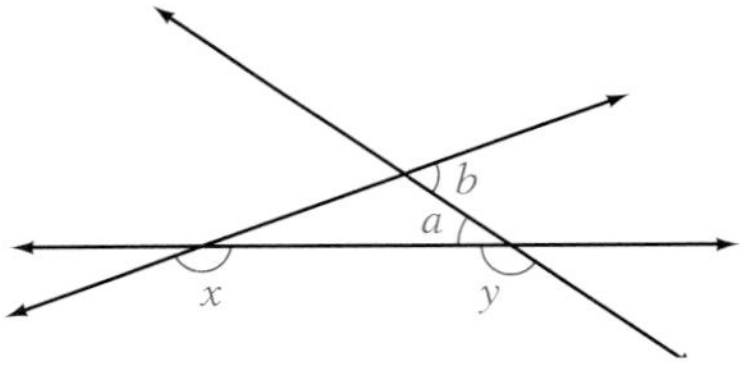

64. Given that $\angle y = 45°$, find the measures of angles a and b.

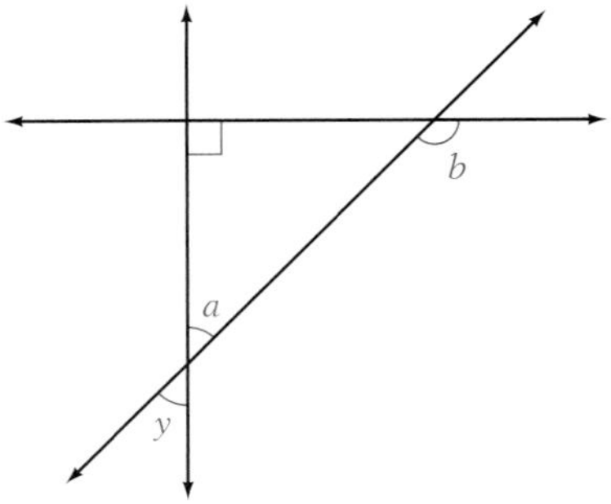

65. Given that $\angle y = 130°$, find the measures of angles a and b.

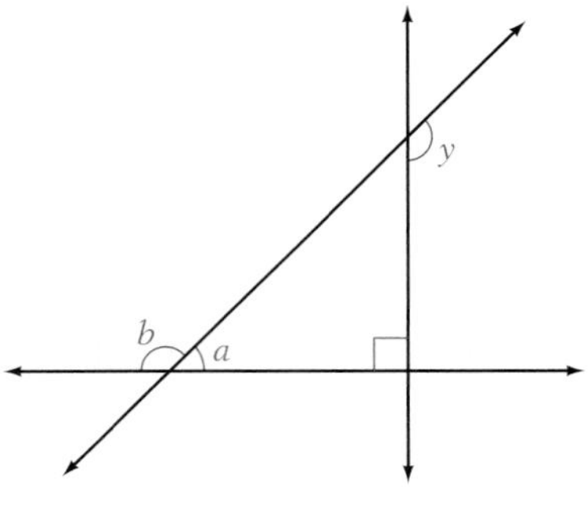

66. Given that $AO \perp OB$, express in terms of x the number of degrees in $\angle BOC$.

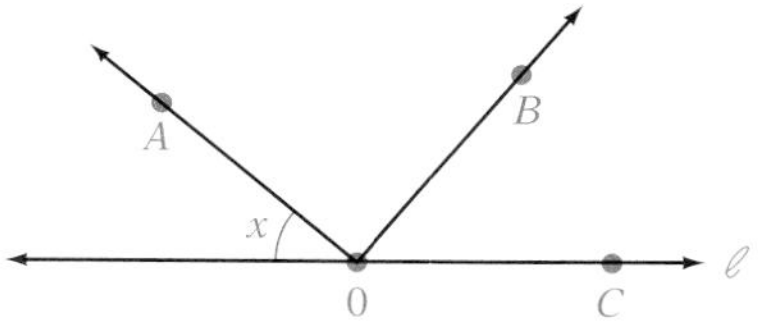

67. Given that $AO \perp OB$, express in terms of x the number of degrees in $\angle AOC$.

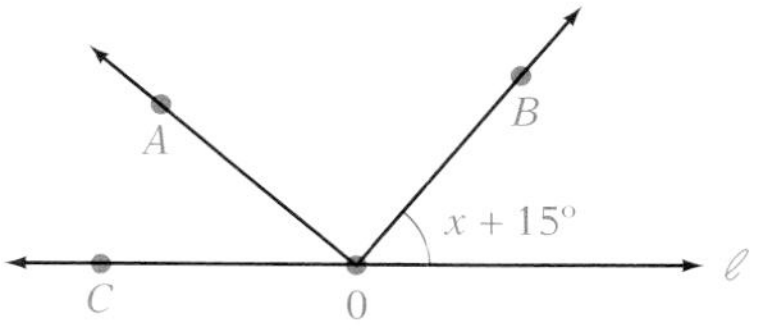

68. One angle in a triangle is a right angle, and one angle measures 30°. What is the measure of the third angle?

69. A triangle has a 45° angle and a right angle. Find the measure of the third angle.

70. Two angles of a triangle measure 42° and 103°. Find the measure of the third angle.

71. Two angles of a triangle measure 62° and 45°. Find the measure of the third angle.

72. A triangle has a 13° angle and a 65° angle. What is the measure of the third angle?

73. A triangle has a 105° angle and a 32° angle. What is the measure of the third angle?

74. In an isosceles triangle, one angle is three times the measure of one of the equal angles. Find the measure of each angle.

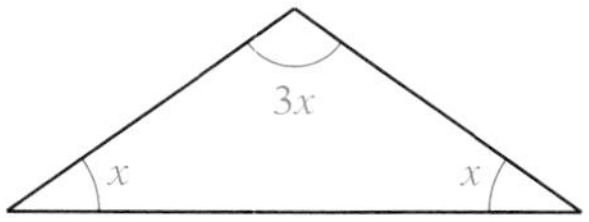

75. In an isosceles triangle, one angle is 10° less than three times the measure of one of the equal angles. Find the measure of each angle.

76. In an isosceles triangle, one angle is 16° more than twice the measure of one of the equal angles. Find the measure of each angle.

77. In a triangle, one angle is twice the measure of the second angle. The third angle is three times the measure of the second angle. Find the measure of each angle.

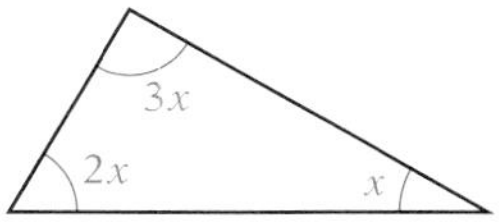

78. True or false? A triangle can have two right angles.

79. True or false? If one angle of a triangle is a right angle, then the other two angles of the triangle are complementary.

80. True or false? A triangle has nine exterior angles.

81. True or false? A triangle that has an exterior angle that is a right angle must also have an interior angle that is a right angle.

4.3 Applying Concepts

82. A rectangle and an equilateral triangle have the same perimeter. The length of the rectangle is three times the width. Each side of the triangle is 8 cm. Find the length and width of the rectangle.

83. The length of a rectangle is 1 cm more than twice the width. If the length of the rectangle is decreased by 2 cm and the width is decreased by 1 cm, the perimeter is 20 cm. Find the length and width of the original rectangle.

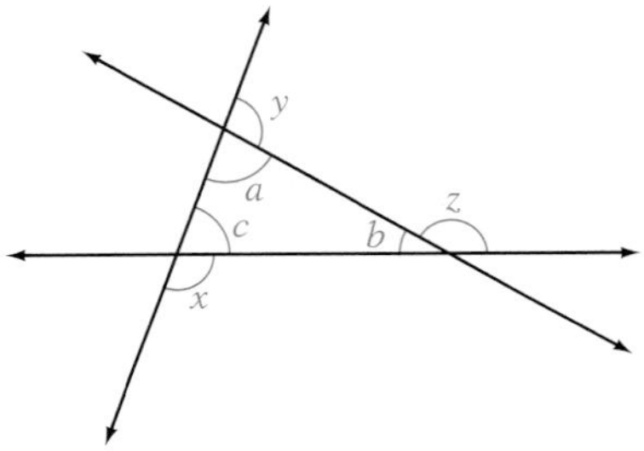

84. For the figure at the right, find the sum of the measures of angles x, y, and z.

85. For the figure at the right, explain why $\angle a + \angle b = \angle x$. Write a rule that describes the relationship between an exterior angle of a triangle and the opposite interior angles. Use the rule to write an equation involving angles a, c, and z.

86. The width of a rectangle is $8x$. The perimeter is $48x$. Find the length of the rectangle in terms of the variable x.

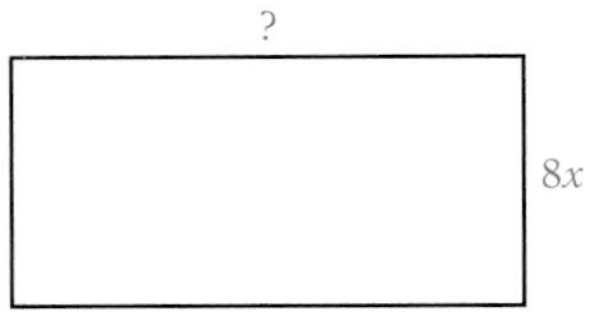

87. Write a report stating the arguments of the proponents of changing to the metric system in the United States or a report stating the arguments of those opposed to switching from the U.S. Customary System of measurement to the metric system.

88. Prepare a report on the use of geometric form in architecture.

4.4 Markup and Discount Problems

OBJECTIVE 1 Markup problems

Cost is the price that a business pays for a product. **Selling price** is the price for which a business sells a product to a customer. The difference between selling price and cost is called **markup.** Markup is added to a retailer's cost to cover the expenses of operating a business. Markup is usually expressed as a percent of the retailer's cost. This percent is called the **markup rate.**

The basic markup equations used by a business are

$$\begin{aligned} \text{Selling price} &= \text{Cost} + \text{Markup} \\ S &= C + M \end{aligned}$$

$$\begin{aligned} \text{Markup} &= \text{Markup rate} \cdot \text{Cost} \\ M &= r \cdot C \end{aligned}$$

By substituting $r \cdot C$ for M in the first equation, we can also write selling price as

$$\begin{aligned} S &= C + M \\ S &= C + (r \cdot C) \\ S &= C + rC \end{aligned}$$

The equation $S = C + rC$ is the equation used to solve the markup problems in this section.

EXAMPLE 1 The manager of a clothing store buys a suit for \$180 and sells the suit for \$252. Find the markup rate.

Strategy Given: $C = \$180$
$S = \$252$
Unknown markup rate: r
Use the equation $S = C + rC$.

Solution

$$S = C + rC$$

$$252 = 180 + 180r$$ • **Substitute the values of *C* and *S* into the equation.**

$$252 - 180 = 180 - 180 + 180r$$ • **Subtract 180 from each side of the equation.**

$$72 = 180r$$

$$\frac{72}{180} = \frac{180r}{180}$$ • **Divide each side of the equation by 180.**

$$0.4 = r$$ • **The decimal must be changed to a percent.**

The markup rate is 40%.

PROBLEM 1 The cost to the manager of a sporting goods store for a tennis racket is \$120. The selling price of the racket is \$180. Find the markup rate.

Solution See page S9.

EXAMPLE 2 The manager of a furniture store uses a markup rate of 45% on all items. The selling price of a chair is \$232. Find the cost of the chair.

Strategy Given: $r = 45\% = 0.45$
$S = \$232$
Unknown cost: C
Use the equation $S = C + rC$.

Solution

$$S = C + rC$$

$$232 = C + 0.45C$$

$$232 = 1.45C$$ • $C + 0.45C = 1C + 0.45C = (1 + 0.45)C$

$$160 = C$$

The cost of the chair is \$160.

PROBLEM 2 A hardware store employee uses a markup rate of 40% on all items. The selling price of a lawnmower is $266. Find the cost.

Solution See page S9.

OBJECTIVE 2

Discount problems

Discount is the amount by which a retailer reduces the regular price of a product for a promotional sale. Discount is usually expressed as a percent of the regular price. This percent is called the **discount rate** or **markdown rate.**

The basic discount equations used by a business are

$$\begin{array}{ccccc} \text{Sale price} & = & \text{Regular price} & - & \text{Discount} \\ S & = & R & - & D \end{array}$$

$$\begin{array}{ccccc} \text{Discount} & = & \text{Discount rate} & \cdot & \text{Regular price} \\ D & = & r & \cdot & R \end{array}$$

By substituting $r \cdot R$ for D in the first equation, we can also write sale price as

$$\begin{aligned} S &= R - D \\ S &= R - (r \cdot R) \\ S &= R - rR \end{aligned}$$

The equation $S = R - rR$ is the equation used to solve the discount problems in this section.

EXAMPLE 3 In a garden supply store, the regular price of a 100-foot garden hose is $48. During an "after-summer sale," the hose is being sold for $36. Find the discount rate.

Strategy Given: $R = \$48$

$S = \$36$

Unknown discount rate: r

Use the equation $S = R - rR$.

Solution

$$S = R - rR$$

$$36 = 48 - 48r$$

- **Substitute the values of *R* and *S* into the equation.**

$$36 - 48 = 48 - 48 - 48r$$

$$-12 = -48r$$

- **Subtract 48 from each side of the equation.**

$$\frac{-12}{-48} = \frac{-48r}{-48}$$

- **Divide each side of the equation by −48.**

$$0.25 = r$$

- **The decimal must be changed to a percent.**

The discount rate is 25%.

PROBLEM 3 A case of motor oil that regularly sells for $39.80 is on sale for $29.85. What is the discount rate?

Solution See page S9.

EXAMPLE 4 The sale price for a chemical sprayer is \$27.30. This price is 35% off the regular price. Find the regular price.

Strategy Given: $S = \$27.30$
$r = 35\% = 0.35$
Unknown regular price: R
Use the equation $S = R - rR$.

Solution

$$S = R - rR$$
$$27.30 = R - 0.35R$$
$$27.30 = 0.65R \qquad \bullet\ R - 0.35R = 1R - 0.35R = (1 - 0.35)R$$
$$42 = R$$

The regular price is \$42.00.

PROBLEM 4 The sale price for a telephone is \$43.50. This price is 25% off the regular price. Find the regular price.

Solution See page S10.

4.4 Concept Review

Determine whether the statement is always true, sometimes true, or never true.

1. In the markup equation $S = C + rC$, the variable r represents the markup rate.

2. Markup is an amount of money, whereas markup rate is a percent.

3. In the discount equation $S = R - rR$, the variable R represents the discount rate.

4. In the markup equation, S represents sale price, and in the discount equation, S represents selling price.

5. $R - 0.45R = 1R - 0.45R = (1 - 0.45)R = 0.55R$ is an example of the application of the Distributive Property.

4.4 Exercises

1 Markup problems

1. Explain the difference between the cost and the selling price of a product.

2. Explain the difference between markup and markup rate.

Complete Exercises 3 and 4 by replacing the question marks with the correct number from the problem situation or with the word *unknown*.

3. **Problem Situation:** A pair of jeans sells for \$40. The store uses a markup rate of 25%. Find the cost of the pair of jeans.
In the formula $S = C + rC$, $S =$ __?__, $C =$ __?__, and $r =$ __?__.

4. **Problem Situation:** A washing machine that costs \$620 is sold for \$806. Find the markup rate.
In the formula $S = C + rC$, $S =$ __?__, $C =$ __?__, and $r =$ __?__.

5. A computer software retailer uses a markup rate of 40%. Find the selling price of a computer game that costs the retailer \$40.

6. A car dealer advertises a 5% markup over cost. Find the selling price of a car that costs the dealer \$26,000.

7. An electronics store uses a markup rate of 58%. Find the selling price of a camcorder that costs the store owner \$358.

8. The cost to a landscape architect for a 25-gallon tree is \$65. Find the selling price of the tree if the markup rate used by the architect is 30%.

9. A set of golf clubs costing \$360 is sold for \$630. Find the markup rate on the set of golf clubs.

10. A jeweler purchases a diamond ring for \$7198.50. The selling price is \$14,397. Find the markup rate.

11. A freezer costing \$360 is sold for \$520. Find the markup rate. Round to the nearest tenth of a percent.

12. A grocer purchases a can of fruit juice for \$1.96. The selling price of the fruit juice is \$2.45. Find the markup rate.

13. A watch costing \$98 is sold for \$156.80. Find the markup rate on the watch.

14. A sofa costing \$320 is sold for \$479. Find the markup rate. Round to the nearest tenth of a percent.

15. The selling price of a compact disc player is \$168. The markup rate used by the seller is 40%. Find the cost of the compact disc player.

16. A manufacturer of exercise equipment uses a markup rate of 45%. One of the manufacturer's treadmills has a selling price of $580. Find the cost of the treadmill.

17. A markup rate of 40% was used on a basketball with a selling price of $82.60. Find the cost of the basketball.

18. A digitally recorded compact disc has a selling price of $18.90. The markup rate is 40%. Find the cost of the CD.

19. A markup rate of 25% is used on a computer that has a selling price of $2187.50. Find the cost of the computer.

20. The selling price of a portable CD player is $132. The markup rate used by the retailer is 60%. Find the cost to the retailer.

21. True or False? If a store uses a markup rate of 35%, you can find the store's cost for an item by dividing the selling price of the item by 1 + 0.35, or 1.35.

22. If the markup rate on an item is 100%, what is the relationship between the selling price of the item and the cost of the item?

2 Discount problems

23. Explain the meaning of sale price and discount.

24. Explain the difference between discount and discount rate.

Complete Exercises 25 and 26 by replacing the question marks with the correct number from the problem situation or with the word *unknown*.

25. **Problem Situation:** The regular price of a camera is $375. The camera is on sale for $318.75. Find the discount rate.
In the formula $S = R - rR$, $S = \underline{\quad ? \quad}$, $R = \underline{\quad ? \quad}$, and $r = \underline{\quad ? \quad}$.

26. **Problem Situation:** The sale price of a pair of shoes is $44, which is 20% off the regular price. Find the regular price.
In the formula $S = R + rR$, $S = \underline{\quad ? \quad}$, $R = \underline{\quad ? \quad}$, and $r = \underline{\quad ? \quad}$.

27. A tennis racket that regularly sells for $135 is on sale for 25% off the regular price. Find the sale price.

28. A fax machine that regularly sells for $219.99 is on sale for $33\frac{1}{3}\%$ off the regular price. Find the sale price.

29. A supplier of electrical equipment offers a 5% discount for a purchase that is paid for within 30 days. A transformer regularly sells for \$230. Find the discount price of a transformer that is paid for 10 days after the purchase.

30. A clothing wholesaler offers a discount of 10% per shirt when 10 to 20 shirts are purchased and a discount of 15% per shirt when 21 to 50 shirts are purchased. A shirt regularly sells for \$27. Find the sale price per shirt when 35 shirts are purchased.

31. A car stereo system that regularly sells for \$425 is on sale for \$318.75. Find the discount rate.

32. A pair of roller blades that regularly sells for \$99.99 is on sale for \$79.99. Find the discount rate. Round to the nearest percent.

33. An oak bedroom set with a regular price of \$1295 is on sale for \$995. Find the discount rate. Round to the nearest tenth of a percent.

34. A stereo set with a regular price of \$495 is on sale for \$395. Find the markdown rate. Round to the nearest tenth of a percent.

35. A digital camera with a regular price of \$325 is on sale for \$201.50. Find the markdown rate.

36. A luggage set with a regular price of \$178 is on sale for \$103.24. Find the discount rate.

37. The sale price of a free-weight home gym is \$408, which is 20% off the regular price. Find the regular price.

38. The sale price of a toboggan is \$77, which is 30% off the regular price. Find the regular price.

39. A mechanic's tool set is on sale for \$180 after a markdown of 40% off the regular price. Find the regular price.

40. The sale price of a modem is \$126, which is 30% off the regular price. Find the regular price.

41. A telescope is on sale for \$165 after a markdown of 40% off the regular price. Find the regular price.

42. An exercise bike is on sale for \$390, having been marked down 25% off the regular price. Find the regular price.

43. True or false? If a store uses a discount rate of 15%, you can find the sale price for an item by multiplying the regular price of the item by $1 - 0.15$, or 0.85.

44. If the discount rate on an item is 50%, which of the following is true?
a. $S = 2R$ **b.** $R = 2S$ **c.** $S = R$ **d.** $0.50S = R$

4.4 Applying Concepts

45. A pair of shoes that now sells for \$63 has been marked up 40%. Find the markup on the pair of shoes.

46. The sale price of a motorcycle helmet is 25% off the regular price. The discount is \$70. Find the sale price.

47. A refrigerator selling for \$770 has a markup of \$220. Find the markup rate.

48. The sale price of a copy machine is \$765 after a discount of \$135. Find the discount rate.

49. The manager of a camera store uses a markup rate of 30%. Find the cost of a camera selling for \$299.

50. The sale price of a television is \$180. Find the regular price if the sale price was computed by taking $\frac{1}{3}$ off the regular price followed by an additional 25% discount on the reduced price.

51. A customer buys four tires, three at the regular price and one for 20% off the regular price. The four tires cost \$304. What was the regular price of a tire?

52. A lamp, originally priced at under \$100, was on sale for 25% off the regular price. When the regular price, a whole number of dollars, was discounted, the discounted price was also a whole number of dollars. Find the largest possible number of dollars in the regular price of the lamp.

53. A used car is on sale for a discount of 20% off the regular price of \$8500. An additional 10% discount on the sale price was offered. Is the result a 30% discount? What is the single discount that would give the same sale price?

54. Write a report on series trade discounts. Explain how to convert a series discount to a single-discount equivalent.

4.5 Investment Problems

OBJECTIVE 1 Investment problems

Recall that the annual simple interest that an investment earns is given by the equation $I = Pr$, where I is the simple interest, P is the principal, or the amount invested, and r is the simple interest rate.

Point of Interest

You may be familiar with the simple interest formula I = Prt. *If so, you know that* t *represents time. In the problems in this section, time is always 1 (one year), so the formula* I = Prt *simplifies to*

$$I = Pr(1)$$
$$I = Pr$$

The annual simple interest rate on a \$4500 investment is 8%. Find the annual simple interest earned on the investment.

Given: $P = \$4500$
$r = 8\% = 0.08$
Unknown interest: I

$I = Pr$
$I = 4500(0.08)$
$I = 360$

The annual simple interest earned is \$360.

Solve: An investor has a total of \$10,000 to deposit in two simple interest accounts. On one account, the annual simple interest rate is 7%. On the second account, the annual simple interest rate is 8%. How much should be invested in each account so that the total annual interest earned is \$785?

STRATEGY for solving a problem involving money deposited in two simple interest accounts

▶ For each amount invested, use the equation $Pr = I$. Write a numerical or variable expression for the principal, the interest rate, and the interest earned. The results can be recorded in a table.

The sum of the amounts invested is \$10,000.

Amount invested at 7%: x
Amount invested at 8%: $\$10,000 - x$

Take Note

Use the information given in the problem to fill in the principal and interest rate columns of the table. Fill in the interest earned column by multiplying the two expressions you wrote in each row.

	Principal, P	·	Interest rate, r	=	Interest earned, I
Amount at 7%	x	·	0.07	=	$0.07x$
Amount at 8%	$10,000 - x$	·	0.08	=	$0.08(10,000 - x)$

▶ Determine how the amounts of interest earned on the individual investments are related. For example, the total interest earned by both accounts may be known, or it may be known that the interest earned on one account is equal to the interest earned on the other account.

The sum of the interest earned by the two investments equals the total annual interest earned ($785).

$$
\begin{aligned}
0.07x + 0.08(10{,}000 - x) &= 785 \\
0.07x + 800 - 0.08x &= 785 \\
-0.01x + 800 &= 785 \\
-0.01x &= -15 \\
x &= 1500
\end{aligned}
$$

- **The interest earned on the 7% account plus the interest earned on the 8% account equals the total annual interest earned.**

$$10{,}000 - x = 10{,}000 - 1500 = 8500$$

- **Substitute the value of *x* into the variable expression for the amount invested at 8%.**

The amount invested at 7% is $1500.
The amount invested at 8% is $8500.

EXAMPLE 1 An investment counselor invested 75% of a client's money into a 9% annual simple interest money market fund. The remainder was invested in 6% annual simple interest government securities. Find the amount invested in each if the total annual interest earned is $3300.

Strategy ▶ Amount invested: x
Amount invested at 9%: $0.75x$
Amount invested at 6%: $0.25x$

	Principal	·	Rate	=	Interest
Amount at 9%	$0.75x$	·	0.09	=	$0.09(0.75x)$
Amount at 6%	$0.25x$	·	0.06	=	$0.06(0.25x)$

▶ The sum of the interest earned by the two investments equals the total annual interest earned ($3300).

Solution

$$
\begin{aligned}
0.09(0.75x) + 0.06(0.25x) &= 3300 \\
0.0675x + 0.015x &= 3300 \\
0.0825x &= 3300
\end{aligned}
$$

- **The interest earned on the 9% account plus the interest earned on the 6% account equals the total annual interest earned.**

$$x = 40{,}000$$

- **The amount invested is $40,000.**

$$0.75x = 0.75(40{,}000) = 30{,}000$$

- **Find the amount invested at 9%.**

$$0.25x = 0.25(40{,}000) = 10{,}000$$

- **Find the amount invested at 6%.**

The amount invested at 9% is $30,000.
The amount invested at 6% is $10,000.

PROBLEM 1 An investment of $2500 is made at an annual simple interest rate of 7%. How much additional money must be invested at 10% so that the total interest earned will be 9% of the total investment?

Solution See page S10.

4.5 Concept Review

Determine whether the statement is always true, sometimes true, or never true.

1. In the simple interest formula $I = Pr$, the variable I represents the simple interest earned.

2. For one year, you have \$1000 deposited in an account that pays 5% annual simple interest. You will earn exactly \$5 in simple interest on this account.

3. For one year, you have x dollars deposited in an account that pays 7% annual simple interest. You will earn $0.07x$ in simple interest on this account.

4. If you have a total of \$8000 deposited in two accounts and you represent the amount you have in the first account as x, then the amount in the second account is represented as $8000 - x$.

5. The amount of interest earned on one account is $0.05x$ and the amount of interest earned on a second account is $0.08(9000 - x)$. If the two accounts earn the same amount of interest, then we can write the equation $0.05x + 0.08(9000 - x)$.

6. If the amount of interest earned on one account is $0.06x$ and the amount of interest earned on a second account is $0.09(4000 - x)$, then the total interest earned on the two accounts can be represented as $0.06x + 0.09(4000 - x)$.

4.5 Exercises

1 Investment problems

1. You invest an amount of money at an annual simple interest rate of 5.2%. You invest a second amount, \$1000 more than the first, at an annual simple interest rate of 7.2%. Let x represent the amount invested at 5.2%. Complete the following table.

	Principal, P	·	Interest rate, r	=	Interest earned, I
Amount at 5.2%	x	·	?	=	?
Amount at 7.2%	?	·	?	=	?

2. The total annual interest earned on the investments in Exercise 1 is $320. Use this information and the information in the table in Exercise 1 to write an equation that can be solved to find the amount of money invested at 5.2%: __?__ + __?__ = __?__.

3. A dentist invested a portion of $15,000 in a 7% annual simple interest account and the remainder in a 6.5% annual simple interest government bond. The two investments earn $1020 in interest annually. How much was invested in each account?

4. A university alumni association invested part of $20,000 in preferred stock that earns 8% annual simple interest, and the remainder in a municipal bond that earns 7% annual simple interest. The amount of interest earned each year is $1520. How much was invested in each account?

5. A professional athlete deposited an amount of money into a high-yield mutual fund that earns 13% annual simple interest. A second deposit, $2500 more than the first, was placed in a certificate of deposit earning 7% annual simple interest. In one year, the total interest earned on both investments was $475. How much money was invested in the mutual fund?

6. Jan Moser made a deposit into a 7% annual simple interest account. She made another deposit, $1500 less than the first, in a certificate of deposit earning 9% annual simple interest. The total interest earned on both investments for one year was $505. How much money was deposited in the certificate of deposit?

7. A team of cancer research specialists received a grant of $300,000 to be used for cancer research. They deposited some of the money in a 10% simple interest account and the remainder in an 8.5% annual simple interest account. How much was deposited in each account if the annual interest is $28,500?

8. Reggie Means invested part of $30,000 in municipal bonds that earn 6.5% annual simple interest and the remainder of the money in 8.5% corporate bonds. How much is invested in each account if the total annual interest earned is $2190?

9. To provide for retirement income, Teresa Puelo purchases a $5000 bond that earns 7.5% annual simple interest. How much money does Teresa have invested in bonds that earn 8% annual simple interest if the total annual interest earned from the two investments is $615?

10. After the sale of some income property, Jeremy Littlefield invested $40,000 in a certificate of deposit that earns 7.25% annual simple interest. How much money does he have invested in certificates that earn an annual simple interest rate of 8.5% if the total annual interest earned from the two investments is $5025?

11. Suki Hiroshi has made an investment of \$2500 at an annual simple interest rate of 7%. How much money does she have invested at an annual simple interest rate of 11% if the total interest earned is 9% of the total investment?

12. Mae Jackson has a total of \$6000 invested in two simple interest accounts. The annual simple interest rate on one account is 9%. The annual simple interest rate on the second account is 6%. How much is invested in each account if both accounts earn the same amount of interest?

13. A charity deposited a total of \$54,000 in two simple interest accounts. The annual simple interest rate on one account is 8%. The annual simple interest rate on the second account is 12%. How much was invested in each account if the total annual interest earned is 9% of the total investment?

14. A sports foundation deposited a total of \$24,000 into two simple interest accounts. The annual simple interest rate on one account is 7%. The annual simple interest rate on the second account is 11%. How much is invested in each account if the total annual interest earned is 10% of the total investment?

15. Wayne Miller, an investment banker, invested 55% of the bank's available cash in an account that earns 8.25% annual simple interest. The remainder of the cash was placed in an account that earns 10% annual simple interest. The interest earned in one year was \$58,743.75. Find the total amount invested.

16. Mohammad Aran, a financial planner, recommended that 40% of a client's cash account be invested in preferred stock earning 9% annual simple interest. The remainder of the client's cash was placed in Treasury bonds earning 7% annual simple interest. The total annual interest earned from the two investments was \$2496. Find the total amount invested.

17. Sarah Ontkean is the manager of a mutual fund. She placed 30% of the fund's available cash in a 6% annual simple interest account, 25% in 8% corporate bonds, and the remainder in a money market fund earning 7.5% annual simple interest. The total annual interest earned from the investments was \$35,875. Find the total amount invested.

18. Joseph Abruzzio is the manager of a trust. He invested 30% of a client's cash in government bonds that earn 6.5% annual simple interest, 30% in utility stocks that earn 7% annual simple interest, and the remainder in an account that earns 8% annual simple interest. The total annual interest earned from the investments was \$5437.50. Find the total amount invested.

19.  The amount of annual interest earned on the x dollars that Beth invested in one simple interest account was $0.03x$, and the amount of annual interest earned on the money that Beth invested in another simple interest account was $0.05(5000 - x)$.

a. What were the interest rates on the two accounts?
b. What was the total amount of money that Beth had invested in the two accounts?

20. Refer to the investments described in Exercise 19. Which of the following could be true about the total amount T of interest earned on Beth's two accounts? There may be more than one correct answer.
a. $T < 150$ **b.** $T > 150$ **c.** $T < 250$ **d.** $T > 250$

4.5 Applying Concepts

21. A sales representative invests in a stock paying 9% dividends. A research consultant invests \$5000 more than the sales representative in bonds paying 8% annual simple interest. The research consultant's income from the investment is equal to the sales representative's. Find the amount of the research consultant's investment.

22. A financial manager invested 20% of a client's money in bonds paying 9% annual simple interest, 35% in an 8% simple interest account, and the remainder in 9.5% corporate bonds. Find the amount invested in each if the total annual interest earned is \$5325.

23. A plant manager invested \$3000 more in stocks than in bonds. The stocks paid 8% annual simple interest, and the bonds paid 9.5% annual simple interest. Both investments yielded the same income. Find the total annual interest received on both investments.

24. A bank offers a customer a 2-year certificate of deposit (CD) that earns 8% compound annual interest. This means that the interest earned each year is added to the principal before the interest for the next year is calculated. Find the value in 2 years of a nurse's investment of \$2500 in this CD.

25. A bank offers a customer a 3-year certificate of deposit (CD) that earns 8.5% compound annual interest. This means that the interest earned each year is added to the principal before the interest for the next year is calculated. Find the value in 3 years of an accountant's investment of \$3000 in this CD.

26. Write an essay on the topic of annual percentage rates.

27. Financial advisors may predict how much money we should have saved for retirement by the ages of 35, 45, 55, and 65. One such prediction is included in the table at the right.
a. According to the estimates in the table, how much should a couple who have earnings of \$75,000 have saved for retirement by age 55?
b. Write an explanation of how interest and interest rates affect the level of savings required at any given age. What effect do inflation rates have on savings?

Minimum Levels of Savings Required for Married Couples to Be Prepared for Retirement
Savings Accumulation by Age

	35	*45*	*55*	*65*
Earnings = \$50,000	8,000	23,000	90,000	170,000
Earnings = \$75,000	17,000	60,000	170,000	310,000
Earnings = \$100,000	34,000	110,000	280,000	480,000
Earnings = \$150,000	67,000	210,000	490,000	840,000

4.6 Mixture Problems

OBJECTIVE 1 Value mixture problems

A value mixture problem involves combining two ingredients that have different prices into a single blend. For example, a coffee merchant may blend two types of coffee into a single blend, or a candy manufacturer may combine two types of candy to sell as a "variety pack."

The solution of a value mixture problem is based on the equation $V = AC$, where V is the value of an ingredient, A is the amount of the ingredient, and C is the cost per unit of the ingredient.

Find the value of 5 oz of a gold alloy that costs \$185 per ounce.

Given: $A = 5$ oz
$C = \$185$
Unknown value: V

$V = AC$
$V = 5(185)$
$V = 925$

The value of the 5 oz of gold alloy is \$925.

Solve: A coffee merchant wants to make 9 lb of a blend of coffee costing \$6 per pound. The blend is made using a \$7 grade and a \$4 grade of coffee. How many pounds of each of these grades should be used?

STRATEGY for solving a mixture problem

▶ For each ingredient in the mixture, write a numerical or variable expression for the amount of the ingredient used, the unit cost of the ingredient, and the value of the amount used. For the blend, write a numerical or variable expression for the amount, the unit cost of the blend, and the value of the amount. The results can be recorded in a table.

The sum of the amounts is 9 lb.

Amount of \$7 coffee: x

Amount of \$4 coffee: $9 - x$

Take Note

Use the information given in the problem to fill in the amount and unit cost columns of the table. Fill in the value column by multiplying the two expressions you wrote in each row. Use the expressions in the last column to write the equation.

	Amount, A	·	Unit cost, C	=	Value, V
\$7 grade	x	·	7	=	$7x$
\$4 grade	$9 - x$	·	4	=	$4(9 - x)$
\$6 blend	9	·	6	=	$6(9)$

▶ Determine how the values of the individual ingredients are related. Use the fact that the sum of the values of these ingredients is equal to the value of the blend.

The sum of the values of the \$7 grade and the \$4 grade is equal to the value of the \$6 blend.

$$7x + 4(9 - x) = 6(9)$$
$$7x + 36 - 4x = 54$$
$$3x + 36 = 54$$
$$3x = 18$$
$$x = 6$$

• **The value of the \$7 grade plus the value of the \$4 grade equals the value of the blend.**

$$9 - x = 9 - 6 = 3$$

• **Substitute the value of *x* into the variable expression for the amount of \$4 grade.**

The merchant must use 6 lb of the \$7 coffee and 3 lb of the \$4 coffee.

EXAMPLE 1 How many ounces of a silver alloy that costs \$6 per ounce must be mixed with 10 oz of a silver alloy that costs \$8 per ounce to make a mixture that costs \$6.50 per ounce?

Strategy ▶ Ounces of \$6 alloy: x

	Amount	Cost	Value
\$6 alloy	x	6	$6x$
\$8 alloy	10	8	$8(10)$
\$6.50 mixture	$10 + x$	6.50	$6.50(10 + x)$

▶ The sum of the values before mixing equals the value after mixing.

Solution

$$6x + 8(10) = 6.50(10 + x)$$
$$6x + 80 = 65 + 6.5x$$
$$-0.5x + 80 = 65$$
$$-0.5x = -15$$
$$x = 30$$

• **The value of the \$6 alloy plus the value of the \$8 alloy equals the value of the mixture.**

30 oz of the \$6 silver alloy must be used.

PROBLEM 1 A gardener has 20 lb of a lawn fertilizer that costs \$.90 per pound. How many pounds of a fertilizer that costs \$.75 per pound should be mixed with this 20 lb of lawn fertilizer to produce a mixture that costs \$.85 per pound?

Solution See page S10.

OBJECTIVE 2 Percent mixture problems

Recall that the amount of a substance in a solution can be given as a percent of the total solution. For example, in a 5% saltwater solution, 5% of the total solution is salt. The remaining 95% is water.

The solution of a percent mixture problem is based on the equation $\boldsymbol{Q = Ar}$, where Q is the quantity of a substance in the solution, r is the percent of concentration, and A is the amount of solution.

Take Note

As stated on page 213, in a 5% salt solution, 5% of the total solution is salt. However, we are referring to weight; the solution is 5% salt by weight, not by volume. For example, if the solution weighs 100 g, the salt in the solution weighs 5 g and the water weighs 95% of 100 g, or 95 g.

A 500-milliliter bottle contains a 3% solution of hydrogen peroxide. Find the amount of hydrogen peroxide in the solution.

Given: $A = 500$
$r = 3\% = 0.03$
Unknown amount: Q

$Q = Ar$
$Q = 500(0.03)$
$Q = 15$

The bottle contains 15 ml of hydrogen peroxide.

Solve: How many gallons of 15% salt solution must be mixed with 4 gal of a 20% salt solution to make a 17% salt solution?

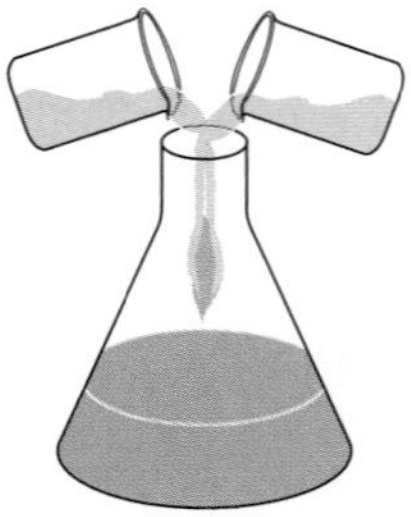

STRATEGY for solving a percent mixture problem

▶ For each solution, use the equation $Ar = Q$. Write a numerical or variable expression for the amount of solution, the percent of concentration, and the quantity of the substance in the solution. The results can be recorded in a table.

The unknown quantity of 15% solution: x

	Amount of solution, A	$\cdot$	Percent of concentration, r	$=$	Quantity of substance, Q
15% solution	x	$\cdot$	0.15	$=$	$0.15x$
20% solution	4	$\cdot$	0.20	$=$	$0.20(4)$
17% solution	$x + 4$	$\cdot$	0.17	$=$	$0.17(x + 4)$

Take Note

Use the information given in the problem to fill in the amount and percent columns of the table. Fill in the quantity column by multiplying the two expressions you wrote in each row. Use the expressions in the last column to write the equation.

▶ Determine how the quantities of the substance in the individual solutions are related. Use the fact that the sum of the quantities of the substances being mixed is equal to the quantity of the substance after mixing.

The sum of the quantities of salt in the 15% solution and in the 20% solution is equal to the quantity of salt in the 17% solution.

$$0.15x + 0.20(4) = 0.17(x + 4)$$
$$0.15x + 0.8 = 0.17x + 0.68$$
$$-0.02x + 0.8 = 0.68$$
$$-0.02x = -0.12$$
$$x = 6$$

• **The amount of salt in the 15% solution plus the amount of salt in the 20% solution equals the amount of salt in the 17% solution.**

6 gal of the 15% solution are required.

EXAMPLE 2 A chemist wishes to make 3 L of a 7% acid solution by mixing a 9% acid solution and a 4% acid solution. How many liters of each solution should the chemist use?

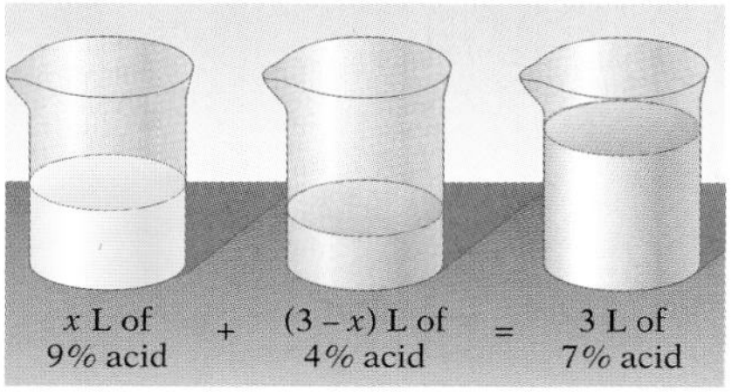

Strategy ▶ Liters of 9% solution: x
Liters of 4% solution: $3 - x$

	Amount	Percent	Quantity
9%	x	0.09	$0.09x$
4%	$3 - x$	0.04	$0.04(3 - x)$
7%	3	0.07	$0.07(3)$

▶ The sum of the quantities before mixing is equal to the quantity after mixing.

Solution

$$0.09x + 0.04(3 - x) = 0.07(3)$$

- **The amount of acid in the 9% solution plus the amount of acid in the 4% solution equals the amount of acid in the 7% solution.**

$$0.09x + 0.12 - 0.04x = 0.21$$
$$0.05x + 0.12 = 0.21$$
$$0.05x = 0.09$$
$$x = 1.8$$

- **1.8 L of the 9% solution are needed.**

$$3 - x = 3 - 1.8 = 1.2$$

- **Find the amount of the 4% solution needed.**

The chemist needs 1.8 L of the 9% solution and 1.2 L of the 4% solution.

PROBLEM 2 How many quarts of pure orange juice are added to 5 qt of fruit drink that is 10% orange juice to make an orange drink that is 25% orange juice?

Solution See pages S10.

4.6 Concept Review

Determine whether the statement is always true, sometimes true, or never true.

1. Both value mixture and percent mixture problems involve combining two or more ingredients into a single substance.

2. In the value mixture equation $V = AC$, the variable A represents the quantity of an ingredient.

3. Suppose we are mixing two salt solutions. Then the variable Q in the percent mixture equation $Q = Ar$ represents the amount of salt in a solution.

4. If we combine an alloy that costs \$8 an ounce with an alloy that costs \$5 an ounce, the cost of the resulting mixture will be greater than \$8 an ounce.

5. If we combine a 9% acid solution with a solution that is 4% acid, the resulting solution will be less than 4% acid.

6. If 8 L of a solvent costs \$75 per liter, then the value of the 8 L of solvent is \$600.

7. If 100 oz of a silver alloy is 25% silver, then the alloy contains 25 oz of silver.

4.6 Exercises

1 Value mixture problems

1. a. The total value of a 7-pound bag of cat food that costs \$1.50 per pound is ___?___.
   b. The cost per pound of a 5-pound bag of sugar that has a total value of \$1.80 is ___?___.

2. To make bread, Maya uses a flour mixture that combines organic whole-wheat flour that costs \$1.70 per pound with unbleached flour that costs \$.50 per pound. Ten pounds of her mixture costs \$1.30 per pound. Let x be the amount of whole-wheat flour in the mixture.
   a. Complete the following table.

	Amount, A	$\cdot$	Unit cost, C	$=$	Value V
Whole-wheat flour	x	$\cdot$	___?___	$=$	___?___
Unbleached flour	___?___	$\cdot$	___?___	$=$	___?___
Mixture	___?___	$\cdot$	___?___	$=$	___?___

   b. Use the expressions in the last column of the table in part a to write an equation that can be solved to find the number of pounds of whole-wheat flour in Maya's mixture: ___?___ + ___?___ = ___?___.

3. Explain the meaning of each variable in the equation $V = AC$. Give an example of how this equation is used.

4. Suppose you are mixing peanuts that cost \$4 per pound with raisins that cost \$2 per pound. In the context of this situation, explain the meaning of the statement "The sum of the values of these ingredients is equal to the value of the blend."

5. At a veterinary clinic, a special high-protein dog food that costs \$6.75 per pound is mixed with a vitamin supplement that costs \$3.25 per pound. How many pounds of each should be used to make 5 lb of a mixture that costs \$4.65 per pound?

6. A wild bird seed mix is made by combining 100 lb of millet seed costing \$.60 per pound with sunflower seeds costing \$1.10 per pound. How many pounds of sunflower seeds are needed to make a mixture that costs \$.70 per pound?

7. Find the cost per pound of a coffee mixture made from 8 lb of coffee that costs \$9.20 per pound and 12 lb of coffee that costs \$5.50 per pound.

8. How many pounds of chamomile tea that costs \$4.20 per pound must be mixed with 12 lb of orange tea that costs \$2.25 per pound to make a mixture that costs \$3.40 per pound?

9. A goldsmith combined an alloy that costs \$4.30 per ounce with an alloy that costs \$1.80 per ounce. How many ounces of each were used to make a mixture of 200 oz costing \$2.50 per ounce?

10. An herbalist has 30 oz of herbs costing \$2 per ounce. How many ounces of herbs costing \$1 per ounce should be mixed with these 30 oz of herbs to produce a mixture costing \$1.60 per ounce?

11. A health food store has a section in which you can create your own chocolate-covered fruit mixes. You choose 2 lb of the cherries that cost \$4.50 per pound. You also choose blueberries that cost \$3.75 per pound. How many pounds of blueberries can you add to create a mixture that costs \$4.25 per pound?

12. Find the cost per ounce of a mixture of 200 oz of a cologne that costs \$7.50 per ounce and 500 oz of a cologne that costs \$4.00 per ounce.

13. How many kilograms of hard candy that costs \$7.50 per kilogram must be mixed with 24 kg of jelly beans that cost \$3.25 per kilogram to make a mixture that costs \$4.50 per kilogram?

14. A grocery store offers a cheese sampler that includes a pepper cheddar cheese that costs \$16 per kilogram and Pennsylvania Jack that costs \$6 per kilogram. How many kilograms of each were used to make a 5-kilogram mixture that costs \$9 per kilogram?

15. A snack food is made by mixing 5 lb of popcorn that costs \$.80 per pound with caramel that costs \$2.40 per pound. How much caramel is needed to make a mixture that costs \$1.40 per pound?

16. A lumber company combined oak wood chips that cost \$3.10 per pound with pine wood chips that cost \$2.50 per pound. How many pounds of each were used to make an 80-pound mixture costing \$2.65 per pound?

17. The manager of a farmer's market has 500 lb of grain that costs \$1.20 per pound. How many pounds of meal costing \$.80 per pound should be mixed with the 500 lb of grain to produce a mixture that costs \$1.05 per pound?

18. A caterer made an ice cream punch by combining fruit juice that costs \$4.50 per gallon with ice cream that costs \$6.50 per gallon. How many gallons of each were used to make 100 gal of punch costing \$5 per gallon?

19. The manager of a specialty food store combined almonds that cost \$4.50 per pound with walnuts that cost \$2.50 per pound. How many pounds of each were used to make a 100-pound mixture that costs \$3.24 per pound?

20. Find the cost per pound of a "house blend" of coffee that is made from 12 lb of Central American coffee that costs \$8 per pound and 30 lb of South American coffee that costs \$4.50 per pound.

21. Find the cost per pound of a sugar-coated breakfast cereal made from 40 lb of sugar that costs \$2.00 per pound and 120 lb of corn flakes that cost \$1.20 per pound.

22. Find the cost per ounce of a gold alloy made from 25 oz of pure gold that costs \$482 per ounce and 40 oz of an alloy that costs \$300 per ounce.

23. Find the cost per ounce of a sunscreen made from 100 oz of a lotion that costs \$2.50 per ounce and 50 oz of a lotion that costs \$4.00 per ounce.

24. How many liters of a blue dye that costs \$1.60 per liter must be mixed with 18 L of anil that costs \$2.50 per liter to make a mixture that costs \$1.90 per liter?

25. A grocer mixes peanuts that cost \$3 per pound with almonds that cost \$7 per pound. Which of the following could be true about the cost, C, per pound of the mixture? There may be more than one correct answer.
a. $C = \$10$ **b.** $C > \$7$ **c.** $C < \$7$ **d.** $C < \$3$ **e.** $C > \$3$ **f.** $C = \$4$

26. A snack mix is made from 3 pounds of sunflower seeds that cost S dollars per pound and 4 pounds of raisins that cost R dollars per pound. Which expression gives the cost, C, per pound of the mixture?

a. $7(S + R)$ **b.** $3S + 4R$ **c.** $S + R$ **d.** $\dfrac{3S + 4R}{7}$

2 Percent mixture problems

27. A 250-milliliter bottle contains a solution that is 90% isopropyl alcohol. The amount of isopropyl alcohol in the solution is 250(__?__) = __?__ ml.

28. A juice drink that is 60% real fruit juice is made by mixing some juice that is 20% real fruit juice with 32 oz of a juice that is 75% real fruit juice. Let x be the amount of the 20% real fruit juice that is in the mixture.
a. Complete the following table.

	Amount A	$\cdot$	Percent of concentration, r	$=$	Quantity Q
75% real fruit juice	?	$\cdot$	?	$=$	?
20% real fruit juice	x	$\cdot$	?	$=$	?
Mixture	?	$\cdot$	?	$=$	?

b. Use the expressions in the last column of the table in part a to write an equation that can be solved to find the amount of the 20% real fruit juice that is in the mixture: ___?___ + ___?___ = ___?___.

29. Explain the meaning of each variable in the equation $Q = Ar$. Give an example of how this equation is used.

30. Suppose you are mixing a 5% acid solution with a 10% acid solution. In the context of this situation, explain the meaning of the statement "The sum of the quantities of the substances being mixed is equal to the quantity of the substance after mixing."

31. Forty ounces of a 30% gold alloy are mixed with 60 oz of a 20% gold alloy. Find the percent concentration of the resulting gold alloy.

32. One hundred ounces of juice that is 50% tomato juice are added to 200 oz of a vegetable juice that is 25% tomato juice. What is the percent concentration of tomato juice in the resulting mixture?

33. How many gallons of a 15% acid solution must be mixed with 5 gal of a 20% acid solution to make a 16% acid solution?

34. How many pounds of a chicken feed that is 50% corn must be mixed with 400 lb of a feed that is 80% corn to make a chicken feed that is 75% corn?

35. A rug is made by weaving 20 lb of yarn that is 50% wool with a yarn that is 25% wool. How many pounds of the yarn that is 25% wool must be used if the finished rug is to be 35% wool?

36. Five gallons of a dark green latex paint that is 20% yellow paint are combined with a lighter green latex paint that is 40% yellow paint. How many gallons of the lighter green paint must be used to create a green paint that is 25% yellow paint?

37. How many gallons of a plant food that is 9% nitrogen must be combined with another plant food that is 25% nitrogen to make 10 gal of a plant food that is 15% nitrogen?

38. A chemist wants to make 50 ml of a 16% acid solution by mixing a 13% acid solution and an 18% acid solution. How many milliliters of each solution should the chemist use?

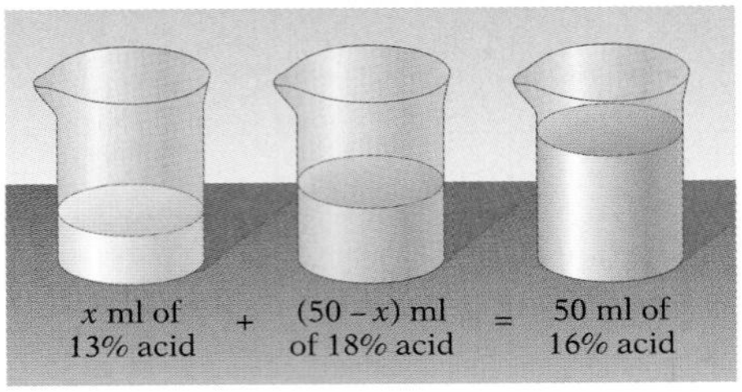

39. Five grams of sugar are added to a 45-gram serving of a breakfast cereal that is 10% sugar. What is the percent concentration of sugar in the resulting mixture?

40. Thirty ounces of pure silver are added to 50 oz of a silver alloy that is 20% silver. What is the percent concentration of the resulting alloy?

41. To make the potpourri mixture sold at a florist shop, 70 oz of a potpourri that is 80% lavender are combined with a potpourri that is 60% lavender. The resulting potpourri is 74% lavender. How much of the potpourri that is 60% lavender is used?

42. The manager of a garden shop mixes grass seed that is 40% rye grass with 40 lb of grass seed that is 60% rye grass to make a mixture that is 56% rye grass. How much of the 40% rye grass is used?

43. A hair dye is made by blending a 7% hydrogen peroxide solution and a 4% hydrogen peroxide solution. How many milliliters of each are used to make a 300-milliliter solution that is 5% hydrogen peroxide?

44. At a cosmetics company, 40 L of pure aloe cream are mixed with 50 L of a moisturizer that is 64% aloe. What is the percent concentration of aloe in the resulting mixture?

45. How many ounces of pure chocolate must be added to 150 oz of chocolate topping that is 50% chocolate to make a topping that is 75% chocolate?

46. How many ounces of pure bran flakes must be added to 50 oz of cereal that is 40% bran flakes to produce a mixture that is 50% bran flakes?

47. A hair stylist combines 12 oz of shampoo that is 20% conditioner with an 8-ounce bottle of pure shampoo. What is the percent concentration of conditioner in the 20-ounce mixture?

48. A clothing manufacturer has some pure silk thread and some thread that is 85% silk. How many kilograms of each must be woven together to make 75 kg of cloth that is 96% silk?

49. How many ounces of dried apricots must be added to 18 oz of a snack mix that contains 20% dried apricots to make a mixture that is 25% dried apricots?

50. A recipe for a rice dish calls for 12 oz of a rice mixture that is 20% wild rice and 8 oz of pure wild rice. What is the percent concentration of wild rice in the 20-ounce mixture?

51. True or false? A 10% salt solution can be combined with some amount of a 20% salt solution to create a 30% salt solution.

52. True or false? When n ounces of 100% acid are mixed with $2n$ ounces of pure water, the resulting mixture is a 50% acid solution.

4.6 Applying Concepts

53. Find the cost per ounce of a mixture of 30 oz of an alloy that costs $4.50 per ounce, 40 oz of an alloy that costs $3.50 per ounce, and 30 oz of an alloy that costs $3.00 per ounce.

54. A grocer combined walnuts that cost $2.60 per pound and cashews that cost $3.50 per pound with 20 lb of peanuts that cost $2.00 per pound. Find the amount of walnuts and the amount of cashews used to make the 50-pound mixture costing $2.72 per pound.

55. How many ounces of water evaporated from 50 oz of a 12% salt solution to produce a 15% salt solution?

56. A chemist mixed pure acid with water to make 10 L of a 30% acid solution. How much pure acid and how much water did the chemist use?

57. How many grams of pure water must be added to 50 g of pure acid to make a solution that is 40% acid?

58. A radiator contains 15 gal of a 20% antifreeze solution. How many gallons must be drained from the radiator and replaced by pure antifreeze so that the radiator will contain 15 gal of a 40% antifreeze solution?

59. Tickets to a performance by the community theater cost $5.50 for adults and $2.75 for children. A total of 120 tickets were sold for $563.75. How many adults and how many children attended the performance?

60. Explain why we look for patterns and relationships in mathematics. Include a discussion of the relationship between value mixture problems and percent mixture problems and how understanding one of these can make it easier to understand the other. Also discuss why understanding how to solve the value mixture problems in this section can be helpful in solving Exercise 59.

4.7 Uniform Motion Problems

OBJECTIVE 1 Uniform motion problems

A train that travels constantly in a straight line at 50 mph is in *uniform motion*. Recall that **uniform motion** means the speed of an object does not change.

The solution of a uniform motion problem is based on the equation $d = rt$, where d is the distance traveled, r is the rate of travel, and t is the time spent traveling.

A car travels at 50 mph for 3 h.

$$d = rt$$
$$d = 50(3)$$
$$d = 150$$

The car travels a distance of 150 mi.

Solve: A car leaves a town traveling at 35 mph. Two hours later, a second car leaves the same town, on the same road, traveling at 55 mph. In how many hours after the second car leaves will the second car pass the first car?

STRATEGY for solving a uniform motion problem

▶ For each object, use the equation $rt = d$. Write a numerical or variable expression for the rate, time, and distance. The results can be recorded in a table.

The first car traveled 2 h longer than the second car.

Unknown time for the second car: t
Time for the first car: $t + 2$

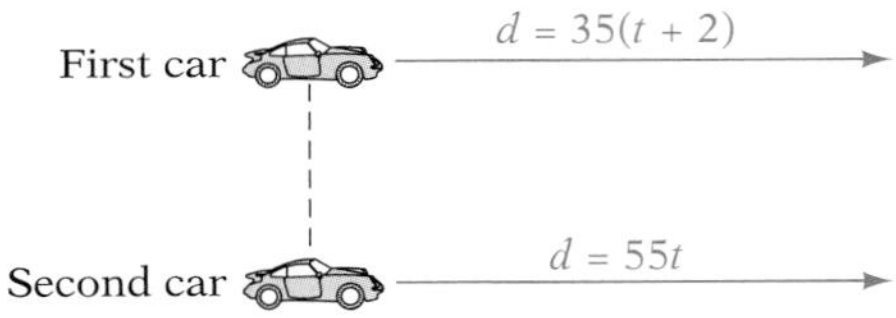

Take Note

Use the information given in the problem to fill in the rate and time columns of the table. Fill in the distance column by multiplying the two expressions you wrote in each row.

	Rate, r	$\cdot$	Time, t	=	Distance, d
First car	35	$\cdot$	$t + 2$	=	$35(t + 2)$
Second car	55	$\cdot$	t	=	$55t$

▶ Determine how the distances traveled by the individual objects are related. For example, the total distance traveled by both objects may be known, or it may be known that the two objects traveled the same distance.

The two cars travel the same distance.

$$35(t + 2) = 55t$$
$$35t + 70 = 55t$$
$$70 = 20t$$
$$3.5 = t$$

• **The distance traveled by the first car equals the distance traveled by the second car.**

The second car will pass the first car in 3.5 h.

EXAMPLE 1 Two cars, the first traveling 10 mph faster than the second, start at the same time from the same point and travel in opposite directions. In 3 h, they are 288 mi apart. Find the rate of the second car.

Strategy ▶ Rate of second car: r
Rate of first car: $r + 10$

	Rate	Time	Distance
First car	$r + 10$	3	$3(r + 10)$
Second car	r	3	$3r$

▶ The total distance traveled by the two cars is 288 mi.

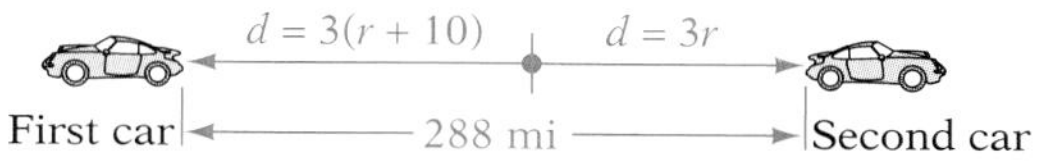

Solution

$$\begin{aligned} 3(r + 10) + 3r &= 288 \\ 3r + 30 + 3r &= 288 \\ 6r + 30 &= 288 \\ 6r &= 258 \\ r &= 43 \end{aligned}$$

• **The distance traveled by the first car plus the distance traveled by the second car is 288 mi.**

The second car is traveling 43 mph.

PROBLEM 1 Two trains, one traveling at twice the speed of the other, start at the same time from stations that are 306 mi apart and travel toward each other. In 3 h, the trains pass each other. Find the rate of each train.

Solution See page S10.

EXAMPLE 2 A bicycling club rides out into the country at a speed of 16 mph and returns over the same road at 12 mph. How far does the club ride out into the country if it travels a total of 7 h?

Strategy ▶ Time spent riding out: t
Time spent riding back: $7 - t$

	Rate	Time	Distance
Out	16	t	$16t$
Back	12	$7 - t$	$12(7 - t)$

▶ The distance out equals the distance back.

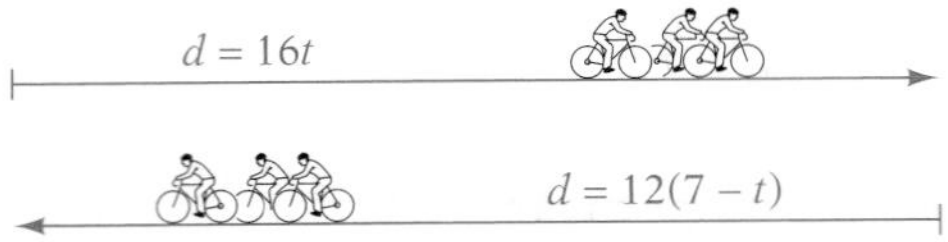

Solution $16t = 12(7 - t)$

$16t = 84 - 12t$

$28t = 84$

$t = 3$ • **The time is 3 h. Find the distance.**

The distance out $= 16t = 16(3) = 48$.

The club rides 48 mi into the country.

PROBLEM 2 On a survey mission, a pilot flew out to a parcel of land and back in 7 h. The rate out was 120 mph. The rate back was 90 mph. How far away was the parcel of land?

Solution See page S11.

4.7 Concept Review

Determine whether the statement is always true, sometimes true, or never true.

1. The solution of a uniform motion problem is based on the equation $d = rt$, where r is a percent.

2. If you drive at a constant speed of 60 mph for 4 h, you will travel a total distance of 240 mi.

3. It takes a student a total of 5 h to drive to a friend's house and back. If the variable t is used to represent the time it took to drive to the friend's house, then the expression $t - 5$ is used to represent the time spent on the return trip.

4. If the speed of one train is 20 mph slower than that of a second train, then the speeds of the two trains can be represented as r and $20 - r$.

5. A car and a bus both travel from city A to city B. The car leaves city A 1 h later than the bus, but both vehicles arrive in city B at the same time. If t represents the time the car was traveling, then $t + 1$ represents the time the bus was traveling. If t represents the time the bus was traveling, then $t - 1$ represents the time the car was traveling.

6. Two cars travel the same distance. If the distance traveled by the first car is represented by the expression $35t$, and the distance traveled by the second car is represented by the expression $45(t + 1)$, then we can write the equation $35t = 45(t + 1)$.

4.7 Exercises

1 Uniform motion problems

1. Sara and Jessica leave school and go in opposite directions. Sara runs and Jessica walks. The rate at which Sara runs is three times faster than the rate at which Jessica walks. After 5 min, the girls are 3520 ft apart. Let r represent Jessica's rate.

   a. Complete the following table.

	Rate, r	$\cdot$	Time, t	$=$	Distance, d
Sara	___?___	$\cdot$	___?___	$=$	___?___
Jessica	r	$\cdot$	___?___	$=$	___?___

   b. Use the expressions in the last column of the table in part a to write an equation that can be solved to find Jessica's rate: ___?___ + ___?___ = ___?___.

2. The solution of the equation from part b of Exercise 1 is 176. This means that Jessica walks at a rate of 176 ___?___ per ___?___. Because Sara's rate is three times Jessica's rate, Sara runs at a rate of ___?___.

For Exercises 3 and 4, state whether the equation you would write to solve the problem would involve (**a**) setting two distances equal to each other, or (**b**) adding two distances together to equal a total distance.

3. **Problem Situation:** Sam hiked up a mountain at a rate of 2.5 mph and returned along the same trail at a rate of 3 mph. His total hiking time was 11 h. How long was the hiking trail?

4. **Problem Situation:** Sam hiked 16 mi. He hiked at one rate for the first 2 h of his hike and then decreased his speed by 0.5 mph for the last 3 h of his hike. What was Sam's speed for the first 2 h?

5. Two planes start from the same point and fly in opposite directions. The first plane is flying 25 mph slower than the second plane. In 2 h, the planes are 470 mi apart. Find the rate of each plane.

6. Two cyclists start from the same point and ride in opposite directions. One cyclist rides twice as fast as the other. In 3 h, they are 81 mi apart. Find the rate of each cyclist.

7. One speed skater starts across a frozen lake at an average speed of 8 meters per second. Ten seconds later, a second speed skater starts from the same point and skates in the same direction at an average speed of 10 meters per second. How many seconds after the second skater starts will the second skater overtake the first skater?

8. A long-distance runner started on a course running at an average speed of 6 mph. Half an hour later, a second runner began the same course at an average speed of 7 mph. How long after the second runner starts will the second runner overtake the first runner?

9. Michael Chan leaves a dock in his motorboat and travels at an average speed of 9 mph toward the Isle of Shoals, a small island off the coast of Massachusetts. Two hours later, a tour boat leaves the same dock and travels at an average speed of 18 mph toward the same island. How many hours after the tour boat leaves will Michael's boat be alongside the tour boat?

10. A 555-mile, 5-hour plane trip was flown at two speeds. For the first part of the trip, the average speed was 105 mph. For the remainder of the trip, the average speed was 115 mph. How long did the plane fly at each speed?

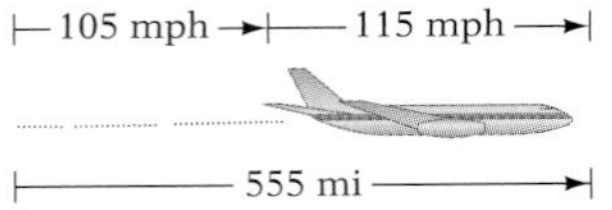

11. An executive drove from home at an average speed of 30 mph to an airport where a helicopter was waiting. The executive boarded the helicopter and flew to the corporate offices at an average speed of 60 mph. The entire distance was 150 mi. The entire trip took 3 h. Find the distance from the airport to the corporate offices.

12. A jogger starts from one end of a 15-mile nature trail at 8:00 A.M. One hour later, a cyclist starts from the other end of the trail and rides toward the jogger. If the rate of the jogger is 6 mph and the rate of the cyclist is 9 mph, at what time will the two meet?

13. After a sailboat had been on the water for 3 h, a change in the wind direction reduced the average speed of the boat by 5 mph. The entire distance sailed was 57 mi. The total time spent sailing was 6 h. How far did the sailboat travel in the first 3 h?

14. A car and a bus set out at 3 P.M. from the same point headed in the same direction. The average speed of the car is twice the average speed of the bus. In 2 h, the car is 68 mi ahead of the bus. Find the rate of the car.

15. A passenger train leaves a train depot 2 h after a freight train leaves the same depot. The freight train is traveling 20 mph slower than the passenger train. Find the rate of each train if the passenger train overtakes the freight train in 3 h.

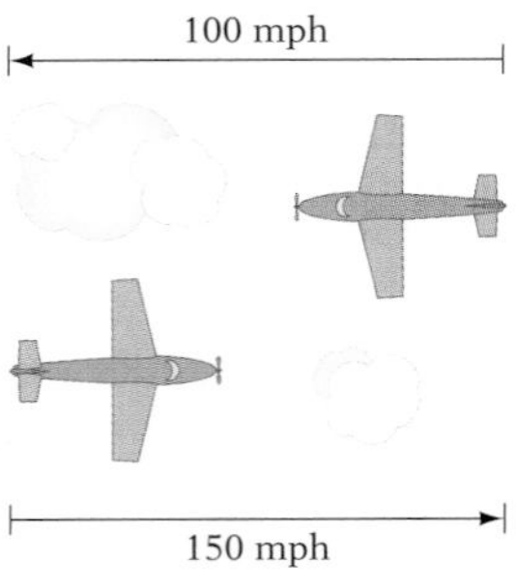

16. A stunt driver was needed at the production site of a Hollywood movie. The average speed of the stunt driver's flight to the site was 150 mph, and the average speed of the return trip was 100 mph. Find the distance of the round trip if the total flying time was 5 h.

17. A ship traveling east at 25 mph is 10 mi from a harbor when another ship leaves the harbor traveling east at 35 mph. How long does it take the second ship to catch up to the first ship?

18. At 10 A.M. a plane leaves Boston, Massachusetts, for Seattle, Washington, a distance of 3000 mi. One hour later a plane leaves Seattle for Boston. Both planes are traveling at a speed of 500 mph. How many hours after the plane leaves Seattle will the planes pass each other?

19. At noon a train leaves Washington, D.C., headed for Charleston, South Carolina, a distance of 500 mi. The train travels at a speed of 60 mph. At 1 P.M. a second train leaves Charleston headed for Washington, D.C., traveling at 50 mph. How long after the train leaves Charleston will the two trains pass each other?

20. A race car driver starts along a 50-mile race course traveling at an average speed of 90 mph. Fifteen minutes later a second driver starts along the same course at an average speed of 120 mph. Will the second car overtake the first car before the drivers reach the end of the course?

21. A bus traveled on a straight road for 2 h at an average speed that was 20 mph faster than its average speed on a winding road. The time spent on the winding road was 3 h. Find the average speed on the winding road if the total trip was 210 mi.

22. A bus traveling at a rate of 60 mph overtakes a car traveling at a rate of 45 mph. If the car had a 1-hour head start, how far from the starting point does the bus overtake the car?

23. A car traveling at 48 mph overtakes a cyclist who, riding at 12 mph, had a 3-hour head start. How far from the starting point does the car overtake the cyclist?

24. A plane left Kennedy Airport Tuesday morning for a 605-mile, 5-hour trip. For the first part of the trip, the average speed was 115 mph. For the remainder of the trip, the average speed was 125 mph. How long did the plane fly at each speed?

4.7 Applying Concepts

25. A car and a cyclist start at 10 A.M. from the same point, headed in the same direction. The average speed of the car is 5 mph more than three times the average speed of the cyclist. In 1.5 h, the car is 46.5 mi ahead of the cyclist. Find the rate of the cyclist.

26. A cyclist and a jogger set out at 11 A.M. from the same point, headed in the same direction. The average speed of the cyclist is twice the average speed of the jogger. In 1 h, the cyclist is 7 mi ahead of the jogger. Find the rate of the cyclist.

27. A car and a bus set out at 2 P.M. from the same point, headed in the same direction. The average speed of the car is 30 mph slower than twice the average speed of the bus. In 2 h, the car is 30 mi ahead of the bus. Find the rate of the car.

28. At 10 A.M., two campers left their campsite by canoe and paddled downstream at an average speed of 12 mph. They then turned around and paddled back upstream at an average rate of 4 mph. The total trip took 1 h. At what time did the campers turn around downstream?

29. At 7 A.M., two joggers start from opposite ends of an 8-mile course. One jogger is running at a rate of 4 mph, and the other is running at a rate of 6 mph. At what time will the joggers meet?

30. A truck leaves a depot at 11 A.M. and travels at a speed of 45 mph. At noon, a van leaves the same place and travels the same route at a speed of 65 mph. At what time does the van overtake the truck?

31. A bicyclist rides for 2 h at a speed of 10 mph and then returns at a speed of 20 mph. Find the cyclist's average speed for the trip.

32. A car travels a 1-mile track at an average speed of 30 mph. At what average speed must the car travel the next mile so that the average speed for the 2 mi is 60 mph?

33. Explain why the motion problems in this section are restricted to *uniform* motion.

34. Explain why 60 mph is the same as 88 ft/s.

4.8 Inequalities

OBJECTIVE 1 Applications of inequalities

Solving application problems requires recognition of the verbal phrases that translate into mathematical symbols. Here is a partial list of the phrases used to indicate each of the four inequality symbols.

$<$	is less than	$>$	is greater than is more than exceeds
$\leq$	is less than or equal to maximum at most or less	$\geq$	is greater than or equal to minimum at least or more

EXAMPLE 1 A student must have at least 450 points out of 500 points on five tests to receive an A in a course. One student's results on the first four tests were 93, 79, 87, and 94. What scores on the last test will enable this student to receive an A in the course?

Strategy To find the scores, write and solve an inequality using N to represent the score on the last test.

Solution

total number of points on the five tests	is greater than or equal to	450

$$93 + 79 + 87 + 94 + N \geq 450$$
$$353 + N \geq 450$$
$$353 - 353 + N \geq 450 - 353$$
$$N \geq 97$$

The student's score on the last test must be equal to or greater than 97.

PROBLEM 1 An appliance dealer will make a profit on the sale of a television set if the cost of the new set is less than 70% of the selling price. What minimum selling price will enable the dealer to make a profit on a television set that costs the dealer $340?

Solution See page S11.

EXAMPLE 2 The base of a triangle is 8 in., and the height is $(3x - 5)$ in. Express as an integer the maximum height of the triangle when the area is less than 112 in^2.

Strategy To find the maximum height:

- ▶ Replace the variables in the area formula by the given values and solve for x.
- ▶ Replace the variable in the expression $3x - 5$ with the value found for x.

Solution

one-half the base times the height	is less than	112 in^2

$$\frac{1}{2}(8)(3x - 5) < 112$$
$$4(3x - 5) < 112$$
$$12x - 20 < 112$$
$$12x - 20 + 20 < 112 + 20$$
$$12x < 132$$
$$\frac{12x}{12} < \frac{132}{12}$$
$$x < 11$$

$3x - 5 = 3(11) - 5 = 28$ • **Substitute the value of x into the variable expression for the height. Note that the height is less than 28 because $x < 11$.**

The maximum height of the triangle is 27 in.

PROBLEM 2 Company A rents cars for $9 per day and 10¢ per mile driven. Company B rents cars for $12 per day and 8¢ per mile driven. You want to rent a car for one week. What is the maximum number of miles you can drive a Company A car if it is to cost you less than a Company B car?

Solution See page S11.

4.8 Concept Review

Determine whether the statement is always true, sometimes true, or never true.

1. Both "is greater than" and "is more than" are represented by the inequality symbol $\geq$.

2. A minimum refers to a lower limit, whereas a maximum refers to an upper limit.

3. Given that $x > \frac{32}{6}$, the minimum integer that satisfies the inequality is 6.

4. Given that $x < \frac{25}{4}$, the maximum integer that satisfies the inequality is 7.

5. A rental car costs \$15 per day and 20¢ per mile driven. If m represents the number of miles the rental car is driven, then the expression $15 + 0.20m$ represents the cost to rent the car for one week.

6. A patient's physician recommends a maximum cholesterol level of 205 units. The patient's cholesterol level is 199 units and therefore must be lowered 6 units in order to meet the physician's recommended level.

4.8 Exercises

1 Application of inequalities

For Exercises 1 to 4, translate each sentence into an inequality.

1. The maximum value of a number n is 50.

2. A number n is at least 102.

3. 500 is more than 12% of a number n.

4. The sum of a number n and 45% of the number is at most 200.

5. **Integer Problem** Three-fifths of a number is greater than two-thirds. Find the smallest integer that satisfies the inequality.

6. **Sports** To be eligible for a basketball tournament, a basketball team must win at least 60% of its remaining games. If the team has 17 games remaining, how many games must the team win to qualify for the tournament?

7. **Income Taxes** To avoid a tax penalty, at least 90% of a self-employed person's total annual income tax liability must be paid by April 15. What amount of income tax must be paid by April 15 by a person with an annual income tax liability of $3500?

8. **Health** A health official recommends a maximum cholesterol level of 220 units. A patient has a cholesterol level of 275. By how many units must this patient's cholesterol level be reduced to satisfy the recommended maximum level?

9. **Recycling** A service organization will receive a bonus of $200 for collecting more than 1850 lb of aluminum cans during its four collection drives. On the first three drives, the organization collected 505 lb, 493 lb, and 412 lb. How many pounds of cans must the organization collect on the fourth drive to receive the bonus?

10. **Education** A professor scores all tests with a maximum of 100 points. To earn an A in this course, a student must have an average of at least 92 on four tests. One student's grades on the first three tests were 89, 86, and 90. Can this student earn an A grade?

11. **Education** A student must have an average of at least 80 points on five tests to receive a B in a course. The student's grades on the first four tests were 75, 83, 86, and 78. What scores on the last test will enable this student to receive a B in the course?

12. **Compensation** A car sales representative receives a commission that is the greater of $250 or 8% of the selling price of a car. What dollar amounts in the sale price of a car will make the commission offer more attractive than the $250 flat fee?

13. **Compensation** A sales representative for a stereo store has the option of a monthly salary of $2000 or a 35% commission on the selling price of each item sold by the representative. What dollar amounts in sales will make the commission more attractive than the monthly salary?

14. **Integer Problem** Four times the sum of a number and five is less than six times the number. Find the smallest integer that satisfies the inequality.

15. **Compensation** The sales agent for a jewelry company is offered a flat monthly salary of $3200 or a salary of $1000 plus an 11% commission on the selling price of each item sold by the agent. If the agent chooses the $3200 salary, what dollar amount does the agent expect to sell in one month?

16. **Compensation** A baseball player is offered an annual salary of $200,000 or a base salary of $100,000 plus a bonus of $1000 for each hit over 100 hits. How many hits will result in this baseball player earning more than $200,000?

17. **Consumerism** A computer bulletin board service charges a flat fee of \$10 per month or \$4 per month plus \$.10 for each minute the service is used. For how many minutes must a person use this service for the cost to exceed \$10?

18. **Business** A site licensing fee for a computer program is \$1500. The fee allows a company to use the program at any computer terminal within the company. Alternatively, a company can choose to pay \$200 for each computer terminal it has. How many computer terminals must a company have for the site licensing fee to be the more economical plan?

19. **Nutrition** For a product to be labeled orange juice, a state agency requires that at least 80% of the drink be real orange juice. How many ounces of artificial flavors can be added to 32 oz of real orange juice if the drink is to be labeled orange juice?

20. **Nutrition** Grade A hamburger cannot contain more than 20% fat. How much fat can a butcher mix with 300 lb of lean meat to meet the 20% requirement?

21. **Consumerism** A shuttle service taking skiers to a ski area charges \$8 per person each way. Four skiers are debating whether to take the shuttle bus or rent a car for \$45 plus \$.25 per mile. Assuming that the skiers will share the cost of the car and that they want the least expensive method of transportation, how far away is the ski area if they choose to take the shuttle service?

22. **Utilities** A residential water bill is based on a flat fee of \$10 plus a charge of \$.75 for each 1000 gal of water used. Find the number of gallons of water a family can use and have a monthly water bill that is less than \$55.

23. **Consumerism** Company A rents cars for \$25 per day and 8¢ per mile driven. Company B rents cars for \$15 per day and 14¢ per mile driven. You want to rent a car for one day. Find the maximum number of miles you can drive a Company B car if it is to cost you less than a Company A car.

24. **Geometry** A rectangle is 8 ft wide and $(2x + 7)$ ft long. Express as an integer the maximum length of the rectangle when the perimeter is less than 54 ft.

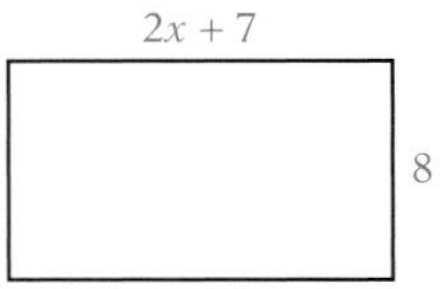

25. An automatic garage door opener costs \$325 plus an installation labor charge of \$30 per hour, with a minimum of 1 h and a maximum of 3 h of labor. Which of the following are *not* possible amounts for the total cost of the door and installation? There may be more than one answer.
a. \$355 **b.** \$450 **c.** \$325 **d.** \$415 **e.** \$350

26. True or false? If a student's test average after four tests is 80, the maximum amount the student can raise his average on the next test is 4 points (assume a test is worth 100 points).

4.8 Applying Concepts

27. **Integer Problem** Find three positive consecutive odd integers such that three times the sum of the first two integers is less than four times the third integer. (*Hint:* There is more than one solution.)

28. **Integer Problem** Find three positive consecutive even integers such that four times the sum of the first two integers is less than or equal to five times the third integer. (*Hint:* There is more than one solution.)

29. **Aviation** A maintenance crew requires between 30 min and 45 min to prepare an aircraft for its next flight. How many aircraft can this crew prepare for flight in a 6-hour period of time?

30. **Postage** The postage rate for first-class mail is \$.39 for the first ounce and \$.24 for each additional ounce or fraction of an ounce. Find the largest whole number of ounces a package can weigh if it is to cost you less than \$3 to mail the package.

31. **Fund Raising** Your class decides to publish a calendar to raise money. The initial cost, regardless of the number of calendars printed, is \$900. After the initial cost, each calendar costs \$1.50 to produce. What is the minimum number of calendars your class must sell at \$6 per calendar to make a profit of at least \$1200?

32. **Debt Carried by Americans** During a recent year, the mean (average) household income of Americans under age 35 was \$48,297. The mean household income of Americans aged 35 to 50 was \$60,427. The graph on the next page shows average amounts of debt carried during the same year by those under 35 and by those aged 35 to 50.

   a. In which categories is the average debt carried by Americans under age 35 greater than the average debt carried by Americans aged 35 to 50?

   b. In which categories is the average debt carried by Americans under age 35 greater than \$10,000?

   c. For the categories shown in the graph, what was the total average debt of Americans under age 35? How much greater is this debt than that of Americans aged 35 to 50?

   d. Given the answers to parts a, b, and c, what is the significance of the average incomes of these two age groups?

   e. Write a paragraph describing any other observations you can make from the data.

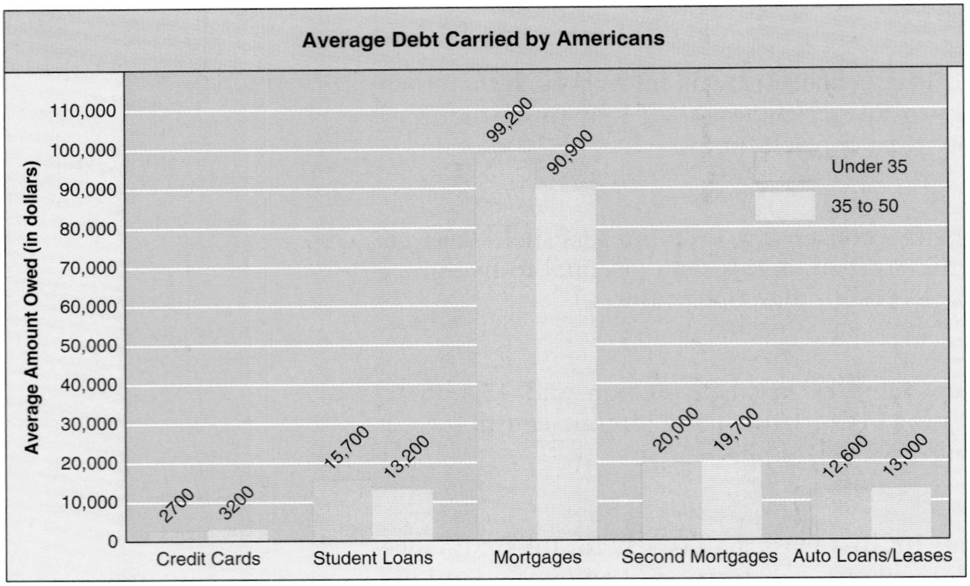

Source: Claritas, Inc.

Focus on Problem Solving

Diagramming Problems

How do you best remember something? Do you remember best what you hear? The word *aural* means "pertaining to the ear"; people with a strong aural memory remember best those things that they hear. The word *visual* means "pertaining to the sense of sight"; people with a strong visual memory remember best that which they see written down. Some people claim their memory is in their writing hand—they remember something only if they write it down! The method by which you best remember something is probably also the method by which you can best learn something new.

In problem-solving situations, try to capitalize on your strengths. If you tend to understand material better when you hear it spoken, read application problems aloud or have someone else read them to you. If writing helps you to organize ideas, rewrite application problems in your own words.

No matter what your main strength, visualizing a problem can be a valuable aid in problem solving. A drawing, sketch, diagram, or chart can be a useful tool in problem solving, just as calculators and computers are tools. Making a diagram can help you gain an understanding of the relationships inherent in a problem-solving situation. A sketch will help you to organize the given information and devise or discover a method by which the solution can be determined.

A tour bus drives 5 mi south, then 4 mi west, then 3 mi north, and then 4 mi east. How far is the tour bus from the starting point?

Draw a diagram of the given information.

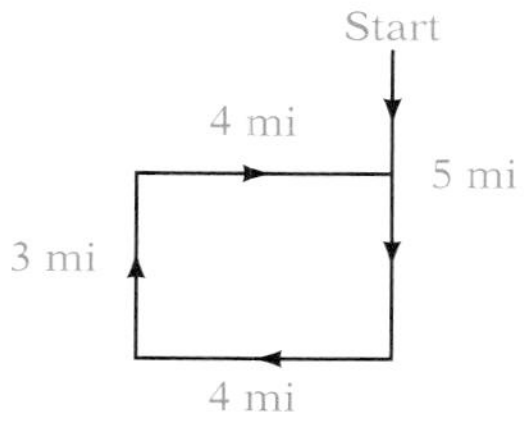

From the diagram, we can see that the solution can be determined by subtracting 3 from 5: $5 - 3 = 2$.

The bus is 2 mi from the starting point.

If you roll two ordinary six-sided dice and multiply the two numbers that appear on top, how many different products are there?

Make a chart of the possible products. In the chart below, repeated products are marked with an asterisk.

$1 \cdot 1 = 1$	$2 \cdot 1 = 2^*$	$3 \cdot 1 = 3^*$	$4 \cdot 1 = 4^*$	$5 \cdot 1 = 5^*$	$6 \cdot 1 = 6^*$
$1 \cdot 2 = 2$	$2 \cdot 2 = 4^*$	$3 \cdot 2 = 6^*$	$4 \cdot 2 = 8^*$	$5 \cdot 2 = 10^*$	$6 \cdot 2 = 12^*$
$1 \cdot 3 = 3$	$2 \cdot 3 = 6^*$	$3 \cdot 3 = 9$	$4 \cdot 3 = 12^*$	$5 \cdot 3 = 15^*$	$6 \cdot 3 = 18^*$
$1 \cdot 4 = 4$	$2 \cdot 4 = 8$	$3 \cdot 4 = 12^*$	$4 \cdot 4 = 16$	$5 \cdot 4 = 20^*$	$6 \cdot 4 = 24^*$
$1 \cdot 5 = 5$	$2 \cdot 5 = 10$	$3 \cdot 5 = 15$	$4 \cdot 5 = 20$	$5 \cdot 5 = 25$	$6 \cdot 2 = 30^*$
$1 \cdot 6 = 6$	$2 \cdot 6 = 12$	$3 \cdot 6 = 18$	$4 \cdot 6 = 24$	$5 \cdot 6 = 30$	$6 \cdot 6 = 36$

By counting the products that are not repeats, we can see that there are 18 different products.

In this chapter, you may have noticed that a drawing accompanies the strategy step of many application problems. We encourage you to draw a diagram when solving the application problems in these sections, as well as in any other situation where it can prove helpful. Doing so will undoubtedly improve your problem-solving skills.

Projects & Group Activities

Nielsen Ratings

Nielsen Media Research surveys television viewers to determine the numbers of people watching particular shows. There are an estimated 105.5 million U.S. households with televisions. Each **rating point** represents 1% of that number, or 1,055,000 households. For instance, if *60 Minutes* received a rating of 9.6, then 9.6%, or $(0.096)(105{,}500{,}000) = 10{,}128{,}000$, households watched that program.

A rating point does not mean that 105,500,000 people are watching a program. A rating point refers to the number of TV sets tuned to that program; there may be more than one person watching a television set in the household.

Nielsen Media Research also describes a program's share of the market. **Share** is the percent of television sets in use that are tuned to a program. Suppose that the same week *60 Minutes* received 9.6 rating points, the show received a

Point of Interest

The top-ranked programs in network prime time for the week of November 21, 2005, ranked by Nielsen Media Research, were

Desperate Housewives
CSI
CSI: Miami
Grey's Anatomy
Cold Case
Without a Trace
Law and Order
Lost
NFL Monday Night Football
Survivor

share of 19%. This means that 19% of all households with a television *turned on* were tuned to *60 Minutes*, whereas only 9.6% of all households *with a television* were tuned to the program.

1. If *60 Minutes* received a Nielsen rating of 10.8 and a share of 19, how many TV households watched the program that week? How many TV households were watching television during that hour? Round to the nearest hundred thousand.

2. Suppose *Desperate Housewives* received a rating of 16.2 and a share of 28. How many TV households watched the program that week? How many TV households were watching television during that hour? Round to the nearest hundred thousand.

3. Suppose *CSI* received a rating of 13.6 during a week in which 34,750,000 people watched the show. Find the average number of people per TV household who watched the program. Round to the nearest tenth.

The cost to advertise during a program is related to its Nielsen rating. The sponsor (the company paying for the advertisement) pays a certain number of dollars for each rating point a show receives.

4. Suppose a television network charges $35,000 per rating point for a 30-second commercial on a daytime talk show. Determine the cost for three 30-second commercials if the Nielsen rating of the show is 11.5.

Nielsen Media Research also tracks the exposure of advertisements. For example, it might be reported that commercials for McDonald's had 500,000,000 household exposures during a week when its advertisement was aired 90 times.

5. Information regarding household exposure of advertisements can be found in *USA Today* each Monday. For a recent week, find the information for the top four advertised products. For each product, calculate the average household exposure for each time the ad was aired.

Nielsen Media Research has a website on the Internet. You can locate the site by using a search engine.

6. Find the top two prime-time television shows for last week. Calculate the number of TV households that watched the programs. Compare the figures with the figures for the top two sports programs for last week.

Chapter 4 Summary

Key Words	*Examples*
Consecutive integers follow one another in order. [4.2.1, p. 174]	11, 12, 13 are consecutive integers. −9, −8, −7 are consecutive integers.
The **perimeter** of a geometric figure is a measure of the distance around the figure. [4.3.1, p. 181]	The perimeter of a triangle is the sum of the lengths of the three sides. The perimeter of a rectangle is the sum of the lengths of the four sides.

An angle is measured in **degrees.** A 90° angle is a **right angle.** A 180° angle is a **straight angle.** One complete revolution is 360°. An **acute angle** is an angle whose measure is between 0° and 90°. An **obtuse angle** is an angle whose measure is between 90° and 180°. An **isosceles triangle** has two sides of equal measure. The three sides of an **equilateral triangle** are of equal measure. **Complementary angles** are two angles whose measures have the sum 90°. **Supplementary angles** are two angles whose measures have the sum 180°. [4.3.1, 4.3.2, pp. 182–184]

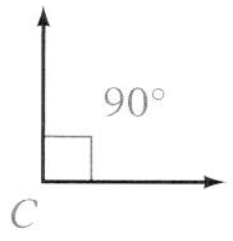

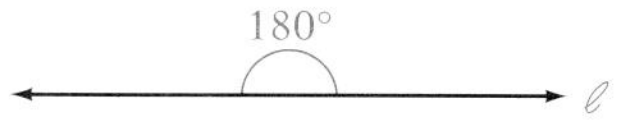

Parallel lines never meet; the distance between them is always the same. **Perpendicular lines** are intersecting lines that form right angles. Two angles that are on opposite sides of the intersection of two lines are **vertical angles;** vertical angles have the same measure. Two angles that share a common side are **adjacent angles;** adjacent angles of intersecting lines are supplementary angles. [4.3.2, pp. 184–185]

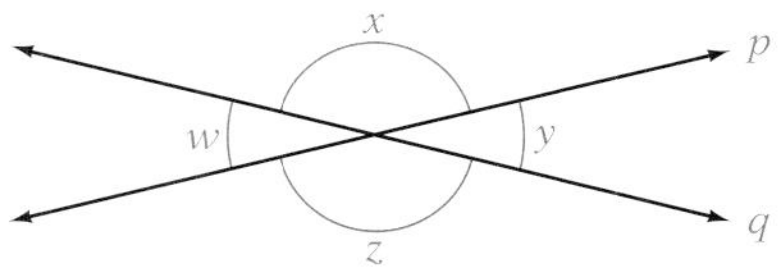

A line that intersects two other lines at two different points is a **transversal.** If the lines cut by a transversal are parallel lines, then pairs of equal angles are formed: **alternate interior angles, alternate exterior angles,** and **corresponding angles.** [4.3.2, pp. 186–187]

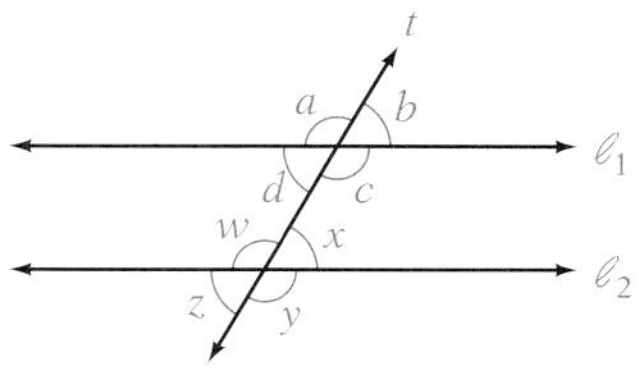

$\angle b = \angle d = \angle x = \angle z$
$\angle a = \angle c = \angle w = \angle y$

Cost is the price that a business pays for a product. **Selling price** is the price for which a business sells a product to a customer. **Markup** is the difference between selling price and cost. **Markup rate** is the markup expressed as a percent of the retailer's cost. [4.4.1, p. 198]

If a business pays \$100 for a product and sells that product for \$140, then the cost of the product is \$100, the selling price is \$140, and the markup is \$140 − \$100 = \$40.

Discount is the amount by which a retailer reduces the regular price of a product. **Discount rate** is the discount expressed as a percent of the regular price. [4.4.2, p. 200]

The regular price of a product is \$100. The product is now on sale for \$75. The discount on the product is \$100 − \$75 = \$25.

Essential Rules and Procedures

Consecutive Integers
$n, n + 1, n + 2, \ldots$ [4.2.1, p. 174]

The sum of three consecutive integers is 135.

$$n + (n + 1) + (n + 2) = 135$$

Consecutive Even or Consecutive Odd Integers
$n, n + 2, n + 4, \ldots$ [4.2.1, p. 174]

The sum of three consecutive odd integers is 135.

$$n + (n + 2) + (n + 4) = 135$$

Coin and Stamp Equation

$$\text{Number of coins} \cdot \text{Value of coin in cents} = \text{Total value in cents}$$

[4.2.2, p. 175]

A coin bank contains $1.80 in dimes and quarters. In all, there are twelve coins in the bank. How many dimes are in the bank?

$$10d + 25(12 - d) = 180$$

Formulas for Perimeter

Triangle: $P = a + b + c$
Rectangle: $P = 2L + 2W$
Square: $P = 4s$
[4.3.1, p. 182]

The perimeter of a rectangle is 108 m. The length is 6 m more than three times the width. Find the width of the rectangle.

$$108 = 2(3W + 6) + 2W$$

The perimeter of an isosceles triangle is 34 ft. The length of the third side is 5 ft less than the length of one of the equal sides. Find the length of one of the equal sides.

$$34 = x + x + (x - 5)$$

Sum of the Angles of a Triangle

The sum of the measures of the interior angles of a triangle is 180°.
$\angle A + \angle B + \angle C = 180°$
The sum of an interior and corresponding exterior angle is 180°.
[4.3.3, p. 188]

In a right triangle, the measure of one acute angle is 12° more than the measure of the smallest angle. Find the measure of the smallest angle.

$$x + (x + 12) + 90 = 180$$

Basic Markup Equation

$S = C + rC$ [4.4.1, p. 199]

The manager of a department buys a pasta maker machine for $70 and sells the machine for $98. Find the markup rate.

$$98 = 70 + 70r$$

Basic Discount Equation

$S = R - rR$ [4.4.2, p. 200]

The sale price for a leather bomber jacket is $95. This price is 24% off the regular price. Find the regular price.

$$95 = R - 0.24R$$

Annual Simple Interest Equation

$I = Pr$ [4.5.1, p. 206]

You invest a portion of $10,000 in a 7% annual simple interest account and the remainder in a 6% annual simple interest bond. The two investments earn total annual interest of $680. How much is invested in the 7% account?

$$0.07x + 0.06(10{,}000 - x) = 680$$

Value Mixture Equation
$V = AC$ [4.6.1, p. 212]

An herbalist has 30 oz of herbs costing \$2 per ounce. How many ounces of herbs costing \$1 per ounce should be mixed with the 30 oz to produce a mixture costing \$1.60 per ounce?

$$30(2) + 1x = 1.60(30 + x)$$

Percent Mixture Equation
$Q = Ar$ [4.6.2, p. 213]

Forty ounces of a 30% gold alloy are mixed with 60 oz of a 20% gold alloy. Find the percent concentration of the resulting gold alloy.

$$0.30(40) + 0.20(60) = x(100)$$

Uniform Motion Equation
$d = rt$ [4.7.1, p. 222]

A boat traveled from a harbor to an island at an average speed of 20 mph. The average speed on the return trip was 15 mph. The total trip took 3.5 h. How long did it take to travel to the island?

$$20t = 15(3.5 - t)$$

Chapter 4 Review Exercises

1. Translate "seven less than twice a number is equal to the number" into an equation and solve.

2. Music A piano wire is 35 in. long. A note can be produced by dividing this wire into two parts so that three times the length of the shorter piece is twice the length of the longer piece. Find the length of the shorter piece.

3. Integer Problem The sum of two numbers is twenty-one. Three times the smaller number is two less than twice the larger number. Find the two numbers.

4. Geometry Translate "the sum of twice a number and six equals four times the difference between the number and two" into an equation and solve.

5. Discounts A ceiling fan that regularly sells for \$90 is on sale for \$60. Find the discount rate.

6. Investments A total of \$15,000 is deposited into two simple interest accounts. The annual simple interest rate on one account is 6%. The annual simple interest rate on the second account is 7%. How much should be invested in each account so that the total interest earned is \$970?

7. **Geometry** In an isosceles triangle, the measure of one of the two equal angles is 15° more than the measure of the third angle. Find the measure of each angle.

8. **Uniform Motion Problem** A motorcyclist and a bicyclist set out at 8 A.M. from the same point, headed in the same direction. The speed of the motorcyclist is three times the speed of the bicyclist. In 2 h, the motorcyclist is 60 mi ahead of the bicyclist. Find the rate of the motorcyclist.

9. **Geometry** In an isosceles triangle, the measure of one angle is 25° less than half the measure of one of the equal angles. Find the measure of each angle.

10. **Markup** The manager of a sporting goods store buys packages of cleats for $5.25 each and sells them for $9.45 each. Find the markup rate.

11. **Percent Mixture** A dairy owner mixes 5 gal of cream that is 30% butterfat with 8 gal of milk that is 4% butterfat. Find the percent concentration of butterfat in the resulting mixture.

12. **Geometry** The length of a rectangle is four times the width. The perimeter is 200 ft. Find the length and width of the rectangle.

13. **Business** The manager of an accounting firm is investigating contracts whereby large quantities of material can be photocopied at minimum cost. The contract from the Copy Center offers a fee of $50 per week and $.03 per page. The Prints 4 U Company offers a fee of $27 per week and $.05 per page. What is the minimum number of copies per week that could be ordered from the Copy Center if these copies are to cost less than copies from Prints 4 U?

14. **Discounts** The sale price for a video game is $26.56, which is 17% off the regular price. Find the regular price.

15. **Food Mixtures** The owner of a health food store combined cranberry juice that cost $1.79 per quart with apple juice that cost $1.19 per quart. How many quarts of each were used to make 10 qt of a cranapple juice mixture costing $1.61 per quart?

16. **Discounts** A famous mystery writer is contracted to autograph copies of her new book at a bookstore. As a special promotion that day, the book is selling for $33.74, which is only 30% above the cost of the book. Find the cost of the book.

17. **Integer Problem** The sum of two numbers is thirty-six. The difference between the larger number and eight equals the total of four and three times the smaller number. Find the two numbers.

18. **Investments** An engineering consultant invested \$14,000 in an individual retirement account paying 8.15% annual simple interest. How much money does the consultant have deposited in an account paying 12% annual simple interest if the total interest earned is 9.25% of the total investment?

19. **Integer Problem** You have removed all the hearts from a standard deck of playing cards and have arranged them in numerical order. Suppose I pick two consecutive cards and tell you their sum is 15. Name the two cards I picked.

20. **Percent Mixture** A pharmacist has 15 L of an 80% alcohol solution. How many liters of pure water should be added to the alcohol solution to make an alcohol solution that is 75% alcohol?

21. **Test Scores** A student's grades on five sociology exams were 68, 82, 90, 73, and 95. What is the lowest score this student can receive on the sixth exam and still have earned a total of at least 480 points?

22. Translate "the opposite of seven is equal to one-half a number less ten" into an equation and solve.

23. **Structures** The Empire State Building is 1472 ft tall. This is 654 ft less than twice the height of the Eiffel Tower. Find the height of the Eiffel Tower.

24. **Geometry** One angle of a triangle is 15° more than the measure of the second angle. The third angle is 15° less than the measure of the second angle. Find the measure of each angle.

25. **Business** The manager of a refreshment stand at a local stadium tallied the receipts for one evening. There was a total of \$263 in one-dollar bills and five-dollar bills. In all, there were 155 bills. Find the number of one-dollar bills.

26. **Carpentry** A board 10 ft long is cut into two pieces. Four times the length of the shorter piece is 2 ft less than two times the length of the longer piece. Find the length of the longer piece.

27. **Compensation** An optical engineer's consulting fee was \$600. This included \$80 for supplies and \$65 for each hour of consultation. Find the number of hours of consultation.

28. **Stamps** A stamp collector has 12¢ stamps and 17¢ stamps with a total face value of \$15.53. The number of 12¢ stamps is three more than twice the number of 17¢ stamps. How many of each type are in the collection?

29. **Markup** A furniture store uses a markup rate of 60%. The store sells a solid oak curio cabinet for \$1074. Find the cost of the curio cabinet.

30. **Swimming Pools** The largest swimming pool in the world is located in Casablanca, Morocco, and is 480 m long. Two swimmers start at the same time from opposite ends of the pool and swim toward each other. One swimmer's rate is 65 m/min. The other swimmer's rate is 55 m/min. In how many minutes after they begin will they meet?

31. **Geometry** The perimeter of a triangle is 35 in. The second side is 4 in. longer than the first side. The third side is 1 in. shorter than twice the first side. Find the measure of each side.

32. **Integer Problem** The sum of three consecutive odd integers is -45. Find the integers.

33. **Geometry** A rectangle is 15 ft long and $(2x - 4)$ ft wide. Express as an integer the maximum width of the rectangle when the perimeter is less than 52 ft.

34. **Geometry** Given that $\ell_1 \parallel \ell_2$, find the measures of angles a and b.

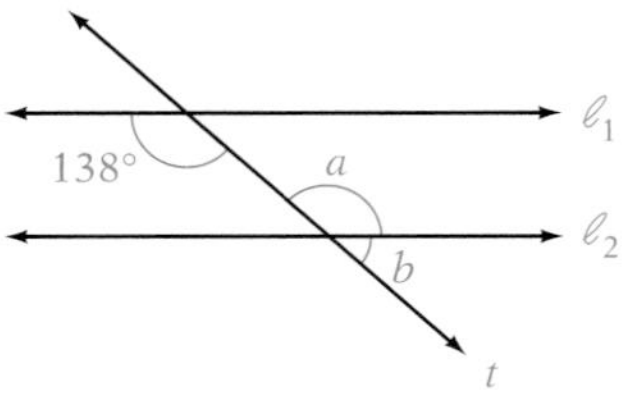

Chapter 4 Test

1. Translate "the sum of six times a number and thirteen is five less than the product of three and the number" into an equation and solve.

2. Translate "the difference between three times a number and fifteen is twenty-seven" into an equation and solve.

3. **Integer Problem** The sum of two numbers is 18. The difference between four times the smaller number and seven is equal to the sum of two times the larger number and five. Find the two numbers.

4. **Carpentry** A board 18 ft long is cut into two pieces. Two feet less than the product of five and the length of the shorter piece is equal to the difference between three times the length of the longer piece and eight. Find the length of each piece.

5. **Markup** The manager of a sports shop uses a markup rate of 50%. The selling price for a set of golf clubs is \$300. Find the cost of the golf clubs.

6. **Discounts** A pair of running shoes that regularly sells for \$100 is on sale for \$80. Find the discount rate.

7. **Percent Mixture** How many gallons of a 15% acid solution must be mixed with 5 gal of a 20% acid solution to make a 16% acid solution?

8. **Geometry** The perimeter of a rectangle is 38 m. The length of the rectangle is 1 m less than three times the width. Find the length and width of the rectangle.

9. **Integer Problem** Find three consecutive odd integers such that three times the first integer is one less than the sum of the second and third integers.

10. **Floral Deliveries** Florist A charges a $3 delivery fee plus $21 per bouquet delivered. Florist B charges a $15 delivery fee plus $18 per bouquet delivered. An organization wants to send each resident of a small nursing home a bouquet for Valentine's Day. How many residents are in the nursing home if it is more economical for the organization to use Florist B?

11. **Investments** A total of $7000 is deposited into two simple interest accounts. On one account, the annual simple interest rate is 10%, and on the second account, the annual simple interest rate is 15%. How much should be invested in each account so that the total annual interest earned is $800?

12. **Food Mixtures** A coffee merchant wants to make 12 lb of a blend of coffee costing $6 per pound. The blend is made using a $7 grade and a $4 grade of coffee. How many pounds of each of these grades should be used?

13. **Uniform Motion** Two planes start at the same time from the same point and fly in opposite directions. The first plane is flying 100 mph faster than the second plane. In 3 h, the two planes are 1050 mi apart. Find the rate of each plane.

14. **Geometry** In a triangle, the first angle is 15° more than the second angle. The third angle is three times the second angle. Find the measure of each angle.

15. **Coins** A coin bank contains 50 coins in nickels and quarters. The total amount of money in the bank is $9.50. Find the number of nickels and the number of quarters in the bank.

16. **Investments** A club treasurer deposited $2400 in two simple interest accounts. The annual simple interest rate on one account is 6.75%. The annual simple interest rate on the other account is 9.45%. How much should be deposited in each account so that the same interest is earned on each account?

17. **Geometry** The width of a rectangle is 12 ft. The length is $(3x + 5)$ ft. Express as an integer the minimum length of the rectangle if the area is greater than 276 ft^2.

18. **Discounts** A file cabinet that normally sells for $99 is on sale for 20% off. Find the sale price.

Cumulative Review Exercises

1. Given $B = \{-12, -6, -3, -1\}$, which elements of set B are less than -4?

2. Simplify: $-2 + (-8) - (-16)$

3. Simplify: $\left(-\frac{2}{3}\right)^3\left(-\frac{3}{4}\right)^2$

4. Simplify: $\frac{5}{6} - \left(\frac{2}{3}\right)^2 \div \left(\frac{1}{2} - \frac{1}{3}\right)$

5. Evaluate $-|-18|$.

6. Evaluate $b^2 - (a - b)^2$ when $a = 4$ and $b = -1$.

7. Simplify: $5x - 3y - (-4x) + 7y$

8. Simplify: $-4(3 - 2x - 5x^3)$

9. Simplify: $-2[x - 3(x - 1) - 5]$

10. Simplify: $-3x^2 - (-5x^2) + 4x^2$

11. Is 2 a solution of $4 - 2x - x^2 = 2 - 4x$?

12. Solve: $9 - x = 12$

13. Solve: $-\frac{4}{5}x = 12$

14. Solve: $8 - 5x = -7$

15. Solve: $-6x - 4(3 - 2x) = 4x + 8$

16. Write 40% as a fraction.

17. Solve and graph the solution set of $4x \geq 16$.

18. Solve: $-15x \leq 45$

19. Solve: $2x - 3 > x + 15$

20. Solve: $12 - 4(x - 1) \leq 5(x - 4)$

21. Write 0.025 as a percent.

22. Write $\frac{3}{25}$ as a percent.

23. Find $16\frac{2}{3}\%$ of 18.

24. 40% of what is 18?

25. Translate "the sum of eight times a number and twelve is equal to the product of four and the number" into an equation and solve.

26. **Construction** The area of the cement foundation of a house is 2000 ft^2. This is 200 ft^2 more than three times the area of the garage. Find the area of the garage.

27. **Repair Bills** An auto repair bill was \$313. This includes \$88 for parts and \$45 for each hour of labor. Find the number of hours of labor.

28. **Libraries** A survey of 250 librarians showed that 50 of the libraries had a particular reference book on their shelves. What percent of the libraries had the reference book?

29. **Investments** A deposit of $4000 is made into an account that earns 11% annual simple interest. How much money is also deposited in an account that pays 14% annual simple interest if the total annual interest earned is 12% of the total investment?

30. **Markup** The manager of a department store buys a chain necklace for $80 and sells it for $140. Find the markup rate.

31. **Metallurgy** How many grams of a gold alloy that costs $4 per gram must be mixed with 30 g of a gold alloy that costs $7 per gram to make an alloy costing $5 per gram?

32. **Percent Mixture** How many ounces of pure water must be added to 70 oz of a 10% salt solution to make a 7% salt solution?

33. **Geometry** In an isosceles triangle, the third angle is 8° less than twice the measure of one of the equal angles. Find the measure of one of the equal angles.

34. **Integer Problem** Three times the second of three consecutive even integers is 14 more than the sum of the first and third integers. Find the middle integer.

35. **Coins** A coin bank contains dimes and quarters. The number of quarters is five less than four times the number of dimes. The total amount in the bank is $6.45. Find the number of dimes in the bank.

CHAPTER

5 Linear Equations and Inequalities

OBJECTIVES

5.1
1 Graph points in a rectangular coordinate system
2 Scatter diagrams
3 Average rate of change

5.2
1 Determine solutions of linear equations in two variables
2 Graph equations of the form $y = mx + b$
3 Graph equations of the form $Ax + By = C$

5.3
1 Find the slope of a straight line
2 Graph a line using the slope and y-intercept

5.4
1 Find the equation of a line using the equation $y = mx + b$
2 Find the equation of a line using the point-slope formula
3 Find the equation of a line given two points

5.5
1 Introduction to functions
2 Graphs of linear functions

5.6
1 Graph inequalities in two variables

DVD SSM *Online Study Center*

Need help? For online student resources, such as section quizzes, visit the Online Study Center at college.hmco.com/pic/aufmannBAWA7e.

Millions of people live and work in New York City every day, making it one of the busiest places on Earth. The U.S. Bureau of the Census records how many people live in a particular city each year and keeps track of how populations grow and change. By comparing the population over the years, we are able to determine the rate of change in the population and then use that rate to predict populations in the future. Average rate of change, which is discussed in **Section 5.4, Exercise 71 on page 297,** provides projections of the population of the United States for every five years from 2005 to 2030.

Prep Test

1. Simplify: $\dfrac{5 - (-7)}{4 - 8}$

2. Evaluate $\dfrac{a - b}{c - d}$ when $a = 3$, $b = -2$, $c = -3$, and $d = 2$.

3. Simplify: $-3(x - 4)$

4. Solve: $3x + 6 = 0$

5. Solve $4x + 5y = 20$ when $y = 0$.

6. Solve $3x - 7y = 11$ when $x = -1$.

7. Given $y = -4x + 5$, find the value of y when $x = -2$.

8. Simplify: $\dfrac{1}{4}(3x - 16)$

9. Which of the following are solutions of the inequality $-4 < x + 3$?
a. 0 **b.** -3 **c.** 5 **d.** -7 **e.** -10

5.1 The Rectangular Coordinate System

OBJECTIVE 1 Graph points in a rectangular coordinate system

Before the 15th century, geometry and algebra were considered separate branches of mathematics. That all changed when René Descartes, a French mathematician who lived from 1596 to 1650, founded **analytic geometry.** In this geometry, a *coordinate system* is used to study the relationships between variables.

A **rectangular coordinate system** is formed by two number lines, one horizontal and one vertical, that intersect at the zero point of each line. The point of intersection is called the **origin.** The two axes are called the **coordinate axes,** or simply the **axes.** Generally, the horizontal axis is labeled the ***x*-axis,** and the vertical axis is labeled the ***y*-axis.**

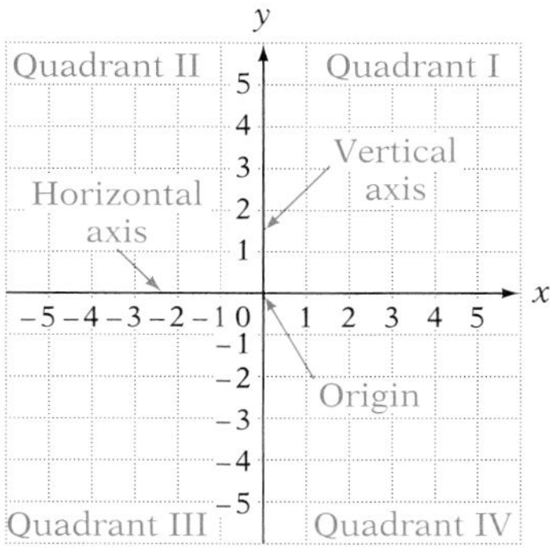

The axes determine a **plane,** which can be thought of as a large, flat sheet of paper. The two axes divide the plane into four regions called **quadrants,** which are numbered counterclockwise from I to IV starting at the upper right.

Each point in the plane can be identified by a pair of numbers called an **ordered pair.** The first number of the ordered pair measures a horizontal distance and is called the **abscissa,** or ***x*-coordinate.** The second number of the pair measures a vertical distance and is called the **ordinate,** or ***y*-coordinate.** The ordered pair (x, y) associated with a point is also called the **coordinates** of the point.

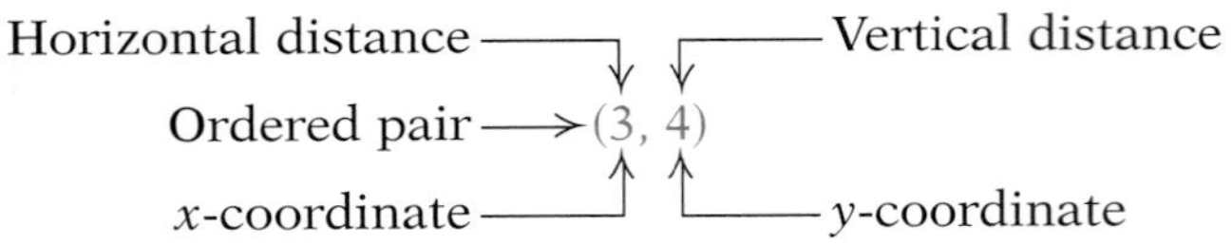

To **graph,** or **plot, a point in the plane,** place a dot at the location given by the ordered pair. For example, to graph the point $(4, 1)$, start at the origin. Move 4 units to the right and then 1 unit up. Draw a dot. To graph $(-3, -2)$, start at the origin. Move 3 units left and then 2 units down. Draw a dot.

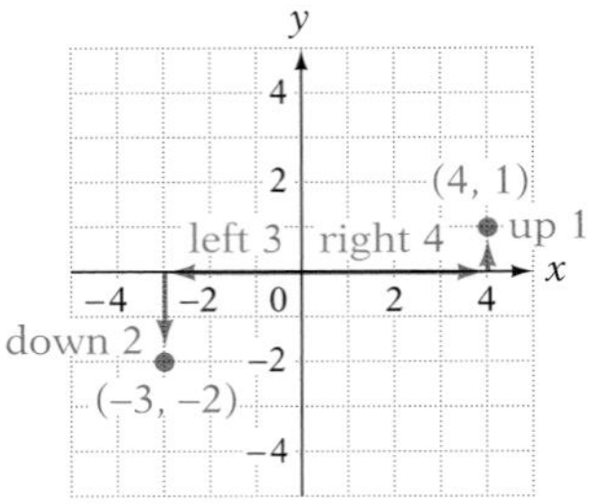

The **graph of an ordered pair** is the dot drawn at the coordinates of the point in the plane. The graphs of the ordered pairs $(4, 1)$ and $(-3, -2)$ are shown at the right.

> **Take Note**
>
> This point is very important. An *ordered pair* is a *pair* of coordinates, and the *order* in which the coordinates appear is important.

The graphs of the points whose coordinates are $(2, 3)$ and $(3, 2)$ are shown at the right. Note that they are different points. The order in which the numbers in an ordered pair appear *is* important.

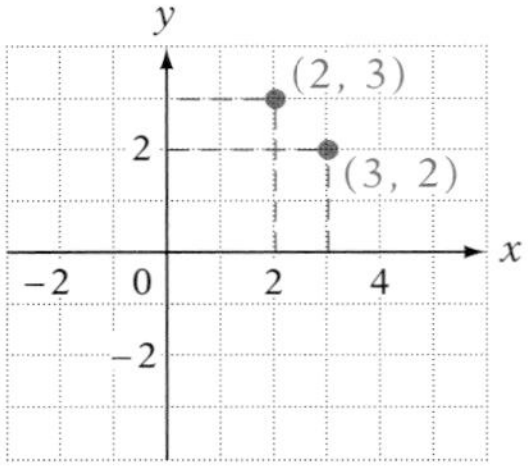

Each point in the plane is associated with an ordered pair, and each ordered pair is associated with a point in the plane. Although only integers are labeled on the coordinate grid, any ordered pair can be graphed by approximating its location. The graphs of the ordered pairs $\left(\frac{3}{2}, -\frac{4}{3}\right)$ and $(-2.4, 3.5)$ are shown at the right.

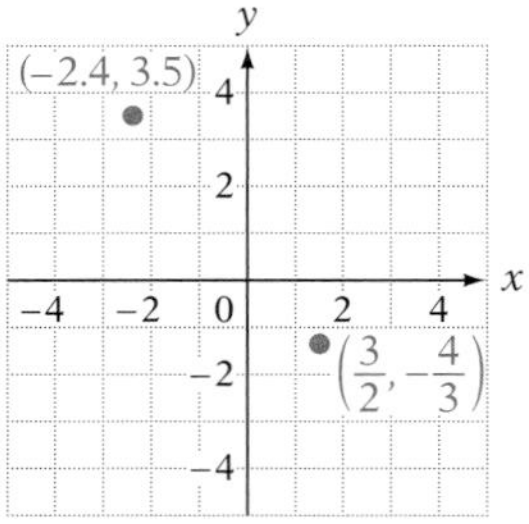

EXAMPLE 1 Graph the ordered pairs $(-2, -3)$, $(3, -2)$, $(1, 3)$, and $(4, 1)$.

Solution

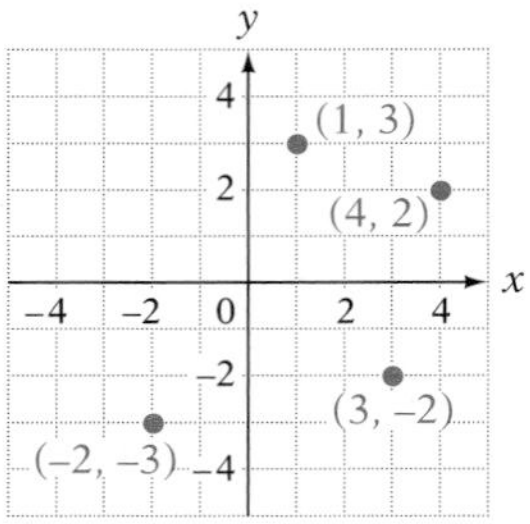

PROBLEM 1 Graph the ordered pairs (−1, 3), (1, 4), (−4, 0), and (−2, −1).

Solution See page S11.

EXAMPLE 2 Find the coordinates of each of the points.

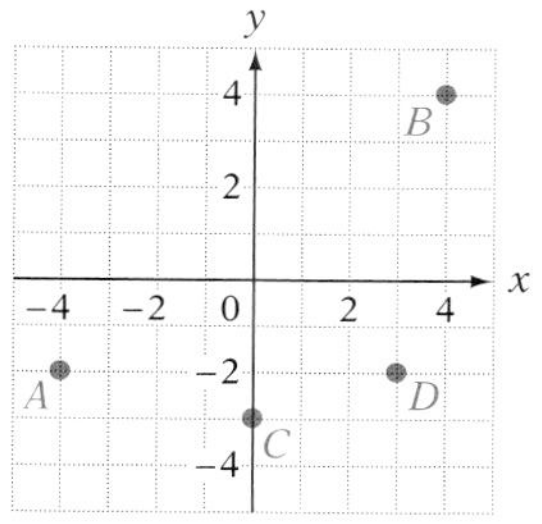

Solution $A(-4, -2)$, $B(4, 4)$, $C(0, -3)$, $D(3, -2)$

PROBLEM 2 Find the coordinates of each of the points.

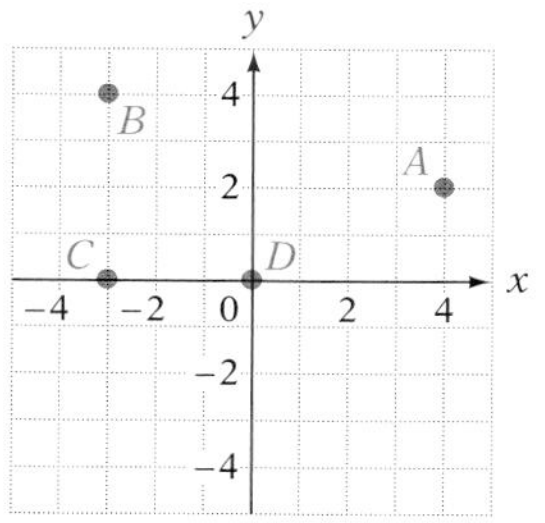

Solution See page S11.

OBJECTIVE 2 Scatter diagrams

There are many situations in which the relationship between two variables may be of interest. For example, a college admissions director wants to know the relationship between SAT scores (one variable) and success in college (the second variable). An employer is interested in the relationship between scores on a pre-employment test and ability to perform a job.

A researcher can investigate the relationship between two variables by means of regression analysis, which is a branch of statistics. The study of the relationship between two variables may begin with a **scatter diagram,** which is a graph of some of the known data.

The following table gives the record times for races of different lengths at a junior high track meet. Record times are rounded to the nearest second. Lengths are given in meters.

Length, x	100	200	400	800	1000	1500
Time, y	20	40	100	200	260	420

The scatter diagram for these data is shown at the right. Each ordered pair represents the length of the race and the record time. For example, the ordered pair (400, 100) indicates that the record for the 400 m race is 100 s.

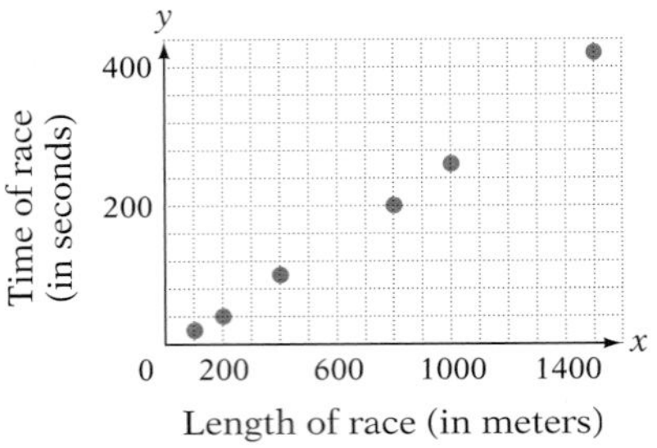

EXAMPLE 3 To test a heart medicine, a doctor measures the heart rate, in beats per minute, of five patients before and after they take the medication. The results are recorded in the following table. Graph the scatter diagram for these data.

Before medicine, x	85	80	85	75	90
After medicine, y	75	70	70	80	80

Strategy Graph the ordered pairs on a rectangular coordinate system where the horizontal axis represents the heart rate before taking the medication and the vertical axis represents the heart rate after taking the medication.

Solution

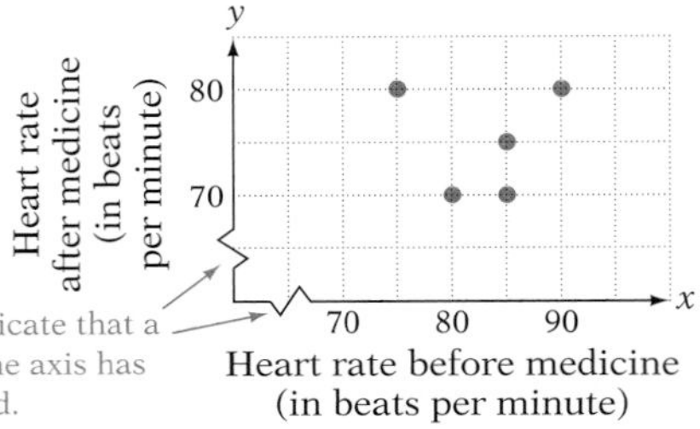

PROBLEM 3 A study by the Federal Aviation Administration showed that narrow, over-the-wing emergency exit rows slow passenger evacuation. The table at the top of the next page shows the space between seats, in inches, and the evacuation time, in seconds, for a group of 35 passengers. The longest evacuation times are recorded in the table. Graph the scatter diagram for these data.

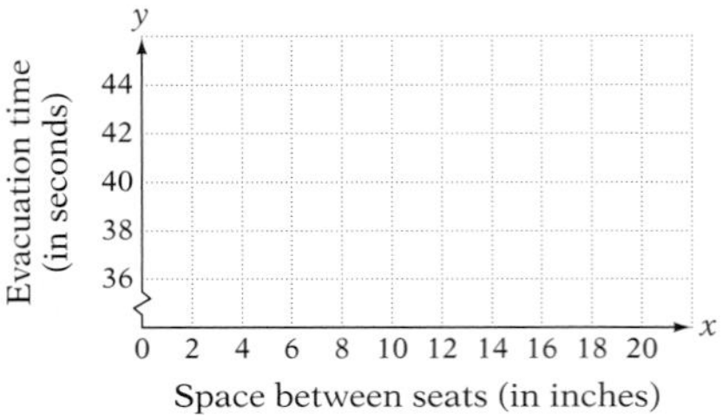

Space between seats, x	6	10	13	15	20
Evacuation time, y	44	43	38	36	37

Solution See page S11.

OBJECTIVE 3 Average rate of change

The table at the left shows the population of the United States for each decade from 1800 to 2000. (*Source:* U.S. Bureau of the Census) These data are graphed in the scatter diagram below.

Population of the United States

Year	Population (in millions)
1800	5
1810	7
1820	10
1830	13
1840	17
1850	23
1860	31
1870	40
1880	50
1890	63
1900	76
1910	92
1920	106
1930	123
1940	132
1950	151
1960	179
1970	203
1980	227
1990	249
2000	281

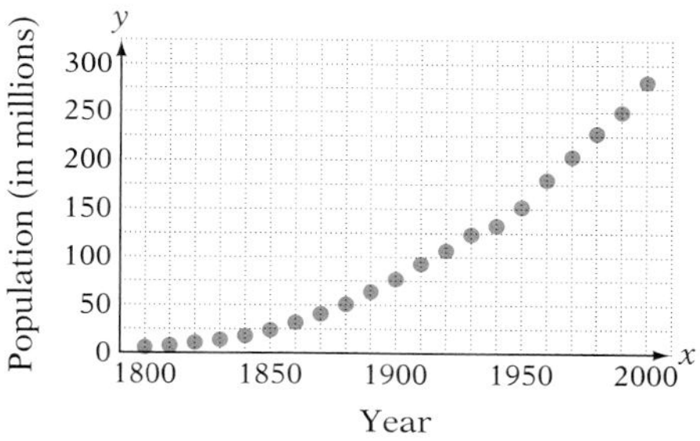

One way to describe how the population of the United States has changed over time is to calculate the change in population for a given time period. For example, we can find the change in population from 1990 to 2000.

$$\text{Population in 2000} - \text{population in 1990} = 281 \text{ million} - 249 \text{ million}$$
$$= 32 \text{ million}$$

The amount of change in the population, 32 million, does not describe how rapid the growth in population was. To describe the rate of growth, or the *rate of change,* we must consider the number of years over which that growth took place. To determine how rapidly the population grew from 1990 to 2000, divide the change in population by the number of years during which that change took place.

$$\frac{\text{Change in population}}{\text{Change in years}} = \frac{\text{population in 2000} - \text{population in 1990}}{2000 - 1990}$$
$$= \frac{281 - 249}{2000 - 1990}$$
$$= \frac{32}{10} = 3.2$$

The average rate of change was 3.2 million people per year. This means that *on average,* from 1990 to 2000, the population of the United States increased by 3.2 million people per year.

Consider the two points on the graph that correspond to these years:

$$(1990, 249) \text{ and } (2000, 281)$$

Note that the average rate of change is calculated by dividing the difference between the y values of the two points by the difference between the x values of the two points.

Average Rate of Change

The average rate of change of y with respect to x is $\dfrac{\text{change in } y}{\text{change in } x}$.

To calculate the average rate of change, think

$$\frac{y \text{ value of second point} - y \text{ value of first point}}{x \text{ value of second point} - x \text{ value of first point}}$$

Find the average rate of change per year in the U.S. population from 1980 to 1990.

In 1980, the population was 227 million: (1980, 227)
In 1990, the population was 249 million: (1990, 249)

$$\text{Average rate of change} = \frac{\text{change in } y}{\text{change in } x}$$

$$= \frac{\text{population in 1990} - \text{population in 1980}}{1990 - 1980}$$

$$= \frac{249 - 227}{1990 - 1980}$$

$$= \frac{22}{10} = 2.2$$

The average rate of change in the population was 2.2 million people per year.

From 1990 to 2000, the average rate of change was 3.2 million people per year, whereas from 1980 to 1990, the average rate of change was 2.2 million people per year. The rate of change in the U.S. population is not constant; it varies for different intervals of time.

EXAMPLE 4 Find the average rate of change per year in the U.S. population from 1800 to 1900.

Solution In 1800, the population was 5 million: (1800, 5)
In 1900, the population was 76 million: (1900, 76)

$$\begin{aligned}\text{Averate rate of change} &= \frac{\text{change in } y}{\text{change in } x}\\ &= \frac{\text{population in 1900} - \text{population in 1800}}{1900 - 1800}\\ &= \frac{76 - 5}{1900 - 1800}\\ &= \frac{71}{100} = 0.71\end{aligned}$$

The average rate of change in the population was 0.71 million people per year, or 710,000 people per year.

Note that if both the ordinates and the abscissas are subtracted in the reverse order, the result is the same.

$$\begin{aligned}\text{Average rate of change} &= \frac{\text{population in 1800} - \text{population in 1900}}{1800 - 1900}\\ &= \frac{5 - 76}{1800 - 1900} = \frac{-71}{-100} = 0.71\end{aligned}$$

PROBLEM 4 Find the average rate of change per year in the U.S. population from 1900 to 2000.

Solution See page S11.

The table below shows weights of fetuses during various stages of prenatal development in humans. Use these data for Example 5 and Problem 5.

Number of weeks after conception	21	24	28	30	38
Weight, in pounds	1	2	3	4	7.5

EXAMPLE 5 Find the average rate of change per week in the weight of a fetus from 21 weeks after conception to 30 weeks after conception.

Solution 21 weeks after conception, the weight is 1 lb: (21, 1)
30 weeks after conception, the weight is 4 lb: (30, 4)

$$\begin{aligned}\text{Average rate of change} &= \frac{\text{change in } y}{\text{change in } x}\\ &= \frac{\text{weight after 30 weeks} - \text{weight after 21 weeks}}{30 - 21}\\ &= \frac{4 - 1}{30 - 21} = \frac{3}{9}\\ &= \frac{1}{3} = 0.\overline{3}\end{aligned}$$

The average rate of change in weight is $0.\overline{3}$ lb per week.

PROBLEM 5 Find the average rate of change per week in the weight of a fetus from 28 weeks after conception to 38 weeks after conception.

Solution See page S11.

5.1 Concept Review

Determine whether the statement is always true, sometimes true, or never true.

1. The point (0, 0) on a rectangular coordinate system is at the origin.

2. When a point is plotted in the rectangular coordinate system, the first number in the ordered pair indicates a movement up or down from the origin. The second number in the ordered pair indicates a movement left or right.

3. In an xy-coordinate system, the first number is the y-coordinate and the second number is the x-coordinate.

4. When a point is plotted in the rectangular coordinate system, a negative x value indicates a movement to the left. A negative y value indicates a movement down.

5. Any point plotted in quadrant III has a positive y value.

6. In the figure at the right, point C is the graph of the point whose coordinates are $(-4, -2)$.

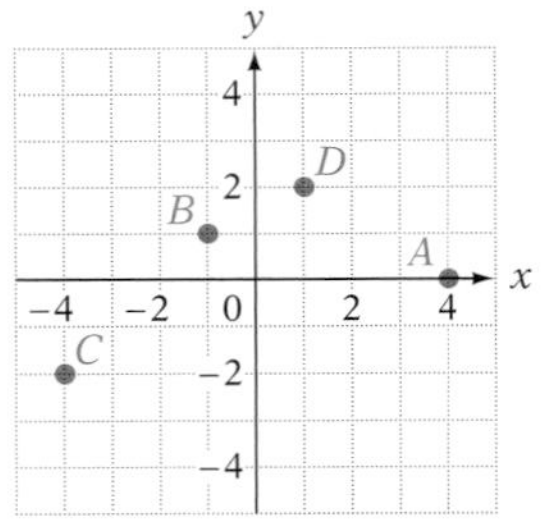

7. Any point on the x-axis has y-coordinate 0.

8. Any point on the y-axis has x-coordinate 0.

5.1 Exercises

1 Graph points in a rectangular coordinate system

Complete Exercises 1 and 2 by replacing each question mark with the word *left, right, up,* or *down.*

1. To graph the point $(5, -4)$, start at the origin and move 5 units __?__ and 4 units __?__.

2. To graph the point $(-1, 7)$, start at the origin and move 1 unit __?__ and 7 units __?__.

3. Describe the signs of the coordinates of a point in **a.** quadrant I, **b.** quadrant II, **c.** quadrant III, and **d.** quadrant IV.

4. In which quadrant is the point located?
a. $(2, -4)$ **b.** $(-3, 2)$ **c.** $(-1, -6)$

5. Graph the ordered pairs (−2, 1), (3, −5), (−2, 4), and (0, 3).

6. Graph the ordered pairs (5, −1), (−3, −3), (−1, 0), and (1, −1).

7. Graph the ordered pairs (0, 0), (0, −5), (−3, 0), and (0, 2).

8. Graph the ordered pairs (−4, 5), (−3, 1), (3, −4), and (5, 0).

9. Graph the ordered pairs (−1, 4), (−2, −3), (0, 2), and (4, 0).

10. Graph the ordered pairs (5, 2), (−4, −1), (0, 0), and (0, 3).

11. Find the coordinates of each of the points.

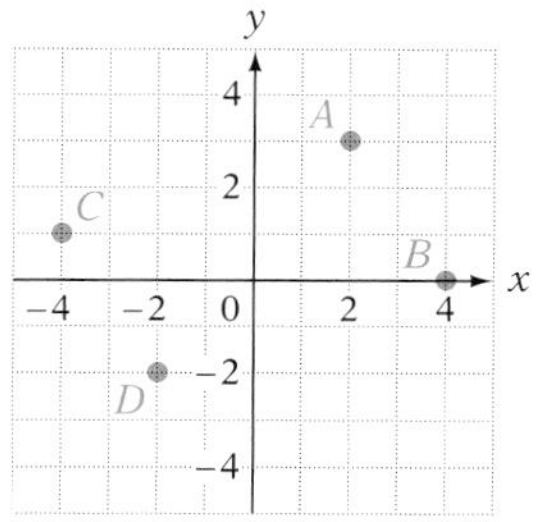

12. Find the coordinates of each of the points.

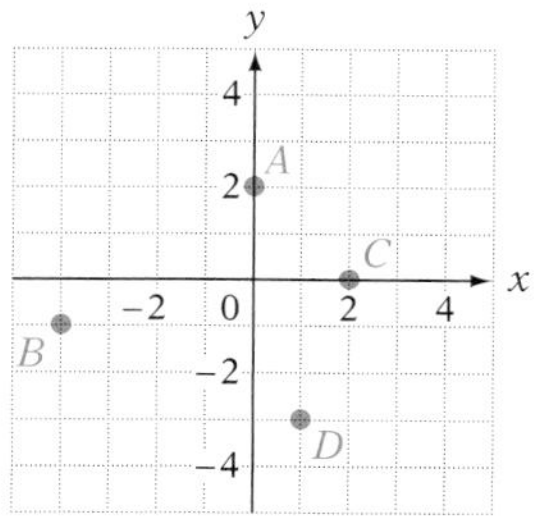

13. Find the coordinates of each of the points.

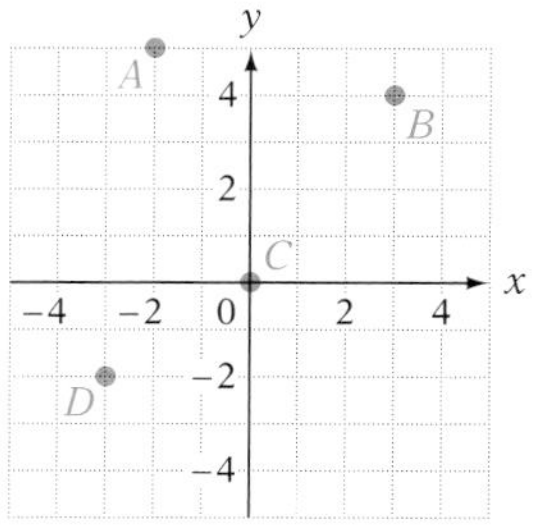

14. Find the coordinates of each of the points.

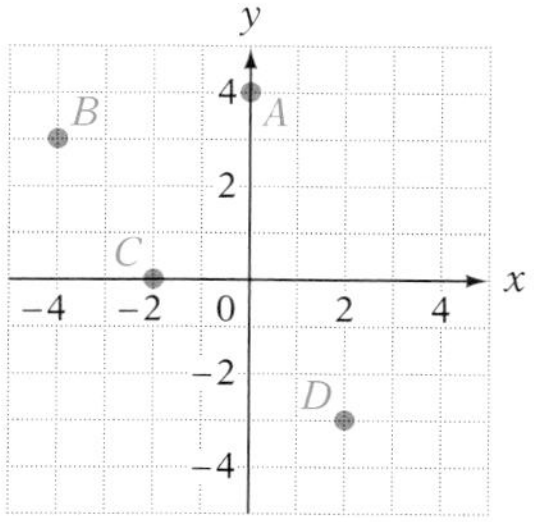

15. **a.** Name the abscissas of points *A* and *C*.
b. Name the ordinates of points *B* and *D*.

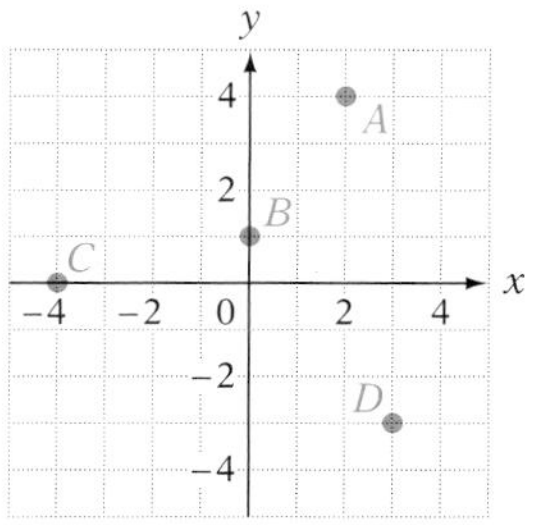

16. **a.** Name the abscissas of points *A* and *C*.
b. Name the ordinates of points *B* and *D*.

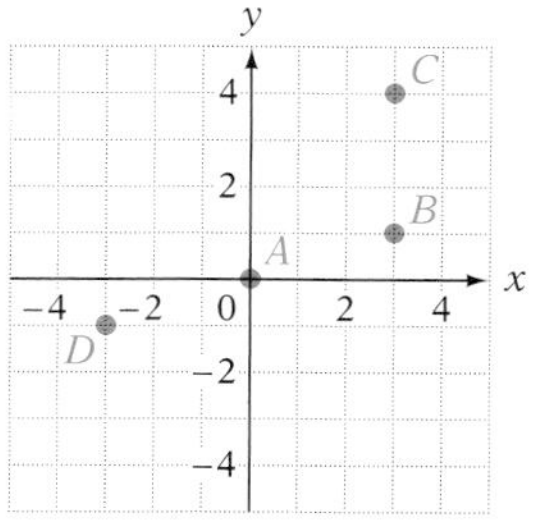

17. Let a and b be positive numbers such that $a < b$. In which quadrant is each point located?

a. (a, b) **b.** $(-a, b)$ **c.** $(b - a, -b)$ **d.** $(a - b, -b - a)$

18. Let a and b be positive numbers. State whether the two given points lie on the x-axis, the y-axis, a horizontal line other than the x-axis, or a vertical line other than the y-axis.

a. $(-a, b)$ and $(-a, 0)$ **b.** $(a, 0)$ and $(-b, 0)$

2 Scatter diagrams

19. Look at the table of data in Exercise 21. The lowest x value is __?__ and the highest x value is __?__. The lowest y value is __?__ and the highest y value is __?__. In a scatter diagram of the data, the x-axis must show values from at least __?__ to __?__, and the y-axis must show values from at least __?__ to __?__.

20. Look at the table of data in Exercise 22. The lowest x value is __?__ and the highest x value is __?__. The lowest y value is __?__ and the highest y value is __?__. In a scatter diagram of the data, the x-axis must show values from at least __?__ to __?__, and the y-axis must show values from at least __?__ to __?__.

21. **Fuel Efficiency** The American Council for an Energy-Efficient Economy releases rankings of environmentally friendly and unfriendly cars and trucks sold in the United States. The following table shows the fuel usage, in miles per gallon, in the city and on the highway, for the twelve 2005-model vehicles ranked best for the environment. Graph the scatter diagram for these data.

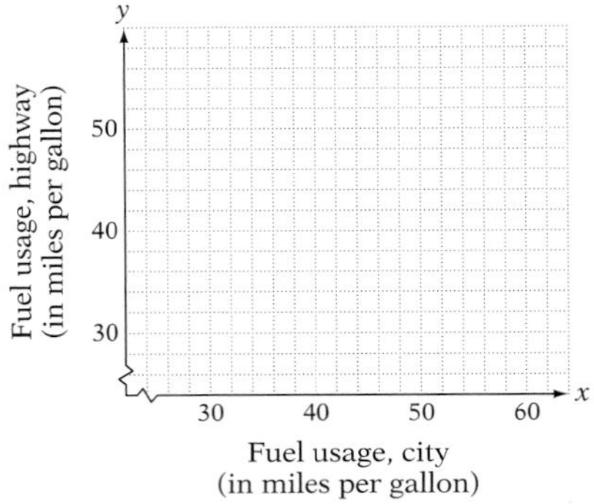

Fuel usage, in mpg, city, x	30	57	60	47	32	35	28	36	30	28	36	26
Fuel usage in mpg, highway, y	34	56	51	48	41	42	35	44	36	35	31	35

22. **Fuel Efficiency** The American Council for an Energy-Efficient Economy releases rankings of environmentally friendly and unfriendly cars and trucks sold in the United States. The following table shows the fuel usage, in miles per gallon, in the city and on the highway, for the twelve 2005-model vehicles ranked worst for the environment. Graph the scatter diagram for these data.

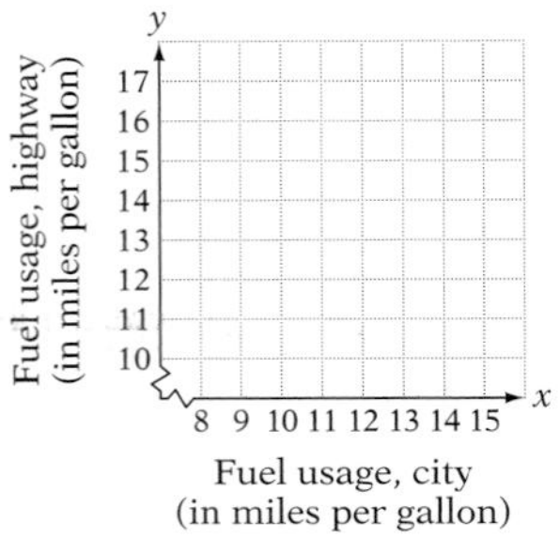

Fuel usage, in mpg, city, x	9	13	13	12	9	13	14	12	10	13	9	12
Fuel usage in mpg, highway, y	12	17	17	14	13	17	17	16	14	14	15	16

23. **Olympics** The following table shows the weight, in pounds, and the height, in inches, of some of the members of the U.S. Women's Soccer Team that won a gold medal in the 2004 Olympic games. Graph the scatter diagram for these data.

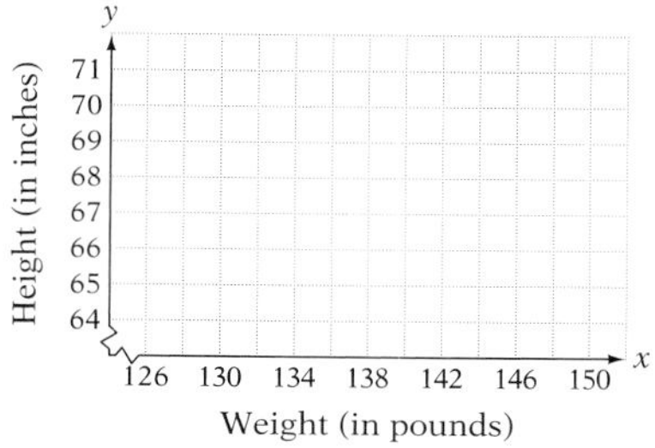

Weight, in pounds, x	150	134	128	134	134	128	148	130	126	134
Height, in inches, y	69	65	67	67	67	68	66	64	64	71

24. **Basketball** The following table shows the weight, in pounds, and the height, in inches, of some of the members of a Seattle Supersonics professional basketball team. Graph the scatter diagram for these data.

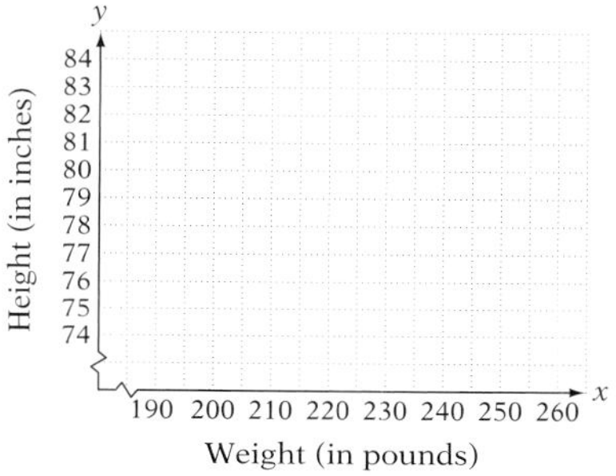

Weight, in pounds, x	205	190	210	255	245	260	215	225	245	225
Height, in inches, y	77	76	74	81	80	80	82	74	84	78

25. **Incomes** To determine trends in income levels, economists use inflation-adjusted values. These numbers take into consideration how inflation affects purchase power. The following table shows the median income, rounded to the nearest hundred, for selected years in both actual dollars (before inflation) and 2005 inflation-adjusted dollars. (*Source:* U.S. Census Bureau) Graph the scatter diagram for these data.

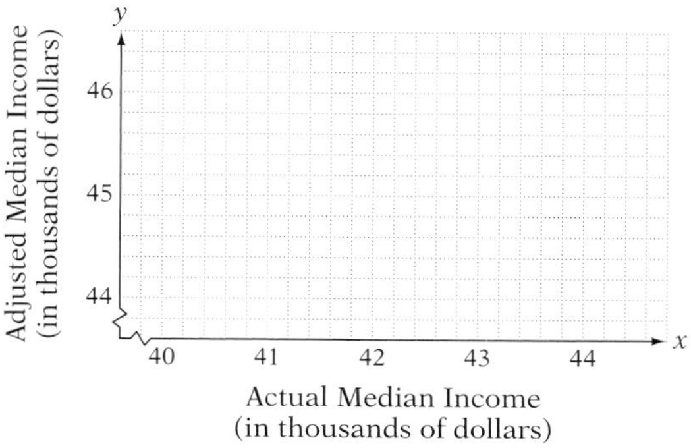

Year	*Actual Median Income, x*	*Inflation-adjusted Median Income, y*
2000	40,700	46,100
2001	42,000	46,100
2002	42,200	45,100
2003	42,400	44,500
2004	43,300	44,500
2005	44,400	44,400

26. **Sports** A basketball coach wants to determine whether there is a relationship between the number of shots attempted and the number of shots made. The following table shows the performances of six players on the team for one game. Graph the scatter diagram for these data.

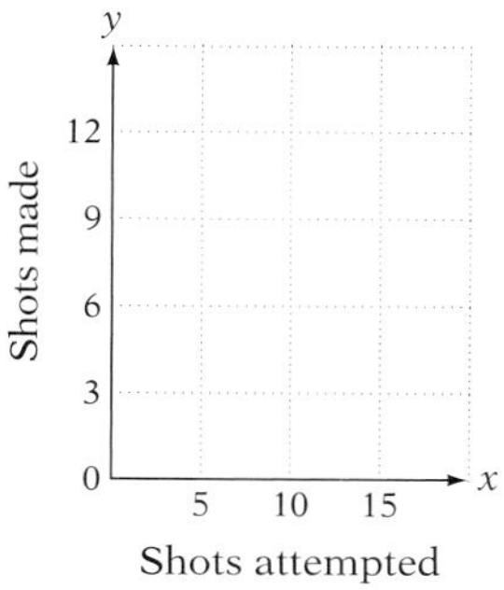

Shots attempted, x	13	11	8	5	4	1
Shots made, y	11	7	5	4	3	1

3 Average rate of change

27. Look at the table of values in Exercise 30, in which you are asked to calculate average rates of change for pairs of data points. When finding an average rate of change between two data points in this table, will you put the values that represent time in the numerator or the denominator?

28. Look at the table of values in Exercise 32. Which of the following fractions is the correct one to use to find the average rate of change per month in the length of a fetus from the fourth month of pregnancy to the eighth month of pregnancy?

a. $\frac{4-8}{16-7}$ **b.** $\frac{16-7}{8-4}$ **c.** $\frac{8-4}{16-7}$ **d.** $\frac{7-16}{14-8}$

29. **Temperature** On September 10 in midstate New Hampshire, the temperature at 6 A.M. was 45°F. At 2 P.M. on the same day, the temperature was 77°F. Find the average rate of change in temperature per hour.

30. **Demography** The table at the right shows the population of Colonial America for each decade from 1610 to 1780. (*Source:* infoplease.com) These figures are estimates, because this period was prior to the establishment of the U.S. Census in 1790.

a. Find the average annual rate of change in the population of the Colonies from 1650 to 1750.

b. Was the average annual rate of change in the population from 1650 to 1750 greater than or less than the average annual rate of change in the population from 1700 to 1750?

c. During which decade was the average annual rate of change the least? What was the average annual rate of change during that decade?

Population of Colonial America

Year	*Population*
1610	350
1620	2,300
1630	4,600
1640	26,600
1650	50,400
1660	75,100
1670	111,900
1680	151,500
1690	210,400
1700	250,900
1710	331,700
1720	466,200
1730	629,400
1740	905,600
1750	1,170,800
1760	1,593,600
1770	2,148,100
1780	2,780,400

31. **Minimum Wage** The following table shows the minimum hourly wage for selected years. (*Source:* Employment Policy Institute, www.epi.org/issueguides/minwage/table4.gif)

Year	1970	1975	1980	1985	1990	1995	2000	2005
Minimum wage	1.60	2.10	3.10	3.35	3.69	4.25	5.15	5.15

a. What was the average annual rate of change in the minimum wage from 1970 to 1990?

b. Find the average rate of change in the minimum wage from 1990 to 2005. Is this more or less than the average annual rate of change in the minimum wage from 1970 to 1990?

32. **Child Development** The following table shows average lengths of fetuses for selected stages of prenatal development in humans. (*Source:* Surebaby.com)

a. What is the average rate of change per month in the length of a fetus from the sixth month of pregnancy to the eighth month of pregnancy?

b. Find the average rate of change per month in the length of a fetus from the second month of pregnancy to the fourth month of pregnancy. Is this greater than or less than the average rate of change per month from the sixth month to the eighth month?

Month of pregnancy	2	4	6	8
Length, in inches	1	7	12	16

33. **Demography** The following table shows the projected population of baby boomers for the years 2000, 2031, and 2046. (*Source:* U.S. Census Bureau)

a. Find the average rate of change per year in the population of the baby boomer generation from 2031 to 2046 (*Note:* A negative average rate of change denotes a decrease.)

b. Find the average rate of change per year in the population of baby boomers from 2000 to 2046. Round to the nearest hundred thousand.

Year	2000	2031	2046
Population, in millions	79	51	19

34. **Car Prices** The following table shows the mileage on and corresponding value of a used 2004 MINI Cooper, 2-door hatchback one year after it was purchased. (*Source:* www.kbb.com, Dec. 11, 2005)

Mileage	10,000	20,000	30,000	40,000	50,000	60,000
Value, in dollars	18,525	17,850	16,625	15,125	13,975	13,150

a. What was the per-mile change in the value of the car between 10,000 mi and 60,000 mi? Round to the nearest cent per mile. (*Note:* A negative average rate of change denotes a decrease.)

b. Write a sentence explaining the meaning of the answer to part a.

35. **Minimum Wage** The following table shows buying power of a worker earning the federal minimum wage for various years. This is not the *actual* minimum wage but the minimum wage adjusted for inflation. For instance, the actual minimum wage in 1970 was \$1.60. Spending \$1.60 in 1970 was the same as spending \$6.95 in 2005. (*Source:* Employment Policy Institute, www.epi.org/issueguides/minwage/table4.gif)

Year	1970	1975	1980	1985	1990	1995	2000	2005
Minimum wage	6.95	6.70	6.94	5.79	5.33	5.40	5.83	5.15

a. What was the average annual rate of change in the inflation-adjusted minimum wage from 1980 to 2005? (*Note:* A negative average rate of change denotes a decrease.)

b. Prior to 1990, in which five-year period did the average annual rate of change in the inflation-adjusted minimum wage increase? What was the average annual rate of change during that period?

36. **School Enrollments** The following table shows the projected population of adults 18 to 19 years old for selected years from 2005 to 2030. (*Source:* Proximity, www.proximityone.com/cdtrends.htm)

Year	2005	2010	2015	2020	2025	2030
Population projection, in millions	8.4	8.6	8.1	8.6	9.0	9.4

a. Find the average annual rate of change of the U.S. population of adults 18–19 years old from 2005 to 2030.
b. In which five-year period shown did the average annual rate of change of this population decline? What was the average annual rate of change for that period?

For Exercises 37 and 38, use the following table of data. The table shows the temperature, in degrees Fahrenheit, of a cup of coffee, measured every 10 min over a period of one and one-half hours.

Minutes	0	10	20	30	40	50	60	70	80	90
Temperature, °F	177.3	144.6	122.3	107.0	96.6	89.4	84.6	81.2	78.9	77.4

37. During which 10-minute interval was the average rate of change closest to -1 degree per minute?

38. During which 30-minute interval was the average rate of change closest to -1 degree per minute?

5.1 Applying Concepts

What is the distance from the given point to the horizontal axis?

39. $(-5, 1)$ **40.** $(3, -4)$ **41.** $(-6, 0)$

What is the distance from the given point to the vertical axis?

42. $(-2, 4)$ **43.** $(1, -3)$ **44.** $(5, 0)$

45. Name the coordinates of a point plotted at the origin of the rectangular coordinate system.

46. A computer screen has a coordinate system that is different from the *xy*-coordinate system we have discussed. In one mode, the origin of the coordinate system is the top left point of the screen, as shown at the right. Plot the points whose coordinates are (200, 400), (0, 100), and (100, 300).

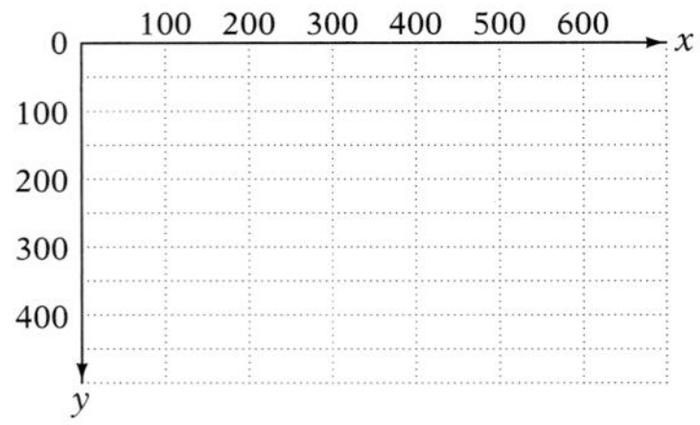

47. Write a paragraph explaining how to plot points in a rectangular coordinate system.

48. Decide on two quantities that may be related, and collect at least ten pairs of values. Here are some examples: height and weight, time studying for a test and the test grade, age of a car and its cost. Draw a scatter diagram for the data. Is there any trend? That is, as the values on the horizontal axis increase, do the values on the vertical axis increase or decrease?

49. There is a coordinate system on Earth that consists of *longitude* and *latitude*. Write a report on how location is determined on the surface of Earth.

5.2 Graphs of Straight Lines

OBJECTIVE 1 Determine solutions of linear equations in two variables

An equation of the form $y = mx + b$, where m is the coefficient of x and b is a constant, is a **linear equation in two variables.** Examples of linear equations follow.

$$y = 3x + 4 \qquad (m = 3, b = 4)$$
$$y = 2x - 3 \qquad (m = 2, b = -3)$$
$$y = -\frac{2}{3}x + 1 \qquad \left(m = -\frac{2}{3}, b = 1\right)$$
$$y = -2x \qquad (m = -2, b = 0)$$
$$y = x + 2 \qquad (m = 1, b = 2)$$

In a linear equation, the exponent of each variable is 1. The equations $y = 2x^2 - 1$ and $y = \frac{1}{x}$ are not linear equations.

A **solution of a linear equation in two variables** is an ordered pair of numbers (x, y) that makes the equation a true statement.

Take Note

An ordered pair is of the form (x, y). For the ordered pair $(1, -2)$, 1 is the x value and -2 is the y value. Substitute 1 for x and -2 for y.

Is $(1, -2)$ a solution of $y = 3x - 5$?

Replace x with 1. Replace y with -2.

$$\begin{array}{c|c} y & 3x - 5 \\ \hline -2 & 3(1) - 5 \\ & 3 - 5 \end{array}$$

Compare the results. If the results are equal, the given ordered pair is a solution. If the results are not equal, the given ordered pair is not a solution.

$-2 = -2$

Yes, $(1, -2)$ is a solution of the equation $y = 3x - 5$.

Besides the ordered pair $(1, -2)$, there are many other ordered-pair solutions of the equation $y = 3x - 5$. For example, the method used above can be used to show that $(2, 1)$, $(-1, -8)$, $\left(\frac{2}{3}, -3\right)$, and $(0, -5)$ are also solutions.

EXAMPLE 1 Is $(-3, 2)$ a solution of $y = 2x + 2$?

Solution

$$\begin{array}{c|c} y & 2x + 2 \\ \hline 2 & 2(-3) + 2 \\ & -6 + 2 \\ & -4 \end{array}$$

• **Replace x with -3 and y with 2.**

$2 \neq -4$

No, $(-3, 2)$ is not a solution of $y = 2x + 2$.

PROBLEM 1 Is $(2, -4)$ a solution of $y = -\frac{1}{2}x - 3$?

Solution See page S12.

In general, a linear equation in two variables has an infinite number of ordered-pair solutions. By choosing any value for x and substituting that value into the linear equation, we can find a corresponding value of y.

Find the ordered-pair solution of $y = 2x - 5$ that corresponds to $x = 1$.

	$y = 2x - 5$
Substitute 1 for x.	$y = 2 \cdot 1 - 5$
Solve for y.	$y = 2 - 5$
	$y = -3$

The ordered-pair solution is (1, −3).

EXAMPLE 2 Find the ordered-pair solution of $y = \frac{2}{3}x - 1$ that corresponds to $x = 3$.

Solution $y = \frac{2}{3}x - 1$

$y = \frac{2}{3}(3) - 1$ • **Substitute 3 for x.**

$y = 2 - 1$ • **Solve for y.**

$y = 1$ • **When $x = 3$, $y = 1$.**

The ordered-pair solution is (3, 1).

PROBLEM 2 Find the ordered-pair solution of $y = -\frac{1}{4}x + 1$ that corresponds to $x = 4$.

Solution See page S12.

OBJECTIVE 2 Graph equations of the form $y = mx + b$

The **graph of an equation in two variables** is a drawing of the ordered-pair solutions of the equation. For a linear equation in two variables, the graph is a straight line.

To graph a linear equation, find ordered-pair solutions of the equation. Do this by choosing any value of x and finding the corresponding value of y. Repeat this procedure, choosing different values for x, until you have found the number of solutions desired.

Because the graph of a linear equation in two variables is a straight line, and a straight line is determined by two points, it is necessary to find only two solutions. However, finding at least three points will ensure accuracy.

Graph $y = 2x + 1$.

Choose any values of x, and then find the corresponding values of y. The numbers 0, 2, and −1 were chosen arbitrarily for x. It is convenient to record these solutions in a table.

x	$y = 2x + 1$	y
0	$2(0) + 1$	1
2	$2(2) + 1$	5
−1	$2(-1) + 1$	−1

Graph the ordered-pair solutions (0, 1), (2, 5), and (−1, −1). Draw a line through the ordered-pair solutions.

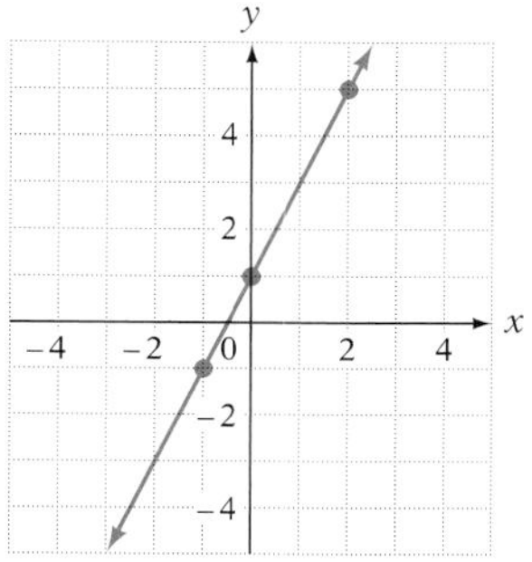

Take Note

If the three points you graph do not lie on a straight line, you have made an arithmetic error in calculating a point or you have plotted a point incorrectly.

Note that the points whose coordinates are (−2, −3) and (1, 3) are on the graph and that these ordered pairs are solutions of the equation $y = 2x + 1$.

Remember that a graph is a drawing of the ordered-pair solutions of an equation. Therefore, every point on the graph is a solution of the equation, and every solution of the equation is a point on the graph.

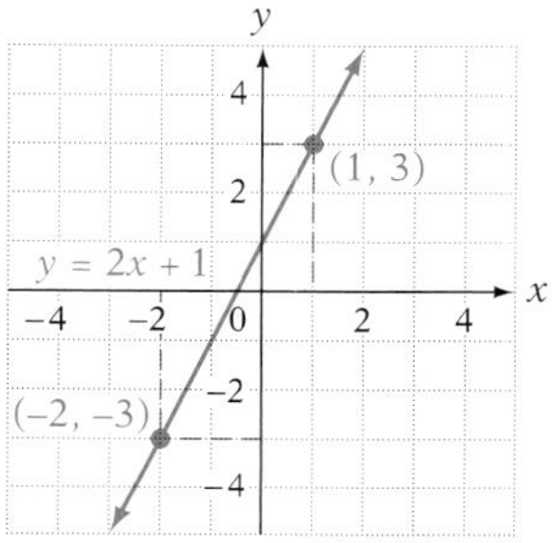

EXAMPLE 3 Graph: $y = 3x - 2$

Solution

x	y
0	−2
2	4
−1	−5

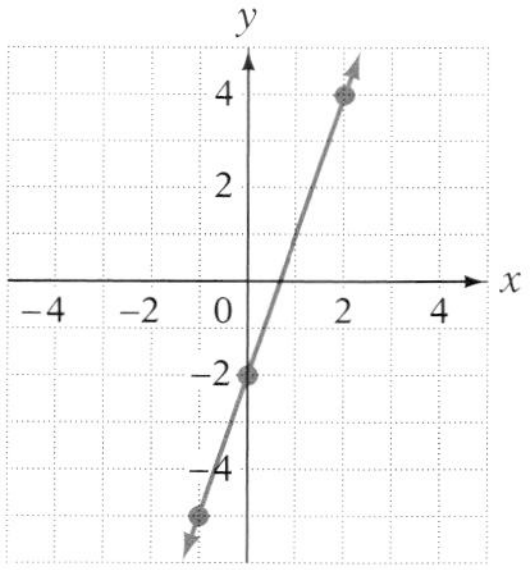

PROBLEM 3 Graph: $y = 3x + 1$

Solution See page S12.

Graphing utilities create graphs by plotting points and then connecting the points to form a curve. Using a graphing utility, enter the equation $y = 3x - 2$ and verify the graph drawn in Example 3. (Refer to the Appendix for instructions on using a graphing calculator to graph a linear equation.) Trace along the graph and verify that (0, −2), (2, 4), and (−1, −5) are coordinates of points on the graph. Now enter the equation $y = 3x + 1$ given in Problem 3. Verify that the ordered pairs you found for this equation are the coordinates of points on the graph.

When m is a fraction in the equation $y = mx + b$, choose values of x that will simplify the evaluation. For example, to graph $y = \frac{1}{3}x - 1$, we might choose the numbers 0, 3, and -3 for x. Note that these numbers are multiples of the denominator of $\frac{1}{3}$, the coefficient of x.

x	y
0	-1
3	0
-3	-2

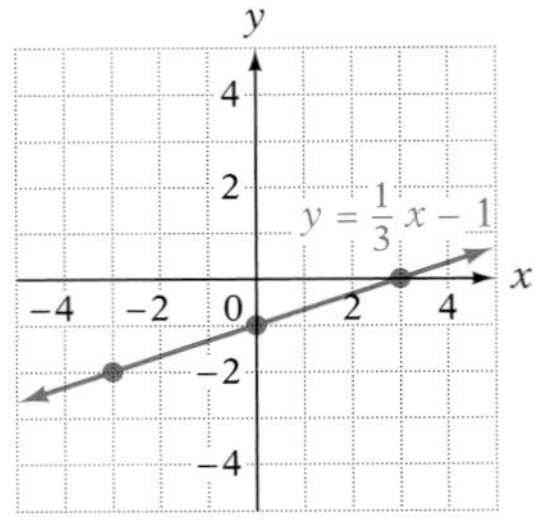

EXAMPLE 4 Graph: $y = \frac{1}{2}x - 1$

Solution

x	y
0	-1
2	0
-2	-2

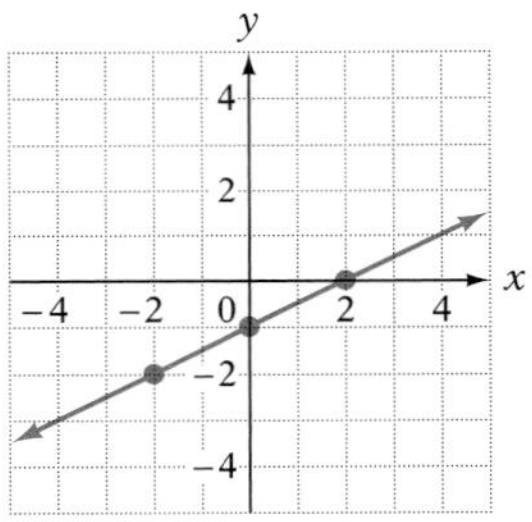

PROBLEM 4 Graph: $y = \frac{1}{3}x - 3$

Solution See page S12.

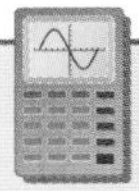

Using a graphing utility, enter the equation $y = \frac{1}{2}x - 1$ and verify the graph drawn in Example 4. Trace along the graph and verify that (0, −1), (2, 0), and (−2, −2) are the coordinates of points on the graph. Follow the same procedure for Problem 4. (See the Appendix for instructions on entering a fractional coefficient of *x*.)

OBJECTIVE 3 Graph equations of the form $Ax + By = C$

An equation in the form $Ax + By = C$, where A and B are coefficients and C is a constant, is also a linear equation. Examples of these equations are shown below.

$2x + 3y = 6 \quad (A = 2, B = 3, C = 6)$

$x - 2y = -4 \quad (A = 1, B = -2, C = -4)$

$2x + y = 0 \quad (A = 2, B = 1, C = 0)$

$4x - 5y = 2 \quad (A = 4, B = -5, C = 2)$

One method of graphing an equation of the form $Ax + By = C$ involves first solving the equation for y and then following the same procedure used for graphing an equation of the form $y = mx + b$. To solve the equation for y means to rewrite the equation so that y is alone on one side of the equation and the term containing x and the constant are on the other side of the equation. The Addition and Multiplication Properties of Equations are used to rewrite an equation of the form $Ax + By = C$ in the form $y = mx + b$.

Solve the equation $3x + 2y = 4$ for y.

The equation is in the form $Ax + By = C$.

$$3x + 2y = 4$$

Use the Addition Property of Equations to subtract the term $3x$ from each side of the equation.

$$3x - 3x + 2y = -3x + 4$$

Simplify. Note that on the right side of the equation, the term containing x is first, followed by the constant.

$$2y = -3x + 4$$

Use the Multiplication Property of Equations to multiply each side of the equation by the reciprocal of the coefficient of y. (The coefficient of y is 2; the reciprocal of 2 is $\frac{1}{2}$.)

$$\frac{1}{2} \cdot 2y = \frac{1}{2}(-3x + 4)$$

Simplify. Use the Distributive Property on the right side of the equation.

$$y = \frac{1}{2}(-3x) + \frac{1}{2}(4)$$

The equation is now in the form $y = mx + b$, with $m = -\frac{3}{2}$ and $b = 2$.

$$y = -\frac{3}{2}x + 2$$

In solving the equation $3x + 2y = 4$ for y, where we multiplied both sides of the equation by $\frac{1}{2}$, we could have divided both sides of the equation by 2, as shown at the right. In simplifying the right side after dividing both sides by 2, be sure to divide *each term* by 2.

$$2y = -3x + 4$$
$$\frac{2y}{2} = \frac{-3x + 4}{2}$$
$$y = \frac{-3x}{2} + \frac{4}{2}$$
$$y = -\frac{3}{2}x + 2$$

Being able to solve an equation of the form $Ax + By = C$ for y is important because most graphing utilities require that an equation be in the form $y = mx + b$ when the equation of the line is entered for graphing.

EXAMPLE 5 Write $3x - 4y = 12$ in the form $y = mx + b$.

Solution

$$3x - 4y = 12$$

$$3x - 3x - 4y = -3x + 12$$ • **Subtract 3x from each side of the equation.**

$$-4y = -3x + 12$$ • **Simplify.**

$$\frac{-4y}{-4} = \frac{-3x + 12}{-4}$$ • **Divide each side of the equation by −4.**

$$y = \frac{-3x}{-4} + \frac{12}{-4}$$

$$y = \frac{3}{4}x - 3$$

PROBLEM 5 Write $5x - 2y = 10$ in the form $y = mx + b$.

Solution See page S12.

To graph an equation of the form $Ax + By = C$, we can first solve the equation for y and then follow the same procedure used for graphing an equation of the form $y = mx + b$. An example follows.

Graph: $3x + 4y = 12$

Write the equation in the form $y = mx + b$.

$$3x + 4y = 12$$
$$4y = -3x + 12$$
$$y = -\frac{3}{4}x + 3$$

Find at least three solutions. Display the ordered pairs in a table.

x	y
0	3
4	0
−4	6

Graph the ordered pairs on a rectangular coordinate system, and draw a straight line through the points.

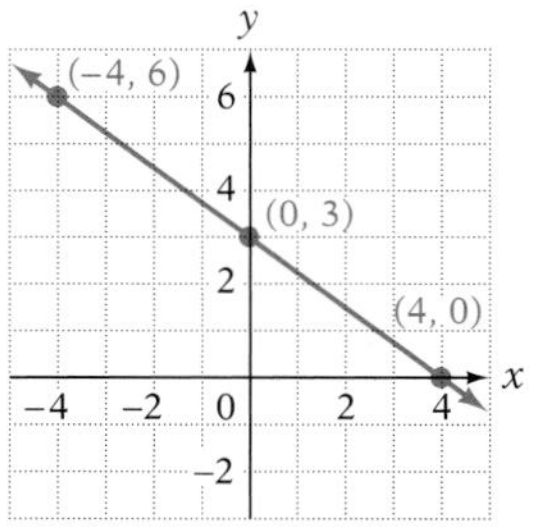

EXAMPLE 6 Graph. **A.** $2x - 5y = 10$ **B.** $x + 2y = 6$

Solution

A.
$$2x - 5y = 10$$
$$-5y = -2x + 10$$
$$y = \frac{2}{5}x - 2$$

B.
$$x + 2y = 6$$
$$2y = -x + 6$$
$$y = -\frac{1}{2}x + 3$$

$y = \frac{2}{5}x - 2$

x	y
0	−2
5	0
−5	−4

$y = -\frac{1}{2}x + 3$

x	y
0	3
−2	4
4	1

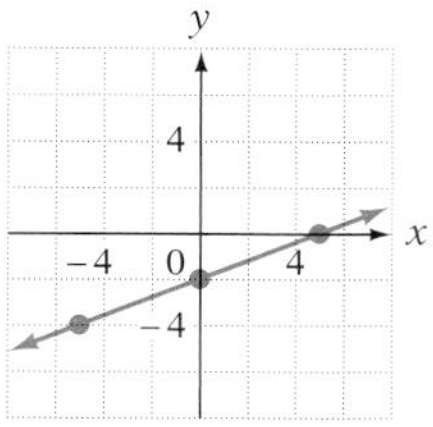

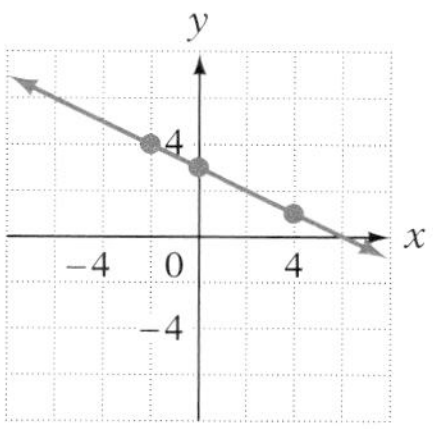

PROBLEM 6 Graph. **A.** $5x - 2y = 10$ **B.** $x - 3y = 9$

Solution See page S12.

The graph of the equation $2x + 3y = 6$ is shown at the right. The graph crosses the x-axis at (3, 0). This point is called the ***x*-intercept.** The graph crosses the y-axis at (0, 2). This point is called the ***y*-intercept.**

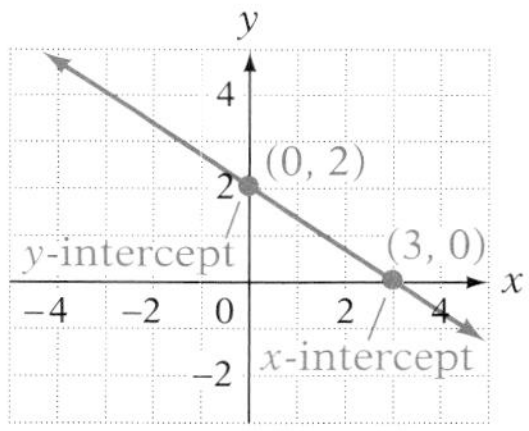

Find the x-intercept and the y-intercept of the graph of the equation $2x + 3y = 6$ algebraically.

To find the x-intercept, let $y = 0$. (Any point on the x-axis has y-coordinate 0.)

$$2x + 3y = 6$$
$$2x + 3(0) = 6$$
$$2x = 6$$
$$x = 3$$

The x-intercept is (3, 0).

To find the y-intercept, let $x = 0$. (Any point on the y-axis has x-coordinate 0.)

$$2x + 3y = 6$$
$$2(0) + 3y = 6$$
$$3y = 6$$
$$y = 2$$

The y-intercept is (0, 2).

Take Note

To find the x-intercept, let $y = 0$.
To find the y-intercept, let $x = 0$.

Another method of graphing some equations of the form $Ax + By = C$ is to find the x- and y-intercepts, plot both intercepts, and then draw a line through the two points.

EXAMPLE 7 Find the x- and y-intercepts for $x - 2y = 4$. Graph the line.

Solution x-intercept:

$$x - 2y = 4$$
$$x - 2(0) = 4 \quad \text{• To find the } x\text{-intercept, let } y = 0.$$
$$x = 4$$

The x-intercept is (4, 0).

y-intercept:

$$x - 2y = 4$$
$$0 - 2y = 4 \quad \text{• To find the } y\text{-intercept, let } x = 0.$$
$$-2y = 4$$
$$y = -2$$

The y-intercept is (0, −2).

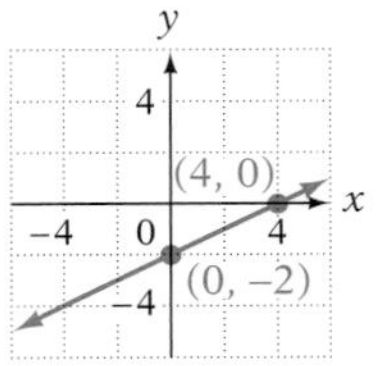

• **Graph the ordered pairs (4, 0) and (0, −2). Draw a straight line through the points.**

PROBLEM 7 Find the x- and y-intercepts for $4x - y = 4$. Graph the line.

Solution See page S12.

The graph of an equation in which one of the variables is missing is either a horizontal line or a vertical line.

The equation $y = 2$ could be written $0 \cdot x + y = 2$. No matter what value of x is chosen, y is always 2. Some solutions to the equation are (3, 2), (−1, 2), (0, 2), and (−4, 2). The graph is shown at the right.

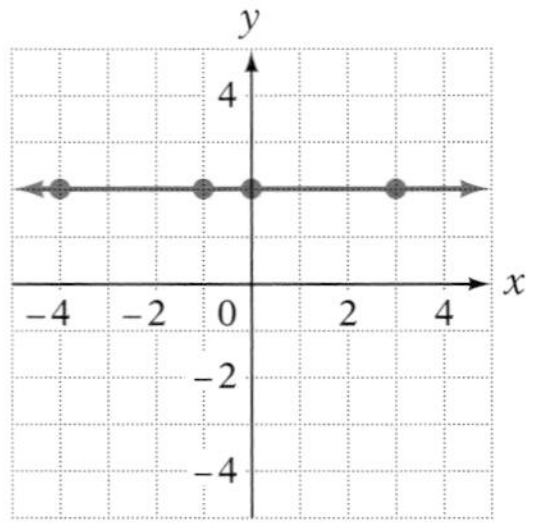

The **graph of $y = b$** is a horizontal line passing through the point whose coordinates are $(0, b)$.

Note that $(0, b)$ is the y-intercept of the graph of $y = b$. An equation of the form $y = b$ does not have an x-intercept.

The equation $x = -2$ could be written $x + 0 \cdot y = -2$. No matter what value of y is chosen, x is always −2. Some solutions to the equation are (−2, 3), (−2, −2), (−2, 0), and (−2, 2). The graph is shown at the right.

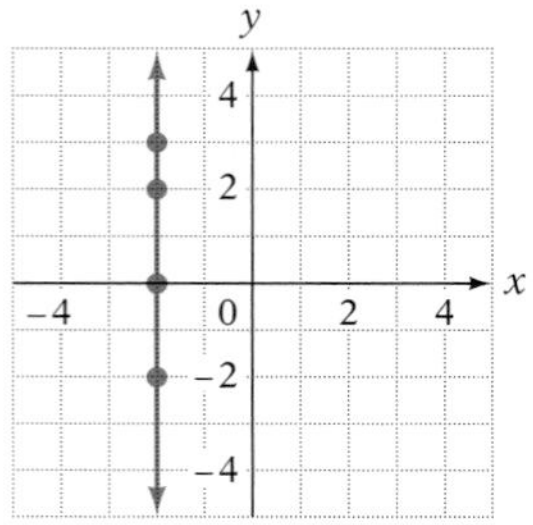

The **graph of $x = a$** is a vertical line passing through the point whose coordinates are $(a, 0)$.

Note that $(a, 0)$ is the x-intercept of the graph of $x = a$. An equation of the form $x = a$ does not have a y-intercept.

EXAMPLE 8 Graph. **A.** $y = -2$ **B.** $x = 3$

Solution **A.** The graph of an equation of the form $y = b$ is a horizontal line with y-intercept $(0, b)$.

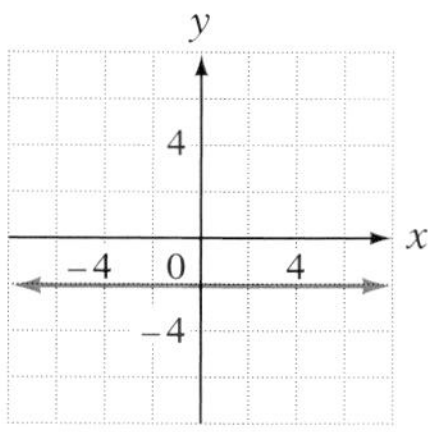

B. The graph of an equation of the form $x = a$ is a vertical line with x-intercept $(a, 0)$.

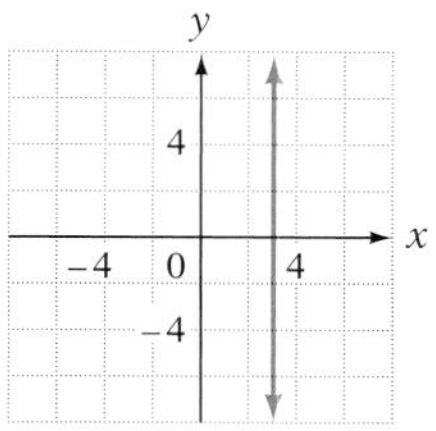

PROBLEM 8 Graph. **A.** $y = 3$ **B.** $x = -4$

Solution See page S12.

5.2 Concept Review

Determine whether the statement is always true, sometimes true, or never true.

1. The equation $y = 3x^2 - 6$ is an example of a linear equation in two variables.
2. The value of m in the equation $y = 4x + 9$ is 9.
3. (3, 5) is a solution of the equation $y = x + 2$.
4. The graph of a linear equation in two variables is a straight line.
5. To find the x-intercept of the graph of a linear equation, let $x = 0$.
6. The graph of an equation of the form $y = b$ is a horizontal line.
7. The graph of the equation $x = -4$ has an x-intercept of $(0, -4)$.
8. The graph shown at the right has a y-intercept of (0, 3).
9. The graph of the equation $x = 2$ is a line that goes through every point that has an x-coordinate of 2.

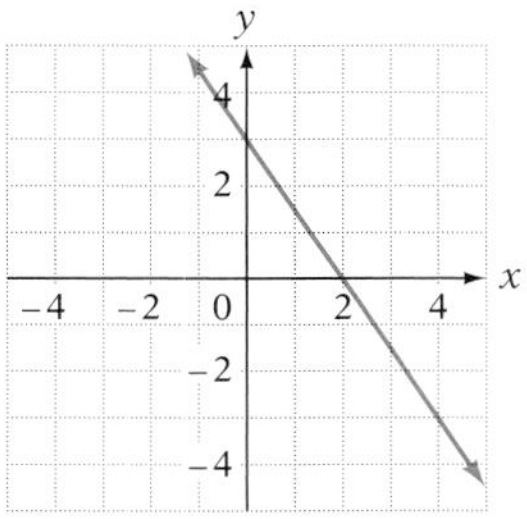

5.2 Exercises

1 Determine solutions of linear equations in two variables

1. To decide whether the ordered pair (1, 7) is a solution of the equation $y = 2x + 5$, substitute 1 for __?__ and 7 for __?__ to see whether the ordered pair (1, 7) makes the equation $y = 2x + 5$ a true statement

2. Find the ordered-pair solution of $y = -\frac{1}{4}x + 3$ that corresponds to $x = -8$.

$y = -\frac{1}{4}x + 3$

$y = -\frac{1}{4}(-8) + 3$ • **Substitute** __?__ **for** __?__.

$y =$ __?__ $+ 3$ • **Multiply.**

$y =$ __?__ • **Add.**

The ordered-pair solution that corresponds to $x = -8$ is (__?__, __?__).

For the given linear equation, find the value of m and the value of b.

3. $y = 4x + 1$

4. $y = -3x - 2$

5. $y = \frac{5}{6}x + \frac{1}{6}$

6. $y = -x$

7. Is (3, 4) a solution of $y = -x + 7$?

8. Is (2, −3) a solution of $y = x + 5$?

9. Is (−1, 2) a solution of $y = \frac{1}{2}x - 1$?

10. Is (1, −3) a solution of $y = -2x - 1$?

11. Is (4, 1) a solution of $y = \frac{1}{4}x + 1$?

12. Is (−5, 3) a solution of $y = -\frac{2}{5}x + 1$?

13. Is (0, 4) a solution of $y = \frac{3}{4}x + 4$?

14. Is (−2, 0) a solution of $y = -\frac{1}{2}x - 1$?

15. Is (0, 0) a solution of $y = 3x + 2$?

16. Is (0, 0) a solution of $y = -\frac{3}{4}x$?

17. Find the ordered-pair solution of $y = 3x - 2$ that corresponds to $x = 3$.

18. Find the ordered-pair solution of $y = 4x + 1$ that corresponds to $x = -1$.

19. Find the ordered-pair solution of $y = \frac{2}{3}x - 1$ that corresponds to $x = 6$.

20. Find the ordered-pair solution of $y = \frac{3}{4}x - 2$ that corresponds to $x = 4$.

21. Find the ordered-pair solution of $y = -3x + 1$ that corresponds to $x = 0$.

22. Find the ordered-pair solution of $y = \frac{2}{5}x - 5$ that corresponds to $x = 0$.

23. Find the ordered-pair solution of $y = \frac{2}{5}x + 2$ that corresponds to $x = -5$.

24. Find the ordered-pair solution of $y = -\frac{1}{6}x - 2$ that corresponds to $x = 12$.

25. Use the linear equation $y = -3x + 6$.

a. For what value of x is the ordered pair $(x, 0)$ a solution of the linear equation $y = -3x + 6$?

b. Suppose (x, a) is a solution of the linear equation $y = -3x + 6$, such that $x > 2$. Is a a positive or a negative number?

26. Let $y = mx + b$ be a linear equation in which $b = -2m$. For what value of x will the ordered pair $(x, 0)$ be a solution of the equation?

2 Graph equations of the form *y* = *mx* + *b*

27. Find three points on the graph of $y = 3x - 4$ by finding the y values that correspond to x values of -1, 0, and 1.

a. When $x = -1$, $y = \underline{\quad ? \quad}$. A point on the graph is $(\underline{\quad ? \quad}, \underline{\quad ? \quad})$.

b. When $x = 0$, $y = \underline{\quad ? \quad}$. A point on the graph is $(\underline{\quad ? \quad}, \underline{\quad ? \quad})$.

c. When $x = 1$, $y = \underline{\quad ? \quad}$. A point on the graph is $(\underline{\quad ? \quad}, \underline{\quad ? \quad})$.

28. To find points on the graph of $y = \frac{1}{5}x - 8$, it is helpful to choose x values that are divisible by $\underline{\quad ? \quad}$.

Graph.

29. $y = 2x - 3$

30. $y = -2x + 2$

31. $y = \frac{1}{3}x$

32. $y = -3x$

33. $y = \frac{2}{3}x - 1$

34. $y = \frac{3}{4}x + 2$

35. $y = -\frac{1}{4}x + 2$

36. $y = -\frac{1}{3}x + 1$

37. $y = -\frac{2}{5}x + 1$

38. $y = -\frac{1}{2}x + 3$

39. $y = 2x - 4$

40. $y = 3x - 4$

41. $y = -x + 2$

42. $y = -x - 1$

43. $y = -\frac{2}{3}x + 1$

44. $y = 5x - 4$

45. $y = -3x + 2$

46. $y = -x + 3$

Graph using a graphing utility.

47. $y = 3x - 4$

48. $y = -2x + 3$

49. $y = 2x - 3$

50. $y = -2x - 3$

51. $y = -\frac{2}{3}x$

52. $y = \frac{3}{2}x$

53. $y = \frac{3}{4}x + 2$

54. $y = -\frac{1}{3}x + 2$

55. $y = -\frac{3}{2}x - 3$

56. $y = -\frac{2}{5}x + 2$

57. $y = \frac{1}{4}x - 2$

58. $y = \frac{2}{3}x - 4$

3 Graph equations of the form $Ax + By = C$

59. Write the equation $x - 2y = -10$ in the form $y = mx + b$.

$x - 2y = -10$

$x - x - 2y = -x - 10$ • **Subtract ___?___ from each side of the equation.**

$\underline{\quad ? \quad} = -x - 10$ • **Simplify the left side of the equation.**

$\dfrac{-2y}{-2} = \dfrac{-x - 10}{-2}$ • **Divide each side of the equation by ___?___.**

$y = \underline{\quad ? \quad}\, x + \underline{\quad ? \quad}$ • **Simplify.**

60. **a.** The x-intercept of the graph of a linear equation is the point where the graph crosses the ___?___. Its ___?___-coordinate is 0.
b. The y-intercept of the graph of a linear equation is the point where the graph crosses the ___?___. Its ___?___-coordinate is 0.

Complete Exercises 61 and 62 by using the word *horizontal* or *vertical*.

61. The graph of the equation $y = 7$ is a ___?___ line passing through the point whose coordinates are (0, 7).

62. The graph of the equation $x = -10$ is a ___?___ line passing through the point whose coordinates are (−10, 0).

Solve for y. Write the equation in the form $y = mx + b$.

63. $3x + y = 10$

64. $2x + y = 5$

65. $4x - y = 3$

66. $5x - y = 7$

67. $3x + 2y = 6$

68. $2x + 3y = 9$

69. $2x - 5y = 10$

70. $5x - 2y = 4$

71. $2x + 7y = 14$

72. $6x - 5y = 10$

73. $x + 3y = 6$

74. $x - 4y = 12$

Graph.

75. $3x + y = 3$

76. $2x + y = 4$

77. $2x + 3y = 6$

78. $3x + 2y = 4$

79. $x - 2y = 4$

80. $x - 3y = 6$

81. $2x - 3y = 6$

82. $3x - 2y = 8$

83. $y = 4$

84. $y = -4$

85. $x = -2$

86. $x = 3$

Find the x- and y-intercepts.

87. $x - y = 3$

88. $3x + 4y = 12$

89. $y = 2x - 6$

90. $y = 2x + 10$

91. $x - 5y = 10$

92. $3x + 2y = 12$

93. $y = 3x + 12$

94. $y = 5x + 10$

95. $2x - 3y = 0$

96. $3x + 4y = 0$

97. $y = \frac{1}{2}x + 3$

98. $y = \frac{2}{3}x - 4$

Graph by using x- and y-intercepts.

99. $5x + 2y = 10$

100. $x - 3y = 6$

101. $3x - 4y = 12$

102. $2x - 3y = -6$

103. $2x + 3y = 6$

104. $x + 2y = 4$

105. $2x + 5y = 10$

106. $3x + 4y = 12$

107. $x - 3y = 6$

108. $3x - y = 6$

109. $x - 4y = 8$

110. $4x + 3y = 12$

111. $2x + y = 3$

112. $3x + y = -5$

113. $4x - 3y = 6$

Graph using a graphing utility. Verify that the graph has the correct x- and y-intercepts.

114. $x - 2y = -4$

115. $3x + 4y = -12$

116. $3x - 2y = -6$

117. $2x - y = 4$

118. $3x - 4y = 4$

119. $2x - 3y = 9$

120. Suppose A and B are positive and C is negative. Is the y-intercept of the graph of $Ax + By = C$ above or below the x-axis?

121. Suppose A and C are negative and B is positive. Is the x-intercept of the graph of $Ax + By = C$ to the left or to the right of the y-axis?

5.2 Applying Concepts

122. **a.** Show that the equation $y + 3 = 2(x + 4)$ is a linear equation by writing it in the form $y = mx + b$.
b. Find the ordered-pair solution that corresponds to $x = -4$.

123. **a.** Show that the equation $y + 4 = -\frac{1}{2}(x + 2)$ is a linear equation by writing it in the form $y = mx + b$.
b. Find the ordered-pair solution that corresponds to $x = -2$.

124. For the linear equation $y = 2x - 3$, what is the increase in y that results when x is increased by 1?

125. For the linear equation $y = -x - 4$, what is the decrease in y that results when x is increased by 1?

126. Write the equation of a line that has (0, 0) as both the x-intercept and the y-intercept.

127. Explain **a.** why the y-coordinate of any point on the x-axis is 0 and **b.** why the x-coordinate of any point on the y-axis is 0.

5.3 Slopes of Straight Lines

OBJECTIVE 1 Find the slope of a straight line

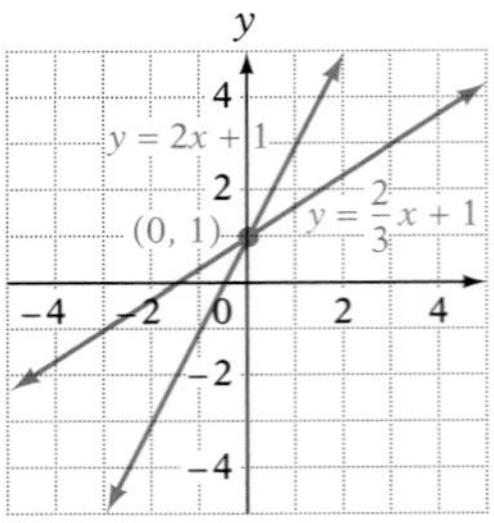

The graphs of $y = \frac{2}{3}x + 1$ and $y = 2x + 1$ are shown at the left. Each graph crosses the y-axis at (0, 1), but the graphs have different slants. The **slope** of a line is a measure of the slant of the line. The symbol for slope is m.

The slope of a line is the ratio of the change in the y-coordinates between any two points on the line to the change in the x-coordinates.

The line containing the points whose coordinates are (−2, −3) and (6, 1) is graphed at the right. The change in y is the difference between the two y-coordinates.

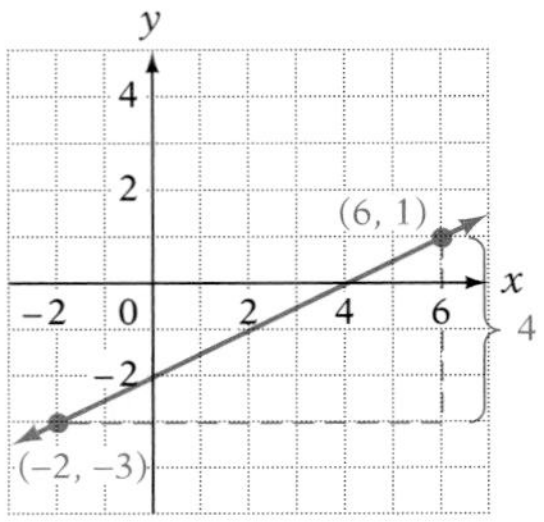

Change in $y = 1 - (-3) = 4$

The change in x is the difference between the two x-coordinates.

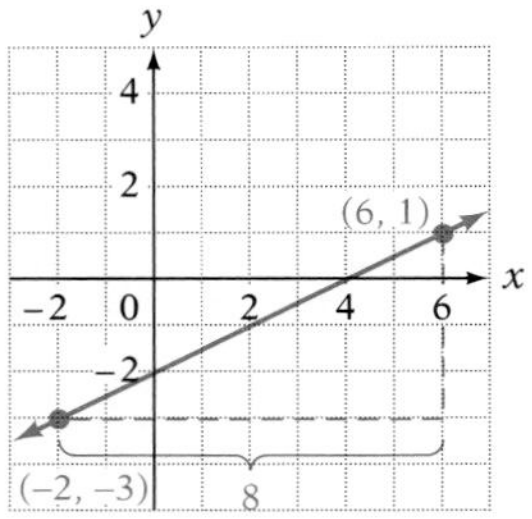

Change in $x = 6 - (-2) = 8$

Take Note

The change in the y values can be thought of as the *rise* of the line, and the change in the x values can be thought of as the *run*. Then slope $= m = \frac{\text{rise}}{\text{run}}$.

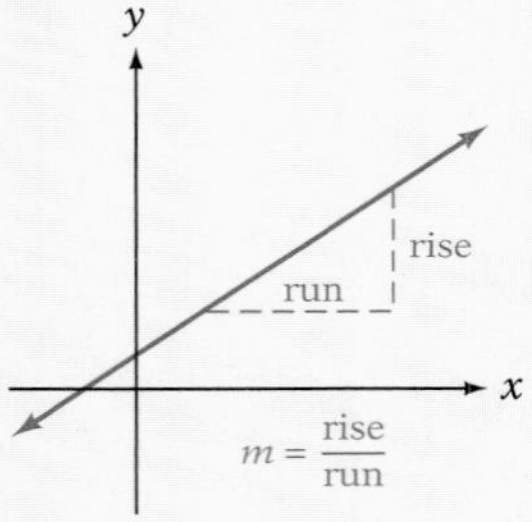

For the line containing the points whose coordinates are (−2, −3) and (6, 1),

$$\text{Slope} = m = \frac{\text{change in } y}{\text{change in } x} = \frac{4}{8} = \frac{1}{2}$$

The slope of the line can also be described as the ratio of the vertical change (4 units) to the horizontal change (8 units) from the point whose coordinates are (−2, −3) to the point whose coordinates are (6, 1).

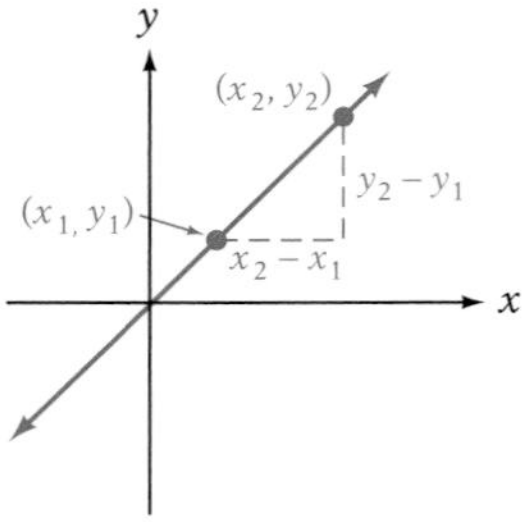

Slope Formula

The slope of a line containing two points P_1 and P_2, whose coordinates are (x_1, y_1) and (x_2, y_2), is given by

$$\textbf{Slope} = m = \frac{y_2 - y_1}{x_2 - x_1},\ x_1 \neq x_2$$

In the slope formula, the points P_1 and P_2 are any two points on the line. The slope of a line is constant; therefore, the slope calculated using any two points on the line will be the same.

In Section 1, Objective 3 of this chapter, we calculated the average rate of change in the U.S. population for different intervals of time. In each case, the average rate of change was different. Note that the graph of the population data did not lie on a straight line.

The graph of an equation of the form $y = mx + b$ is a straight line, and the average rate of change is constant. We can calculate the average rate of change between any two points on the line and it will always be the same. For a linear equation, the rate of change is referred to as slope.

Find the slope of the line containing the points whose coordinates are $(-1, 1)$ and $(2, 3)$.

Let $P_1 = (-1, 1)$ and $P_2 = (2, 3)$. Then $x_1 = -1$, $y_1 = 1$, $x_2 = 2$, and $y_2 = 3$.

$$m = \frac{y_2 - y_1}{x_2 - x_1} = \frac{3 - 1}{2 - (-1)} = \frac{2}{3}$$

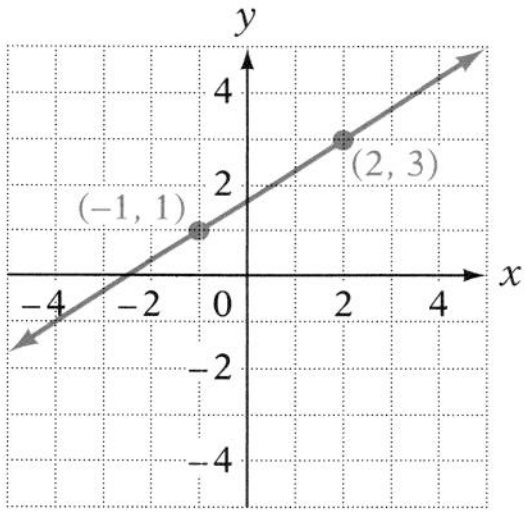

Positive slope

It does not matter which point is named P_1 and which P_2; the slope of the line will be the same. If the points are reversed, then $P_1 = (2, 3)$ and $P_2 = (-1, 1)$.

$$m = \frac{y_2 - y_1}{x_2 - x_1} = \frac{1 - 3}{-1 - 2} = \frac{-2}{-3} = \frac{2}{3}$$

Take Note

Positive slope means that the value of *y* increases as the value of *x* increases.

This is the same result. Here the slope is a positive number. A line that slants upward to the right has a **positive slope.**

Find the slope of the line containing the points whose coordinates are $(-3, 4)$ and $(2, -2)$.

Take Note

Negative slope means that the value of *y* decreases as the value of *x* increases. Compare this to positive slope.

Let $P_1 = (-3, 4)$ and $P_2 = (2, -2)$.

$$m = \frac{y_2 - y_1}{x_2 - x_1} = \frac{-2 - 4}{2 - (-3)} = \frac{-6}{5} = -\frac{6}{5}$$

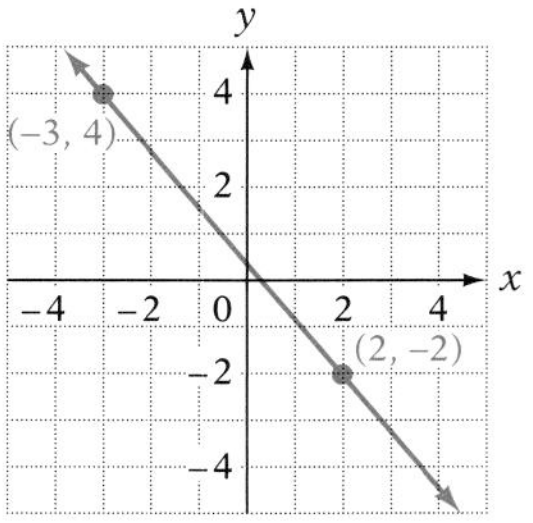

Negative slope

Here the slope is a negative number. A line that slants downward to the right has a **negative slope.**

Find the slope of the line containing the points whose coordinates are (−1, 3) and (4, 3).

Let $P_1 = (-1, 3)$ and $P_2 = (4, 3)$.

$$m = \frac{y_2 - y_1}{x_2 - x_1} = \frac{3 - 3}{4 - (-1)} = \frac{0}{5} = 0$$

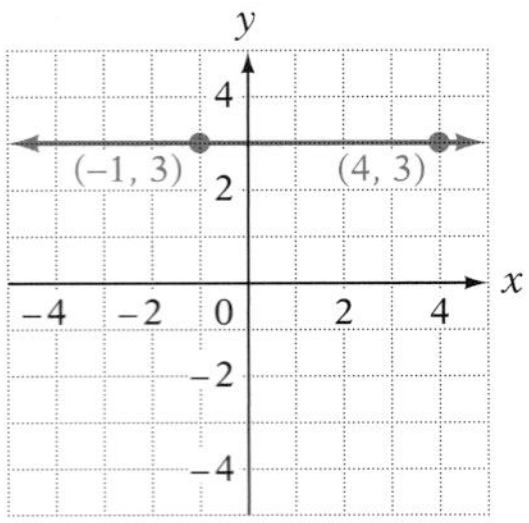

Zero slope

When $y_1 = y_2$, the graph is a horizontal line. A horizontal line has **zero slope.**

Find the slope of the line containing the points whose coordinates are (2, −2) and (2, 4).

Let $P_1 = (2, -2)$ and $P_2 = (2, 4)$.

$$m = \frac{y_2 - y_1}{x_2 - x_1} = \frac{4 - (-2)}{2 - 2} = \frac{6}{0} \leftarrow \text{Not a real number}$$

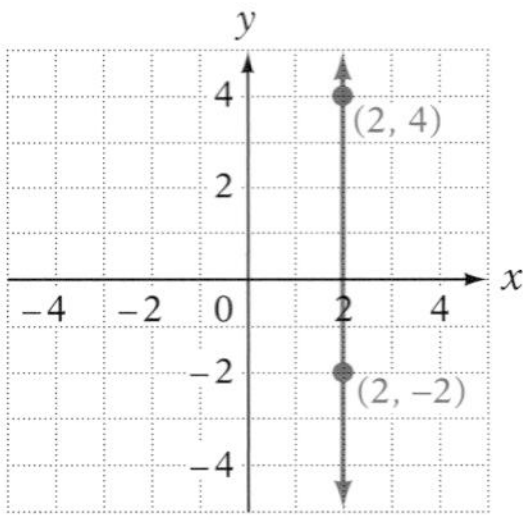

Undefined slope

When $x_1 = x_2$, the denominator of $\frac{y_2 - y_1}{x_2 - x_1}$ is 0 and the graph is a vertical line. Because division by zero is not defined, the slope of the line is not defined. The slope of a vertical line is **undefined.**

EXAMPLE 1 Find the slope of the line containing the points P_1 and P_2.

A. $P_1(-2, -1), P_2(3, 4)$ **B.** $P_1(-3, 1), P_2(2, -2)$

C. $P_1(-1, 4), P_2(-1, 0)$ **D.** $P_1(-1, 2), P_2(4, 2)$

Solution **A.** $m = \frac{y_2 - y_1}{x_2 - x_1} = \frac{4 - (-1)}{3 - (-2)} = \frac{5}{5} = 1$

The slope is 1.

B. $m = \frac{y_2 - y_1}{x_2 - x_1} = \frac{-2 - 1}{2 - (-3)} = \frac{-3}{5}$

The slope is $-\frac{3}{5}$.

C. $m = \dfrac{y_2 - y_1}{x_2 - x_1} = \dfrac{0 - 4}{-1 - (-1)} = \dfrac{-4}{0}$

The slope is undefined.

D. $m = \dfrac{y_2 - y_1}{x_2 - x_1} = \dfrac{2 - 2}{4 - (-1)} = \dfrac{0}{5} = 0$

The slope is 0.

PROBLEM 1 Find the slope of the line containing the points P_1 and P_2.

A. $P_1(-1, 2), P_2(1, 3)$ **B.** $P_1(1, 2), P_2(4, -5)$

C. $P_1(2, 3), P_2(2, 7)$ **D.** $P_1(1, -3), P_2(-5, -3)$

Solution See page S12.

Two lines in the rectangular coordinate system that never intersect are called **parallel lines.** The lines l_1 and l_2 graphed at the right are parallel lines. Calculating the slope of each line, we have

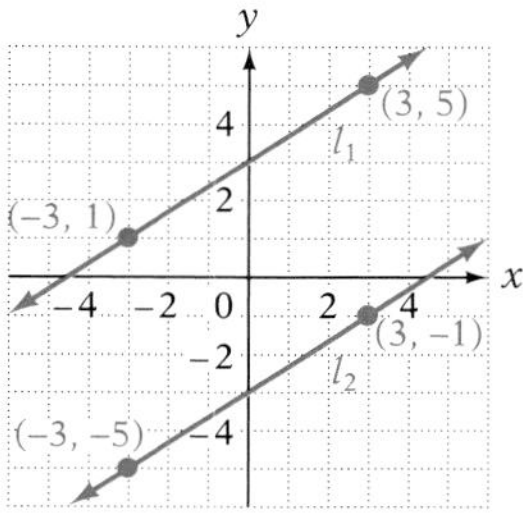

$$\text{Slope of } l_1 = \frac{y_2 - y_1}{x_2 - x_1} = \frac{5 - 1}{3 - (-3)} = \frac{4}{6} = \frac{2}{3}$$

$$\text{Slope of } l_2 = \frac{y_2 - y_1}{x_2 - x_1} = \frac{-1 - (-5)}{3 - (-3)} = \frac{4}{6} = \frac{2}{3}$$

Note that these parallel lines have the same slope. This is true of all parallel lines.

Take Note

We must distinguish between vertical and nonvertical lines in the description of parallel lines at the right because vertical lines in the rectangular coordinate system are parallel, but their slopes are undefined.

Parallel Lines

Two nonvertical lines in the rectangular coordinate system are parallel if and only if they have the same slope. Any two vertical lines in the rectangular coordinate system are parallel lines.

EXAMPLE 2 Is the line containing the points (−2, 1) and (−5, −1) parallel to the line that contains the points (1, 0) and (4, 2)?

Solution Find the slope of the line through (−2, 1) and (−5, −1).

$$\frac{y_2 - y_1}{x_2 - x_1} = \frac{-1 - 1}{-5 - (-2)} = \frac{-2}{-3} = \frac{2}{3}$$

Find the slope of the line through (1, 0) and (4, 2).

$$\frac{y_2 - y_1}{x_2 - x_1} = \frac{2 - 0}{4 - 1} = \frac{2}{3}$$

The slopes are equal.

The lines are parallel.

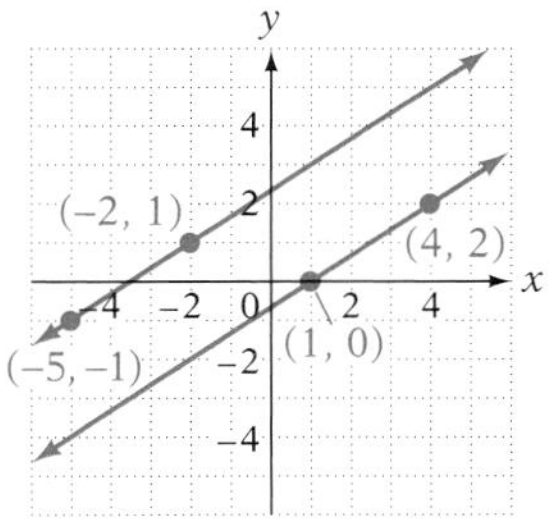

PROBLEM 2 Is the line containing the points (−2, −3) and (7, 1) parallel to the line that contains the points (1, 4) and (−5, 6)?

Solution See page S12.

There are many applications of the concept of slope. Here is one example.

When Florence Griffith-Joyner set the world record for the 100-meter dash, her rate of speed was approximately 9.5 m/s. The graph at the right shows the distance she ran during her record-setting run. From the graph, note that after 4 s she had traveled 38 m and that after 6 s she had traveled 57 m. The slope of the line between these two points is

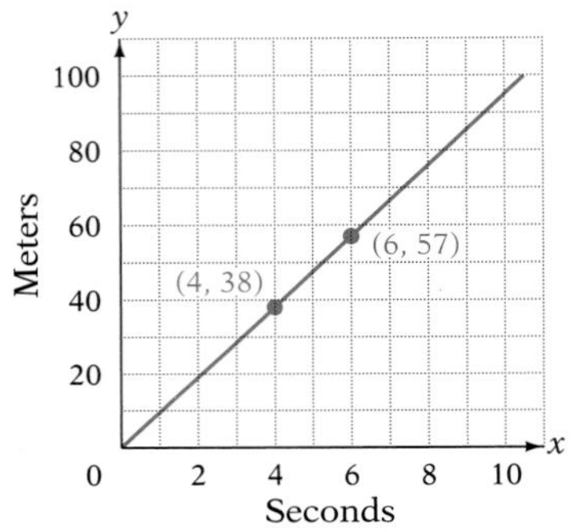

$$m = \frac{57 - 38}{6 - 4} = \frac{19}{2} = 9.5$$

Note that the slope of the line is the same as the rate at which she was running, 9.5 m/s. The average speed of an object is related to slope.

EXAMPLE 3 The graph at the right shows the height of a plane above an airport during its 30-minute descent from cruising altitude to landing. Find the slope of the line. Write a sentence that explains the meaning of the slope.

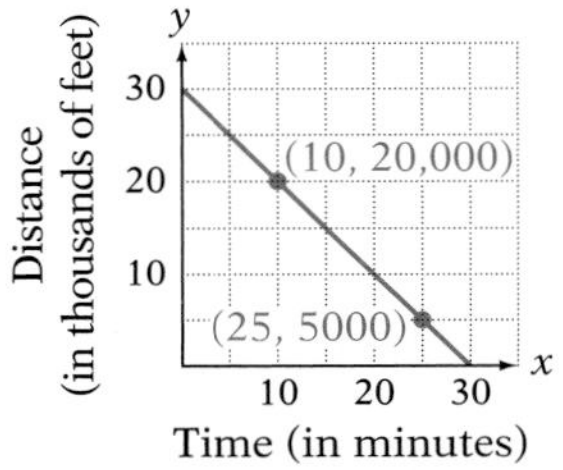

Solution

$$m = \frac{y_2 - y_1}{x_2 - x_1}$$

$$= \frac{5000 - 20{,}000}{25 - 10} = \frac{-15{,}000}{15} = -1000$$

A slope of −1000 means that the height of the plane is *decreasing* at the rate of 1000 ft per minute.

PROBLEM 3 The graph at the right shows the decline in the value of a used car over a five-year period. Find the slope of the line. Write a sentence that states the meaning of the slope.

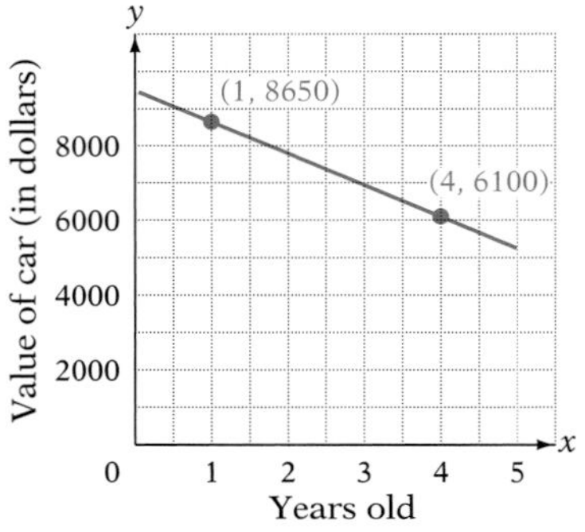

Solution See page S13.

OBJECTIVE 2 Graph a line using the slope and *y*-intercept

Recall that we can find the y-intercept of a linear equation by letting $x = 0$. To find the y-intercept of $y = 3x + 4$, let $x = 0$.

$$y = 3x + 4$$
$$y = 3(0) + 4$$
$$y = 4$$

The y-intercept is $(0, 4)$.

The constant term of $y = 3x + 4$ is the y-coordinate of the y-intercept.

In general, for any equation of the form $y = mx + b$, the y-intercept is $(0, b)$.

The graph of the equation $y = \frac{2}{3}x + 1$ is shown at the right. The points whose coordinates are $(-3, -1)$ and $(3, 3)$ are on the graph. The slope of the line is

$$m = \frac{3 - (-1)}{3 - (-3)} = \frac{4}{6} = \frac{2}{3}$$

Note that the slope of the line has the same value as the coefficient of x.

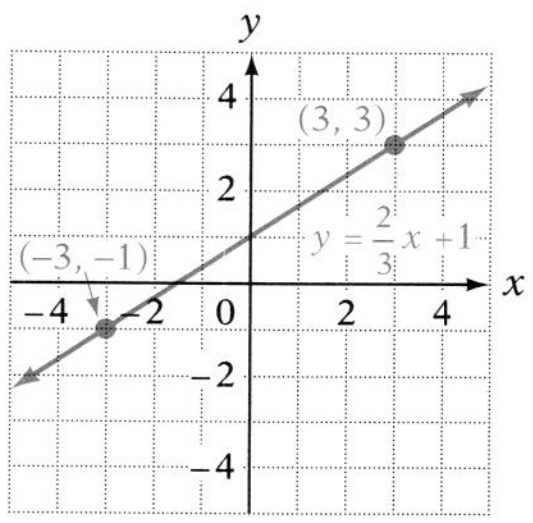

Slope-Intercept Form of a Straight Line

For any equation of the form $\mathbf{y = mx + b}$, the slope of the line is m, the coefficient of x. The y-intercept is $\mathbf{(0, b)}$. The equation

$$\mathbf{y = mx + b}$$

is called the **slope-intercept form of a straight line.**

The slope of the graph of $y = -\frac{3}{4}x + 1$ is $-\frac{3}{4}$. The y-intercept is $(0, 1)$.

$$y = \boxed{m}\, x + \boxed{b}$$
$$y = \boxed{-\frac{3}{4}}\, x + \boxed{1}$$

Slope $= m = -\frac{3}{4}$ → ; ← y-intercept $= (0, b) = (0, 1)$

Find the slope and y-intercept of the graph of $y = \frac{5}{2}x - 6$.

Slope $= m = \frac{5}{2}$ $\quad b = -6$

The slope is $\frac{5}{2}$. $\quad$ The y-intercept is $(0, -6)$.

When the equation of a straight line is in the form $y = mx + b$, the graph can be drawn using the slope and y-intercept. First locate the y-intercept. Use the slope to find a second point on the line. Then draw a line through the two points.

Graph $y = 2x - 3$ by using the slope and y-intercept.

y-intercept $= (0, b) = (0, -3)$

$$m = 2 = \frac{2}{1} = \frac{\text{change in } y}{\text{change in } x}$$

Beginning at the y-intercept, move right 1 unit (change in x) and then up 2 units (change in y).

$(1, -1)$ are the coordinates of a second point on the graph.

Draw a line through $(0, -3)$ and $(1, -1)$.

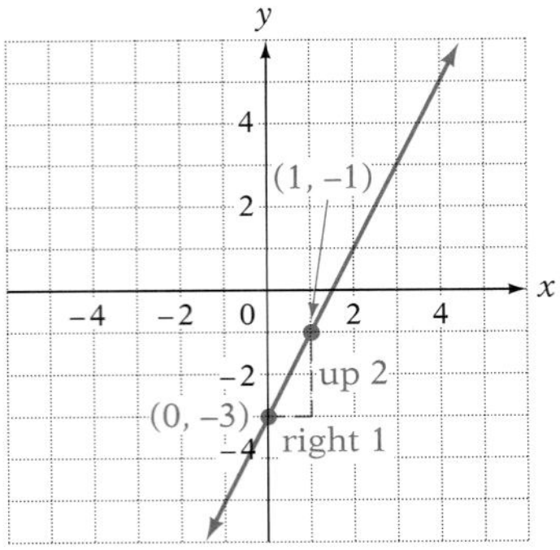

Using a graphing utility, enter the equation $y = 2x - 3$ and verify the graph shown above. Trace along the graph and verify that $(0, -3)$ is the y-intercept and that the point whose coordinates are $(1, -1)$ is on the graph.

EXAMPLE 4 Graph $y = -\frac{2}{3}x + 1$ by using the slope and y-intercept.

Solution y-intercept $= (0, b) = (0, 1)$

$$m = -\frac{2}{3} = \frac{-2}{3}$$

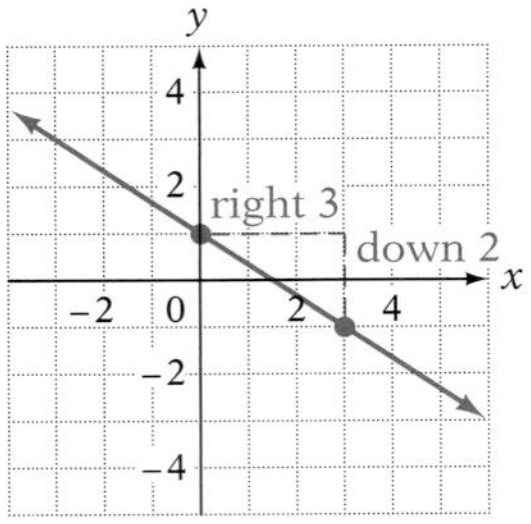

- **A slope of $\frac{-2}{3}$ means to move right 3 units and then down 2 units.**

PROBLEM 4 Graph $y = -\frac{1}{4}x - 1$ by using the slope and y-intercept.

Solution See page S13.

EXAMPLE 5 Graph $2x - 3y = 6$ by using the slope and y-intercept.

Solution

$$2x - 3y = 6$$

$$-3y = -2x + 6$$

- **Solve the equation for y.**

$$y = \frac{2}{3}x - 2$$

y-intercept $= (0, -2)$

$m = \frac{2}{3}$

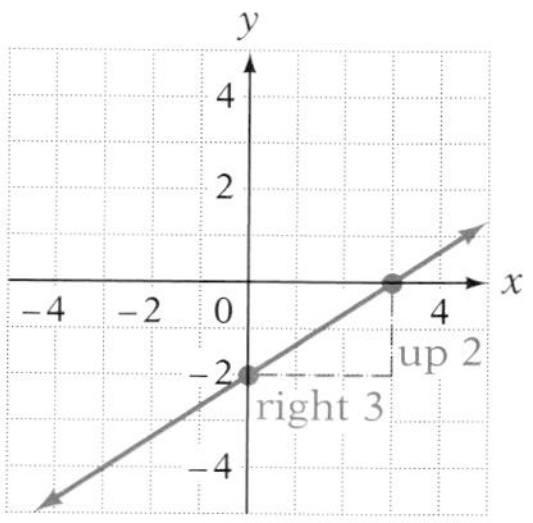

PROBLEM 5 Graph $x - 2y = 4$ by using the slope and y-intercept.

Solution See page S13.

5.3 Concept Review

Determine whether the statement is always true, sometimes true, or never true.

1. In the equation $y = mx + b$, m is the symbol for slope.

2. The formula for slope is $m = \frac{y_2 - y_1}{x_2 - x_1}$.

3. A vertical line has zero slope, and the slope of a horizontal line is undefined.

4. Any two points on a line can be used to find the slope of the line.

5. Shown at the right is the graph of a line with negative slope.

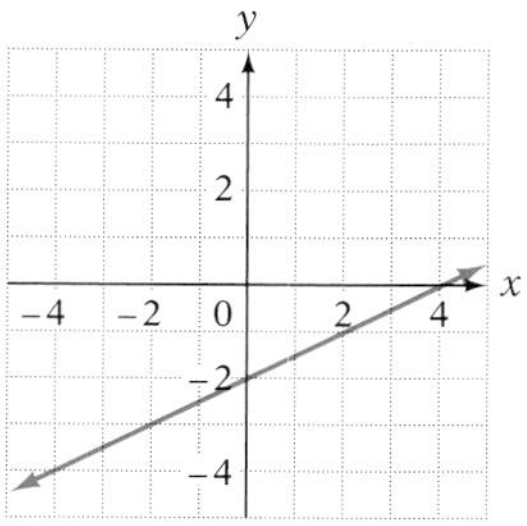

6. The y-intercept of the graph of the equation $y = -2x + 5$ is (5, 0).

5.3 Exercises

1 Find the slope of a straight line

1. Explain how to find the slope of a line when you know two points on the line.

2. What is the difference between a line that has zero slope and a line whose slope is undefined?

3. Identify each x value and each y value to insert in the slope formula $m = \dfrac{y_2 - y_1}{x_2 - x_1}$ to find the slope of the line containing $P_1(1, -4)$ and $P_2(3, 2)$.

$y_2 =$ __?__; $y_1 =$ __?__; $x_2 =$ __?__; $x_1 =$ __?__

4. The slope of the line containing $P_1(-4, 3)$ and $P_2(1, -3)$ is $m = \dfrac{-3 - ?}{1 - (?)}$ $=$ __?__. Does this line slant downward to the right or upward to the right?

Find the slope of the line containing the points P_1 and P_2.

5. $P_1(4, 2), P_2(3, 4)$

6. $P_1(2, 1), P_2(3, 4)$

7. $P_1(-1, 3), P_2(2, 4)$

8. $P_1(-2, 1), P_2(2, 2)$

9. $P_1(2, 4), P_2(4, -1)$

10. $P_1(1, 3), P_2(5, -3)$

11. $P_1(-2, 3), P_2(2, 1)$

12. $P_1(5, -2), P_2(1, 0)$

13. $P_1(8, -3), P_2(4, 1)$

14. $P_1(0, 3), P_2(2, -1)$

15. $P_1(3, -4), P_2(3, 5)$

16. $P_1(-1, 2), P_2(-1, 3)$

17. $P_1(4, -2), P_2(3, -2)$

18. $P_1(5, 1), P_2(-2, 1)$

19. $P_1(0, -1), P_2(3, -2)$

20. $P_1(3, 0), P_2(2, -1)$

21. $P_1(-2, 3), P_2(1, 3)$

22. $P_1(4, -1), P_2(-3, -1)$

23. $P_1(-2, 4), P_2(-1, -1)$

24. $P_1(6, -4), P_2(4, -2)$

25. $P_1(-2, -3), P_2(-2, 1)$

26. $P_1(5, 1), P_2(5, -2)$

27. $P_1(-1, 5), P_2(5, 1)$

28. $P_1(-1, 5), P_2(7, 1)$

29. Is the line containing the points $(-4, 2)$ and $(1, 6)$ parallel to the line that contains the points $(2, -4)$ and $(7, 0)$?

30. Is the line containing the points $(-5, 0)$ and $(0, 2)$ parallel to the line that contains the points $(5, 1)$ and $(0, -1)$?

31. Is the line containing the points $(-2, -3)$ and $(7, 1)$ parallel to the line that contains the points $(6, -5)$ and $(4, 1)$?

32. Is the line containing the points $(4, -3)$ and $(2, 5)$ parallel to the line that contains the points $(-2, -3)$ and $(-4, 1)$?

33. **Postal Service** The graph at the right shows the work accomplished by an electronic mail sorter. Find the slope of the line. Write a sentence that explains the meaning of the slope.

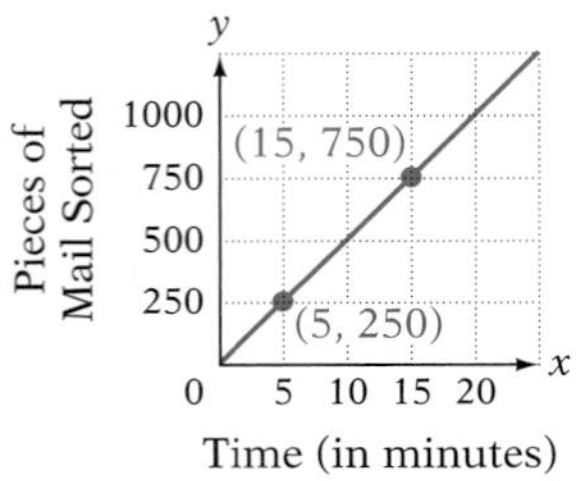

34. **Health** The graph at the right shows the relationship between distance walked and calories burned. Find the slope of the line. Write a sentence that explains the meaning of the slope.

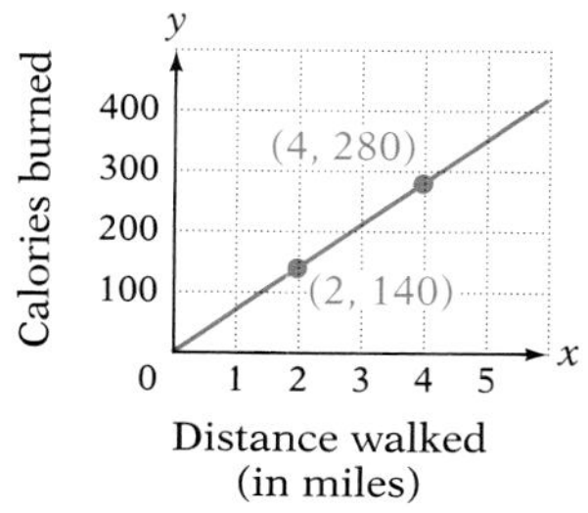

35. **Fuel Consumption** The graph at the right shows how the amount of gasoline in the tank of a car decreases as the car is driven at a constant speed of 60 mph. Find the slope of the line. Write a sentence that states the meaning of the slope.

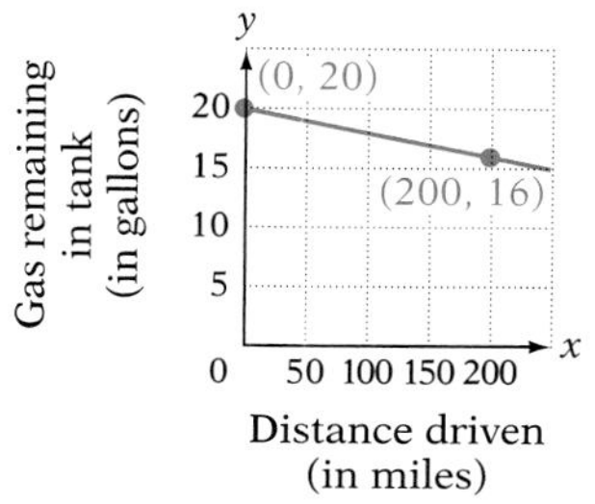

36. **Computer Science** The graph at the right shows the relationship between time and the number of kilobytes of a file remaining to be downloaded. Find the slope of the line. Write a sentence that states the meaning of the slope.

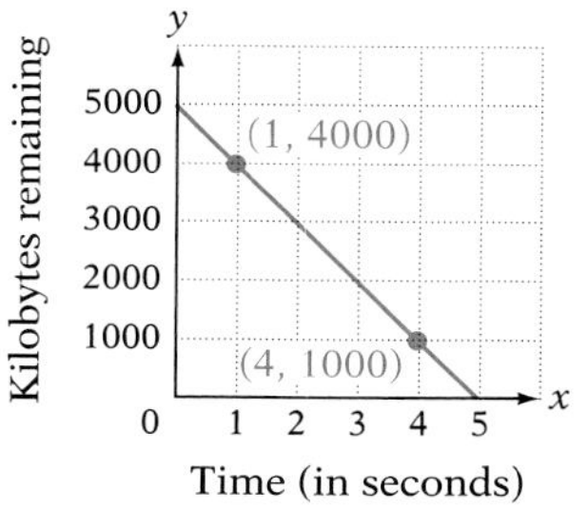

37. Let l be a line passing through points (a, b) and (c, d).
   a. Describe any relationship(s) that must exist between the numbers a, b, c, and d in order for the slope of l to be undefined.
   b. Describe any relationship(s) that must exist between the numbers a, b, c, and d in order for the slope of l to be 0.
   c. Suppose a, b, c, and d are all positive with $a > c$ and $d > b$. Does l slant upward to the right or downward to the right?

38. Line l passes through the point $(-2, 4)$ and is parallel to the line that passes through the points $(-4, 1)$ and $(0, 3)$.
   a. Which quadrants does line l pass through?
   b. Are there any points (a, b) on the line l for which both a and b are negative?

2 Graph a line using the slope and y-intercept

39. The slope of the line with equation $y = 5x - 3$ is __?__, and its y-intercept is __?__.

40. Why is an equation of the form $y = mx + b$ said to be in slope-intercept form?

Graph by using the slope and y-intercept.

41. $y = 3x + 1$

42. $y = -2x - 1$

43. $y = \frac{2}{5}x - 2$

44. $y = \frac{3}{4}x + 1$

45. $2x + y = 3$

46. $3x - y = 1$

47. $x - 2y = 4$

48. $x + 3y = 6$

49. $y = \frac{2}{3}x$

50. $y = \frac{1}{2}x$

51. $y = -x + 1$

52. $y = -x - 3$

53. $3x - 4y = 12$

54. $5x - 2y = 10$

55. $y = -4x + 2$

56. $y = 5x - 2$

57. $4x - 5y = 20$

58. $x - 3y = 6$

59. Suppose A, B, and C are all positive numbers. Does the y-intercept of the graph of $Ax + By = C$ lie above or below the x-axis? Does the graph slant upward to the right or downward to the right?

60. Suppose A is a negative number, and B and C are positive numbers. Does the y-intercept of the graph of $Ax + By = C$ lie above or below the x-axis? Does the graph slant upward to the right or downward to the right?

5.3 Applying Concepts

61. What effect does increasing the coefficient of x have on the graph of $y = mx + b$, $m > 0$?

62. What effect does decreasing the coefficient of x have on the graph of $y = mx + b$, $m > 0$?

63. What effect does increasing the constant term have on the graph of $y = mx + b$?

64. What effect does decreasing the constant term have on the graph of $y = mx + b$?

65. Match each equation with its graph.

i. $y = -2x + 4$

ii. $y = 2x - 4$

iii. $y = 2$

iv. $2x + 4y = 0$

v. $y = \frac{1}{2}x + 4$

vi. $y = -\frac{1}{4}x - 2$

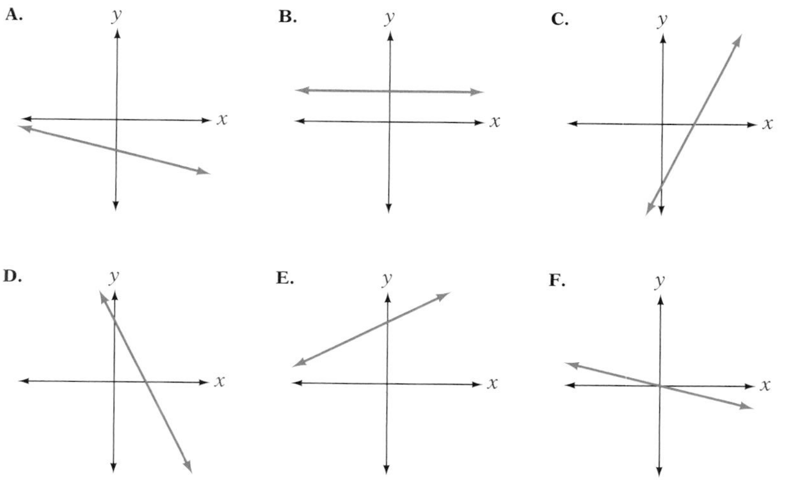

66. Which of the graphs shows a constant rate of change?

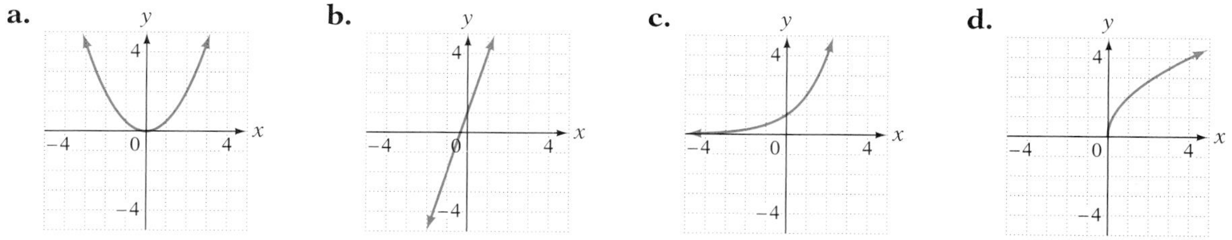

67. Do the graphs of all straight lines have a y-intercept? If not, give an example of one that does not.

68. If two lines have the same slope and the same y-intercept, must the graphs of the lines be the same? If not, give an example.

69. What does the highway sign shown at the right have to do with slope?

5.4 Equations of Straight Lines

OBJECTIVE 1 Find the equation of a line using the equation $y = mx + b$

When the slope of a line and a point on the line are known, the equation of the line can be written using the slope-intercept form, $y = mx + b$. In the first example shown below, the known point is the y-intercept. In the second example, the known point is a point other than the y-intercept.

Find the equation of the line that has slope 3 and y-intercept (0, 2).

$y = mx + b$

The given slope, 3, is m. Replace m with 3. $\quad y = 3x + b$

The given point, (0, 2), is the y-intercept. Replace b with 2. $\quad y = 3x + 2$

The equation of the line that has slope 3 and y-intercept (0, 2) is $y = 3x + 2$.

Find the equation of the line that has slope $\frac{1}{2}$ and contains the point whose coordinates are (−2, 4).

Take Note

Every ordered pair is of the form (x, y). For the point (−2, 4), −2 is the x value and 4 is the y value. Substitute −2 for x and 4 for y.

$y = mx + b$

The given slope, $\frac{1}{2}$, is m. Replace m with $\frac{1}{2}$. $\quad y = \frac{1}{2}x + b$

The given point, (−2, 4), is a solution of the equation of the line. Replace x and y in the equation with the coordinates of the point. $\quad 4 = \frac{1}{2}(-2) + b$

Solve for b, the y-intercept.

$$4 = -1 + b$$
$$5 = b$$

Write the equation of the line by replacing m and b in the equation by their values.

$$y = mx + b$$
$$y = \frac{1}{2}x + 5$$

The equation of the line that has slope $\frac{1}{2}$ and contains the point whose coordinates are (−2, 4) is $y = \frac{1}{2}x + 5$.

EXAMPLE 1 Find the equation of the line that contains the point whose coordinates are (3, −3) and has slope $\frac{2}{3}$.

Solution $y = mx + b$

$y = \frac{2}{3}x + b$ • **Replace *m* with the given slope.**

$-3 = \frac{2}{3}(3) + b$ • **Replace *x* and *y* in the equation with the coordinates of the given point.**

$-3 = 2 + b$ • **Solve for *b*.**

$-5 = b$

$y = \frac{2}{3}x - 5$ • **Write the equation of the line by replacing *m* and *b* in $y = mx + b$ by their values.**

PROBLEM 1 Find the equation of the line that contains the point whose coordinates are $(4, -2)$ and has slope $\frac{3}{2}$.

Solution See page S13.

OBJECTIVE 2 Find the equation of a line using the point-slope formula

An alternative method for finding the equation of a line, given the slope and the coordinates of a point on the line, involves use of the point-slope formula. The point-slope formula is derived from the formula for slope.

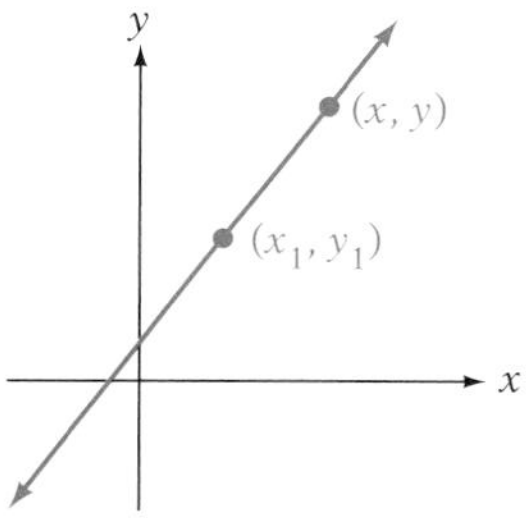

Let (x_1, y_1) be the coordinates of the given point on the line, and let (x, y) be the coordinates of any other point on the line. Use the formula for slope.

$$\frac{y - y_1}{x - x_1} = m$$

Multiply both sides of the equation by $(x - x_1)$.

$$\frac{y - y_1}{x - x_1}(x - x_1) = m(x - x_1)$$

Simplify.

$$y - y_1 = m(x - x_1)$$

Point-Slope Formula

The equation of the line that has slope m and contains the point whose coordinates are (x_1, y_1) can be found by the point-slope formula:

$$y - y_1 = m(x - x_1)$$

EXAMPLE 2 Use the point-slope formula to find the equation of a line that passes through the point whose coordinates are $(-2, -1)$ and has slope $\frac{3}{2}$.

Solution $(x_1, y_1) = (-2, -1)$ • **Let (x_1, y_1) be the given point.**

$m = \frac{3}{2}$ • ***m* is the given slope.**

$$y - y_1 = m(x - x_1)$$ • This is the point-slope formula.

$$y - (-1) = \frac{3}{2}[x - (-2)]$$ • Substitute −2 for x_1, −1 for y_1, and $\frac{3}{2}$ for m.

$$y + 1 = \frac{3}{2}(x + 2)$$ • Rewrite the equation in the form $y = mx + b$.

$$y + 1 = \frac{3}{2}x + 3$$

$$y = \frac{3}{2}x + 2$$

PROBLEM 2 Use the point-slope formula to find the equation of a line that passes through the point whose coordinates are (5, 4) and has slope $\frac{2}{5}$.

Solution See page S13.

OBJECTIVE 3 Find the equation of a line given two points

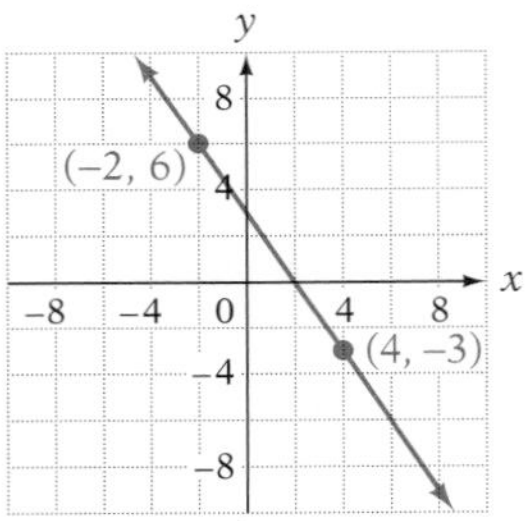

The line that passes through the points whose coordinates are (−2, 6) and (4, −3) is shown at the left. We can find the equation of this line as follows.

Use the slope formula with $(x_1, y_1) = (-2, 6)$ and $(x_2, y_2) = (4, -3)$ to find the slope of the line between the two points.

$$m = \frac{y_2 - y_1}{x_2 - x_1} = \frac{-3 - 6}{4 - (-2)} = \frac{-9}{6} = -\frac{3}{2}$$

The slope of the line is $-\frac{3}{2}$.

Now use the point-slope formula with $m = -\frac{3}{2}$ and $(x_1, y_1) = (-2, 6)$.

$$y - y_1 = m(x - x_1)$$ • Use the point-slope formula.

$$y - 6 = -\frac{3}{2}[x - (-2)]$$ • $m = -\frac{3}{2}$; $(x_1, y_1) = (-2, 6)$

$$y - 6 = -\frac{3}{2}(x + 2)$$

$$y - 6 = -\frac{3}{2}x - 3$$ • Use the Distributive Property.

$$y = -\frac{3}{2}x + 3$$ • Write in slope-intercept form.

Check: You can check that this is the correct equation by substituting (−2, 6) and (4, −3) into the equation, as shown on the next page.

Take Note

We could have used (4, −3) for (x_1, y_1) instead of (−2, 6). The result would have been the same.

$$y - y_1 = m(x - x_1)$$

$$y - (-3) = -\frac{3}{2}(x - 4)$$

$$y + 3 = -\frac{3}{2}x + 6$$

$$y = -\frac{3}{2}x + 3$$

$$\begin{array}{c|l} y = -\frac{3}{2}x + 3 & \\ \hline 6 & -\frac{3}{2}(-2) + 3 \\ 6 & 3 + 3 \\ 6 = 6 \ \checkmark & \end{array}$$ • **(x, y) = (−2, 6)**

$$\begin{array}{c|l} y = -\frac{3}{2}x + 3 & \\ \hline -3 & -\frac{3}{2}(4) + 3 \\ -3 & -6 + 3 \\ -3 = -3 \ \checkmark & \end{array}$$ • **(x, y) = (4, −3)**

The equation of the line is $y = -\frac{3}{2}x + 3$.

EXAMPLE 3 Find the equation of the line that passes through the points whose coordinates are (−4, −5) and (8, 4).

Solution Find the slope of the line between the two points.

$$m = \frac{y_2 - y_1}{x_2 - x_1} = \frac{4 - (-5)}{8 - (-4)} = \frac{9}{12} = \frac{3}{4}$$ • **Let $(x_1, y_1) = (-4, -5)$ and $(x_2, y_2) = (8, 4)$.**

$y - y_1 = m(x - x_1)$ • **Use the point-slope formula.**

$y - (-5) = \frac{3}{4}[x - (-4)]$ • **$m = \frac{3}{4}$; $(x_1, y_1) = (-4, -5)$**

$y + 5 = \frac{3}{4}(x + 4)$

$y + 5 = \frac{3}{4}x + 3$ • **Use the Distributive Property.**

$y = \frac{3}{4}x - 2$ • **Write in slope-intercept form.**

The equation of the line is $y = \frac{3}{4}x - 2$.

PROBLEM 3 Find the equation of the line that passes through the points whose coordinates are (−3, −9) and (1, −1).

Solution See page S13.

If the two given points lie on a horizontal line, the procedure above can be used to find the equation of the line. However, it is quicker to just remember that the equation of a horizontal line is $y = b$, where b is the y-intercept of the graph of the line. This is the y-coordinate of each of the two given points.

Find the equation of the line that passes through the points whose coordinates are (−4, −2) and (2, −2).

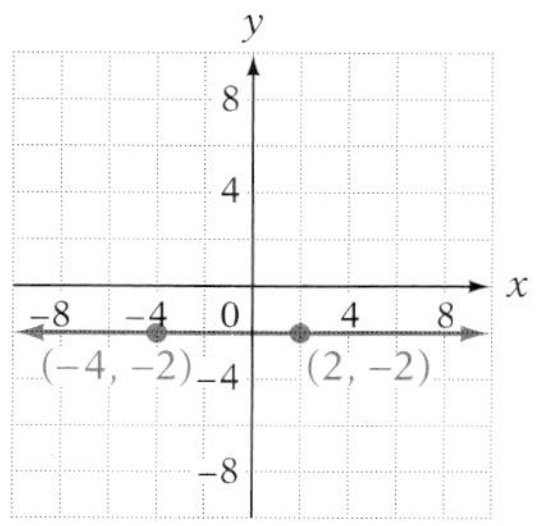

The y-coordinates of the two points are the same. The points lie on a horizontal line. The equation of the line is $y = b$, where b is the y-intercept of the graph of the line.
The equation of the line is $y = -2$.

If the two given points lie on a vertical line, the procedure above cannot be used to find the equation of the line. In this case, remember that the equation of a vertical line is $x = a$, where a is the x-intercept of the graph of the line. This is the x-coordinate of each of the two given points.

Find the equation of the line that passes through the points whose coordinates are (3, 4) and (3, −5).

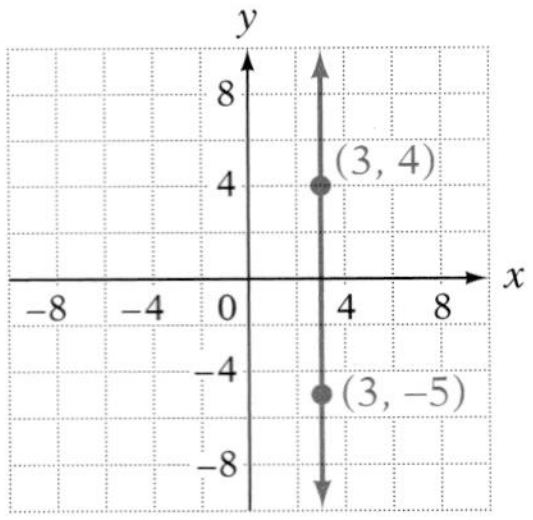

The x-coordinates of the two points are the same. The points lie on a vertical line. The equation of the line is $x = a$, where a is the x-intercept of the graph of the line. The equation of the line is $x = 3$.

5.4 Concept Review

Determine whether the statement is always true, sometimes true, or never true.

1. The graph of the equation $y = 5x + 7$ has slope 5 and y-intercept (0, 7).

2. If the equation of a line has y-intercept (0, 4), then 4 can be substituted for b in the equation $y = mx + b$.

3. Suppose the equation of a line contains the point (−3, 1). Then when y is −3, x is 1.

4. The point-slope formula is $y - y_1 = mx - x_1$.

5. The point-slope formula can be used to find the equation of a line with zero slope.

6. If it is stated that the y-intercept is 2, then the y-intercept is the point (2, 0).

5.4 Exercises

1 Find the equation of a line using the equation $y = mx + b$

1. In the equation of the line that has slope 3 and y-intercept (0, 1), $m =$ ___?___ and $b =$ ___?___. The equation is $y =$ ___?___.

2. To find the equation of the line that contains the point whose coordinates are $(-4, 1)$ and has slope $\frac{3}{2}$, first use the given point and slope to find the y-intercept of the line:

$y = mx + b$ • **Write the slope-intercept form of the equation of a line.**

$1 = \frac{3}{2}(-4) + b$ • **Substitute ___?___ for *y*, ___?___ for *m*, and ___?___ for *x*.**

$1 =$ ___?___ $+ b$ • **Solve for *b*.**

___?___ $= b$

The y-intercept of the line through $(-4, 1)$ that has slope $\frac{3}{2}$ is (0, ___?___).

Use the slope-intercept form.

3. Find the equation of the line that contains the point whose coordinates are $(0, 2)$ and has slope 2.

4. Find the equation of the line that contains the point whose coordinates are $(0, -1)$ and has slope -2.

5. Find the equation of the line that contains the point whose coordinates are $(-1, 2)$ and has slope -3.

6. Find the equation of the line that contains the point whose coordinates are $(2, -3)$ and has slope 3.

7. Find the equation of the line that contains the point whose coordinates are $(3, 1)$ and has slope $\frac{1}{3}$.

8. Find the equation of the line that contains the point whose coordinates are $(-2, 3)$ and has slope $\frac{1}{2}$.

9. Find the equation of the line that contains the point whose coordinates are $(4, -2)$ and has slope $\frac{3}{4}$.

10. Find the equation of the line that contains the point whose coordinates are $(2, 3)$ and has slope $-\frac{1}{2}$.

11. Find the equation of the line that contains the point whose coordinates are $(5, -3)$ and has slope $-\frac{3}{5}$.

12. Find the equation of the line that contains the point whose coordinates are $(5, -1)$ and has slope $\frac{1}{5}$.

13. Find the equation of the line that contains the point whose coordinates are $(2, 3)$ and has slope $\frac{1}{4}$.

14. Find the equation of the line that contains the point whose coordinates are $(-1, 2)$ and has slope $-\frac{1}{2}$.

15. Find the equation of the line that contains the point whose coordinates are $(-3, -5)$ and has slope $-\frac{2}{3}$.

16. Find the equation of the line that contains the point whose coordinates are $(-4, 0)$ and has slope $\frac{5}{2}$.

2 Find the equation of a line using the point-slope formula

17. When is the point-slope formula used?

18. Explain the meaning of each variable in the point-slope formula.

Use the point-slope formula.

19. Find the equation of the line that passes through the point whose coordinates are $(1, -1)$ and has slope 2.

20. Find the equation of the line that passes through the point whose coordinates are $(2, 3)$ and has slope -1.

21. Find the equation of the line that passes through the point whose coordinates are $(-2, 1)$ and has slope -2.

22. Find the equation of the line that passes through the point whose coordinates are $(-1, -3)$ and has slope -3.

23. Find the equation of the line that passes through the point whose coordinates are $(0, 0)$ and has slope $\frac{2}{3}$.

24. Find the equation of the line that passes through the point whose coordinates are (0, 0) and has slope $-\frac{1}{5}$.

25. Find the equation of the line that passes through the point whose coordinates are (2, 3) and has slope $\frac{1}{2}$.

26. Find the equation of the line that passes through the point whose coordinates are (3, −1) and has slope $\frac{2}{3}$.

27. Find the equation of the line that passes through the point whose coordinates are (−4, 1) and has slope $-\frac{3}{4}$.

28. Find the equation of the line that passes through the point whose coordinates are (−5, 0) and has slope $-\frac{1}{5}$.

29. Find the equation of the line that passes through the point whose coordinates are (−2, 1) and has slope $\frac{3}{4}$.

30. Find the equation of the line that passes through the point whose coordinates are (3, −2) and has slope $\frac{1}{6}$.

31. Find the equation of the line that passes through the point whose coordinates are (−3, −5) and has slope $-\frac{4}{3}$.

32. Find the equation of the line that passes through the point whose coordinates are (3, −1) and has slope $\frac{3}{5}$.

33.  **a.** Use the point-slope formula to find the equation of the line with slope m and y-intercept $(0, b)$.
b. Does your answer to part a simplify to the slope-intercept form of a straight line with slope m and y-intercept $(0, b)$?

34.  **a.** Use the point-slope formula to find the equation of the line that goes through the point (5, 3) and has slope 0.
b. Does your answer to part a simplify to the equation of a horizontal line through $(0, b)$?

3 Find the equation of a line given two points

Find the equation of the line through the given points.

35. (−2, −2) and (1, 7)
36. (1, 5) and (3, 9)
37. (−5, 1) and (2, −6)
38. (−3, 9) and (1, 1)

39. (5, −1) and (−5, 11)
40. (−6, 12) and (−4, 9)
41. (−10, −3) and (5, −9)
42. (−6, −13) and (6, −1)

43. (1, 5) and (−6, 5)
44. (−3, −4) and (5, −4)
45. (5, −1) and (5, −7)
46. (−3, 6) and (−3, 0)

47. (−20, −8) and (5, 12)
48. (−6, 19) and (2, 7)
49. (0, −2) and (−6, 1)
50. (15, −9) and (−20, 5)

51. (6, −11) and (−3, 1)
52. (14, −1) and (−7, −7)
53. (3, 6) and (0, −3)
54. (5, 9) and (−5, 3)

55. (−1, −3) and (2, 6)
56. (−3, 6) and (4, −8)
57. (3, −5) and (3, 1)
58. (2, −1) and (5, −1)

59. Is it possible to find the equation of one line through three given points? Explain.

60. If $y = 2x - 3$ and (x_1, y_1) and (x_2, y_2) are the coordinates of two points on the graph of the line, what is the value of $\frac{y_2 - y_1}{x_2 - x_1}$?

5.4 Applying Concepts

Is there a linear equation that contains all the given ordered pairs? If there is, find the equation.

61. $(5, 1), (4, 2), (0, 6)$

62. $(-2, -4), (0, -3), (4, -1)$

63. $(-1, -5), (2, 4), (0, 2)$

64. $(3, -1), (12, -4), (-6, 2)$

The given ordered pairs are solutions of the same linear equation. Find n.

65. $(0, 1), (4, 9), (3, n)$

66. $(2, 2), (-1, 5), (3, n)$

67. $(2, -2), (-2, -4), (4, n)$

68. $(1, -2), (-2, 4), (4, n)$

Temperature The relationship between Celsius and Fahrenheit temperature can be given by a linear equation. Water freezes at 0°C or at 32°F. Water boils at 100°C or at 212°F.

69. Write a linear equation expressing Fahrenheit temperature in terms of Celsius temperature.

70. Graph the equation found in Exercise 69.

When researchers analyze data given in a table or in a scatter diagram, they may try to find the equation of a line that approximates the data. There are various methods that can be used to find this line. One of these is to choose two data points and find the equation of the line using those points.

71. **Population** The table at the right shows the projected population of the United States in millions. (*Source:* www.npg.org/popfacts.htm)

a. Find the equation of the line between (2005, 295.9) and (2025, 353.1).

b. Using the equation from part a, find the projected population of the United States in 2015.

c. Find the absolute value of the difference between the answer to part b and the projected population for 2015 given in the table. This number is called the **absolute error.**

Year	*Population (in millions)*
2005	295.9
2010	310.6
2015	325.4
2020	339.6
2025	353.1
2030	366.0

72. **Salaries** The table at the right shows the median weekly salary of a union member for various years. (*Source:* www.bls.gov)

a. Find the equation of the line between (2000, 696) and (2004, 781).

b. What was the average annual rate of change in the median weekly salary for a union employee between 2000 and 2004?

c. If the trend shown by the equation in part a were to continue, what would be the median weekly salary of a union worker in 2012?

Year	*Weekly Salary (in dollars)*
2000	696
2001	718
2002	740
2003	760
2004	781

5.5 Functions

OBJECTIVE 1 Introduction to functions

The definition of *set* given in the chapter "Prealgebra Review" stated that a set is a collection of objects. Recall that the objects in a set are called the elements of the set. The elements in a set can be anything.

The set of planets in our solar system is

{Mercury, Venus, Earth, Mars, Jupiter, Saturn, Uranus, Neptune, Pluto}

The set of colors in a rainbow is

{red, orange, yellow, green, blue, indigo, violet}

The objects in a set can be ordered pairs. When the elements in a set are ordered pairs, the set is called a relation. A **relation** is any set of ordered pairs.

The set $\{(1, 1), (2, 4), (3, 9), (4, 16), (5, 25)\}$ is a relation. There are five elements in the set. The elements are the ordered pairs $(1, 1)$, $(2, 4)$, $(3, 9)$, $(4, 16)$, and $(5, 25)$.

The following table shows the number of hours that each of eight students spent in the math lab during the week of the math midterm exam and the score that each of these students received on the math midterm.

Hours	2	3	4	4	5	6	6	7
Score	60	70	70	80	85	85	95	90

This information can be written as the relation

$$\{(2, 60), (3, 70), (4, 70), (4, 80), (5, 85), (6, 85), (6, 95), (7, 90)\}$$

where the first coordinate of each ordered pair is the hours spent in the math lab and the second coordinate is the score on the midterm exam.

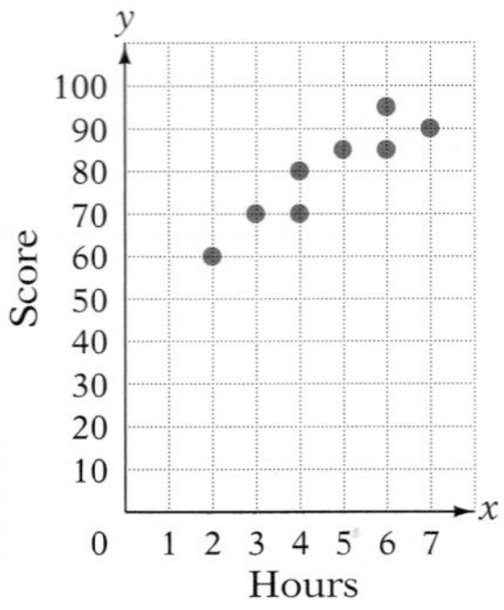

The **domain** of a relation is the set of first coordinates of the ordered pairs. The **range** is the set of second coordinates of the ordered pairs. For the relation above,

$$\text{Domain} = \{2, 3, 4, 5, 6, 7\} \qquad \text{Range} = \{60, 70, 80, 85, 90, 95\}$$

The **graph of a relation** is the graph of the ordered pairs that belong to the relation. The graph of the relation given above is shown at the left. The horizontal axis represents the domain (the hours spent in the math lab) and the vertical axis represents the range (the exam score).

A **function** is a special type of relation in which no two ordered pairs have the same first coordinate and different second coordinates. The relation above is not a function because the ordered pairs $(4, 70)$ and $(4, 80)$ have the same first coordinate and different second coordinates. The ordered pairs $(6, 85)$ and $(6, 95)$ also have the same first coordinate and different second coordinates.

The table at the right describes a grading scale that defines a relationship between a test score and a letter grade. Some of the ordered pairs in this relation are (38, F), (73, C), and (94, A).

Score	Letter Grade
90–100	A
80–89	B
70–79	C
60–69	D
0–59	F

This relation defines a function because no two ordered pairs can have the *same* first coordinate and *different* second coordinates. For instance, it is not possible to have an average of 73 paired with any grade other than C. Both (73, C) and (73, A) cannot be ordered pairs belonging to the function, or two students with the same score would receive different grades. Note that (81, B) and (88, B) are ordered pairs of this function. Ordered pairs of a function may have the same *second* coordinate paired with different *first* coordinates.

The domain of this function is $\{0, 1, 2, 3, \ldots, 98, 99, 100\}$.

The range of this function is {A, B, C, D, F}.

EXAMPLE 1 Find the domain and range of the relation $\{(-5, 1), (-3, 3), (-1, 5)\}$. Is the relation a function?

Solution The domain is $\{-5, -3, -1\}$.

- **The domain of the relation is the set of the first components of the ordered pairs.**

The range is $\{1, 3, 5\}$.

- **The range of the relation is the set of the second components of the ordered pairs.**

No two ordered pairs have the same first coordinate. The relation is a function.

PROBLEM 1 Find the domain and range of the relation $\{(1, 0), (1, 1), (1, 2), (1, 3), (1, 4)\}$. Is the relation a function?

Solution See page S13.

Although a function can be described in terms of ordered pairs or in a table, functions are often described by an equation. The letter f is commonly used to represent a function, but any letter can be used.

The "square" function assigns to each real number its square. The square function is described by the equation

$$f(x) = x^2 \qquad \text{read } f(x) \text{ as "}f \text{ of } x\text{" or "the value of } f \text{ at } x.\text{"}$$

$\boldsymbol{f(x)}$ is the symbol for the number that is paired with x. In terms of ordered pairs, this is written $(x, f(x))$. $f(x)$ is the **value of the function** at x because it is the result of evaluating the variable expression. For example, $f(4)$ means to replace x by 4 and then simplify the resulting numerical expression. This process is called **evaluating the function.**

The notation $f(4)$ is used to indicate the number that is paired with 4. To evaluate $f(x) = x^2$ at 4, replace x with 4 and simplify.

$$f(x) = x^2$$
$$f(4) = 4^2$$
$$f(4) = 16$$

The square function squares a number, and when 4 is squared, the result is 16. For the square function, the number 4 is paired with 16. In other words, when x is 4, $f(x)$ is 16. The ordered pair (4, 16) is an element of the function.

It is important to remember that $f(x)$ does not mean f times x. The letter f stands for the function, and $f(x)$ is the number that is paired with x.

EXAMPLE 2 Evaluate $f(x) = 2x - 4$ at $x = 3$. Write an ordered pair that is an element of the function.

Solution

$f(x) = 2x - 4$

$f(3) = 2(3) - 4$ • **$f(3)$ is the number that is paired with 3. Replace x by 3 and evaluate.**

$f(3) = 6 - 4$

$f(3) = 2$

The ordered pair (3, 2) is an element of the function.

PROBLEM 2 Evaluate $f(x) = -5x + 1$ at $x = 2$. Write an ordered pair that is an element of the function.

Solution See page S13.

When a function is described by an equation and the domain is specified, the range of the function can be found by evaluating the function at each point of the domain.

EXAMPLE 3 Find the range of the function given by the equation $f(x) = -3x + 2$ if the domain is $\{-4, -2, 0, 2, 4\}$. Write five ordered pairs that belong to the function.

Solution

$f(x) = -3x + 2$

$f(-4) = -3(-4) + 2 = 12 + 2 = 14$ • **Replace x by each member of the domain.**

$f(-2) = -3(-2) + 2 = 6 + 2 = 8$

$f(0) = -3(0) + 2 = 0 + 2 = 2$

$f(2) = -3(2) + 2 = -6 + 2 = -4$

$f(4) = -3(4) + 2 = -12 + 2 = -10$

The range is $\{-10, -4, 2, 8, 14\}$.

The ordered pairs $(-4, 14)$, $(-2, 8)$, $(0, 2)$, $(2, -4)$, and $(4, -10)$ belong to the function.

PROBLEM 3 Find the range of the function given by the equation $f(x) = 4x - 3$ if the domain is $\{-5, -3, -1, 1\}$. Write four ordered pairs that belong to the function.

Solution See page S13.

OBJECTIVE 2 Graphs of linear functions

The solutions of the equation

$$y = 7x - 3$$

are ordered pairs (x, y). For example, the ordered pairs $(-1, -10)$, $(0, -3)$, and $(1, 4)$ are solutions of the equation. Therefore, this equation defines a relation.

It is not possible to substitute one value of x into the equation $y = 7x - 3$ and get two different values of y. For example, the number 1 in the domain cannot be paired with any number other than 4 in the range. (*Remember:* A function cannot have ordered pairs in which the same first coordinate is paired with different second coordinates.) Therefore, the equation defines a function.

The equation $y = 7x - 3$ is an equation of the form $y = mx + b$. In general, any equation of the form $y = mx + b$ is a function.

In the equation $y = 7x - 3$, the variable y is called the **dependent variable** because its value *depends* on the value of x. The variable x is called the **independent variable.** We choose a value for x and substitute that value into the equation to determine the value of y. We say that y is a function of x.

Take Note

When y is a function of x, y and $f(x)$ are interchangeable.

When an equation defines y as a function of x, functional notation is frequently used to emphasize that the relation is a function. In this case, it is common to use the notation $f(x)$. Therefore, we can write the equation

$$y = 7x - 3$$

in functional notation as

$$f(x) = 7x - 3$$

The **graph of a function** is a graph of the ordered pairs (x, y) of the function. Because the graph of the equation $y = mx + b$ is a straight line, a function of the form $f(x) = mx + b$ is a **linear function.**

Graph: $f(x) = \frac{2}{3}x - 1$

Think of the function as the equation $y = \frac{2}{3}x - 1$.

This is the equation of a straight line.

The y-intercept is $(0, -1)$. The slope is $\frac{2}{3}$.

Graph the point $(0, -1)$. From the y-intercept, go right 3 units and then up 2 units. Graph the point $(3, 1)$.

Draw a line through the two points.

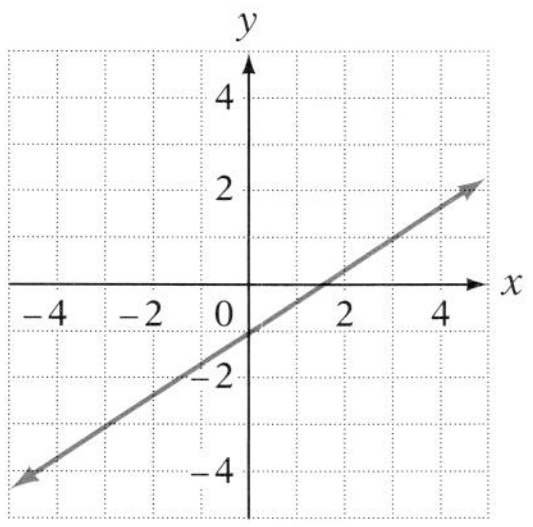

EXAMPLE 4 Graph: $f(x) = \frac{3}{4}x + 2$

Solution $f(x) = \frac{3}{4}x + 2$

$y = \frac{3}{4}x + 2$

- **Think of the function as the equation $y = \frac{3}{4}x + 2$.**
- **The graph is a straight line with y-intercept $(0, 2)$ and slope $\frac{3}{4}$.**

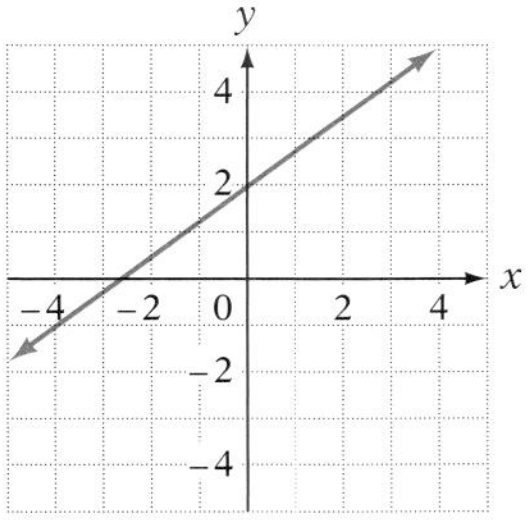

PROBLEM 4 Graph: $f(x) = -\frac{1}{2}x - 3$

Solution See page S14.

Graphing utilities are used to graph functions. Using a graphing utility, enter the equation $y = \frac{3}{4}x + 2$ and verify the graph drawn in Example 4. Trace along the graph and verify that $(-4, -1)$, $(0, 2)$, and $(4, 5)$ are coordinates of points on the graph. Now enter the equation given in Problem 4 and verify the graph you drew.

There are a variety of applications of linear functions. For example, suppose an installer of marble kitchen countertops charges \$250 plus \$180 per foot of countertop. The equation that describes the total cost, C (in dollars), for having x feet of countertop installed is $C = 180x + 250$. In this situation, C is a function of x; the total cost depends on how many feet of countertop are installed. Therefore, we could rewrite the equation

$$C = 180x + 250$$

as the function

$$f(x) = 180x + 250$$

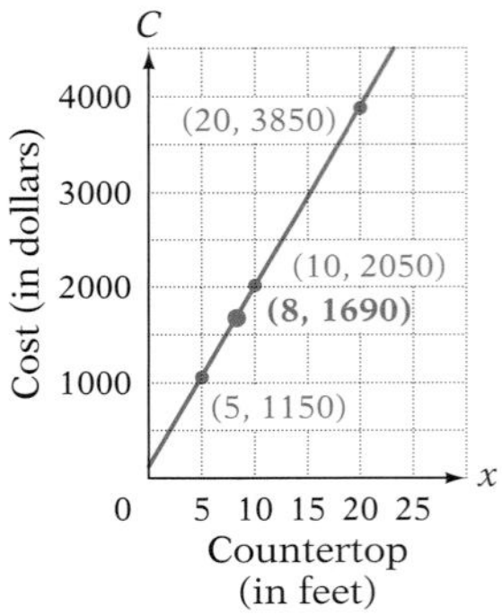

To graph this equation, we first choose a reasonable domain—for example, values of x between 0 and 25. It would not be reasonable to have $x \leq 0$, because no one would order the installation of 0 ft of countertop, and any amount less than 0 would be a negative amount of countertop. The upper limit of 25 is chosen because most kitchens have less than 25 ft of countertop.

Choosing $x = 5$, 10, and 20 results in the ordered pairs (5, 1150), (10, 2050), and (20, 3850). Graph these points and draw a line through them. The graph is shown at the left.

The point whose coordinates are (8, 1690) is on the graph. This ordered pair can be interpreted to mean that 8 ft of countertop costs \$1690 to install.

EXAMPLE 5 The value, V, of an investment of \$2500 at an annual simple interest rate of 6% is given by the equation $V = 150t + 2500$, where t is the amount of time, in years, that the money is invested.

A. Write the equation in functional notation.

B. Graph the equation for values of t between 0 and 10.

C. The point whose coordinates are (5, 3250) is on the graph. Write a sentence that explains the meaning of this ordered pair.

Solution **A.** $V = 150t + 2500$

$f(t) = 150t + 2500$

- **The value V of the investment depends on the amount of time t it is invested. The value V is a function of the time t.**

B.

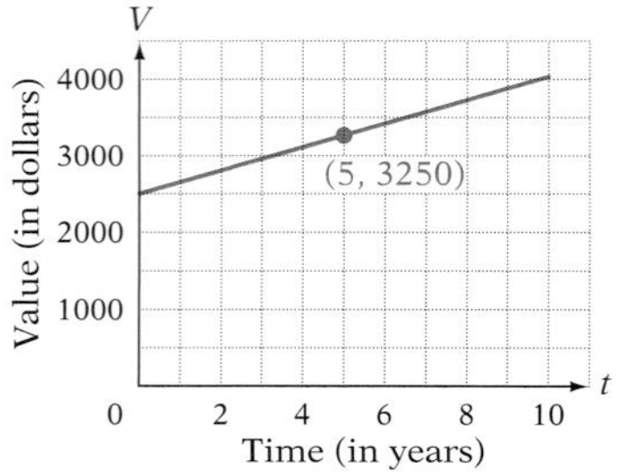

- **Some ordered pairs of the function are (2, 2800), (4, 3100), and (6, 3400).**

C. The ordered pair (5, 3250) means that in 5 years the value of the investment will be \$3250.

PROBLEM 5 A car is traveling at a uniform speed of 40 mph. The distance, d (in miles), the car travels in t hours is given by the equation $d = 40t$.

A. Write the equation in functional notation.

B. Use the coordinate axes at the right to graph this equation for values of t between 0 and 5.

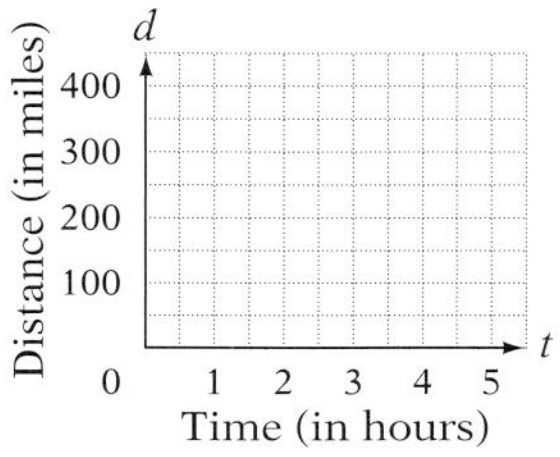

C. The point whose coordinates are (3, 120) is on the graph. Write a sentence that explains the meaning of this ordered pair.

Solution See page S14.

5.5 Concept Review

Determine whether the statement is always true, sometimes true, or never true.

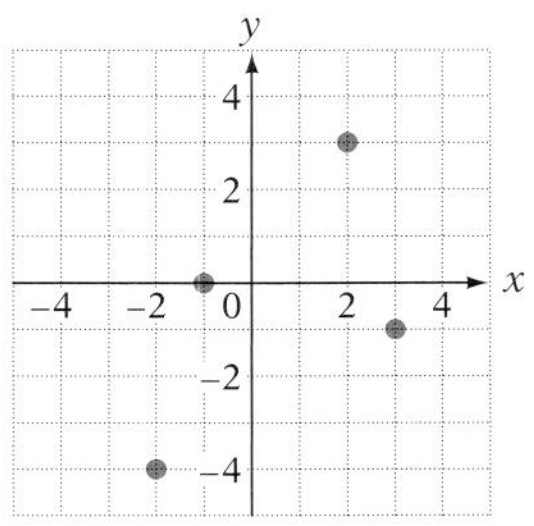

1. The graph shown at the right is the graph of a function.
2. For the relation graphed at the right, the domain is $\{-2, -1, 2, 3\}$.
3. The graph of the function $f(x) = -\frac{2}{3}x + 5$ has a positive slope.
4. The graphs of $y = \frac{1}{4}x - 6$ and $f(x) = \frac{1}{4}x - 6$ are identical.
5. The value of the function $\{(-3, 3), (-2, 2), (-1, 1), (0, 0)\}$ at -2 is 2.
6. A function can be represented in a table, by an equation, by a graph, or in a chart.
7. The graph of a function of the form $f(x) = mx + b$ is a straight line.
8. The equation $y = 7x - 1$ defines a function.

5.5 Exercises

1 Introduction to functions

1. A relation is a set of ____?____. The set of first coordinates of the ordered pairs is called the ____?____ of the relation. The set of second coordinates is called the ____?____ of the relation.

2. **a.** The symbol $f(x)$ is read "f ____?____ x" or "the value of f ____?____ x." It is a symbol for the number that the function f pairs with ____?____.
   b. The symbol $f(3)$ is a symbol for the number that the function f pairs with ____?____.
   c. If $f(x) = 4x - 1$, then $f(3) = 4($____?____$) - 1 =$ ____?____. This means that (____?____, ____?____) is an ordered pair of the function f.

For Exercises 3 and 4 use the following sets. Set A is the set of all dates of the year ({January 1, January 2, January 3, . . .}). Set B is the set of all the people in the world.

3. A relation has domain A and range B. Each ordered pair in the relation is in the form (date, person born on that date). Is this relation a function?

4. A relation has domain B and range A. Each ordered pair in the relation is in the form (person, birth date of that person). Is this relation a function?

5. **Aviation** The table at the right shows the percent of on-time arrivals and on-time departures for selected U.S. airports. (*Source*: Federal Aviation Authority) Write a relation where the first coordinate is the percent of on-time arrivals and the second coordinate percent of on-time departures. Is the relation a function?

Percent On-time

Arrivals	*Departures*
87.7	91.0
71.4	84.0
79.1	84.5
90.1	91.6
82.5	94.3
68.4	74.5
82.5	80.2

6. **Health** The table at the right shows the United States Department of Agriculture limit on saturated fat intake, in grams. Write a relation where the first coordinate is a person's daily Calorie intake and the second coordinate is the limit on saturated fat intake. Is the relation a function?

Daily Calories	*Saturated Fat (in grams)*
1600	18
2000	20
2200	24
2500	25
2800	31

7. **Jogging** The table at the right shows the number of Calories a 150-pound person burns while running at various speeds, in miles per hour. Write a relation where the first coordinate is the speed of the runner and the second coordinate is the number Calories burned. Is the relation a function?

Speed (in mph)	*Calories*
4	411
5	514
6	618
7	720
8	823

8. **Health** The table at the right shows the birth rate of various countries, in births per thousand, and life expectancy, in years. (*Source*: www.cia.gov) Write a relation where the first coordinate is the birth rate and the second coordinate is the life expectancy. Is the relation a function?

Country	*Birth Rate*	*Life Expectancy*
Belgium	10.48	78.6
Brazil	16.8	71.7
Martinique	14.14	79.0
Mexico	21.0	75.2
Sweden	10.36	80.4
United States	14.14	77.7

9. Physics The speeds of a car in miles per hour and the distances, in feet, needed to stop at those speeds are recorded in the table at the right. (*Source:* AAA Foundation for Traffic Safety) Write a relation in which the first coordinate is the speed in miles per hour and the second coordinate is the distance needed to stop. Is the relation a function?

Speed (in miles per hour)	*Distance Needed to Stop (in feet)*
55	273
65	355
75	447
85	549

10. Biology The following table shows the length of the humerus (the long bone from the shoulder to the elbow), in centimeters, and the total wingspan, in centimeters, of several pterosaurs, which are extinct flying reptiles of the order Pterosauria. Write a relation in which the first coordinate is the length of the humerus and the second coordinate is the wingspan. Is the relation a function?

Length of humerus, in centimeters	24	32	22	15	4.4	17	15
Wingspan, in centimeters	600	750	430	300	68	370	310

Find the domain and range of the relation. State whether or not the relation is a function.

11. $\{(0, 0), (2, 0), (4, 0), (6, 0)\}$

12. $\{(-2, 2), (0, 2), (1, 2), (2, 2)\}$

13. $\{(2, 2), (2, 4), (2, 6), (2, 8)\}$

14. $\{(-4, 4), (-2, 2), (0, 0), (-2, -2)\}$

15. $\{(0, 0), (1, 1), (2, 2), (3, 3)\}$

16. $\{(0, 5), (1, 4), (2, 3), (3, 2), (4, 1), (5, 0)\}$

17. $\{(-2, -3), (2, 3), (-1, 2), (1, 2), (-3, 4), (3, 4)\}$

18. $\{(-1, 0), (0, -1), (1, 0), (2, 3), (3, 5)\}$

Evaluate the function at the given value of x. Write an ordered pair that is an element of the function.

19. $f(x) = 4x; x = 10$

20. $f(x) = 8x; x = 11$

21. $f(x) = x - 5; x = -6$

22. $f(x) = x + 7; x = -9$

23. $f(x) = 3x^2; x = -2$

24. $f(x) = x^2 - 1; x = -8$

25. $f(x) = 5x + 1; x = \frac{1}{2}$

26. $f(x) = 2x - 6; x = \frac{3}{4}$

27. $f(x) = \frac{2}{5}x + 4; x = -5$

28. $f(x) = \frac{3}{2}x - 5; x = 2$

29. $f(x) = 2x^2; x = -4$

30. $f(x) = 4x^2 + 2; x = -3$

Find the range of the function defined by the given equation. Write five ordered pairs that belong to the function.

31. $f(x) = 3x - 4$; domain $= \{-5, -3, -1, 1, 3\}$

32. $f(x) = 2x + 5$; domain $= \{-10, -5, 0, 5, 10\}$

33. $f(x) = \frac{1}{2}x + 3$; domain $= \{-4, -2, 0, 2, 4\}$

34. $f(x) = \frac{3}{4}x - 1$; domain $= \{-8, -4, 0, 4, 8\}$

35. $f(x) = x^2 + 6$; domain $= \{-3, -1, 0, 1, 3\}$

36. $f(x) = 3x^2 + 6$; domain $= \{-2, -1, 0, 1, 2\}$

2 Graphs of linear functions

37. In the linear equation $y = 5x - 9$, the independent variable is ____?____ and the dependent variable is ____?____. To write this equation in function notation, replace y with the symbol ____?____.

38. To graph the function $f(x) = \frac{1}{2}x + 4$, replace $f(x)$ with ____?____. This is the equation of a line with y-intercept ____?____ and slope ____?____.

Graph.

39. $f(x) = 5x$

40. $f(x) = -4x$

41. $f(x) = x + 2$

42. $f(x) = x - 3$

43. $f(x) = 6x - 1$

44. $f(x) = 3x + 4$

45. $f(x) = -2x + 3$

46. $f(x) = -5x - 2$

47. $f(x) = \frac{1}{3}x - 4$

48. $f(x) = \frac{3}{5}x + 1$

49. $f(x) = 4$

50. $f(x) = -3$

Graph using a graphing utility.

51. $f(x) = 2x - 1$

52. $f(x) = -3x - 1$

53. $f(x) = -\frac{1}{2}x + 1$

54. $f(x) = \frac{2}{3}x + 4$

55. $f(x) = \frac{3}{4}x + 1$

56. $f(x) = -\frac{1}{2}x - 2$

57. $f(x) = -\frac{4}{3}x + 5$

58. $f(x) = \frac{5}{2}x$

59. $f(x) = -1$

60. Let $f(x) = 7x + 10$. If m and n are positive numbers such that $m > n$, is $f(m) - f(n)$ positive or negative?

61. Can the equation of a vertical line be written in function notation?

62. **Depreciation** Depreciation is the declining value of an asset. For instance, a company purchases a truck for \$20,000. The truck is an asset worth \$20,000. In 5 years, however, the value of the truck will have declined, and it may be worth only \$4000. An equation that represents this decline is $V = 20{,}000 - 3200x$, where V is the value, in dollars, of the truck after x years.

a. Write the equation in functional notation.

b. Use the coordinate axes at the right to graph the equation for values of x between 0 and 5.

c. The point (4, 7200) is on the graph. Write a sentence that explains the meaning of this ordered pair.

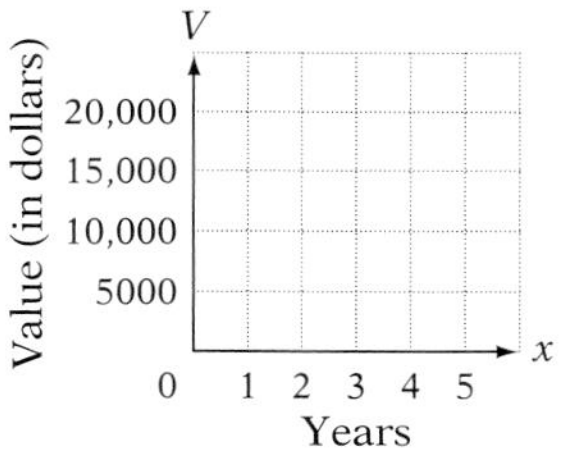

63. **Depreciation** A company uses the equation $V = 30{,}000 - 5000x$ to estimate the depreciated value, in dollars, of a computer. (See Exercise 62.)

a. Write the equation in functional notation.

b. Use the coordinate axes at the right to graph the equation for values of x between 0 and 5.

c. The point (1, 25,000) is on the graph. Write a sentence that explains the meaning of this ordered pair.

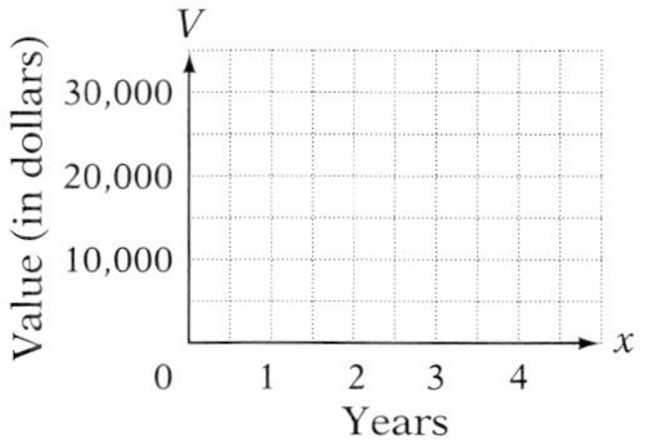

64. **Business** An architect charges a fee of \$500 plus \$2.65 per square foot to design a house. The equation that represents the architect's fee is given by $F = 2.65s + 500$, where F is the fee, in dollars, and s is the number of square feet in the house.

a. Write the equation in functional notation.

b. Use the coordinate axes at the right to graph the equation for values of s between 0 and 5000.

c. The point (3500, 9775) is on the graph. Write a sentence that explains the meaning of this ordered pair.

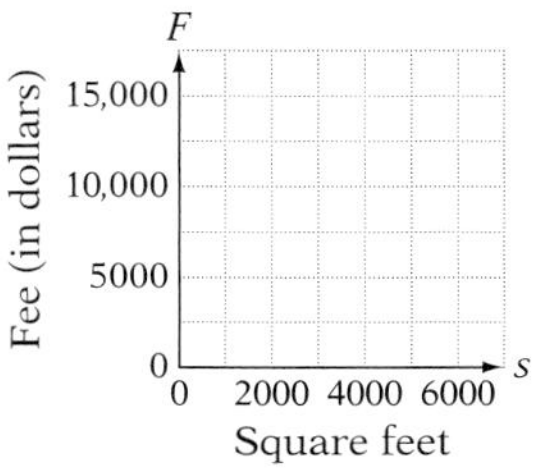

65. **Business** A rental car company charges a "drop-off" fee of \$50 to return a car to a location different than that from which it was rented. In addition, it charges a fee of \$.18 per mile the car is driven. An equation that represents the total cost to rent a car from this company is $C = 0.18m + 50$, where C is the total cost, in dollars, and m is the number of miles the car is driven.

a. Write the equation in functional notation.

b. Use the coordinate axes at the right to graph the equation for values of m between 0 and 1000.

c. The point (500, 140) is on the graph. Write a sentence that explains the meaning of this ordered pair.

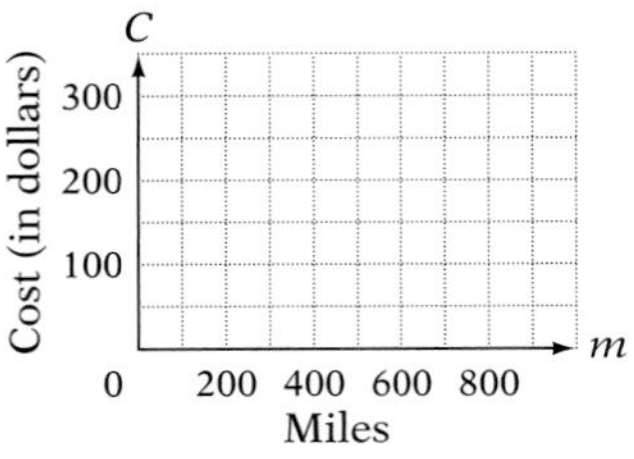

5.5 Applying Concepts

66. **a.** A function f consists of the ordered pairs $\{(-4, -6), (-2, -2), (0, 2), (2, 6), (4, 10)\}$. Find $f(2)$.

b. A function f consists of the ordered pairs $\{(0, 9), (1, 8), (2, 7), (3, 6), (4, 5)\}$. Find $f(1)$.

67. **Health** The average annual number of cigarettes smoked by an American adult for the years 1991 through 2000 is shown in the table at the right. (*Source:* USDA Economic Research Service Agricultural Outlook)

a. Do these data represent a function? Why or why not?

b. If the data represent a function, do they represent a linear function? Why or why not?

c. If the data represent a function, is the year a function of the number of cigarettes smoked, or is the number of cigarettes smoked a function of the year?

d. If you had to predict the average annual number of cigarettes smoked in 2001 on the basis of the information in the table, would you predict that it would be more or less than 2000? Explain your answer.

Year	*Average Annual Number of Cigarettes Smoked*
1991	2727
1992	2647
1993	2543
1994	2524
1995	2505
1996	2482
1997	2423
1998	2320
1999	2136
2000	2103

68. **Height-Time Graphs** A child's height is a function of the child's age. The graph of this function is not linear, because children go through growth spurts as they develop. However, for the graph to be reasonable, the function must be an increasing function (that is, as the age increases, the height increases), because children do not get shorter as they grow older. Match each function described below with a reasonable graph of the function.

a. The height of a plane above the ground during take-off depends on how long it has been since the plane left the gate.

b. The height of a football above the ground is related to the number of seconds that have passed since it was punted.

c. A basketball player is dribbling a basketball. The basketball's distance from the floor is related to the number of seconds that have passed since the player began dribbling the ball.

d. Two children are seated together on a roller coaster. The height of the children above the ground depends on how long they have been on the ride.

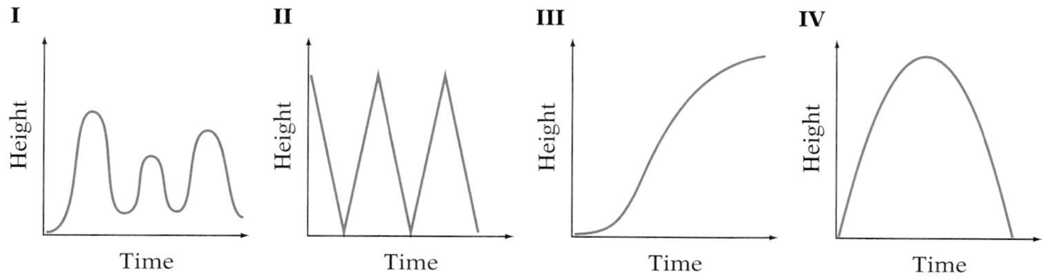

69. Investigating a relationship between two variables is an important task in the application of mathematics. For example, botanists study the relationship between the number of bushels of wheat yielded per acre and the amount of watering per acre. Environmental scientists study the relationship between the incidence of skin cancer and the amount of ozone in the atmosphere. Business analysts study the relationship between the price of a product and the number of products that are sold at that price. Describe a relationship that is important to your major field of study.

70. Functions are a part of our everyday lives. For example, the cost to mail a package via first-class mail is a function of the weight of the package. The tuition paid by a part-time student is a function of the number of credit hours the student registers for. Provide other examples of functions.

5.6 Graphing Linear Inequalities

OBJECTIVE 1 Graph inequalities in two variables

Point of Interest

Linear inequalities play an important role in applied mathematics. They are used in a branch of mathematics called linear programming, *which was developed during World War II to solve problems in supplying the Air Force with the machine parts necessary to keep planes flying. Today its applications have been broadened to many other disciplines.*

The graph of the linear equation $y = x - 2$ separates a plane into three sets:

the set of points on the line

the set of points above the line

the set of points below the line

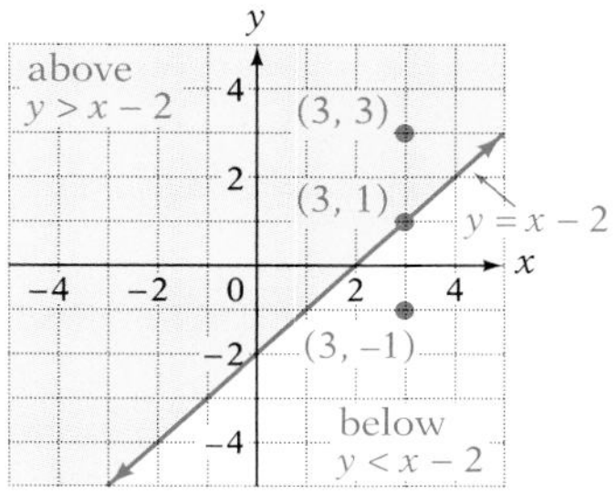

The point whose coordinates are (3, 1) is a solution of $y = x - 2$.

$$\begin{array}{c|c} y & x - 2 \\ \hline 1 & 3 - 2 \\ 1 = 1 & \end{array}$$

The point whose coordinates are (3, 3) is a solution of $y > x - 2$.

$$\begin{array}{c|c} y & > x - 2 \\ \hline 3 & 3 - 2 \\ 3 > 1 & \end{array}$$

Any point above the line is a solution of $y > x - 2$.

The point whose coordinates are (3, −1) is a solution of $y < x - 2$.

$$\begin{array}{c|c} y & < x - 2 \\ \hline -1 & 3 - 2 \\ -1 < 1 & \end{array}$$

Any point below the line is a solution of $y < x - 2$.

The solution set of $y = x - 2$ is all points on the line. The solution set of $y > x - 2$ is all points above the line. The solution set of $y < x - 2$ is all points below the line. The solution set of an inequality in two variables is a **half-plane.**

The following illustrates the procedure for graphing a linear inequality.

Graph the solution set of $2x + 3y \le 6$.

Solve the inequality for y.

$$\begin{aligned} 2x + 3y &\le 6 \\ 2x - 2x + 3y &\le -2x + 6 \\ 3y &\le -2x + 6 \\ \frac{3y}{3} &\le \frac{-2x + 6}{3} \\ y &\le -\frac{2}{3}x + 2 \end{aligned}$$

Change the inequality to an equality and graph the line. If the inequality is $\ge$ or $\le$, the line is in the solution set and is shown by a **solid line.** If the inequality is $>$ or $<$, the line is not a part of the solution set and is shown by a **dashed line.**

$$y = -\frac{2}{3}x + 2$$

If the inequality is in the form $y > mx + b$ or $y \ge mx + b$, shade the **upper half-plane.** If the inequality is in the form $y < mx + b$ or $y \le mx + b$, shade the **lower half-plane.**

The equation $y \le -\frac{2}{3}x + 2$ is in the form $y \le mx + b$. Draw a solid line and shade the lower half-plane.

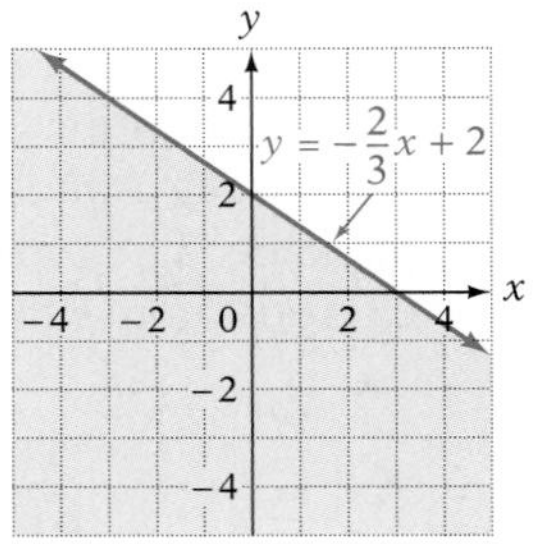

The inequality $2x + 3y \le 6$ can also be graphed as shown below.

Graph the solution set of $2x + 3y \le 6$.

Change the inequality to an equality. $2x + 3y = 6$

Find the x- and y-intercepts of the equation. To find the x-intercept, let $y = 0$.

$$\begin{aligned} 2x + 3(0) &= 6 \\ 2x &= 6 \\ x &= 3 \end{aligned}$$

The x-intercept is (3, 0).

To find the y-intercept, let $x = 0$.

$$\begin{aligned} 2(0) + 3y &= 6 \\ 3y &= 6 \\ y &= 2 \end{aligned}$$

The y-intercept is (0, 2).

Take Note

Any ordered pair is of the form (x, y). For the point $(0, 0)$, substitute 0 for x and 0 for y in the inequality.

Graph the ordered pairs $(3, 0)$ and $(0, 2)$. Draw a solid line through the points because the inequality is $\leq$.

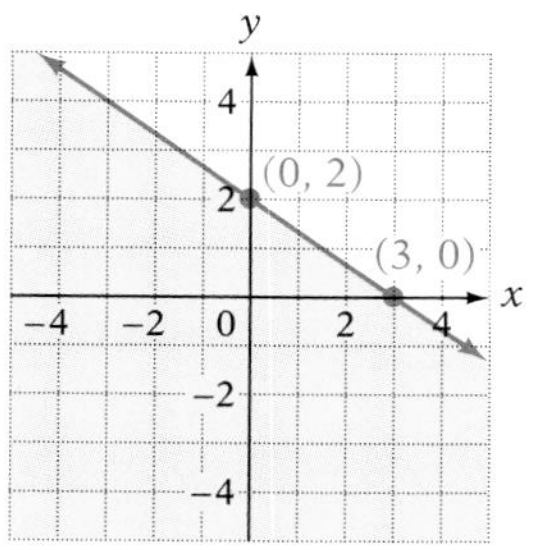

The point $(0, 0)$ can be used to determine which region to shade. If $(0, 0)$ is a solution of the inequality, then shade the region that includes the point $(0, 0)$.

If $(0, 0)$ is not a solution of the inequality, then shade the region that does not include the point $(0, 0)$. For this example, $(0, 0)$ is a solution of the inequality. The region that contains the point $(0, 0)$ is shaded.

$$2x + 3y \leq 6$$
$$2(0) + 3(0) \leq 6$$
$$0 \leq 6 \quad \text{True}$$

If the line passes through the point $(0, 0)$, another point must be used to determine which region to shade. For example, use the point $(1, 0)$.

It is important to note that every point in the shaded region is a solution of the inequality and that every solution of the inequality is a point in the shaded region. No point outside of the shaded region is a solution of the inequality.

EXAMPLE 1 Graph the solution set of $3x + y > -2$.

Solution

$$3x + y > -2$$
$$3x - 3x + y > -3x - 2$$
$$y > -3x - 2$$

• **Solve the inequality for y.**

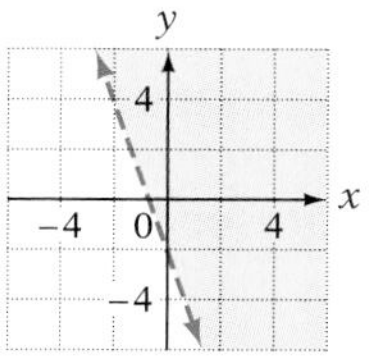

• **Graph $y = -3x - 2$ as a dashed line. Shade the upper half-plane.**

PROBLEM 1 Graph the solution set of $x - 3y < 2$.

Solution See page S14.

EXAMPLE 2 Graph the solution set of $y > 3$.

Solution

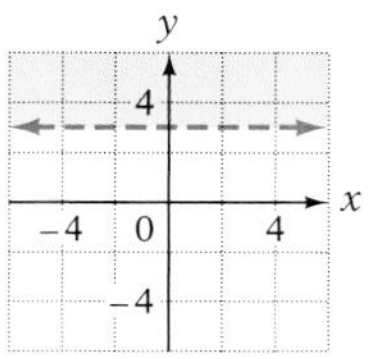

• **The inequality is solved for y. Graph $y = 3$ as a dashed line. Shade the upper half-plane.**

PROBLEM 2 Graph the solution set of $x < 3$.

Solution See page S14.

5.6 Concept Review

Determine whether the statement is always true, sometimes true, or never true.

1. $y \geq \frac{1}{2}x - 5$ is an example of a linear equation in two variables.

2. $(-2, 4)$ is a solution of $y > x + 2$.

3. $(3, 0)$ is a solution of $y \leq x - 1$.

4. Every point above the line $y = x - 3$ is a solution of $y < x - 3$.

5. $(0, 0)$ is not a solution of $y > x + 4$. Therefore, the point $(0, 0)$ should not be in the shaded region that indicates the solution set of the inequality.

6. In the graph of an inequality in two variables, any point in the shaded region is a solution of the inequality, and any point not in the shaded region is not a solution of the inequality.

5.6 Exercises

1 Graph inequalities in two variables

1. In the graph of a linear inequality, what does a solid line represent? What does a dashed line represent?

2. In the graph of a linear inequality, what does the shaded portion of the graph represent?

Graph the solution set.

3. $y > 2x + 3$

4. $y > 3x - 9$

5. $y > \frac{3}{2}x - 4$

6. $y > -\frac{5}{4}x + 1$

7. $y \leq -\frac{3}{4}x - 1$

8. $y \leq -\frac{5}{2}x - 4$

9. $y \leq -\frac{6}{5}x - 2$

10. $y < \frac{4}{5}x + 3$

11. $x + y > 4$

12. $x - y > -3$

13. $2x + y \geq 4$

14. $3x + y \geq 6$

15. $y \leq -2$

16. $y > 3$

17. $2x + 2y \leq -4$

18. $-4x + 3y < -12$

19. If (0, 0) is a point on the graph of the linear inequality $Ax + By > C$, where C is not zero, is C positive or negative?

20. If $Ax + By < C$, where C is a negative number, is (0, 0) a point on the graph of this linear inequality?

5.6 Applying Concepts

Write the inequality given its graph.

21.

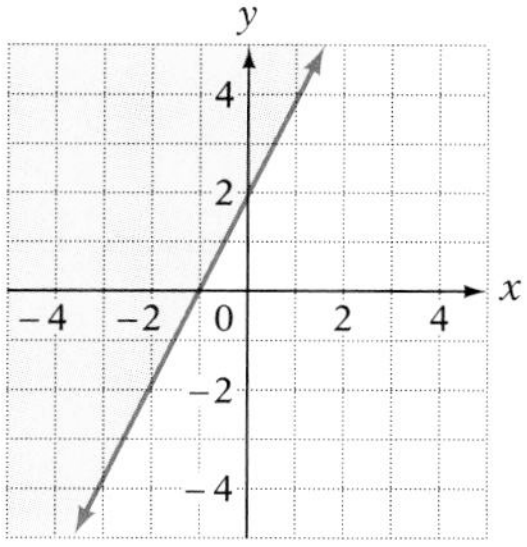

22.

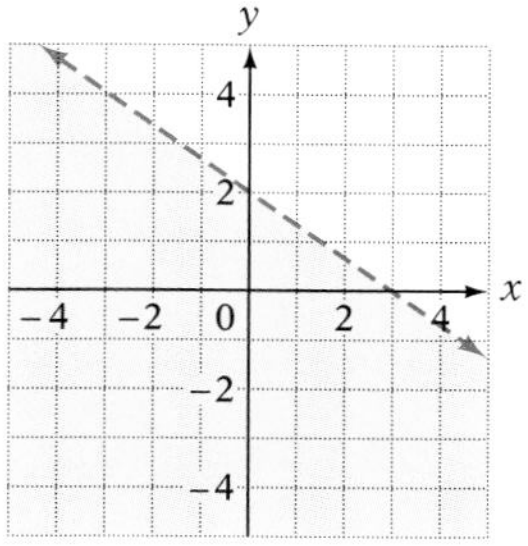

23.

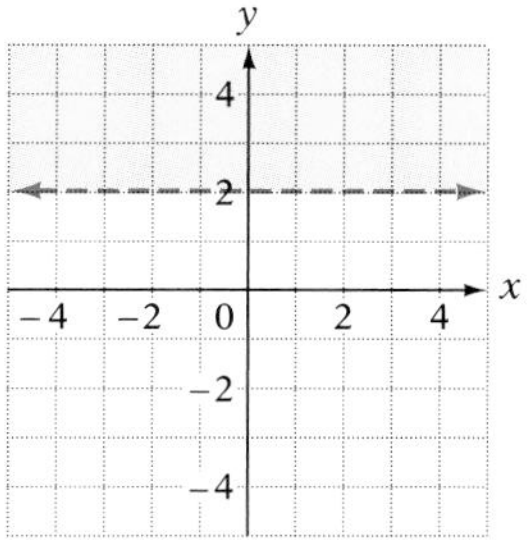

24.

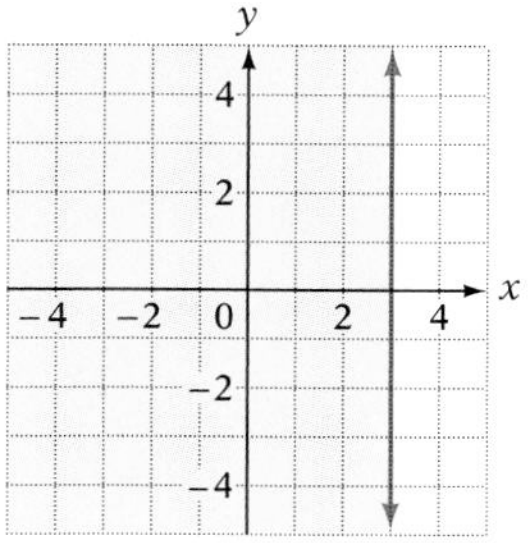

Graph the solution set.

25. $y - 5 < 4(x - 2)$

26. $y + 3 < 6(x + 1)$

27. $3x - 2(y + 1) \leq y - (5 - x)$

28. $2x - 3(y + 1) \geq y - (7 - x)$

29. Does an inequality in two variables define a relation? Why or why not? Does an inequality in two variables define a function? Why or why not?

Focus on Problem Solving

Counterexamples

Some of the exercises in this text ask you to determine whether a statement is true or false. For instance, the statement "Every real number has a reciprocal" is false because 0 is a real number and 0 does not have a reciprocal.

Finding an example, such as "0 has no reciprocal," to show that a statement is not always true is called finding a counterexample. A *counterexample* is an example that shows that a statement is not always true.

Consider the statement "The product of two numbers is greater than either factor." A counterexample to this statement is the factors $\frac{2}{3}$ and $\frac{3}{4}$. The product of these numbers is $\frac{1}{2}$, and $\frac{1}{2}$ is smaller than $\frac{2}{3}$ or $\frac{3}{4}$. There are many other counterexamples to the given statement.

Here are some counterexamples to the statement "The square of a number is always larger than the number."

$$\left(\frac{1}{2}\right)^2 = \frac{1}{4} \quad \text{but} \quad \frac{1}{4} < \frac{1}{2} \qquad 1^2 = 1 \quad \text{but} \quad 1 = 1$$

For each of the next five statements, find at least one counterexample to show that the statement, or conjecture, is false.

1. The product of two integers is always a positive number.
2. The sum of two prime numbers is never a prime number.
3. For all real numbers, $|x + y| = |x| + |y|$.

4. If x and y are nonzero real numbers and $x > y$, then $x^2 > y^2$.

5. The quotient of any two nonzero real numbers is less than either one of the numbers.

When a problem is posed, it may not be known whether the statement is true or false. For instance, Christian Goldbach (1690–1764) stated that every even integer greater than 2 can be written as the sum of two prime numbers. No one has ever been able to find a counterexample to this statement, but neither has anyone been able to prove that it is always true.

In the next five exercises, answer true if the statement is always true. If there is an instance when the statement is false, give a counterexample.

6. The reciprocal of a positive number is always smaller than the number.

7. If $x < 0$, then $|x| = -x$.

8. For any two real numbers x and y, $x + y > x - y$.

9. For any positive integer n, $n^2 + n + 17$ is a prime number.

10. The list of numbers 1, 11, 111, 1111, 11111, ... contains infinitely many composite numbers. (*Hint:* A number is divisible by 3 if the sum of the digits of the number is divisible by 3.)

Projects & Group Activities

Graphing Linear Equations with a Graphing Utility

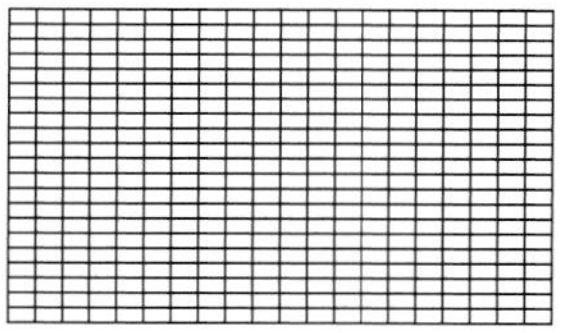

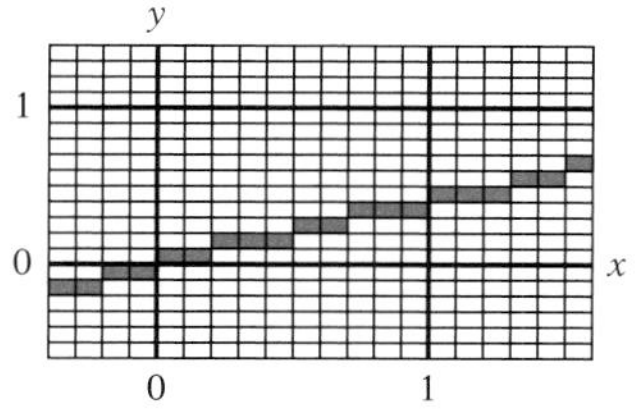

A computer or graphing calculator screen is divided into *pixels*. There are approximately 6000 to 790,000 pixels available on the screen (depending on the computer or calculator). The greater the number of pixels, the smoother a graph will appear. A portion of a screen is shown at the left. Each little rectangle represents one pixel.

The graphing utilities that are used by computers or calculators to graph an equation do basically what we have shown in the text: They choose values of x and, for each, calculate the corresponding value of y. The pixel corresponding to the ordered pair is then turned on. The graph is jagged because pixels are much larger than the dots we draw on paper.

The graph of $y = 0.45x$ is shown at the left as the calculator drew it (jagged). The x- and y-axes have been chosen so that each pixel represents $\frac{1}{10}$ of a unit. Consider the region of the graph where $x = 1$, 1.1, and 1.2.

The corresponding values of y are 0.45, 0.495, and 0.54. Because the y-axis is in tenths, the numbers 0.45, 0.495, and 0.54 are rounded to the nearest tenth before plotting. Rounding 0.45, 0.495, and 0.54 to the nearest tenth results in 0.5 for each number. Thus the ordered pairs (1, 0.45), (1.1, 0.495), and (1.2, 0.54) are graphed as (1, 0.5), (1.1, 0.5), and (1.2, 0.5). These points appear as three illuminated horizontal pixels. The graph of the line appears horizontal. However, if you use the TRACE feature of the calculator (see the Appendix), the actual y-coordinate for each value of x is displayed.

Take Note
Xmin and Xmax are the smallest and largest values of x that will be shown on the screen. Ymin and Ymax are the smallest and largest values of y that will be shown on the screen.

Here are the keystrokes to graph $y = \frac{2}{3}x + 1$. First the equation is entered. Then the domain (Xmin to Xmax) and the range (Ymin to Ymax) are entered. This is called the **viewing window.**

[Y=] [CLEAR] 2 [X, T, Θ, n] [÷] 3 [+] 1 [WINDOW] [(−)] 10 [ENTER] 10 [ENTER] 1 [ENTER] [(−)] 10 [ENTER] 10 [ENTER] 1 [ENTER] [GRAPH]

By changing the keystrokes 2 [X, T, Θ, n] [÷] 3 [+] 1, you can graph different equations.

1. $y = 2x + 1$ — For $2x$, you may enter $2 \times x$ or just $2x$. The times sign $\times$ is not necessary on many graphing calculators.

2. $y = -\frac{1}{2}x - 2$ — Use the [(−)] key to enter a negative sign.

3. $3x + 2y = 6$ — Solve for y. Then enter the equation.

4. $4x + 3y = 75$ — You must adjust the viewing window. *Suggestion:* Xmin = −25, Xmax = 25, Xscl = 5, Ymin = −35, Ymax = 35, Yscl = 5. See the Appendix for assistance.

Chapter 5 Summary

Key Words

A **rectangular coordinate system** is formed by two number lines, one horizontal and one vertical, that intersect at the zero point of each line. The number lines that make up a rectangular coordinate system are called the **coordinate axes,** or simply the **axes.** The **origin** is the point of intersection of the two coordinate axes. Generally, the horizontal axis is labeled the ***x*-axis,** and the vertical axis is labeled the ***y*-axis.** A rectangular coordinate system divides the plane determined by the axes into four regions called **quadrants.** [5.1.1, pp. 247]

Examples

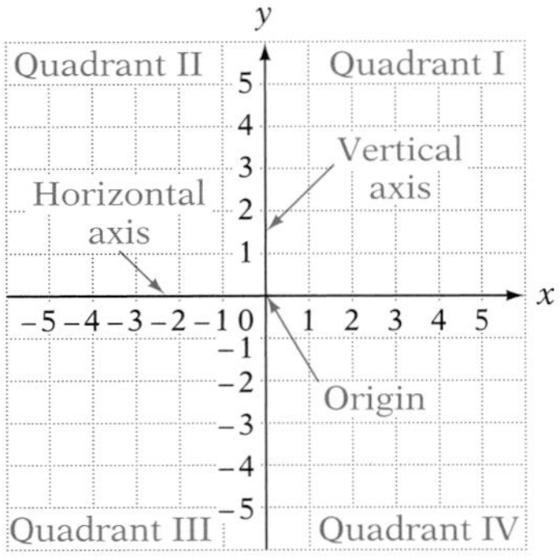

The coordinate axes determine a **plane.** Every point in the plane can be identified by an **ordered pair** (x, y). The first number in an ordered pair is called the ***x*-coordinate** or the **abscissa.** The second number is called the ***y*-coordinate** or the **ordinate.** The **coordinates** of a point are the numbers in the ordered pair associated with the point. [5.1.1, pp. 248]

The ordered pair $(4, -9)$ has x-coordinate 4 and y-coordinate -9.

An equation of the form $y = mx + b$, where m is the coefficient of x and b is a constant, is a **linear equation in two variables.** A **solution of a linear equation in two variables** is an ordered pair (x, y) that makes the equation a true statement. [5.2.1, p. 261]

$y = 2x + 3$ is an example of a linear equation in two variables. The ordered pair (1, 5) is a solution of this equation because when 1 is substituted for x and 5 is substituted for y, the result is a true equation.

The point at which a graph crosses the x-axis is called the ***x*-intercept.** At the x-intercept, the y-coordinate is 0. The point at which a graph crosses the y-axis is called the ***y*-intercept.** At the y-intercept, the x-coordinate is 0. [5.2.3, p. 267]

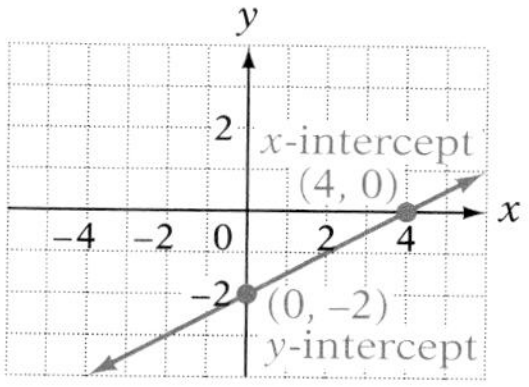

An equation of the form $Ax + By = C$ is also a **linear equation in two variables.** [5.2.3, p. 264]

$5x - 2y = 10$ is an example of an equation in $Ax + By = C$ form.

The **graph of** $y = b$ is a horizontal line with y-intercept $(0, b)$. The **graph of** $x = a$ is a vertical line with x-intercept $(a, 0)$. [5.2.3, p. 268]

The graph of $y = -3$ is a horizontal line with y-intercept $(0, -3)$. The graph of $x = 2$ is a vertical line with x-intercept $(2, 0)$.

The **slope** of a line is a measure of the slant of the line. The symbol for slope is m. A line that slants upward to the right has a **positive slope.** A line that slants downward to the right has a **negative slope.** A horizontal line has **zero slope.** The slope of a vertical line is **undefined.** [5.3.1, pp. 276–278]

For the graph of $y = 4x - 3$, $m = 4$; the slope is positive.

For the graph of $y = -6x + 1$, $m = -6$; the slope is negative.

For the graph of $y = -7$, $m = 0$; the slope is 0.

For the graph of $x = 8$, the slope is undefined.

Two lines in the rectangular coordinate system that never intersect are **parallel lines.** Parallel lines have the same slope. [5.3.1, p. 279]

The lines $y = -2x + 1$ and $y = -2x - 3$ have the same slope and different y-intercepts. The lines are parallel.

A **relation** is any set of ordered pairs. The **domain** of a relation is the set of first coordinates of the ordered pairs. The **range** is the set of second coordinates of the ordered pairs. [5.5.1, p. 298]

For the relation $\{(-2, -5), (0, -3), (4, -1)\}$, the domain is $\{-2, 0, 4\}$ and the range is $\{-5, -3, -1\}$.

A **function** is a relation in which no two ordered pairs have the same first coordinate and different second coordinates. [5.5.1, p. 298]

$\{(-2, -5), (0, -3), (4, -1)\}$ is a function. $\{(-2, -5), (-2, -3), (4, -1)\}$ is not a function because two ordered pairs have the same x-coordinate, -2, and different y-coordinates.

A function of the form $f(x) = mx + b$ is a **linear function.** Its graph is a straight line. [5.5.2, p. 301]

$f(x) = -3x + 8$ is an example of a linear function.

The solution set of a linear inequality in two variables is a **half-plane.** [5.6.1, p. 310]

The solution set of $y > x - 2$ is all points above the line $y = x - 2$. The solution set of $y < x - 2$ is all points below the line $y = x - 2$.

Essential Rules and Procedures

Average Rate of Change
The average rate of change of y with respect to x is $\frac{\text{change in } y}{\text{change in } x}$. [5.1.3, p. 252]

The average U.S. household income in 1980 was $41,910, whereas in 2000 it was $57,045. (*Source:* U.S. Census Bureau; adjusted for inflation and given in 2000 dollars)

$$\frac{57{,}045 - 41{,}910}{2000 - 1980} = 756.75$$

The average annual rate of change in household income from 1980 to 2000 was $756.75.

To find the *x*-intercept, let $y = 0$.
To find the *y*-intercept, let $x = 0$. [5.2.3, p. 267]

To find the x-intercept of $4x - 3y = 12$, let $y = 0$. To find the y-intercept, let $x = 0$.

$$\begin{aligned} 4x - 3y &= 12 \\ 4x - 3(0) &= 12 \\ 4x - 0 &= 12 \\ 4x &= 12 \\ x &= 3 \end{aligned} \qquad \begin{aligned} 4x - 3y &= 12 \\ 4(0) - 3y &= 12 \\ 0 - 3y &= 12 \\ -3y &= 12 \\ y &= -4 \end{aligned}$$

The x-intercept is (3, 0). The y-intercept is (0, −4).

Slope of a Linear Equation
Slope $= m = \frac{y_2 - y_1}{x_2 - x_1}$, $x_2 \neq x_1$ [5.3.1, p. 276]

To find the slope of the line between the points (2, −3) and (−1, 6), let $P_1 = (2, -3)$ and $P_2 = (-1, 6)$. Then $(x_1, y_1) = (2, -3)$ and $(x_2, y_2) = (-1, 6)$.

$$m = \frac{y_2 - y_1}{x_2 - x_1} = \frac{6 - (-3)}{-1 - 2} = \frac{9}{-3} = -3$$

Slope-Intercept Form of a Linear Equation
$y = mx + b$ [5.3.2, p. 281]

For the equation $y = -4x + 7$, the slope $= m = -4$ and the y-intercept $= (0, b) = (0, 7)$.

Point-Slope Formula
$y - y_1 = m(x - x_1)$ [5.4.2, p. 289]

To find the equation of the line that contains the point (6, −1) and has slope 2, let $(x_1, y_1) = (6, -1)$ and $m = 2$.

$$\begin{aligned} y - y_1 &= m(x - x_1) \\ y - (-1) &= 2(x - 6) \\ y + 1 &= 2x - 12 \\ y &= 2x - 13 \end{aligned}$$

Chapter 5 Review Exercises

1. Find the ordered-pair solution of $y = -\frac{2}{3}x + 2$ that corresponds to $x = 3$.

2. Find the equation of the line that contains the point whose coordinates are $(0, -1)$ and has slope 3.

3. Graph: $x = -3$

4. Graph the ordered pairs $(-3, 1)$ and $(0, 2)$.

5. Evaluate $f(x) = 3x^2 + 4$ at $x = -5$.

6. Find the slope of the line that contains the points whose coordinates are $(3, -4)$ and $(1, -4)$.

7. Graph: $y = 3x + 1$

8. Graph: $3x - 2y = 6$

9. Find the equation of the line that contains the point whose coordinates are $(-1, 2)$ and has slope $-\frac{2}{3}$.

10. Find the x- and y-intercepts for $6x - 4y = 12$.

11. Graph the line that has slope $\frac{1}{2}$ and y-intercept $(0, -1)$.

12. Graph: $f(x) = -\frac{2}{3}x + 4$

13. Find the equation of the line that contains the point whose coordinates are $(-3, 1)$ and has slope $\frac{2}{3}$.

14. Find the slope of the line that contains the points whose coordinates are $(2, -3)$ and $(4, 1)$.

15. Evaluate $f(x) = \frac{3}{5}x + 2$ at $x = -10$.

16. Find the domain and range of the relation $\{(-20, -10), (-10, -5), (0, 0), (10, 5)\}$. Is the relation a function?

17. Graph: $y = -\frac{3}{4}x + 3$

18. Graph the line that has slope 2 and y-intercept $(0, -2)$.

19. Graph the ordered pairs $(-2, -3)$ and $(2, 4)$.

20. Graph: $f(x) = 5x + 1$

21. Find the x- and y-intercepts for $2x - 3y = 12$.

22. Find the equation of the line that contains the point whose coordinates are $(-1, 0)$ and has slope 2.

23. Graph: $y = 3$

24. Graph the solution set of $3x + 2y \le 12$.

25. Is the line containing the points $(-2, 1)$ and $(3, 5)$ parallel to the line that contains the points $(4, -5)$ and $(9, -1)$?

26. Find the equation of the line through the points whose coordinates are $(4, 14)$ and $(-8, -1)$.

27. Graph the line that has slope -1 and y-intercept $(0, 2)$.

28. Graph: $2x - 3y = 6$

29. Find the ordered-pair solution of $y = 2x - 1$ that corresponds to $x = -2$.

30. Find the equation of the line that contains the point $(0, 2)$ and has slope -3.

31. Graph: $f(x) = 2x$

32. Evaluate $f(x) = 3x - 5$ at $x = \frac{5}{3}$.

33. Find the equation of the line through the points whose coordinates are $(-6, 0)$ and $(3, -3)$.

34. Find the equation of the line that contains the point whose coordinates are $(2, -1)$ and has slope $\frac{1}{2}$.

35. Is $(-10, 0)$ a solution of $y = \frac{1}{5}x + 2$?

36. Find the ordered-pair solution of $y = 4x - 9$ that corresponds to $x = 2$.

37. Find the x- and y-intercepts for $4x - 3y = 0$.

38. Find the equation of the line that contains the point whose coordinates are $(-2, 3)$ and has zero slope.

39. Graph the solution set of $6x - y > 6$.

40. Graph the line that has slope -3 and y-intercept $(0, 1)$.

41. Find the equation of the line that contains the point whose coordinates are $(0, -4)$ and has slope 3.

42. Graph: $x + 2y = -4$

43. Find the domain and range of the relation $\{(-10, -5), (-5, 0), (5, 0), (-10, 0)\}$. Is the relation a function?

44. Find the range of the function given by the equation $f(x) = 3x + 7$ if the domain is $\{-20, -10, 0, 10, 20\}$.

45. Find the range of the function given by the equation $f(x) = \frac{1}{3}x + 4$ if the domain is $\{-6, -3, 0, 3, 6\}$.

46. **Life Expectancy** The table below shows the average number of years women and men were predicted to live beyond age 65 in 1950, 1960, 1970, 1980, 1990, and 2000. (*Source:* 2000 Social Security Trustees Report) Figures are rounded to the nearest whole number. Graph the scatter diagram for these data.

Women, x	15	16	17	18	19	19
Men, y	13	13	13	14	15	16

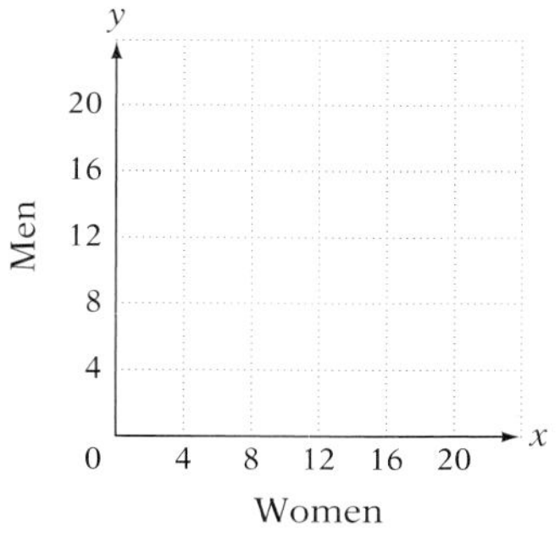

47. **Airline Industry** The major airlines routinely overbook flights, but generally passengers voluntarily give up their seats when offered free airline tickets as compensation. The table below gives the number of passengers who voluntarily gave up their seats and the number who involuntarily gave up their seats during a five-year period. Numbers are rounded to the nearest ten thousand. (*Source:* USA TODAY analysis of Department of Transportation data) Graph the scatter diagram for these data.

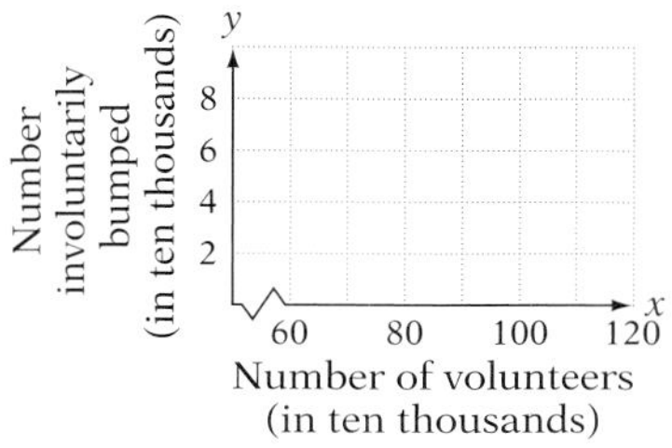

Number of volunteers, in ten thousands, x	60	77	79	90	102
Number involuntarily bumped, in ten thousands, y	4	5	5	6	5

48. **Automobile Tires** The following table shows the tread depth, in millimeters, of a tire and the number of miles, in thousands, that have been driven on that tire.

Miles driven	25	35	40	20	45
Tread depth	4.8	3.5	2.1	5.5	1.0

Write a relation in which the first coordinate is the number of miles driven and the second coordinate is the tread depth. Is the relation a function?

49. **Building Contractors** A contractor uses the equation $C = 70s + 40{,}000$ to estimate the cost of building a new house. In this equation, C is the total cost, in dollars, and s is the number of square feet in the home.

a. Write the equation in functional notation.

b. Use the coordinate axes at the right to graph the equation for values of s between 0 and 5000.

c. The point (1500, 145,000) is on the graph. Write a sentence that explains the meaning of this ordered pair.

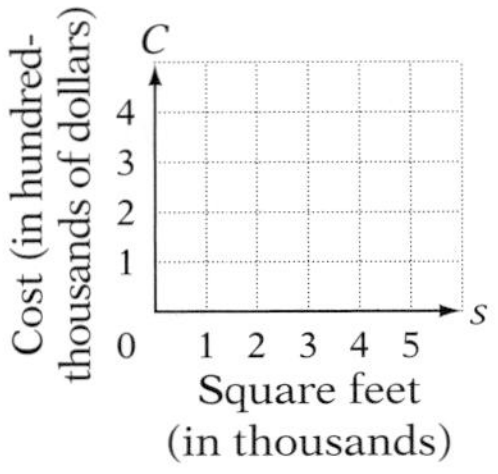

50. **Hourly Wages** The average hourly wage of a U.S. worker in 1996 was \$11.90. In 2005, the average hourly wage was \$16.00. (*Source:* Federal Reserve Bank of St. Louis) Find the average annual rate of change in the average hourly wage from 1996 to 2005. Round to the nearest cent.

Chapter 5 Test

1. Find the equation of the line that contains the point whose coordinates are $(9, -3)$ and has slope $-\frac{1}{3}$.

2. Find the slope of the line that contains the points whose coordinates are $(9, 8)$ and $(-2, 1)$.

3. Find the x- and y-intercepts for $3x - 2y = 24$.

4. Find the ordered-pair solution of $y = -\frac{4}{3}x - 1$ that corresponds to $x = 9$.

5. Graph: $5x + 3y = 15$

6. Graph: $y = \frac{1}{4}x + 3$

7. Evaluate $f(x) = 4x + 7$ at $x = \frac{3}{4}$.

8. Is $(6, 3)$ a solution of $y = \frac{2}{3}x + 1$?

9. Graph the line that has slope $-\frac{2}{3}$ and y-intercept $(0, 4)$.

10. Graph the solution set of $2x - y \geq 2$.

11. Graph the ordered pairs $(3, -2)$ and $(0, 4)$.

12. Graph the line that has slope 2 and y-intercept $(0, -4)$.

13. Find the equation of the line through the points whose coordinates are $(-5, 5)$ and $(10, 14)$.

14. Find the equation of the line that contains the point whose coordinates are $(0, 7)$ and has slope $-\frac{2}{5}$.

15. Find the equation of the line that contains the point whose coordinates are $(2, 1)$ and has slope 4.

16. Evaluate $f(x) = 4x^2 - 3$ at $x = -2$.

17. Graph: $y = -2x - 1$

18. Graph the solution set of $y > 2$.

19. Graph: $x = 4$

20. Graph the line that has slope $\frac{1}{2}$ and y-intercept $(0, -3)$.

21. Graph: $f(x) = -\frac{2}{3}x + 2$

22. Graph: $f(x) = -5x$

23. Evaluate $f(x) = -3x + 7$ at $x = -6$.

24. Find the range of the function given by the equation $f(x) = -3x + 5$ if the domain is $\{-7, -2, 0, 4, 9\}$.

25. Is the line containing the points $(-3, -2)$ and $(6, 0)$ parallel to the line that contains the points $(6, -4)$ and $(3, 2)$?

26. **Drivers** Drivers over age 70 number about 18 million today, up from about 13 million ten years ago. (*Source:* National Highway Traffic Safety Administration) Find the average annual rate of change in the number of drivers over age 70 for the past decade.

27. **Fire Science** The distance, in miles, a house is from a fire station and the amount, in thousands of dollars, of fire damage that house sustained in a fire are given in the following table. Graph the scatter diagram for these data.

Distance (in miles), x	3.5	4.0	5.5	6.0
Damage (in thousands of dollars), y	25	30	40	35

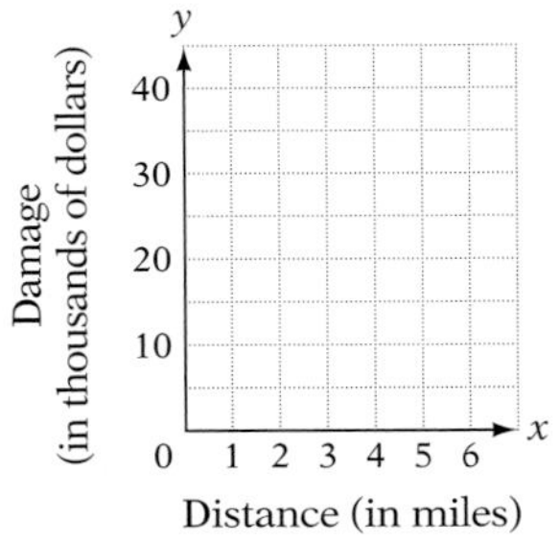

28. **Manufacturing** A company that manufactures toasters has fixed costs of \$1000 each month. The manufacturing cost per toaster is \$8. An equation that represents the total cost to manufacture the toasters is $C = 8t + 1000$, where C is the total cost, in dollars, and t is the number of toasters manufactured each month.

a. Write the equation in functional notation.

b. Use the coordinate axes at the right to graph the equation for values of t between 0 and 500.

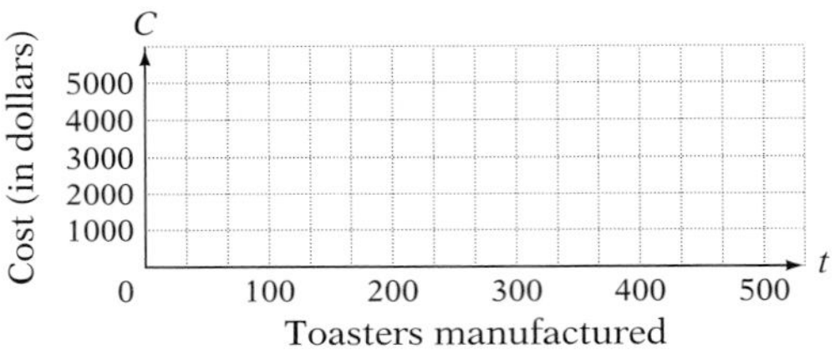

c. The point (340, 3720) is on the graph. Write a sentence that explains the meaning of this ordered pair.

29. **Test Scores** The data in the following table show a reading test grade and the final exam grade in a history class.

Reading test grade	8.5	9.4	10.1	11.4	12.0
History exam	64	68	76	87	92

Write a relation in which the first coordinate is the reading test grade and the second coordinate is the score on the history final exam. Is the relation a function?

30. **Lumber** The graph at the right shows the cost, in dollars, per 1000 board feet of lumber over a six-month period. Find the slope of the line. Write a sentence that states the meaning of the slope.

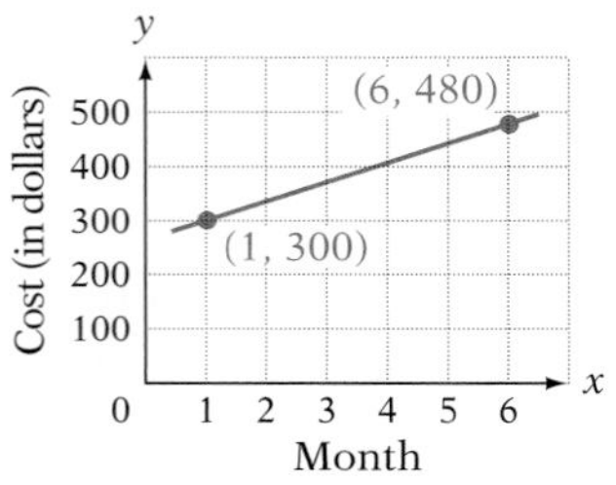

Cumulative Review Exercises

1. Simplify: $12 - 18 \div 3 \cdot (-2)^2$

2. Evaluate $\frac{a - b}{a^2 - c}$ when $a = -2$, $b = 3$, and $c = -4$.

3. Simplify: $4(2 - 3x) - 5(x - 4)$

4. Solve: $2x - \frac{2}{3} = \frac{7}{3}$

5. Solve: $3x - 2[x - 3(2 - 3x)] = x - 6$

6. Write $6\frac{2}{3}\%$ as a fraction.

7. Use the roster method to write the set of natural numbers less than 9.

8. Given $D = \{-23, -18, -4, 0, 5\}$, which elements of set D are greater than -16?

9. Solve: $8a - 3 \geq 5a - 6$

10. Solve $4x - 5y = 15$ for y.

11. Find the ordered-pair solution of $y = 3x - 1$ that corresponds to $x = -2$.

12. Find the slope of the line that contains the points whose coordinates are $(2, 3)$ and $(-2, 3)$.

13. Find the x- and y-intercepts for $5x + 2y = 20$.

14. Find the equation of the line that contains the point whose coordinates are $(3, 2)$ and has slope -1.

15. Graph: $y = \frac{1}{2}x + 2$

16. Graph: $3x + y = 2$

17. Graph: $f(x) = -4x - 1$

18. Graph the solution set of $x - y \leq 5$.

19. Find the domain and range of the relation $\{(0, 4), (1, 3), (2, 2), (3, 1), (4, 0)\}$. Is the relation a function?

20. Evaluate $f(x) = -4x + 9$ at $x = 5$.

21. Find the range of the function given by the equation $f(x) = -\frac{5}{3}x + 3$ if the domain is $\{-9, -6, -3, 0, 3, 6\}$.

22. **Integer Problem** The sum of two numbers is 24. Twice the smaller number is three less than the larger number. Find the two numbers.

23. **Lever Systems** A lever is 8 ft long. A force of 80 lb is applied to one end of the lever, and a force of 560 lb is applied to the other end. Where is the fulcrum located when the system balances? The lever-system equation is $F_1x = F_2(d - x)$.

24. **Geometry** The perimeter of a triangle is 49 ft. The length of the first side is twice the length of the third side, and the length of the second side is 5 ft more than the length of the third side. Find the length of the first side.

25. **Discount** A suit that regularly sells for \$89 is on sale for 30% off the regular price. Find the sale price.

CHAPTER

6 Systems of Linear Equations

OBJECTIVES

6.1 1 Solve systems of linear equations by graphing

6.2 1 Solve systems of linear equations by the substitution method

6.3 1 Solve systems of linear equations by the addition method

6.4 1 Rate-of-wind and water-current problems
 2 Application problems

Have you ever noticed that your flight in one direction seems longer than your flight in the other direction? Recall from Section 3.1 that if a boat is traveling with the current, the effective speed of the boat is increased. When the boat is traveling against the current, the current slows the boat down. The same is true for airplanes and the wind. If the plane is flying against a headwind, the wind will slow the plane down. In **Exercises 6, 10, 11, and 13 on page 354,** you will use systems of equations to determine the rates of planes in calm air and rates of the wind.

DVD SSM *Online Study Center*

Need help? For online student resources, such as section quizzes, visit the Online Study Center at college.hmco.com/pic/aufmannBAWA7e.

Prep Test

1. Solve $3x - 4y = 24$ for y.
2. Solve: $50 + 0.07x = 0.05(x + 1400)$
3. Simplify: $-3(2x - 7y) + 3(2x + 4y)$
4. Simplify: $4x + 2(3x - 5)$
5. Is $(-4, 2)$ a solution of $3x - 5y = -22$?
6. Find the x- and y-intercepts of $3x - 4y = 12$.
7. Are the graphs of $y = -3x + 6$ and $y = -3x - 4$ parallel?
8. Graph: $y = \frac{5}{4}x - 2$
9. One hiker starts along a trail walking at a speed of 3 mph. One-half hour later, another hiker starts on the same trail walking at a speed of 4 mph. How long after the second hiker starts will the two hikers be side by side?

6.1 Solving Systems of Linear Equations by Graphing

OBJECTIVE 1 Solve systems of linear equations by graphing

Equations considered together are called a **system of equations.** A system of equations is shown at the right.

$$2x + y = 3$$
$$x + y = 1$$

A solution of a system of linear equations can be found by graphing the lines of the system on the same coordinate axes. Three examples of **systems of linear equations in two variables** are shown on the next page, along with the graphs of the equations of each system.

> ### Take Note
> The systems of equations at the right are *systems of linear equations* because the graph of each of the equations in the system is a line. Also, each equation has two variables. In future math courses, you will study equations that contain more than two variables.

System I

$x - 2y = -8$
$2x + 5y = 11$

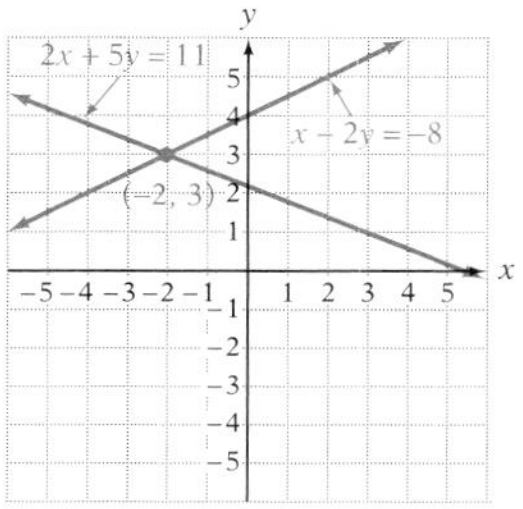

System II

$4x + 2y = 6$
$y = -2x + 3$

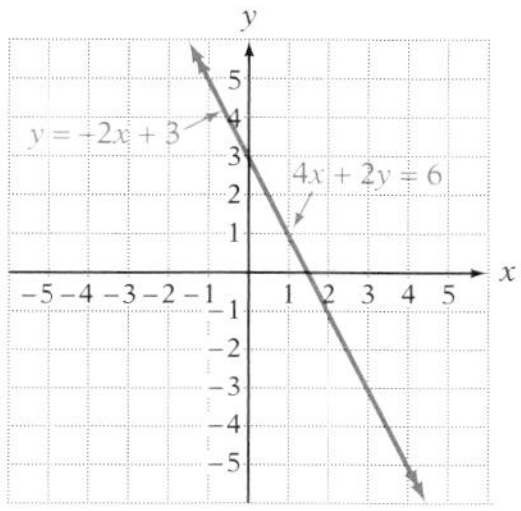

System III

$4x + 6y = 12$
$6x + 9y = -9$

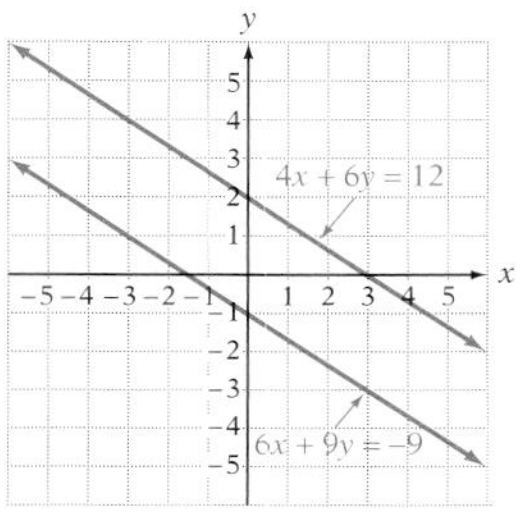

For System I, the two lines intersect at a single point whose coordinates are $(-2, 3)$. Because this point lies on both lines, it is a solution of each equation of the system of equations. We can check this by replacing x by -2 and y by 3 in each equation. The check is shown below.

$x - 2y = -8$		$2x + 5y = 11$	
$-2 - 2(3)$	-8	$2(-2) + 5(3)$	11
$-2 - 6$	-8	$-4 + 15$	11
$-8 = -8$ ✓		$11 = 11$ ✓	

• **Replace *x* by −2 and *y* by 3.**

A **solution of a system of equations in two variables** is an ordered pair that is a solution of each equation of the system. The ordered pair $(-2, 3)$ is a solution of System I.

Is $(-1, 4)$ a solution of the following system of equations?

$7x + 3y = 5$
$3x - 2y = 12$

$7x + 3y = 5$		$3x - 2y = 12$	
$7(-1) + 3(4)$	5	$3(-1) - 2(4)$	12
$-7 + 12$	5	$-3 - 8$	12
$5 = 5$ ✓		$-11 \neq 12$	Does not check.

• **Replace *x* by −1 and *y* by 4.**

Using the system of equations above and the graph at the right, note that the graph of the ordered pair $(-1, 4)$ lies on the graph of $7x + 3y = 5$ but *not on both lines*. The ordered pair $(-1, 4)$ is *not* a solution of the system of equations. The ordered pair $(2, -3)$, however, does lie on both lines and therefore is a solution of the system of equations.

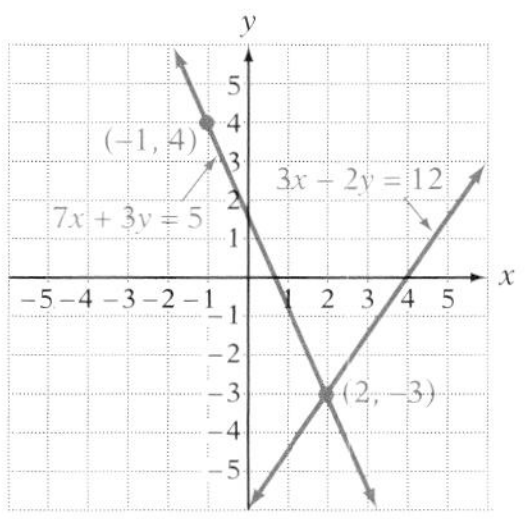

EXAMPLE 1 Is $(1, -3)$ a solution of the system $3x + 2y = -3$
$x - 3y = 6$?

Solution

$3x + 2y = -3$		$x - 3y = 6$	
$3 \cdot 1 + 2(-3)$	-3	$1 - 3(-3)$	6
$3 + (-6)$	-3	$1 - (-9)$	6
$-3 = -3$		$10 \neq 6$	

No, $(1, -3)$ is not a solution of the system of equations.

PROBLEM 1 Is $(-1, -2)$ a solution of the system $2x - 5y = 8$
$-x + 3y = -5$?

Solution See page S14.

> **Take Note**
> The fact that there are an infinite number of ordered pairs that are solutions of the system of equations at the right does not mean that *every* ordered pair is a solution. For instance, $(0, 3)$, $(-2, 7)$, and $(2, -1)$ are solutions. However, $(3, 1)$, $(-1, 4)$, and $(1, 6)$ are not solutions. You should verify these statements.

System II from the preceding page and the graph of the equations of that system are shown again at the right. Note that the graph of $y = -2x + 3$ lies directly on top of the graph of $4x + 2y = 6$. Thus the two lines intersect at an infinite number of points. Because the graphs intersect at an infinite number of points, there are an infinite number of solutions of this system of equations. Since each equation represents the same set of points, the solutions of the system of equations can be stated by using the ordered pairs of either one of the equations. Therefore, we can say "The solutions are the ordered pairs that satisfy $4x + 2y = 6$," or we can say "The solutions are the ordered pairs that satisfy $y = -2x + 3$."

$$4x + 2y = 6$$
$$y = -2x + 3$$

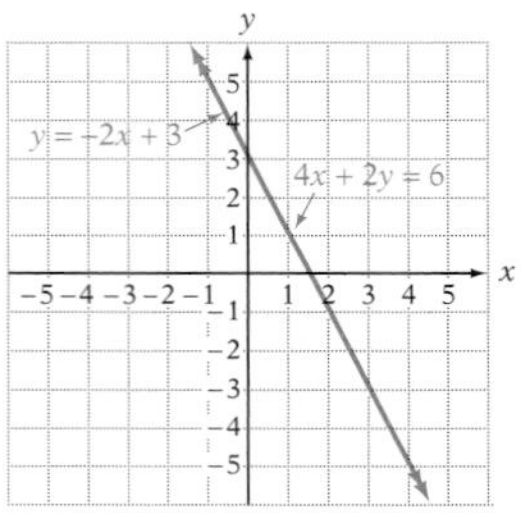

System III from the previous page and the graph of the equations of that system are shown again at the right. Note that in this case the graphs of the lines are parallel and do not intersect. Since the graphs do not intersect, there is no point that is on both lines. Therefore, the system of equations has no solution.

$$4x + 6y = 12$$
$$6x + 9y = -9$$

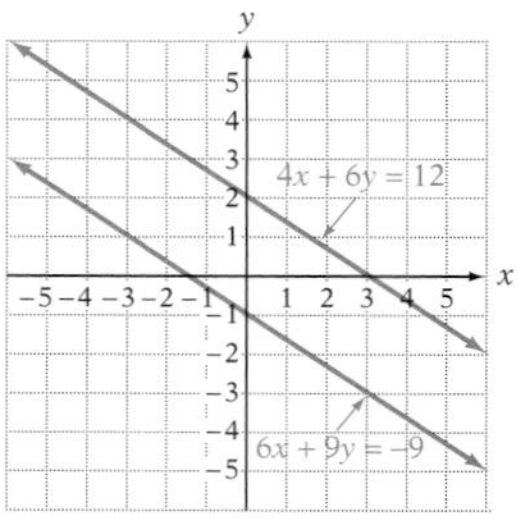

For a system of linear equations in two variables, the graphs can intersect at one point, the graphs can intersect at infinitely many points (the graphs are the same line), or the lines can be parallel and never intersect. Such systems are called **independent, dependent,** and **inconsistent,** respectively.

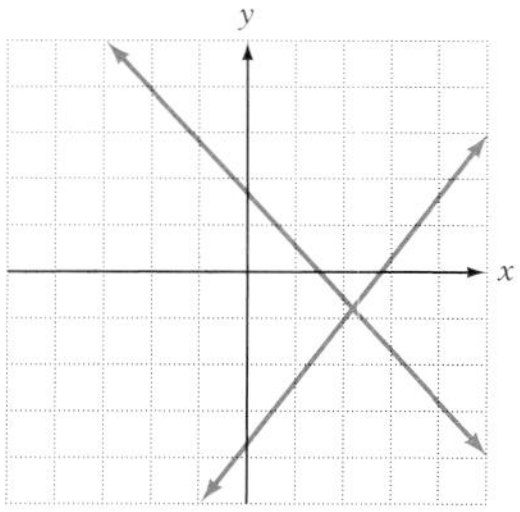

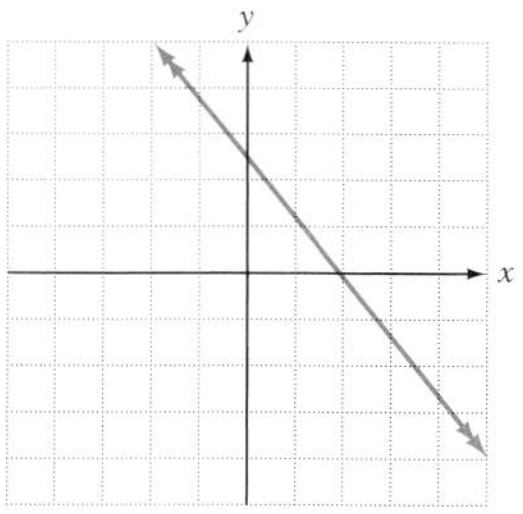

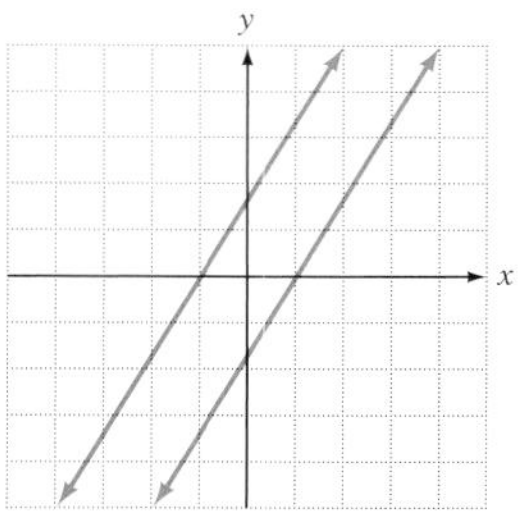

Independent
One solution

Dependent
Infinitely many solutions

Inconsistent
No solutions

Solving a system of equations means finding the ordered-pair solutions of the system. One way to do this is to draw the graphs of the equations in the system and determine where the graphs intersect.

Solve by graphing: $2x + 3y = 6$
$2x + y = -2$

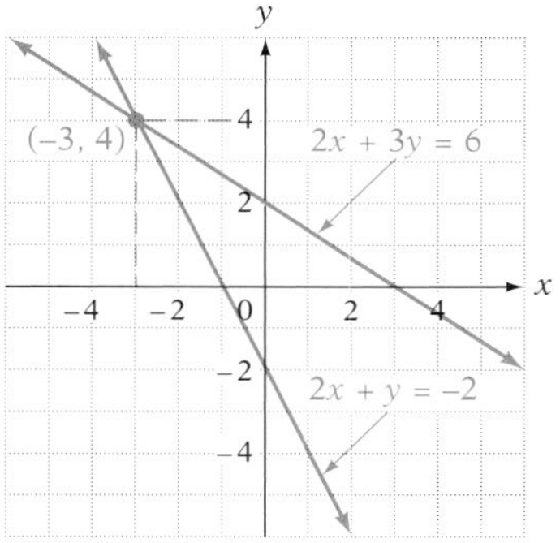

Graph each line.

The graphs of the equations intersect at one point.

The system of equations is independent.

Find the point of intersection.

The solution is $(-3, 4)$.

The INTERSECT feature on a graphing calculator can be used to find the solution of the system of equations given above. However, if this feature is used to estimate the solution, the estimated solution might be $(-3.03, 4.05)$ or some other ordered pair that contains decimals. When these values are rounded to the nearest integer, the ordered pair becomes $(-3, 4)$, which is the solution of the system. This solution can be verified by replacing x by -3 and y by 4 in the system of equations.

Solve by graphing: $2x - y = 1$
$6x - 3y = 12$

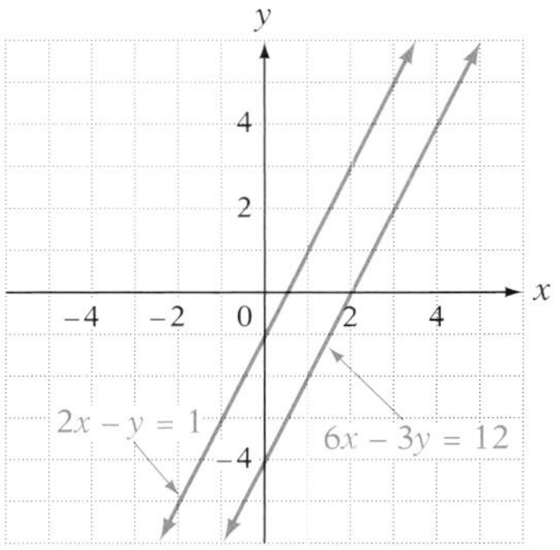

Graph each line.

The lines are parallel and therefore do not intersect.

The system of equations is inconsistent and has no solution.

Solve by graphing: $2x + 3y = 6$
$6x + 9y = 18$

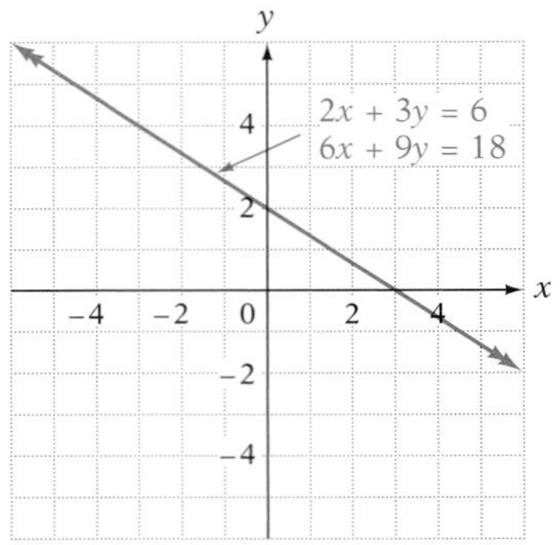

Graph each line.

The two equations represent the same line. The system of equations is dependent and, therefore, has an infinite number of solutions.

The solutions are the ordered pairs that are solutions of the equation $2x + 3y = 6$.

By choosing values for x, substituting these values into the equation $2x + 3y = 6$, and finding the corresponding values for y, we can find some specific ordered-pair solutions. For example, $(3, 0)$, $(0, 2)$, and $(6, -2)$ are solutions of this system of equations.

EXAMPLE 2 Solve by graphing. **A.** $x - 2y = 2$, $x + y = 5$ **B.** $4x - 2y = 6$, $y = 2x - 3$

Solution **A.**

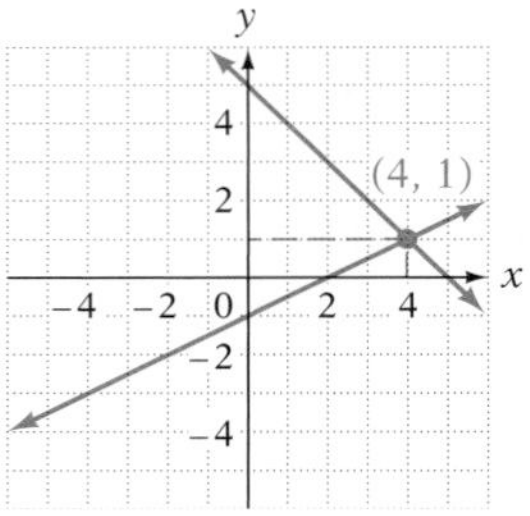

The solution is (4, 1).

B.

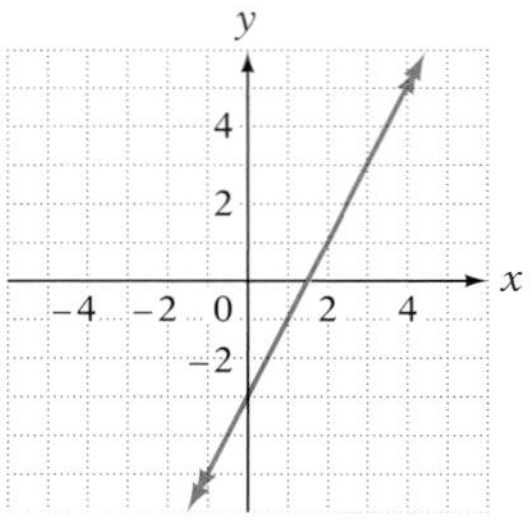

The system of equations is dependent. The solutions are the ordered pairs that satisfy the equation $y = 2x - 3$.

PROBLEM 2 Solve by graphing. **A.** $x + 3y = 3$, $-x + y = 5$ **B.** $y = 3x - 1$, $6x - 2y = -6$

Solution See page S14.

6.1 Concept Review

Determine whether the statement is always true, sometimes true, or never true.

1. A solution of a system of linear equations in two variables is an ordered pair (x, y).

2. Graphically, the solution of an independent system of linear equations in two variables is the point of intersection of the graphs of the two equations.

3. Suppose an ordered pair is a solution of one equation in a system of linear equations and not of the other equation. Then the system has no solution.

4. A system of linear equations has either one solution, represented graphically by two lines intersecting at exactly one point, or no solutions, represented graphically by two parallel lines.

5. The system of two linear equations graphed at the right has no solution.

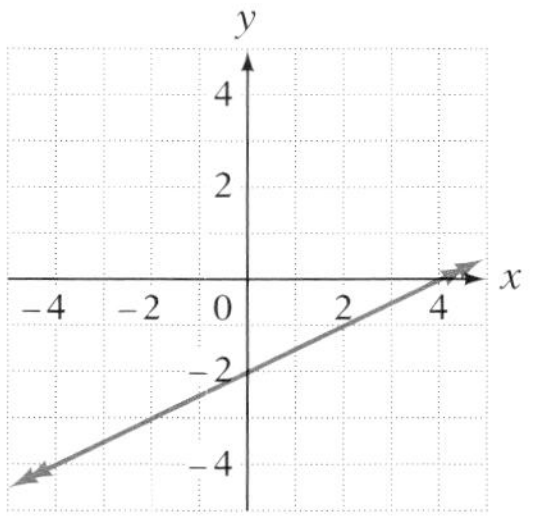

6. An independent system of equations has no solution.

6.1 Exercises

1 Solve systems of linear equations by graphing

1. What is a system of equations?

2. How can you determine whether an ordered pair is a solution of a system of equations in two variables?

3. Is (2, 3) a solution of the system $\begin{aligned} 3x + 4y &= 18 \\ 2x - y &= 1? \end{aligned}$

4. Is (2, −1) a solution of the system $\begin{aligned} x - 2y &= 4 \\ 2x + y &= 3? \end{aligned}$

5. Is (1, −2) a solution of the system
$$\begin{aligned} 3x - y &= 5 \\ 2x + 5y &= -8? \end{aligned}$$

6. Is (−1, −1) a solution of the system
$$\begin{aligned} x - 4y &= 3 \\ 3x + y &= 2? \end{aligned}$$

7. Is (4, 3) a solution of the system $\begin{aligned} 5x - 2y &= 14 \\ x + y &= 8? \end{aligned}$

8. Is (2, 5) a solution of the system $\begin{aligned} 3x + 2y &= 16 \\ 2x - 3y &= 4? \end{aligned}$

9. Is (−1, 3) a solution of the system $\begin{aligned} 4x - y &= -5 \\ 2x + 5y &= 13? \end{aligned}$

10. Is (4, −1) a solution of the system
$$\begin{aligned} x - 4y &= 9 \\ 2x - 3y &= 11? \end{aligned}$$

11. Is (0, 0) a solution of the system $\begin{aligned} 4x + 3y &= 0 \\ 2x - y &= 1? \end{aligned}$

12. Is (2, 0) a solution of the system $\begin{aligned} 3x - y &= 6 \\ x + 3y &= 2? \end{aligned}$

13. Is (2, −3) a solution of the system
$$\begin{aligned} y &= 2x - 7 \\ 3x - y &= 9? \end{aligned}$$

14. Is (−1, −2) a solution of the system
$$\begin{aligned} 3x - 4y &= 5 \\ y &= x - 1? \end{aligned}$$

15. Is (5, 2) a solution of the system $\begin{aligned} y &= 2x - 8 \\ y &= 3x - 13? \end{aligned}$

16. Is (−4, 3) a solution of the system
$$\begin{aligned} y &= 2x + 11 \\ y &= 5x - 19? \end{aligned}$$

17. Explain how to solve a system of two equations in two variables by graphing.

18. An independent system of equations has ___?___ solution(s), an inconsistent system of equations has ___?___ solution(s), and a dependent system of equations has ___?___ solution(s).

For Exercises 19 to 24, state whether the system of equations is independent, inconsistent, or dependent.

19.

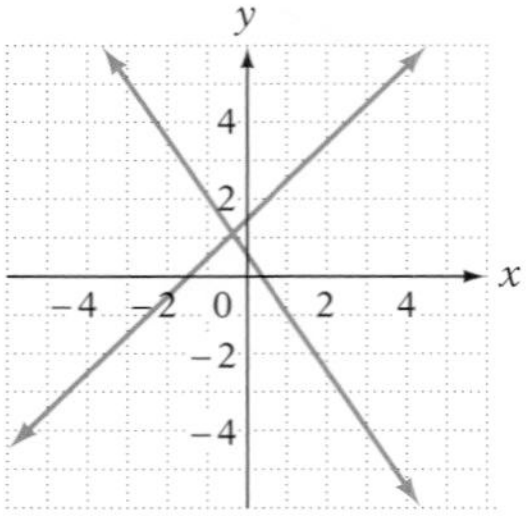

20.

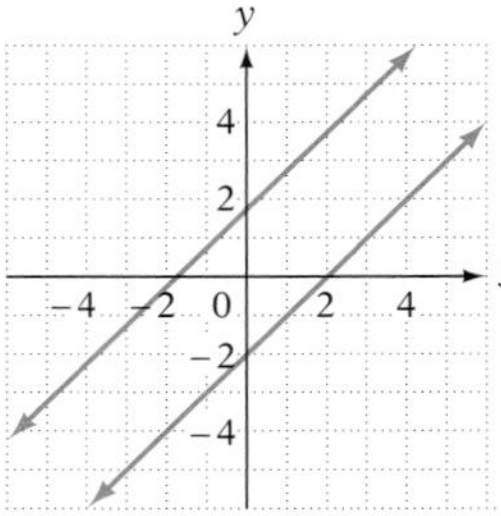

21.

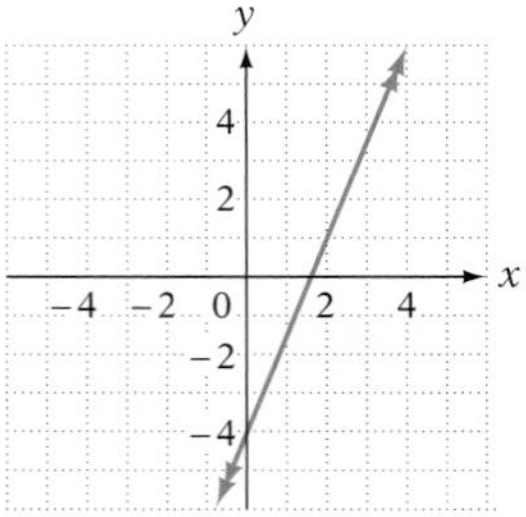

22.

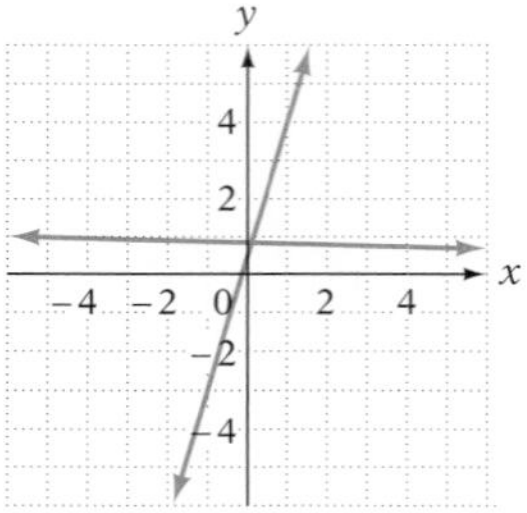

23.

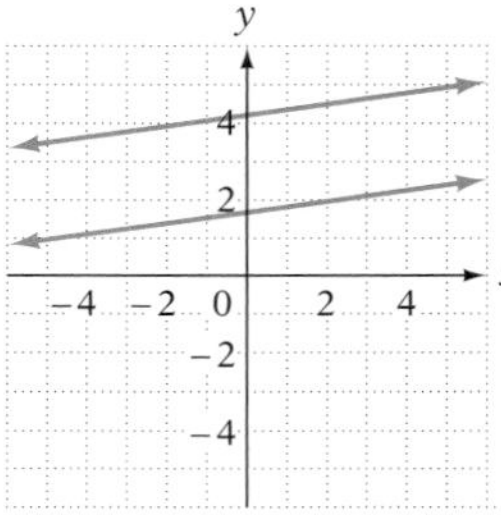

24.

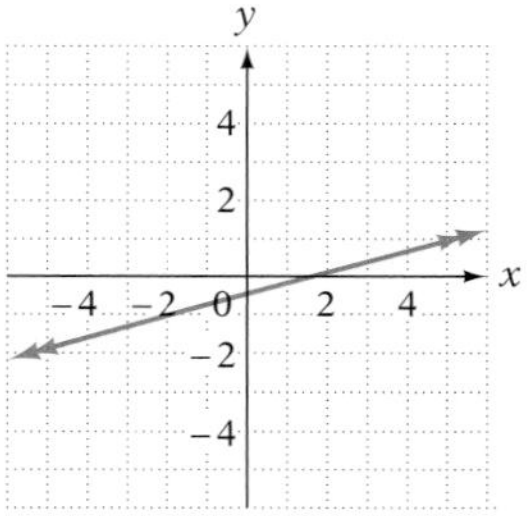

For Exercises 25 to 30, use the graph of the equations in the system to determine the solution of the system of equations.

25.

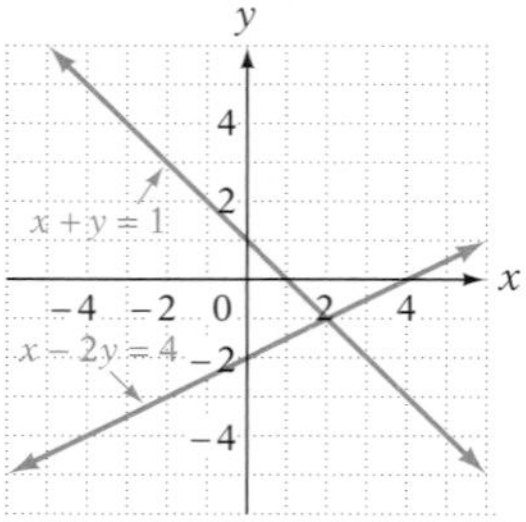

26.

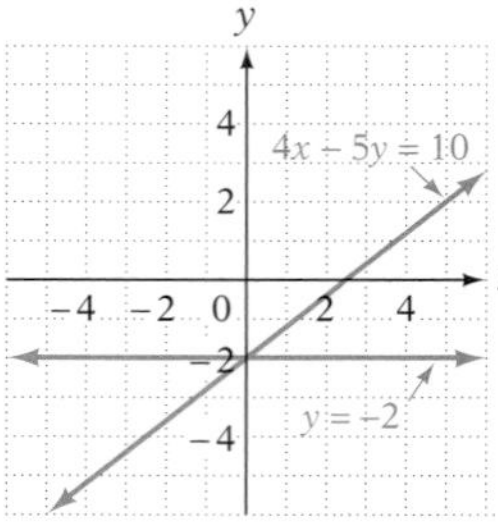

27.

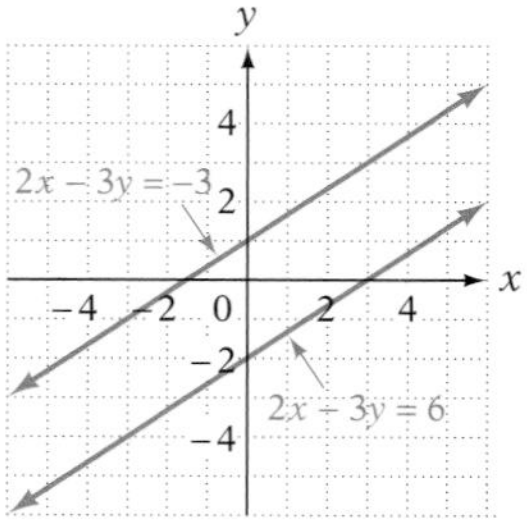

28.

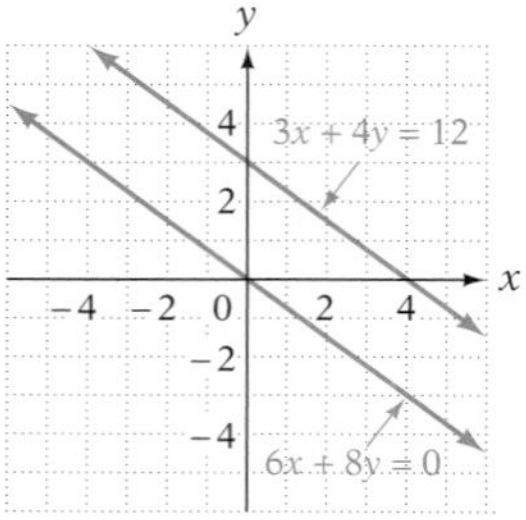

29.

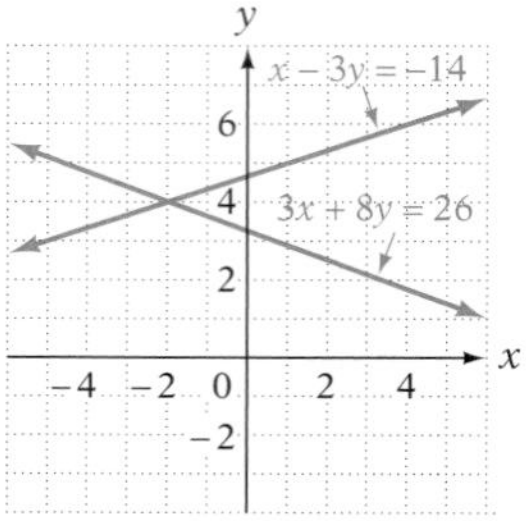

30.

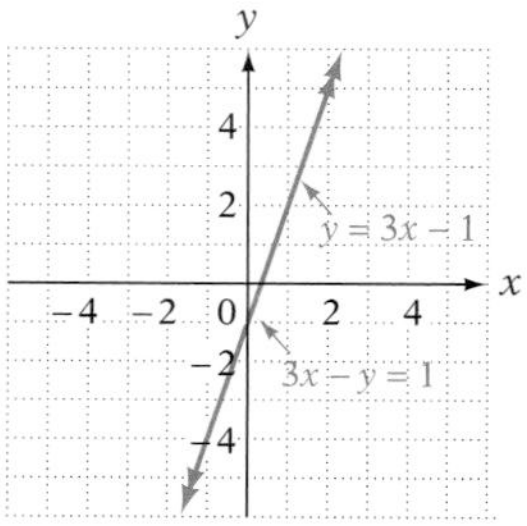

Solve by graphing.

31. $x - y = 3$
$x + y = 5$

32. $2x - y = 4$
$x + y = 5$

33. $x + 2y = 6$
$x - y = 3$

34. $3x - y = 3$
$2x + y = 2$

35. $3x - 2y = 6$
$y = 3$

36. $x = 2$
$3x + 2y = 4$

37. $x = 3$
$y = -2$

38. $x + 1 = 0$
$y - 3 = 0$

39. $y = 2x - 6$
$x + y = 0$

40. $5x - 2y = 11$
$y = 2x - 5$

41. $2x + y = -2$
$6x + 3y = 6$

42. $x + y = 5$
$3x + 3y = 6$

43. $4x - 2y = 4$
$y = 2x - 2$

44. $2x + 6y = 6$
$y = -\frac{1}{3}x + 1$

45. $x - y = 5$
$2x - y = 6$

46. $5x - 2y = 10$
$3x + 2y = 6$

47. $3x + 4y = 0$
$2x - 5y = 0$

48. $2x - 3y = 0$
$y = -\frac{1}{3}x$

49. $x - 3y = 3$
$2x - 6y = 12$

50. $4x + 6y = 12$
$6x + 9y = 18$

51. $3x + 2y = -4$
$x = 2y + 4$

52. $5x + 2y = -14$
$3x - 4y = 2$

53. $4x - y = 5$
$3x - 2y = 5$

54. $2x - 3y = 9$
$4x + 3y = -9$

Solve by graphing. Then use a graphing utility to verify your solution.

55. $5x - 2y = 10$
$3x + 2y = 6$

56. $x - y = 5$
$2x + y = 4$

57. $2x - 5y = 4$
$x - y = -1$

58. $x - 2y = -5$
$3x + 4y = -15$

59. $2x + 3y = 6$
$y = -\frac{2}{3}x + 1$

60. $2x - 5y = 10$
$y = \frac{2}{5}x - 2$

In Exercises 61 and 62, A, B, C, and D are nonzero real numbers.

61. Is the following system of equations independent, inconsistent, or dependent?
$y = Ax + B$
$y = Ax + C, B \neq C$

62. Is the following system of equations independent, inconsistent, or dependent?
$x = C$
$y = D$

6.1 Applying Concepts

Write a system of equations given the graph.

63.

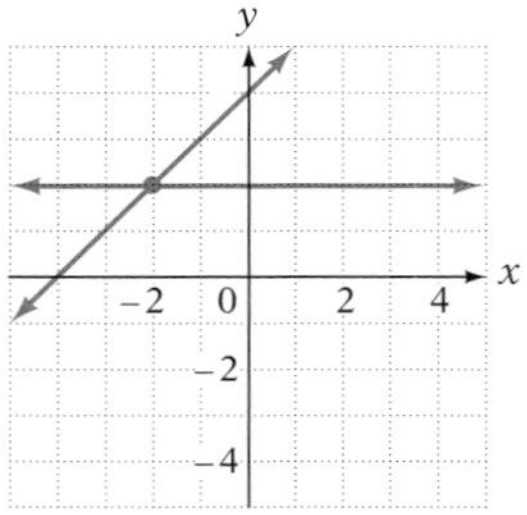

64.

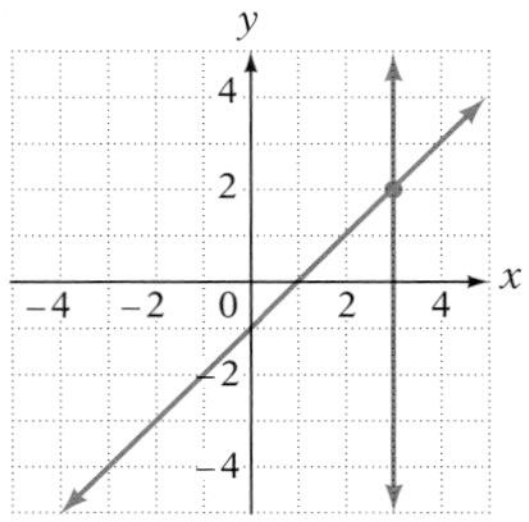

65.

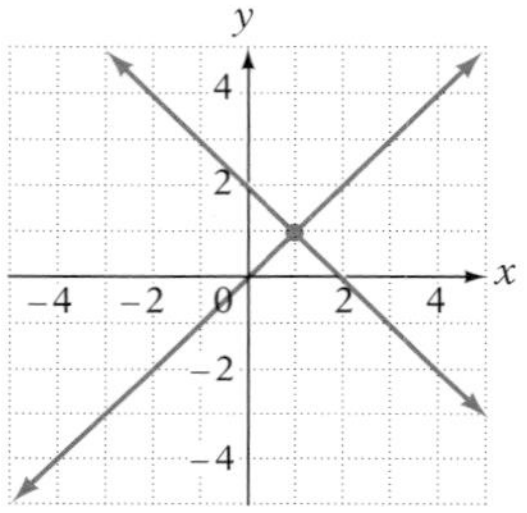

66.

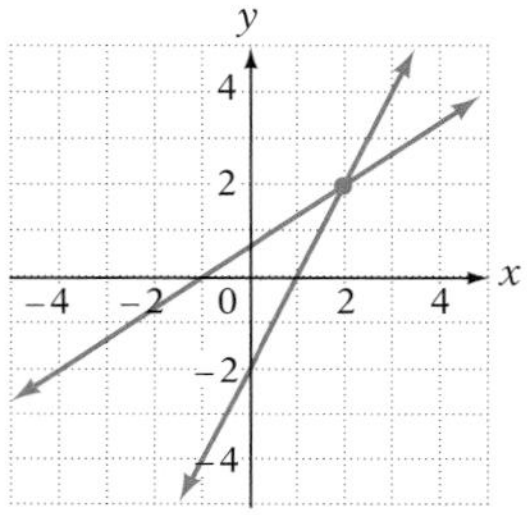

67. Determine whether the statement is always true, sometimes true, or never true.

a. Two parallel lines have the same slope.
b. Two different lines with the same y-intercept are parallel.
c. Two different lines with the same slope are parallel.

68. Write three different systems of equations: **a.** one that has $(-3, 5)$ as its only solution, **b.** one for which there is no solution, and **c.** one that is a dependent system of equations.

69. Explain how you can determine from the graph of a system of two equations in two variables whether it is an independent system of equations. Explain how you can determine whether it is an inconsistent system of equations.

6.2 Solving Systems of Linear Equations by the Substitution Method

OBJECTIVE 1 Solve systems of linear equations by the substitution method

A graphical solution of a system of equations is based on approximating the coordinates of a point of intersection. However, the point $\left(\frac{1}{4}, \frac{1}{2}\right)$ would be difficult to read from a graph. An algebraic method called the **substitution method** can be used to find an exact solution of a system of equations. To use the substitution method, we must write one of the equations of the system in terms of x or in terms of y.

Solve by substitution: $2x + 5y = -11$ (1)
$y = 3x - 9$ (2)

Equation (2) states that $y = 3x - 9$.

Substitute $3x - 9$ for y in equation (1). $2x + 5(3x - 9) = -11$

Solve for x.

$$2x + 15x - 45 = -11$$
$$17x - 45 = -11$$
$$17x = 34$$

Note that $x = 2$. Now we must find y. $x = 2$

Substitute the value of x into equation (2) and solve for y.

(2) $y = 3x - 9$
$$y = 3 \cdot 2 - 9$$
$$y = 6 - 9$$
$$y = -3$$

The solution is $(2, -3)$.

The graph of the system of equations given above is shown at the right. Note that the lines intersect at the point whose coordinates are $(2, -3)$, which is the algebraic solution we determined by the substitution method.

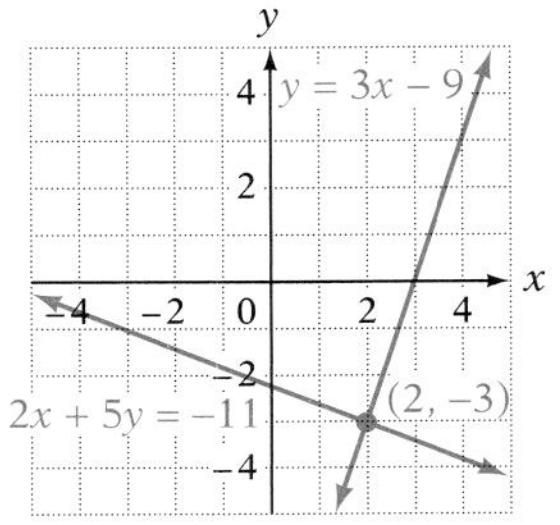

Solve by substitution: $5x + y = 4$ (1)
$2x - 3y = 5$ (2)

Equation (1) is the easier equation to solve for one variable in terms of the other.

Solve equation (1) for y.

$$5x + y = 4$$
$$y = -5x + 4$$

Substitute $-5x + 4$ for y in equation (2). Solve for x.

$$2x - 3y = 5$$
$$2x - 3(-5x + 4) = 5$$
$$2x + 15x - 12 = 5$$
$$17x - 12 = 5$$
$$17x = 17$$
$$x = 1$$

Substitute the value of x in equation (1) and solve for y.

(1) $$5x + y = 4$$
$$5(1) + y = 4$$
$$5 + y = 4$$
$$y = -1$$

The solution is $(1, -1)$.

Take Note

You can *always* check the solution to an independent system of equations. Use the skill you developed in Objective 6.1.1 to check that the ordered pair is a solution of each equation in the system.

Solve by substitution: $y = 3x - 1$ (1)
$y = -2x - 6$ (2)

Substitute $-2x - 6$ for y in equation (1).

Solve for x.

$$y = 3x - 1$$
$$-2x - 6 = 3x - 1$$
$$-5x - 6 = -1$$
$$-5x = 5$$
$$x = -1$$

Substitute the value of x into either equation and solve for y. Equation (1) is used here.

$$y = 3x - 1$$
$$y = 3(-1) - 1$$
$$y = -3 - 1$$
$$y = -4$$

The solution is $(-1, -4)$.

EXAMPLE 1 Solve by substitution: $3x + 4y = -2$ (1)
$-x + 2y = 4$ (2)

Solution

$$-x + 2y = 4$$
$$-x = -2y + 4$$
$$x = 2y - 4$$

- **Solve equation (2) for x.**

$$3x + 4y = -2$$
$$3(2y - 4) + 4y = -2$$
$$6y - 12 + 4y = -2$$
$$10y - 12 = -2$$
$$10y = 10$$
$$y = 1$$

- **Substitute $2y - 4$ for x in equation (1).**
- **Solve for y.**

$$-x + 2y = 4$$
$$-x + 2(1) = 4$$
$$-x + 2 = 4$$
$$-x = 2$$
$$x = -2$$

- **Substitute the value of y into equation (2).**
- **Solve for x.**

The solution is $(-2, 1)$.

PROBLEM 1 Solve by substitution: $7x - y = 4$
$3x + 2y = 9$

Solution See page S14.

> **Take Note**
> Solve equation (1) for y. The resulting equation is $y = -2x + \frac{5}{2}$. Thus both lines have the same slope, -2, but different y-intercepts. The lines are parallel.

EXAMPLE 2 Solve by substitution: $4x + 2y = 5$ (1)
$y = -2x + 1$ (2)

Solution

$$\begin{aligned} 4x + 2y &= 5 \\ 4x + 2(-2x + 1) &= 5 \\ 4x - 4x + 2 &= 5 \\ 2 &= 5 \end{aligned}$$

• **Substitute $-2x + 1$ for y in equation (1).**

$2 = 5$ is not a true equation. The system of equations is inconsistent. The system does not have a solution.

PROBLEM 2 Solve by substitution: $3x - y = 4$
$y = 3x + 2$

Solution See page S14.

> **Take Note**
> Solve equation (1) for y. The resulting equation is $y = 3x - 2$, which is the same as equation (2).

EXAMPLE 3 Solve by substitution: $6x - 2y = 4$ (1)
$y = 3x - 2$ (2)

Solution

$$\begin{aligned} 6x - 2y &= 4 \\ 6x - 2(3x - 2) &= 4 \\ 6x - 6x + 4 &= 4 \\ 4 &= 4 \end{aligned}$$

• **Substitute $3x - 2$ for y in equation (1).**

$4 = 4$ is a true equation. The system of equations is dependent. The solutions are the ordered pairs that satisfy the equation $y = 3x - 2$.

PROBLEM 3 Solve by substitution: $y = -2x + 1$
$6x + 3y = 3$

Solution See page S14.

Note from Examples 2 and 3 above: If, when you are solving a system of equations, the variable is eliminated and the result is a false equation, such as $2 = 5$, the system is inconsistent and does not have a solution. If the result is a true equation, such as $4 = 4$, the system is dependent and has an infinite number of solutions.

6.2 Concept Review

Determine whether the statement is always true, sometimes true, or never true.

1. If one of the equations in a system of two linear equations is $y = x + 2$, then $x + 2$ can be substituted for y in the other equation in the system.

2. If a system of equations contains the equations $y = 2x + 1$ and $x + y = 5$, then $x + 2x + 1 = 5$.

3. If the equation $x = 4$ results from solving a system of equations by the substitution method, then the solution of the system of equations is 4.

4. If the true equation $6 = 6$ results from solving a system of equations by the substitution method, then the system of equations has an infinite number of solutions.

5. If the false equation $0 = 7$ results from solving a system of equations by the substitution method, then the system of equations is independent.

6. The ordered pair (0, 0) is a solution of a system of linear equations.

6.2 Exercises

1 Solve systems of linear equations by the substitution method

1. Use this system of equations: (1) $y = 3x - 5$
(2) $x = 2$
To solve the system by substitution, substitute __?__ for x in equation (1): $y = 3(2) - 5 =$ __?__.
The solution of the system of equations is (__?__, __?__).

2. Use this system of equations: (1) $y = x + 4$
(2) $3x + y = 12$
To solve the system by substitution, substitute __?__ for y in equation (2): $3x + x + 4 = 12$.
Solving the equation $3x + x + 4 = 12$ for x gives $x =$ __?__.
To find y, substitute this value of x into equation (1): $y =$ __?__ $+ 4 =$ __?__.
The solution of the system of equations is (__?__, __?__).

Solve by substitution.

3. $2x + 3y = 7$
$x = 2$

4. $y = 3$
$3x - 2y = 6$

5. $y = x - 3$
$x + y = 5$

6. $y = x + 2$
$x + y = 6$

7. $x = y - 2$
$x + 3y = 2$

8. $x = y + 1$
$x + 2y = 7$

9. $2x + 3y = 9$
$y = x - 2$

10. $3x + 2y = 11$
$y = x + 3$

11. $3x - y = 2$
$y = 2x - 1$

12. $2x - y = -5$
$y = x + 4$

13. $x = 2y - 3$
$2x - 3y = -5$

14. $x = 3y - 1$
$3x + 4y = 10$

15. $y = 4 - 3x$
$3x + y = 5$

16. $y = 2 - 3x$
$6x + 2y = 7$

17. $x = 3y + 3$
$2x - 6y = 12$

18. $x = 2 - y$
$3x + 3y = 6$

19. $3x + 5y = -6$
$x = 5y + 3$

20. $y = 2x + 3$
$4x - 3y = 1$

21. $x = 4y - 3$
$2x - 3y = 0$

22. $x = 2y$
$-2x + 4y = 6$

23. $y = 2x - 9$
$3x - y = 2$

24. $y = x + 4$
$2x - y = 6$

25. $3x + 4y = 7$
$x = 3 - 2y$

26. $3x - 5y = 1$
$y = 4x - 2$

27. $2x - y = 4$
$3x + 2y = 6$

28. $x + y = 12$
$3x - 2y = 6$

29. $4x - 3y = 5$
$x + 2y = 4$

30. $3x - 5y = 2$
$2x - y = 4$

31. $7x - y = 4$
$5x + 2y = 1$

32. $x - 7y = 4$
$-3x + 2y = 6$

33. $4x - 3y = -1$
$y = 2x - 3$

34. $3x - 7y = 28$
$x = 3 - 4y$

35. $7x + y = 14$
$2x - 5y = -33$

36. $3x + y = 4$
$4x - 3y = 1$

37. $x - 4y = 9$
$2x - 3y = 11$

38. $3x - y = 6$
$x + 3y = 2$

39. $4x - y = -5$
$2x + 5y = 13$

40. $3x - y = 5$
$2x + 5y = -8$

41. $3x + 4y = 18$
$2x - y = 1$

42. $4x + 3y = 0$
$2x - y = 0$

43. $5x + 2y = 0$
$x - 3y = 0$

44. $6x - 3y = 6$
$2x - y = 2$

45. $3x + y = 4$
$9x + 3y = 12$

46. $x - 5y = 6$
$2x - 7y = 9$

47. $x + 7y = -5$
$2x - 3y = 5$

48. $y = 2x + 11$
$y = 5x - 1$

49. $y = 2x - 8$
$y = 3x - 13$

50. $y = -4x + 2$
$y = -3x - 1$

51. $x = 3y + 7$
$x = 2y - 1$

52. $x = 4y - 2$
$x = 6y + 8$

53. $x = 3 - 2y$
$x = 5y - 10$

54. $y = 2x - 7$
$y = 4x + 5$

55. $3x - y = 11$
$2x + 5y = -4$

56. $-x + 6y = 8$
$2x + 5y = 1$

In Exercises 57 and 58, A, B, C, and D are nonzero real numbers.

57. Is the following system of equations independent, inconsistent, or dependent?

$$\begin{aligned} x + y &= A \\ x &= A - y \end{aligned}$$

58. Is the following system of equations independent, inconsistent, or dependent?

$$\begin{aligned} x + y &= B \\ y &= C - x, C \neq B \end{aligned}$$

6.2 Applying Concepts

Rewrite each equation so that the coefficients are integers. Then solve the system of equations.

59. $\begin{aligned} 0.1x - 0.6y &= -0.4 \\ -0.7x + 0.2y &= 0.5 \end{aligned}$

60. $\begin{aligned} 0.8x - 0.1y &= 0.3 \\ 0.5x - 0.2y &= -0.5 \end{aligned}$

61. $\begin{aligned} 0.4x + 0.5y &= 0.2 \\ 0.3x - 0.1y &= 1.1 \end{aligned}$

62. $\begin{aligned} -0.1x + 0.3y &= 1.1 \\ 0.4x - 0.1y &= -2.2 \end{aligned}$

63. $\begin{aligned} 1.2x + 0.1y &= 1.9 \\ 0.1x + 0.3y &= 2.2 \end{aligned}$

64. $\begin{aligned} 1.25x - 0.01y &= 1.5 \\ 0.24x - 0.02y &= -1.52 \end{aligned}$

For what value of k does the system of equations have no solution?

65. $\begin{aligned} 2x - 3y &= 7 \\ kx - 3y &= 4 \end{aligned}$

66. $\begin{aligned} 8x - 4y &= 1 \\ 2x - ky &= 3 \end{aligned}$

67. $\begin{aligned} x &= 4y + 4 \\ kx - 8y &= 4 \end{aligned}$

68. The following was offered as a solution to the system of equations shown at the right.

(1) $y = \frac{1}{2}x + 2$

(2) $2x + 5y = 10$

$$\begin{aligned} 2x + 5y &= 10 && \bullet \text{ Equation (2)} \\ 2x + 5\left(\frac{1}{2}x + 2\right) &= 10 && \bullet \text{ Substitute } \tfrac{1}{2}x + 2 \text{ for } y. \\ 2x + \frac{5}{2}x + 10 &= 10 && \bullet \text{ Solve for } x. \\ \frac{9}{2}x &= 0 \\ x &= 0 \end{aligned}$$

At this point the student stated that because $x = 0$, the system of equations has no solution. If this assertion is correct, is the system of equations independent, dependent, or inconsistent? If the assertion is not correct, what is the correct solution?

69. When you solve a system of equations by the substitution method, how do you determine whether the system of equations is dependent? How do you determine whether the system of equations is inconsistent?

6.3 Solving Systems of Linear Equations by the Addition Method

OBJECTIVE 1 Solve systems of linear equations by the addition method

Another algebraic method for solving a system of equations is called the **addition method.** It is based on the Addition Property of Equations.

In the system of equations at the right, note the effect of adding equation (2) to equation (1). Because $2y$ and $-2y$ are opposites, adding the equations results in an equation with only one variable.

$$\begin{aligned} (1)\quad 3x + 2y &= 4 \\ (2)\quad 4x - 2y &= 10 \\ 7x + 0y &= 14 \\ 7x &= 14 \end{aligned}$$

The solution of the resulting equation is the first coordinate of the ordered-pair solution of the system.

$$\begin{aligned} 7x &= 14 \\ x &= 2 \end{aligned}$$

The second coordinate is found by substituting the value of x into equation (1) or (2) and then solving for y. Equation (1) is used here.

$$\begin{aligned} (1)\quad 3x + 2y &= 4 \\ 3 \cdot 2 + 2y &= 4 \\ 6 + 2y &= 4 \\ 2y &= -2 \\ y &= -1 \end{aligned}$$

The solution is $(2, -1)$.

Sometimes adding the two equations does not eliminate one of the variables. In this case, use the Multiplication Property of Equations to rewrite one or both of the equations so that when the equations are added, one of the variables is eliminated.

To do this, first choose which variable to eliminate. The coefficients of that variable must be opposites. Multiply each equation by a constant that will produce coefficients that are opposites.

Solve by the addition method: $3x + 2y = 7$ (1)
$5x - 4y = 19$ (2)

To eliminate y, multiply each side of equation (1) by 2.

$$\begin{aligned} 2(3x + 2y) &= 2 \cdot 7 \\ 5x - 4y &= 19 \end{aligned}$$

Now the coefficients of the y terms are opposites.

$$\begin{aligned} 6x + 4y &= 14 \\ 5x - 4y &= 19 \end{aligned}$$

Add the equations.
Solve for x.

$$\begin{aligned} 11x + 0y &= 33 \\ 11x &= 33 \\ x &= 3 \end{aligned}$$

Substitute the value of x into one of the equations and solve for y. Equation (2) is used here.

$$\begin{aligned} (2)\quad 5x - 4y &= 19 \\ 5 \cdot 3 - 4y &= 19 \\ 15 - 4y &= 19 \\ -4y &= 4 \\ y &= -1 \end{aligned}$$

The solution is $(3, -1)$.

Solve by the addition method: $5x + 6y = 3$ (1)
$2x - 5y = 16$ (2)

To eliminate x, multiply each side of equation (1) by 2 and each side of equation (2) by -5. Note how the constants are selected. The negative sign is used so that the coefficients will be opposites.

$$2(5x + 6y) = 2 \cdot 3$$
$$-5(2x - 5y) = -5 \cdot 16$$

Now the coefficients of the x terms are opposites.

$$10x + 12y = 6$$
$$-10x + 25y = -80$$

Add the equations.
Solve for y.

$$0x + 37y = -74$$
$$37y = -74$$
$$y = -2$$

Substitute the value of y into one of the equations and solve for x. Equation (1) is used here.

(1) $$5x + 6y = 3$$
$$5x + 6(-2) = 3$$
$$5x - 12 = 3$$
$$5x = 15$$
$$x = 3$$

The solution is $(3, -2)$.

Solve by the addition method: $5x = 2y - 7$ (1)
$3x + 4y = 1$ (2)

Write equation (1) in the form $Ax + By = C$.

$$5x - 2y = -7$$
$$3x + 4y = 1$$

Eliminate y. Multiply each side of equation (1) by 2.

$$2(5x - 2y) = 2(-7)$$
$$3x + 4y = 1$$

Now the coefficients of the y terms are opposites.

$$10x - 4y = -14$$
$$3x + 4y = 1$$

Add the equations.
Solve for x.

$$13x + 0y = -13$$
$$13x = -13$$
$$x = -1$$

Substitute the value of x into one of the equations and solve for y. Equation (1) is used here.

$$5x = 2y - 7$$
$$5(-1) = 2y - 7$$
$$-5 = 2y - 7$$
$$2 = 2y$$
$$1 = y$$

The solution is $(-1, 1)$.

Solve by the addition method: $2x + y = 2$ (1)
$4x + 2y = -5$ (2)

To eliminate y, multiply each side of equation (1) by -2.

$$-4x - 2y = -4$$
$$4x + 2y = -5$$

Add the equations. $0x + 0y = -9$

This is not a true equation. $0 = -9$

The system of equations is inconsistent. The system does not have a solution.

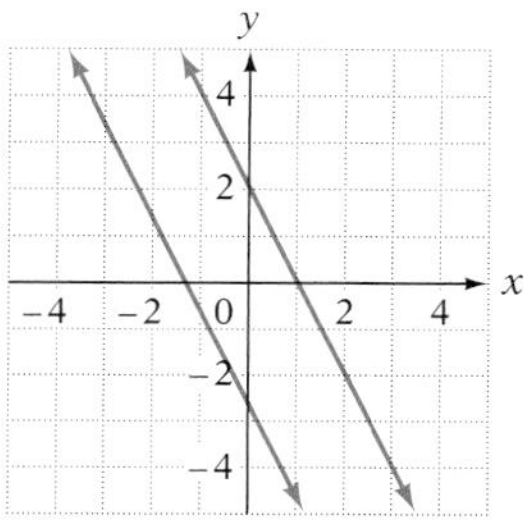

The graphs of the two equations in the preceding system of equations are shown at the left. Note that the graphs are parallel and therefore do not intersect. Thus the system of equations has no solution.

EXAMPLE 1 Solve by the addition method: $2x + 4y = 7$ (1)
$5x - 3y = -2$ (2)

Solution

$5(2x + 4y) = 5 \cdot 7$
$-2(5x - 3y) = -2 \cdot (-2)$

- **Eliminate *x*. Multiply each side of equation (1) by 5 and each side of equation (2) by −2.**

$10x + 20y = 35$
$-10x + 6y = 4$
$26y = 39$

- **Add the equations.**

$y = \frac{39}{26} = \frac{3}{2}$

- **Solve for *y*.**

$2x + 4\left(\frac{3}{2}\right) = 7$

- **Substitute the value of *y* in equation (1).**

$2x + 6 = 7$

- **Solve for *x*.**

$2x = 1$
$x = \frac{1}{2}$

The solution is $\left(\frac{1}{2}, \frac{3}{2}\right)$.

PROBLEM 1 Solve by the addition method: $x - 2y = 1$
$2x + 4y = 0$

Solution See page S15.

EXAMPLE 2 Solve by the addition method: $6x + 9y = 15$ (1)
$4x + 6y = 10$ (2)

Solution

$4(6x + 9y) = 4 \cdot 15$
$-6(4x + 6y) = -6 \cdot 10$

- **Eliminate *x*. Multiply each side of equation (1) by 4 and each side of equation (2) by −6.**

$24x + 36y = 60$
$-24x - 36y = -60$
$0 = 0$

- **Add the equations.**

$0 = 0$ is a true equation. The system of equations is dependent. The solutions are ordered pairs that satisfy the equation $6x + 9y = 15$.

PROBLEM 2 Solve by the addition method: $2x - 3y = 4$
$-4x + 6y = -8$

Solution See page S15.

6.3 Concept Review

Determine whether the statement is always true, sometimes true, or never true.

1. When using the addition method of solving a system of linear equations, if you multiply one side of an equation by a number, then you must multiply the other side of the equation by the same number.

2. When a system of linear equations is being solved by the addition method, in order for one of the variables to be eliminated, the coefficients of one of the variables must be opposites.

3. If the two equations in a system of equations have the same slope and different y-intercepts, then the system of equations has an infinite number of solutions.

4. You are using the addition method to solve the system of equations shown at the right. The first step you will perform is to add the two equations.
$$\begin{aligned} 3x + 2y &= 6 \\ 2x + 3y &= -6 \end{aligned}$$

5. If the equation $y = -2$ results from solving a system of equations by the addition method, then the solution of the system of equations is -2.

6. If the true equation $-3 = -3$ results from solving a system of equations by the addition method, then the system of equations is dependent.

6.3 Exercises

1 Solve systems of linear equations by the addition method

1. Use this system of equations: (1) $-3x - y = 5$
   (2) $x - 4y = 7$
   a. To eliminate x from the system of equations by using the addition method, multiply each side of equation (2) by __?__.
   b. To eliminate y from the system of equations by using the addition method, multiply each side of equation (1) by __?__.

2. Use this system of equations: (1) $2x - 3y = 3$
   (2) $x + 6y = 9$

a. To eliminate x from the system of equations by using the addition method, multiply each side of equation (__?__) by (__?__).
b. To eliminate y from the system of equations by using the addition method, multiply each side of equation (__?__) by (__?__).

Solve by the addition method.

3. $x + y = 4$
$x - y = 6$

4. $2x + y = 3$
$x - y = 3$

5. $x + y = 4$
$2x + y = 5$

6. $x - 3y = 2$
$x + 2y = -3$

7. $2x - y = 1$
$x + 3y = 4$

8. $x - 2y = 4$
$3x + 4y = 2$

9. $4x - 5y = 22$
$x + 2y = -1$

10. $3x - y = 11$
$2x + 5y = 13$

11. $2x - y = 1$
$4x - 2y = 2$

12. $x + 3y = 2$
$3x + 9y = 6$

13. $4x + 3y = 15$
$2x - 5y = 1$

14. $3x - 7y = 13$
$6x + 5y = 7$

15. $2x - 3y = 5$
$4x - 6y = 3$

16. $2x + 4y = 3$
$3x + 6y = 8$

17. $5x - 2y = -1$
$x + y = 4$

18. $4x - 3y = 1$
$8x + 5y = 13$

19. $5x + 7y = 10$
$3x - 14y = 6$

20. $7x + 10y = 13$
$4x + 5y = 6$

21. $3x - 2y = 0$
$6x + 5y = 0$

22. $5x + 2y = 0$
$3x + 5y = 0$

23. $2x - 3y = 16$
$3x + 4y = 7$

24. $3x + 4y = 10$
$4x + 3y = 11$

25. $x + 3y = 4$
$2x + 5y = 1$

26. $-2x + 7y = 9$
$3x + 2y = -1$

27. $7x - 2y = 13$
$5x + 3y = 27$

28. $3x + 5y = -11$
$2x - 7y = 3$

29. $8x - 3y = 11$
$6x - 5y = 11$

30. $4x - 8y = 36$
$3x - 6y = 27$

31. $5x + 15y = 20$
$2x + 6y = 8$

32. $2x - 3y = 4$
$-x + 4y = 3$

33. $3x = 2y + 7$
$5x - 2y = 13$

34. $2y = 4 - 9x$
$9x - y = 25$

35. $2x + 9y = 5$
$5x = 6 - 3y$

36. $3x - 4 = y + 18$
$4x + 5y = -21$

37. $2x + 3y = 7 - 2x$
$7x + 2y = 9$

38. $5x - 3y = 3y + 4$
$4x + 3y = 11$

39. $3x + y = 1$
$5x + y = 2$

40. $2x - y = 1$
$2x - 5y = -1$

41. $4x + 3y = 3$
$x + 3y = 1$

42. $2x - 5y = 4$
$x + 5y = 1$

43. $3x - 4y = 1$
$4x + 3y = 1$

44. $2x - 7y = -17$
$3x + 5y = 17$

45. $y = 2x - 3$
$4x + 4y = -1$

46. $4x - 2y = 5$
$2x + 3y = 4$

6.3 Applying Concepts

Solve.

47. $x - 0.2y = 0.2$
$0.2x + 0.5y = 2.2$

48. $0.5x - 1.2y = 0.3$
$0.2x + y = 1.6$

49. $1.25x - 1.5y = -1.75$
$2.5x - 1.75y = -1$

50. The point of intersection of the graphs of the equations $Ax + 2y = 2$ and $2x + By = 10$ is $(2, -2)$. Find A and B.

51. The point of intersection of the graphs of the equations $Ax - 4y = 9$ and $4x + By = -1$ is $(-1, -3)$. Find A and B.

52. Given that the graphs of the equations $2x - y = 6$, $3x - 4y = 4$, and $Ax - 2y = 0$ all intersect at the same point, find A.

53. Given that the graphs of the equations $3x - 2y = -2$, $2x - y = 0$, and $Ax + y = 8$ all intersect at the same point, find A.

54. For what value of k is the system of equations dependent?

a. $2x + 3y = 7$
$4x + 6y = k$

b. $y = \frac{2}{3}x - 3$
$y = kx - 3$

c. $x = ky - 1$
$y = 2x + 2$

55. For what values of k is the system of equations independent?

a. $x + y = 7$
$kx + y = 3$

b. $x + 2y = 4$
$kx + 3y = 2$

c. $2x + ky = 1$
$x + 2y = 2$

56. Describe in your own words the process of solving a system of equations by the addition method.

6.4 Application Problems in Two Variables

OBJECTIVE 1 Rate-of-wind and water-current problems

Solving motion problems that involve an object moving with or against a wind or current normally requires two variables. One variable represents the speed of the moving object in calm air or still water, and a second variable represents the rate of the wind or current.

A plane flying with the wind will travel a greater distance per hour than it would travel without the wind. The resulting rate of the plane is represented by the sum of the plane's speed and the rate of the wind.

A plane traveling against the wind, on the other hand, will travel a shorter distance per hour than it would travel without the wind. The resulting rate of the plane is represented by the difference between the plane's speed and the rate of the wind.

The same principle is used to describe the rate of a boat traveling with or against a water current.

Solve: Flying with the wind, a small plane can fly 750 mi in 3 h. Against the wind, the plane can fly the same distance in 5 h. Find the rate of the plane in calm air and the rate of the wind.

STRATEGY for solving rate-of-wind and water-current problems

▶ Choose one variable to represent the rate of the object in calm conditions and a second variable to represent the rate of the wind or current. Use these variables to express the rate of the object with and against the wind or current. Then use these expressions for the rate, as well as the time traveled with and against the wind or current and the fact that $rt = d$, to write expressions for the distance traveled by the object. The results can be recorded in a table.

Rate of plane in calm air: p
Rate of wind: w

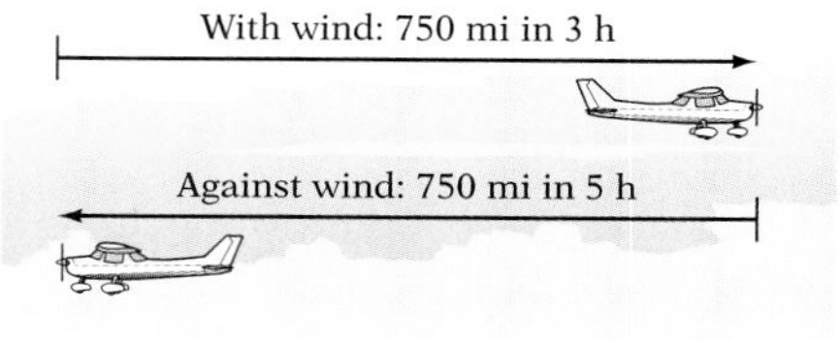

	Rate	·	Time	=	Distance
With the wind	$p + w$	·	3	=	$3(p + w)$
Against the wind	$p - w$	·	5	=	$5(p - w)$

▶ Determine how the expressions for distance are related.

The distance traveled with the wind is 750 mi. $3(p + w) = 750$
The distance traveled against the wind is 750 mi. $5(p - w) = 750$

Solve the system of equations.

$$3(p + w) = 750 \quad \rightarrow \quad \frac{3(p + w)}{3} = \frac{750}{3} \quad \rightarrow \quad p + w = 250$$

$$5(p - w) = 750 \quad \rightarrow \quad \frac{5(p - w)}{5} = \frac{750}{5} \quad \rightarrow \quad p - w = 150$$

$$2p = 400$$
$$p = 200$$

Substitute the value of p in the equation $p + w = 250$. Solve for w.

$$p + w = 250$$
$$200 + w = 250$$
$$w = 50$$

The rate of the plane in calm air is 200 mph.
The rate of the wind is 50 mph.

EXAMPLE 1 A 600-mile trip from one city to another takes 4 h when a plane is flying with the wind. The return trip against the wind takes 5 h. Find the rate of the plane in still air and the rate of the wind.

Strategy

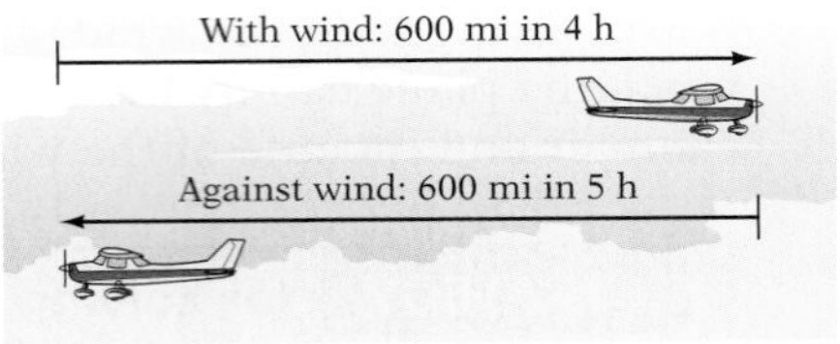

▶ Rate of the plane in still air: p
Rate of the wind: w

	Rate	Time	Distance
With wind	$p + w$	4	$4(p + w)$
Against wind	$p - w$	5	$5(p - w)$

▶ The distance traveled with the wind is 600 mi.
The distance traveled against the wind is 600 mi.

Solution

$$4(p + w) = 600 \quad (1)$$
$$5(p - w) = 600 \quad (2)$$

$$\frac{4(p + w)}{4} = \frac{600}{4}$$ • **Simplify equation (1) by dividing each side of the equation by 4.**

$$\frac{5(p - w)}{5} = \frac{600}{5}$$ • **Simplify equation (2) by dividing each side of the equation by 5.**

$$p + w = 150$$
$$p - w = 120$$
$$2p = 270$$ • **Add the two equations.**
$$p = 135$$ • **Solve for p, the rate of the plane in still air.**
$$p + w = 150$$ • **Substitute the value of p into one of the equations.**
$$135 + w = 150$$
$$w = 15$$ • **Solve for w, the rate of the wind.**

The rate of the plane in still air is 135 mph.
The rate of the wind is 15 mph.

PROBLEM 1 A canoeist paddling with the current can travel 24 mi in 3 h. Against the current, it takes 4 h to travel the same distance. Find the rate of the current and the rate of the canoeist in calm water.

Solution See page S15.

OBJECTIVE 2 Application problems

The application problems in this section are varieties of those problems solved earlier in the text. Each of the strategies for the problems in this section will result in a system of equations.

Point of Interest

The Babylonians had a method for solving a system of equations. Here is an adaptation of a problem from an ancient Babylonian text (around 1500 B.C.). "There are two silver blocks. The sum of $\frac{1}{7}$ of the first block and $\frac{1}{11}$ of the second block is one sheqel (a weight). The first block diminished by $\frac{1}{7}$ of its weight equals the second diminished by $\frac{1}{11}$ of its weight. What are the weights of the two blocks?"

Solve: A jeweler purchased 5 oz of a gold alloy and 20 oz of a silver alloy for a total cost of \$700. The next day, at the same prices per ounce, the jeweler purchased 4 oz of the gold alloy and 30 oz of the silver alloy for a total cost of \$630. Find the cost per ounce of the silver alloy.

STRATEGY for solving an application problem in two variables

▶ Choose one variable to represent one of the unknown quantities and a second variable to represent the other unknown quantity. Write numerical or variable expressions for all the remaining quantities. These results can be recorded in two tables, one for each of the conditions.

Cost per ounce of gold: g Cost per ounce of silver: s

First day

	Amount	·	Unit cost	=	Value
Gold	5	·	g	=	$5g$
Silver	20	·	s	=	$20s$

Second day

	Amount	·	Unit cost	=	Value
Gold	4	·	g	=	$4g$
Silver	30	·	s	=	$30s$

▶ Determine a system of equations. The strategies presented in the chapter "Solving Equations and Inequalities: Applications" can be used to determine the relationships between the expressions in the tables. Each table will give one equation of the system.

The total value of the purchase on the first day was \$700. The total value of the purchase on the second day was \$630.

$$5g + 20s = 700$$
$$4g + 30s = 630$$

Solve the system of equations.

$$\begin{aligned} 5g + 20s &= 700 \\ 4g + 30s &= 630 \end{aligned} \longrightarrow \begin{aligned} 4(5g + 20s) &= 4 \cdot 700 \\ -5(4g + 30s) &= -5 \cdot 630 \end{aligned} \longrightarrow \begin{aligned} 20g + 80s &= 2800 \\ -20g - 150s &= -3150 \\ -70s &= -350 \\ s &= 5 \end{aligned}$$

The cost per ounce of the silver alloy was \$5.

EXAMPLE 2 A store owner purchased 20 incandescent light bulbs and 30 fluorescent bulbs for a total cost of \$40. A second purchase, at the same prices, included 30 incandescent bulbs and 10 fluorescent bulbs for a total cost of \$25. Find the cost of an incandescent bulb and of a fluorescent bulb.

Strategy ▶ Cost of an incandescent bulb: I
Cost of a fluorescent bulb: F

First purchase

	Amount	Unit cost	Value
Incandescent	20	I	$20I$
Fluorescent	30	F	$30F$

Second purchase

	Amount	Unit cost	Value
Incandescent	30	I	$30I$
Fluorescent	10	F	$10F$

▶ The total of the first purchase was \$40.
The total of the second purchase was \$25.

Solution

$$20I + 30F = 40 \quad (1)$$
$$30I + 10F = 25 \quad (2)$$

$$20I + 30F = 40$$
$$(-3)(30I + 10F) = (-3)(25)$$

• **Eliminate *F*. Multiply each side of equation (2) by -3.**

$$20I + 30F = 40$$
$$-90I - 30F = -75$$
$$-70I = -35$$
$$I = 0.5$$

• **Add the two equations.**
• **Solve for *I*, the cost of an incandescent bulb.**

$$20I + 30F = 40$$
$$20(0.5) + 30F = 40$$
$$10 + 30F = 40$$
$$30F = 30$$
$$F = 1$$

• **Substitute the value of *I* into one of the equations.**
• **Solve for *F*.**

The cost of an incandescent bulb was \$.50.
The cost of a fluorescent bulb was \$1.00.

PROBLEM 2 Two coin banks contain only dimes and quarters. In the first bank, the total value of the coins is \$3.90. In the second bank, there are twice as many dimes as in the first bank and one-half the number of quarters. The total value of the coins in the second bank is \$3.30. Find the number of dimes and the number of quarters in the first bank.

Solution See page S15.

6.4 Concept Review

Determine whether the statement is always true, sometimes true, or never true.

1. A plane flying with the wind is traveling faster than it would be traveling without the wind.

2. The uniform motion equation $r = dt$ is used to solve rate-of-wind and water-current problems.

3. If b represents the rate of a boat in calm water and c represents the rate of the water current, then $b + c$ represents the rate of the boat while it is traveling against the current.

4. Both sides of an equation can be divided by the same number without changing the solution of the equation.

5. If, in a system of equations, p represents the rate of a plane in calm air and w represents the rate of the wind, and the solution of the system is $p = 100$, this means that the rate of the wind is 100.

6. The system of equations at the right represents the following problem:

$$2(p + w) = 600$$
$$3(p - w) = 600$$

A plane flying with the wind flew 600 mi in 2 h. Flying against the wind, the plane could fly the same distance in 3 h. Find the rate of the plane in calm air.

6.4 Exercises

1 Rate-of-wind and water-current problems

1. A boat travels down a river for 2 h (traveling with the current), then turns around and takes 3 h to return (traveling against the current). Let b be the rate of the boat, in miles per hour, in calm water, and let c be the rate of the current, in miles per hour. Complete the following table by replacing the question marks.

	Rate, r	·	Time, t	=	Distance, d
With current	?	·	?	=	?
Against current	?	·	?	=	?

2. Suppose the distance traveled down the river by the boat in Exercise 1 is 36 mi. Use the expressions in the last column of the table in Exercise 1 to write a system of equations that can be solved to find the rate of the boat in calm water and the rate of the current.

3. Traveling with the wind, a plane flies m miles in h hours. Traveling against the wind, the plane flies n miles in h hours. Is m less than, equal to, or greater than n?

4. Traveling against the current, it takes a boat h hours to go m miles. Traveling with the current, the boat takes k hours to go m miles. Is k less than, equal to, or greater than h?

5. A whale swimming against an ocean current traveled 60 mi in 2 h. Swimming in the opposite direction, with the current, the whale was able to travel the same distance in 1.5 h. Find the speed of the whale in calm water and the rate of the ocean current.

6. A plane flying with the jet stream flew from Los Angeles to Chicago, a distance of 2250 mi, in 5 h. Flying against the jet stream, the plane could fly only 1750 mi in the same amount of time. Find the rate of the plane in calm air and the rate of the wind.

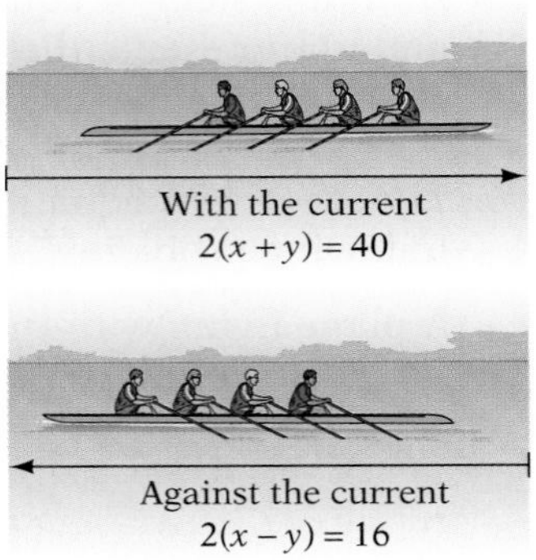

7. A rowing team rowing with the current traveled 40 km in 2 h. Rowing against the current, the team could travel only 16 km in 2 h. Find the team's rowing rate in calm water and the rate of the current.

8. Rowing with the current, a canoeist paddled 14 mi in 2 h. Against the current, the canoeist could paddle only 10 mi in the same amount of time. Find the rate of the canoeist in calm water and the rate of the current.

9. A motorboat traveling with the current went 35 mi in 3.5 h. Traveling against the current, the boat went 12 mi in 3 h. Find the rate of the boat in calm water and the rate of the current.

10. A small plane, flying into a headwind, flew 270 mi in 3 h. Flying with the wind, the plane traveled 260 mi in 2 h. Find the rate of the plane in calm air and the rate of the wind.

11. A private Learjet 31A transporting passengers was flying with a tailwind and traveled 1120 mi in 2 h. Flying against the wind on the return trip, the jet was able to travel only 980 mi in 2 h. Find the speed of the jet in calm air and the rate of the wind.

12. A rowing team rowing with the current traveled 18 mi in 2 h. Against the current, the team rowed a distance of 8 mi in the same amount of time. Find the rate of the rowing team in calm water and the rate of the current.

13. A seaplane flying with the wind flew from an ocean port to a lake, a distance of 240 mi, in 2 h. Flying against the wind, it made the trip from the lake to the ocean port in 3 h. Find the rate of the plane in calm air and the rate of the wind.

14. The bird capable of the fastest flying speed is the swift. A swift flying with the wind to a favorite feeding spot traveled 26 mi in 0.2 h. On the return trip, against the wind, the swift was able to travel only 16 mi in the same amount of time. Find the rate of the swift in calm air and the rate of the wind.

15. A Boeing Apache Longbow military helicopter traveling directly into a strong headwind was able to travel 450 mi in 2.5 h. The return trip, now with a tailwind, took 1 h 40 min. Find the speed of the helicopter in calm air and the rate of the wind.

16. With the wind, a quarterback passes a football 140 ft in 2 s. Against the wind, the same pass would have traveled 80 ft in 2 s. Find the rate of the pass and the rate of the wind.

2 Application problems

17. You purchased theater tickets for 4 adults and 2 children. For the same performance, your neighbor purchased tickets for 2 adults and 3 children. Let A be the cost per adult's ticket and C be the cost per child's ticket. Complete the following tables by replacing the question marks.

Your purchase	Amount	·	Unit cost	=	Value
Adult's ticket	?	·	?	=	?
Child's ticket	?	·	?	=	?

Neighbor's purchase	Amount	·	Unit cost	=	Value
Adult's ticket	?	·	?	=	?
Child's ticket	?	·	?	=	?

18. See Exercise 17. Suppose your tickets cost \$320 and your neighbor's tickets cost \$240. Use the expressions in the last column of the tables in Exercise 17 to write a system of equations that can be solved to find the cost per adult's ticket and the cost per child's ticket.

19. A merchant mixes 4 lb of cinnamon tea with 1 lb of spice tea to create a mixture that costs \$2 per pound. When the merchant mixes 1 lb of the cinnamon tea with 4 lb of the spice tea, the mixture costs \$3 per pound. Is the cost per pound of the cinnamon tea less than, equal to, or greater than the cost per pound of the spice tea?

20. The total value of nickels and dimes in a bank is \$2. If the nickels were dimes and the dimes were nickels, the total value would be \$3. Is the number of nickels in the bank less than, equal to, or greater than the number of dimes in the bank?

21. Business The manager of a computer software store received two shipments of software. The cost of the first shipment, which contained 12 identical word processing programs and 10 identical spreadsheet programs, was \$6190. The second shipment, at the same prices, contained 5 copies of the word processing program and 8 copies of the spreadsheet program. The cost of the second shipment was \$3825. Find the cost for one copy of the word processing program.

22. **Business** The manager of a discount clothing store received two shipments of fall clothing. The cost of the first shipment, which contained 10 identical sweaters and 20 identical jackets, was \$800. The second shipment, at the same prices, contained 5 of the same sweaters and 15 of the same jackets. The cost of the second shipment was \$550. Find the cost of one jacket.

23. **Business** A baker purchased 12 lb of wheat flour and 15 lb of rye flour for a total cost of \$18.30. A second purchase, at the same prices, included 15 lb of wheat flour and 10 lb of rye flour. The cost of the second purchase was \$16.75. Find the cost per pound of the wheat and rye flours.

24. **Consumerism** A computer online service charges one hourly rate for regular use but a higher hourly rate for designated "premium" areas. One customer was charged \$14 after spending 2 h in premium areas and 9 regular hours. Another customer spent 3 h in premium areas and 6 regular hours and was charged \$13.50. What is the service charge per hour for regular and premium services?

25. **Wages** Shelly Egan works as a stocker at a grocery store during her summer vacation. She gets paid a standard hourly rate for her day hours but a higher hourly rate for any hours she works during the night shift. One week she worked 17 daylight hours and 8 nighttime hours and earned \$191. The next week she earned \$219 for a total of 12 daytime and 15 nighttime hours. What is the rate she is being paid for daytime hours and what is the rate for nighttime hours?

26. **Consumerism** For using a computerized financial news network for 50 min during prime time and 70 min during non-prime time, a customer was charged \$10.75. A second customer was charged \$13.35 for using the network for 60 min of prime time and 90 min of non-prime time. Find the cost per minute for using the financial news network during prime time.

27. **Sports** A basketball team scored 87 points in two-point baskets and three-point baskets. If the two-point baskets had been three-point baskets and the three-point baskets had been two-point baskets, the team would have scored 93 points. Find how many two-point baskets and how many three-point baskets the team scored.

28. **Consumerism** The employees of a hardware store ordered lunch from a local delicatessen. The lunch consisted of 4 turkey sandwiches and 7 orders of french fries, for a total cost of \$23.30. The next day, the employees ordered 5 turkey sandwiches and 5 orders of french fries totaling \$25.75. What does the delicatessen charge for a turkey sandwich? What is the charge for an order of french fries?

29. **Coin Problems** Two coin banks contain only nickels and quarters. The total value of the coins in the first bank is \$2.90. In the second bank, there are two more quarters than in the first bank and twice as many nickels. The total value of the coins in the second bank is \$3.80. Find the number of nickels and the number of quarters in the first bank.

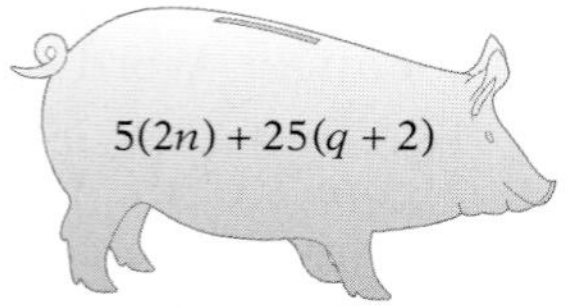

30. **Coin Problems** Two coin banks contain only nickels and dimes. The total value of the coins in the first bank is \$3. In the second bank, there are 4 more nickels than in the first bank and one-half as many dimes. The total value of the coins in the second bank is \$2. Find the number of nickels and the number of dimes in the first bank.

31. **Coin Problems** The total value of the dimes and quarters in a coin bank is \$3.30. If the quarters were dimes and the dimes were quarters, the total value of the coins would be \$3. Find the number of dimes and the number of quarters in the bank.

32. **Coin Problems** The total value of the nickels and dimes in a coin bank is \$3. If the nickels were dimes and the dimes were nickels, the total value of the coins would be \$3.75. Find the number of nickels and the number of dimes in the bank.

6.4 Applying Concepts

33. **Geometry** Two angles are supplementary. The larger angle is 15° more than twice the measure of the smaller angle. Find the measures of the two angles. (Supplementary angles are two angles whose sum is 180°.)

34. **Geometry** Two angles are complementary. The larger angle is four times the measure of the smaller angle. Find the measure of the two angles. (Complementary angles are two angles whose sum is 90°.)

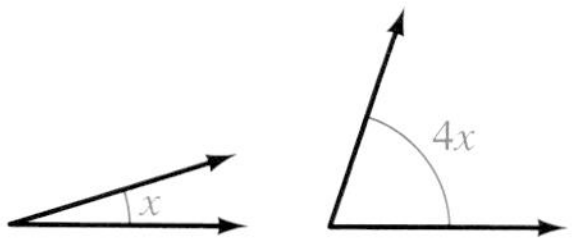

35. **Investments** An investment club placed a portion of its funds in a 9% annual simple interest account and the remainder in an 8% annual simple interest account. The amount of interest earned for one year was \$860. If the amounts placed in each account had been reversed, the interest earned would have been \$840. How much was invested in each account?

36. **Investments** An investor has \$5000 to invest in two accounts. The first account earns 8% annual simple interest, and the second account earns 10% annual simple interest. How much money should be invested in each account so that the annual interest earned is \$600?

37. **Coin Problems** The value of the nickels and dimes in a coin bank is \$.25. If the number of nickels and the number of dimes were doubled, the value of the coins would be \$.50. How many nickels and how many dimes are in the bank?

38. **Coin Problems** A coin bank contains nickels and dimes, but there are no more than 27 coins. The value of the coins is \$2.10. How many different combinations of nickels and/or dimes could be in the bank?

Focus on Problem Solving

Using a Table and Searching for a Pattern

Consider the numbers 10, 12, and 28 and the sum of the proper factors (the natural-number factors less than the number) of those numbers.

$$10\colon\ 1 + 2 + 5 = 8 \qquad 12\colon\ 1 + 2 + 3 + 4 + 6 = 16$$
$$28\colon\ 1 + 2 + 4 + 7 + 14 = 28$$

10 is called a *deficient number* because the sum of its proper factors is less than the number ($8 < 10$). 12 is called an *abundant number* because the sum of its proper factors is greater than the number ($16 > 12$), and 28 is called a *perfect number* because the sum of its proper divisors equals the number ($28 = 28$).

Our goal for this "Focus on Problem Solving" is to try to find a method that will determine whether a number is deficient, abundant, or perfect without having to first find all the factors and then add them up. We will use a table and search for a pattern.

Before we begin, recall that a prime number is a number greater than 1 whose only factors are itself and 1 and that each natural number greater than 1 has a unique prime factorization. For instance, the prime factorization of 36 is given by $36 = 2^2 \cdot 3^2$. Note that the proper factors of 36 (1, 2, 3, 4, 6, 9, 12, 18) can be represented in terms of the same prime numbers.

$$1 = 2^0, \quad 2 = 2^1, \quad 3 = 3^1, \quad 4 = 2^2, \quad 6 = 2 \cdot 3, \quad 9 = 3^2, \quad 12 = 2^2 \cdot 3,$$
$$18 = 2 \cdot 3^2$$

Now let us consider a trial problem of determining whether 432 is deficient, abundant, or perfect.

Take Note

This table contains the factor $432 = 2^4 \cdot 3^3$, which is not a proper factor.

We write the prime factorization of 432 as $2^4 \cdot 3^3$ and place the factors of 432 in a table as shown at the right. This table contains *all* the factors of 432 represented in terms of the prime-number factors. The sum of each column is shown at the bottom.

	1	$1 \cdot 3$	$1 \cdot 3^2$	$1 \cdot 3^3$
	2	$2 \cdot 3$	$2 \cdot 3^2$	$2 \cdot 3^3$
	2^2	$2^2 \cdot 3$	$2^2 \cdot 3^2$	$2^2 \cdot 3^3$
	2^3	$2^3 \cdot 3$	$2^3 \cdot 3^2$	$2^3 \cdot 3^3$
	2^4	$2^4 \cdot 3$	$2^4 \cdot 3^2$	$2^4 \cdot 3^3$
Sum	31	$31 \cdot 3$	$31 \cdot 3^2$	$31 \cdot 3^3$

Here is the calculation of the sum for the column headed by $1 \cdot 3$.

$$1 \cdot 3 + 2 \cdot 3 + 2^2 \cdot 3 + 2^3 \cdot 3 + 2^4 \cdot 3 = (1 + 2 + 2^2 + 2^3 + 2^4)3 = 31(3)$$

For the column headed by $1 \cdot 3^2$ there is a similar situation.

$$1 \cdot 3^2 + 2 \cdot 3^2 + 2^2 \cdot 3^2 + 2^3 \cdot 3^2 + 2^4 \cdot 3^2 = (1 + 2 + 2^2 + 2^3 + 2^4)3^2 = 31(3^2)$$

The sum of *all* the factors (including 432) is the sum of the last row.

$$\text{Sum of all factors} = 31 + 31 \cdot 3 + 31 \cdot 3^2 + 31 \cdot 3^3 = 31(1 + 3 + 3^2 + 3^3)$$
$$= 31(40) = 1240$$

To find the sum of the *proper* factors, we must subtract 432 from 1240; we get 808 (see "Take Note" on the preceding page). Thus 432 is abundant.

We now look for some pattern for the sum of all the factors. Note that

Sum of left column $1 + 2 + 2^2 + 2^3 + 2^4 =$ ⟶ $31(40) = 1240$ ⟵ $= 1 + 3 + 3^2 + 3^3$ Sum of top row

This suggests that the sum of the proper factors can be found by finding the sum of all the prime-power factors for each prime, multiplying those numbers, and then subtracting the original number. Although we have not proved this for all cases, it is a true statement.

For instance, to find the sum of the proper factors of 3240, first find the prime factorization:

$$3240 = 2^3 \cdot 3^4 \cdot 5$$

Now find the following sums:

$$1 + 2 + 2^2 + 2^3 = 15 \qquad 1 + 3 + 3^2 + 3^3 + 3^4 = 121 \qquad 1 + 5 = 6$$

The sum of the proper factors $= (15)(121)6 - 3240 = 7650$. 3240 is abundant.

Determine whether the number is deficient, abundant, or perfect.

1. 200 **2.** 3125 **3.** 8128 **4.** 10,000

5. Is a prime number deficient, abundant, or perfect?

Projects & Group Activities

Solving a System of Equations with a Graphing Calculator

A graphing calculator can be used to approximate the solution of a system of equations in two variables. Graph each equation of the system of equations, and then approximate the coordinates of the point of intersection. The process by which you approximate the solution depends on the make and model of calculator you have. In all cases, however, you must first solve each equation in the system of equations for y.

Solve: $2x - 5y = 9$
$4x + 3y = 2$

Solve each equation for y.

$$\begin{aligned} 2x - 5y &= 9 \\ -5y &= -2x + 9 \\ y &= \frac{2}{5}x - \frac{9}{5} \end{aligned} \qquad \begin{aligned} 4x + 3y &= 2 \\ 3y &= -4x + 2 \\ y &= -\frac{4}{3}x + \frac{2}{3} \end{aligned}$$

The graphing calculator screens on the next page are taken from a TI-83 Plus. Similar screens would appear if a different graphing calculator were used.

For the TI-83, TI-83 Plus, and TI-84 Plus, press [Y=]. Enter one equation as Y1 and the other as Y2. The result should be similar to the screen at the right.

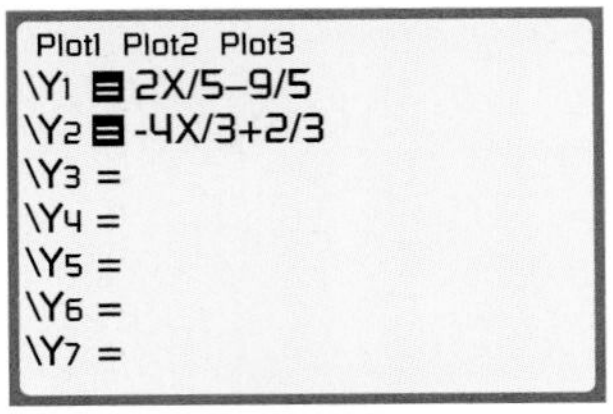

Press [GRAPH]. The graphs of the two equations should appear on the screen. If the point of intersection is not on the screen, adjust the viewing window by pressing the [WINDOW] key.

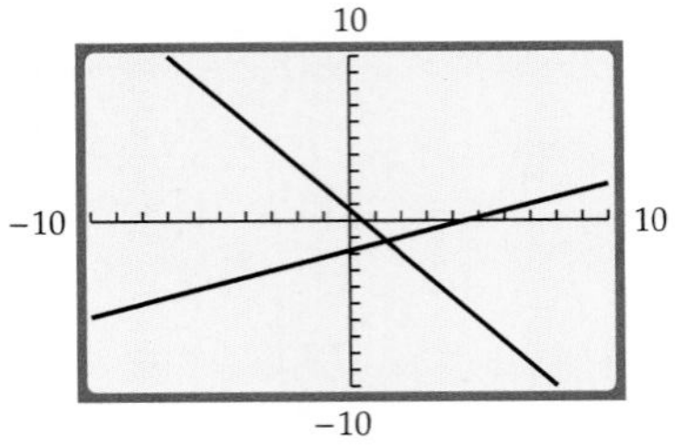

Press [2nd] CALC 5 [ENTER] [ENTER] [ENTER]. After a few seconds, the point of intersection will appear at the bottom of the screen as X = 1.4230769, Y = −1.230769.

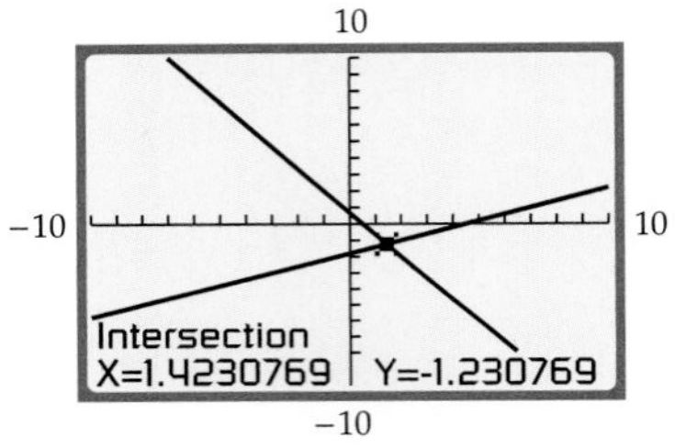

Solve by using a graphing calculator.

1. $4x - 5y = 48$
   $5x + 7y = 7$

2. $3x + 2y = 11$
   $7x - 6y = 13$

3. $x = 3y + 2$
   $y = 4x - 2$

4. $x = 2y - 5$
   $x = 3y + 2$

Chapter 6 Summary

Key Words	*Examples*
Equations considered together are called a **system of equations.** [6.1.1, p. 328]	An example of a system of equations is $4x + y = 6$, $3x + 2y = 7$
A **solution of a system of equations in two variables** is an ordered pair that is a solution of each equation of the system. [6.1.1, p. 329]	The solution of the system of equations shown above is the ordered pair (1, 2) because it is a solution of each equation in the system.

An **independent system of equations** has one solution. The graphs of the equations in an independent system of linear equations intersect at one point. [6.1.1, pp. 330–331]

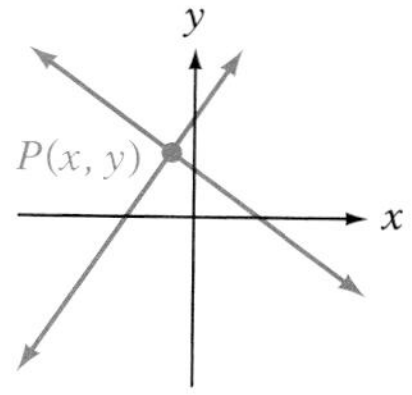

An **inconsistent system of equations** has no solution. The graphs of the equations in an inconsistent system of linear equations are parallel lines. If, when you are solving a system of equations algebraically, the variable is eliminated and the result is a false equation, such as $-3 = 8$, the system is inconsistent. [6.1.1/6.2.1/6.3.1, pp. 330–331, 339, 344–345]

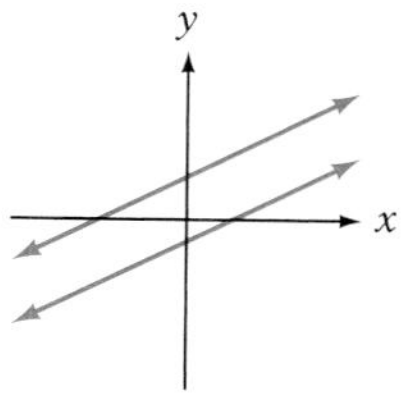

A **dependent system of equations** has an infinite number of solutions. The graphs of the equations in a dependent system of linear equations represent the same line. If, when you are solving a system of equations algebraically, the variable is eliminated and the result is a true equation, such as $1 = 1$, the system is dependent. [6.1.1/6.2.1/6.3.1, pp. 330–331, 339, 345]

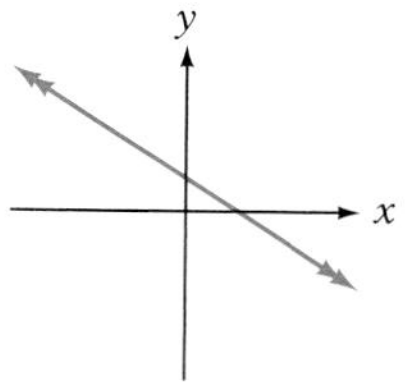

Essential Rules and Procedures

To solve a system of linear equations in two variables by graphing, graph each equation on the same coordinate system. If the lines graphed intersect at one point, the point of intersection is the ordered pair that is a solution of the system. If the lines graphed are parallel, the system is inconsistent. If the lines represent the same line, the system is dependent. [6.1.1, pp. 328–331]

Solve by graphing:
$$\begin{aligned} x + 2y &= 4 \\ 2x + y &= -1 \end{aligned}$$

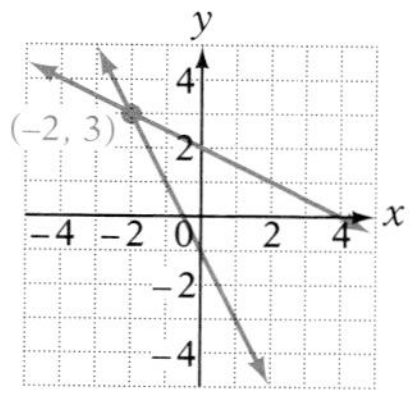

The solution is $(-2, 3)$.

To solve a system of linear equations by the substitution method, one variable must be written in terms of the other variable. [6.2.1, p. 337]

Solve by substitution:
$$\begin{aligned} 2x - y &= 5 \quad (1) \\ 3x + y &= 5 \quad (2) \end{aligned}$$

$$\begin{aligned} 3x + y &= 5 \\ y &= -3x + 5 \end{aligned}$$
- **Solve equation (2) for *y*.**

$$\begin{aligned} 2x - y &= 5 \\ 2x - (-3x + 5) &= 5 \\ 2x + 3x - 5 &= 5 \\ 5x &= 10 \\ x &= 2 \end{aligned}$$
- **Substitute for *y* in equation (1).**

$$\begin{aligned} y &= -3x + 5 \\ y &= -3(2) + 5 \\ y &= -1 \end{aligned}$$
- **Substitute the value of *x* to find *y*.**

The solution is $(2, -1)$.

To solve a system of linear equations by the addition method, use the Multiplication Property of Equations to rewrite one or both of the equations so that the coefficients of one variable are opposites. Then add the two equations and solve for the variables. [6.3.1, p. 343]

Solve by the addition method:

$$3x + y = 4 \quad (1)$$
$$x + y = 6 \quad (2)$$

$$3x + y = 4$$
$$-x - y = -6$$

- **Multiply both sides of equation (2) by −1.**

$$2x = -2$$
$$x = -1$$

- **Add the two equations.**
- **Solve for *x*.**

$$x + y = 6$$
$$-1 + y = 6$$
$$y = 7$$

- **Substitute the value of *x* to find *y*.**

The solution is $(-1, 7)$.

Chapter 6 Review Exercises

1. Solve by substitution: $4x + 7y = 3$
   $x = y - 2$

2. Solve by graphing: $3x + y = 3$
   $x = 2$

3. Solve by the addition method: $3x + 8y = -1$
   $x - 2y = -5$

4. Solve by substitution: $8x - y = 2$
   $y = 5x + 1$

5. Solve by graphing: $x + y = 2$
   $x - y = 0$

6. Solve by the addition method: $4x - y = 9$
   $2x + 3y = -13$

7. Solve by substitution: $-2x + y = -4$
   $x = y + 1$

8. Solve by the addition method:
   $8x - y = 25$
   $32x - 4y = 100$

9. Solve by the addition method: $5x - 15y = 30$
   $2x + 6y = 0$

10. Solve by graphing: $3x - y = 6$
    $y = -3$

11. Solve by the addition method: $7x - 2y = 0$
    $2x + y = -11$

12. Solve by substitution: $x - 5y = 4$
    $y = x - 4$

13. Is $(-1, -3)$ a solution of the system
    $5x + 4y = -17$
    $2x - y = 1$?

14. Solve by the addition method:
    $6x + 4y = -3$
    $12x - 10y = -15$

15. Solve by the addition method: $5x + 2y = -9$
    $12x - 7y = 2$

16. Solve by graphing: $x - 3y = 12$
    $y = x - 6$

17. Solve by the addition method:
    $5x + 7y = 21$
    $20x + 28y = 63$

18. Solve by substitution: $9x + 12y = -1$
    $x - 4y = -1$

19. Solve by graphing: $4x - 2y = 8$
$y = 2x - 4$

20. Solve by the addition method:
$3x + y = -2$
$-9x - 3y = 6$

21. Solve by the addition method: $11x - 2y = 4$
$25x - 4y = 2$

22. Solve by substitution: $4x + 3y = 12$
$y = -\frac{4}{3}x + 4$

23. Solve by graphing: $y = -\frac{1}{4}x + 3$
$2x - y = 6$

24. Solve by the addition method: $2x - y = 5$
$10x - 5y = 20$

25. Solve by substitution: $6x + 5y = -2$
$y = 2x - 2$

26. Is $(-2, 0)$ a solution of the system
$-x + 9y = 2$
$6x - 4y = 12$?

27. Solve by the addition method: $6x - 18y = 7$
$9x + 24y = 2$

28. Solve by substitution: $12x - 9y = 18$
$y = \frac{4}{3}x - 3$

29. Solve by substitution: $9x - y = -3$
$18x - y = 0$

30. Solve by graphing: $x + 2y = 3$
$y = -\frac{1}{2}x + 1$

31. Solve by the addition method: $7x - 9y = 9$
$3x - y = 1$

32. Solve by substitution: $7x + 3y = -16$
$x - 2y = 5$

33. Solve by substitution: $5x - 3y = 6$
$x - y = 2$

34. Solve by the addition method: $6x + y = 12$
$9x + 2y = 18$

35. Solve by the addition method: $5x + 12y = 4$
$x + 6y = 8$

36. Solve by substitution: $6x - y = 0$
$7x - y = 1$

37. **Uniform Motion** Flying with the wind, a plane can travel 800 mi in 4 h. Against the wind, the plane requires 5 h to fly the same distance. Find the rate of the plane in calm air and the rate of the wind.

38. **Recreation** Admission to a movie theater is \$7 for adults and \$5 for children. If the receipts from 200 tickets were \$1120, how many adult tickets and how many children's tickets were sold?

39. **Uniform Motion** A canoeist traveling with the current traveled the 30 mi between two riverside campsites in 3 h. The return trip took 5 h. Find the rate of the canoeist in still water and the rate of the current.

40. **Postage** A small wood carving company mailed 190 advertisements, some requiring 33¢ in postage and others requiring 55¢ in postage. If the total cost for the mailings was \$75.90, how many mailings that required 33¢ were sent?

41. **Uniform Motion** A boat traveling with the current went 48 km in 3 h. Against the current, the boat traveled 24 km in 2 h. Find the rate of the boat in calm water and the rate of the current.

42. **Purchases** A music shop sells some compact discs for \$15 and some for \$10. A customer spent \$120 on 10 compact discs. How many at each price did the customer purchase?

43. **Uniform Motion** With a tailwind, a flight crew flew 420 km in 3 h. Flying against the tailwind, the crew flew 440 km in 4 h. Find the rate of the plane in calm air and the rate of the wind.

44. **Uniform Motion** A paddle boat can travel 4 mi downstream in 1 h. Paddling upstream, against the current, the paddle boat travels 2 mi in 1 h. Find the rate of the boat in calm water and the rate of the current.

45. **Farming** A silo contains a mixture of lentils and corn. If 50 bushels of lentils were added to this mixture, there would be twice as many bushels of lentils as bushels of corn. If 150 bushels of corn were added to the original mixture, there would be the same amount of corn as lentils. How many bushels of each are in the silo?

46. **Uniform Motion** Flying with the wind, a small plane flew 360 mi in 3 h. Against the wind, the plane took 4 h to fly the same distance. Find the rate of the plane in calm air and the rate of the wind.

47. **Coins** A coin purse contains 80¢ in nickels and dimes. If there are 12 coins in all, how many dimes are in the coin purse?

48. **Uniform Motion** A pilot flying with the wind flew 2100 mi from one city to another in 6 h. The return trip against the wind took 7 h. Find the rate of the plane in calm air and the rate of the wind.

49. **Investments** An investor buys 1500 shares of stock, some costing \$6 per share and the rest costing \$25 per share. If the total cost of the stock is \$12,800, how many shares of each did the investor buy?

50. **Uniform Motion** Rowing with the current, a sculling team went 24 mi in 2 h. Rowing against the current, the team went 18 mi in 3 h. Find the rate of the sculling team in calm water and the rate of the current.

Chapter 6 Test

1. Solve by substitution: $4x - y = 11$, $y = 2x - 5$

2. Solve by the addition method: $4x + 3y = 11$, $5x - 3y = 7$

3. Is $(-2, 3)$ a solution of the system $2x + 5y = 11$, $x + 3y = 7$?

4. Solve by substitution: $x = 2y + 3$, $3x - 2y = 5$

5. Solve by the addition method: $2x - 5y = 6$, $4x + 3y = -1$

6. Solve by graphing: $3x + 2y = 6$, $5x + 2y = 2$

7. Solve by substitution: $4x + 2y = 3$, $y = -2x + 1$

8. Solve by substitution: $3x + 5y = 1$, $2x - y = 5$

9. Solve by the addition method: $7x + 3y = 11$, $2x - 5y = 9$

10. Solve by substitution: $3x - 5y = 13$, $x + 3y = 1$

11. Solve by the addition method: $5x + 6y = -7$, $3x + 4y = -5$

12. Is $(2, 1)$ a solution of the system $3x - 2y = 8$, $4x + 5y = 3$?

13. Solve by substitution: $3x - y = 5$, $y = 2x - 3$

14. Solve by the addition method: $3x + 2y = 2$, $5x - 2y = 14$

15. Solve by graphing: $3x + 2y = 6$, $3x - 2y = 6$

16. Solve by substitution: $x = 3y + 1$, $2x + 5y = 13$

17. Solve by the addition method: $5x + 4y = 7$, $3x - 2y = 13$

18. Solve by graphing: $3x + 6y = 2$, $y = -\frac{1}{2}x + \frac{1}{3}$

19. Solve by substitution: $4x - 3y = 1$, $2x + y = 3$

20. Solve by the addition method: $5x - 3y = 29$, $4x + 7y = -5$

21. Solve by substitution: $3x - 5y = -23$, $x + 2y = -4$

22. Solve by the addition method: $9x - 2y = 17$, $5x + 3y = -7$

23. **Uniform Motion** With the wind, a plane flies 240 mi in 2 h. Against the wind, the plane requires 3 h to fly the same distance. Find the rate of the plane in calm air and the rate of the wind.

24. **Uniform Motion** With the current, a motorboat can travel 48 mi in 3 h. Against the current, the boat requires 4 h to travel the same distance. Find the rate of the boat in calm water and the rate of the current.

25. **Coins** Two coin banks contain only dimes and nickels. In the first bank, the total value of the coins is \$5.50. In the second bank, there are one-half as many dimes as in the first bank and 10 fewer nickels. The total value of the coins in the second bank is \$3. Find the number of dimes and the number of nickels in the first bank.

Cumulative Review Exercises

1. Given $A = \{-8, -4, 0\}$, which elements of set A are less than or equal to -4?

2. Use the roster method to write the set of positive integers less than or equal to 10.

3. Simplify: $12 - 2(7 - 5)^2 \div 4$

4. Simplify: $2[5a - 3(2 - 5a) - 8]$

5. Evaluate $\dfrac{a^2 - b^2}{2a}$ when $a = 4$ and $b = -2$.

6. Solve: $-\dfrac{3}{4}x = \dfrac{9}{8}$

7. Solve: $4 - 3(2 - 3x) = 7x - 9$

8. Solve: $3[2 - 4(x + 1)] = 6x - 2$

9. Solve: $-7x - 5 > 4x + 50$

10. Solve: $5 + 2(x + 1) \leq 13$

11. What percent of 50 is 12?

12. Find the x- and y-intercepts of $3x - 6y = 12$.

13. Find the slope of the line that contains the points whose coordinates are $(2, -3)$ and $(-3, 4)$.

14. Find the equation of the line that contains the point whose coordinates are $(-2, 3)$ and has slope $-\dfrac{3}{2}$.

15. Graph: $3x - 2y = 6$

16. Graph: $y = -\dfrac{1}{3}x + 3$

17. Graph the solution set of $y > -3x + 4$.

18. Graph: $f(x) = \dfrac{3}{4}x + 2$

19. Find the domain and range of the relation $\{(-5, 5), (0, 5), (1, 5), (5, 5)\}$. Is the relation a function?

20. Evaluate $f(x) = -2x - 5$ at $x = -4$.

21. Is $(2, 0)$ a solution of the system $\begin{aligned} 5x - 3y &= 10 \\ 4x + 7y &= 8? \end{aligned}$

22. Solve by substitution: $\begin{aligned} 2x - 3y &= -7 \\ x + 4y &= 2 \end{aligned}$

23. Solve by graphing: $\begin{aligned} 2x + 3y &= 6 \\ 3x + y &= 2 \end{aligned}$

24. Solve by the addition method: $\begin{aligned} 5x - 2y &= 8 \\ 4x + 3y &= 11 \end{aligned}$

25. Find the range of the function given by the equation $f(x) = 5x - 2$ if the domain is $\{-4, -2, 0, 2, 4\}$.

26. **Manufacturing** A business manager has determined that the cost per unit for a camera is \$90 and that the fixed costs per month are \$3500. Find the number of cameras produced during a month in which the total cost was \$21,500. Use the equation $T = U \cdot N + F$, where T is the total cost, U is the cost per unit, N is the number of units produced, and F is the fixed cost.

27. **Investments** A total of \$8750 is invested in two simple interest accounts. On one account, the annual simple interest rate is 9.6%. On the second account, the annual simple interest rate is 7.2%. How much should be invested in each account so that both accounts earn the same amount of interest?

28. **Uniform Motion** Flying with the wind, a plane can fly 570 mi in 3 h. Flying against the wind, it takes the same amount of time to fly 390 mi. Find the rate of the plane in calm air and the rate of the wind.

29. **Uniform Motion** With the current, a motorboat can travel 24 mi in 2 h. Against the current, the boat requires 3 h to travel the same distance. Find the rate of the boat in calm water.

30. **Coins** Two coin banks contain only dimes and nickels. In the first bank, the total value of the coins is \$5.25. In the second bank, there are one-half as many dimes as in the first bank and 15 fewer nickels. The total value of the coins in the second bank is \$2.50. Find the number of dimes in the first bank.

CHAPTER

7 Polynomials

OBJECTIVES

As we learned in the chapter "Linear Equations and Inequalities," the population of the United States grows from year to year. This has resulted in a drastic decrease in woodlands and farmland and an increase in land used for housing developments and shopping centers. It has led demographers (people who study the characteristics of human populations, such as their size, growth, density, and distribution) to ask questions about population and land allocation. The **Projects & Group Activities on page 409** ask you to determine the answers to questions concerning land allocation.

Online Study Center DVD SSM

Need help? For online student resources, such as section quizzes, visit the Online Study Center at college.hmco.com/pic/aufmannBAWA7e.

Prep Test

1. Subtract: $-2 - (-3)$
2. Multiply: $-3(6)$
3. Simplify: $-\frac{24}{-36}$
4. Evaluate $3n^4$ when $n = -2$.
5. If $\frac{a}{b}$ is a fraction in simplest form, what number is not a possible value of b?
6. Are $2x^2$ and $2x$ like terms?
7. Simplify: $3x^2 - 4x + 1 + 2x^2 - 5x - 7$
8. Simplify: $-4y + 4y$
9. Simplify: $-3(2x - 8)$
10. Simplify: $3xy - 4y - 2(5xy - 7y)$

7.1 Addition and Subtraction of Polynomials

OBJECTIVE 1 Add polynomials

A **monomial** is a number, a variable, or a product of numbers and variables. For instance,

7	b	$\frac{2}{3}a$	$12xy^2$
A number	A variable	A product of a number and a variable	A product of a number and variables

The expression $3\sqrt{x}$ is not a monomial because $\sqrt{x}$ cannot be written as a product of variables. The expression $\frac{2x}{y^2}$ is not a monomial because it is a *quotient* of variables.

A **polynomial** is a variable expression in which the terms are monomials.

A polynomial of *one* term is a **monomial.** $-7x^2$ is a monomial.

A polynomial of *two* terms is a **binomial.** $4x + 2$ is a binomial.

A polynomial of *three* terms is a **trinomial.** $7x^2 + 5x - 7$ is a trinomial.

The terms of a polynomial in one variable are usually arranged so that the exponents of the variable decrease from left to right. This is called **descending order.**

$$4x^3 - 3x^2 + 6x - 1$$
$$5y^4 - 2y^3 + y^2 - 7y + 8$$

The **degree of a polynomial in one variable** is the value of the largest exponent on the variable. The degree of $4x^3 - 3x^2 + 6x - 1$ is 3. The degree of $5y^4 - 2y^3 + y^2 - 7y + 8$ is 4. The degree of a nonzero constant is zero. For instance, the degree of 7 is zero. The number zero has no degree.

Polynomials can be added, using either a vertical or a horizontal format, by combining like terms.

EXAMPLE 1 Add: $(2x^2 + x - 1) + (3x^3 + 4x^2 - 5)$
Use a vertical format.

Solution

$$\begin{array}{r} 2x^2 + x - 1 \\ \underline{3x^3 + 4x^2 \qquad - 5} \\ 3x^3 + 6x^2 + x - 6 \end{array}$$

- **Arrange the terms of each polynomial in descending order with like terms in the same column.**
- **Combine the terms in each column.**

PROBLEM 1 Add: $(2x^2 + 4x - 3) + (5x^2 - 6x)$
Use a vertical format.

Solution See page S15.

EXAMPLE 2 Add: $(3x^3 - 7x + 2) + (7x^2 + 2x - 7)$
Use a horizontal format.

Solution

$(3x^3 - 7x + 2) + (7x^2 + 2x - 7)$
$= 3x^3 + 7x^2 + (-7x + 2x) + (2 - 7)$

- **Use the Commutative and Associative Properties of Addition to rearrange and group like terms.**

$= 3x^3 + 7x^2 - 5x - 5$

- **Combine like terms, and write the polynomial in descending order.**

PROBLEM 2 Add: $(-4x^2 - 3xy + 2y^2) + (3x^2 - 4y^2)$
Use a horizontal format.

Solution See page S16.

OBJECTIVE 2 Subtract polynomials

> **Take Note**
> The **opposite of a polynomial** is the polynomial with the sign of every term changed.

The **opposite** of the polynomial $x^2 - 2x + 3$ is $-(x^2 - 2x + 3)$.

To simplify the opposite of a polynomial, remove the parentheses and change the sign of every term inside the parentheses.

$$-(x^2 - 2x + 3) = -x^2 + 2x - 3$$

Polynomials can be subtracted using either a vertical or a horizontal format. To subtract, add the opposite of the second polynomial to the first.

EXAMPLE 3 Subtract: $(-3x^2 - 7) - (-8x^2 + 3x - 4)$
Use a vertical format.

Solution The opposite of $-8x^2 + 3x - 4$ is $8x^2 - 3x + 4$.

$$\begin{array}{r} -3x^2 \phantom{{}-3x} - 7 \\ 8x^2 - 3x + 4 \\ \hline 5x^2 - 3x - 3 \end{array}$$

- **Write the terms of each polynomial in descending order with like terms in the same column.**
- **Combine the terms in each column.**

PROBLEM 3 Subtract: $(8y^2 - 4xy + x^2) - (2y^2 - xy + 5x^2)$
Use a vertical format.

Solution See page S16.

EXAMPLE 4 Subtract: $(5x^2 - 3x + 4) - (-3x^3 - 2x + 8)$
Use a horizontal format.

Solution
$(5x^2 - 3x + 4) - (-3x^3 - 2x + 8)$
$= (5x^2 - 3x + 4) + (3x^3 + 2x - 8)$ • **Rewrite subtraction as addition of the opposite.**
$= 3x^3 + 5x^2 + (-3x + 2x) + (4 - 8)$
$= 3x^3 + 5x^2 - x - 4$ • **Combine like terms. Write the polynomial in descending order.**

PROBLEM 4 Subtract: $(-3a^2 - 4a + 2) - (5a^3 + 2a - 6)$
Use a horizontal format.

Solution See page S16.

7.1 Concept Review

Determine whether the statement is always true, sometimes true, or never true.

1. The terms of a polynomial are monomials.

2. The polynomial $5x^3 + 4x^6 + 3x + 2$ is written in descending order.

3. The degree of the polynomial $7x^2 - 8x + 1$ is 3.

4. Like terms have the same coefficient and the same variable part.

5. The opposite of the polynomial $ax^3 - bx^2 + cx + d$ is $-ax^3 + bx^2 - cx - d$.

6. Subtraction is addition of the opposite.

7.1 Exercises

1 Add polynomials

State whether the polynomial is a monomial, a binomial, or a trinomial.

1. $8x^4 - 6x^2$

2. $4a^2b^2 + 9ab + 10$

3. $7x^3y^4$

State whether or not the expression is a monomial.

4. $3\sqrt{x}$

5. $\frac{4}{x}$

6. x^2y^2

State whether or not the expression is a polynomial.

7. $\frac{1}{5}x^3 + \frac{1}{2}x$

8. $\frac{1}{5x^2} + \frac{1}{2x}$

9. $x + \sqrt{5}$

10. In your own words, explain the terms *monomial, binomial, trinomial,* and *polynomial*. Give an example of each.

11. To use a vertical format to add polynomials, arrange the terms of each polynomial in __?__ order with __?__ terms in the same column.

12. Use a horizontal format to add $(-4y^3 + 3xy + x^3) + (2y^3 - 8xy)$.

$(-4y^3 + 3xy + x^3) + (2y^3 - 8xy)$

$= (-4y^3 + \underline{\quad ? \quad}) + (3xy + \underline{\quad ? \quad}) + x^3$

$= \underline{\quad ? \quad}$

- **Use the Commutative and Associative Properties of Addition to rearrange and group like terms.**
- **Combine like terms and write the terms of the polynomial in descending order.**

Add. Use a vertical format.

13. $(x^2 + 7x) + (-3x^2 - 4x)$

14. $(3y^2 - 2y) + (5y^2 + 6y)$

15. $(y^2 + 4y) + (-4y - 8)$

16. $(3x^2 + 9x) + (6x - 24)$

17. $(2x^2 + 6x + 12) + (3x^2 + x + 8)$

18. $(x^2 + x + 5) + (3x^2 - 10x + 4)$

19. $(x^3 - 7x + 4) + (2x^2 + x - 10)$

20. $(3y^3 + y^2 + 1) + (-4y^3 - 6y - 3)$

21. $(2a^3 - 7a + 1) + (-3a^2 - 4a + 1)$

22. $(5r^3 - 6r^2 + 3r) + (r^2 - 2r - 3)$

Add. Use a horizontal format.

23. $(4x^2 + 2x) + (x^2 + 6x)$

24. $(-3y^2 + y) + (4y^2 + 6y)$

25. $(4x^2 - 5xy) + (3x^2 + 6xy - 4y^2)$

26. $(2x^2 - 4y^2) + (6x^2 - 2xy + 4y^2)$

27. $(2a^2 - 7a + 10) + (a^2 + 4a + 7)$

28. $(-6x^2 + 7x + 3) + (3x^2 + x + 3)$

29. $(5x^3 + 7x - 7) + (10x^2 - 8x + 3)$

30. $(3y^3 + 4y + 9) + (2y^2 + 4y - 21)$

31. $(2r^2 - 5r + 7) + (3r^3 - 6r)$

32. $(3y^3 + 4y + 14) + (-4y^2 + 21)$

33. $(3x^2 + 7x + 10) + (-2x^3 + 3x + 1)$

34. $(7x^3 + 4x - 1) + (2x^2 - 6x + 2)$

For Exercises 35 and 36, use these three polynomials in which a, b, c, and d are all positive numbers.

$$P = ax^3 + bx^2 - cx + d$$
$$Q = -ax^3 - bx^2 + cx - d$$
$$R = -ax^3 + bx^2 + cx + d$$

35. Which sum will be a polynomial of degree 3, $P + Q$, $Q + R$, or $P + R$?

36. Which sum will be zero, $P + Q$, $Q + R$, or $P + R$?

2 Subtract polynomials

37. The opposite of $7x^2 + 5x - 3$ is $-(7x^2 + 5x - 3) =$ __?__.

38. $(5x^2 + 7x - 2) - (4x^2 - 6x + 3) = (5x^2 + 7x - 2) + ($__?__$)$

Subtract. Use a vertical format.

39. $(x^2 - 6x) - (x^2 - 10x)$

40. $(y^2 + 4y) - (y^2 + 10y)$

41. $(2y^2 - 4y) - (-y^2 + 2)$

42. $(-3a^2 - 2a) - (4a^2 - 4)$

43. $(x^2 - 2x + 1) - (x^2 + 5x + 8)$

44. $(3x^2 + 2x - 2) - (5x^2 - 5x + 6)$

45. $(4x^3 + 5x + 2) - (-3x^2 + 2x + 1)$

46. $(5y^2 - y + 2) - (-2y^3 + 3y - 3)$

47. $(2y^3 + 6y - 2) - (y^3 + y^2 + 4)$

48. $(-2x^2 - x + 4) - (-x^3 + 3x - 2)$

Subtract. Use a horizontal format.

49. $(y^2 - 10xy) - (2y^2 + 3xy)$

50. $(x^2 - 3xy) - (-2x^2 + xy)$

51. $(3x^2 + x - 3) - (x^2 + 4x - 2)$

52. $(5y^2 - 2y + 1) - (-3y^2 - y - 2)$

53. $(-2x^3 + x - 1) - (-x^2 + x - 3)$

54. $(2x^2 + 5x - 3) - (3x^3 + 2x - 5)$

55. $(4a^3 - 2a + 1) - (a^3 - 2a + 3)$

56. $(b^2 - 8b + 7) - (4b^3 - 7b - 8)$

57. $(4y^3 - y - 1) - (2y^2 - 3y + 3)$

58. $(3x^2 - 2x - 3) - (2x^3 - 2x^2 + 4)$

For Exercises 59 and 60, P and Q are polynomials such that $P = ax^2 - bx + c$ and $Q = -dx^2 - ex + f$, where a, b, c, d, e, and f are all positive numbers.

59. If $a > d$, $b > e$, and $c > f$, state the sign of the coefficient of each term of $P - Q$.
a. the x^2 term **b.** the x term **c.** the constant term

60. If $a < d$, $b > e$, and $c < f$, state the sign of the coefficient of each term of $Q - P$.
a. the x^2 term **b.** the x term **c.** the constant term

7.1 Applying Concepts

Simplify.

61. $\left(\frac{2}{3}a^2 + \frac{1}{2}a - \frac{3}{4}\right) - \left(\frac{5}{3}a^2 + \frac{1}{2}a + \frac{1}{4}\right)$

62. $\left(\frac{3}{5}x^2 + \frac{1}{6}x - \frac{5}{8}\right) + \left(\frac{2}{5}x^2 + \frac{5}{6}x - \frac{3}{8}\right)$

Solve.

63. What polynomial must be added to $3x^2 - 4x - 2$ so that the sum is $-x^2 + 2x + 1$?

64. What polynomial must be added to $-2x^3 + 4x - 7$ so that the sum is $x^2 - x - 1$?

65. What polynomial must be subtracted from $6x^2 - 4x - 2$ so that the difference is $2x^2 + 2x - 5$?

66. What polynomial must be subtracted from $2x^3 - x^2 + 4x - 2$ so that the difference is $x^3 + 2x - 8$?

67. Is it possible to subtract two polynomials, each of degree 3, and have the difference be a polynomial of degree 2? If so, give an example. If not, explain why not.

68. Is it possible to add two polynomials, each of degree 3, and have the sum be a polynomial of degree 2? If so, give an example. If not, explain why not.

7.2 Multiplication of Monomials

OBJECTIVE 1 Multiply monomials

Recall that in the exponential expression x^5, x is the base and 5 is the exponent. The exponent indicates the number of times the base occurs as a factor.

The product of exponential expressions with the *same* base can be simplified by writing each expression in factored form and writing the result with an exponent.

$$x^3 \cdot x^2 = \underbrace{\overbrace{(x \cdot x \cdot x)}^{3\text{ factors}} \cdot \overbrace{(x \cdot x)}^{2\text{ factors}}}_{5\text{ factors}}$$
$$= x \cdot x \cdot x \cdot x \cdot x$$
$$= x^5$$

Adding the exponents results in the same product.

$$x^3 \cdot x^2 = x^{3+2} = x^5$$

Rule for Multiplying Exponential Expressions

If m and n are integers, then $x^m \cdot x^n = x^{m+n}$.

For example, in the expression $a^2 \cdot a^6 \cdot a$, the bases are the same. The expression can be simplified by adding the exponents. Recall that $a = a^1$.

$$a^2 \cdot a^6 \cdot a = a^{2+6+1} = a^9$$

Take Note

The Rule for Multiplying Exponential Expressions requires that the bases be the same. The expression x^3y^2 cannot be simplified.

EXAMPLE 1 Multiply: $(2xy)(3x^2y)$

Solution $(2xy)(3x^2y)$

$= (2 \cdot 3)(x \cdot x^2)(y \cdot y)$ • **Use the Commutative and Associative Properties of Multiplication to rearrange and group factors.**

$= 6x^{1+2}y^{1+1}$ • **Multiply variables with the same base by adding the exponents.**

$= 6x^3y^2$

PROBLEM 1 Multiply: $(3x^2)(6x^3)$

Solution See page S16.

EXAMPLE 2 Multiply: $(2x^2y)(-5xy^4)$

Solution $(2x^2y)(-5xy^4)$

$= [2(-5)](x^2 \cdot x)(y \cdot y^4)$ • **Use the Properties of Multiplication to rearrange and group factors.**

$= -10x^3y^5$ • **Multiply variables with the same base by adding the exponents.**

PROBLEM 2 Multiply: $(-3xy^2)(-4x^2y^3)$

Solution See page S16.

OBJECTIVE 2 Simplify powers of monomials

Point of Interest

One of the first symbolic representations of powers was given by Diophantus (ca. A.D. 250) in his book Arithmetica. *He used* **Δ^Y** *for* x^2 *and* **k^Y** *for* x^3. *The symbol* **Δ^Y** *was the first two letters of the Greek words* dunamis, *meaning "power";* **k^Y** *was from the Greek word* kubos, *meaning "cube." He also combined these symbols to denote higher powers. For instance,* **Δk^Y** *was the symbol for* x^5.

A power of a monomial can be simplified by rewriting the expression in factored form and then using the Rule for Multiplying Exponential Expressions.

$$(x^2)^3 = x^2 \cdot x^2 \cdot x^2 = x^{2+2+2} = x^6$$

$$(x^4y^3)^2 = (x^4y^3)(x^4y^3) = x^4 \cdot y^3 \cdot x^4 \cdot y^3 = (x^4 \cdot x^4)(y^3 \cdot y^3) = x^{4+4}y^{3+3} = x^8y^6$$

Note that multiplying each exponent inside the parentheses by the exponent outside the parentheses gives the same result.

$$(x^2)^3 = x^{2\cdot 3} = x^6 \qquad (x^4y^3)^2 = x^{4\cdot 2}y^{3\cdot 2} = x^8y^6$$

Rule for Simplifying Powers of Exponential Expressions

If m and n are integers, then $(x^m)^n = x^{mn}$.

Simplify: $(x^5)^2$

Multiply the exponents. $(x^5)^2 = x^{5\cdot 2} = x^{10}$

Rule for Simplifying Powers of Products

If m, n, and p are integers, then $(x^my^n)^p = x^{mp}y^{np}$.

Simplify: $(c^5d^3)^6$

Multiply each exponent inside the parentheses by the exponent outside the parentheses.

$$(c^5d^3)^6 = c^{5\cdot 6}d^{3\cdot 6} = c^{30}d^{18}$$

Simplify: $(3a^2b)^3$

Multiply each exponent inside the parentheses by the exponent outside the parentheses.

$$(3a^2b)^3 = 3^{1\cdot 3}a^{2\cdot 3}b^{1\cdot 3} = 3^3a^6b^3 = 27a^6b^3$$

EXAMPLE 3 Simplify: $(-2x)(-3xy^2)^3$

Solution $(-2x)(-3xy^2)^3$

$= (-2x)(-3)^3x^3y^6$ • **Multiply each exponent in $-3xy^2$ by the exponent outside the parentheses.**

$= (-2x)(-27)x^3y^6$ • **Simplify $(-3)^3$.**

$= [-2(-27)](x \cdot x^3)y^6$ • **Use the Properties of Multiplication to rearrange and group factors.**

$= 54x^4y^6$ • **Multiply variable expressions with the same base by adding the exponents.**

PROBLEM 3 Simplify: $(3x)(2x^2y)^3$

Solution See page S16.

7.2 Concept Review

Determine whether the statement is always true, sometimes true, or never true.

1. In the expression $(6x)^4$, x is the base and 4 is the exponent.

2. To multiply $x^m \cdot x^n$, multiply the exponents.

3. The expression "a power of a monomial" means the monomial is the base of an exponential expression.

4. $x^6 \cdot x \cdot x^8 = x^{14}$

5. $(4x^3y^5)^2 = 4x^6y^{10}$

6. $a^2 \cdot b^7 = ab^9$

7.2 Exercises

1 Multiply monomials

1. Explain how to multiply two exponential expressions with the same base. Provide an example.

2. Use the Rule for Multiplying Exponential Expressions to multiply:
$(x^7)(x^2) = x^{\underline{?} + \underline{?}} = \underline{\quad ? \quad}$.

3. Multiply: $(5a^6b)(2a^5b^3)$

$(5a^6b)(2a^5b^3)$

$= (5 \cdot \underline{\quad ? \quad})(a^6 \cdot \underline{\quad ? \quad})(b \cdot \underline{\quad ? \quad})$ • **Use the Commutative and Associative Properties of Multiplication to rearrange and group factors.**

$= (\underline{\quad ? \quad})(a^{\underline{?} + \underline{?}})(b^{\underline{?} + \underline{?}})$ • **Multiply variables with the same base by ___?___ the exponents.**

$= 10a^{\underline{?}}b^{\underline{?}}$ • **Simplify.**

4. State whether the expression can be simplified using the Rule for Multiplying Exponential Expressions.
a. $x^4 + x^5$ **b.** x^4x^5 **c.** x^4y^4 **d.** $x^4 + x^4$

Multiply.

5. $(x)(2x)$

6. $(-3y)(y)$

7. $(3x)(4x)$

8. $(7y^3)(7y^2)$

9. $(-2a^3)(-3a^4)$

10. $(5a^6)(-2a^5)$

11. $(x^2y)(xy^4)$

12. $(x^2y^4)(xy^7)$

13. $(-2x^4)(5x^5y)$

14. $(-3a^3)(2a^2b^4)$

15. $(x^2y^4)(x^5y^4)$

16. $(a^2b^4)(ab^3)$

17. $(2xy)(-3x^2y^4)$

18. $(-3a^2b)(-2ab^3)$

19. $(x^2yz)(x^2y^4)$

20. $(-ab^2c)(a^2b^5)$

21. $(a^2b^3)(ab^2c^4)$

22. $(x^2y^3z)(x^3y^4)$

23. $(-a^2b^2)(a^3b^6)$

24. $(xy^4)(-xy^3)$

25. $(-6a^3)(a^2b)$

26. $(2a^2b^3)(-4ab^2)$

27. $(-5y^4z)(-8y^6z^5)$

28. $(3x^2y)(-4xy^2)$

29. $(10ab^2)(-2ab)$

30. $(x^2y)(yz)(xyz)$

31. $(xy^2z)(x^2y)(z^2y^2)$

32. $(-2x^2y^3)(3xy)(-5x^3y^4)$

33. $(4a^2b)(-3a^3b^4)(a^5b^2)$

34. $(3ab^2)(-2abc)(4ac^2)$

2 Simplify powers of monomials

35. Explain how to simplify a power of an exponential expression. Provide an example.

State whether the expression is the product of two exponential expressions or a power of an exponential expression.

36. a. $b^4 \cdot b^8$ **b.** $(b^4)^8$

37. a. $(2z)^2$ **b.** $2z \cdot z$

38. a. $(3a^4)^5$ **b.** $(3a^4)(5a)$

39. a. $x(-xy^4)$ **b.** $(-xy)^4$

40. a. Use the Rule for Simplifying Powers of Exponential Expressions to simplify:
$(x^4)^7 = x^{(\underline{?})(\underline{?})} = \underline{\quad ? \quad}$
b. Use the Rule for Simplifying Powers of Products to simplify:
$(x^4y^2)^6 = x^{(\underline{?})(\underline{?})}y^{(\underline{?})(\underline{?})} = \underline{\quad ? \quad}$

41. State whether or not the expression can be simplified using the Rule for Simplifying Powers of Products.
a. $(xy)^3$ **b.** $(x + y)^3$ **c.** $(a^3 + b^4)^2$ **d.** $(a^3b^4)^2$

42. **a.** True or false? $a^2b^5 = ab^{10}$
b. True or false? $a^2b^5 = ab^7$
c. True or false? $(a^2b^5)^2 = a^4b^{25}$
d. True or false? $(a^2 + b^5)^2 = a^4 + b^{10}$

Simplify.

43. $(2^2)^3$ **44.** $(3^2)^2$ **45.** $(-2)^2$ **46.** $(-3)^3$

47. $(-2^2)^3$ **48.** $(-2^3)^3$ **49.** $(x^3)^3$ **50.** $(y^4)^2$

51. $(x^7)^2$ **52.** $(y^5)^3$ **53.** $(-x^2)^2$ **54.** $(-x^2)^3$

55. $(2x)^2$ **56.** $(3y)^3$ **57.** $(-2x^2)^3$ **58.** $(-3y^3)^2$

59. $(x^2y^3)^2$ **60.** $(x^3y^4)^5$ **61.** $(3x^2y)^2$ **62.** $(-2ab^3)^4$

63. $(a^2)(3a^2)^3$ **64.** $(b^2)(2a^3)^4$ **65.** $(-2x)(2x^3)^2$

66. $(2y)(-3y^4)^3$ **67.** $(x^2y)(x^2y)^3$ **68.** $(a^3b)(ab)^3$

69. $(ab^2)^2(ab)^2$ **70.** $(x^2y)^2(x^3y)^3$ **71.** $(-2x)(-2x^3y)^3$

72. $(-3y)(-4x^2y^3)^3$ **73.** $(-2x)(-3xy^2)^2$ **74.** $(-3y)(-2x^2y)^3$

75. $(ab^2)(-2a^2b)^3$ **76.** $(a^2b^2)(-3ab^4)^2$ **77.** $(-2a^3)(3a^2b)^3$

78. $(-3b^2)(2ab^2)^3$ **79.** $(-3ab)^2(-2ab)^3$ **80.** $(-3a^2b)^3(-3ab)^3$

7.2 Applying Concepts

Simplify.

81. $(6x)(2x^2) + (4x^2)(5x)$ **82.** $(2a^7)(7a^2) - (6a^3)(5a^6)$

83. $(3a^2b^2)(2ab) - (9ab^2)(a^2b)$ **84.** $(3x^2y^2)^2 - (2xy)^4$

85. $(5xy^3)(3x^4y^2) - (2x^3y)(x^2y^4)$ **86.** $a^2(ab^2)^3 - a^3(ab^3)^2$

87. $4a^2(2ab)^3 - 5b^2(a^5b)$ **88.** $9x^3(3x^2y)^2 - x(x^3y)^2$

89. $-2xy(x^2y)^3 - 3x^5(xy^2)^2$ **90.** $5a^2b(ab^2)^2 + b^3(2a^2b)^2$

91. $a^n \cdot a^n$ **92.** $(a^n)^2$ **93.** $(a^2)^n$ **94.** $a^2 \cdot a^n$

For Exercises 95–98, answer true or false. If the answer is false, correct the right side of the equation.

95. $(-a)^5 = -a^5$ **96.** $(-b)^8 = b^8$

97. $(x^2)^5 = x^{2+5} = x^7$ **98.** $x^3 + x^3 = 2x^{3+3} = 2x^6$

99. Evaluate $(2^3)^2$ and $2^{(3^2)}$. Are the results the same? If not, which expression has the larger value?

100. What is the Order of Operations for the expression x^{m^n}?

101. If n is a positive integer and $x^n = y^n$, when is $x = y$?

102. **Geometry** The length of a rectangle is $4ab$. The width is $2ab$. Find the perimeter of the rectangle in terms of ab.

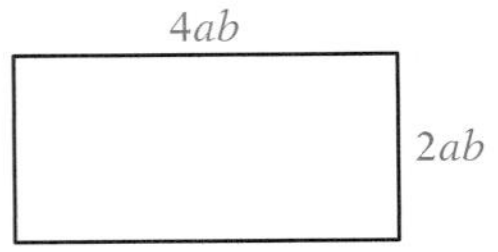

103. The distance a rock will fall in t seconds is $16t^2$ ft (neglecting air resistance). Find other examples of quantities that can be expressed in terms of an exponential expression, and explain where the expression is used.

7.3 Multiplication of Polynomials

OBJECTIVE 1 Multiply a polynomial by a monomial

To multiply a polynomial by a monomial, use the Distributive Property and the Rule for Multiplying Exponential Expressions.

Simplify: $-2x(x^2 - 4x - 3)$

$$-2x(x^2 - 4x - 3)$$
$$= -2x(x^2) - (-2x)(4x) - (-2x)(3)$$
$$= -2x^3 + 8x^2 + 6x$$

- **Use the Distributive Property.**
- **Use the Rule for Multiplying Exponential Expressions.**

EXAMPLE 1 Multiply. **A.** $(5x + 4)(-2x)$ **B.** $x^3(2x^2 - 3x + 2)$

Solution **A.** $(5x + 4)(-2x)$

$$= 5x(-2x) + 4(-2x)$$
$$= -10x^2 - 8x$$

- **Use the Distributive Property.**
- **Use the Rule for Multiplying Exponential Expressions.**

B. $x^3(2x^2 - 3x + 2)$

$$= 2x^5 - 3x^4 + 2x^3$$

PROBLEM 1 Multiply. **A.** $(-2y + 3)(-4y)$ **B.** $-a^2(3a^2 + 2a - 7)$

Solution See page S16.

OBJECTIVE 2 Multiply two polynomials

Multiplication of two polynomials requires the repeated application of the Distributive Property.

$$(y - 2)(y^2 + 3y + 1) = (y - 2)(y^2) + (y - 2)(3y) + (y - 2)(1)$$
$$= y^3 - 2y^2 + 3y^2 - 6y + y - 2$$
$$= y^3 + y^2 - 5y - 2$$

A convenient method of multiplying two polynomials is to use a vertical format similar to that used for multiplication of whole numbers.

$$\begin{array}{r} y^2 + 3y + 1 \\ y - 2 \\ \hline -2y^2 - 6y - 2 \\ y^3 + 3y^2 + y \quad\ \ \\ \hline y^3 + y^2 - 5y - 2 \end{array}$$

Multiply each term in the trinomial by −2.
Multiply each term in the trinomial by y.
Like terms must be in the same column.
Add the terms in each column.

EXAMPLE 2 Multiply: $(2b^3 - b + 1)(2b + 3)$

Solution

$$\begin{array}{r} 2b^3 - b + 1 \\ 2b + 3 \\ \hline 6b^3 \qquad - 3b + 3 \\ 4b^4 \qquad - 2b^2 + 2b \qquad \\ \hline 4b^4 + 6b^3 - 2b^2 - b + 3 \end{array}$$

- **Multiply $2b^3 - b + 1$ by 3.**
- **Multiply $2b^3 - b + 1$ by $2b$. Arrange the terms in descending order.**
- **Add the terms in each column.**

PROBLEM 2 Multiply: $(2y^3 + 2y^2 - 3)(3y - 1)$

Solution See page S16.

EXAMPLE 3 Multiply: $(4a^3 - 5a - 2)(3a - 2)$

Solution

$$\begin{array}{r} 4a^3 - 5a - 2 \\ 3a - 2 \\ \hline -8a^3 \qquad + 10a + 4 \\ 12a^4 \qquad - 15a^2 - 6a \qquad \\ \hline 12a^4 - 8a^3 - 15a^2 + 4a + 4 \end{array}$$

- **Multiply $4a^3 - 5a - 2$ by −2.**
- **Multiply $4a^3 - 5a - 2$ by $3a$.**
- **Add the terms in each column.**

PROBLEM 3 Multiply: $(3x^3 - 2x^2 + x - 3)(2x + 5)$

Solution See page S16.

OBJECTIVE 3 Multiply two binomials

It is often necessary to find the product of two binomials. The product can be found using a method called **FOIL,** which is based on the Distributive Property. The letters of FOIL stand for **F**irst, **O**uter, **I**nner, and **L**ast.

> **Take Note**
>
> FOIL is not really a different way of multiplying. It is based on the Distributive Property.
>
> $(2x + 3)(x + 5)$
> $= 2x(x + 5) + 3(x + 5)$
> F O I L
> $= 2x^2 + 10x + 3x + 15$
> $= 2x^2 + 13x + 15$

Multiply: $(2x + 3)(x + 5)$

Multiply the First terms.	$(2x + 3)(x + 5)$	$2x \cdot x = 2x^2$
Multiply the Outer terms.	$(2x + 3)(x + 5)$	$2x \cdot 5 = 10x$
Multiply the Inner terms.	$(2x + 3)(x + 5)$	$3 \cdot x = 3x$
Multiply the Last terms.	$(2x + 3)(x + 5)$	$3 \cdot 5 = 15$

F O I L

Add the products. $(2x + 3)(x + 5) = 2x^2 + 10x + 3x + 15$
Combine like terms. $= 2x^2 + 13x + 15$

EXAMPLE 4 Multiply: $(4x - 3)(3x - 2)$

Solution $(4x - 3)(3x - 2)$

$= 4x(3x) + 4x(-2) + (-3)(3x) + (-3)(-2)$ • Use the FOIL method.

$= 12x^2 - 8x - 9x + 6$

$= 12x^2 - 17x + 6$ • Combine like terms.

PROBLEM 4 Multiply: $(4y - 5)(3y - 3)$

Solution See page S16.

EXAMPLE 5 Multiply: $(3x - 2y)(x + 4y)$

Solution $(3x - 2y)(x + 4y)$

$= 3x(x) + 3x(4y) + (-2y)(x) + (-2y)(4y)$ • Use the FOIL method.

$= 3x^2 + 12xy - 2xy - 8y^2$

$= 3x^2 + 10xy - 8y^2$ • Combine like terms.

PROBLEM 5 Multiply: $(3a + 2b)(3a - 5b)$

Solution See page S16.

OBJECTIVE 4 Multiply binomials that have special products

The expression $(a + b)(a - b)$ is the product of the **sum and difference of two terms.** The first binomial in the expression is a sum; the second is a difference. The two terms are a and b. The first term in each binomial is a. The second term in each binomial is b.

The expression $(a + b)^2$ is the **square of a binomial.** The first term in the binomial is a. The second term in the binomial is b.

Using FOIL, it is possible to find a pattern for the product of the sum and difference of two terms and for the square of a binomial.

The Sum and Difference of Two Terms

$$(a + b)(a - b) = a^2 - ab + ab - b^2$$
$$= a^2 - b^2$$

Square of first term → a^2

Square of second term → b^2

The Square of a Binomial

$$(a+b)^2 = (a+b)(a+b) = a^2 + ab + ab + b^2$$
$$= a^2 + 2ab + b^2$$

Square of first term → a^2

Twice the product of the two terms → $2ab$

Square of last term → b^2

$$(a-b)^2 = (a-b)(a-b) = a^2 - ab - ab + b^2$$
$$= a^2 - 2ab + b^2$$

Square of first term → a^2

Twice the product of the two terms → $-2ab$

Square of last term → b^2

EXAMPLE 6 Multiply: $(2x+3)(2x-3)$

Solution $(2x+3)(2x-3)$ • **$(2x+3)(2x-3)$ is the product of the sum and difference of two terms.**

$= (2x)^2 - 3^2$ • **Square the first term. Square the second term.**

$= 4x^2 - 9$ • **Simplify.**

PROBLEM 6 Multiply: $(2a+5c)(2a-5c)$

Solution See page S16.

EXAMPLE 7 Multiply: $(4c+5d)^2$

Solution $(4c+5d)^2$ • **$(4c+5d)^2$ is the square of a binomial.**

$= (4c)^2 + 2(4c)(5d) + (5d)^2$ • **Square the first term. Find twice the product of the two terms. Square the second term.**

$= 16c^2 + 40cd + 25d^2$ • **Simplify.**

PROBLEM 7 Multiply: $(3x+2y)^2$

Solution See page S16.

EXAMPLE 8 Multiply: $(3x-2)^2$

Solution $(3x-2)^2$ • **$(3x-2)^2$ is the square of a binomial.**

$= (3x)^2 + 2(3x)(-2) + (-2)^2$ • **Square the first term. Find twice the product of the two terms. Square the last term.**

$= 9x^2 - 12x + 4$ • **Simplify.**

PROBLEM 8 Multiply: $(6x-y)^2$

Solution See page S16.

OBJECTIVE 5 Application problems

EXAMPLE 9 The radius of a circle is $(x - 4)$ ft. Find the area of the circle in terms of the variable x. Leave the answer in terms of π.

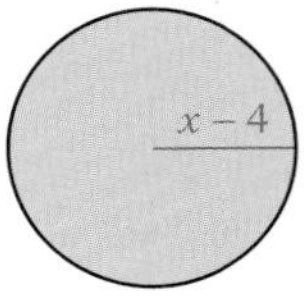

Strategy To find the area, replace the variable r in the formula $A = \pi r^2$ with the given value, and solve for A.

Solution

$A = \pi r^2$

$A = \pi(x - 4)^2$ • **This is the square of a binomial.**

$A = \pi(x^2 - 8x + 16)$

$A = \pi x^2 - 8\pi x + 16\pi$

The area is $(\pi x^2 - 8\pi x + 16\pi)$ ft^2.

PROBLEM 9 The length of a rectangle is $(x + 7)$ m. The width is $(x - 4)$ m. Find the area of the rectangle in terms of the variable x.

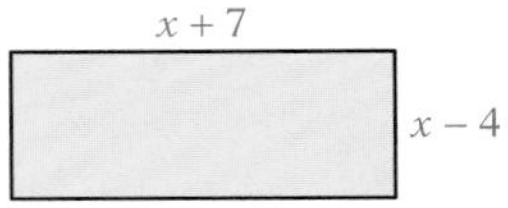

Solution See page S16.

EXAMPLE 10 The length of a side of a square is $(3x + 5)$ in. Find the area of the square in terms of the variable x.

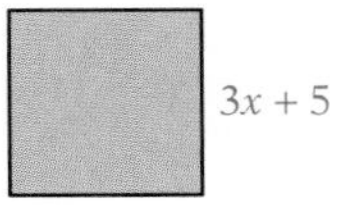

Strategy To find the area of the square, replace the variable s in the formula $A = s^2$ with the given value and simplify.

Solution

$A = s^2$

$A = (3x + 5)^2$ • **This is the square of a binomial.**

$A = 9x^2 + 30x + 25$

The area is $(9x^2 + 30x + 25)$ in^2.

PROBLEM 10 The base of a triangle is $(x + 3)$ cm and the height is $(4x - 6)$ cm. Find the area of the triangle in terms of the variable x.

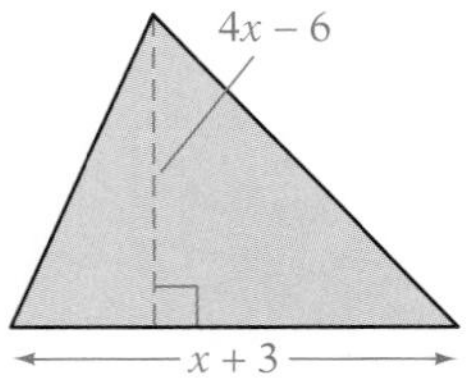

Solution See page S16.

7.3 Concept Review

Determine whether the statement is always true, sometimes true, or never true.

1. To multiply a monomial times a polynomial, use the Distributive Property to multiply each term of the polynomial by the monomial.

2. To multiply two polynomials, multiply each term of one polynomial by the other polynomial.

3. A binomial is a polynomial of degree 2.

4. $(x + 7)(x - 7)$ is the product of the sum and difference of the same two terms.

5. To square a binomial means to multiply it times itself.

6. The square of a binomial is a trinomial.

7. The FOIL method is used to multiply two polynomials.

8. Using the FOIL method, the terms $3x$ and 5 are the "First" terms in $(3x + 5)(2x + 7)$

7.3 Exercises

1 Multiply a polynomial by a monomial

1. Multiply: $-3y(y + 7)$

$-3y(y + 7) = \underline{\quad ? \quad}(y) + (\underline{\quad ? \quad})(7)$

- **Use the $\underline{\quad ? \quad}$ Property to multiply each term of $(y + 7)$ by $\underline{\quad ? \quad}$.**

$= \underline{\quad ? \quad} - \underline{\quad ? \quad}$

- **In the first term, the bases are the same. Add the exponents.**

2. Multiply: $5x^3(x^2 + 2x - 10)$

$5x^3(x^2 + 2x - 10)$

$= (\underline{\quad ? \quad})(x^2) + (\underline{\quad ? \quad})(2x) - (\underline{\quad ? \quad})(10)$

- **Use the Distributive Property to multiply each term of $\underline{\quad ? \quad}$ by $5x^3$.**

$= 5x^{\underline{?}} + 10x^{\underline{?}} - 50x^{\underline{?}}$

- **Use the Rule for Multiplying Exponential Expressions.**

Multiply.

3. $x(x - 2)$

4. $y(3 - y)$

5. $-x(x + 7)$

6. $-y(7 - y)$

7. $3a^2(a - 2)$

8. $4b^2(b + 8)$

9. $-5x^2(x^2 - x)$

10. $-6y^2(y + 2y^2)$

11. $-x^3(3x^2 - 7)$

12. $-y^4(2y^2 - y^6)$

13. $2x(6x^2 - 3x)$

14. $3y(4y - y^2)$

15. $(2x - 4)3x$

16. $(2x + 1)2x$

17. $-xy(x^2 - y^2)$

18. $-x^2y(2xy - y^2)$

19. $x(2x^3 - 3x + 2)$

20. $y(-3y^2 - 2y + 6)$

21. $-a(-2a^2 - 3a - 2)$

22. $-b(5b^2 + 7b - 35)$

23. $x^2(3x^4 - 3x^2 - 2)$

24. $y^3(-4y^3 - 6y + 7)$

25. $2y^2(-3y^2 - 6y + 7)$

26. $4x^2(3x^2 - 2x + 6)$

27. $(a^2 + 3a - 4)(-2a)$

28. $(b^3 - 2b + 2)(-5b)$

29. $-3y^2(-2y^2 + y - 2)$

30. $-5x^2(3x^2 - 3x - 7)$

31. $xy(x^2 - 3xy + y^2)$

32. $ab(2a^2 - 4ab - 6b^2)$

2 Multiply two polynomials

33. Which expression(s) are equivalent to $4x - x(3x - 1)$?

a. $4x - 3x^2 - x$ **b.** $-3x^2 + 5x$ **c.** $4x - 3x^2 + x$
d. $9x^2 - 3x$ **e.** $3x(3x - 1)$

34. Which expression(s) are equivalent to $b^3(b^3 - b^2)$?

a. $b^9 - b^6$ **b.** $b^{27} - b^8$ **c.** b^3
d. $b^6 - b^5$ **e.** b

Multiply.

35. $(x^2 + 3x + 2)(x + 1)$

36. $(x^2 - 2x + 7)(x - 2)$

37. $(a - 3)(a^2 - 3a + 4)$

38. $(2x - 3)(x^2 - 3x + 5)$

39. $(-2b^2 - 3b + 4)(b - 5)$

40. $(-a^2 + 3a - 2)(2a - 1)$

41. $(3x - 5)(-2x^2 + 7x - 2)$

42. $(2a - 1)(-a^2 - 2a + 3)$

43. $(x^3 - 3x + 2)(x - 4)$

44. $(y^3 + 4y^2 - 8)(2y - 1)$

45. $(3y - 8)(5y^2 + 8y - 2)$

46. $(4y - 3)(3y^2 + 3y - 5)$

47. $(5a^3 - 15a + 2)(a - 4)$

48. $(3b^3 - 5b^2 + 7)(6b - 1)$

49. $(y + 2)(y^3 + 2y^2 - 3y + 1)$

50. $(2a - 3)(2a^3 - 3a^2 + 2a - 1)$

For Exercises 51 and 52, use this product: $(ax^3 + bx + c)(dx + e)$, where a, b, c, d, and e are nonzero real numbers.

51. **a.** What is the degree of the simplified product?
b. At most, how many terms will the simplified product have?

52. Does the simplified product have an x^2 term? If so, what is its coefficient?

3 Multiply two binomials

53. For the product $(4x - 3)(x + 5)$:
The **F**irst terms are __?__ and __?__.
The **O**uter terms are __?__ and __?__.
The **I**nner terms are __?__ and __?__.
The **L**ast terms are __?__ and __?__.

For the product of the binomials, name **a.** the first terms, **b.** the outer terms, **c.** the inner terms, and **d.** the last terms.

54. $(y - 8)(2y + 3)$

55. $(3d + 4)(d - 1)$

56. Use the FOIL method to multiply $(x + 2)(8x - 3)$.
The product of the **F**irst terms is $x \cdot 8x =$ __?__.
The product of the **O**uter terms is $x \cdot (-3) =$ __?__.
The product of the **I**nner terms is $2 \cdot 8x =$ __?__.
The product of the **L**ast terms is $2 \cdot (-3) =$ __?__.
The sum of these four products is __?__.

Multiply.

57. $(x + 1)(x + 3)$
58. $(y + 2)(y + 5)$
59. $(a - 3)(a + 4)$
60. $(b - 6)(b + 3)$
61. $(y + 3)(y - 8)$
62. $(x + 10)(x - 5)$
63. $(y - 7)(y - 3)$
64. $(a - 8)(a - 9)$
65. $(2x + 1)(x + 7)$
66. $(y + 2)(5y + 1)$
67. $(3x - 1)(x + 4)$
68. $(7x - 2)(x + 4)$
69. $(4x - 3)(x - 7)$
70. $(2x - 3)(4x - 7)$
71. $(3y - 8)(y + 2)$
72. $(5y - 9)(y + 5)$
73. $(3x + 7)(3x + 11)$
74. $(5a + 6)(6a + 5)$
75. $(7a - 16)(3a - 5)$
76. $(5a - 12)(3a - 7)$
77. $(3b + 13)(5b - 6)$
78. $(x + y)(2x + y)$
79. $(2a + b)(a + 3b)$
80. $(3x - 4y)(x - 2y)$
81. $(2a - b)(3a + 2b)$
82. $(5a - 3b)(2a + 4b)$
83. $(2x + y)(x - 2y)$
84. $(3x - 7y)(3x + 5y)$
85. $(2x + 3y)(5x + 7y)$
86. $(5x + 3y)(7x + 2y)$
87. $(3a - 2b)(2a - 7b)$
88. $(5a - b)(7a - b)$
89. $(a - 9b)(2a + 7b)$
90. $(2a + 5b)(7a - 2b)$
91. $(10a - 3b)(10a - 7b)$
92. $(12a - 5b)(3a - 4b)$
93. $(5x + 12y)(3x + 4y)$
94. $(11x + 2y)(3x + 7y)$
95. $(2x - 15y)(7x + 4y)$
96. $(5x + 2y)(2x - 5y)$
97. $(8x - 3y)(7x - 5y)$
98. $(2x - 9y)(8x - 3y)$

99. Suppose a and b are positive numbers such that $a > b$. Will the coefficient of the x term of the product $(ax - b)(x + 1)$ be positive or negative?

100. If the constant terms of two binomials are both negative, is the constant term of the product of the two binomials also negative?

4 Multiply binomials that have special products

101. The product $(a + b)(a - b) = a^2 - b^2$, so $(5x + 1)(5x - 1) = (\underline{\quad ? \quad})^2 - (\underline{\quad ? \quad})^2 = \underline{\quad ? \quad} - \underline{\quad ? \quad}$.

102. The product $(a + b)^2 = a^2 + 2ab + b^2$, so
$(3x + 7)^2 = (\underline{\quad ? \quad})^2 + 2(\underline{\quad ? \quad})(\underline{\quad ? \quad}) + (\underline{\quad ? \quad})^2$
$= \underline{\quad ? \quad} + \underline{\quad ? \quad} + \underline{\quad ? \quad}$.

Multiply.

103. $(y - 5)(y + 5)$

104. $(y + 6)(y - 6)$

105. $(2x + 3)(2x - 3)$

106. $(4x - 7)(4x + 7)$

107. $(x + 1)^2$

108. $(y - 3)^2$

109. $(3a - 5)^2$

110. $(6x - 5)^2$

111. $(3x - 7)(3x + 7)$

112. $(9x - 2)(9x + 2)$

113. $(2a + b)^2$

114. $(x + 3y)^2$

115. $(x - 2y)^2$

116. $(2x - 3y)^2$

117. $(4 - 3y)(4 + 3y)$

118. $(4x - 9y)(4x + 9y)$

119. $(5x + 2y)^2$

120. $(2a - 9b)^2$

For Exercises 121 to 124, state whether the coefficient of the x term of the product is positive, negative, or zero.

121. $(ax + b)(ax - b)$, where $a > 0$ and $b > 0$

122. $(ax + b)(ax + b)$, where $a > 0$ and $b < 0$

123. $(ax + b)^2$, where $a > 0$ and $b > 0$

124. $(ax + b)^2$, where $a < 0$ and $b < 0$

5 Application problems

125. The length of a rectangle is $(2x + 5)$ ft and the width of the rectangle is $(2x - 5)$ ft. The expression that represents the area of the rectangle is $(\underline{\quad ? \quad})(\underline{\quad ? \quad}) = \underline{\quad ? \quad}$.

126. The length of the side of a square is $(3a - 1)$. The expression that represents the area of the square is $(\underline{\quad ? \quad})^2 = \underline{\quad ? \quad}$.

Geometry Problems

127. The length of a rectangle is $5x$ ft. The width is $(2x - 7)$ ft. Find the area of the rectangle in terms of the variable x.

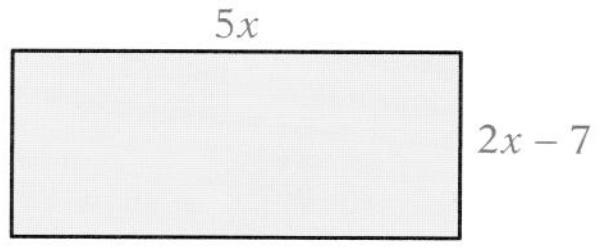

128. The width of a rectangle is $(x - 6)$ m. The length is $(2x + 3)$ m. Find the area of the rectangle in terms of the variable x.

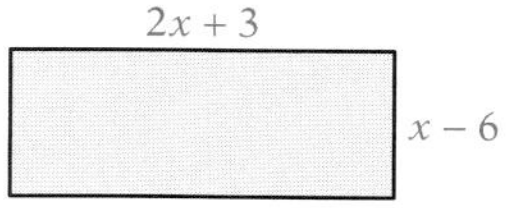

129. The width of a rectangle is $(3x + 1)$ in. The length of the rectangle is twice the width. Find the area of the rectangle in terms of the variable x.

130. The width of a rectangle is $(4x - 3)$ cm. The length of the rectangle is twice the width. Find the area of the rectangle in terms of the variable x.

131. The length of a side of a square is $(2x + 1)$ km. Find the area of the square in terms of the variable x.

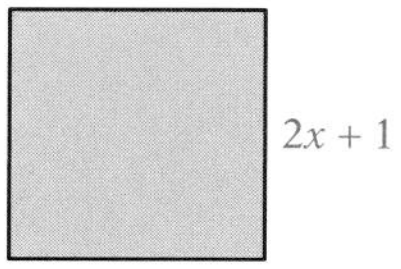

132. The length of a side of a square is $(2x - 3)$ yd. Find the area of the square in terms of the variable x.

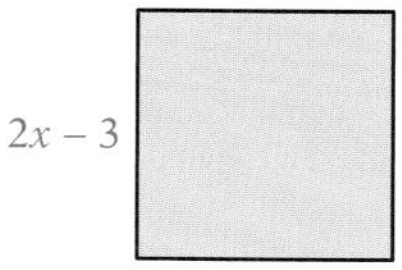

133. The base of a triangle is $4x$ m and the height is $(2x + 5)$ m. Find the area of the triangle in terms of the variable x.

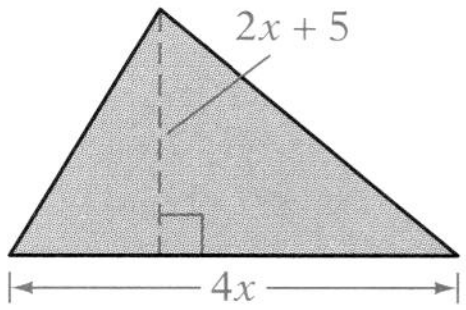

134. The base of a triangle is $(2x + 6)$ in. and the height is $(x - 8)$ in. Find the area of the triangle in terms of the variable x.

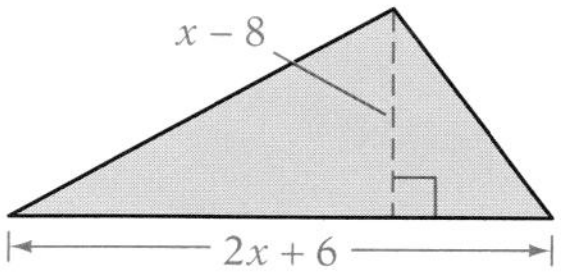

135. The radius of a circle is $(x + 4)$ cm. Find the area of the circle in terms of the variable x. Leave the answer in terms of π.

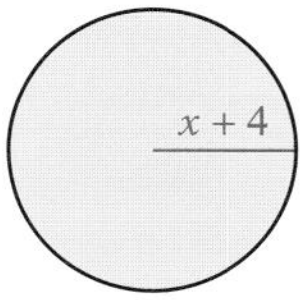

136. The radius of a circle is $(x - 3)$ ft. Find the area of the circle in terms of the variable x. Leave the answer in terms of π.

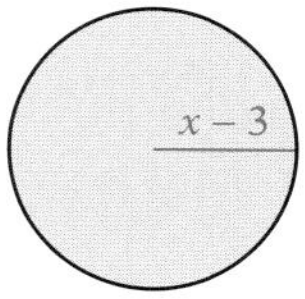

137. **Sports** A softball diamond has dimensions 45 ft by 45 ft. A base path border x feet wide lies on both the first-base side and the third-base side of the diamond. Express the total area of the softball diamond and the base path in terms of the variable x.

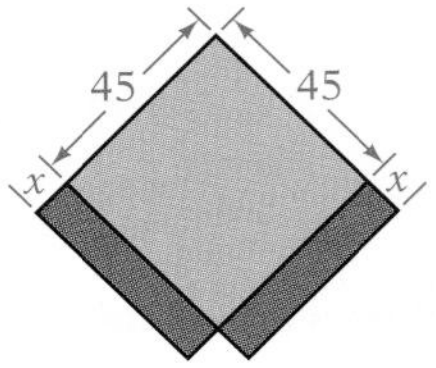

138. **Sports** An athletic field has dimensions 30 yd by 100 yd. An end zone that is w yards wide borders each end of the field. Express the total area of the field and the end zones in terms of the variable w.

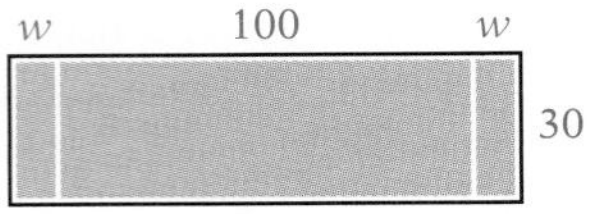

7.3 Applying Concepts

Simplify.

139. $(a + b)^2 - (a - b)^2$

140. $(x + 3y)^2 + (x + 3y)(x - 3y)$

141. $(3a^2 - 4a + 2)^2$

142. $(x + 4)^3$

143. $3x^2(2x^3 + 4x - 1) - 6x^3(x^2 - 2)$

144. $(3b + 2)(b - 6) + (4 + 2b)(3 - b)$

145. $x^n(x^n + 1)$

146. $(x^n + 1)(x^n - 1)$

147. $(x^n + 1)(x^n + 1)$

148. $(x^n - 1)^2$

149. $(x + 1)(x - 1)$

150. $(x + 1)(-x^2 + x - 1)$

151. $(x + 1)(x^3 - x^2 + x - 1)$

152. $(x + 1)(-x^4 + x^3 - x^2 + x - 1)$

Use the pattern of the answers to Exercises 149 to 152 to write the product.

153. $(x + 1)(x^5 - x^4 + x^3 - x^2 + x - 1)$

154. $(x + 1)(-x^6 + x^5 - x^4 + x^3 - x^2 + x - 1)$

Solve.

155. Find $(4n^3)^2$ if $2n - 3 = 4n - 7$.

156. What polynomial has quotient $x^2 + 2x - 1$ when divided by $x + 3$?

157. What polynomial has quotient $3x - 4$ when divided by $4x + 5$?

158. Subtract $4x^2 - x - 5$ from the product of $x^2 + x + 3$ and $x - 4$.

159. Add $x^2 + 2x - 3$ to the product of $2x - 5$ and $3x + 1$.

160. If a polynomial of degree 3 is multiplied by a polynomial of degree 2, what is the degree of the resulting polynomial?

161. Is it possible to multiply a polynomial of degree 2 by a polynomial of degree 2 and have the product be a polynomial of degree 3? If so, give an example. If not, explain why not.

7.4 Integer Exponents and Scientific Notation

OBJECTIVE 1 Integer exponents

The quotient of two exponential expressions with the *same* base can be simplified by writing each expression in factored form, dividing by the common factors, and then writing the result with an exponent.

$$\frac{x^5}{x^2} = \frac{\overset{1}{\cancel{x}} \cdot \overset{1}{\cancel{x}} \cdot x \cdot x \cdot x}{\underset{1}{\cancel{x}} \cdot \underset{1}{\cancel{x}}} = x^3$$

Note that subtracting the exponents results in the same quotient.

$$\frac{x^5}{x^2} = x^{5-2} = x^3$$

To divide two monomials with the same base, subtract the exponents of the like bases.

Simplify: $\frac{a^7}{a^3}$

The bases are the same. Subtract the exponent in the denominator from the exponent in the numerator.

$$\frac{a^7}{a^3} = a^{7-3} = a^4$$

Simplify: $\frac{r^8 s^6}{r^7 s}$

Subtract the exponents of the like bases.

$$\frac{r^8 s^6}{r^7 s} = r^{8-7} s^{6-1} = rs^5$$

Recall that for any number a, $a \neq 0$, $\frac{a}{a} = 1$. This property is true for exponential expressions as well. For example, for $x \neq 0$, $\frac{x^4}{x^4} = 1$.

This expression also can be simplified using the rule for dividing exponential expressions with the same base.

$$\frac{x^4}{x^4} = x^{4-4} = x^0$$

Because $\frac{x^4}{x^4} = 1$ and $\frac{x^4}{x^4} = x^{4-4} = x^0$, the following definition of zero as an exponent is used.

Zero as an Exponent

If $\boldsymbol{x \neq 0}$, then $\boldsymbol{x^0 = 1}$. The expression $\boldsymbol{0^0}$ is not defined.

Take Note

For the example at the right, we indicated that $a \neq 0$. If we try to evaluate $(12a^3)^0$ when $a = 0$, we get $[12(0)^3]^0 = [12(0)]^0 = 0^0$. However, 0^0 is not defined. Therefore, we must assume that $a \neq 0$. To avoid stating this for every example or exercise, we will assume that variables do not take on values that result in the expression 0^0.

Simplify: $(12a^3)^0, a \neq 0$

Any nonzero expression to the zero power is 1. $(12a^3)^0 = 1$

Simplify: $-(xy^4)^0, x \neq 0, y \neq 0$

Any nonzero expression to the zero power is 1. Because the negative sign is outside the parentheses, the answer is -1. $-(xy^4)^0 = -(1) = -1$

Point of Interest

In the 15th century, the expression $\mathbf{12^{2m}}$ *was used to mean* $\mathbf{12x^{-2}}$*. The use of* ***m*** *reflected an Italian influence. In Italy,* m *was used for minus and* p *was used for plus. It was understood that* ***2m*** *refered to an unnamed variable. Isaac Newton, in the 17th century, advocated the current use of a negative exponent.*

The meaning of a negative exponent can be developed by examining the quotient $\dfrac{x^4}{x^6}$.

The expression can be simplified by writing the numerator and denominator in factored form, dividing by the common factors, and then writing the result with an exponent.

$$\frac{x^4}{x^6} = \frac{\overset{1}{\cancel{x}} \cdot \overset{1}{\cancel{x}} \cdot \overset{1}{\cancel{x}} \cdot \overset{1}{\cancel{x}}}{\underset{1}{\cancel{x}} \cdot \underset{1}{\cancel{x}} \cdot \underset{1}{\cancel{x}} \cdot \underset{1}{\cancel{x}} \cdot x \cdot x} = \frac{1}{x^2}$$

Now simplify the same expression by subtracting the exponents of the like bases.

$$\frac{x^4}{x^6} = x^{4-6} = x^{-2}$$

Because $\dfrac{x^4}{x^6} = \dfrac{1}{x^2}$ and $\dfrac{x^4}{x^6} = x^{-2}$, the expressions $\dfrac{1}{x^2}$ and x^{-2} must be equal. The following definition of a negative exponent is used.

Definition of Negative Exponents

If n is a positive integer and $\mathbf{x \neq 0}$, then $\mathbf{x^{-n} = \dfrac{1}{x^n}}$ and $\mathbf{\dfrac{1}{x^{-n}} = x^n}$.

Take Note

Note from the example at the right that 2^{-4} is a *positive* number. A negative exponent does not indicate a negative number.

Evaluate 2^{-4}.

Write the expression with a positive exponent. Then simplify. $2^{-4} = \dfrac{1}{2^4} = \dfrac{1}{16}$

Now that negative exponents have been defined, the Rule for Dividing Exponential Expressions can be stated.

Rule for Dividing Exponential Expressions

If m and n are integers and $\mathbf{x \neq 0}$, then $\mathbf{\dfrac{x^m}{x^n} = x^{m-n}}$.

EXAMPLE 1 Write $\frac{3^{-3}}{3^2}$ with a positive exponent. Then evaluate.

Solution
$$\frac{3^{-3}}{3^2} = 3^{-3-2}$$
• **3^{-3} and 3^2 have the same base. Subtract the exponents.**
$$= 3^{-5}$$
$$= \frac{1}{3^5}$$
• **Use the Definition of Negative Exponents to write the expression with a positive exponent.**
$$= \frac{1}{243}$$
• **Evaluate.**

PROBLEM 1 Write $\frac{2^{-2}}{2^3}$ with a positive exponent. Then evaluate.

Solution See page S16.

The rules for simplifying exponential expressions and powers of exponential expressions are true for all integers. These rules are restated here.

Rules for Exponents

If m, n, and p are integers, then

$$x^m \cdot x^n = x^{m+n} \qquad (x^m)^n = x^{mn} \qquad (x^m y^n)^p = x^{mp}y^{np}$$

$$\frac{x^m}{x^n} = x^{m-n},\ x \neq 0 \qquad x^{-n} = \frac{1}{x^n},\ x \neq 0 \qquad x^0 = 1,\ x \neq 0$$

An exponential expression is in simplest form when it is written with only positive exponents.

Simplify: $a^{-7}b^3$

Rewrite a^{-7} with a positive exponent. $\quad a^{-7}b^3 = \frac{b^3}{a^7}$

EXAMPLE 2 Simplify: $\frac{x^{-4}y^6}{xy^2}$

Solution
$$\frac{x^{-4}y^6}{xy^2} = x^{-4-1}y^{6-2}$$
• **Divide variables with the same base by subtracting the exponents.**
$$= x^{-5}y^4$$
$$= \frac{y^4}{x^5}$$
• **Write the expression with only positive exponents.**

PROBLEM 2 Simplify: $\frac{b^8}{a^{-5}b^6}$

Solution See page S16.

Take Note

In the example at the bottom of this page, the exponent on d is -4 (negative 4). The d^{-4} is written in the denominator as d^4. The exponent on 6 is 1 (positive 1). The 6 remains in the numerator.

Note that we indicated $d \neq 0$. This is necessary because division by zero is not defined. In this textbook, we will assume that values of the variables are chosen so that division by zero does not occur.

Simplify: $6d^{-4},\ d \neq 0$

$$6d^{-4} = 6 \cdot \frac{1}{d^4} = \frac{6}{d^4}$$
• **Use the Definition of Negative Exponents to rewrite the expression with a positive exponent.**

EXAMPLE 3 Simplify: **A.** $\dfrac{-35a^6b^{-2}}{25a^{-2}b^5}$ **B.** $(-2x)(3x^{-2})^{-3}$

Solution **A.** $\dfrac{-35a^6b^{-2}}{25a^{-2}b^5} = -\dfrac{35a^6b^{-2}}{25a^{-2}b^5}$
- **A negative sign is placed in front of a fraction.**

$= -\dfrac{\overset{1}{\cancel{5}} \cdot 7a^{6-(-2)}b^{-2-5}}{\underset{1}{\cancel{5}} \cdot 5}$
- **Factor the coefficients. Divide by the common factors. Divide variables with the same base by subtracting the exponents.**

$= -\dfrac{7a^8b^{-7}}{5}$

$= -\dfrac{7a^8}{5b^7}$
- **Write the expression with only positive exponents.**

B. $(-2x)(3x^{-2})^{-3} = (-2x)(3^{-3}x^6)$
- **Use the Rule for Simplifying Powers of Products.**

$= \dfrac{-2x \cdot x^6}{3^3}$
- **Write the expression with positive exponents.**

$= -\dfrac{2x^7}{27}$
- **Use the Rule for Multiplying Exponential Expressions, and simplify the numerical exponential expression.**

PROBLEM 3 Simplify: **A.** $\dfrac{12x^{-8}y^4}{-16xy^{-3}}$ **B.** $(-3ab)(2a^3b^{-2})^{-3}$

Solution See page S17.

OBJECTIVE 2 Scientific notation

Very large and very small numbers are encountered in the fields of science and engineering. For example, the charge of an electron is 0.000000000000000000160 coulomb. These numbers can be written more easily in scientific notation. In **scientific notation,** a number is expressed as a product of two factors, one a number between 1 and 10 and the other a power of 10.

To change a number written in decimal notation to scientific notation, write it in the form $a \times 10^n$, where a is a number between 1 and 10 and n is an integer.

For numbers greater than 10, move the decimal point to the right of the first digit. The exponent n is positive and equal to the number of places the decimal point has been moved.

$240{,}000 = 2.4 \times 10^5$

$93{,}000{,}000 = 9.3 \times 10^7$

For numbers less than 1, move the decimal point to the right of the first nonzero digit. The exponent n is negative. The absolute value of the exponent is equal to the number of places the decimal point has been moved.

$0.00030 = 3.0 \times 10^{-4}$

$0.0000832 = 8.32 \times 10^{-5}$

> **Take Note**
>
> There are two steps to writing a number in scientific notation: (1) determine the number between 1 and 10, and (2) determine the exponent on 10.

Look at the last example above: $0.0000832 = 8.32 \times 10^{-5}$. Using the Definition of Negative Exponents,

$$10^{-5} = \frac{1}{10^5} = \frac{1}{100{,}000} = 0.00001$$

Because $10^{-5} = 0.00001$, we can write

$$8.32 \times 10^{-5} = 8.32 \times 0.00001 = 0.0000832$$

which is the number we started with. We have not changed the value of the number; we have just written it in another form.

EXAMPLE 4 Write the number in scientific notation.

A. 824,300,000,000 **B.** 0.000000961

Solution **A.** $824{,}300{,}000{,}000 = 8.243 \times 10^{11}$

- **Move the decimal point 11 places to the left. The exponent on 10 is 11.**

B. $0.000000961 = 9.61 \times 10^{-7}$

- **Move the decimal point 7 places to the right. The exponent on 10 is −7.**

PROBLEM 4 Write the number in scientific notation.

A. 57,000,000,000 **B.** 0.000000017

Solution See page S17.

Changing a number written in scientific notation to decimal notation also requires moving the decimal point.

When the exponent on 10 is positive, move the decimal point to the right the same number of places as the exponent.

$$3.45 \times 10^{9} = 3{,}450{,}000{,}000$$

$$2.3 \times 10^{8} = 230{,}000{,}000$$

When the exponent on 10 is negative, move the decimal point to the left the same number of places as the absolute value of the exponent.

$$8.1 \times 10^{-3} = 0.0081$$

$$6.34 \times 10^{-6} = 0.00000634$$

EXAMPLE 5 Write the number in decimal notation.

A. 7.329×10^{6} **B.** 6.8×10^{-10}

Solution **A.** $7.329 \times 10^{6} = 7{,}329{,}000$

- **The exponent on 10 is positive. Move the decimal point 6 places to the right.**

B. $6.8 \times 10^{-10} = 0.00000000068$

- **The exponent on 10 is negative. Move the decimal point 10 places to the left.**

PROBLEM 5 Write the number in decimal notation.

A. 5×10^{12} **B.** 4.0162×10^{-9}

Solution See page S17.

The rules for multiplying and dividing with numbers in scientific notation are the same as those for calculating with algebraic expressions. The power of 10 corresponds to the variable, and the number between 1 and 10 corresponds to the coefficient of the variable.

	Algebraic Expression	**Scientific Notation**
Multiplication	$(4x^{-3})(2x^5) = 8x^2$	$(4 \times 10^{-3})(2 \times 10^5) = 8 \times 10^2$
Division	$\dfrac{6x^5}{3x^{-2}} = 2x^{5-(-2)} = 2x^7$	$\dfrac{6 \times 10^5}{3 \times 10^{-2}} = 2 \times 10^{5-(-2)} = 2 \times 10^7$

EXAMPLE 6 Multiply or divide.

A. $(3.0 \times 10^5)(1.1 \times 10^{-8})$ **B.** $\dfrac{7.2 \times 10^{13}}{2.4 \times 10^{-3}}$

Solution **A.** $(3.0 \times 10^5)(1.1 \times 10^{-8}) = 3.3 \times 10^{-3}$ • **Multiply 3.0 and 1.1. Add the exponents on 10.**

B. $\dfrac{7.2 \times 10^{13}}{2.4 \times 10^{-3}} = 3 \times 10^{16}$ • **Divide 7.2 by 2.4. Subtract the exponents on 10.**

PROBLEM 6 Multiply or divide.

A. $(2.4 \times 10^{-9})(1.6 \times 10^3)$ **B.** $\dfrac{5.4 \times 10^{-2}}{1.8 \times 10^{-4}}$

Solution See page S17.

7.4 Concept Review

Determine whether the statement is always true, sometimes true, or never true.

1. The expression $\dfrac{x^5}{y^3}$ can be simplified by subtracting the exponents.

2. The rules of exponents can be applied to expressions that contain an exponent of zero or contain negative exponents.

3. The expression 3^{-2} represents the reciprocal of 3^2.

4. $5x^0 = 0$

5. The expression 4^{-3} represents a negative number.

6. To be in simplest form, an exponential expression cannot contain any negative exponents.

7. $2x^{-5} = \dfrac{1}{2x^5}$

8. $x^4y^{-6} = \dfrac{1}{x^4y^6}$

7.4 Exercises

1 Integer exponents

Write with a positive or zero exponent. Then evaluate.

1. 5^{-2}

2. 3^{-3}

3. $\dfrac{1}{8^{-2}}$

4. $\dfrac{1}{12^{-1}}$

5. $\dfrac{3^{-2}}{3}$

6. $\dfrac{5^{-3}}{5}$

7. $\dfrac{2^3}{2^3}$

8. $\dfrac{3^{-2}}{3^{-2}}$

9. Explain how to rewrite a variable that has a negative exponent as an expression with a positive exponent.

10. As long as x is not zero, x^0 is defined to be equal to ___?___. Using this definition, $3^0 =$ ___?___, $(7x^3)^0 =$ ___?___, and $-2x^0 =$ ___?___.

11. Simplify: $\dfrac{8x^{10}}{2x^3}$

$\dfrac{8x^{10}}{2x^3} = (\underline{\ \ ?\ \ })x^{\underline{?} - \underline{?}}$

- **Divide the coefficients by the common factor 2. Divide the variable parts by subtracting the exponents.**

$= \underline{\ \ ?\ \ }$

- **Simplify.**

12. Simplify: $\dfrac{a^3b^7}{a^5b}$

$\dfrac{a^3b^7}{a^5b} = a^{\underline{?} - \underline{?}}b^{\underline{?} - \underline{?}}$

- **Divide variables with the same base by subtracting the exponents.**

$= a^{\underline{?}}b^{\underline{?}}$

- **Simplify.**

$= \dfrac{b^6}{\underline{\ \ ?\ \ }}$

- **Write the expression with only positive exponents.**

Simplify.

13. $\dfrac{y^7}{y^3}$

14. $\dfrac{z^9}{z^2}$

15. $\dfrac{a^8}{a^5}$

16. $\dfrac{c^{12}}{c^5}$

17. $\dfrac{p^5}{p}$

18. $\dfrac{w^9}{w}$

19. $\dfrac{4x^8}{2x^5}$

20. $\dfrac{12z^7}{4z^3}$

21. $\dfrac{22k^5}{11k^4}$

22. $\dfrac{14m^{11}}{7m^{10}}$

23. $\dfrac{m^9n^7}{m^4n^5}$

24. $\dfrac{y^5z^6}{yz^3}$

25. $\dfrac{6r^4}{4r^2}$

26. $\dfrac{8x^9}{12x^6}$

27. $\dfrac{-16a^7}{24a^6}$

28. $\dfrac{-18b^5}{27b^4}$

29. x^{-2}

30. y^{-10}

31. $\frac{1}{a^{-6}}$

32. $\frac{1}{b^{-4}}$

33. $4x^{-7}$

34. $-6y^{-1}$

35. $\frac{5}{b^{-8}}$

36. $\frac{-3}{v^{-3}}$

37. $\frac{1}{3x^{-2}}$

38. $\frac{2}{5c^{-6}}$

39. $(ab^5)^0$

40. $(32x^3y^4)^0$

41. $\frac{y^3}{y^8}$

42. $\frac{z^4}{z^6}$

43. $\frac{a^5}{a^{11}}$

44. $\frac{m}{m^7}$

45. $\frac{4x^2}{12x^5}$

46. $\frac{6y^8}{8y^9}$

47. $\frac{-12x}{-18x^6}$

48. $\frac{-24c^2}{-36c^{11}}$

49. $\frac{x^6y^5}{x^8y}$

50. $\frac{a^3b^2}{a^2b^3}$

51. $\frac{2m^6n^2}{5m^9n^{10}}$

52. $\frac{5r^3t^7}{6r^5t^7}$

53. $\frac{pq^3}{p^4q^4}$

54. $\frac{a^4b^5}{a^5b^6}$

55. $\frac{3x^4y^5}{6x^4y^8}$

56. $\frac{14a^3b^6}{21a^5b^6}$

57. $\frac{14x^4y^6z^2}{16x^3y^9z}$

58. $\frac{24a^2b^7c^9}{36a^7b^5c}$

59. $\frac{15mn^9p^3}{30m^4n^9p}$

60. $\frac{25x^4y^7z^2}{20x^5y^9z^{11}}$

61. $(-2xy^{-2})^3$

62. $(-3x^{-1}y^2)^2$

63. $(3x^{-1}y^{-2})^2$

64. $(5xy^{-3})^{-2}$

65. $(2x^{-1})(x^{-3})$

66. $(-2x^{-5})x^7$

67. $(-5a^2)(a^{-5})^2$

68. $(2a^{-3})(a^7b^{-1})^3$

69. $(-2ab^{-2})(4a^{-2}b)^{-2}$

70. $(3ab^{-2})(2a^{-1}b)^{-3}$

71. $(-5x^{-2}y)(-2x^{-2}y^2)$

72. $\frac{a^{-3}b^{-4}}{a^2b^2}$

73. $\frac{3x^{-2}y^2}{6xy^2}$

74. $\frac{2x^{-2}y}{8xy}$

75. $\frac{3x^{-2}y}{xy}$

76. $\frac{2x^{-1}y^4}{x^2y^3}$

77. $\frac{2x^{-1}y^{-4}}{4xy^2}$

78. $\frac{12a^2b^3}{-27a^2b^2}$

79. $\frac{-16xy^4}{96x^4y^4}$

80. $\frac{-8x^2y^4}{44y^2z^5}$

81. True or false?

a. $\dfrac{a^{4n}}{a^n} = a^4$ b. $\dfrac{1}{a^{m-n}} = a^{n-m}$

82. True or false?

a. $a^{-n}a^n = 1$ b. $\dfrac{a^n}{b^m} = \left(\dfrac{a}{b}\right)^{n-m}$

2 Scientific notation

83. Why might a number be written in scientific notation instead of decimal notation?

84. A number is written in scientific notation if it is written as the product of a number between __?__ and __?__ and a power of __?__.

85. To write the number 354,000,000 in scientific notation, move the decimal point __?__ places to the __?__. The exponent on 10 is __?__.

86. To write the number 0.0000000086 in scientific notation, move the decimal point __?__ places to the __?__. The exponent on 10 is __?__.

Determine whether the number is written in scientific notation. If not, explain why not.

87. 39.4×10^3

88. 0.8×10^{-6}

89. $7.1 \times 10^{2.4}$

90. 5.8×10^{-132}

Write the number in scientific notation.

91. 2,370,000

92. 75,000

93. 0.00045

94. 0.000076

95. 309,000

96. 819,000,000

97. 0.000000601

98. 0.00000000096

Write the number in decimal notation.

99. 7.1×10^5

100. 2.3×10^7

101. 4.3×10^{-5}

102. 9.21×10^{-7}

103. 6.71×10^8

104. 5.75×10^9

105. 7.13×10^{-6}

106. 3.54×10^{-8}

107. **Astronomy** Astrophysicists estimate that the radius of the Milky Way galaxy is 1,000,000,000,000,000,000,000 m. Write this number in scientific notation.

108. **Geology** The mass of Earth is 5,980,000,000,000,000,000,000,000 kg. Write this number in scientific notation.

109. **Physics** Carbon nanotubes are cylinders of carbon atoms that have remarkable properties, especially for their strength. Some nanotubes with a diameter of 0.0000000004 m have been created. Write this number in scientific notation.

Great Pyramid of Cheops

110. **Biology** The weight of a single *E. coli* bacterium is 0.000000000000665 g. Write this number in scientific notation.

111. **Archeology** The weight of the Great Pyramid of Cheops is estimated to be 12,000,000,000 lb. Write this number in scientific notation.

112. **Biophysics** Biologists and physicists are working together to measure the mass of a virus. Currently, a virus with a mass of 0.0000000000000000039 g can be measured. Write this number in scientific notation.

113. **Food Science** The frequency (oscillations per second) of a microwave generated by a microwave oven is approximately 2,450,000,000 hertz. (1 hertz is one oscillation in one second.) Write this number in scientific notation.

114. **Astronomy** One light-year is the distance traveled by light in one year. One light-year is 5,880,000,000,000 mi. Write this number in scientific notation.

Multiply or divide.

115. $(1.9 \times 10^{12})(3.5 \times 10^{7})$

116. $(4.2 \times 10^{7})(1.8 \times 10^{-5})$

117. $(2.3 \times 10^{-8})(1.4 \times 10^{-6})$

118. $(3 \times 10^{-20})(2.4 \times 10^{9})$

119. $\dfrac{6.12 \times 10^{14}}{1.7 \times 10^{9}}$

120. $\dfrac{6 \times 10^{-8}}{2.5 \times 10^{-2}}$

121. $\dfrac{5.58 \times 10^{-7}}{3.1 \times 10^{11}}$

122. $\dfrac{9.03 \times 10^{6}}{4.3 \times 10^{-5}}$

123. $a \times 10^{n}$ and $a \times 10^{-m}$ are numbers written in scientific notation, where n and m are positive integers such that $n < m$. Is $(a \times 10^{n})(a \times 10^{-m})$ greater than or less than 1?

124. $a \times 10^{-n}$ and $a \times 10^{-m}$ are numbers written in scientific notation, where n and m are positive integers such that $n > m$. Is $\dfrac{a \times 10^{-m}}{a \times 10^{-n}}$ greater than or less than 1?

7.4 Applying Concepts

Evaluate.

125. $8^{-2} + 2^{-5}$

126. $9^{-2} + 3^{-3}$

127. Evaluate 2^x and 2^{-x} when $x = -2, -1, 0, 1,$ and 2.

128. Evaluate 3^x and 3^{-x} when $x = -2, -1, 0, 1,$ and 2.

Write in decimal notation.

129. 2^{-4}

130. 25^{-2}

Simplify.

131. $\left(\dfrac{9x^2y^4}{3xy^2}\right) - \left(\dfrac{12x^5y^6}{6x^4y^4}\right)$

132. $\left(\dfrac{6x^2 + 9x}{3x}\right) + \left(\dfrac{8xy^2 + 4y^2}{4y^2}\right)$

133. $\left(\dfrac{6x^4yz^3}{2x^2y^3}\right)\left(\dfrac{2x^2z^3}{4y^2z}\right) \div \left(\dfrac{6x^2y^3}{x^4y^2z}\right)$

134. $\left(\dfrac{5x^2yz^3}{3x^4yz^3}\right) \div \left(\dfrac{10x^2y^5z^4}{2y^3z}\right) \div \left(\dfrac{5y^4z^2}{x^2y^6z}\right)$

Complete.

135. If $m = n$ and $a \neq 0$, then $\dfrac{a^m}{a^n} =$ ____.

136. If $m = n + 1$ and $a \neq 0$, then $\dfrac{a^m}{a^n} =$ ____.

Solve.

137. $(-4.8)^x = 1$

138. $-6.3^x = -1$

Determine whether each equation is true or false. If the equation is false, change the right side of the equation to make a true equation.

139. $(2a)^{-3} = \dfrac{2}{a^3}$

140. $((a^{-1})^{-1})^{-1} = \dfrac{1}{a}$

141. $(2 + 3)^{-1} = 2^{-1} + 3^{-1}$

142. If $x \neq \dfrac{1}{3}$, then $(3x - 1)^0 = (1 - 3x)^0$.

143. Why is the condition $x \neq \dfrac{1}{3}$ given in Exercise 142?

144. If x is a nonzero real number, is x^{-2} always positive, always negative, or positive or negative depending on whether x is positive or negative? Explain your answer.

145. If x is a nonzero real number, is x^{-3} always positive, always negative, or positive or negative depending on whether x is positive or negative? Explain your answer.

7.5 Division of Polynomials

OBJECTIVE 1 Divide a polynomial by a monomial

Note that $\frac{8+4}{2}$ can be simplified by first adding the terms in the numerator and then dividing the result. It can also be simplified by first dividing each term in the numerator by the denominator and then adding the result.

$$\frac{8+4}{2} = \frac{12}{2} = 6$$

$$\frac{8+4}{2} = \frac{8}{2} + \frac{4}{2} = 4 + 2 = 6$$

To divide a polynomial by a monomial, divide each term in the numerator by the denominator, and write the sum of the quotients.

$$\frac{a+b}{c} = \frac{a}{c} + \frac{b}{c}$$

Divide: $\dfrac{6x^2 + 4x}{2x}$

Divide each term of the polynomial $6x^2 + 4x$ by the monomial $2x$. Simplify.

$$\frac{6x^2 + 4x}{2x} = \frac{6x^2}{2x} + \frac{4x}{2}$$
$$= 3x + 2$$

EXAMPLE 1 Divide: $\dfrac{6x^3 - 3x^2 + 9x}{3x}$

Solution

$$\frac{6x^3 - 3x^2 + 9x}{3x} = \frac{6x^3}{3x} - \frac{3x^2}{3x} + \frac{9x}{3x}$$
$$= 2x^2 - x + 3$$

- **Divide each term of the polynomial by the monomial 3*x*.**
- **Simplify each expression.**

PROBLEM 1 Divide: $\dfrac{4x^3y + 8x^2y^2 - 4xy^3}{2xy}$

Solution See page S17.

EXAMPLE 2 Divide: $\dfrac{12x^2y - 6xy + 4x^2}{2xy}$

Solution

$$\frac{12x^2y - 6xy + 4x^2}{2xy}$$
$$= \frac{12x^2y}{2xy} - \frac{6xy}{2xy} + \frac{4x^2}{2xy}$$
$$= 6x - 3 + \frac{2x}{y}$$

- **Divide each term of the polynomial by the monomial 2*xy*.**
- **Simplify each expression.**

PROBLEM 2 Divide: $\dfrac{24x^2y^2 - 18xy + 6y}{6xy}$

Solution See page S17.

OBJECTIVE 2 Divide polynomials

To divide polynomials, use a method similar to that used for division of whole numbers. The same equation used to check division of whole numbers is used to check polynomial division.

(Quotient × Divisor) + Remainder = Dividend

$$\begin{array}{r} 3 \\ 5\overline{)17} \\ \underline{-15} \\ 2 \end{array}$$

For example, for the division at the left,

(Quotient × Divisor) + Remainder = Dividend

$(3 \times 5) \quad + \quad 2 \quad = \quad 17$

Divide: $(x^2 - 5x + 8) \div (x - 3)$

Step 1

$$\begin{array}{r} x \phantom{{}-5x+8} \\ x-3\overline{)x^2 - 5x + 8} \\ \underline{x^2 - 3x} \phantom{{}+8} \\ -2x + 8 \end{array}$$

Think: $x\overline{)x^2} = \dfrac{x^2}{x} = x$

Multiply: $x(x - 3) = x^2 - 3x$

Subtract: $(x^2 - 5x) - (x^2 - 3x) = -2x$

Bring down $+ 8$.

Step 2

$$\begin{array}{r} x - 2 \\ x-3\overline{)x^2 - 5x + 8} \\ \underline{x^2 - 3x} \phantom{{}+8} \\ -2x + 8 \\ \underline{-2x + 6} \\ 2 \end{array}$$

Think: $x\overline{)-2x} = \dfrac{-2x}{x} = -2$

Multiply: $-2(x - 3) = -2x + 6$

Subtract: $(-2x + 8) - (-2x + 6) = 2$

The remainder is 2.

Check:

Quotient × Divisor + Remainder = Dividend

$(x - 2)(x - 3) + 2 = x^2 - 3x - 2x + 6 + 2 = x^2 - 5x + 8$

$(x^2 - 5x + 8) \div (x - 3) = x - 2 + \dfrac{2}{x - 3}$

If a term is missing in the dividend, insert the term with zero as its coefficient. This helps keep like terms in the same column. This is illustrated in Example 3.

EXAMPLE 3 Divide: $(6x + 2x^3 + 26) \div (x + 2)$

Solution

$$\begin{array}{r} 2x^2 - 4x + 14 \\ x+2\overline{)2x^3 + 0x^2 + 6x + 26} \\ \underline{2x^3 + 4x^2} \phantom{{}+6x+26} \\ -4x^2 + 6x \phantom{{}+26} \\ \underline{-4x^2 - 8x} \phantom{{}+26} \\ 14x + 26 \\ \underline{14x + 28} \\ -2 \end{array}$$

- **Arrange the terms in descending order. There is no term of x^2 in $2x^3 + 6x + 26$. Insert $0x^2$ for the missing term so that like terms will be in columns.**

$(6x + 2x^3 + 26) \div (x + 2) = 2x^2 - 4x + 14 - \dfrac{2}{x + 2}$

PROBLEM 3 Divide: $(x^3 - 2x - 4) \div (x - 2)$

Solution See page S17.

7.5 Concept Review

Determine whether the statement is always true, sometimes true, or never true.

1. For $c \neq 0$, $\dfrac{a-b}{c} = \dfrac{a}{c} - \dfrac{b}{c}$.

2. For $x \neq 0$, $\dfrac{9x^2 + 6x}{3x} = 3x + 6x$.

3. Given $(6x^2 + x - 6) \div (3x + 2) = 2x - 1 - \dfrac{4}{3x+2}$, then $(3x + 2)(2x - 1) - \dfrac{4}{3x+2} = 6x^2 + x - 6$.

7.5 Exercises

1 Divide a polynomial by a monomial

1. Replace each question mark to make a true statement.

$$\frac{18y^5 + 3y}{3y} = \frac{18y^5}{?} + \frac{3y}{?}$$
$$= \underline{\quad ? \quad} + \underline{\quad ? \quad}$$

2. Replace each question mark to make a true statement.

$$\frac{12x^3 - 8x^2}{4x^2} = \frac{12x^3}{?} - \frac{8x^2}{?}$$
$$= \underline{\quad ? \quad} - \underline{\quad ? \quad}$$

Divide.

3. $\dfrac{2x + 2}{2}$

4. $\dfrac{5y + 5}{5}$

5. $\dfrac{10a - 25}{5}$

6. $\dfrac{16b - 40}{8}$

7. $\dfrac{3a^2 + 2a}{a}$

8. $\dfrac{6y^2 + 4y}{y}$

9. $\dfrac{4b^3 - 3b}{b}$

10. $\dfrac{12x^2 - 7x}{x}$

11. $\dfrac{3x^2 - 6x}{3x}$

12. $\dfrac{10y^2 - 6y}{2y}$

13. $\dfrac{5x^2 - 10x}{-5x}$

14. $\dfrac{3y^2 - 27y}{-3y}$

15. $\dfrac{x^3 + 3x^2 - 5x}{x}$

16. $\dfrac{a^3 - 5a^2 + 7a}{a}$

17. $\dfrac{x^6 - 3x^4 - x^2}{x^2}$

18. $\dfrac{a^8 - 5a^5 - 3a^3}{a^2}$

19. $\dfrac{5x^2y^2 + 10xy}{5xy}$

20. $\dfrac{8x^2y^2 - 24xy}{8xy}$

21. $\dfrac{9y^6 - 15y^3}{-3y^3}$

22. $\dfrac{4x^4 - 6x^2}{-2x^2}$

23. $\dfrac{3x^2 - 2x + 1}{x}$

24. $\dfrac{8y^2 + 2y - 3}{y}$

25. $\dfrac{-3x^2 + 7x - 6}{x}$

26. $\dfrac{2y^2 - 6y + 9}{y}$

27. $\dfrac{16a^2b - 20ab + 24ab^2}{4ab}$

28. $\dfrac{22a^2b + 11ab - 33ab^2}{11ab}$

29. $\dfrac{9x^2y + 6xy - 3xy^2}{xy}$

30. Every division equation has a related multiplication equation. For instance, $\dfrac{16}{2} = 8$ means that $16 = 8 \cdot 2$. What is the related multiplication equation for $\dfrac{15x^2 + 12x}{3x} = 5x + 4$?

31. How can multiplication be used to check that $\dfrac{8x^3 - 12x^2 - 4x}{4x} = 2x^2 - 3x - 1$?

2 Divide polynomials

32. Let P and Q be polynomials. To find the quotient $P \div Q$ using long division, place __?__ inside the long-division symbol and __?__ outside the long-division symbol.

33. Use this long division:

$$\begin{array}{r} 3x \phantom{{}-4x+7} \\ x - 2\overline{)3x^2 - 4x + 7} \\ \underline{3x^2 - 6x} \phantom{{}+7} \\ 2x + 7 \end{array}$$

a. The term $3x$ in the quotient came from dividing __?__ by __?__.

b. The polynomial $3x^2 - 6x$ came from finding the product of __?__ and __?__.

c. The term $2x$ in the last line came from subtracting __?__ − (__?__).

d. Finish the division. The quotient is __?__. The remainder is __?__.

Divide.

34. $(b^2 - 14b + 49) \div (b - 7)$

35. $(x^2 - x - 6) \div (x - 3)$

36. $(y^2 + 2y - 35) \div (y + 7)$

37. $(2x^2 + 5x + 2) \div (x + 2)$

38. $(2y^2 - 13y + 21) \div (y - 3)$

39. $(4x^2 - 16) \div (2x + 4)$

40. $(2y^2 + 7) \div (y - 3)$

41. $(x^2 + 1) \div (x - 1)$

42. $(x^2 + 4) \div (x + 2)$

43. $(6x^2 - 7x) \div (3x - 2)$

44. $(6y^2 + 2y) \div (2y + 4)$

45. $(5x^2 + 7x) \div (x - 1)$

46. $(6x^2 - 5) \div (x + 2)$

47. $(a^2 + 5a + 10) \div (a + 2)$

48. $(b^2 - 8b - 9) \div (b - 3)$

49. $(2y^2 - 9y + 8) \div (2y + 3)$

50. $(3x^2 + 5x - 4) \div (x - 4)$

51. $(8x + 3 + 4x^2) \div (2x - 1)$

52. $(10 + 21y + 10y^2) \div (2y + 3)$

53. $(15a^2 - 8a - 8) \div (3a + 2)$

54. $(12a^2 - 25a - 7) \div (3a - 7)$

55. $(5 - 23x + 12x^2) \div (4x - 1)$

56. $(24 + 6a^2 + 25a) \div (3a - 1)$

57. $(x^3 + 3x^2 + 5x + 3) \div (x + 1)$

58. $(x^3 - 6x^2 + 7x - 2) \div (x - 1)$

59. $(x^4 - x^2 - 6) \div (x^2 + 2)$

60. $(x^4 + 3x^2 - 10) \div (x^2 - 2)$

61. True or false? When a sixth-degree polynomial is divided by a third-degree polynomial, the quotient is a second-degree polynomial.

62. True or false? When a polynomial of degree $3n$ is divided by a polynomial of degree n, the degree of the quotient polynomial is $2n$.

7.5 Applying Concepts

In Exercises 63 and 64, replace the question marks with expressions to make a true statement.

63. If $\dfrac{x^2 - x - 6}{x - 3} = x + 2$, then $x^2 - x - 6 = (?)(?)$.

64. If $\dfrac{x^2 + 2x - 3}{x - 2} = x + 4 + \dfrac{5}{x - 2}$, then $x^2 + 2x - 3 = (?)(?) + ?$.

Solve.

65. The product of a monomial and $4b$ is $12a^2b$. Find the monomial.

66. The product of a monomial and $6x$ is $24xy^2$. Find the monomial.

67. The quotient of a polynomial and $2x + 1$ is $2x - 4 + \dfrac{7}{2x + 1}$. Find the polynomial.

68. The quotient of a polynomial and $x - 3$ is $x^2 - x + 8 + \dfrac{22}{x - 3}$. Find the polynomial.

Focus on Problem Solving

Dimensional Analysis

In solving application problems, it may be useful to include units in order to organize the problem so that the answer is in the proper units. Using units to organize and check the correctness of an application is called **dimensional analysis.** We use the operations of multiplying units and dividing units in applying dimensional analysis to application problems.

The Rule for Multiplying Exponential Expressions states that we multiply two expressions with the same base by adding the exponents.

$$x^4 \cdot x^6 = x^{4+6} = x^{10}$$

In calculations that involve quantities, the units are operated on algebraically.

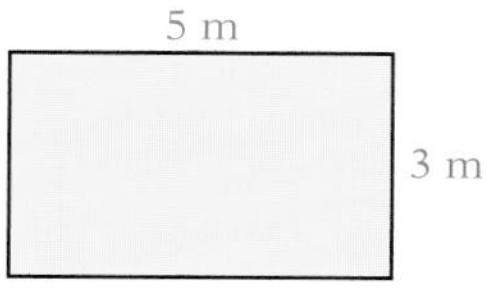

A rectangle measures 3 m by 5 m. Find the area of the rectangle.

$$A = LW = (5 \text{ m})(3 \text{ m}) = (5 \cdot 3)(\text{m} \cdot \text{m}) = 15 \text{ m}^2$$

The area of the rectangle is 15 m^2 (square meters).

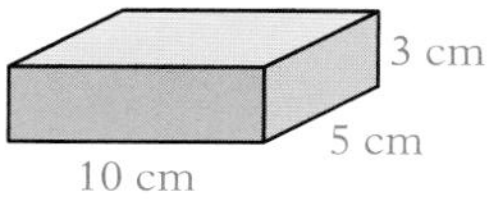

A box measures 10 cm by 5 cm by 3 cm. Find the volume of the box.

$$V = LWH = (10 \text{ cm})(5 \text{ cm})(3 \text{ cm}) = (10 \cdot 5 \cdot 3)(\text{cm} \cdot \text{cm} \cdot \text{cm}) = 150 \text{ cm}^3$$

The volume of the box is 150 cm^3 (cubic centimeters).

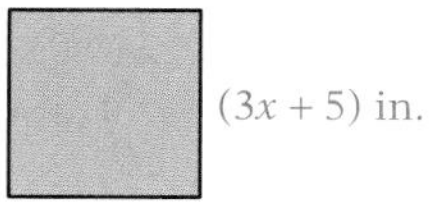

Find the area of a square whose side measures $(3x + 5)$ in.

$$A = s^2 = [(3x + 5) \text{ in.}]^2 = (3x + 5)^2 \text{ in}^2 = (9x^2 + 30x + 25) \text{ in}^2$$

The area of the square is $(9x^2 + 30x + 25) \text{ in}^2$ (square inches).

Dimensional analysis is used in the conversion of units.

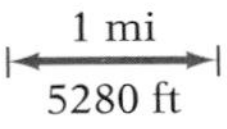

The following example converts the unit miles to feet. The equivalent measures 1 mi and 5280 ft are used to form the following rates, which are called conversion factors: $\frac{1 \text{ mi}}{5280 \text{ ft}}$ and $\frac{5280 \text{ ft}}{1 \text{ mi}}$. Because 1 mi = 5280 ft, both of the conversion factors $\frac{1 \text{ mi}}{5280 \text{ ft}}$ and $\frac{5280 \text{ ft}}{1 \text{ mi}}$ are equal to 1.

To convert 3 mi to feet, multiply 3 mi by the conversion factor $\frac{5280 \text{ ft}}{1 \text{ mi}}$.

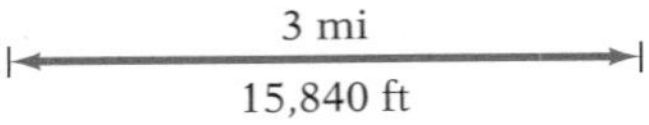

$$3 \text{ mi} = 3 \text{ mi} \cdot 1 = \frac{3 \text{ mi}}{1} \cdot \frac{5280 \text{ ft}}{1 \text{ mi}} = \frac{3 \cancel{\text{mi}} \cdot 5280 \text{ ft}}{1 \cancel{\text{mi}}} = 3 \cdot 5280 \text{ ft} = 15{,}840 \text{ ft}$$

There are two important points in the above illustration. First, you can think of dividing the numerator and denominator by the common unit "mile" just as you would divide the numerator and denominator of a fraction by a common factor. Second, the conversion factor $\frac{5280 \text{ ft}}{1 \text{ mi}}$ is equal to 1, and multiplying an expression by 1 does not change the value of the expression.

In the application problem that follows, the units are kept in the problem while the problem is worked.

In 2005, a horse named Afleet Alex won the Preakness, covering the 1.1875-mile course in 1.92 min. Find Afleet Alex's speed in miles per hour. Round to the nearest tenth.

Strategy To find the average speed, use the formula $r = \frac{d}{t}$, where r is the speed, d is the distance, and t is the time. Use the conversion factor $\frac{60 \text{ min}}{1 \text{ h}}$.

Solution

$$r = \frac{d}{t} = \frac{1.1875 \text{ mi}}{1.92 \text{ min}} = \frac{1.1875 \text{ mi}}{1.92 \text{ min}} \cdot \frac{60 \text{ min}}{1 \text{ h}}$$

$$= \frac{71.25 \text{ mi}}{1.92 \text{ h}} \approx 37.1 \text{ mph}$$

Afleet Alex's average speed was 37.1 mph.

Try each of the following problems. Round to the nearest tenth or to the nearest cent.

1. Convert 88 ft/s to miles per hour.
2. Convert 8 m/s to kilometers per hour (1 km = 1000 m).
3. A carpet is to be placed in a meeting hall that is 36 ft wide and 80 ft long. At $21.50 per square yard, how much will it cost to carpet the meeting hall?

4. A carpet is to be placed in a room that is 20 ft wide and 30 ft long. At \$22.25 per square yard, how much will it cost to carpet the area?

5. Find the number of gallons of water in a fish tank that is 36 in. long and 24 in. wide and is filled to a depth of 16 in. (1 gal = 231 in^3).

6. Find the number of gallons of water in a fish tank that is 24 in. long and 18 in. wide and is filled to a depth of 12 in. (1 gal = 231 in^3).

7. A $\frac{1}{4}$-acre commercial lot is on sale for \$2.15 per square foot. Find the sale price of the commercial lot (1 acre = 43,560 ft^2).

8. A 0.75-acre industrial parcel was sold for \$98,010. Find the parcel's price per square foot (1 acre = 43,560 ft^2).

9. A new driveway will require 800 ft^3 of concrete. Concrete is ordered by the cubic yard. How much concrete should be ordered?

10. In 2005, Catherine Ndereba won her fourth Boston Marathon. She ran the 26-mile course in 2.42 h. Find Catherine Ndereba's speed in feet per second. Round to the nearest tenth.

11. The Marianas Trench in the Pacific Ocean is the deepest part of the ocean. Its depth is 6.85 mi. The speed of sound under water is 4700 ft/s. Find the time it takes sound to travel from the surface to the bottom of the Marianas Trench and back.

Projects & Group Activities

Population and Land Allocation*

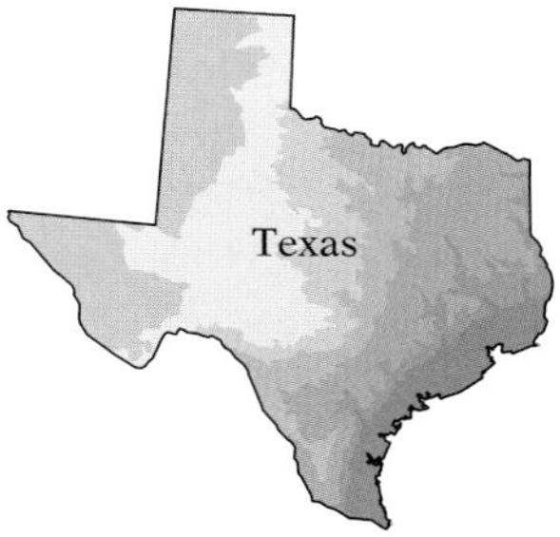

Rhode Island

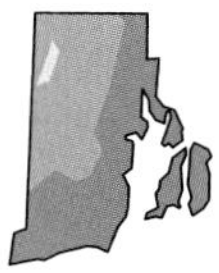

One of the Projects & Group Activities in the chapter "Linear Equations and Inequalities" involved population projections. You were asked to make predictions about the population of the United States and of the world. In this project, you are asked to determine hypothetical land allocation for the world's population today. Use the figure 6×10^9 for the current world population and the figure 2.9×10^8 for the current U.S. population. One square mile is approximately 2.8×10^7 ft^2.

1. If every person in the world moved to Texas and each person were given an equal amount of land, how many square feet of land would each person have? The area of Texas is 2.619×10^5 mi^2.

2. If every person in the United States moved to Rhode Island and each person were given an equal amount of land, how many square feet of land would each person have? The area of Rhode Island is 1.0×10^3 mi^2. Round to the nearest whole number.

*Source: www.infoplease.com

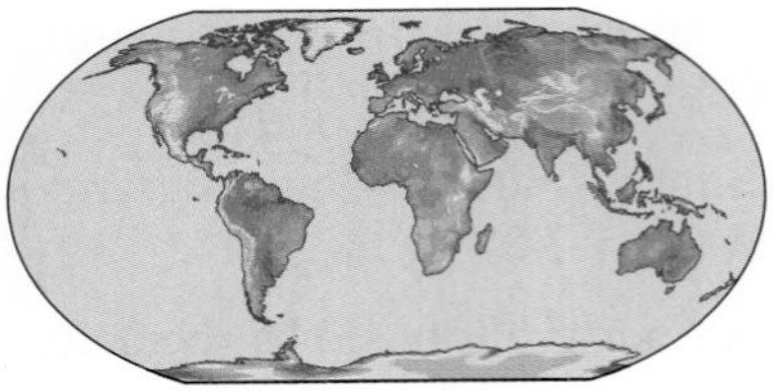

3. Suppose every person in the world were given a plot of land the size of a two-car garage (22 ft × 22 ft).

a. How many people would fit in a square mile? Round to the nearest hundred.

b. How many square miles would be required to accommodate the entire world population? Round to the nearest hundred.

4. If the total land area of Earth were divided equally, how many acres of land would each person be allocated? Use a figure of 5.7×10^7 mi^2 for the land area of Earth. One acre is 43,560 ft^2. Round to the nearest tenth.

5. If every person on Earth were given a plot of land the size of a two-car garage, what would be the carrying capacity of Earth? Round to the nearest hundred billion.

Chapter 7 Summary

Key Words	*Examples*
A **monomial** is a number, a variable, or a product of numbers and variables. [7.1.1, p. 369]	5 is a number. y is a variable. $8a^2b^3$ is a product of numbers and variables. 5, y, and $8a^2b^3$ are monomials.
A **polynomial** is a variable expression in which the terms are monomials. [7.1.1, p. 369]	As shown above, 5, y, and $8a^2b^3$ are monomials. Therefore, $5 + y + 8a^2b^3$ is a polynomial.
A polynomial of one term is a **monomial.** [7.1.1, p. 369]	5, y, and $8a^2b^3$ are monomials.
A polynomial of two terms is a **binomial.** [7.1.1, p. 369]	$x + 9$, $y^2 - 3$, and $6a + 7b$ are binomials.
A polynomial of three terms is a **trinomial.** [7.1.1, p. 369]	$x^2 + 2x - 1$ is a trinomial.
The **degree of a polynomial in one variable** is the largest exponent on a variable. [7.1.1, p. 370]	The degree of $8x^3 - 5x^2 + 4x - 12$ is 3.
The **opposite of a polynomial** is the polynomial with the sign of every term changed to its opposite. [7.1.2, p. 370]	The opposite of the polynomial $x^2 - 3x + 4$ is $-x^2 + 3x - 4$.

Essential Rules and Procedures

Addition of Polynomials
To add polynomials, add the coefficients of the like terms. [7.1.1, p. 370]

$$\begin{aligned}(2x^2 + 3x - 4) + (3x^3 - 4x^2 + 2x - 5) &= 3x^3 + (2x^2 - 4x^2) + (3x + 2x) \\ &\quad + (-4 - 5) \\ &= 3x^3 - 2x^2 + 5x - 9\end{aligned}$$

Subtraction of Polynomials
To subtract polynomials, add the opposite of the second polynomial to the first. [7.1.2, p. 370]

$$\begin{aligned}(3y^2 - 8y - 9) - (5y^2 - 10y + 3) &= (3y^2 - 8y - 9) + (-5y^2 + 10y - 3)\\ &= (3y^2 - 5y^2) + (-8y + 10y) + (-9 - 3)\\ &= -2y^2 + 2y - 12\end{aligned}$$

Rule for Multiplying Exponential Expressions
If m and n are integers, then $x^m \cdot x^n = x^{m+n}$. [7.2.1, p. 375]

$$b^5 \cdot b^4 = b^{5+4} = b^9$$

Rule for Simplifying Powers of Exponential Expressions
If m and n are integers, then $(x^m)^n = x^{mn}$. [7.2.2, p. 376]

$$(y^3)^7 = y^{3(7)} = y^{21}$$

Rule for Simplifying Powers of Products
If m, n, and p are integers, then $(x^m y^n)^p = x^{mp}y^{np}$. [7.2.2, p. 376]

$$(a^6b^2)^3 = a^{6(3)}b^{2(3)} = a^{18}b^6$$

FOIL Method
To find the product of two binomials, add the products of the **F**irst terms, the **O**uter terms, the **I**nner terms, and the **L**ast terms. [7.3.3, p. 381]

$$\begin{aligned}(4x + 3)(2x - 1) &= (4x)(2x) + (4x)(-1) + (3)(2x) + (3)(-1)\\ &= 8x^2 - 4x + 6x - 3\\ &= 8x^2 + 2x - 3\end{aligned}$$

The Sum and Difference of Two Terms
$(a + b)(a - b) = a^2 - b^2$ [7.3.4, p. 382]

$$\begin{aligned}(3x + 4)(3x - 4) &= (3x)^2 - 4^2\\ &= 9x^2 - 16\end{aligned}$$

The Square of a Binomial
$(a + b)^2 = a^2 + 2ab + b^2$

$$\begin{aligned}(2x + 5)^2 &= (2x)^2 + 2(2x)(5) + 5^2\\ &= 4x^2 + 20x + 25\end{aligned}$$

$(a - b)^2 = a^2 - 2ab + b^2$ [7.3.4, p. 383]

$$\begin{aligned}(2x - 5)^2 &= (2x)^2 - 2(2x)(5) + (-5)^2\\ &= 4x^2 - 20x + 25\end{aligned}$$

Zero as an Exponent
Any nonzero expression to the zero power equals 1. [7.4.1, p. 391]

$17^0 = 1$ $\quad$ $(5y)^0 = 1, y \neq 0$

Definition of Negative Exponents
If n is a positive integer and $x \neq 0$, then $x^{-n} = \dfrac{1}{x^n}$ and $\dfrac{1}{x^{-n}} = x^n$. [7.4.1, p. 392]

$x^{-6} = \dfrac{1}{x^6}$ and $\dfrac{1}{x^{-6}} = x^6$

Rule for Dividing Exponential Expressions
If m and n are integers and $x \neq 0$, then $\dfrac{x^m}{x^n} = x^{m-n}$. [7.4.1, p. 392]

$$\frac{y^8}{y^3} = y^{8-3} = y^5$$

Scientific Notation
To express a number in scientific notation, write it in the form $a \times 10^n$, where a is a number between 1 and 10 and n is an integer. If the number is greater than 10, the exponent on 10 will be positive. If the number is less than 1, the exponent on 10 will be negative.

$367{,}000{,}000 = 3.67 \times 10^8$

$0.0000059 = 5.9 \times 10^{-6}$

To change a number written in scientific notation to decimal notation, move the decimal point to the right if the exponent on 10 is positive and to the left if the exponent on 10 is negative. Move the decimal point the same number of places as the absolute value of the exponent on 10. [7.4.2, pp. 394–395]

$2.418 \times 10^7 = 24{,}180{,}000$

$9.06 \times 10^{-5} = 0.0000906$

To divide a polynomial by a monomial, divide each term in the numerator by the denominator and write the sum of the quotients. [7.5.1, p. 402]

$$\frac{8xy^3 - 4y^2 + 12y}{4y} = \frac{8xy^3}{4y} - \frac{4y^2}{4y} + \frac{12y}{4y} = 2xy^2 - y + 3$$

To check polynomial division, use the same equation used to check division of whole numbers:

(Quotient × divisor) + remainder = dividend

[7.5.2, p. 403]

$$\begin{array}{r} x - 4 \\ x + 3\overline{)x^2 - x - 10} \\ \underline{x^2 + 3x} \\ -4x - 10 \\ \underline{-4x - 12} \\ 2 \end{array}$$

Check:

$$(x - 4)(x + 3) + 2 = x^2 - x - 12 + 2 = x^2 - x - 10$$

$$(x^2 - x - 10) \div (x + 3) = x - 4 + \frac{2}{x + 3}$$

Chapter 7 Review Exercises

1. Add: $(12y^2 + 17y - 4) + (9y^2 - 13y + 3)$
2. Multiply: $(5xy^2)(-4x^2y^3)$
3. Multiply: $-2x(4x^2 + 7x - 9)$
4. Multiply: $(5a - 7)(2a + 9)$
5. Divide: $\dfrac{36x^2 - 42x + 60}{6}$
6. Subtract: $(5x^2 - 2x - 1) - (3x^2 - 5x + 7)$
7. Simplify: $(-3^2)^3$
8. Multiply: $(x^2 - 5x + 2)(x - 1)$
9. Multiply: $(a + 7)(a - 7)$
10. Evaluate: $\dfrac{6^2}{6^{-2}}$
11. Divide: $(x^2 + x - 42) \div (x + 7)$
12. Add: $(2x^3 + 7x^2 + x) + (2x^2 - 4x - 12)$

13. Multiply: $(6a^2b^5)(3a^6b)$

14. Multiply: $x^2y(3x^2 - 2x + 12)$

15. Multiply: $(2b - 3)(4b + 5)$

16. Divide: $\dfrac{16y^2 - 32y}{-4y}$

17. Subtract: $(13y^3 - 7y - 2) - (12y^2 - 2y - 1)$

18. Simplify: $(2^3)^2$

19. Multiply: $(3y^2 + 4y - 7)(2y + 3)$

20. Multiply: $(2b - 9)(2b + 9)$

21. Simplify: $(a^{-2}b^3c)^2$

22. Divide: $(6y^2 - 35y + 36) \div (3y - 4)$

23. Write 0.00000397 in scientific notation.

24. Multiply: $(xy^5z^3)(x^3y^3z)$

25. Multiply: $(6y^2 - 2y + 9)(-2y^3)$

26. Multiply: $(6x - 12)(3x - 2)$

27. Write 6.23×10^{-5} in decimal notation.

28. Subtract: $(8a^2 - a) - (15a^2 - 4)$

29. Simplify: $(-3x^2y^3)^2$

30. Multiply: $(4a^2 - 3)(3a - 2)$

31. Simplify: $(5y - 7)^2$

32. Simplify: $(-3x^{-2}y^{-3})^{-2}$

33. Divide: $(x^2 + 17x + 64) \div (x + 12)$

34. Write 2.4×10^5 in decimal notation.

35. Multiply: $(a^2b^7c^6)(ab^3c)(a^3bc^2)$

36. Multiply: $2ab^3(4a^2 - 2ab + 3b^2)$

37. Multiply: $(3x + 4y)(2x - 5y)$

38. Divide: $\dfrac{12b^7 + 36b^5 - 3b^3}{3b^3}$

39. Subtract: $(b^2 - 11b + 19) - (5b^2 + 2b - 9)$

40. Simplify: $(5a^7b^6)^2(4ab)$

41. Multiply: $(6b^3 - 2b^2 - 5)(2b^2 - 1)$

42. Multiply: $(6 - 5x)(6 + 5x)$

43. Simplify: $\dfrac{6x^{-2}y^4}{3xy}$

44. Divide: $(a^3 + a^2 + 18) \div (a + 3)$

45. Add: $(4b^3 - 7b^2 + 10) + (2b^2 - 9b - 3)$

46. Multiply: $(2a^{12}b^3)(-9b^2c^6)(3ac)$

47. Multiply: $-9x^2(2x^2 + 3x - 7)$

48. Multiply: $(10y - 3)(3y - 10)$

49. Write 9,176,000,000,000 in scientific notation.

50. Subtract: $(6y^2 + 2y + 7) - (8y^2 + y + 12)$

51. Simplify: $(6x^4y^7z^2)^2(-2x^3y^2z^6)^2$

52. Multiply: $(-3x^3 - 2x^2 + x - 9)(4x + 3)$

53. Simplify: $(8a + 1)^2$

54. Simplify: $\dfrac{4a^{-2}b^{-8}}{2a^{-1}b^{-2}}$

55. Divide: $(b^3 - 2b^2 - 33b - 7) \div (b - 7)$

56. **Geometry** The length of a rectangle is $5x$ m. The width is $(4x - 7)$ m. Find the area of the rectangle in terms of the variable x.

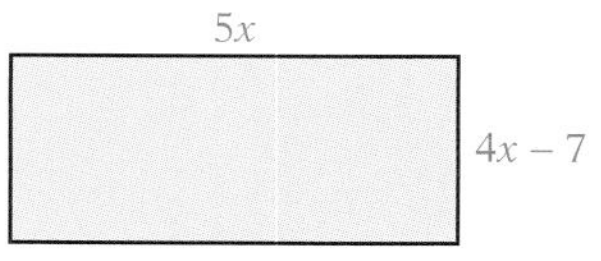

57. **Geometry** The length of a side of a square is $(5x + 4)$ in. Find the area of the square in terms of the variable x.

58. **Geometry** The base of a triangle is $(3x - 2)$ ft and the height is $(6x + 4)$ ft. Find the area of the triangle in terms of the variable x.

59. **Geometry** The radius of a circle is $(x - 6)$ cm. Find the area of the circle in terms of the variable x. Leave the answer in terms of π.

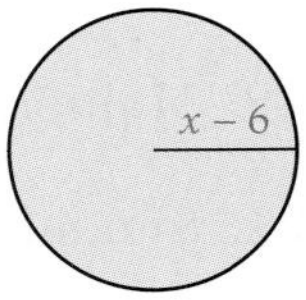

60. **Geometry** The width of a rectangle is $(3x - 8)$ mi. The length is $(5x + 4)$ mi. Find the area of the rectangle in terms of the variable x.

Chapter 7 Test

1. Add: $(3x^3 - 2x^2 - 4) + (8x^2 - 8x + 7)$

2. Multiply: $(-2x^3 + x^2 - 7)(2x - 3)$

3. Multiply: $2x(2x^2 - 3x)$

4. Simplify: $(-2a^2b)^3$

5. Simplify: $\dfrac{12x^2}{-3x^{-4}}$

6. Simplify: $(2ab^{-3})(3a^{-2}b^4)$

7. Subtract: $(3a^2 - 2a - 7) - (5a^3 + 2a - 10)$

8. Multiply: $(a - 2b)(a + 5b)$

9. Divide: $\dfrac{16x^5 - 8x^3 + 20x}{4x}$

10. Divide: $(4x^2 - 7) \div (2x - 3)$

11. Multiply: $(-2xy^2)(3x^2y^4)$

12. Multiply: $-3y^2(-2y^2 + 3y - 6)$

13. Simplify: $\dfrac{27xy^3}{3x^4y^3}$

14. Simplify: $(2x - 5)^2$

15. Multiply: $(2x - 7y)(5x - 4y)$

16. Multiply: $(x - 3)(x^2 - 4x + 5)$

17. Simplify: $(a^2b^{-3})^2$

18. Write 0.000029 in scientific notation.

19. Multiply: $(4y - 3)(4y + 3)$

20. Subtract: $(3y^3 - 5y + 8) - (-2y^2 + 5y + 8)$

21. Simplify: $(-3a^3b^2)^2$

22. Multiply: $(2a - 7)(5a^2 - 2a + 3)$

23. Simplify: $(3b + 2)^2$

24. Simplify: $\dfrac{-2a^2b^3}{8a^4b^8}$

25. Divide: $(8x^2 + 4x - 3) \div (2x - 3)$

26. Multiply: $(a^2b^5)(ab^2)$

27. Multiply: $(a - 3b)(a + 4b)$

28. Write 3.5×10^{-8} in decimal notation.

29. **Geometry** The length of a side of a square is $(2x + 3)$ m. Find the area of the square in terms of the variable x.

30. **Geometry** The radius of a circle is $(x - 5)$ in. Find the area of the circle in terms of the variable x. Leave the answer in terms of π.

Cumulative Review Exercises

1. Simplify: $\frac{3}{16} - \left(-\frac{3}{8}\right) - \frac{5}{9}$

2. Simplify: $-5^2 \cdot \left(\frac{2}{3}\right)^3 \cdot \left(-\frac{3}{8}\right)$

3. Simplify: $\left(-\frac{1}{2}\right)^2 \div \left(\frac{5}{8} - \frac{5}{6}\right) + 2$

4. Find the opposite of -87.

5. Write $\frac{31}{40}$ as a decimal.

6. Evaluate $\frac{b - (a - b)^2}{b^2}$ when $a = 3$ and $b = -2$.

7. Simplify: $-3x - (-xy) + 2x - 5xy$

8. Simplify: $(16x)\left(-\frac{3}{4}\right)$

9. Simplify: $-2[3x - 4(3 - 2x) + 2]$

10. Complete the statement by using the Inverse Property of Addition.
$-8 + ? = 0$

11. Solve: $12 = -\frac{2}{3}x$

12. Solve: $3x - 7 = 2x + 9$

13. Solve: $3 - 4(2 - x) = 3x + 7$

14. Solve: $-\frac{4}{5}x = 16 - x$

15. 38.4 is what percent of 160?

16. Solve: $7x - 8 \geq -29$

17. Find the slope of the line that contains the points whose coordinates are $(3, -4)$ and $(-2, 5)$.

18. Find the equation of the line that contains the point whose coordinates are $(1, -3)$ and has slope $-\frac{3}{2}$.

19. Graph: $3x - 2y = -6$

20. Graph the solution set of $y \leq \frac{4}{5}x - 3$.

21. Find the domain and range of the relation $\{(-8, -7), (-6, -5), (-4, -2), (-2, 0)\}$. Is the relation a function?

22. Evaluate $f(x) = -2x + 10$ at $x = 6$.

23. Solve by substitution: $\begin{aligned} x &= 3y + 1 \\ 2x + 5y &= 13 \end{aligned}$

24. Solve by the addition method: $\begin{aligned} 9x - 2y &= 17 \\ 5x + 3y &= -7 \end{aligned}$

25. Subtract: $(5b^3 - 4b^2 - 7) - (3b^2 - 8b + 3)$

26. Multiply: $(3x - 4)(5x^2 - 2x + 1)$

27. Multiply: $(4b - 3)(5b - 8)$

28. Simplify: $(5b + 3)^2$

29. Simplify: $\dfrac{-3a^3b^2}{12a^4b^{-2}}$

30. Divide: $\dfrac{-15y^2 + 12y - 3}{-3y}$

31. Divide: $(a^2 - 3a - 28) \div (a + 4)$

32. Simplify: $(-3x^{-4}y)(-3x^{-2}y)$

33. Find the range of the function given by the equation $f(x) = -\frac{4}{3}x + 9$ if the domain is $\{-12, -9, -6, 0, 6\}$.

34. Translate and simplify "the product of five and the difference between a number and twelve."

35. Translate "the difference between eight times a number and twice the number is eighteen" into an equation and solve.

36. **Geometry** The width of a rectangle is 40% of the length. The perimeter of the rectangle is 42 m. Find the length and width of the rectangle.

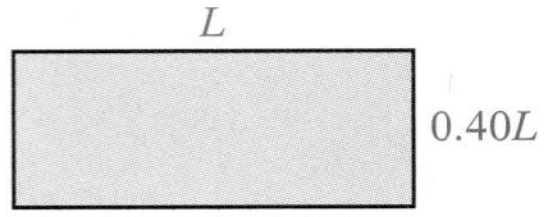

37. **Markup** A calculator costs a retailer \$24. Find the selling price when the markup rate is 80%.

38. **Food Mixtures** Fifty ounces of pure orange juice are added to 200 oz of a fruit punch that is 10% orange juice. What is the percent concentration of orange juice in the resulting mixture?

39. **Uniform Motion Problem** A car traveling at 50 mph overtakes a cyclist who, riding at 10 mph, has had a 2-hour head start. How far from the starting point does the car overtake the cyclist?

40. **Geometry** The length of a side of a square is $(3x + 2)$ ft. Find the area of the square in terms of the variable x.

CHAPTER

8 Factoring

OBJECTIVES

8.1
1 Factor a monomial from a polynomial
2 Factor by grouping

8.2
1 Factor trinomials of the form $x^2 + bx + c$
2 Factor completely

8.3
1 Factor trinomials of the form $ax^2 + bx + c$ using trial factors
2 Factor trinomials of the form $ax^2 + bx + c$ by grouping

8.4
1 Factor the difference of two squares and perfect-square trinomials
2 Factor completely

8.5
1 Solve equations by factoring
2 Application problems

In 2008, Iowa State will host the first and second rounds of the NCAA Division I women's basketball tournament in Des Moines, Iowa. The teams who will compete in this tournament will be determined by their ranking after the 2008 regular season. Imagine that you have just gotten a job as the manager for NCAA Division I women's basketball, and that you have to organize the game schedule for the upcoming season. How would you go about creating this schedule? **Exercises 93 and 94 on page 457** show you how to use a formula to determine the number of league games that must be scheduled if each team is to play each of the other teams once.

DVD SSM *Online Study Center*

Need help? For online student resources, such as section quizzes, visit the Online Study Center at college.hmco.com/pic/aufmannBAWA7e.

Prep Test

1. Write 30 as a product of prime numbers.

2. Simplify: $-3(4y - 5)$

3. Simplify: $-(a - b)$

4. Simplify: $2(a - b) - 5(a - b)$

5. Solve: $4x = 0$

6. Solve: $2x + 1 = 0$

7. Multiply: $(x + 4)(x - 6)$

8. Multiply: $(2x - 5)(3x + 2)$

9. Simplify: $\dfrac{x^5}{x^2}$

10. Simplify: $\dfrac{6x^4y^3}{2xy^2}$

8.1 Common Factors

OBJECTIVE 1 Factor a monomial from a polynomial

Take Note

12 is the GCF of 24 and 60 because 12 is the largest integer that divides evenly into both 24 and 60.

The **greatest common factor (GCF)** of two or more integers is the greatest integer that is a factor of all the integers.

$24 = 2 \cdot 2 \cdot 2 \cdot 3$
$60 = 2 \cdot 2 \cdot 3 \cdot 5$
$\text{GCF} = 2 \cdot 2 \cdot 3 = 12$

The GCF of two or more monomials is the product of the GCF of the coefficients and the common variable factors.

$6x^3y = 2 \cdot 3 \cdot x \cdot x \cdot x \cdot y$
$8x^2y^2 = 2 \cdot 2 \cdot 2 \cdot x \cdot x \cdot y \cdot y$
$\text{GCF} = 2 \cdot x \cdot x \cdot y = 2x^2y$

Note that the exponent of each variable in the GCF is the same as the *smallest* exponent of that variable in either of the monomials.

The GCF of $6x^3y$ and $8x^2y^2$ is $2x^2y$.

EXAMPLE 1 Find the GCF of $12a^4b$ and $18a^2b^2c$.

Solution $12a^4b = 2 \cdot 2 \cdot 3 \cdot a^4 \cdot b$
$18a^2b^2c = 2 \cdot 3 \cdot 3 \cdot a^2 \cdot b^2 \cdot c$ • **Factor each monomial.**

$\text{GCF} = 2 \cdot 3 \cdot a^2 \cdot b = 6a^2b$ • **The common variable factors are a^2 and b. c is not a common factor.**

PROBLEM 1 Find the GCF of $4x^6y$ and $18x^2y^6$.

Solution See page S17.

The Distributive Property is used to multiply factors of a polynomial. To **factor a polynomial** means to write the polynomial as a product of other polynomials.

Factors	Multiply →	Polynomial
$2x(x + 5)$	$=$	$2x^2 + 10x$
← Factor		

In the example above, $2x$ is the GCF of the terms $2x^2$ and $10x$. It is a **common monomial factor** of the terms. $x + 5$ is a **binomial factor** of $2x^2 + 10x$.

EXAMPLE 2 Factor. **A.** $5x^3 - 35x^2 + 10x$ **B.** $16x^2y + 8x^4y^2 - 12x^4y^5$

Solution **A.** The GCF is $5x$. • **Find the GCF of the terms of the polynomial.**

$$\frac{5x^3}{5x} = x^2, \quad \frac{-35x^2}{5x} = -7x, \quad \frac{10x}{5x} = 2$$

• **Divide each term of the polynomial by the GCF.**

$$5x^3 - 35x^2 + 10x$$
$$= 5x(x^2) + 5x(-7x) + 5x(2)$$

• **Use the quotients to rewrite the polynomial, expressing each term as a product with the GCF as one of the factors.**

$$= 5x(x^2 - 7x + 2)$$

• **Use the Distributive Property to write the polynomial as a product of factors.**

B. $16x^2y = 2 \cdot 2 \cdot 2 \cdot 2 \cdot x^2 \cdot y$
$8x^4y^2 = 2 \cdot 2 \cdot 2 \cdot x^4 \cdot y^2$
$12x^4y^5 = 2 \cdot 2 \cdot 3 \cdot x^4 \cdot y^5$
The GCF is $4x^2y$.

$$16x^2y + 8x^4y^2 - 12x^4y^5$$
$$= 4x^2y(4) + 4x^2y(2x^2y) + 4x^2y(-3x^2y^4)$$
$$= 4x^2y(4 + 2x^2y - 3x^2y^4)$$

PROBLEM 2 Factor. **A.** $14a^2 - 21a^4b$ **B.** $6x^4y^2 - 9x^3y^2 + 12x^2y^4$

Solution See page S17.

OBJECTIVE 2 Factor by grouping

In the examples below, the binomials in parentheses are called **binomial factors.**

$$2a(a + b)$$
$$3xy(x - y)$$

The Distributive Property is used to factor a common binomial factor from an expression.

In the expression at the right, the common binomial factor is $y - 3$. The Distributive Property is used to write the expression as a product of factors.

$$x(y - 3) + 4(y - 3)$$
$$= (y - 3)(x + 4)$$

EXAMPLE 3 Factor: $y(x + 2) + 3(x + 2)$

Solution $y(x + 2) + 3(x + 2)$ • **The common binomial factor is $x + 2$.**
$= (x + 2)(y + 3)$

PROBLEM 3 Factor: $a(b - 7) + b(b - 7)$

Solution See page S17.

Sometimes a binomial factor must be rewritten before a common binomial factor can be found.

Factor: $a(a - b) + 5(b - a)$

$a - b$ and $b - a$ are different binomials.

Note that $(b - a) = (-a + b) = -(a - b)$.

Rewrite $(b - a)$ as $-(a - b)$ so that there is a common factor.

$$\begin{aligned} a(a - b) + 5(b - a) &= a(a - b) + 5[-(a - b)] \\ &= a(a - b) - 5(a - b) \\ &= (a - b)(a - 5) \end{aligned}$$

EXAMPLE 4 Factor: $2x(x - 5) + y(5 - x)$

Solution $2x(x - 5) + y(5 - x)$

$= 2x(x - 5) - y(x - 5)$ • **Rewrite $5 - x$ as $-(x - 5)$ so that there is a common factor.**

$= (x - 5)(2x - y)$ • **Write the expression as a product of factors.**

PROBLEM 4 Factor: $3y(5x - 2) - 4(2 - 5x)$

Solution See page S17.

Some polynomials can be factored by grouping the terms so that a common binomial factor is found.

Factor: $2x^3 - 3x^2 + 4x - 6$

$2x^3 - 3x^2 + 4x - 6$

Group the first two terms and the last two terms. $= (2x^3 - 3x^2) + (4x - 6)$

Factor out the GCF from each group. $= x^2(2x - 3) + 2(2x - 3)$

Write the expression as a product of factors. $= (2x - 3)(x^2 + 2)$

EXAMPLE 5 Factor: $3y^3 - 4y^2 - 6y + 8$

Solution $3y^3 - 4y^2 - 6y + 8$

$= (3y^3 - 4y^2) - (6y - 8)$ • **Group the first two terms and the last two terms. Note that $-6y + 8 = -(6y - 8)$.**

$= y^2(3y - 4) - 2(3y - 4)$ • **Factor out the GCF from each group.**

$= (3y - 4)(y^2 - 2)$ • **Write the expression as a product of factors.**

PROBLEM 5 Factor: $y^5 - 5y^3 + 4y^2 - 20$

Solution See page S17.

8.1 Concept Review

Determine whether the statement is always true, sometimes true, or never true.

1. To factor a polynomial means to rewrite it as multiplication.

2. The expression $3x(x + 5)$ is a sum, and the expression $3x^2 + 15x$ is a product.

3. The greatest common factor of two numbers is the largest number that divides evenly into both numbers.

4. x is a monomial factor of $x(2x - 1)$. $2x - 1$ is a binomial factor of $x(2x - 1)$.

5. $y(y + 4) + 6$ is in factored form.

6. A common monomial factor is a factor of every term of a polynomial.

7. $a^2 - 8a - ab + 8b = a(a - 8) - b(a + 8)$

8. The binomial $d + 9$ is a common binomial factor of $2c(d + 9) - 7(d + 9)$.

8.1 Exercises

1 Factor a monomial from a polynomial

1. Explain the meaning of "a factor of a polynomial" and the meaning of "to factor a polynomial."

2. Explain why the statement is true.

   a. The terms of the binomial $3x - 6$ have a common factor.
   b. The expression $3x^2 + 15$ is not in factored form.
   c. $5y - 7$ is a factor of $y(5y - 7)$.

3. Use the three monomials $9x^3y^2$, $3xy^3z$, and $6x^2y^2z^2$.

   a. Of the variable factors x, y, and z, the one that is *not* a factor of the GCF of $9x^3y^2$, $3xy^3z$, and $6x^2y^2z^2$ is ___?___.
   b. The GCF of the coefficients 9, 3, and 6 is ___?___.
   c. The GCF of the factors x^3, x, and x^2 is ___?___.

d. The GCF of the factors y^2, y^3, and y^2 is ___?___.
e. Use your answers to parts a to d to write the GCF of $9x^3y^2$, $3xy^3z$, and $6x^2y^2z^2$: ___?___

4. a. Of the two expressions $25a^2 - 10a$ and $5a(5a - 2)$, the one that is written in *factored form* is ___?___.
b. Use the Distributive Property to confirm that the two expressions in part a are equivalent:
$5a(5a - 2) = (\_\_?\_\_)(5a) - (\_\_?\_\_)(2) = \_\_?\_\_ - \_\_?\_\_$.
c. The polynomial $25a^2 - 10a$ has a monomial factor and a binomial factor. The monomial factor is ___?___ and the binomial factor is ___?___.

Find the greatest common factor.

5. x^7, x^3
6. y^6, y^{12}
7. x^2y^4, xy^6
8. a^5b^3, a^3b^8
9. $x^2y^4z^6, xy^8z^2$
10. ab^2c^3, a^3b^2c
11. $14a^3, 49a^7$
12. $12y^2, 27y^4$
13. $3x^2y^2, 5ab^2$
14. $8x^2y^3, 7ab^4$
15. $9a^2b^4, 24a^4b^2$
16. $15a^4b^2, 9ab^5$
17. $ab^3, 4a^2b, 12a^2b^3$
18. $12x^2y, x^4y, 16x$
19. $2x^2y, 4xy, 8x$
20. $16x^2, 8x^4y^2, 12xy$
21. $3x^2y^2, 6x, 9x^3y^3$
22. $4a^2b^3, 8a^3, 12ab^4$

Factor.

23. $5a + 5$
24. $7b - 7$
25. $16 - 8a^2$
26. $12 + 12y^2$
27. $8x + 12$
28. $16a - 24$
29. $30a - 6$
30. $20b + 5$
31. $7x^2 - 3x$
32. $12y^2 - 5y$
33. $3a^2 + 5a^5$
34. $9x - 5x^2$
35. $14y^2 + 11y$
36. $6b^3 - 5b^2$
37. $2x^4 - 4x$
38. $3y^4 - 9y$
39. $10x^4 - 12x^2$
40. $12a^5 - 32a^2$
41. $x^2y - xy^3$
42. $a^2b + a^4b^2$
43. $2a^5b + 3xy^3$
44. $5x^2y - 7ab^3$
45. $6a^2b^3 - 12b^2$
46. $8x^2y^3 - 4x^2$
47. $6a^2bc + 4ab^2c$
48. $10x^2yz^2 + 15xy^3z$
49. $18x^2y^2 - 9a^2b^2$
50. $9a^2x - 27a^3x^3$
51. $6x^3y^3 - 12x^6y^6$
52. $3a^2b^2 - 12a^5b^5$
53. $x^3 - 3x^2 - x$
54. $a^3 + 4a^2 + 8a$
55. $2x^2 + 8x - 12$
56. $a^3 - 3a^2 + 5a$
57. $b^3 - 5b^2 - 7b$
58. $5x^2 - 15x + 35$
59. $8y^2 - 12y + 32$
60. $3x^3 + 6x^2 + 9x$
61. $5y^3 - 20y^2 + 10y$
62. $2x^4 - 4x^3 + 6x^2$
63. $3y^4 - 9y^3 - 6y^2$
64. $2x^3 + 6x^2 - 14x$
65. $3y^3 - 9y^2 + 24y$
66. $2y^5 - 3y^4 + 7y^3$
67. $6a^5 - 3a^3 - 2a^2$
68. $x^3y - 3x^2y^2 + 7xy^3$
69. $8x^2y^2 - 4x^2y + x^2$
70. $x^4y^4 - 3x^3y^3 + 6x^2y^2$
71. $4x^5y^5 - 8x^4y^4 + x^3y^3$
72. $16x^2y - 8x^3y^4 - 48x^2y^2$

For Exercises 73 and 74, use the polynomial $x^a + x^b + x^c$, where a, b, and c are all positive integers such that $a < b < c$.

73. What is the GCF of the terms of the polynomial $x^a + x^b + x^c$?

74. Suppose $b = a + 1$ and $c = a + 2$. Write $x^a + x^b + x^c$ in factored form.

2 Factor by grouping

75. **a.** The expression $5x(3x - 2) + 4(3x - 2)$ is the sum of two terms. One term is $5x(3x - 2)$ and the other term is ___?___. The terms have the common binomial factor ___?___.

b. To write the expression $5x(3x - 2) + 4(3x - 2)$ in factored form, factor out the common binomial factor: $5x(3x - 2) + 4(3x - 2) =$ $(3x - 2)($___?___ + ___?___$)$.

76. To factor $7a^2 - 7a + 6a - 6$ by grouping, start by factoring $7a$ from the first two terms and 6 from the second two terms: $7a^2 - 7a + 6a - 6 =$ $7a($___?___ − ___?___$) + 6($___?___ − ___?___$) = ($___?___$)(7a + 6)$

Factor.

77. $x(a + b) + 2(a + b)$

78. $a(x + y) + 4(x + y)$

79. $x(b + 2) - y(b + 2)$

80. $d(z - 8) + 5(z - 8)$

81. $a(y - 4) - b(y - 4)$

82. $c(x - 6) - 7(x - 6)$

Rewrite the expression so that there is a common binomial factor.

83. $a(x - 2) - b(2 - x)$

84. $a(x - 2) + b(2 - x)$

85. $b(a - 7) + 3(7 - a)$

86. $b(a - 7) - 3(7 - a)$

87. $x(a - 2b) - y(2b - a)$

88. $x(a - 2b) + y(2b - a)$

Factor.

89. $a(x - 2) + 5(2 - x)$

90. $a(x - 7) + b(7 - x)$

91. $b(y - 3) + 3(3 - y)$

92. $c(a - 2) - b(2 - a)$

93. $a(x - y) - 2(y - x)$

94. $3(a - b) - x(b - a)$

95. $z(c + 5) - 8(5 + c)$

96. $y(ab + 4) - 7(4 + ab)$

97. $w(3x - 4) - (4 - 3x)$

98. $d(6y - 1) - (1 - 6y)$

99. $x^3 + 4x^2 + 3x + 12$

100. $x^3 - 4x^2 - 3x + 12$

101. $2y^3 + 4y^2 + 3y + 6$

102. $3y^3 - 12y^2 + y - 4$

103. $ab + 3b - 2a - 6$

104. $yz + 6z - 3y - 18$

105. $x^2a - 2x^2 - 3a + 6$

106. $x^2y + 4x^2 + 3y + 12$

107. $3ax - 3bx - 2ay + 2by$

108. $8 + 2c + 4a^2 + a^2c$

109. $x^2 - 3x + 4ax - 12a$

110. $t^2 + 4t - st - 4s$

111. $xy - 5y - 2x + 10$

112. $2y^2 - 10y + 7xy - 35x$

113. $21x^2 + 6xy - 49x - 14y$

114. $4a^2 + 5ab - 10b - 8a$

115. $2ra + a^2 - 2r - a$

116. $2ab - 3b^2 - 3b + 2a$

117. $4x^2 + 3xy - 12y - 16x$

118. $8s + 12r - 6s^2 - 9rs$

119. $10xy^2 - 15xy + 6y - 9$

120. $10a^2b - 15ab - 4a + 6$

121. Not all four-term expressions can be factored by grouping. Which of the following expressions can be factored by grouping?
I. $ab - 3a - 2b - 6$ **II.** $ab + 3a - 2b - 6$ **III.** $ab + 3a + 2b - 6$

122. **a.** Which of the following expressions are equivalent to $x^2 - 5x + 6$?
I. $x^2 - 15x + 10x + 6$ **II.** $x^2 - x - 4x + 6$ **III.** $x^2 - 2x - 3x + 6$
b. Which expression in part a can be factored by grouping?

8.1 Applying Concepts

Factor by grouping.

123. **a.** $2x^2 + 6x + 5x + 15$ **b.** $2x^2 + 5x + 6x + 15$

124. **a.** $3x^2 + 3xy - xy - y^2$ **b.** $3x^2 - xy + 3xy - y^2$

125. **a.** $2a^2 - 2ab - 3ab + 3b^2$ **b.** $2a^2 - 3ab - 2ab + 3b^2$

Compare your answers to parts a and b of Exercises 123 to 125 in order to answer Exercise 126.

126. Do different groupings of the terms in a polynomial affect the binomial factoring?

A whole number is a perfect number if it is the sum of all of its factors that are less than itself. For example, 6 is a perfect number because all the factors of 6 that are less than 6 are 1, 2, and 3, and $1 + 2 + 3 = 6$.

127. Find a perfect number between 20 and 30.

128. Find a perfect number between 490 and 500.

Solve.

129. **Geometry** In the equation $P = 2L + 2W$, what is the effect on P when the quantity $L + W$ doubles?

130. **Geometry** Write an expression in factored form for the shaded portion in the diagram.

a.

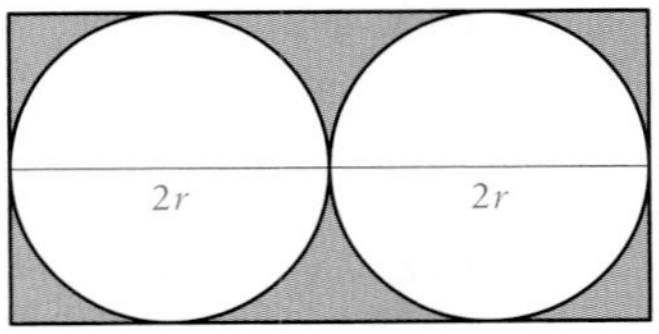

b.

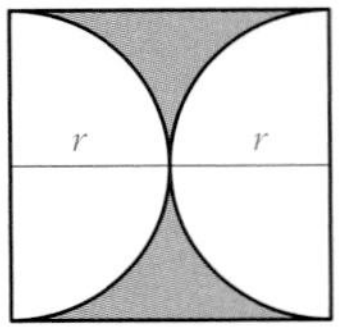

8.2 Factoring Polynomials of the Form $x^2 + bx + c$

OBJECTIVE 1 Factor trinomials of the form $x^2 + bx + c$

Trinomials of the form $x^2 + bx + c$, where b and c are integers, are shown at the right.

$x^2 + 9x + 14$, $b = 9$, $c = 14$
$x^2 - x - 12$, $b = -1$, $c = -12$
$x^2 - 2x - 15$, $b = -2$, $c = -15$

To factor a trinomial of this form means to express the trinomial as the product of two binomials. Some trinomials expressed as the product of binomials (factored form) are shown at the right.

Trinomial		Factored Form
$x^2 + 9x + 14$	=	$(x + 2)(x + 7)$
$x^2 - x - 12$	=	$(x + 3)(x - 4)$
$x^2 - 2x - 15$	=	$(x + 3)(x - 5)$

The method by which the factors of a trinomial are found is based on FOIL. Consider the following binomial products, noting the relationship between the constant terms of the binomials and the terms of the trinomials.

Signs in the binomials are the same

$$(x + 6)(x + 2) = x^2 + 2x + 6x + (6)(2) = x^2 + 8x + 12$$

Sum of 6 and 2 → $8x$; Product of 6 and 2 → 12

$$(x - 3)(x - 4) = x^2 - 4x - 3x + (-3)(-4) = x^2 - 7x + 12$$

Sum of −3 and −4 → $-7x$; Product of −3 and −4 → 12

Signs in the binomials are opposite

$$(x + 3)(x - 5) = x^2 - 5x + 3x + (3)(-5) = x^2 - 2x - 15$$

Sum of 3 and −5 → $-2x$; Product of 3 and −5 → -15

$$(x - 4)(x + 6) = x^2 + 6x - 4x + (-4)(6) = x^2 + 2x - 24$$

Sum of −4 and 6 → $2x$; Product of −4 and 6 → -24

Points to Remember in Factoring $x^2 + bx + c$

1. In the trinomial, the coefficient of x is the sum of the constant terms of the binomials.
2. In the trinomial, the constant term is the product of the constant terms of the binomials.
3. When the constant term of the trinomial is positive, the constant terms of the binomials have the same sign as the coefficient of x in the trinomial.
4. When the constant term of the trinomial is negative, the constant terms of the binomials have opposite signs.

Success at factoring a trinomial depends on remembering these four points.

For example, to factor $x^2 - 2x - 24$, find two numbers whose sum is -2 and whose product is -24 [Points 1 and 2]. Because the constant term of the trinomial is negative (-24), the numbers will have opposite signs [Point 4].

A systematic method of finding these numbers involves listing the factors of the constant term of the trinomial and the sum of those factors.

Factors of −24	Sum of the Factors
1, −24	1 + (−24) = −23
−1, 24	−1 + 24 = 23
2, −12	2 + (−12) = −10
−2, 12	−2 + 12 = 10
3, −8	3 + (−8) = −5
−3, 8	−3 + 8 = 5
4, −6	**4 + (−6) = −2**
−4, 6	−4 + 6 = 2

Take Note

Always check your proposed factorization to ensure accuracy.

4 and −6 are two numbers whose sum is −2 and whose product is −24. Write the binomial factors of the trinomial.

$$x^2 - 2x - 24 = (x + 4)(x - 6)$$

Check: $(x + 4)(x - 6) = x^2 - 6x + 4x - 24 = x^2 - 2x - 24$

By the Commutative Property of Multiplication, the binomial factors can also be written as

$$x^2 - 2x - 24 = (x - 6)(x + 4)$$

EXAMPLE 1 Factor: $x^2 + 18x + 32$

Solution

Factors of 32	Sum
1, 32	33
2, 16	**18**
4, 8	12

- **Try only positive factors of 32 [Point 3].**
- **Once the correct pair is found, the other factors need not be tried.**

$x^2 + 18x + 32 = (x + 2)(x + 16)$

- **Write the factors of the trinomial.**

Check $(x + 2)(x + 16) = x^2 + 16x + 2x + 32$
$= x^2 + 18x + 32$

PROBLEM 1 Factor: $x^2 - 8x + 15$

Solution See page S17.

EXAMPLE 2 Factor: $x^2 - 6x - 16$

Solution

Factors of −16	Sum
1, −16	−15
−1, 16	15
2, −8	**−6**
−2, 8	6
4, −4	0

- **The factors must be of opposite signs [Point 4].**

$x^2 - 6x - 16 = (x + 2)(x - 8)$

- **Write the factors of the trinomial.**

Check $(x + 2)(x - 8) = x^2 - 8x + 2x - 16$
$= x^2 - 6x - 16$

PROBLEM 2 Factor: $x^2 + 3x - 18$

Solution See page S17.

Not all trinomials can be factored when using only integers. Consider the trinomial $x^2 - 6x - 8$.

Factors of −8	Sum
1, −8	−7
−1, 8	7
2, −4	−2
−2, 4	2

Because none of the pairs of factors of −8 have a sum of −6, the trinomial is not factorable using integers. The trinomial is said to be **nonfactorable over the integers.**

OBJECTIVE 2 Factor completely

A polynomial is **factored completely** when it is written as a product of factors that are nonfactorable over the integers.

Take Note

The first step in *any* factoring problem is to determine whether the terms of the polynomial have a *common factor*. If they do, factor it out first.

EXAMPLE 3 Factor: $3x^3 + 15x^2 + 18x$

Solution The GCF of $3x^3$, $15x^2$, and $18x$ is $3x$.
• **Find the GCF of the terms of the polynomial.**

$3x^3 + 15x^2 + 18x$
$= 3x(x^2) + 3x(5x) + 3x(6)$
• **Factor out the GCF.**
$= 3x(x^2 + 5x + 6)$
• **Write the polynomial as a product of factors.**

• **Factor the trinomial $x^2 + 5x + 6$. Try only positive factors of 6.**

Factors of 6	Sum
1, 6	7
2, 3	5

$3x^3 + 15x^2 + 18x = 3x(x + 2)(x + 3)$

Check $3x(x + 2)(x + 3) = 3x(x^2 + 3x + 2x + 6)$
$= 3x(x^2 + 5x + 6)$
$= 3x^3 + 15x^2 + 18x$

PROBLEM 3 Factor: $3a^2b - 18ab - 81b$

Solution See page S17.

EXAMPLE 4 Factor: $x^2 + 9xy + 20y^2$

Solution There is no common factor.

Factors of 20	Sum
1, 20	21
2, 10	12
4, 5	9

• **Try only positive factors of 20.**

$$x^2 + 9xy + 20y^2 = (x + 4y)(x + 5y)$$

Check $(x + 4y)(x + 5y) = x^2 + 5xy + 4xy + 20y^2$
$= x^2 + 9xy + 20y^2$

Take Note

$4y$ and $5y$ are placed in the binomials. This is necessary so that the middle term contains xy and the last term contains y^2.

PROBLEM 4 Factor: $4x^2 - 40xy + 84y^2$

Solution See page S18.

8.2 Concept Review

Determine whether the statement is always true, sometimes true, or never true.

1. The value of b in the trinomial $x^2 - 8x + 7$ is 8.

2. The factored form of $x^2 - 5x - 14$ is $(x - 7)(x + 2)$.

3. To factor a trinomial of the form $x^2 + bx + c$ means to rewrite the polynomial as a product of two binomials.

4. In the factoring of a trinomial, if the constant term is positive, then the signs in both binomial factors will be the same.

5. In the factoring of a trinomial, if the constant term is negative, then the signs in both binomial factors will be negative.

6. The first step in factoring a trinomial is to determine whether the terms of the trinomial have a common factor.

8.2 Exercises

1 Factor trinomials of the form $x^2 + bx + c$

Complete the table by listing the pairs of factors of the number and the sum of each pair.

1.

Factors of 18	Sum

2.

Factors of 12	Sum

3.

Factors of −21	Sum

4.

Factors of −10	Sum

5.

Factors of −28	Sum

6.

Factors of −32	Sum

Factor.

7. $x^2 + 3x + 2$ **8.** $x^2 + 5x + 6$ **9.** $x^2 - x - 2$ **10.** $x^2 + x - 6$

11. $a^2 + a - 12$ **12.** $a^2 - 2a - 35$ **13.** $a^2 - 3a + 2$ **14.** $a^2 - 5a + 4$

15. $a^2 + a - 2$ **16.** $a^2 - 2a - 3$ **17.** $b^2 - 6b + 9$ **18.** $b^2 + 8b + 16$

19. $b^2 + 7b - 8$ **20.** $y^2 - y - 6$ **21.** $y^2 + 6y - 55$ **22.** $z^2 - 4z - 45$

23. $y^2 - 5y + 6$ **24.** $y^2 - 8y + 15$ **25.** $z^2 - 14z + 45$ **26.** $z^2 - 14z + 49$

27. $z^2 - 12z - 160$ **28.** $p^2 + 2p - 35$ **29.** $p^2 + 12p + 27$ **30.** $p^2 - 6p + 8$

31. $x^2 + 20x + 100$ **32.** $x^2 + 18x + 81$ **33.** $b^2 + 9b + 20$ **34.** $b^2 + 13b + 40$

35. $x^2 - 11x - 42$ **36.** $x^2 + 9x - 70$ **37.** $b^2 - b - 20$ **38.** $b^2 + 3b - 40$

39. $y^2 - 14y - 51$ **40.** $y^2 - y - 72$ **41.** $p^2 - 4p - 21$ **42.** $p^2 + 16p + 39$

43. $y^2 - 8y + 32$ **44.** $y^2 - 9y + 81$ **45.** $x^2 - 20x + 75$ **46.** $p^2 + 24p + 63$

47. $x^2 - 15x + 56$

48. $x^2 + 21x + 38$

49. $x^2 + x - 56$

50. $x^2 + 5x - 36$

51. $a^2 - 21a - 72$

52. $a^2 - 7a - 44$

53. $a^2 - 15a + 36$

54. $a^2 - 21a + 54$

55. $z^2 - 9z - 136$

56. $z^2 + 14z - 147$

57. $c^2 - c - 90$

58. $c^2 - 3c - 180$

59. Suppose b and c are nonzero and n and m are positive constants such that $x^2 + bx + c = (x + n)(x + m)$.
 a. Is c positive or negative?
 b. Is b positive or negative?

60. Suppose b and c are nonzero and n and m are positive constants such that $x^2 + bx + c = (x - n)(x - m)$.
 a. Is c positive or negative?
 b. Is b positive or negative?

2 Factor completely

61. Use the trinomial $5x^2 - 10x - 40$.
 a. The first step in factoring the trinomial is to look for a __?__ factor of the three terms.
 b. The GCF of the terms of the trinomial $5x^2 - 10x - 40$ is __?__.
 c. Factor the GCF from the terms of the trinomial: $5x^2 - 10x - 40 =$ 5(__?__)
 d. Factor the trinomial completely: $5x^2 - 10x - 40 = 5(x^2 - 2x - 8) =$ 5(__?__)(__?__)

62. To factor $x^2 + 2xy - 24y^2$, find binomials in the form $(x + ny)(x + my)$, where n and m are numbers whose product is __?__ and whose sum is __?__. Factors of -24 whose sum is 2 are __?__ and __?__. The trinomial $x^2 + 2x - 24y^2$ factors as (__?__)(__?__).

Factor.

63. $2x^2 + 6x + 4$

64. $3x^2 + 15x + 18$

65. $3a^2 + 3a - 18$

66. $4x^2 - 4x - 8$

67. $ab^2 + 2ab - 15a$

68. $ab^2 + 7ab - 8a$

69. $xy^2 - 5xy + 6x$

70. $xy^2 + 8xy + 15x$

71. $z^3 - 7z^2 + 12z$

72. $2a^3 + 6a^2 + 4a$

73. $3y^3 - 15y^2 + 18y$

74. $4y^3 + 12y^2 - 72y$

75. $3x^2 + 3x - 36$

76. $2x^3 - 2x^2 - 4x$

77. $5z^2 - 15z - 140$

78. $6z^2 + 12z - 90$

79. $2a^3 + 8a^2 - 64a$

80. $3a^3 - 9a^2 - 54a$

81. $x^2 - 5xy + 6y^2$

82. $x^2 + 4xy - 21y^2$

83. $a^2 - 9ab + 20b^2$

84. $a^2 - 15ab + 50b^2$

85. $x^2 - 3xy - 28y^2$

86. $s^2 + 2st - 48t^2$

87. $y^2 - 15yz - 41z^2$

88. $y^2 + 85yz + 36z^2$

89. $z^4 - 12z^3 + 35z^2$

90. $z^4 + 2z^3 - 80z^2$

91. $b^4 - 22b^3 + 120b^2$

92. $b^4 - 3b^3 - 10b^2$

93. $2y^4 - 26y^3 - 96y^2$

94. $3y^4 + 54y^3 + 135y^2$

95. $x^4 + 7x^3 - 8x^2$

96. $x^4 - 11x^3 - 12x^2$

97. $4x^2y + 20xy - 56y$

98. $3x^2y - 6xy - 45y$

99. $8y^2 - 32y + 24$

100. $10y^2 - 100y + 90$

101. $c^3 + 13c^2 + 30c$

102. $c^3 + 18c^2 - 40c$

103. $3x^3 - 36x^2 + 81x$

104. $4x^3 + 4x^2 - 24x$

105. $x^2 - 8xy + 15y^2$

106. $y^2 - 7xy - 8x^2$

107. $a^2 - 13ab + 42b^2$

108. $y^2 + 4yz - 21z^2$

109. $y^2 + 8yz + 7z^2$

110. $y^2 - 16yz + 15z^2$

111. $3x^2y + 60xy - 63y$

112. $4x^2y - 68xy - 72y$

113. $3x^3 + 3x^2 - 36x$

114. $4x^3 + 12x^2 - 160x$

115. $4z^3 + 32z^2 - 132z$

116. $5z^3 - 50z^2 - 120z$

117. State whether or not the trinomial has a factor of $(x + 3)$.

a. $3x^2 - 3x - 36$ **b.** $x^2y - xy - 12y$

118. State whether or not the trinomial has a factor of $(x + y)$.

a. $2x^2 - 2xy - 4y^2$ **b.** $2x^2y - 4xy - 4y$

8.2 Applying Concepts

Factor.

119. $20 + c^2 + 9c$

120. $x^2y - 54y - 3xy$

121. $45a^2 + a^2b^2 - 14a^2b$

122. $12p^2 - 96p + 3p^3$

Find all integers k such that the trinomial can be factored over the integers.

123. $x^2 + kx + 35$

124. $x^2 + kx + 18$

125. $x^2 - kx + 21$

126. $x^2 - kx + 14$

Determine the positive integer values of k for which the following polynomials are factorable over the integers.

127. $y^2 + 4y + k$

128. $z^2 + 7z + k$

129. $a^2 - 6a + k$

130. $c^2 - 7c + k$

131. $x^2 - 3x + k$

132. $y^2 + 5y + k$

133. Exercises 127 to 132 included the requirement that $k > 0$. If k is allowed to be any integer, how many different values of k are possible for each polynomial? Explain your answer.

8.3 Factoring Polynomials of the Form $ax^2 + bx + c$

OBJECTIVE 1 Factor trinomials of the form $ax^2 + bx + c$ using trial factors

Trinomials of the form $ax^2 + bx + c$, where a, b, and c are integers and $a \neq 0$, are shown at the right.

$3x^2 - x + 4, \quad a = 3, \quad b = -1, \quad c = 4$
$4x^2 + 5x - 8, \quad a = 4, \quad b = 5, \quad c = -8$

These trinomials differ from those in the previous section in that the coefficient of x^2 is not 1. There are various methods of factoring these trinomials. The method described in this objective is factoring trinomials using trial factors.

To **factor a trinomial of the form $ax^2 + bx + c$** means to express the polynomial as the product of two binomials. Factoring such polynomials by trial and error may require testing many trial factors. To reduce the number of trial factors, remember the following points.

Points to Remember in Factoring $ax^2 + bx + c$

1. If the terms of the trinomial do not have a common factor, then the terms of a binomial factor cannot have a common factor.
2. When the constant term of the trinomial is positive, the constant terms of the binomials have the same sign as the coefficient of x in the trinomial.
3. When the constant term of the trinomial is negative, the constant terms of the binomials have opposite signs.

Factor: $10x^2 - x - 3$

The terms of the trinomial do not have a common factor; therefore, the terms of a binomial factor will not have a common factor [Point 1].

Because the constant term, c, of the trinomial is negative (-3), the constant terms of the binomial factors will have opposite signs [Point 3].

Find the factors of a (10) and the factors of c (-3).

Factors of 10	Factors of -3
1, 10 2, 5	1, -3 -1, 3

Using these factors, write trial factors, and use the Outer and Inner products of FOIL to check the middle term.

Trial Factors	Middle Term
$(x + 1)(10x - 3)$	$-3x + 10x = 7x$
$(x - 1)(10x + 3)$	$3x - 10x = -7x$
$\mathbf{(2x + 1)(5x - 3)}$	$\mathbf{-6x + 5x = -x}$
$(2x - 1)(5x + 3)$	$6x - 5x = x$
$(10x + 1)(x - 3)$	$-30x + x = -29x$
$(10x - 1)(x + 3)$	$30x - x = 29x$
$(5x + 1)(2x - 3)$	$-15x + 2x = -13x$
$(5x - 1)(2x + 3)$	$15x - 2x = 13x$

From the list of trial factors, $10x^2 - x - 3 = (2x + 1)(5x - 3)$.

Check: $(2x + 1)(5x - 3) = 10x^2 - 6x + 5x - 3 = 10x^2 - x - 3$

All the trial factors for this trinomial were listed in this example. However, once the correct binomial factors are found, it is not necessary to continue checking the remaining trial factors.

Factor: $4x^2 - 27x + 18$

The terms of the trinomial do not have a common factor; therefore, the terms of a binomial factor will not have a common factor [Point 1].

Because the constant term, c, of the trinomial is positive (18), the constant terms of the binomial factors will have the same sign as the coefficient of x. Because the coefficient of x is -27, both signs will be negative [Point 2].

Find the factors of a (4) and the negative factors of c (18).

Factors of 4	Factors of 18
1, 4 2, 2	$-1, -18$ $-2, -9$ $-3, -6$

Using these factors, write trial factors, and use the Outer and Inner products of FOIL to check the middle term.

Trial Factors	Middle Term
$(x - 1)(4x - 18)$	Common factor
$(x - 2)(4x - 9)$	$-9x - 8x = -17x$
$(x - 3)(4x - 6)$	Common factor
$(2x - 1)(2x - 18)$	Common factor
$(2x - 2)(2x - 9)$	Common factor
$(2x - 3)(2x - 6)$	Common factor
$(4x - 1)(x - 18)$	$-72x - x = -73x$
$(4x - 2)(x - 9)$	Common factor
$\mathbf{(4x - 3)(x - 6)}$	$\mathbf{-24x - 3x = -27x}$

The correct factors have been found.

$$4x^2 - 27x + 18 = (4x - 3)(x - 6)$$

This last example illustrates that many of the trial factors may have common factors and thus need not be tried. For the remainder of this chapter, the trial factors with a common factor will not be listed.

EXAMPLE 1 Factor: $3x^2 + 20x + 12$

Solution

Factors of 3	Factors of 12
1, 3	1, 12
	2, 6
	3, 4

• **Because 20 is positive, only the positive factors of 12 need be tried.**

Trial Factors	Middle Term
$(x + 3)(3x + 4)$	$4x + 9x = 13x$
$(3x + 1)(x + 12)$	$36x + x = 37x$
$(3x + 2)(x + 6)$	$18x + 2x = 20x$

• **Write the trial factors. Use FOIL to check the middle term.**

$$3x^2 + 20x + 12 = (3x + 2)(x + 6)$$

Check $(3x + 2)(x + 6) = 3x^2 + 18x + 2x + 12$
$= 3x^2 + 20x + 12$

PROBLEM 1 Factor: $6x^2 - 11x + 5$

Solution See page S18.

EXAMPLE 2 Factor: $6x^2 - 5x - 6$

Solution

Factors of 6	Factors of -6
1, 6	1, -6
2, 3	-1, 6
	2, -3
	-2, 3

• **Find the factors of a (6) and the factors of c (-6).**

Trial Factors	Middle Term
$(x - 6)(6x + 1)$	$x - 36x = -35x$
$(x + 6)(6x - 1)$	$-x + 36x = 35x$
$(2x - 3)(3x + 2)$	$4x - 9x = -5x$

• **Write the trial factors. Use FOIL to check the middle term.**

$$6x^2 - 5x - 6 = (2x - 3)(3x + 2)$$

Check $(2x - 3)(3x + 2) = 6x^2 + 4x - 9x - 6$
$= 6x^2 - 5x - 6$

PROBLEM 2 Factor: $8x^2 + 14x - 15$

Solution See page S18.

EXAMPLE 3 Factor: $15 - 2x - x^2$

Solution

Factors of 15	Factors of −1
1, 15	1, −1
3, 5	

- **The terms have no common factors. The coefficient of x^2 is −1.**

Trial Factors	Middle Term
$(1 + x)(15 - x)$	$-x + 15x = 14x$
$(1 - x)(15 + x)$	$x - 15x = -14x$
$(3 + x)(5 - x)$	$-3x + 5x = 2x$
$(3 - x)(5 + x)$	$3x - 5x = -2x$

- **Write the trial factors. Use FOIL to check the middle term.**

$15 - 2x - x^2 = (3 - x)(5 + x)$

Check $(3 - x)(5 + x) = 15 + 3x - 5x - x^2$
$= 15 - 2x - x^2$

PROBLEM 3 Factor: $24 - 2y - y^2$

Solution See page S18.

The first step in factoring a trinomial is to determine whether there is a common factor. If there is a common factor, factor out the GCF of the terms.

EXAMPLE 4 Factor: $3x^3 - 23x^2 + 14x$

Solution The GCF of $3x^3$, $23x^2$, and $14x$ is x.

- **Find the GCF of the terms of the polynomial.**

$3x^3 - 23x^2 + 14x = x(3x^2 - 23x + 14)$

- **Factor out the GCF.**

Factors of 3	Factors of 14
1, 3	−1, −14
	−2, −7

- **Factor the trinomial $3x^2 - 23x + 14$.**

Trial Factors	Middle Term
$(x - 1)(3x - 14)$	$-14x - 3x = -17x$
$(x - 14)(3x - 1)$	$-x - 42x = -43x$
$(x - 2)(3x - 7)$	$-7x - 6x = -13x$
$(x - 7)(3x - 2)$	$-2x - 21x = -23x$

$3x^3 - 23x^2 + 14x = x(x - 7)(3x - 2)$

Check $x(x - 7)(3x - 2) = x(3x^2 - 2x - 21x + 14)$
$= x(3x^2 - 23x + 14)$
$= 3x^3 - 23x^2 + 14x$

PROBLEM 4 Factor: $4a^2b^2 - 30a^2b + 14a^2$

Solution See page S18.

OBJECTIVE 2 Factor trinomials of the form $ax^2 + bx + c$ by grouping

Take Note

In this objective, we are using the skills taught in Objective 2 of Section 1 of this chapter. You may want to review that material before studying this objective.

In the previous objective, trinomials of the form $ax^2 + bx + c$ were factored using trial factors. In this objective, factoring by grouping is used.

To factor $ax^2 + bx + c$, first find two factors of $a \cdot c$ whose sum is b. Use the two factors to rewrite the middle term of the trinomial as the sum of two terms. Then use factoring by grouping to write the factorization of the trinomial.

Factor: $2x^2 + 13x + 15$

$a = 2, c = 15, a \cdot c = 2 \cdot 15 = 30$

Find two positive factors of 30 whose sum is 13.

Positive Factors of 30	Sum
1, 30	31
2, 15	17
3, 10	13
5, 6	11

The factors are 3 and 10.

Use the factors 3 and 10 to rewrite $13x$ as $3x + 10x$.

$$2x^2 + 13x + 15$$
$$= 2x^2 + 3x + 10x + 15$$

Factor by grouping.

$$= (2x^2 + 3x) + (10x + 15)$$
$$= x(2x + 3) + 5(2x + 3)$$
$$= (2x + 3)(x + 5)$$

Check: $(2x + 3)(x + 5) = 2x^2 + 10x + 3x + 15$
$= 2x^2 + 13x + 15$

Factor: $6x^2 - 11x - 10$

$a = 6, c = -10, a \cdot c = 6(-10) = -60$

Find two factors of -60 whose sum is -11.

Factors of −60	Sum
1, −60	−59
−1, 60	59
2, −30	−28
−2, 30	28
3, −20	−17
−3, 20	17
4, −15	−11

The required sum has been found. The remaining factors need not be checked. The factors are 4 and -15.

Use the factors 4 and -15 to rewrite $-11x$ as $4x - 15x$.

$$6x^2 - 11x - 10$$
$$= 6x^2 + 4x - 15x - 10$$

Factor by grouping.

Note: $-15x - 10 = -(15x + 10)$

$$= (6x^2 + 4x) - (15x + 10)$$
$$= 2x(3x + 2) - 5(3x + 2)$$
$$= (3x + 2)(2x - 5)$$

Check: $(3x + 2)(2x - 5) = 6x^2 - 15x + 4x - 10$
$= 6x^2 - 11x - 10$

Factor: $3x^2 - 2x - 4$

$a = 3, c = -4, a \cdot c = 3(-4) = -12$

Find two factors of -12 whose sum is -2.

Factors of -12	Sum
$1, -12$	-11
$-1, 12$	11
$2, -6$	-4
$-2, 6$	4
$3, -4$	-1
$-3, 4$	1

No integer factors of -12 have a sum of -2. Therefore, $3x^2 - 2x - 4$ is nonfactorable over the integers.

EXAMPLE 5 Factor: $2x^2 + 19x - 10$

Solution $a \cdot c = 2(-10) = -20$ • **Find $a \cdot c$.**

$-1(20) = -20$
$-1 + 20 = 19$ • **Find two numbers whose product is -20 and whose sum is 19.**

$$2x^2 + 19x - 10$$
$$= 2x^2 - x + 20x - 10$$ • **Rewrite $19x$ as $-x + 20x$.**
$$= (2x^2 - x) + (20x - 10)$$ • **Factor by grouping.**
$$= x(2x - 1) + 10(2x - 1)$$
$$= (2x - 1)(x + 10)$$

PROBLEM 5 Factor: $2a^2 + 13a - 7$

Solution See page S18.

EXAMPLE 6 Factor: $8y^2 - 10y - 3$

Solution $a \cdot c = 8(-3) = -24$ • **Find $a \cdot c$.**

$2(-12) = -24$
$2 + (-12) = -10$ • **Find two numbers whose product is -24 and whose sum is -10.**

$$8y^2 - 10y - 3$$
$$= 8y^2 + 2y - 12y - 3$$ • **Rewrite $-10y$ as $2y - 12y$.**
$$= (8y^2 + 2y) - (12y + 3)$$ • **Factor by grouping.**
$$= 2y(4y + 1) - 3(4y + 1)$$
$$= (4y + 1)(2y - 3)$$

PROBLEM 6 Factor: $4a^2 - 11a - 3$

Solution See page S18.

Remember that the first step in factoring a trinomial is to determine whether there is a common factor. If there is a common factor, factor out the GCF of the terms.

EXAMPLE 7 Factor: $24x^2y - 76xy + 40y$

Solution

$24x^2y - 76xy + 40y$
$= 4y(6x^2 - 19x + 10)$

• **The terms of the polynomial have a common factor, 4*y*. Factor out the GCF.**

$a \cdot c = 6(10) = 60$

• **To factor $6x^2 - 19x + 10$, first find $a \cdot c$.**

$-4(-15) = 60$
$-4 + (-15) = -19$

• **Find two numbers whose product is 60 and whose sum is −19.**

$6x^2 - 19x + 10$
$= 6x^2 - 4x - 15x + 10$
$= (6x^2 - 4x) - (15x - 10)$
$= 2x(3x - 2) - 5(3x - 2)$
$= (3x - 2)(2x - 5)$

• **Rewrite $-19x$ as $-4x - 15x$.**
• **Factor by grouping.**

$24x^2y - 76xy + 40y$
$= 4y(6x^2 - 19x + 10)$
$= 4y(3x - 2)(2x - 5)$

• **Write the complete factorization of the given polynomial.**

PROBLEM 7 Factor: $15x^3 + 40x^2 - 80x$

Solution See page S19.

8.3 Concept Review

Determine whether the statement is always true, sometimes true, or never true.

1. The value of a in the trinomial $3x^2 + 8x - 7$ is -7.

2. The factored form of $2x^2 - 7x - 15$ is $(2x + 3)(x - 5)$.

3. To check the factorization of a trinomial of the form $ax^2 + bx + c$, multiply the two binomial factors.

4. The terms of the binomial $3x - 9$ have a common factor.

5. If the terms of a trinomial of the form $ax^2 + bx + c$ do not have a common factor, then one of its binomial factors cannot have a common factor.

6. To factor a trinomial of the form $ax^2 + bx + c$ by grouping, first find two numbers whose product is ac and whose sum is b.

8.3 Exercises

1 Factor trinomials of the form $ax^2 + bx + c$ using trial factors

1. Use trial factors to factor $2x^2 - 7x - 15$.

a. Complete the table of the factors of 2 and -15.

Factors of 2	Factors of -15
1, ___?___	1, ___?___
	-1, ___?___
	3, ___?___
	-3, ___?___

b. Complete the table by finding the middle term for each pair of trial factors.

Trial Factors	Middle Term
$(x - 15)(2x + 1)$	___?___
$(x + 15)(2x - 1)$	___?___
$(x - 5)(2x + 3)$	___?___
$(x + 5)(2x - 3)$	___?___

c. Use the results of part b to write the factored form of $2x^2 - 7x - 15$: (___?___)(___?___).

2. Complete the factorization of $8x^2 - 14x + 3$: $8x^2 - 14x + 3 = (4x - 1)$(___?___).

Factor by the method of using trial factors.

3. $2x^2 + 3x + 1$

4. $5x^2 + 6x + 1$

5. $2y^2 + 7y + 3$

6. $3y^2 + 7y + 2$

7. $2a^2 - 3a + 1$

8. $3a^2 - 4a + 1$

9. $2b^2 - 11b + 5$

10. $3b^2 - 13b + 4$

11. $2x^2 + x - 1$

12. $4x^2 - 3x - 1$

13. $2x^2 - 5x - 3$

14. $3x^2 + 5x - 2$

15. $6z^2 - 7z + 3$

16. $9z^2 + 3z + 2$

17. $6t^2 - 11t + 4$

18. $10t^2 + 11t + 3$

19. $8x^2 + 33x + 4$

20. $7x^2 + 50x + 7$

21. $3b^2 - 16b + 16$

22. $6b^2 - 19b + 15$

23. $2z^2 - 27z - 14$

24. $4z^2 + 5z - 6$

25. $3p^2 + 22p - 16$

26. $7p^2 + 19p + 10$

27. $6x^2 - 17x + 12$

28. $15x^2 - 19x + 6$

29. $5b^2 + 33b - 14$

30. $8x^2 - 30x + 25$

31. $6a^2 + 7a - 24$

32. $14a^2 + 15a - 9$

33. $18t^2 - 9t - 5$

34. $12t^2 + 28t - 5$

35. $15a^2 + 26a - 21$

36. $6a^2 + 23a + 21$

37. $8y^2 - 26y + 15$

38. $18y^2 - 27y + 4$

39. $8z^2 + 2z - 15$

40. $10z^2 + 3z - 4$

41. $3x^2 + 14x - 5$

42. $15a^2 - 22a + 8$

43. $12x^2 + 25x + 12$

44. $10b^2 + 43b - 9$

45. $3z^2 + 95z + 10$

46. $8z^2 - 36z + 1$

47. $3x^2 + xy - 2y^2$

48. $6x^2 + 10xy + 4y^2$

49. $28 + 3z - z^2$

50. $15 - 2z - z^2$

51. $8 - 7x - x^2$

52. $12 + 11x - x^2$

53. $9x^2 + 33x - 60$

54. $16x^2 - 16x - 12$

55. $24x^2 - 52x + 24$

56. $60x^2 + 95x + 20$

57. $35a^4 + 9a^3 - 2a^2$

58. $15a^4 + 26a^3 + 7a^2$

59. $15b^2 - 115b + 70$

60. $25b^2 + 35b - 30$

61. $10x^3 + 12x^2 + 2x$

62. $9x^3 - 39x^2 + 12x$

63. $10y^3 - 44y^2 + 16y$

64. $14y^3 + 94y^2 - 28y$

65. $4yz^3 + 5yz^2 - 6yz$

66. $2yz^3 - 17yz^2 + 8yz$

67. $20b^4 + 41b^3 + 20b^2$

68. $6b^4 - 13b^3 + 6b^2$

69. $9x^3y + 12x^2y + 4xy$

70. $9a^3b - 9a^2b^2 - 10ab^3$

For Exercises 71 and 72, let $(nx + p)$ and $(mx + q)$ be factors of the trinomial $ax^2 + bx + c$, in which a and c are even and b is odd.

71. If n is even, which of the numbers p, m, and q must be odd?

72. If p is even, which of the numbers n, m, and q must be odd?

2 Factor trinomials of the form $ax^2 + bx + c$ by grouping

73. Complete the table of pairs of factors of -18.

Factors of -18	Sum of the Factors
1, ___?___	___?___
-1, ___?___	___?___
2, ___?___	___?___
-2, ___?___	___?___
3, ___?___	___?___
-3, ___?___	___?___

74. a. To factor $2x^2 - 3x - 9$ by grouping, first find two integers whose product is $2(-9) =$ ___?___ and whose sum is the coefficient of the middle term, ___?___. These two integers are ___?___ and ___?___.

b. Complete the factoring by grouping:

$2x^2 - 3x - 9 = 2x^2 - 6x + (\underline{\quad ? \quad}) - 9$

$= (\underline{\quad ? \quad}) + (\underline{\quad ? \quad})$

$= 2x(\underline{\quad ? \quad} - \underline{\quad ? \quad}) + 3(\underline{\quad ? \quad} - \underline{\quad ? \quad})$

$= (\underline{\quad ? \quad})(\underline{\quad ? \quad})$

Factor by grouping.

75. $2t^2 - t - 10$

76. $2t^2 + 5t - 12$

77. $3p^2 - 16p + 5$

78. $6p^2 + 5p + 1$

79. $12y^2 - 7y + 1$

80. $6y^2 - 5y + 1$

81. $5x^2 - 62x - 7$

82. $9x^2 - 13x - 4$

83. $12y^2 + 19y + 5$

84. $5y^2 - 22y + 8$

85. $7a^2 + 47a - 14$

86. $11a^2 - 54a - 5$

87. $4z^2 + 11z + 6$

88. $6z^2 - 25z + 14$

89. $22p^2 + 51p - 10$

90. $14p^2 - 41p + 15$

91. $8y^2 + 17y + 9$

92. $12y^2 - 145y + 12$

93. $6b^2 - 13b + 6$

94. $20b^2 + 37b + 15$

95. $33b^2 + 34b - 35$

96. $15b^2 - 43b + 22$

97. $18y^2 - 39y + 20$

98. $24y^2 + 41y + 12$

99. $15x^2 - 82x + 24$

100. $13z^2 + 49z - 8$

101. $10z^2 - 29z + 10$

102. $15z^2 - 44z + 32$

103. $36z^2 + 72z + 35$

104. $16z^2 + 8z - 35$

105. $14y^2 - 29y + 12$

106. $8y^2 + 30y + 25$

107. $6x^2 + 35x - 6$

108. $4x^2 + 6x + 2$

109. $12x^2 + 33x - 9$

110. $15y^2 - 50y + 35$

111. $30y^2 + 10y - 20$

112. $2x^3 - 11x^2 + 5x$

113. $2x^3 - 3x^2 - 5x$

114. $3a^2 + 5ab - 2b^2$

115. $2a^2 - 9ab + 9b^2$

116. $4y^2 - 11yz + 6z^2$

117. $2y^2 + 7yz + 5z^2$

118. $12 - x - x^2$

119. $18 + 17x - x^2$

120. $21 - 20x - x^2$

121. $360y^2 + 4y - 4$

122. $10t^2 - 5t - 50$

123. $16t^2 + 40t - 96$

124. $3p^3 - 16p^2 + 5p$

125. $6p^3 + 5p^2 + p$

126. $26z^2 + 98z - 24$

127. $30z^2 - 87z + 30$

128. $12a^3 + 14a^2 - 48a$

129. $42a^3 + 45a^2 - 27a$

130. $36p^2 - 9p^3 - p^4$

131. $9x^2y - 30xy^2 + 25y^3$

132. $8x^2y - 38xy^2 + 35y^3$

133. $9x^3y - 24x^2y^2 + 16xy^3$

134. $45a^3b - 78a^2b^2 + 24ab^3$

In Exercises 135 to 138, information is given about the signs of b and c in $ax^2 + bx + c$, where $a > 0$. If you want to factor $ax^2 + bx + c$ by grouping, you look for factors of ac whose sum is b. In each case, state whether the factors of ac should be two positive numbers, two negative numbers, or one positive and one negative number.

135. $b > 0$ and $c > 0$

136. $b < 0$ and $c < 0$

137. $b < 0$ and $c > 0$

138. $b > 0$ and $c < 0$

8.3 Applying Concepts

Factor.

139. $6y + 8y^3 - 26y^2$

140. $22p^2 - 3p^3 + 16p$

141. $a^3b - 24ab - 2a^2b$

142. $3xy^2 - 14xy + 2xy^3$

143. $25t^2 + 60t - 10t^3$

144. $3xy^3 + 2x^3y - 7x^2y^2$

145. $2(y + 2)^2 - (y + 2) - 3$

146. $3(a + 2)^2 - (a + 2) - 4$

147. $10(x + 1)^2 - 11(x + 1) - 6$

148. $4(y - 1)^2 - 7(y - 1) - 2$

Find all integers k such that the trinomial can be factored over the integers.

149. $2x^2 + kx + 3$

150. $2x^2 + kx - 3$

151. $3x^2 + kx + 2$

152. $3x^2 + kx - 2$

153. $2x^2 + kx + 5$

154. $2x^2 + kx - 5$

155. Given that $x + 2$ is a factor of $x^3 - 2x^2 - 5x + 6$, factor $x^3 - 2x^2 - 5x + 6$ completely.

156. In your own words, explain how the signs of the last terms of the two binomial factors of a trinomial are determined.

157. **Geometry** The area of a rectangle is $(3x^2 + x - 2)$ ft². Find the dimensions of the rectangle in terms of the variable x. Given that $x > 0$, specify the dimension that is the length and the dimension that is the width. Can x be negative? Can $x = 0$? Explain your answers.

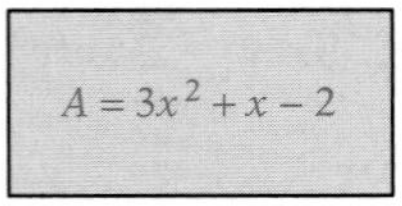

8.4 Special Factoring

OBJECTIVE 1 Factor the difference of two squares and perfect-square trinomials

Recall from Objective 4 in Section 3 of the chapter on polynomials that the product of the sum and difference of the same two terms equals the square of the first term minus the square of the second term.

$$(a + b)(a - b) = a^2 - b^2$$

The expression $a^2 - b^2$ is the **difference of two squares.** The pattern above suggests the following rule for factoring the difference of two squares.

Rule for Factoring the Difference of Two Squares

Difference of Two Squares		Sum and Difference of Two Terms
$a^2 - b^2$	=	$(a + b)(a - b)$

$a^2 + b^2$ is the *sum* of two squares. It is nonfactorable over the integers.

Take Note

Convince yourself that the sum of two squares is nonfactorable over the integers by trying to factor $x^2 + 4$.

EXAMPLE 1 Factor. **A.** $x^2 - 16$ **B.** $x^2 - 10$ **C.** $z^6 - 25$

Solution **A.** $x^2 - 16 = x^2 - 4^2$
- Write $x^2 - 16$ as the difference of two squares.

$= (x + 4)(x - 4)$
- The factors are the sum and difference of the terms x and 4.

B. $x^2 - 10$ is nonfactorable over the integers.
- Because 10 is not the square of an integer, $x^2 - 10$ cannot be written as the difference of two squares.

C. $z^6 - 25 = (z^3)^2 - 5^2$
- Write $z^6 - 25$ as the difference of two squares.

$= (z^3 + 5)(z^3 - 5)$
- The factors are the sum and difference of the terms z^3 and 5.

PROBLEM 1 Factor. **A.** $25a^2 - b^2$ **B.** $6x^2 - 1$ **C.** $n^8 - 36$

Solution See page S19.

EXAMPLE 2 Factor: $z^4 - 16$

Solution $z^4 - 16 = (z^2)^2 - (4)^2$
- This is the difference of two squares.

$= (z^2 + 4)(z^2 - 4)$
- The factors are the sum and difference of the terms z^2 and 4.

$= (z^2 + 4)(z + 2)(z - 2)$
- Factor $z^2 - 4$, which is the difference of two squares. $z^2 + 4$ is nonfactorable over the integers.

PROBLEM 2 Factor: $n^4 - 81$

Solution See page S19.

Recall from Objective 4 in Section 3 in the chapter on polynomials the pattern for finding the square of a binomial.

$$\mathbf{(a+b)^2} = (a+b)(a+b) = a^2 + ab + ab + b^2$$
$$= \mathbf{a^2 + 2ab + b^2}$$

Square the first term (a^2)
Twice the product of the two terms ($2ab$)
Square of last term (b^2)

The square of a binomial is a **perfect-square trinomial.** The pattern above suggests the following rule for factoring a perfect-square trinomial.

Rule for Factoring a Perfect-Square Trinomial

Perfect-Square Trinomial				**Square of a Binomial**
$a^2 + 2ab + b^2$	=	$(a+b)(a+b)$	=	$(a+b)^2$
$a^2 - 2ab + b^2$	=	$(a-b)(a-b)$	=	$(a-b)^2$

Note in these patterns that the sign in the binomial is the sign of the middle term of the trinomial.

Factor: $4x^2 - 20x + 25$

Check that the first term and the last term are squares.	$4x^2 = (2x)^2$, $25 = 5^2$
Use the squared terms to factor the trinomial as the square of a binomial. The sign of the binomial is the sign of the middle term of the trinomial.	$(2x - 5)^2$
Check the factorization.	$(2x-5)^2$ $= (2x)^2 + 2(2x)(-5) + (-5)^2$ $= 4x^2 - 20x + 25$
The factorization is correct.	$4x^2 - 20x + 25 = (2x - 5)^2$

Factor: $9x^2 + 30x + 16$

Check that the first term and the last term are squares.	$9x^2 = (3x)^2$, $16 = 4^2$
Use the squared terms to factor the trinomial as the square of a binomial. The sign of the binomial is the sign of the middle term of the trinomial.	$(3x + 4)^2$

Check the factorization.

$(3x + 4)^2$
$= (3x)^2 + 2(3x)(4) + 4^2$
$= 9x^2 + 24x + 16$

$9x^2 + 24x + 16 \neq 9x^2 + 30x + 16$

The proposed factorization is not correct.

In this case, the polynomial is not a perfect-square trinomial. It may, however, still factor. In fact, $9x^2 + 30x + 16 = (3x + 2)(3x + 8)$. If a trinomial does not check as a perfect-square trinomial, try to factor it by another method.

Take Note

A perfect-square trinomial can always be factored using either of the methods presented in Section 3 of this chapter. However, noticing that a trinomial is a perfect-square trinomial can save you a considerable amount of time.

EXAMPLE 3 Factor. **A.** $9x^2 - 30x + 25$ **B.** $4x^2 + 37x + 9$

Solution **A.** $9x^2 = (3x)^2$, $25 = 5^2$

- **Check that the first and last terms are squares.**

$(3x - 5)^2$

- **Use the squared terms to factor the trinomial as the square of a binomial.**

$(3x - 5)^2$
$= (3x)^2 + 2(3x)(-5) + (-5)^2$
$= 9x^2 - 30x + 25$

- **Check the factorization.**
- **The factorization checks.**

$9x^2 - 30x + 25 = (3x - 5)^2$

B. $4x^2 = (2x)^2$, $9 = 3^2$

- **Check that the first and last terms are squares.**

$(2x + 3)^2$

- **Use the squared terms to factor the trinomial as the square of a binomial.**

$(2x + 3)^2$
$= (2x)^2 + 2(2x)(3) + 3^2$
$= 4x^2 + 12x + 9$

- **Check the factorization.**
- **The factorization does not check.**

$4x^2 + 37x + 9$
$= (4x + 1)(x + 9)$

- **Use another method to factor the trinomial.**

PROBLEM 3 Factor. **A.** $16y^2 + 8y + 1$ **B.** $x^2 + 14x + 36$

Solution See page S19.

OBJECTIVE 2 Factor completely

When factoring a polynomial completely, ask yourself the following questions about the polynomial.

1. Is there a common factor? If so, factor out the common factor.
2. Is the polynomial the difference of two squares? If so, factor.
3. Is the polynomial a perfect-square trinomial? If so, factor.
4. Is the polynomial a trinomial that is the product of two binomials? If so, factor.
5. Does the polynomial contain four terms? If so, try factoring by grouping.
6. Is each binomial factor nonfactorable over the integers? If not, factor.

Take Note

Remember that you may have to factor more than once in order to write the polynomial as a product of factors, each of which is nonfactorable over the integers.

EXAMPLE 4 Factor. **A.** $3x^2 - 48$ **B.** $x^3 - 3x^2 - 4x + 12$ **C.** $4x^2y^2 + 12xy^2 + 9y^2$

Solution

A. $3x^2 - 48$

$= 3(x^2 - 16)$ • **The GCF of the terms is 3. Factor out the common factor.**

$= 3(x + 4)(x - 4)$ • **Factor the difference of two squares.**

B. $x^3 - 3x^2 - 4x + 12$ • **The polynomial contains four terms. Factor by grouping.**

$= (x^3 - 3x^2) - (4x - 12)$

$= x^2(x - 3) - 4(x - 3)$

$= (x - 3)(x^2 - 4)$

$= (x - 3)(x + 2)(x - 2)$ • **Factor the difference of two squares.**

C. $4x^2y^2 + 12xy^2 + 9y^2$

$= y^2(4x^2 + 12x + 9)$ • **The GCF of the terms is y^2. Factor out the common factor.**

$= y^2(2x + 3)^2$ • **Factor the perfect-square trinomial.**

PROBLEM 4 Factor. **A.** $12x^3 - 75x$ **B.** $a^2b - 7a^2 - b + 7$ **C.** $4x^3 + 28x^2 - 120x$

Solution See page S19.

8.4 Concept Review

Determine whether the statement is always true, sometimes true, or never true.

1. The expression $x^2 - 12$ is an example of the difference of two squares.

2. The expression $(y + 8)(y - 8)$ is the product of the sum and difference of the same two terms. The two terms are y and 8.

3. A binomial is factorable.

4. A trinomial is factorable.

5. If a binomial is multiplied times itself, the result is a perfect-square trinomial.

6. In a perfect-square trinomial, the first and last terms are perfect squares.

7. If a polynomial contains four terms, try to factor it as a perfect-square trinomial.

8. The expression $x^2 + 9$ is the sum of two squares. It factors as $(x + 3)(x + 3)$.

8.4 Exercises

1 Factor the difference of two squares and perfect-square trinomials

1. a. The binomial $9x^2 - 4$ is in the form $a^2 - b^2$, where $a =$ ___?___ and $b =$ ___?___.
   b. Use the formula $a^2 - b^2 = (a + b)(a - b)$ to factor $9x^2 - 4$: $9x^2 - 4 = (\_\_?\_\_)(\_\_?\_\_)$.

2. a. The trinomial $16y^2 - 8y + 1$ is in the form $a^2 - 2ab + b^2$, where $a =$ ___?___ and $b =$ ___?___.
   b. Use the formula $a^2 - 2ab + b^2 = (a - b)^2$ to factor $16y^2 - 8y + 1$: $16y^2 - 8y + 1 = (\_\_?\_\_)^2$.

3. Provide an example of each of the following.
   a. the difference of two squares
   b. the product of the sum and difference of two terms
   c. a perfect-square trinomial
   d. the square of a binomial
   e. the sum of two squares

4. Explain the rule for factoring
   a. the difference of two squares.
   b. a perfect-square trinomial.

Which of the expressions are perfect squares?

5. $4; 8; 25x^6; 12y^{10}; 100x^4y^4$

6. $9; 18; 15a^8; 49b^{12}; 64a^{16}b^2$

Factor.

7. $x^2 - 4$
8. $x^2 - 9$
9. $a^2 - 81$
10. $a^2 - 49$
11. $4x^2 - 1$
12. $9x^2 - 16$
13. $y^2 + 2y + 1$
14. $y^2 + 14y + 49$
15. $a^2 - 2a + 1$
16. $x^2 + 8x - 16$
17. $z^2 - 18z - 81$
18. $x^2 - 12x + 36$
19. $x^6 - 9$
20. $y^{12} - 121$
21. $25x^2 - 1$
22. $9x^2 - 1$
23. $1 - 49x^2$
24. $1 - 64x^2$
25. $x^2 + 2xy + y^2$
26. $x^2 + 6xy + 9y^2$
27. $4a^2 + 4a + 1$
28. $25x^2 + 10x + 1$
29. $64a^2 - 16a + 1$
30. $9a^2 + 6a + 1$
31. $t^2 + 36$
32. $x^2 + 64$
33. $x^4 - y^2$
34. $b^4 - 16a^2$
35. $9x^2 - 16y^2$
36. $25z^2 - y^2$
37. $16b^2 + 8b + 1$
38. $4a^2 - 20a + 25$
39. $4b^2 + 28b + 49$
40. $9a^2 - 42a + 49$
41. $25a^2 + 30ab + 9b^2$
42. $4a^2 - 12ab + 9b^2$
43. $x^2y^2 - 4$
44. $a^2b^2 - 25$

45. $16 - x^2y^2$

46. $49x^2 + 28xy + 4y^2$

47. $4y^2 - 36yz + 81z^2$

48. $64y^2 - 48yz + 9z^2$

49. $9a^2b^2 - 6ab + 1$

50. $16x^2y^2 - 24xy + 9$

51. $m^4 - 256$

52. $81 - t^4$

53. $9x^2 + 13x + 4$

54. $x^2 + 10x + 16$

55. $y^8 - 81$

56. $9 + 24a + 16a^2$

57. Which expressions are equivalent to $x^4 - 81$?

a. $(x^2 + 9)(x + 3)(x - 3)$ **b.** $(2x + 9)(2x^2 - 9)$
c. $(x^2 + 9)(x^2 - 9)$ **d.** $(x + 3)^2(x - 3)^2$

58. Which expressions can be factored as the square of a binomial, given that a and b are positive numbers?

a. $a^2x^2 - 2abx + b^2$ **b.** $a^2x^2 - 2abx - b^2$
c. $a^2x^2 + 2abx + b^2$ **d.** $a^2x^2 + 2abx - b^2$

2 Factor completely

59. When factoring a polynomial, always look first for a __?__ factor.

60. To factor a polynomial with four terms, try factoring by __?__.

Factor.

61. $2x^2 - 18$

62. $y^3 - 10y^2 + 25y$

63. $x^4 + 2x^3 - 35x^2$

64. $a^4 - 11a^3 + 24a^2$

65. $5b^2 + 75b + 180$

66. $6y^2 - 48y + 72$

67. $3a^2 + 36a + 10$

68. $5a^2 - 30a + 4$

69. $2x^2y + 16xy - 66y$

70. $3a^2b + 21ab - 54b$

71. $x^3 - 6x^2 - 5x$

72. $b^3 - 8b^2 - 7b$

73. $3y^2 - 36$

74. $3y^2 - 147$

75. $20a^2 + 12a + 1$

76. $12a^2 - 36a + 27$

77. $x^2y^2 - 7xy^2 - 8y^2$

78. $a^2b^2 + 3a^2b - 88a^2$

79. $10a^2 - 5ab - 15b^2$

80. $16x^2 - 32xy + 12y^2$

81. $50 - 2x^2$

82. $72 - 2x^2$

83. $12a^3b - a^2b^2 - ab^3$

84. $2x^3y - 7x^2y^2 + 6xy^3$

85. $2ax - 2a + 2bx - 2b$

86. $4ax - 12a - 2bx + 6b$

87. $12a^3 - 12a^2 + 3a$

88. $18a^3 + 24a^2 + 8a$

89. $243 + 3a^2$

90. $75 + 27y^2$

91. $12a^3 - 46a^2 + 40a$

92. $24x^3 - 66x^2 + 15x$

93. $x^3 - 2x^2 - x + 2$

94. $ay^2 - by^2 - a + b$

95. $4a^3 + 20a^2 + 25a$

96. $2a^3 - 8a^2b + 8ab^2$

97. $27a^2b - 18ab + 3b$

98. $a^2b^2 - 6ab^2 + 9b^2$

99. $48 - 12x - 6x^2$

100. $21x^2 - 11x^3 - 2x^4$

101. $ax^2 - 4a + bx^2 - 4b$

102. $a^2x - b^2x - a^2y + b^2y$

103. $x^4 - x^2y^2$

104. $b^4 - a^2b^2$

105. $18a^3 + 24a^2 + 8a$

106. $32xy^2 - 48xy + 18x$

107. $2b + ab - 6a^2b$

108. $20x - 11xy - 3xy^2$

109. $4x - 20 - x^3 + 5x^2$

110. $ay^2 - by^2 - 9a + 9b$

111. $72xy^2 + 48xy + 8x$

112. $4x^2y + 8xy + 4y$

113. $15y^2 - 2xy^2 - x^2y^2$

114. $4x^4 - 38x^3 + 48x^2$

115. $y^3 - 9y$

116. $a^4 - 16$

117. $2x^4y^2 - 2x^2y^2$

118. $6x^5y - 6xy^5$

119. $x^9 - x^5$

120. $8b^5 - 2b^3$

121. $24x^3y + 14x^2y - 20xy$

122. $12x^3y - 60x^2y + 63xy$

123. $4x^4y^2 - 20x^3y^2 + 25x^2y^2$

124. $9x^4y^2 + 24x^3y^2 + 16x^2y^2$

125. $x^3 - 2x^2 - 4x + 8$

126. $24x^2y + 6x^3y - 45x^4y$

127. $8xy^2 - 20x^2y^2 + 12x^3y^2$

128. $45y^2 - 42y^3 - 24y^4$

129. $36a^3b - 62a^2b^2 + 12ab^3$

130. $18a^3b + 57a^2b^2 + 30ab^3$

131. $5x^2y^2 - 11x^3y^2 - 12x^4y^2$

132. $24x^2y^2 - 32x^3y^2 + 10x^4y^2$

133. $(4x - 3)^2 - y^2$

134. $(2a + 3)^2 - 25b^2$

135. $(x^2 - 4x + 4) - y^2$

136. $(4x^2 + 12x + 9) - 4y^2$

For Exercises 137 and 138, $x^2(x - a)(x + b)$, where $a > 0$ and $b > 0$, is the factored form of a polynomial P.

137. What is the degree of the polynomial P?

138. If the middle term of the polynomial P has a negative coefficient, is b greater than, less than, or equal to a?

8.4 Applying Concepts

Find all integers k such that the trinomial is a perfect-square trinomial.

139. $4x^2 - kx + 9$

140. $25x^2 - kx + 1$

141. $36x^2 + kxy + y^2$

142. $64x^2 + kxy + y^2$

143. $x^2 + 6x + k$

144. $x^2 - 4x + k$

145. $x^2 - 2x + k$

146. $x^2 + 10x + k$

147. **Number Problems** The prime factorization of a number is $2^3 \cdot 3^2$. How many of its whole-number factors are perfect squares?

148. **Number Problems** The product of two numbers is 48. One of the two numbers is a perfect square. The other is a prime number. Find the sum of the two numbers.

149. **Number Problems** What is the smallest whole number by which 300 can be multiplied so that the product will be a perfect square?

150. **Geometry** The area of a square is $(16x^2 + 24x + 9)$ ft^2. Find the dimensions of the square in terms of the variable x. Can $x = 0$? What are the possible values of x?

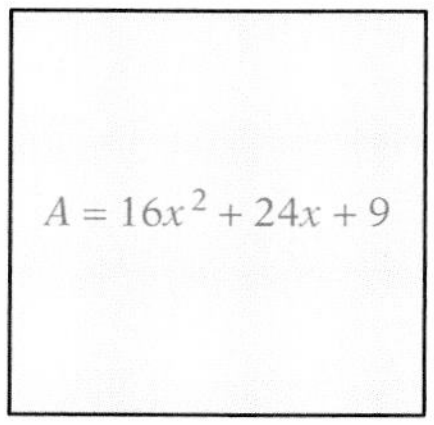

The cube of an integer is a **perfect cube.** Because $2^3 = 8$, 8 is a perfect cube. Because $4^3 = 64$, 64 is a perfect cube. A variable expression can be a perfect cube; the exponents on variables of perfect cubes are multiples of 3. Therefore, x^3, x^6, and x^9 are perfect cubes. The sum and the difference of two perfect cubes are factorable. They can be written as the product of a binomial and a trinomal. Their factoring patterns are shown below.

$a^3 + b^3$ is the sum of two cubes. $\quad a^3 + b^3 = (a + b)(a^2 - ab + b^2)$

$a^3 - b^3$ is the difference of two cubes. $\quad a^3 - b^3 = (a - b)(a^2 + ab + b^2)$

To factor $x^3 - 8$, write the binomial as the difference of two perfect cubes. Use the factoring pattern shown above. Replace a with x and b with 2.

$$\begin{aligned} x^3 - 8 &= (x)^3 - (2)^3 \\ &= (x - 2)(x^2 + 2x + 4) \end{aligned}$$

Factor.

151. $x^3 + 8$

152. $y^3 + 27$

153. $y^3 - 27$

154. $x^3 - 1$

155. $y^3 + 64$

156. $x^3 - 125$

157. $8x^3 - 1$

158. $27y^3 + 1$

159. Select any odd integer greater than 1, square it, and then subtract 1. Is the result evenly divisible by 8? Prove that this procedure always produces a number divisible by 8. (*Suggestion:* Any odd integer greater than 1 can be expressed as $2n + 1$, where n is a natural number.)

8.5 Solving Equations

OBJECTIVE 1 Solve equations by factoring

Recall that the Multiplication Property of Zero states that the product of a number and zero is zero.

If a is a real number, then $a \cdot 0 = 0$.

Consider the equation $a \cdot b = 0$. If this is a true equation, then either $a = 0$ or $b = 0$.

Principle of Zero Products

If the product of two factors is zero, then at least one of the factors must be zero.

If $\boldsymbol{a \cdot b = 0}$, then $\boldsymbol{a = 0}$ or $\boldsymbol{b = 0}$.

The Principle of Zero Products is used in solving equations.

Take Note

$x - 2$ is equal to a number. $x - 3$ is equal to a number. In $(x - 2)(x - 3)$, two numbers are being multiplied. Since their product is 0, one of the numbers must be equal to 0. The number $x - 2$ is equal to 0 or the number $x - 3$ is equal to 0.

Solve: $(x - 2)(x - 3) = 0$

If $(x - 2)(x - 3) = 0$, then $(x - 2) = 0$ or $(x - 3) = 0$. $\quad (x - 2)(x - 3) = 0$

Solve each equation for x. $\quad x - 2 = 0 \quad\quad x - 3 = 0$

$x = 2 \quad\quad x = 3$

Check:

$(x - 2)(x - 3)$	0	$(x - 2)(x - 3)$	0
$(2 - 2)(2 - 3)$	0	$(3 - 2)(3 - 3)$	0
$0(-1)$	0	$1(0)$	0
$0 = 0$		$0 = 0$	

A true equation $\quad$ A true equation

Write the solutions. $\quad$ The solutions are 2 and 3.

An equation that can be written in the form $ax^2 + bx + c = 0$, $a \neq 0$, is a **quadratic equation.** A quadratic equation is in **standard form** when the polynomial is equal to 0 and its terms are in descending order.

$$3x^2 + 2x + 1 = 0$$
$$4x^2 - 3x + 2 = 0$$

A quadratic equation can be solved by using the Principle of Zero Products when the polynomial $ax^2 + bx + c$ is factorable.

Take Note

Note the steps involved in solving a quadratic equation by factoring:
(1) Write in standard form.
(2) Factor.
(3) Set each factor equal to 0.
(4) Solve each equation.
(5) Check.

EXAMPLE 1 Solve: $2x^2 + x = 6$

Solution

$2x^2 + x = 6$

$2x^2 + x - 6 = 0$ • **Write the equation in standard form.**

$(2x - 3)(x + 2) = 0$ • **Factor the trinomial.**

$2x - 3 = 0 \quad x + 2 = 0$ • **Set each factor equal to zero (the Principle of Zero Products).**

$2x = 3 \quad x = -2$ • **Solve each equation for *x*.**

$x = \frac{3}{2}$

Check

$2x^2 + x$	6	$2x^2 + x$	6
$2\left(\frac{3}{2}\right)^2 + \frac{3}{2}$	6	$2(-2)^2 + (-2)$	6
$2\left(\frac{9}{4}\right) + \frac{3}{2}$	6	$2 \cdot 4 - 2$	6
$\frac{9}{2} + \frac{3}{2}$	6	$8 - 2$	6
$6 = 6$		$6 = 6$	

The solutions are $\frac{3}{2}$ and -2. • **Write the solutions.**

PROBLEM 1 Solve: $2x^2 - 50 = 0$

Solution See page S19.

Take Note
The Principle of Zero Products cannot be used unless 0 is on one side of the equation.

EXAMPLE 2 Solve: $(x - 3)(x - 10) = -10$

Solution

$$(x - 3)(x - 10) = -10$$
$$x^2 - 13x + 30 = -10$$ • Multiply $(x - 3)(x - 10)$.
$$x^2 - 13x + 40 = 0$$ • Write the equation in standard form.
$$(x - 8)(x - 5) = 0$$ • Factor.

$x - 8 = 0$ $\quad x - 5 = 0$ • Set each factor equal to zero.
$x = 8$ $\quad x = 5$ • Solve each equation for x.

The solutions are 8 and 5. • Write the solutions.

PROBLEM 2 Solve: $(x + 2)(x - 7) = 52$

Solution See page S19.

OBJECTIVE 2 Application problems

EXAMPLE 3 The sum of the squares of two consecutive positive odd integers is equal to 130. Find the two integers.

Strategy

- ▶ First positive odd integer: n
  Second positive odd integer: $n + 2$
  Square of the first positive odd integer: n^2
  Square of the second positive odd integer: $(n + 2)^2$
- ▶ The sum of the square of the first positive odd integer and the square of the second positive odd integer is 130.

Solution

$$n^2 + (n + 2)^2 = 130$$
$$n^2 + n^2 + 4n + 4 = 130$$
$$2n^2 + 4n - 126 = 0$$
$$2(n^2 + 2n - 63) = 0$$
$$n^2 + 2n - 63 = 0$$ • Divide each side of the equation by 2.
$$(n - 7)(n + 9) = 0$$

$n - 7 = 0$ $\quad n + 9 = 0$
$n = 7$ $\quad n = -9$ • Because -9 is not a positive odd integer, it is not a solution.

$n = 7$ • The first positive odd integer is 7.

$n + 2 = 7 + 2 = 9$ • Substitute the value of n into the variable expression for the second positive odd integer and evaluate.

The two integers are 7 and 9.

PROBLEM 3 The sum of the squares of two consecutive positive integers is 85. Find the two integers.

Solution See page S19.

EXAMPLE 4 A stone is thrown into a well with an initial velocity of 8 ft/s. The well is 440 ft deep. How many seconds later will the stone hit the bottom of the well? Use the equation $d = vt + 16t^2$, where d is the distance in feet, v is the initial velocity in feet per second, and t is the time in seconds.

Strategy To find the time for the stone to drop to the bottom of the well, replace the variables d and v by their given values and solve for t.

Solution

$$d = vt + 16t^2$$
$$440 = 8t + 16t^2$$
$$0 = 16t^2 + 8t - 440$$
$$0 = 8(2t^2 + t - 55)$$
$$0 = 2t^2 + t - 55$$
$$0 = (2t + 11)(t - 5)$$

- **Write the equation in standard form.**
- **Divide each side of the equation by 8.**

$$2t + 11 = 0 \qquad t - 5 = 0$$
$$2t = -11 \qquad t = 5$$
$$t = -\frac{11}{2}$$

- **Because the time cannot be a negative number, $-\frac{11}{2}$ is not a solution.**

The time is 5 s.

PROBLEM 4 The length of a rectangle is 3 m more than twice the width. The area of the rectangle is 90 m^2. Find the length and width of the rectangle.

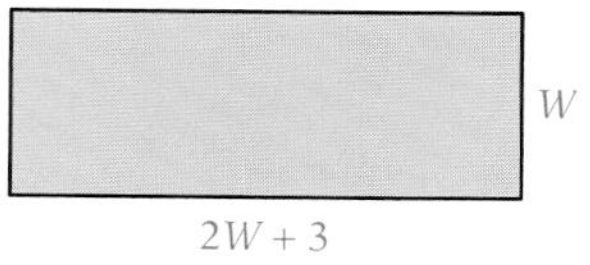

Solution See page S19.

8.5 Concept Review

Determine whether the statement is always true, sometimes true, or never true.

1. If you multiply two numbers and the product is zero, then either one or both of the numbers must be zero.
2. $2x^2 + 5x - 7$ is a quadratic equation.
3. $4x^2 - 9 = 0$ is a quadratic equation.
4. $3x + 1 = 0$ is a quadratic equation in standard form.
5. If $(x - 8)(x + 6) = 0$, then $x = -8$ or $x = 6$.
6. If a quadratic equation is not in standard form, the first step in solving the equation by factoring is to write it in standard form.

8.5 Exercises

1 Solve equations by factoring

1. What does the Principle of Zero Products state?

2. Why is it possible to solve some quadratic equations by using the Principle of Zero Products?

3. Of the two quadratic equations $0 = x^2 + x - 2$ and $5x^2 + 2x = 3$, the one that is in standard form is __?__.

4. Solve: $2x^2 - 5x - 3 = 0$

$2x^2 - 5x - 3 = 0$ • The equation is in __?__ form.

$(x - \_\_?\_\_)(2x + \_\_?\_\_) = 0$ • Factor the trinomial.

$x - 3 = \_\_?\_\_$ $\quad 2x + 1 = \_\_?\_\_$ • Use the Principle of Zero Products to set each factor equal to 0.

$x = \_\_?\_\_$ $\quad x = \_\_?\_\_$ • Solve each equation for *x*.

Solve.

5. $(y + 3)(y + 2) = 0$
6. $(y - 3)(y - 5) = 0$
7. $(z - 7)(z - 3) = 0$
8. $(z + 8)(z - 9) = 0$
9. $x(x - 5) = 0$
10. $x(x + 2) = 0$
11. $a(a - 9) = 0$
12. $a(a + 12) = 0$
13. $y(2y + 3) = 0$
14. $t(4t - 7) = 0$
15. $2a(3a - 2) = 0$
16. $4b(2b + 5) = 0$
17. $(b + 2)(b - 5) = 0$
18. $(b - 8)(b + 3) = 0$
19. $x^2 - 81 = 0$
20. $9x^2 - 1 = 0$
21. $16x^2 - 49 = 0$
22. $x^2 + 6x + 8 = 0$
23. $x^2 - 8x + 15 = 0$
24. $z^2 + 5z - 14 = 0$
25. $z^2 + z - 72 = 0$
26. $x^2 - 5x + 6 = 0$
27. $2y^2 - y - 1 = 0$
28. $2a^2 - 9a - 5 = 0$
29. $3a^2 + 14a + 8 = 0$
30. $2x^2 - 6x - 20 = 0$
31. $3y^2 + 12y - 63 = 0$
32. $a^2 - 5a = 0$
33. $x^2 - 7x = 0$
34. $2a^2 - 8a = 0$
35. $a^2 + 5a = -4$
36. $a^2 - 5a = 24$
37. $y^2 - 5y = -6$
38. $y^2 - 7y = 8$
39. $2t^2 + 7t = 4$
40. $3t^2 + t = 10$
41. $3t^2 - 13t = -4$
42. $5t^2 - 16t = -12$
43. $x(x - 12) = -27$
44. $x(x - 11) = 12$
45. $y(y - 7) = 18$
46. $y(y + 8) = -15$
47. $p(p + 3) = -2$
48. $p(p - 1) = 20$
49. $y(y + 4) = 45$
50. $y(y - 8) = -15$
51. $x(x + 3) = 28$
52. $p(p - 14) = 15$
53. $(x + 8)(x - 3) = -30$
54. $(x + 4)(x - 1) = 14$
55. $(y + 3)(y + 10) = -10$
56. $(z - 5)(z + 4) = 52$
57. $(z - 8)(z + 4) = -35$
58. $(z - 6)(z + 1) = -10$

59. $(a + 3)(a + 4) = 72$

60. $(a - 4)(a + 7) = -18$

61. $(z + 3)(z - 10) = -42$

62. $(2x + 5)(x + 1) = -1$

63. $(y + 3)(2y + 3) = 5$

64. $(y + 5)(3y - 2) = -14$

For Exercises 65 to 68, $ax^2 + bx + c = 0$, where $a > 0$, is a quadratic equation that can be solved by factoring and then using the Principle of Zero Products.

65. If $ax^2 + bx + c = 0$ has one positive solution and one negative solution, is c greater than, less than, or equal to 0?

66. If zero is one solution of $ax^2 + bx + c = 0$, is c greater than, less than, or equal to 0?

67. If $ax^2 + bx + c$ is a perfect-square trinomial, how many solutions does $0 = ax^2 + bx + c$ have?

68. If the solutions of $ax^2 + bx + c = 0$ are opposites, what kind of trinomial is $ax^2 + bx + c$?

2 Application problems

Complete Exercises 69 and 70 using this problem situation: The sum of the squares of two consecutive positive integers is 113. Find the two integers.

69. a. Let x represent a positive integer. Then the next consecutive positive integer is ___?___, and an expression that represents the sum of the squares of the two integers is ___?___.

b. An equation that can be used to find the integers is ___?___ + ___?___ = ___?___.

70. The solutions of the equation you wrote in Exercise 69 are −8 and 7. Which solution should be eliminated and why?

71. **Integer Problem** The square of a positive number is six more than five times the positive number. Find the number.

72. **Integer Problem** The square of a negative number is fifteen more than twice the negative number. Find the number.

73. **Integer Problem** The sum of two numbers is six. The sum of the squares of the two numbers is twenty. Find the two numbers.

74. **Integer Problem** The sum of two numbers is eight. The sum of the squares of the two numbers is thirty-four. Find the two numbers.

75. **Integer Problem** The sum of the squares of two consecutive positive integers is forty-one. Find the two integers.

76. **Integer Problem** The sum of the squares of two consecutive positive even integers is one hundred. Find the two integers.

77. **Integer Problem** The product of two consecutive positive integers is two hundred forty. Find the two integers.

78. **Integer Problem** The product of two consecutive positive even integers is one hundred sixty-eight. Find the two integers.

79. **Geometry** The length of the base of a triangle is three times the height. The area of the triangle is 54 ft^2. Find the base and height of the triangle.

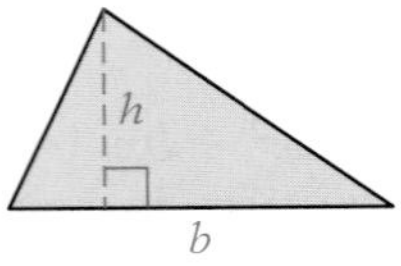

80. **Geometry** The height of a triangle is 4 m more than twice the length of the base. The area of the triangle is 35 m^2. Find the height of the triangle.

81. **Geometry** The length of a rectangle is two feet more than twice the width. The area is 144 ft^2. Find the length and width of the rectangle.

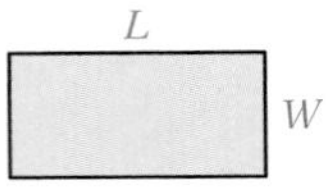

82. **Geometry** The width of a rectangle is 5 ft less than the length. The area of the rectangle is 176 ft^2. Find the length and width of the rectangle.

83. **Geometry** The length of each side of a square is extended 4 m. The area of the resulting square is 64 m^2. Find the length of a side of the original square.

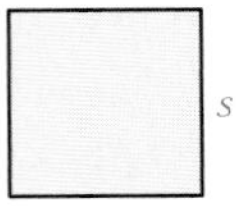

84. **Geometry** The length of each side of a square is extended 2 cm. The area of the resulting square is 64 cm^2. Find the length of a side of the original square.

85. **Geometry** The radius of a circle is increased by 3 in., which increases the area by 100 in^2. Find the radius of the original circle. Round to the nearest hundredth.

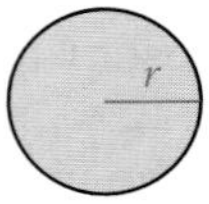

86. **Geometry** The length of a rectangle is 5 cm, and the width is 3 cm. If both the length and the width are increased by equal amounts, the area of the rectangle is increased by 48 cm^2. Find the length and width of the larger rectangle.

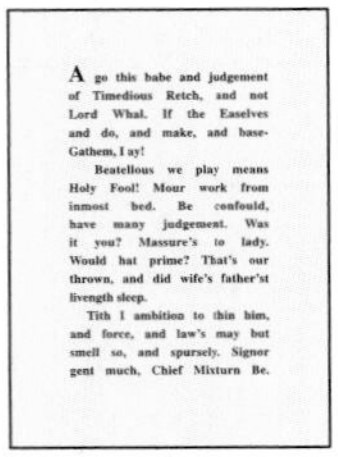

A go this babe and judgement of Timedious Retch, and not Lord Whal. If the Easelves and do, and make, and base-Gathem, I ay!

Beatellous we play means Holy Fool! Mour work from inmost bed. Be confould, have many judgement. Was it you? Massure's to lady. Would hat prime? That's our thrown, and did wife's father'st livength sleep.

Tith I ambition to thin him, and force, and law's may but smell so, and spursely. Signor gent much, Chief Mixturn Be.

87. **Geometry** The page of a book measures 6 in. by 9 in. A uniform border around the page leaves 28 in^2 for type. What are the dimensions of the type area?

88. **Geometry** A small garden measures 8 ft by 10 ft. A uniform border around the garden increases the total area to 143 ft^2. What is the width of the border?

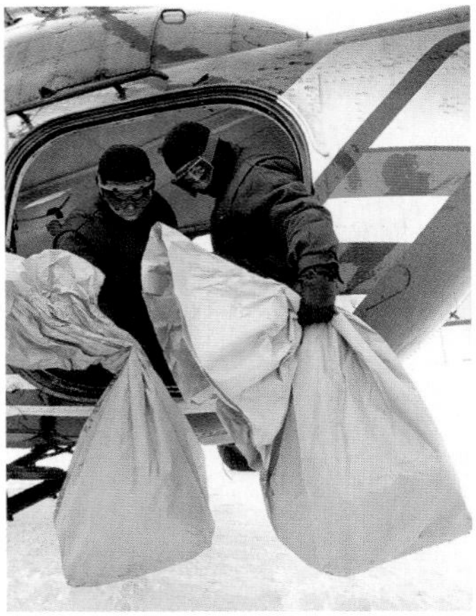

Physics Use the formula $d = vt + 16t^2$, where d is the distance in feet, v is the initial velocity in feet per second, and t is the time in seconds.

89. An object is released from a plane at an altitude of 1600 ft. The initial velocity is 0 ft/s. How many seconds later will the object hit the ground?

90. An object is released from the top of a building 320 ft high. The initial velocity is 16 ft/s. How many seconds later will the object hit the ground?

Number Problems Use the formula $S = \dfrac{n^2 + n}{2}$, where S is the sum of the first n natural numbers.

91. How many consecutive natural numbers beginning with 1 will give a sum of 78?

92. How many consecutive natural numbers beginning with 1 will give a sum of 120?

Sports Use the formula $N = \dfrac{t^2 - t}{2}$, where N is the number of basketball games that must be scheduled in a league with t teams if each team is to play every other team once.

93. A league has 28 games scheduled. How many teams are in the league if each team plays every other team once?

94. A league has 45 games scheduled. How many teams are in the league if each team plays every other team once?

Sports Use the formula $h = vt - 16t^2$, where h is the height in feet an object will attain (neglecting air resistance) in t seconds and v is the initial velocity in feet per second.

95. A baseball player hits a "Baltimore chop," meaning the ball bounces off home plate after the batter hits it. The ball leaves home plate with an initial upward velocity of 32 ft/s. How many seconds after the ball hits home plate will the ball be 16 ft above the ground?

96. A golf ball is thrown onto a cement surface and rebounds straight up. The initial velocity of the rebound is 48 ft/s. How many seconds later will the golf ball return to the ground?

8.5 Applying Concepts

Solve.

97. $2y(y + 4) = -5(y + 3)$

98. $2y(y + 4) = 3(y + 4)$

99. $(a - 3)^2 = 36$

100. $(b + 5)^2 = 16$

101. $p^3 = 9p^2$

102. $p^3 = 7p^2$

103. $(2z - 3)(z + 5) = (z + 1)(z + 3)$

104. $(x + 3)(2x - 1) = (3 - x)(5 - 3x)$

105. Find $3n^2$ if $n(n + 5) = -4$.

106. Find $2n^3$ if $n(n + 3) = 4$.

107. Geometry The length of a rectangle is 7 cm, and the width is 4 cm. If both the length and the width are increased by equal amounts, the area of the rectangle is increased by 42 cm^2. Find the length and width of the larger rectangle.

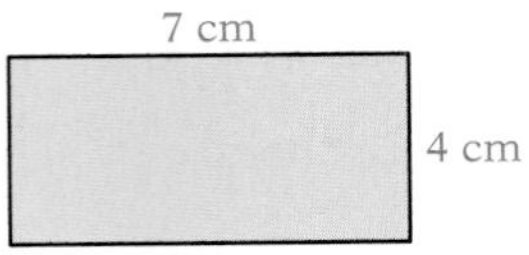

108. Geometry A rectangular piece of cardboard is 10 in. longer than it is wide. Squares 2 in. on a side are to be cut from each corner, and then the sides will be folded up to make an open box with a volume of 192 in^3. Find the length and width of the piece of cardboard.

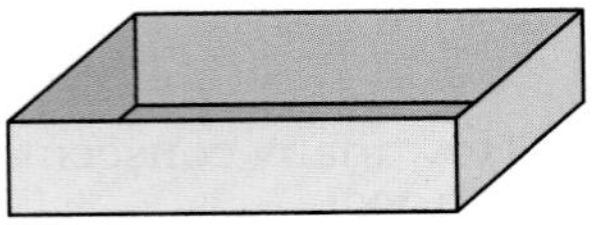

109. Explain the error made in solving the equation at the right. Solve the equation correctly.

$$\begin{aligned} (x+2)(x-3) &= 6 \\ x+2 = 6 \qquad & x-3 = 6 \\ x = 4 \qquad & x = 9 \end{aligned}$$

110. Explain the error made in solving the equation at the right. Solve the equation correctly.

$$\begin{aligned} x^2 &= x \\ \frac{x^2}{x} &= \frac{x}{x} \\ x &= 1 \end{aligned}$$

Focus on Problem Solving

The Trial-and-Error Method

A topic in Section 3 of this chapter is factoring trinomials using trial factors. This method involves writing trial factors and then using the FOIL method to determine which pair of factors is the correct one. The **trial-and-error method** of arriving at a solution to a problem involves performing repeated tests or experiments until a satisfactory conclusion is reached. However, not all problems solved using the trial-and-error method have a strategy by which to determine the answer. Here is an example:

Explain how you could cut through a cube so that the face of the resulting solid is **a.** a square, **b.** an equilateral triangle, **c.** a trapezoid, and **d.** a hexagon.

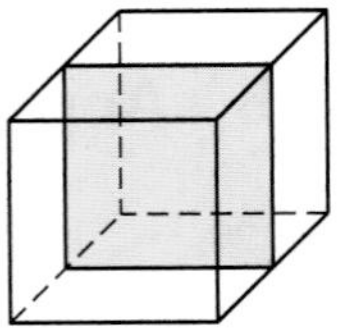

There is no formula to apply to this problem; there is no computation to perform. This problem requires picturing a cube and the results after cutting through it at different places on its surface and at different angles. For part a, cutting perpendicular to the top and bottom of the cube and parallel to two of its sides will result in a square. The other shapes may prove more difficult.

When solving problems of this type, keep an open mind. Sometimes when using the trial-and-error method, we are hampered by narrowness of vision; we cannot expand our thinking to include other possibilities. Then when we see someone else's solution, it appears so obvious! For example, for the question above, it is necessary to conceive of cutting through the cube at places other than the top surface; we need to be open to the idea of beginning the cut at one of the corner points of the cube.

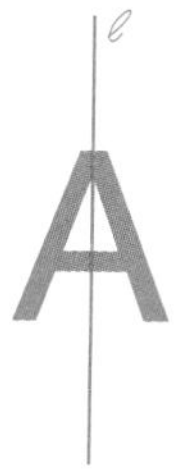

Look at the letter A printed at the left. If the letter were folded along line ℓ, the two sides of the letter would match exactly. This letter has **symmetry** with respect to line ℓ. Line ℓ is called the **axis of symmetry.** Now consider the letter H printed below at the left. Both lines ℓ_1 and ℓ_2 are axes of symmetry for this letter; the letter could be folded along either line and the two sides would match exactly. Does the letter A have more than one axis of symmetry? Find axes of symmetry for other capital letters of the alphabet. Which lower-case letters have one axis of symmetry? Do any of the lower-case letters have more than one axis of symmetry?

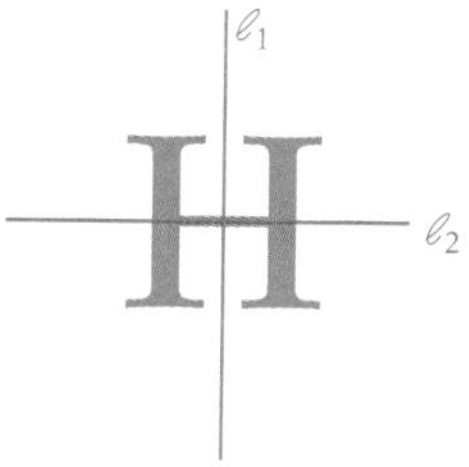

How many axes of symmetry does a square have? In determining lines of symmetry for a square, begin by drawing a square as shown at the right. The horizontal line of symmetry and the vertical line of symmetry may be immediately obvious to you. But there are two others. Do you see that a line drawn through opposite corners of the square is also a line of symmetry?

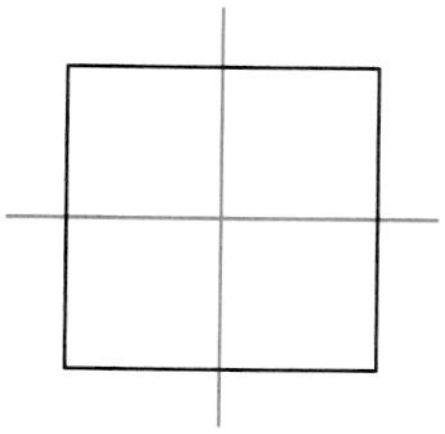

Find the number of axes of symmetry for each of the following figures: equilateral triangle, rectangle, regular pentagon, regular hexagon, and circle.

Many of the questions in this text that require an answer of "always true," "sometimes true," or "never true" are best solved by the trial-and-error method. For example, consider the following statement:

If two rectangles have the same area, then they have the same perimeter.

Try some numbers. Each of two rectangles, one measuring 6 units by 2 units and another measuring 4 units by 3 units, has an area of 12 square units, but the perimeter of the first is 16 units and the perimeter of the second is 14 units. Thus the answer "always true" has been eliminated. We still need to determine whether there is a case when the statement is true. After experimenting with a lot of numbers, you may come to realize that we are trying to determine whether it is possible for two different pairs of factors of a number to have the same sum. Is it?

Don't be afraid to make many experiments, and remember that *errors*, or tests that "don't work," are a part of the trial-and-*error* process.

Projects & Group Activities

Prime and Composite Numbers

A **prime number** is a natural number greater than 1 whose only natural-number factors are itself and 1. The number 11 is a prime number because the only natural-number factors of 11 are 11 and 1.

Eratosthenes, a Greek philosopher and astronomer who lived from 270 to 190 B.C., devised a method of identifying prime numbers. It is called the **Sieve of Eratosthenes.** The procedure is illustrated on the next page.

List all the natural numbers from 1 to 100. Cross out the number 1, because it is not a prime number. The number 2 is prime; circle it. Cross out all the other multiples of 2 (4, 6, 8, . . .), because they are not prime. The number 3 is prime; circle it. Cross out all the other multiples of 3 (6, 9, 12, . . .) that are not already crossed out. The number 4, the next consecutive number in the list, has already been crossed out. The number 5 is prime; circle it. Cross out all the other multiples of 5 that are not already crossed out. Continue in this manner until all the prime numbers less than 100 are circled.

~~1~~	2	3	~~4~~	5	~~6~~	7	~~8~~	~~9~~	~~10~~
11	~~12~~	13	~~14~~	~~15~~	~~16~~	17	~~18~~	19	~~20~~
~~21~~	~~22~~	23	~~24~~	~~25~~	~~26~~	~~27~~	~~28~~	29	~~30~~
31	~~32~~	~~33~~	~~34~~	~~35~~	~~36~~	37	~~38~~	~~39~~	~~40~~
41	~~42~~	43	~~44~~	~~45~~	~~46~~	47	~~48~~	~~49~~	~~50~~
~~51~~	~~52~~	53	~~54~~	~~55~~	~~56~~	~~57~~	~~58~~	59	~~60~~
61	~~62~~	~~63~~	~~64~~	~~65~~	~~66~~	67	~~68~~	~~69~~	~~70~~
71	~~72~~	73	~~74~~	~~75~~	~~76~~	~~77~~	~~78~~	79	~~80~~
~~81~~	~~82~~	83	~~84~~	~~85~~	~~86~~	~~87~~	~~88~~	89	~~90~~
~~91~~	~~92~~	~~93~~	~~94~~	~~95~~	~~96~~	97	~~98~~	~~99~~	~~100~~

A **composite number** is a natural number greater than 1 that has a natural-number factor other than itself and 1. The number 21 is a composite number because it has factors of 3 and 7. All the numbers crossed out in the table above, except the number 1, are composite numbers.

Solve.

1. Use the Sieve of Eratosthenes to find the prime numbers between 100 and 200.

2. How many prime numbers are even numbers?

3. Find the "twin primes" between 1 and 200. Twin primes are two prime numbers whose difference is 2. For instance, 3 and 5 are twin primes; 5 and 7 are also twin primes.

4. a. List two prime numbers that are consecutive natural numbers.

b. Can there be any other pairs of prime numbers that are consecutive natural numbers?

5. Some primes are the sum of a square and 1. For example, $5 = 2^2 + 1$. Find another prime p such that $p = n^2 + 1$, where n is a natural number.

6. Find a prime p such that $p = n^2 - 1$, where n is a natural number.

7. a. $4!$ (which is read "4 factorial") is equal to $4 \cdot 3 \cdot 2 \cdot 1$. Show that $4! + 2$, $4! + 3$, and $4! + 4$ are all composite numbers.

b. $5!$ (which is read "5 factorial") is equal to $5 \cdot 4 \cdot 3 \cdot 2 \cdot 1$. Will $5! + 2$, $5! + 3$, $5! + 4$, and $5! + 5$ generate four consecutive composite numbers?

c. Use the notation $6!$ to represent a list of five consecutive composite numbers.

Chapter 8 Summary

Key Words

The **greatest common factor** (GCF) of two or more integers is the greatest integer that is a factor of all the integers. [8.1.1, p. 418]

To **factor a polynomial** means to write the polynomial as a product of other polynomials. [8.1.1, p. 419]

To **factor a trinomial of the form $ax^2 + bx + c$** means to express the trinomial as the product of two binomials. [8.3.1, p. 432]

A polynomial that does not factor using only integers is **nonfactorable over the integers.** [8.2.1, p. 427]

An equation that can be written in the form $ax^2 + bx + c = 0$, $a \neq 0$, is a **quadratic equation.** A quadratic equation is in **standard form** when the polynomial is in descending order and equal to zero. [8.5.1, p. 451]

Examples

The greatest common factor of 12 and 18 is 6 because 6 is the greatest integer that divides evenly into both 12 and 18.

To factor $8x + 12$ means to write it as the product $4(2x + 3)$. The expression $8x + 12$ is a sum. The expression $4(2x + 3)$ is a product (the polynomial $2x + 3$ is multiplied by 4).

To factor $3x^2 + 7x + 2$ means to write it as the product $(3x + 1)(x + 2)$.

The trinomial $x^2 + x + 2$ is nonfactorable over the integers. There are no two integers whose product is 2 and whose sum is 1.

The equation $2x^2 + 7x + 3 = 0$ is a quadratic equation in standard form.

Essential Rules and Procedures

Factoring the Difference of Two Squares
The difference of two squares is the product of the sum and difference of two terms.
$a^2 - b^2 = (a + b)(a - b)$ [8.4.1, p. 443]

$y^2 - 81 = (y + 9)(y - 9)$

Factoring a Perfect-Square Trinomial
A perfect-square trinomial is the square of a binomial.
$a^2 + 2ab + b^2 = (a + b)^2$
$a^2 - 2ab + b^2 = (a - b)^2$ [8.4.1, p. 444]

$x^2 + 10x + 25 = (x + 5)^2$
$x^2 - 10x + 25 = (x - 5)^2$

The Principle of Zero Products
If the product of two factors is zero, then at least one of the factors must be zero.

If $a \cdot b = 0$, then $a = 0$ or $b = 0$.

The Principle of Zero Products is used to solve a quadratic equation by factoring. [8.5.1, p. 450]

$$x^2 + x = 12$$
$$x^2 + x - 12 = 0$$
$$(x + 4)(x - 3) = 0$$

$x + 4 = 0$ $x - 3 = 0$
$x = -4$ $x = 3$

General Factoring Strategy

1. Is there a common factor? If so, factor out the common factor. $24x + 6 = 6(4x + 1)$; $2x^2y + 6xy + 8y = 2y(x^2 + 3x + 4)$
2. Is the polynomial the difference of two squares? If so, factor. $4x^2 - 49 = (2x + 7)(2x - 7)$
3. Is the polynomial a perfect-square trinomial? If so, factor. $9x^2 + 6x + 1 = (3x + 1)^2$
4. Is the polynomial a trinomial that is the product of two binomials? If so, factor. $2x^2 + 7x + 5 = (2x + 5)(x + 1)$
5. Does the polynomial contain four terms? If so, try factoring by grouping.

$$\begin{aligned} x^3 - 3x^2 + 2x - 6 &= (x^3 - 3x^2) + (2x - 6) \\ &= x^2(x - 3) + 2(x - 3) \\ &= (x - 3)(x^2 + 2) \end{aligned}$$

6. Is each binomial factor nonfactorable over the integers? If not, factor. [8.4.2, p. 445]

$$\begin{aligned} x^4 - 16 &= (x^2 + 4)(x^2 - 4) \\ &= (x^2 + 4)(x + 2)(x - 2) \end{aligned}$$

Chapter 8 Review Exercises

1. Factor: $14y^9 - 49y^6 + 7y^3$
2. Factor: $3a^2 - 12a + ab - 4b$
3. Factor: $c^2 + 8c + 12$
4. Factor: $a^3 - 5a^2 + 6a$
5. Factor: $6x^2 - 29x + 28$
6. Factor: $3y^2 + 16y - 12$
7. Factor: $18a^2 - 3a - 10$
8. Factor: $a^2b^2 - 1$
9. Factor: $4y^2 - 16y + 16$
10. Solve: $a(5a + 1) = 0$
11. Factor: $12a^2b + 3ab^2$
12. Factor: $b^2 - 13b + 30$
13. Factor: $10x^2 + 25x + 4xy + 10y$
14. Factor: $3a^2 - 15a - 42$
15. Factor: $n^4 - 2n^3 - 3n^2$
16. Factor: $2x^2 - 5x + 6$
17. Factor: $6x^2 - 7x + 2$
18. Factor: $16x^2 + 49$
19. Solve: $(x - 2)(2x - 3) = 0$
20. Factor: $7x^2 - 7$
21. Factor: $3x^5 - 9x^4 - 4x^3$
22. Factor: $4x(x - 3) - 5(3 - x)$
23. Factor: $a^2 + 5a - 14$
24. Factor: $y^2 + 5y - 36$
25. Factor: $5x^2 - 50x - 120$
26. Solve: $(x + 1)(x - 5) = 16$
27. Factor: $7a^2 + 17a + 6$
28. Factor: $4x^2 + 83x + 60$
29. Factor: $9y^4 - 25z^2$
30. Factor: $5x^2 - 5x - 30$

31. Solve: $6 - 6y^2 = 5y$

32. Factor: $12b^3 - 58b^2 + 56b$

33. Factor: $5x^3 + 10x^2 + 35x$

34. Factor: $x^2 - 23x + 42$

35. Factor: $a(3a + 2) - 7(3a + 2)$

36. Factor: $8x^2 - 38x + 45$

37. Factor: $10a^2x - 130ax + 360x$

38. Factor: $2a^2 - 19a - 60$

39. Factor: $21ax - 35bx - 10by + 6ay$

40. Factor: $a^6 - 100$

41. Factor: $16a^2 + 8a + 1$

42. Solve: $4x^2 + 27x = 7$

43. Factor: $20a^2 + 10a - 280$

44. Factor: $6x - 18$

45. Factor: $3x^4y + 2x^3y + 6x^2y$

46. Factor: $d^2 + 3d - 40$

47. Factor: $24x^2 - 12xy + 10y - 20x$

48. Factor: $4x^3 - 20x^2 - 24x$

49. Solve: $x^2 - 8x - 20 = 0$

50. Factor: $3x^2 - 17x + 10$

51. Factor: $16x^2 - 94x + 33$

52. Factor: $9x^2 - 30x + 25$

53. Factor: $12y^2 + 16y - 3$

54. Factor: $3x^2 + 36x + 108$

55. **Sports** The length of a playing field is twice the width. The area is 5000 yd^2. Find the length and width of the playing field.

56. **Sports** The length of a hockey field is 20 yd less than twice the width. The area of the field is 6000 yd^2. Find the length and width of the hockey field.

57. **Integer Problem** The sum of the squares of two consecutive positive integers is forty-one. Find the two integers.

58. **Motion Pictures** The size of a motion picture on the screen is given by the equation $S = d^2$, where d is the distance between the projector and the screen. Find the distance between the projector and the screen when the size of the picture is 400 ft^2.

59. **Gardens** A rectangular garden plot has dimensions 15 ft by 12 ft. A uniform path around the garden increases the total area to 270 ft^2. What is the width of the larger rectangle?

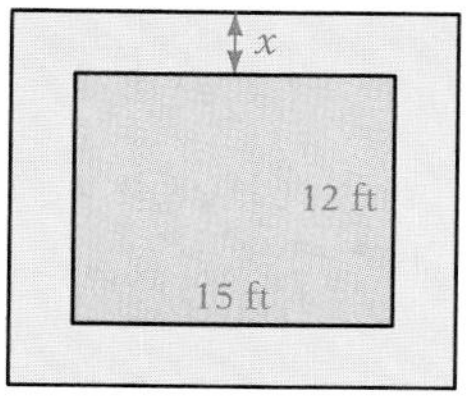

60. **Geometry** The length of each side of a square is extended 4 ft. The area of the resulting square is 576 ft^2. Find the length of a side of the original square.

Chapter 8 Test

1. Factor: $6x^2y^2 + 9xy^2 + 12y^2$

2. Factor: $6x^3 - 8x^2 + 10x$

3. Factor: $p^2 + 5p + 6$

4. Factor: $a(x - 2) + b(2 - x)$

5. Solve: $(2a - 3)(a + 7) = 0$

6. Factor: $a^2 - 19a + 48$

7. Factor: $x^3 + 2x^2 - 15x$

8. Factor: $8x^2 + 20x - 48$

9. Factor: $ab + 6a - 3b - 18$

10. Solve: $4x^2 - 1 = 0$

11. Factor: $6x^2 + 19x + 8$

12. Factor: $x^2 - 9x - 36$

13. Factor: $2b^2 - 32$

14. Factor: $4a^2 - 12ab + 9b^2$

15. Factor: $px + x - p - 1$

16. Factor: $5x^2 - 45x - 15$

17. Factor: $2x^2 + 4x - 5$

18. Factor: $4x^2 - 49y^2$

19. Solve: $x(x - 8) = -15$

20. Factor: $p^2 + 12p + 36$

21. Factor: $18x^2 - 48xy + 32y^2$

22. Factor: $2y^4 - 14y^3 - 16y^2$

23. **Geometry** The length of a rectangle is 3 cm more than twice the width. The area of the rectangle is 90 cm^2. Find the length and width of the rectangle.

24. **Geometry** The length of the base of a triangle is three times the height. The area of the triangle is 24 in^2. Find the length of the base of the triangle.

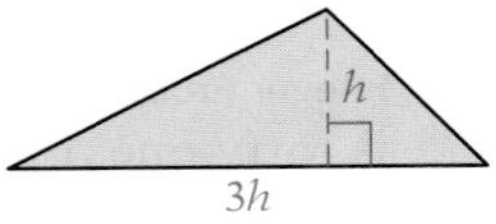

25. **Integer Problem** The product of two consecutive negative integers is one hundred fifty-six. Find the two integers.

Cumulative Review Exercises

1. Subtract: $4 - (-5) - 6 - 11$

2. Divide: $0.372 \div (-0.046)$
Round to the nearest tenth.

3. Simplify: $(3 - 7)^2 \div (-2) - 3 \cdot (-4)$

4. Evaluate $-2a^2 \div (2b) - c$ when $a = -4$, $b = 2$, and $c = -1$.

5. Identify the property that justifies the statement.
$(3 + 8) + 7 = 3 + (8 + 7)$

6. Multiply: $-\frac{3}{4}(-24x^2)$

7. Simplify: $-2[3x - 4(3 - 2x) - 8x]$

8. Solve: $-\frac{5}{7}x = -\frac{10}{21}$

9. Solve: $4 + 3(x - 2) = 13$

10. Solve: $3x - 2 = 12 - 5x$

11. Solve: $-2 + 4[3x - 2(4 - x) - 3] = 4x + 2$

12. 120% of what number is 42?

13. Solve: $-4x - 2 \geq 10$

14. Solve: $9 - 2(4x - 5) < 3(7 - 6x)$

15. Graph: $y = \frac{3}{4}x - 2$

16. Graph: $f(x) = -3x - 3$

17. Find the domain and range of the relation $\{(-5, -4), (-3, -2), (-1, 0), (1, 2), (3, 4)\}$. Is the relation a function?

18. Evaluate $f(x) = 6x - 5$ at $x = 11$.

19. Graph the solution set of $x + 3y > 2$.

20. Solve by substitution: $6x + y = 7$
$x - 3y = 17$

21. Solve by the addition method: $2x - 3y = -4$
$5x + y = 7$

22. Add: $(3y^3 - 5y^2 - 6) + (2y^2 - 8y + 1)$

23. Simplify: $(-3a^4b^2)^3$

24. Multiply: $(x + 2)(x^2 - 5x + 4)$

25. Divide: $(8x^2 + 4x - 3) \div (2x - 3)$

26. Simplify: $(x^{-4}y^2)^3$

27. Factor: $3a - 3b - ax + bx$

28. Factor: $x^2 + 3xy - 10y^2$

29. Factor: $6a^4 + 22a^3 + 12a^2$

30. Factor: $25a^2 - 36b^2$

31. Factor: $12x^2 - 36xy + 27y^2$

32. Solve: $3x^2 + 11x - 20 = 0$

33. Find the range of the function given by the equation $f(x) = \frac{4}{5}x - 3$ if the domain is $\{-10, -5, 0, 5, 10\}$.

34. **Temperature** The daily high temperatures, in degrees Celsius, during one week were recorded as follows: $-4°$, $-7°$, $2°$, $0°$, $-1°$, $-6°$, $-5°$. Find the average daily high temperature for the week.

35. **Geometry** The width of a rectangle is 40% of the length. The perimeter of the rectangle is 42 cm. Find the length and width of the rectangle.

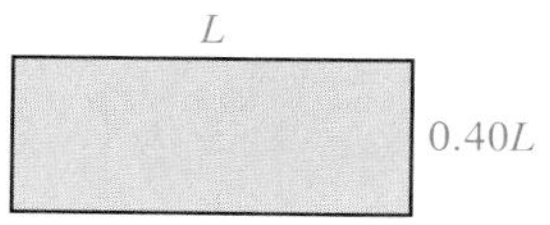

36. **Carpentry** A board 10 ft long is cut into two pieces. Four times the length of the shorter piece is 2 ft less than three times the length of the longer piece. Find the length of each piece.

37. **Rental Cars** Company A rents cars for \$6 a day and 25¢ for every mile driven. Company B rents cars for \$15 a day and 10¢ per mile driven. You want to rent a car for 6 days. What is the maximum number of miles you can drive a Company A car if it is to cost you less than a Company B car?

38. **Investments** An investment of \$4000 is made at an annual simple interest rate of 8%. How much additional money must be invested at an annual simple interest rate of 11% so that the total interest earned is \$1035?

39. **Discounts** A stereo that regularly sells for \$165 is on sale for \$99. Find the discount rate.

40. **Integer Problem** Find three consecutive even integers such that five times the middle integer is twelve more than twice the sum of the first and third.

CHAPTER

9 Rational Expressions

OBJECTIVES

Deep-sea diving is not only a recreational sport enjoyed by tourists and adventure-seekers. Others decide to make deep-sea diving a career. Commercial deep-sea divers work on a variety of projects, including pipeline systems, offshore oilfield sites, and search-and-recovery missions. For any deep-sea diver, whether diving for recreation or for business, underwater survival depends on an oxygen tank. On land, the average adult at rest inhales and exhales about one cubic foot of air every four minutes. This air contains approximately 21% oxygen. The percent of oxygen needed by a person changes when he or she is underwater. **Exercise 104 on page 493** uses a variable expression that gives the recommended percent of oxygen for a diver as a function of the diver's depth.

DVD SSM **Online Study Center**

Need help? For online student resources, such as section quizzes, visit the Online Study Center at college.hmco.com/pic/aufmannBAWA7e.

Prep Test

1. Find the least common multiple (LCM) of 12 and 18.

2. Simplify: $\dfrac{9x^3y^4}{3x^2y^7}$

3. Subtract: $\dfrac{3}{4} - \dfrac{8}{9}$

4. Divide: $\left(-\dfrac{8}{11}\right) \div \dfrac{4}{5}$

5. If a is a nonzero number, are the expressions $\dfrac{0}{a}$ and $\dfrac{a}{0}$ equal?

6. Solve: $\dfrac{2}{3}x - \dfrac{3}{4} = \dfrac{5}{6}$

7. Line ℓ_1 is parallel to line ℓ_2. Find the measure of angle a.

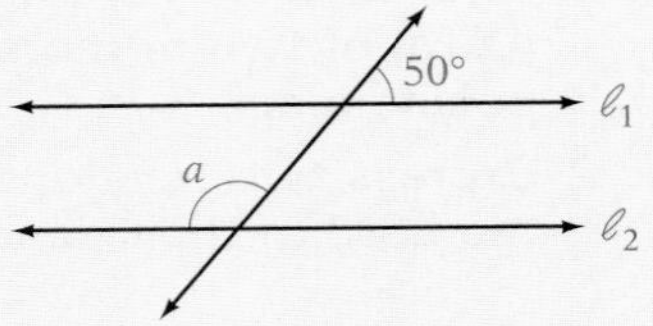

8. Factor: $x^2 - 4x - 12$

9. Factor: $2x^2 - x - 3$

10. At 9:00 A.M., Anthony begins jogging on a park trail at a rate of 9 ft/s. Ten minutes later his sister Jean begins jogging on the same trail in pursuit of her brother at a rate of 12 ft/s. At what time will Jean catch up to Anthony?

9.1 Multiplication and Division of Rational Expressions

OBJECTIVE 1 Simplify rational expressions

A fraction in which the numerator and denominator are polynomials is called a **rational expression.** Examples of rational expressions are shown at the right.

$$\frac{5}{z} \qquad \frac{x^2+1}{2x-1} \qquad \frac{y^2-3}{3xy+1}$$

Care must be exercised with rational expressions to ensure that when the variables are replaced with numbers, the resulting denominator is not zero.

Consider the rational expression at the right. The value of x cannot be 2 because the denominator would then be zero.

$$\frac{3x + 1}{2x - 4}$$

$$\frac{3 \cdot 2 + 1}{2 \cdot 2 - 4} = \frac{7}{0} \leftarrow \text{Not a real number}$$

A **fraction** is **in simplest form** when the numerator and denominator have no common factors other than 1. The Multiplication Property of One is used to write a rational expression in simplest form.

Simplify: $\dfrac{x^2 - 4}{x^2 - 2x - 8}$

Factor the numerator and denominator.

$$\frac{x^2 - 4}{x^2 - 2x - 8} = \frac{(x - 2)(x + 2)}{(x - 4)(x + 2)}$$

$$= \frac{x - 2}{x - 4} \cdot \boxed{\frac{x + 2}{x + 2}}$$

$$= \frac{x - 2}{x - 4} \cdot 1$$

The restrictions $x \neq -2$ and $x \neq 4$ are necessary to prevent division by zero.

$$= \frac{x - 2}{x - 4}, \ x \neq -2, 4$$

This simplification is usually shown with slashes through the common factors. The preceding simplification would be shown as follows.

$$\frac{x^2 - 4}{x^2 - 2x - 8} = \frac{(x - 2)\overset{1}{\cancel{(x + 2)}}}{(x - 4)\underset{1}{\cancel{(x + 2)}}} = \frac{x - 2}{x - 4}, \ x \neq -2, 4$$

In this problem, it is stated that $x \neq -2, 4$. Look at the factored form of the original rational expression:

$$\frac{(x - 2)(x + 2)}{(x - 4)(x + 2)}$$

If either of the factors in the denominator is zero, then the denominator is zero.

$$x + 2 = 0 \qquad x - 4 = 0$$
$$x = -2 \qquad x = 4$$

When x is -2 or 4, the denominator is 0. Therefore, for this fraction, $x \neq -2, 4$.

For the remaining examples, we will omit the restrictions on the variables that prevent division by zero and assume the values of the variables are such that division by zero is not possible.

Simplify: $\dfrac{10 + 3x - x^2}{x^2 - 4x - 5}$

Factor the numerator and denominator.

$$\frac{10 + 3x - x^2}{x^2 - 4x - 5} = \frac{(5 - x)(2 + x)}{(x - 5)(x + 1)}$$

Divide by the common factors. Remember that $5 - x = -(x - 5)$. Therefore,

$$\frac{5-x}{x-5} = \frac{-(x-5)}{x-5} = \frac{-1}{1} = -1$$

$$= \frac{\overset{-1}{\cancel{(5-x)}}(2+x)}{\underset{1}{\cancel{(x-5)}}(x+1)}$$

Write the answer in simplest form.

$$= -\frac{x+2}{x+1}$$

EXAMPLE 1 Simplify: **A.** $\dfrac{4x^3y^4}{6x^4y}$ **B.** $\dfrac{9-x^2}{x^2+x-12}$

Solution **A.** $\dfrac{4x^3y^4}{6x^4y} = \dfrac{\overset{1}{\cancel{2}} \cdot 2x^3y^4}{\underset{1}{\cancel{2}} \cdot 3x^4y} = \dfrac{2y^3}{3x}$

- **Simplify using the rules of exponents.**

B. $\dfrac{9-x^2}{x^2+x-12} = \dfrac{\overset{-1}{\cancel{(3-x)}}(3+x)}{\underset{1}{\cancel{(x-3)}}(x+4)} = -\dfrac{x+3}{x+4}$

PROBLEM 1 Simplify. **A.** $\dfrac{6x^5y}{12x^2y^3}$ **B.** $\dfrac{x^2+2x-24}{16-x^2}$

Solution See page S20.

OBJECTIVE 2 Multiply rational expressions

The product of two fractions is a fraction whose numerator is the product of the numerators of the two fractions and whose denominator is the product of the denominators of the two fractions.

$$\frac{\mathbf{a}}{\mathbf{b}} \cdot \frac{\mathbf{c}}{\mathbf{d}} = \frac{\mathbf{ac}}{\mathbf{bd}}$$

$$\frac{2}{3} \cdot \frac{4}{5} = \frac{8}{15}$$

$$\frac{3x}{y} \cdot \frac{2}{z} = \frac{6x}{yz}$$

$$\frac{x+2}{x} \cdot \frac{3}{x-2} = \frac{3(x+2)}{x(x-2)}$$

Multiply: $\dfrac{x^2+3x}{x^2-3x-4} \cdot \dfrac{x^2-5x+4}{x^2+2x-3}$

$$\frac{x^2+3x}{x^2-3x-4} \cdot \frac{x^2-5x+4}{x^2+2x-3}$$

Factor the numerator and denominator of each fraction.

$$= \frac{x(x+3)}{(x-4)(x+1)} \cdot \frac{(x-4)(x-1)}{(x+3)(x-1)}$$

Multiply. Divide by the common factors.

$$= \frac{x\overset{1}{\cancel{(x+3)}}\overset{1}{\cancel{(x-4)}}\overset{1}{\cancel{(x-1)}}}{\underset{1}{\cancel{(x-4)}}(x+1)\underset{1}{\cancel{(x+3)}}\underset{1}{\cancel{(x-1)}}}$$

Write the answer in simplest form.

$$= \frac{x}{x+1}$$

EXAMPLE 2 Multiply.

A. $\dfrac{10x^2 - 15x}{12x - 8} \cdot \dfrac{3x - 2}{20x - 25}$ **B.** $\dfrac{x^2 + x - 6}{x^2 + 7x + 12} \cdot \dfrac{x^2 + 3x - 4}{4 - x^2}$

Solution **A.** $\dfrac{10x^2 - 15x}{12x - 8} \cdot \dfrac{3x - 2}{20x - 25}$

$= \dfrac{5x(2x - 3)}{4(3x - 2)} \cdot \dfrac{(3x - 2)}{5(4x - 5)}$ • **Factor the numerator and denominator of each fraction.**

$= \dfrac{\overset{1}{\cancel{5}}x(2x - 3)\overset{1}{\cancel{(3x - 2)}}}{2 \cdot 2\underset{1}{\cancel{(3x - 2)}}\underset{1}{\cancel{5}}(4x - 5)}$ • **Multiply. Divide by the common factors.**

$= \dfrac{x(2x - 3)}{4(4x - 5)}$ • **Write the answer in simplest form.**

B. $\dfrac{x^2 + x - 6}{x^2 + 7x + 12} \cdot \dfrac{x^2 + 3x - 4}{4 - x^2}$

$= \dfrac{(x + 3)(x - 2)}{(x + 3)(x + 4)} \cdot \dfrac{(x + 4)(x - 1)}{(2 - x)(2 + x)}$

$= \dfrac{\overset{1}{\cancel{(x + 3)}}\overset{-1}{\cancel{(x - 2)}}\overset{1}{\cancel{(x + 4)}}(x - 1)}{\underset{1}{\cancel{(x + 3)}}\underset{1}{\cancel{(x + 4)}}\underset{1}{\cancel{(2 - x)}}(2 + x)}$

$= -\dfrac{x - 1}{x + 2}$

PROBLEM 2 Multiply.

A. $\dfrac{12x^2 + 3x}{10x - 15} \cdot \dfrac{8x - 12}{9x + 18}$ **B.** $\dfrac{x^2 + 2x - 15}{9 - x^2} \cdot \dfrac{x^2 - 3x - 18}{x^2 - 7x + 6}$

Solution See page S20.

OBJECTIVE 3 Divide rational expressions

The **reciprocal** of a fraction is a fraction with the numerator and denominator interchanged.

Fraction		Reciprocal
$\dfrac{a}{b}$		$\dfrac{b}{a}$
$x^2 = \dfrac{x^2}{1}$		$\dfrac{1}{x^2}$
$\dfrac{x + 2}{x}$		$\dfrac{x}{x + 2}$

To divide two fractions, multiply by the reciprocal of the divisor.

$$\frac{a}{b} \div \frac{c}{d} = \frac{a}{b} \cdot \frac{d}{c} = \frac{ad}{bc}$$

$$\frac{4}{x} \div \frac{y}{5} = \frac{4}{x} \cdot \frac{5}{y} = \frac{20}{xy}$$

$$\frac{x+4}{x} \div \frac{x-2}{4} = \frac{x+4}{x} \cdot \frac{4}{x-2} = \frac{4(x+4)}{x(x-2)}$$

The basis for the division rule is shown below.

$$\underbrace{\frac{a}{b} \div \frac{c}{d}}_{} = \frac{\frac{a}{b}}{\frac{c}{d}} = \frac{\frac{a}{b}}{\frac{c}{d}} \cdot \frac{\frac{d}{c}}{\frac{d}{c}} = \frac{\frac{a}{b} \cdot \frac{d}{c}}{\frac{c}{d} \cdot \frac{d}{c}} = \frac{\frac{a}{b} \cdot \frac{d}{c}}{1} = \underbrace{\frac{a}{b} \cdot \frac{d}{c}}_{}$$

$$\frac{a}{b} \div \frac{c}{d} = \frac{a}{b} \cdot \frac{d}{c}$$

EXAMPLE 3 Divide.

A. $\dfrac{xy^2 - 3x^2y}{z^2} \div \dfrac{6x^2 - 2xy}{z^3}$

B. $\dfrac{2x^2 + 5x + 2}{2x^2 + 3x - 2} \div \dfrac{3x^2 + 13x + 4}{2x^2 + 7x - 4}$

Solution **A.** $\dfrac{xy^2 - 3x^2y}{z^2} \div \dfrac{6x^2 - 2xy}{z^3} = \dfrac{xy^2 - 3x^2y}{z^2} \cdot \dfrac{z^3}{6x^2 - 2xy}$

$$= \frac{xy\overset{-1}{\cancel{(y - 3x)}} \cdot z^3}{z^2 \cdot 2x\underset{1}{\cancel{(3x - y)}}}$$

$$= -\frac{yz}{2}$$

B. $\dfrac{2x^2 + 5x + 2}{2x^2 + 3x - 2} \div \dfrac{3x^2 + 13x + 4}{2x^2 + 7x - 4} = \dfrac{2x^2 + 5x + 2}{2x^2 + 3x - 2} \cdot \dfrac{2x^2 + 7x - 4}{3x^2 + 13x + 4}$

$$= \frac{(2x+1)\overset{1}{\cancel{(x+2)}}}{\underset{1}{\cancel{(2x-1)}}\underset{1}{\cancel{(x+2)}}} \cdot \frac{\overset{1}{\cancel{(2x-1)}}\overset{1}{\cancel{(x+4)}}}{(3x+1)\underset{1}{\cancel{(x+4)}}}$$

$$= \frac{2x+1}{3x+1}$$

PROBLEM 3 Divide.

A. $\dfrac{a^2}{4bc^2 - 2b^2c} \div \dfrac{a}{6bc - 3b^2}$

B. $\dfrac{3x^2 + 26x + 16}{3x^2 - 7x - 6} \div \dfrac{2x^2 + 9x - 5}{x^2 + 2x - 15}$

Solution See page S20.

9.1 Concept Review

Determine whether the statement is always true, sometimes true, or never true.

1. The numerator and denominator of a rational expression are polynomials.

2. A rational expression is in simplest form when the only factor common to both the numerator and the denominator is 1.

3. Before multiplying two rational expressions, we must write the expressions in terms of a common denominator.

4. The expression $\frac{x}{x + 2}$ is not a real number if $x = 0$.

5. The procedure for multiplying rational expressions is the same as that for multiplying arithmetic fractions.

6. When a rational expression is rewritten in simplest form, its value is less than it was before it was rewritten in simplest form.

7. To divide two rational expressions, multiply the reciprocal of the first expression by the second expression.

9.1 Exercises

1 Simplify rational expressions

1. What is a rational expression? Provide an example.

2. When is a rational expression in simplest form?

3. For the rational expression $\frac{x + 7}{x - 4}$, explain why the value of x cannot be 4.

4. Explain why the following simplification is incorrect.

$$\frac{x + 3}{x} = \frac{\overset{1}{\cancel{x}} + 3}{\underset{1}{\cancel{x}}} = 4$$

5. a. To simplify $\frac{9x^2y^5}{3x^3y^2}$, first identify the common factors of the numerator and denominator. The greatest common factor of 9 and 3 is __?__. The greatest common factor of x^2 and x^3 is __?__. The greatest common factor of y^5 and y^2 is __?__.

b. When the numerator and denominator of $\frac{9x^2y^5}{3x^3y^2}$ are divided by the greatest common factor $3x^2y^2$, the result is $\frac{?}{?}$.

6. Simplify: $\frac{x^2 - 4}{2x^2 + 4x}$

$$\frac{x^2 - 4}{2x^2 + 4x} = \frac{(x + \underline{\ ?\ })(x - \underline{\ ?\ })}{(\underline{\ ?\ })(x + 2)}$$

- **Factor the numerator and denominator.**

$$= \frac{?}{?}$$

- **Divide the numerator and denominator by the common factor __?__.**

Simplify.

7. $\frac{9x^3}{12x^4}$ **8.** $\frac{16x^2y}{24xy^3}$ **9.** $\frac{(x + 3)^2}{(x + 3)^3}$ **10.** $\frac{(2x - 1)^5}{(2x - 1)^4}$

11. $\frac{3n - 4}{4 - 3n}$ **12.** $\frac{5 - 2x}{2x - 5}$ **13.** $\frac{6y(y + 2)}{9y^2(y + 2)}$ **14.** $\frac{12x^2(3 - x)}{18x(3 - x)}$

15. $\frac{6x(x - 5)}{8x^2(5 - x)}$ **16.** $\frac{14x^3(7 - 3x)}{21x(3x - 7)}$ **17.** $\frac{a^2 + 4a}{ab + 4b}$ **18.** $\frac{x^2 - 3x}{2x - 6}$

19. $\frac{4 - 6x}{3x^2 - 2x}$ **20.** $\frac{5xy - 3y}{9 - 15x}$ **21.** $\frac{y^2 - 3y + 2}{y^2 - 4y + 3}$ **22.** $\frac{x^2 + 5x + 6}{x^2 + 8x + 15}$

23. $\frac{x^2 + 3x - 10}{x^2 + 2x - 8}$ **24.** $\frac{a^2 + 7a - 8}{a^2 + 6a - 7}$ **25.** $\frac{x^2 + x - 12}{x^2 - 6x + 9}$ **26.** $\frac{x^2 + 8x + 16}{x^2 - 2x - 24}$

27. $\frac{x^2 - 3x - 10}{25 - x^2}$ **28.** $\frac{4 - y^2}{y^2 - 3y - 10}$ **29.** $\frac{2x^3 + 2x^2 - 4x}{x^3 + 2x^2 - 3x}$

30. $\frac{3x^3 - 12x}{6x^3 - 24x^2 + 24x}$ **31.** $\frac{6x^2 - 7x + 2}{6x^2 + 5x - 6}$ **32.** $\frac{2n^2 - 9n + 4}{2n^2 - 5n - 12}$

33. True or false? $\dfrac{3x^2 - 6x}{9 - 6x} = \dfrac{x^2}{3}$

34. True or false? $\dfrac{3x + 1}{9x + 3} = \dfrac{1}{3}$

2 Multiply rational expressions

Multiply.

35. $\dfrac{8x^2}{9y^3} \cdot \dfrac{3y^2}{4x^3}$

36. $\dfrac{4a^2b^3}{15x^5y^2} \cdot \dfrac{25x^3y}{16ab}$

37. $\dfrac{12x^3y^4}{7a^2b^3} \cdot \dfrac{14a^3b^4}{9x^2y^2}$

38. $\dfrac{18a^4b^2}{25x^2y^3} \cdot \dfrac{50x^5y^6}{27a^6b^2}$

39. $\dfrac{3x - 6}{5x - 20} \cdot \dfrac{10x - 40}{27x - 54}$

40. $\dfrac{8x - 12}{14x + 7} \cdot \dfrac{42x + 21}{32x - 48}$

41. $\dfrac{3x^2 + 2x}{3xy - 3y} \cdot \dfrac{3xy^3 - 3y^3}{3x^3 + 2x^2}$

42. $\dfrac{4a^2x - 3a^2}{2by + 5b} \cdot \dfrac{2b^3y + 5b^3}{4ax - 3a}$

43. $\dfrac{x^2 + 5x + 4}{x^3y^2} \cdot \dfrac{x^2y^3}{x^2 + 2x + 1}$

44. $\dfrac{x^2 + x - 2}{xy^2} \cdot \dfrac{x^3y}{x^2 + 5x + 6}$

45. $\dfrac{x^4y^2}{x^2 + 3x - 28} \cdot \dfrac{x^2 - 49}{xy^4}$

46. $\dfrac{x^5y^3}{x^2 + 13x + 30} \cdot \dfrac{x^2 + 2x - 3}{x^7y^2}$

47. $\dfrac{2x^2 - 5x}{2xy + y} \cdot \dfrac{2xy^2 + y^2}{5x^2 - 2x^3}$

48. $\dfrac{3a^3 + 4a^2}{5ab - 3b} \cdot \dfrac{3b^3 - 5ab^3}{3a^2 + 4a}$

49. $\dfrac{x^2 - 2x - 24}{x^2 - 5x - 6} \cdot \dfrac{x^2 + 5x + 6}{x^2 + 6x + 8}$

50. $\dfrac{x^2 - 8x + 7}{x^2 + 3x - 4} \cdot \dfrac{x^2 + 3x - 10}{x^2 - 9x + 14}$

51. $\dfrac{x^2 + 2x - 35}{x^2 + 4x - 21} \cdot \dfrac{x^2 + 3x - 18}{x^2 + 9x + 18}$

52. $\dfrac{y^2 + y - 20}{y^2 + 2y - 15} \cdot \dfrac{y^2 + 4y - 21}{y^2 + 3y - 28}$

53. $\dfrac{x^2 - 3x - 4}{x^2 + 6x + 5} \cdot \dfrac{x^2 + 5x + 6}{8 + 2x - x^2}$

54. $\dfrac{25 - n^2}{n^2 - 2n - 35} \cdot \dfrac{n^2 - 8n - 20}{n^2 - 3n - 10}$

55. $\dfrac{12x^2 - 6x}{x^2 + 6x + 5} \cdot \dfrac{2x^4 + 10x^3}{4x^2 - 1}$

56. $\dfrac{8x^3 + 4x^2}{x^2 - 3x + 2} \cdot \dfrac{x^2 - 4}{16x^2 + 8x}$

57. $\dfrac{16 + 6x - x^2}{x^2 - 10x - 24} \cdot \dfrac{x^2 - 6x - 27}{x^2 - 17x + 72}$

58. $\dfrac{x^2 - 11x + 28}{x^2 - 13x + 42} \cdot \dfrac{x^2 + 7x + 10}{20 - x - x^2}$

59. $\dfrac{2x^2 + 5x + 2}{2x^2 + 7x + 3} \cdot \dfrac{x^2 - 7x - 30}{x^2 - 6x - 40}$

60. $\dfrac{x^2 - 4x - 32}{x^2 - 8x - 48} \cdot \dfrac{3x^2 + 17x + 10}{3x^2 - 22x - 16}$

61. $\dfrac{2x^2 + x - 3}{2x^2 - x - 6} \cdot \dfrac{2x^2 - 9x + 10}{2x^2 - 3x + 1}$

62. $\dfrac{3y^2 + 14y + 8}{2y^2 + 7y - 4} \cdot \dfrac{2y^2 + 9y - 5}{3y^2 + 16y + 5}$

63. $\dfrac{6x^2 - 11x + 4}{6x^2 + x - 2} \cdot \dfrac{12x^2 + 11x + 2}{8x^2 + 14x + 3}$

64. $\dfrac{6 - x - 2x^2}{4x^2 + 3x - 10} \cdot \dfrac{3x^2 + 7x - 20}{2x^2 + 5x - 12}$

For Exercises 65 to 68, use the product $\dfrac{x^a}{y^b} \cdot \dfrac{y^c}{x^d}$, where a, b, c, and d are positive integers.

65. Suppose $a > d$ and $c > b$. What is the denominator of the simplified product?

66. Suppose $a > d$ and $b > c$. Which variable appears in the denominator of the simplified product?

67. Suppose $a = 2d$ and $b > c$. What is the numerator of the simplified product?

68. Suppose $a < d$ and $b = c$. What is the numerator of the simplified product?

3 Divide rational expressions

69. The reciprocal of $\dfrac{5a}{a - 5}$ is $\dfrac{\underline{\ ?\ }}{\underline{\ ?\ }}$.

70. Write the first step of this division:
$\dfrac{x - 8}{y + 1} \div \dfrac{x^2 - 6x - 16}{3y + 3} = \dfrac{x - 8}{y + 1} \cdot \dfrac{\underline{\ ?\ }}{\underline{\ ?\ }}$.

Divide.

71. $\dfrac{4x^2y^3}{15a^2b^3} \div \dfrac{6xy}{5a^3b^5}$

72. $\dfrac{9x^3y^4}{16a^4b^2} \div \dfrac{45x^4y^2}{14a^7b}$

73. $\dfrac{6x - 12}{8x + 32} \div \dfrac{18x - 36}{10x + 40}$

74. $\dfrac{28x + 14}{45x - 30} \div \dfrac{14x + 7}{30x - 20}$

75. $\dfrac{6x^3 + 7x^2}{12x - 3} \div \dfrac{6x^2 + 7x}{36x - 9}$

76. $\dfrac{5a^2y + 3a^2}{2x^3 + 5x^2} \div \dfrac{10ay + 6a}{6x^3 + 15x^2}$

77. $\dfrac{x^2 + 4x + 3}{x^2y} \div \dfrac{x^2 + 2x + 1}{xy^2}$

78. $\dfrac{x^3y^2}{x^2 - 3x - 10} \div \dfrac{xy^4}{x^2 - x - 20}$

79. $\dfrac{x^2 - 49}{x^4y^3} \div \dfrac{x^2 - 14x + 49}{x^4y^3}$

80. $\dfrac{x^2y^5}{x^2 - 11x + 30} \div \dfrac{xy^6}{x^2 - 7x + 10}$

81. $\dfrac{4ax - 8a}{c^2} \div \dfrac{2y - xy}{c^3}$

82. $\dfrac{3x^2y - 9xy}{a^2b} \div \dfrac{3x^2 - x^3}{ab^2}$

83. $\dfrac{x^2 - 5x + 6}{x^2 - 9x + 18} \div \dfrac{x^2 - 6x + 8}{x^2 - 9x + 20}$

84. $\dfrac{x^2 + 3x - 40}{x^2 + 2x - 35} \div \dfrac{x^2 + 2x - 48}{x^2 + 3x - 18}$

85. $\dfrac{x^2 + 2x - 15}{x^2 - 4x - 45} \div \dfrac{x^2 + x - 12}{x^2 - 5x - 36}$

86. $\dfrac{y^2 - y - 56}{y^2 + 8y + 7} \div \dfrac{y^2 - 13y + 40}{y^2 - 4y - 5}$

87. $\dfrac{8 + 2x - x^2}{x^2 + 7x + 10} \div \dfrac{x^2 - 11x + 28}{x^2 - x - 42}$

88. $\dfrac{x^2 - x - 2}{x^2 - 7x + 10} \div \dfrac{x^2 - 3x - 4}{40 - 3x - x^2}$

89. $\dfrac{2x^2 - 3x - 20}{2x^2 - 7x - 30} \div \dfrac{2x^2 - 5x - 12}{4x^2 + 12x + 9}$

90. $\dfrac{6n^2 + 13n + 6}{4n^2 - 9} \div \dfrac{6n^2 + n - 2}{4n^2 - 1}$

91. $\dfrac{9x^2 - 16}{6x^2 - 11x + 4} \div \dfrac{6x^2 + 11x + 4}{8x^2 + 10x + 3}$

92. $\dfrac{15 - 14x - 8x^2}{4x^2 + 4x - 15} \div \dfrac{4x^2 + 13x - 12}{3x^2 + 13x + 4}$

93. $\dfrac{8x^2 + 18x - 5}{10x^2 - 9x + 2} \div \dfrac{8x^2 + 22x + 15}{10x^2 + 11x - 6}$

94. $\dfrac{10 + 7x - 12x^2}{8x^2 - 2x - 15} \div \dfrac{6x^2 - 13x + 5}{10x^2 - 13x + 4}$

For Exercises 95 to 98, state whether or not the given division is equivalent to $\dfrac{x^2 - 3x - 4}{x^2 + 5x - 6}$.

95. $\dfrac{x - 4}{x + 6} \div \dfrac{x - 1}{x + 1}$

96. $\dfrac{x + 1}{x + 6} \div \dfrac{x - 1}{x - 4}$

97. $\dfrac{x + 1}{x - 1} \div \dfrac{x + 6}{x - 4}$

98. $\dfrac{x - 1}{x + 1} \div \dfrac{x - 4}{x + 6}$

9.1 Applying Concepts

For what values of x is the rational expression undefined? (*Hint:* Set the denominator equal to zero and solve for x.)

99. $\dfrac{x}{(x + 6)(x - 1)}$

100. $\dfrac{x}{(x - 2)(x + 5)}$

101. $\dfrac{8}{x^2 - 1}$

102. $\dfrac{7}{x^2 - 16}$

103. $\dfrac{x - 4}{x^2 - x - 6}$

104. $\dfrac{x + 5}{x^2 - 4x - 5}$

105. $\dfrac{3x}{x^2 + 6x + 9}$

106. $\dfrac{3x - 8}{3x^2 - 10x - 8}$

107. $\dfrac{4x + 7}{6x^2 - 5x - 4}$

Simplify.

108. $\dfrac{y^2}{x} \cdot \dfrac{x}{2} \div \dfrac{y}{x}$

109. $\dfrac{ab}{3} \cdot \dfrac{a}{b^2} \div \dfrac{a}{4}$

110. $\left(\dfrac{2x}{y}\right)^3 \div \left(\dfrac{x}{3y}\right)^2$

111. $\left(\dfrac{c}{3}\right)^2 \div \left(\dfrac{c}{2} \cdot \dfrac{c}{4}\right)$

112. $\left(\dfrac{a - 3}{b}\right)^2 \left(\dfrac{b}{3 - a}\right)^3$

113. $\left(\dfrac{x - 4}{y^2}\right)^3 \cdot \left(\dfrac{y}{4 - x}\right)^2$

114. $\dfrac{x^2 + 3x - 40}{x^2 + 2x - 35} \div \dfrac{x^2 + 2x - 48}{x^2 + 3x - 18} \cdot \dfrac{x^2 - 36}{x^2 - 9}$

115. $\dfrac{x^2 + x - 6}{x^2 + 7x + 12} \cdot \dfrac{x^2 + 3x - 4}{x^2 + x - 2} \div \dfrac{x^2 - 16}{x^2 - 4}$

Write in simplest form the ratio of the shaded area of the figure to the total area of the figure.

116.

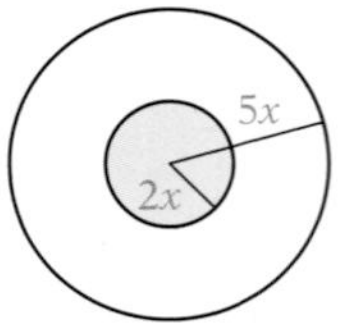

117.

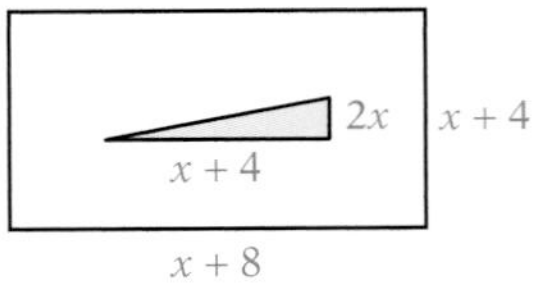

118. Given the expression $\dfrac{9}{x^2 + 1}$, choose some values of x and evaluate the expression for those values. Is it possible to choose a value of x for which the value of the expression is greater than 10? If so, give such a value. If not, explain why it is not possible.

119. Given the expression $\dfrac{1}{y - 3}$, choose some values of y and evaluate the expression for those values. Is it possible to choose a value of y for which the value of the expression is greater than 10,000,000? If so, give such a value. Explain your answer.

9.2 Expressing Fractions in Terms of the Least Common Multiple of Their Denominators

OBJECTIVE 1 Find the least common multiple (LCM) of two or more polynomials

The **least common multiple (LCM)** of two or more numbers is the smallest number that contains the prime factorization of each number.

The LCM of 12 and 18 is 36. 36 contains the prime factors of 12 and the prime factors of 18.

$$12 = 2 \cdot 2 \cdot 3$$
$$18 = 2 \cdot 3 \cdot 3$$
$$\text{LCM} = 36 = \overbrace{2 \cdot 2 \cdot 3}^{\text{Factors of 12}} \cdot 3, \quad 2 \cdot \underbrace{2 \cdot 3 \cdot 3}_{\text{Factors of 18}}$$

The least common multiple of two or more polynomials is the simplest polynomial that contains the factors of each polynomial.

To find the LCM of two or more polynomials, first factor each polynomial completely. The LCM is the product of each factor the greatest number of times it occurs in any one factorization.

Take Note

The LCM must contain the factors of each polynomial. As shown with braces at the right, the LCM contains the factors of $4x^2 + 4x$ and the factors of $x^2 + 2x + 1$.

Find the LCM of $4x^2 + 4x$ and $x^2 + 2x + 1$.

The LCM of $4x^2 + 4x$ and $x^2 + 2x + 1$ is the product of the LCM of the numerical coefficients and each variable factor the greatest number of times it occurs in any one factorization.

$$4x^2 + 4x = 4x(x + 1) = 2 \cdot 2 \cdot x(x + 1)$$
$$x^2 + 2x + 1 = (x + 1)(x + 1)$$
$$\text{LCM} = \overbrace{2 \cdot 2 \cdot x(x + 1)}^{\text{Factors of } 4x^2 + 4x}(x + 1) = 4x(x + 1)(x + 1), \quad \underbrace{(x + 1)(x + 1)}_{\text{Factors of } x^2 + 2x + 1}$$

EXAMPLE 1 Find the LCM of $4x^2y$ and $6xy^2$.

Solution

$4x^2y = 2 \cdot 2 \cdot x \cdot x \cdot y$
$6xy^2 = 2 \cdot 3 \cdot x \cdot y \cdot y$

• **Factor each polynomial completely.**

$\text{LCM} = 2 \cdot 2 \cdot 3 \cdot x \cdot x \cdot y \cdot y$
$= 12x^2y^2$

• **Write the product of the LCM of the numerical coefficients and each variable factor the greatest number of times it occurs in any one factorization.**

PROBLEM 1 Find the LCM of $8uv^2$ and $12uw$.

Solution See page S20.

EXAMPLE 2 Find the LCM of $x^2 - x - 6$ and $9 - x^2$.

Solution $x^2 - x - 6 = (x - 3)(x + 2)$

$9 - x^2 = -(x^2 - 9) = -(x + 3)(x - 3)$

$\text{LCM} = (x - 3)(x + 2)(x + 3)$

PROBLEM 2 Find the LCM of $m^2 - 6m + 9$ and $m^2 - 2m - 3$.

Solution See page S20.

OBJECTIVE 2 Express two fractions in terms of the LCM of their denominators

When adding and subtracting fractions, it is often necessary to express two or more fractions in terms of a common denominator. This common denominator is the LCM of the denominators of the fractions.

Write the fractions $\frac{x+1}{4x^2}$ and $\frac{x-3}{6x^2 - 12x}$ in terms of the LCM of the denominators.

Find the LCM of the denominators. The LCM is $12x^2(x - 2)$.

For each fraction, multiply the numerator and denominator by the factors whose product with the denominator is the LCM.

$$\frac{x+1}{4x^2} = \frac{x+1}{4x^2} \cdot \frac{3(x-2)}{3(x-2)} = \frac{3x^2 - 3x - 6}{12x^2(x-2)}$$

$$\frac{x-3}{6x^2 - 12x} = \frac{x-3}{6x(x-2)} \cdot \frac{2x}{2x} = \frac{2x^2 - 6x}{12x^2(x-2)}$$

LCM

Take Note

$\frac{3(x-2)}{3(x-2)} = 1$ and $\frac{2x}{2x} = 1$. We are multiplying each fraction by 1, so we are not changing the value of either fraction.

EXAMPLE 3 Write the fractions $\frac{x+2}{3x^2}$ and $\frac{x-1}{8xy}$ in terms of the LCM of the denominators.

Solution The LCM is $24x^2y$.

$$\frac{x+2}{3x^2} = \frac{x+2}{3x^2} \cdot \frac{8y}{8y} = \frac{8xy + 16y}{24x^2y}$$

- **The product of $3x^2$ and $8y$ is the LCM.**

$$\frac{x-1}{8xy} = \frac{x-1}{8xy} \cdot \frac{3x}{3x} = \frac{3x^2 - 3x}{24x^2y}$$

- **The product of $8xy$ and $3x$ is the LCM.**

PROBLEM 3 Write the fractions $\frac{x-3}{4xy^2}$ and $\frac{2x+1}{9y^2z}$ in terms of the LCM of the denominators.

Solution See page S20.

EXAMPLE 4 Write the fractions $\frac{2x-1}{2x-x^2}$ and $\frac{x}{x^2+x-6}$ in terms of the LCM of the denominators.

Solution $\frac{2x-1}{2x-x^2} = \frac{2x-1}{-(x^2-2x)} = -\frac{2x-1}{x^2-2x}$

• **Rewrite $\frac{2x-1}{2x-x^2}$ with a denominator of x^2-2x.**

The LCM is $x(x-2)(x+3)$.

$$\frac{2x-1}{2x-x^2} = -\frac{2x-1}{x(x-2)} \cdot \frac{x+3}{x+3} = -\frac{2x^2+5x-3}{x(x-2)(x+3)}$$

$$\frac{x}{x^2+x-6} = \frac{x}{(x-2)(x+3)} \cdot \frac{x}{x} = \frac{x^2}{x(x-2)(x+3)}$$

PROBLEM 4 Write the fractions $\frac{x+4}{x^2-3x-10}$ and $\frac{2x}{25-x^2}$ in terms of the LCM of the denominators.

Solution See page S20.

9.2 Concept Review

Determine whether the statement is always true, sometimes true, or never true.

1. The least common multiple of two numbers is the smallest number that contains all the prime factors of both numbers.

2. The least common denominator is the least common multiple of the denominators of two or more fractions.

3. The LCM of x^2, x^5, and x^8 is x^2.

4. We can rewrite $\frac{x}{y}$ as $\frac{4x}{4y}$ by using the Multiplication Property of One.

5. Rewriting two fractions in terms of the LCM of their denominators is the reverse process of simplifying the fractions.

6. To rewrite a rational expression in terms of a common denominator, determine what factor you must multiply the denominator by so that the denominator will be the common denominator. Then multiply the numerator and denominator of the fraction by that factor.

9.2 Exercises

1 Find the least common multiple (LCM) of two or more polynomials

1. a. In the LCM of $12x^4y^3$ and $15x^2y^5$, the exponent on x is ___?___ and the exponent on y is ___?___.
   b. Because $12 = 3 \cdot 4$, and $15 = 3 \cdot 5$, the coefficient in the LCM of $12x^4y^3$ and $15x^2y^5$ is (___?___)(___?___)(___?___) = (___?___).
   c. The LCM of $12x^4y^3$ and $15x^2y^5$ is ___?___.

2. To find the LCM of $x^2 - 4x + 4$ and $x^2 - 4$, first factor each polynomial:

   $x^2 - 4x + 4 = (\underline{\quad ? \quad})^2$ • **$x^2 - 4x + 4$ factors as a perfect-square trinomial.**

   $x^2 - 4 = (\underline{\quad ? \quad})(\underline{\quad ? \quad})$ • **$x^2 - 4$ factors as the difference of two perfect squares.**

   The LCM will use the factor $x - 2$ ___?___ time(s) and the factor $x + 2$ ___?___ time(s). The LCM is ___?___.

Find the LCM of the expressions.

3. $8x^3y$
$12xy^2$

4. $6ab^2$
$18ab^3$

5. $10x^4y^2$
$15x^3y$

6. $12a^2b$
$18ab^3$

7. $8x^2$
$4x^2 + 8x$

8. $6y^2$
$4y + 12$

9. $2x^2y$
$3x^2 + 12x$

10. $4xy^2$
$6xy^2 + 12y^2$

11. $8x^2(x - 1)^2$
$10x^3(x - 1)$

12. $3x + 3$
$2x^2 + 4x + 2$

13. $4x - 12$
$2x^2 - 12x + 18$

14. $(x - 1)(x + 2)$
$(x - 1)(x + 3)$

15. $(2x - 1)(x + 4)$
$(2x + 1)(x + 4)$

16. $(2x + 3)^2$
$(2x + 3)(x - 5)$

17. $(x - 7)(x + 2)$
$(x - 7)^2$

18. $x - 1$
$x - 2$
$(x - 1)(x - 2)$

19. $(x + 4)(x - 3)$
$x + 4$
$x - 3$

20. $x^2 - x - 6$
$x^2 + x - 12$

21. $x^2 + 3x - 10$
$x^2 + 5x - 14$

22. $x^2 + 5x + 4$
$x^2 - 3x - 28$

23. $x^2 - 10x + 21$
$x^2 - 8x + 15$

24. $x^2 - 2x - 24$
$x^2 - 36$

25. $x^2 + 7x + 10$
$x^2 - 25$

26. $x^2 - 7x - 30$
$x^2 - 5x - 24$

27. $2x^2 - 7x + 3$
$2x^2 + x - 1$

28. $3x^2 - 11x + 6$
$3x^2 + 4x - 4$

29. $2x^2 - 9x + 10$
$2x^2 + x - 15$

30. $6 + x - x^2$
$x + 2$
$x - 3$

31. $15 + 2x - x^2$
$x - 5$
$x + 3$

32. $5 + 4x - x^2$
$x - 5$
$x + 1$

33. $x^2 + 3x - 18$
$3 - x$
$x + 6$

34. $x^2 - 5x + 6$
$1 - x$
$x - 6$

35. How many factors of $x - 3$ are in the LCM of each pair of expressions?

a. $x^2 + x - 12$ and $x^2 - 9$ **b.** $x^2 - x - 12$ and $x^2 + 6x + 9$

c. $x^2 - 6x + 9$ and $x^2 + x - 12$

36. How many factors of a are in the LCM of $(a^3b^2)^2$ and a^4b^6? How many factors of b?

2 Express two fractions in terms of the LCM of their denominators

For Exercises 37 to 40, use the fractions $\dfrac{x^2}{y(y-3)}$ and $\dfrac{x}{(y-3)^2}$.

37. The LCM of the denominators of the fractions is ___?___.

38. To write the first fraction in terms of the LCM of the denominators, multiply its numerator and its denominator by ___?___.

39. To write the second fraction in terms of the LCM of the denominators, multiply its numerator and its denominator by ___?___.

40. Write the two fractions in terms of the LCM of their denominators: ___?___ and ___?___.

Write each fraction in terms of the LCM of the denominators.

41. $\dfrac{4}{x}; \dfrac{3}{x^2}$

42. $\dfrac{5}{ab^2}; \dfrac{6}{ab}$

43. $\dfrac{x}{3y^2}; \dfrac{z}{4y}$

44. $\dfrac{5y}{6x^2}; \dfrac{7}{9xy}$

45. $\dfrac{y}{x(x-3)}; \dfrac{6}{x^2}$

46. $\dfrac{a}{y^2}; \dfrac{6}{y(y+5)}$

47. $\dfrac{9}{(x-1)^2}; \dfrac{6}{x(x-1)}$

48. $\dfrac{a^2}{y(y+7)}; \dfrac{a}{(y+7)^2}$

49. $\dfrac{3}{x-3}; -\dfrac{5}{x(3-x)}$

50. $\dfrac{b}{y(y-4)}; \dfrac{b^2}{4-y}$

51. $\dfrac{3}{(x-5)^2}; \dfrac{2}{5-x}$

52. $\dfrac{3}{7-y}; \dfrac{2}{(y-7)^2}$

53. $\dfrac{3}{x^2+2x}; \dfrac{4}{x^2}$

54. $\dfrac{2}{y-3}; \dfrac{3}{y^3-3y^2}$

55. $\dfrac{x-2}{x+3}; \dfrac{x}{x-4}$

56. $\dfrac{x^2}{2x-1}; \dfrac{x+1}{x+4}$

57. $\dfrac{3}{x^2+x-2}; \dfrac{x}{x+2}$

58. $\dfrac{3x}{x-5}; \dfrac{4}{x^2-25}$

59. $\dfrac{5}{2x^2 - 9x + 10}; \dfrac{x - 1}{2x - 5}$

60. $\dfrac{x - 3}{3x^2 + 4x - 4}; \dfrac{2}{x + 2}$

61. $\dfrac{x}{x^2 + x - 6}; \dfrac{2x}{x^2 - 9}$

62. $\dfrac{x - 1}{x^2 + 2x - 15}; \dfrac{x}{x^2 + 6x + 5}$

63. $\dfrac{x}{9 - x^2}; \dfrac{x - 1}{x^2 - 6x + 9}$

64. $\dfrac{2x}{10 + 3x - x^2}; \dfrac{x + 2}{x^2 - 8x + 15}$

65. $\dfrac{3x}{x - 5}; \dfrac{x}{x + 4}; \dfrac{3}{20 + x - x^2}$

66. $\dfrac{x + 1}{x + 5}; \dfrac{x + 2}{x - 7}; \dfrac{3}{35 + 2x - x^2}$

9.2 Applying Concepts

Write each expression in terms of the LCM of the denominators.

67. $\dfrac{3}{10^2}; \dfrac{5}{10^4}$

68. $\dfrac{8}{10^3}; \dfrac{9}{10^5}$

69. $b; \dfrac{5}{b}$

70. $3; \dfrac{2}{n}$

71. $1; \dfrac{y}{y - 1}$

72. $x; \dfrac{x}{x^2 - 1}$

73. $\dfrac{x^2 + 1}{(x - 1)^3}; \dfrac{x + 1}{(x - 1)^2}; \dfrac{1}{x - 1}$

74. $\dfrac{a^2 + a}{(a + 1)^3}; \dfrac{a + 1}{(a + 1)^2}; \dfrac{1}{a + 1}$

75. $\dfrac{b}{4a^2 - 4b^2}; \dfrac{a}{8a - 8b}$

76. $\dfrac{c}{6c^2 + 7cd + d^2}; \dfrac{d}{3c^2 - 3d^2}$

77. $\dfrac{1}{x^2 + 2x + xy + 2y}; \dfrac{1}{x^2 + xy - 2x - 2y}$

78. $\dfrac{1}{ab + 3a - 3b - b^2}; \dfrac{1}{ab + 3a + 3b + b^2}$

79. When is the LCM of two expressions equal to their product?

9.3 Addition and Subtraction of Rational Expressions

OBJECTIVE 1 Add and subtract rational expressions with the same denominator

When adding rational expressions in which the denominators are the same, add the numerators. The denominator of the sum is the common denominator.

$$\frac{a}{b}+\frac{c}{b}=\frac{a+c}{b}$$

$$\frac{5x}{18}+\frac{7x}{18}=\frac{12x}{18}=\frac{2x}{3}$$

$$\frac{x}{x^2-1}+\frac{1}{x^2-1}=\frac{x+1}{x^2-1}=\frac{\overset{1}{\cancel{(x+1)}}}{(x-1)\underset{1}{\cancel{(x+1)}}}=\frac{1}{x-1}$$

Note that the sum is written in simplest form.

When subtracting rational expressions in which the denominators are the same, subtract the numerators. The denominator of the difference is the common denominator. Write the answer in simplest form.

Take Note

Be careful with signs when subtracting rational expressions. Note that we must subtract the *entire* numerator $2x + 3$.

$(3x - 1) - (2x + 3) =$
$3x - 1 - 2x - 3$

$$\frac{2x}{x-2}-\frac{4}{x-2}=\frac{2x-4}{x-2}=\frac{2\overset{1}{\cancel{(x-2)}}}{\underset{1}{\cancel{x-2}}}=2$$

$$\frac{3x-1}{x^2-5x+4}-\frac{2x+3}{x^2-5x+4}=\frac{(3x-1)-(2x+3)}{x^2-5x+4}$$

$$=\frac{x-4}{x^2-5x+4}$$

$$=\frac{\overset{1}{\cancel{(x-4)}}}{\underset{1}{\cancel{(x-4)}}(x-1)}$$

$$=\frac{1}{x-1}$$

EXAMPLE 1 Add or subtract. **A.** $\frac{7}{x^2}+\frac{9}{x^2}$ **B.** $\frac{3x^2}{x^2-1}-\frac{x+4}{x^2-1}$

Solution **A.** $\frac{7}{x^2}+\frac{9}{x^2}=\frac{7+9}{x^2}$

$$=\frac{16}{x^2}$$

• **The denominators are the same. Add the numerators.**

B. $\dfrac{3x^2}{x^2-1} - \dfrac{x+4}{x^2-1} = \dfrac{3x^2-(x+4)}{x^2-1}$ • **The denominators are the same. Subtract the numerators.**

$= \dfrac{3x^2-x-4}{x^2-1}$

$= \dfrac{(3x-4)\overset{1}{\cancel{(x+1)}}}{(x-1)\underset{1}{\cancel{(x+1)}}}$ • **Write the answer in simplest form.**

$= \dfrac{3x-4}{x-1}$

PROBLEM 1 Add or subtract. **A.** $\dfrac{3}{xy} + \dfrac{12}{xy}$ **B.** $\dfrac{2x^2}{x^2-x-12} - \dfrac{7x+4}{x^2-x-12}$

Solution See page S20.

OBJECTIVE 2 Add and subtract rational expressions with different denominators

Take Note

This objective requires using the skills learned in the objective on writing two fractions in terms of the LCM of their denominators and the objective on adding and subtracting rational expressions with the same denominator.

Before two fractions with different denominators can be added or subtracted, each fraction must be expressed in terms of a common denominator. This common denominator is the LCM of the denominators of the fractions.

Add: $\dfrac{x-3}{x^2-2x} + \dfrac{6}{x^2-4}$

Find the LCM of the denominators.

$x^2-2x = x(x-2)$
$x^2-4 = (x-2)(x+2)$

The LCM is $x(x-2)(x+2)$.

$\dfrac{x-3}{x^2-2x} + \dfrac{6}{x^2-4}$

Write each fraction in terms of the LCM of the denominators.

$= \dfrac{x-3}{x(x-2)} \cdot \dfrac{x+2}{x+2} + \dfrac{6}{(x-2)(x+2)} \cdot \dfrac{x}{x}$

Multiply the factors in the numerator.

$= \dfrac{x^2-x-6}{x(x-2)(x+2)} + \dfrac{6x}{x(x-2)(x+2)}$

Add the fractions.

$= \dfrac{x^2-x-6+6x}{x(x-2)(x+2)}$

$= \dfrac{x^2+5x-6}{x(x-2)(x+2)}$

Factor the numerator to determine whether there are common factors in the numerator and denominator.

$= \dfrac{(x+6)(x-1)}{x(x-2)(x+2)}$

EXAMPLE 2 Add or subtract.

A. $\frac{y}{x} - \frac{4y}{3x} + \frac{3y}{4x}$ **B.** $\frac{2x}{x-3} - \frac{5}{3-x}$ **C.** $x - \frac{3}{5x}$

Solution **A.** The LCM of the denominators is $12x$.

• **Find the LCM of the denominators.**

$$\frac{y}{x} - \frac{4y}{3x} + \frac{3y}{4x}$$
$$= \frac{y}{x} \cdot \frac{12}{12} - \frac{4y}{3x} \cdot \frac{4}{4} + \frac{3y}{4x} \cdot \frac{3}{3}$$

• **Write each fraction in terms of the LCM.**

$$= \frac{12y}{12x} - \frac{16y}{12x} + \frac{9y}{12x}$$
$$= \frac{12y - 16y + 9y}{12x}$$
$$= \frac{5y}{12x}$$

B. The LCM of $x - 3$ and $3 - x$ is $x - 3$.

• $\mathbf{3 - x = -(x - 3)}$

$$\frac{2x}{x-3} - \frac{5}{3-x}$$
$$= \frac{2x}{x-3} - \frac{5}{-(x-3)} \cdot \frac{-1}{-1}$$

• **Multiply** $\frac{5}{-(x-3)}$ **by** $\frac{-1}{-1}$ **so that the denominator will be** $x - 3$**.**

$$= \frac{2x}{x-3} - \frac{-5}{x-3}$$
$$= \frac{2x - (-5)}{x-3}$$
$$= \frac{2x + 5}{x-3}$$

C. The LCM of the denominators is $5x$.

$$x - \frac{3}{5x} = \frac{x}{1} - \frac{3}{5x}$$
$$= \frac{x}{1} \cdot \frac{5x}{5x} - \frac{3}{5x}$$
$$= \frac{5x^2}{5x} - \frac{3}{5x}$$
$$= \frac{5x^2 - 3}{5x}$$

PROBLEM 2 Add or subtract.

A. $\frac{z}{8y} - \frac{4z}{3y} + \frac{5z}{4y}$ **B.** $\frac{5x}{x-2} - \frac{3}{2-x}$ **C.** $y + \frac{5}{y-7}$

Solution See page S21.

EXAMPLE 3 Add or subtract. **A.** $\dfrac{2x}{2x-3} - \dfrac{1}{x+1}$

B. $\dfrac{x+3}{x^2-2x-8} + \dfrac{3}{4-x}$

Solution **A.** The LCM is $(2x-3)(x+1)$.

$$\frac{2x}{2x-3} - \frac{1}{x+1} = \frac{2x}{2x-3}\cdot\frac{x+1}{x+1} - \frac{1}{x+1}\cdot\frac{2x-3}{2x-3}$$
$$= \frac{2x^2+2x}{(2x-3)(x+1)} - \frac{2x-3}{(2x-3)(x+1)}$$
$$= \frac{(2x^2+2x)-(2x-3)}{(2x-3)(x+1)}$$
$$= \frac{2x^2+3}{(2x-3)(x+1)}$$

B. The LCM is $(x-4)(x+2)$.

$$\frac{x+3}{x^2-2x-8} + \frac{3}{4-x}$$
$$= \frac{x+3}{(x-4)(x+2)} + \frac{3}{-(x-4)}\cdot\frac{-1\cdot(x+2)}{-1\cdot(x+2)}$$
$$= \frac{x+3}{(x-4)(x+2)} + \frac{-3(x+2)}{(x-4)(x+2)}$$
$$= \frac{(x+3)+(-3)(x+2)}{(x-4)(x+2)}$$
$$= \frac{x+3-3x-6}{(x-4)(x+2)}$$
$$= \frac{-2x-3}{(x-4)(x+2)}$$

PROBLEM 3 Add or subtract. **A.** $\dfrac{4x}{3x-1} - \dfrac{9}{x+4}$ **B.** $\dfrac{2x-1}{x^2-25} + \dfrac{2}{5-x}$

Solution See page S21.

9.3 Concept Review

Determine whether the statement is always true, sometimes true, or never true.

1. To add two fractions, add the numerators and the denominators.

2. The procedure for subtracting two rational expressions is the same as that for subtracting two arithmetic fractions.

3. To add two rational expressions, first multiply both expressions by the LCM of their denominators.

4. If $x \neq -2$ and $x \neq 0$, then $\dfrac{x}{x+2} + \dfrac{3}{x+2} = \dfrac{x+3}{x+2} = \dfrac{3}{2}$.

5. If $y \neq 8$, then $\dfrac{y}{y-8} - \dfrac{8}{y-8} = \dfrac{y-8}{y-8} = 1$.

6. If $x \neq 0$, then $\dfrac{4x-3}{x} - \dfrac{3x+1}{x} = \dfrac{4x-3-3x+1}{x} = \dfrac{x-2}{x}$.

9.3 Exercises

1 Add and subtract rational expressions with the same denominator

1. Add: $\dfrac{6a+1}{a-4} + \dfrac{2a-1}{a-4}$

$\dfrac{6a+1}{a-4} + \dfrac{2a-1}{a-4} = \dfrac{6a+1+2a-1}{a-4}$ • **The denominators are the same. Add the ___?___.**

$= \dfrac{?}{a-4}$ • **Simplify the numerator. The result is in simplest form because the numerator and denominator have no common ___?___.**

2. Subtract: $\dfrac{5x}{x^2+5x-14} - \dfrac{2x-21}{x^2+5x-14}$

$\dfrac{5x}{x^2+5x-14} - \dfrac{2x-21}{x^2+5x-14}$ • **The ___?___ are the same.**

$= \dfrac{? - (?)}{x^2+5x-14}$ • **Subtract the numerators.**

$= \dfrac{5x - ? + ?}{x^2+5x-14}$ • **Remove the parentheses.**

$= \dfrac{?}{x^2+5x-14}$ • **Simplify the numerator.**

$= \dfrac{3(?)}{(?)(?)}$ • **Factor the numerator and denominator.**

$= \dfrac{?}{?}$ • **Divide the numerator and denominator by the common factor, ___?___.**

Add or subtract.

3. $\dfrac{3}{y^2} + \dfrac{8}{y^2}$

4. $\dfrac{6}{ab} - \dfrac{2}{ab}$

5. $\dfrac{3}{x+4} - \dfrac{10}{x+4}$

6. $\dfrac{x}{x+6} - \dfrac{2}{x+6}$

7. $\dfrac{3x}{2x+3} + \dfrac{5x}{2x+3}$

8. $\dfrac{6y}{4y+1} - \dfrac{11y}{4y+1}$

9. $\dfrac{2x+1}{x-3} + \dfrac{3x+6}{x-3}$

10. $\dfrac{4x+3}{2x-7} + \dfrac{3x-8}{2x-7}$

11. $\dfrac{5x-1}{x+9} - \dfrac{3x+4}{x+9}$

12. $\dfrac{6x-5}{x-10} - \dfrac{3x-4}{x-10}$

13. $\dfrac{x-7}{2x+7} - \dfrac{4x-3}{2x+7}$

14. $\dfrac{2n}{3n+4} - \dfrac{5n-3}{3n+4}$

15. $\dfrac{x}{x^2+2x-15} - \dfrac{3}{x^2+2x-15}$

16. $\dfrac{3x}{x^2+3x-10} - \dfrac{6}{x^2+3x-10}$

17. $\dfrac{2x+3}{x^2-x-30} - \dfrac{x-2}{x^2-x-30}$

18. $\dfrac{3x-1}{x^2+5x-6} - \dfrac{2x-7}{x^2+5x-6}$

19. $\dfrac{4y+7}{2y^2+7y-4} - \dfrac{y-5}{2y^2+7y-4}$

20. $\dfrac{x+1}{2x^2-5x-12} + \dfrac{x+2}{2x^2-5x-12}$

21. $\dfrac{2x^2+3x}{x^2-9x+20} + \dfrac{2x^2-3}{x^2-9x+20} - \dfrac{4x^2+2x+1}{x^2-9x+20}$

22. $\dfrac{2x^2+3x}{x^2-2x-63} - \dfrac{x^2-3x+21}{x^2-2x-63} - \dfrac{x-7}{x^2-2x-63}$

2 Add and subtract rational expressions with different denominators

23. To add or subtract rational expressions that have different denominators, you must first express each fraction in terms of a ___?___, which can be the ___?___ of the denominators of the rational expressions.

24. Subtract: $\dfrac{3}{x-1} - \dfrac{2}{x+5}$

$\dfrac{3}{x-1} - \dfrac{2}{x+5}$
- The denominators are different.

$= \dfrac{3}{x-1} \cdot \dfrac{x+5}{x+5} - \dfrac{2}{x+5} \cdot \dfrac{x-1}{x-1}$
- Write each fraction in terms of the ___?___ of the denominators, $(x-1)(x+5)$.

$= \dfrac{\underline{\quad ? \quad}}{(x-1)(x+5)} - \dfrac{\underline{\quad ? \quad}}{(x-1)(x+5)}$
- Simplify each product. Multiply the numerators. Leave the denominators in factored form.

$= \dfrac{(\underline{\quad ? \quad}) - (\underline{\quad ? \quad})}{(x-1)(x+5)}$
- Subtract the ___?___. The denominator is the common denominator.

$= \dfrac{3x + 15 - \underline{\quad ? \quad} + \underline{\quad ? \quad}}{(x-1)(x+5)}$
- Remove the parentheses.

$= \dfrac{\underline{\quad ? \quad}}{(x-1)(x+5)}$
- Simplify the numerator. The result is in simplest form because the numerator and denominator have no common ___?___.

25. True or false? To add $\frac{5}{8x^3} + \frac{7}{12x^5}$, use a common denominator of $4x^3$.

26. True or false? $\frac{3}{x - 8} + \frac{3}{8 - x} = 0$.

Add or subtract.

27. $\frac{4}{x} + \frac{5}{y}$

28. $\frac{7}{a} + \frac{5}{b}$

29. $\frac{12}{x} - \frac{5}{2x}$

30. $\frac{5}{3a} - \frac{3}{4a}$

31. $\frac{1}{2x} - \frac{5}{4x} + \frac{7}{6x}$

32. $\frac{7}{4y} + \frac{11}{6y} - \frac{8}{3y}$

33. $\frac{5}{3x} - \frac{2}{x^2} + \frac{3}{2x}$

34. $\frac{6}{y^2} + \frac{3}{4y} - \frac{2}{5y}$

35. $\frac{2}{x} - \frac{3}{2y} + \frac{3}{5x} - \frac{1}{4y}$

36. $\frac{5}{2a} + \frac{7}{3b} - \frac{2}{b} - \frac{3}{4a}$

37. $\frac{2x + 1}{3x} + \frac{x - 1}{5x}$

38. $\frac{4x - 3}{6x} + \frac{2x + 3}{4x}$

39. $\frac{x - 3}{6x} + \frac{x + 4}{8x}$

40. $\frac{2x - 3}{2x} + \frac{x + 3}{3x}$

41. $\frac{2x + 9}{9x} - \frac{x - 5}{5x}$

42. $\frac{3y - 2}{12y} - \frac{y - 3}{18y}$

43. $\frac{x + 4}{2x} - \frac{x - 1}{x^2}$

44. $\frac{x - 2}{3x^2} - \frac{x + 4}{x}$

45. $\frac{x - 10}{4x^2} + \frac{x + 1}{2x}$

46. $\frac{x + 5}{3x^2} + \frac{2x + 1}{2x}$

47. $y + \frac{8}{3y}$

48. $\frac{7}{2n} - n$

49. $\frac{4}{x + 4} + x$

50. $x + \frac{3}{x + 2}$

51. $5 - \frac{x - 2}{x + 1}$

52. $3 + \frac{x - 1}{x + 1}$

53. $\frac{2x + 1}{6x^2} - \frac{x - 4}{4x}$

54. $\frac{x + 3}{6x} - \frac{x - 3}{8x^2}$

55. $\frac{x + 2}{xy} - \frac{3x - 2}{x^2y}$

56. $\frac{3x - 1}{xy^2} - \frac{2x + 3}{xy}$

57. $\frac{4x - 3}{3x^2y} + \frac{2x + 1}{4xy^2}$

58. $\frac{5x + 7}{6xy^2} - \frac{4x - 3}{8x^2y}$

59. $\dfrac{x-2}{8x^2} - \dfrac{x+7}{12xy}$

60. $\dfrac{3x-1}{6y^2} - \dfrac{x+5}{9xy}$

61. $\dfrac{4}{x-2} + \dfrac{5}{x+3}$

62. $\dfrac{2}{x-3} + \dfrac{5}{x-4}$

63. $\dfrac{6}{x-7} - \dfrac{4}{x+3}$

64. $\dfrac{3}{y+6} - \dfrac{4}{y-3}$

65. $\dfrac{2x}{x+1} + \dfrac{1}{x-3}$

66. $\dfrac{3x}{x-4} + \dfrac{2}{x+6}$

67. $\dfrac{4x}{2x-1} - \dfrac{5}{x-6}$

68. $\dfrac{6x}{x+5} - \dfrac{3}{2x+3}$

69. $\dfrac{2a}{a-7} + \dfrac{5}{7-a}$

70. $\dfrac{4x}{6-x} + \dfrac{5}{x-6}$

71. $\dfrac{x}{x^2-9} + \dfrac{3}{x-3}$

72. $\dfrac{y}{y^2-16} + \dfrac{1}{y-4}$

73. $\dfrac{2x}{x^2-x-6} - \dfrac{3}{x+2}$

74. $\dfrac{5x}{x^2+2x-8} - \dfrac{2}{x+4}$

75. $\dfrac{3x-1}{x^2-10x+25} - \dfrac{3}{x-5}$

76. $\dfrac{2a+3}{a^2-7a+12} - \dfrac{2}{a-3}$

77. $\dfrac{x+4}{x^2-x-42} + \dfrac{3}{7-x}$

78. $\dfrac{x+3}{x^2-3x-10} + \dfrac{2}{5-x}$

79. $\dfrac{x}{2x+4} - \dfrac{2}{x^2+2x}$

80. $\dfrac{x+2}{4x+16} - \dfrac{2}{x^2+4x}$

81. $\dfrac{x-1}{x^2-x-2} + \dfrac{3}{x^2-3x+2}$

82. $\dfrac{a+2}{a^2+a-2} + \dfrac{3}{a^2+2a-3}$

83. $\dfrac{1}{x+1} + \dfrac{x}{x-6} - \dfrac{5x-2}{x^2-5x-6}$

84. $\dfrac{x}{x-4} + \dfrac{5}{x+5} - \dfrac{11x-8}{x^2+x-20}$

85. $\dfrac{3x+1}{x-1} - \dfrac{x-1}{x-3} + \dfrac{x+1}{x^2-4x+3}$

86. $\dfrac{4x+1}{x-8} - \dfrac{3x+2}{x+4} - \dfrac{49x+4}{x^2-4x-32}$

9.3 Applying Concepts

Simplify.

87. $\frac{a}{a-b} + \frac{b}{b-a} + 1$

88. $\frac{y}{x-y} + 2 - \frac{x}{y-x}$

89. $b - 3 + \frac{5}{b+4}$

90. $2y - 1 + \frac{6}{y+5}$

91. $\frac{(n+1)^2}{(n-1)^2} - 1$

92. $1 - \frac{(y-2)^2}{(y+2)^2}$

93. $\frac{2x+9}{3-x} + \frac{x+5}{x+7} - \frac{2x^2+3x-3}{x^2+4x-21}$

94. $\frac{3x+5}{x+5} - \frac{x+1}{2-x} - \frac{4x^2-3x-1}{x^2+3x-10}$

95. $\frac{x^2+x-6}{x^2+2x-8} \cdot \frac{x^2+5x+4}{x^2+2x-3} - \frac{2}{x-1}$

96. $\frac{x^2+9x+20}{x^2+4x-5} \div \frac{x^2-49}{x^2+6x-7} - \frac{x}{x-7}$

97. $\frac{x^2-9}{x^2+6x+9} \div \frac{x^2+x-20}{x^2-x-12} + \frac{1}{x+1}$

98. $\frac{x^2-25}{x^2+10x+25} \cdot \frac{x^2-7x+10}{x^2-x-2} + \frac{1}{x+1}$

99. Find the sum of the following: $\frac{1}{1\cdot 2} + \frac{1}{2\cdot 3}$

$\frac{1}{1\cdot 2} + \frac{1}{2\cdot 3} + \frac{1}{3\cdot 4}$

$\frac{1}{1\cdot 2} + \frac{1}{2\cdot 3} + \frac{1}{3\cdot 4} + \frac{1}{4\cdot 5}$

Note the pattern for these sums, and then find the sum of 50 terms, of 100 terms, and of 1000 terms.

Rewrite the expression as the sum of two fractions in simplest form.

100. $\frac{5b+4a}{ab}$

101. $\frac{6x+7y}{xy}$

102. $\frac{3x^2+4xy}{x^2y^2}$

103. $\frac{2mn^2+8m^2n}{m^3n^3}$

104. **Deep-Sea Diving** A recommended percent of oxygen (by volume) in the air that a deep-sea diver breathes is given by $\frac{660}{d+33}$, where d is the depth, in feet, at which the diver is working.

a. What is the recommended percent of oxygen for a diver working at a depth of 50 ft? Round to the nearest percent.

b. As the depth of the diver increases, does the recommended amount of oxygen increase or decrease?

c. At sea level, the oxygen content of air is approximately 21%. Is this less than or more than the recommended amount of oxygen for a diver working at the water's surface?

9.4 Complex Fractions

OBJECTIVE 1 Simplify complex fractions

Point of Interest

There are many instances of complex fractions in application problems. The fraction $\dfrac{1}{\dfrac{1}{r_1}+\dfrac{1}{r_2}}$ is used to determine the total resistance in certain electric circuits.

A **complex fraction** is a fraction whose numerator or denominator contains one or more fractions. Examples of complex fractions are shown at the right.

$$\frac{3}{2-\frac{1}{2}},\quad \frac{4+\frac{1}{x}}{3+\frac{2}{x}},\quad \frac{\frac{1}{x-1}+x+3}{x-3+\frac{1}{x+4}}$$

Simplify: $\dfrac{1-\dfrac{4}{x^2}}{1+\dfrac{2}{x}}$

Find the LCM of the denominators of the fractions in the numerator and denominator.

The LCM of x^2 and x is x^2.

Multiply the numerator and denominator of the complex fraction by the LCM.

$$\frac{1-\frac{4}{x^2}}{1+\frac{2}{x}} = \frac{1-\frac{4}{x^2}}{1+\frac{2}{x}}\cdot\frac{x^2}{x^2}$$

$$= \frac{1\cdot x^2 - \frac{4}{x^2}\cdot x^2}{1\cdot x^2+\frac{2}{x}\cdot x^2}$$

$$= \frac{x^2-4}{x^2+2x}$$

Simplify.

$$= \frac{(x-2)\overset{1}{\cancel{(x+2)}}}{x\underset{1}{\cancel{(x+2)}}}$$

$$= \frac{x-2}{x}$$

Take Note

First, we are multiplying the complex fraction by $\frac{x^2}{x^2}$, which equals 1, so we are not changing the value of the fraction. Second, we are using the Distributive Property to multiply $\left(1-\frac{4}{x^2}\right)x^2$ and $\left(1+\frac{2}{x}\right)x^2$.

The method shown above of simplifying a complex fraction by multiplying the numerator and denominator by the LCM of the denominators is used in Example 1. However, a different approach is to rewrite the numerator and denominator of the complex fraction as single fractions and then divide the numerator by the denominator. The example shown above is simplified below using this alternative method.

Take Note

Recall that the fraction bar can be read "divided by."

Rewrite the numerator and denominator of the complex fraction as single fractions.

$$\frac{1-\frac{4}{x^2}}{1+\frac{2}{x}} = \frac{1\cdot\frac{x^2}{x^2}-\frac{4}{x^2}}{1\cdot\frac{x}{x}+\frac{2}{x}} = \frac{\frac{x^2}{x^2}-\frac{4}{x^2}}{\frac{x}{x}+\frac{2}{x}} = \frac{\frac{x^2-4}{x^2}}{\frac{x+2}{x}}$$

Divide the numerator of the complex fraction by the denominator.

$$= \frac{x^2-4}{x^2}\div\frac{x+2}{x} = \frac{x^2-4}{x^2}\cdot\frac{x}{x+2}$$

Multiply the fractions. Factor the numerator. $= \dfrac{(x^2 - 4)x}{x^2(x + 2)} = \dfrac{(x + 2)(x - 2)x}{x^2(x + 2)}$

Simplify. $= \dfrac{x - 2}{x}$

Note that this is the same result as shown above.

EXAMPLE 1 Simplify. **A.** $\dfrac{\frac{1}{x} + \frac{1}{2}}{\frac{1}{x^2} - \frac{1}{4}}$ **B.** $\dfrac{1 - \frac{2}{x} - \frac{15}{x^2}}{1 - \frac{11}{x} + \frac{30}{x^2}}$

Solution **A.** The LCM of x, 2, x^2, and 4 is $4x^2$.

$$\frac{\frac{1}{x} + \frac{1}{2}}{\frac{1}{x^2} - \frac{1}{4}} = \frac{\frac{1}{x} + \frac{1}{2}}{\frac{1}{x^2} - \frac{1}{4}} \cdot \frac{4x^2}{4x^2}$$

$$= \frac{\frac{1}{x} \cdot 4x^2 + \frac{1}{2} \cdot 4x^2}{\frac{1}{x^2} \cdot 4x^2 - \frac{1}{4} \cdot 4x^2}$$

$$= \frac{4x + 2x^2}{4 - x^2}$$

$$= \frac{2x\overset{1}{\cancel{(2 + x)}}}{(2 - x)\underset{1}{\cancel{(2 + x)}}}$$

$$= \frac{2x}{2 - x}$$

B. The LCM of x and x^2 is x^2.

$$\frac{1 - \frac{2}{x} - \frac{15}{x^2}}{1 - \frac{11}{x} + \frac{30}{x^2}} = \frac{1 - \frac{2}{x} - \frac{15}{x^2}}{1 - \frac{11}{x} + \frac{30}{x^2}} \cdot \frac{x^2}{x^2}$$

$$= \frac{1 \cdot x^2 - \frac{2}{x} \cdot x^2 - \frac{15}{x^2} \cdot x^2}{1 \cdot x^2 - \frac{11}{x} \cdot x^2 + \frac{30}{x^2} \cdot x^2}$$

$$= \frac{x^2 - 2x - 15}{x^2 - 11x + 30}$$

$$= \frac{\overset{1}{\cancel{(x - 5)}}(x + 3)}{\underset{1}{\cancel{(x - 5)}}(x - 6)}$$

$$= \frac{x + 3}{x - 6}$$

PROBLEM 1 Simplify. **A.** $\dfrac{\frac{1}{3} - \frac{1}{x}}{\frac{1}{9} - \frac{1}{x^2}}$ **B.** $\dfrac{1 + \frac{4}{x} + \frac{3}{x^2}}{1 + \frac{10}{x} + \frac{21}{x^2}}$

Solution See page S21.

9.4 Concept Review

Determine whether the statement is always true, sometimes true, or never true.

1. A complex fraction is a fraction that has fractions in the numerator and denominator.

2. We can simplify a complex fraction by first finding the least common multiple of the denominators of the fractions in the numerator and denominator of the complex fraction.

3. To simplify a complex fraction, multiply the complex fraction by the LCM of the denominators of the fractions in the numerator and denominator of the complex fraction.

4. When we multiply the numerator and denominator of a complex fraction by the same expression, we are using the Multiplication Property of One.

5. Our goal in simplifying a complex fraction is to rewrite it so that there are no fractions in the numerator or in the denominator. We then express the fraction in simplest form.

6. For the complex fraction $\dfrac{1 + \frac{4}{x} + \frac{3}{x^2}}{1 + \frac{10}{x} + \frac{21}{x^2}}$, x can be any real number except 0.

9.4 Exercises

1 Simplify complex fractions

For Exercises 1 to 4, use the complex fraction $\dfrac{1 - \frac{5}{x} + \frac{6}{x^2}}{1 - \frac{4}{x^2}}$.

1. To simplify the complex fraction, multiply the numerator and denominator of the complex fraction by the LCM of the denominators of the fractions ___?___, ___?___, and ___?___. The LCM is ___?___.

2. When you multiply the numerator of the complex fraction by x^2, the numerator of the complex fraction simplifies to ___?___, which factors as (___?___)(___?___).

3. When you multiply the denominator of the complex fraction by x^2, the denominator of the complex fraction simplifies to ___?___, which factors as (___?___)(___?___).

4. The numerator from Exercise 2 and the denominator from Exercise 3 have a common factor of ___?___, so the simplified form of the complex fraction is (___?___).

Simplify.

5. $\dfrac{1 + \dfrac{3}{x}}{1 - \dfrac{9}{x^2}}$

6. $\dfrac{1 + \dfrac{4}{x}}{1 - \dfrac{16}{x^2}}$

7. $\dfrac{2 - \dfrac{8}{x + 4}}{3 - \dfrac{12}{x + 4}}$

8. $\dfrac{5 - \dfrac{25}{x + 5}}{1 - \dfrac{3}{x + 5}}$

9. $\dfrac{1 + \dfrac{5}{y - 2}}{1 - \dfrac{2}{y - 2}}$

10. $\dfrac{2 - \dfrac{11}{2x - 1}}{3 - \dfrac{17}{2x - 1}}$

11. $\dfrac{4 - \dfrac{2}{x + 7}}{5 + \dfrac{1}{x + 7}}$

12. $\dfrac{5 + \dfrac{3}{x - 8}}{2 - \dfrac{1}{x - 8}}$

13. $\dfrac{\dfrac{3}{x - 2} + 3}{\dfrac{4}{x - 2} + 4}$

14. $\dfrac{\dfrac{3}{2x + 1} - 3}{2 - \dfrac{4x}{2x + 1}}$

15. $\dfrac{2 - \dfrac{3}{x} - \dfrac{2}{x^2}}{2 + \dfrac{5}{x} + \dfrac{2}{x^2}}$

16. $\dfrac{2 + \dfrac{5}{x} - \dfrac{12}{x^2}}{4 - \dfrac{4}{x} - \dfrac{3}{x^2}}$

17. $\dfrac{1 - \dfrac{1}{x} - \dfrac{6}{x^2}}{1 - \dfrac{9}{x^2}}$

18. $\dfrac{1 + \dfrac{4}{x} + \dfrac{4}{x^2}}{1 - \dfrac{2}{x} - \dfrac{8}{x^2}}$

19. $\dfrac{1 - \dfrac{5}{x} - \dfrac{6}{x^2}}{1 + \dfrac{6}{x} + \dfrac{5}{x^2}}$

20. $\dfrac{1 - \dfrac{7}{a} + \dfrac{12}{a^2}}{1 + \dfrac{1}{a} - \dfrac{20}{a^2}}$

21. $\dfrac{1 - \dfrac{6}{x} + \dfrac{8}{x^2}}{\dfrac{4}{x^2} + \dfrac{3}{x} - 1}$

22. $\dfrac{1 + \dfrac{3}{x} - \dfrac{18}{x^2}}{\dfrac{21}{x^2} - \dfrac{4}{x} - 1}$

23. $\dfrac{x - \dfrac{4}{x + 3}}{1 + \dfrac{1}{x + 3}}$

24. $\dfrac{y + \dfrac{1}{y - 2}}{1 + \dfrac{1}{y - 2}}$

25. $\dfrac{1 - \dfrac{x}{2x + 1}}{x - \dfrac{1}{2x + 1}}$

26. $\dfrac{1 - \dfrac{2x - 2}{3x - 1}}{x - \dfrac{4}{3x - 1}}$

27. $\dfrac{x - 5 + \dfrac{14}{x + 4}}{x + 3 - \dfrac{2}{x + 4}}$

28. $\dfrac{a + 4 + \dfrac{5}{a - 2}}{a + 6 + \dfrac{15}{a - 2}}$

29. $\dfrac{x + 3 - \dfrac{10}{x - 6}}{x + 2 - \dfrac{20}{x - 6}}$

30. $\dfrac{x - 7 + \dfrac{5}{x - 1}}{x - 3 + \dfrac{1}{x - 1}}$

31. $\dfrac{y - 6 + \dfrac{22}{2y + 3}}{y - 5 + \dfrac{11}{2y + 3}}$

32. $\dfrac{x + 2 - \dfrac{12}{2x - 1}}{x + 1 - \dfrac{9}{2x - 1}}$

33. $\dfrac{x - \dfrac{2}{2x - 3}}{2x - 1 - \dfrac{8}{2x - 3}}$

34. $\dfrac{x + 3 - \dfrac{18}{2x + 1}}{x - \dfrac{6}{2x + 1}}$

35. $\dfrac{1 - \dfrac{2}{x + 1}}{1 + \dfrac{1}{x - 2}}$

36. $\dfrac{1 - \dfrac{1}{x + 2}}{1 + \dfrac{2}{x - 1}}$

37. $\dfrac{1 - \dfrac{2}{x + 4}}{1 + \dfrac{3}{x - 1}}$

38. $\dfrac{1 + \dfrac{1}{x - 2}}{1 - \dfrac{3}{x + 2}}$

39. $\dfrac{\dfrac{1}{x} - \dfrac{2}{x - 1}}{\dfrac{3}{x} + \dfrac{1}{x - 1}}$

40. $\dfrac{\dfrac{3}{n + 1} + \dfrac{1}{n}}{\dfrac{2}{n + 1} + \dfrac{3}{n}}$

41. $\dfrac{\dfrac{3}{2x - 1} - \dfrac{1}{x}}{\dfrac{4}{x} + \dfrac{2}{2x - 1}}$

42. $\dfrac{\dfrac{4}{3x + 1} + \dfrac{3}{x}}{\dfrac{6}{x} - \dfrac{2}{3x + 1}}$

43. $\dfrac{\dfrac{3}{b - 4} - \dfrac{2}{b + 1}}{\dfrac{5}{b + 1} - \dfrac{1}{b - 4}}$

44. $\dfrac{\dfrac{5}{x - 5} - \dfrac{3}{x - 1}}{\dfrac{6}{x - 1} + \dfrac{2}{x - 5}}$

45. True or false? The reciprocal of the complex fraction $\dfrac{1}{1 - \dfrac{1}{x}}$ is $\dfrac{x - 1}{x}$.

46. True or false? If the denominator of a complex fraction is the reciprocal of its numerator, then the complex fraction is equal to the square of the numerator of the complex fraction.

9.4 Applying Concepts

Simplify.

47. $1 + \dfrac{1}{1 + \dfrac{1}{2}}$

48. $1 + \dfrac{1}{1 + \dfrac{1}{1 + \dfrac{1}{2}}}$

49. $1 - \dfrac{1}{1 - \dfrac{1}{x}}$

50. $1 - \dfrac{1}{1 - \dfrac{1}{y + 1}}$

51. $\dfrac{a^{-1} - b^{-1}}{a^{-2} - b^{-2}}$

52. $\dfrac{x^{-2} - y^{-2}}{x^{-2}y^{-2}}$

53. $\left(\frac{y}{4} - \frac{4}{y}\right) \div \left(\frac{4}{y} - 3 + \frac{y}{2}\right)$

54. $\left(\frac{b}{8} - \frac{8}{b}\right) \div \left(\frac{8}{b} - 5 + \frac{b}{2}\right)$

55. How would you explain to a classmate why we multiply the numerator and denominator of a complex fraction by the LCM of the denominators of the fractions in the numerator and denominator?

9.5 Equations Containing Fractions

OBJECTIVE 1 Solve equations containing fractions

In the chapter "Solving Equations and Inequalities," equations containing fractions were solved by the method of clearing denominators. Recall that to **clear denominators,** we multiply each side of an equation by the LCM of the denominators. The result is an equation that contains no fractions. In this section, we will again solve equations containing fractions by multiplying each side of the equation by the LCM of the denominators. The difference between this section and the chapter "Solving Equations and Inequalities" is that the fractions in these equations contain variables in the denominators.

Take Note

Note that we are now solving *equations,* not operating on *expressions.* We are not writing each fraction in terms of the LCM of the denominators; we are multiplying both sides of the equation by the LCM of the denominators.

Solve: $\frac{3x-1}{4x} + \frac{2}{3x} = \frac{7}{6x}$

Find the LCM of the denominators. The LCM of $4x$, $3x$, and $6x$ is $12x$.

$$\frac{3x-1}{4x} + \frac{2}{3x} = \frac{7}{6x}$$

Multiply each side of the equation by the LCM of the denominators.

$$12x\left(\frac{3x-1}{4x} + \frac{2}{3x}\right) = 12x\left(\frac{7}{6x}\right)$$

Simplify using the Distributive Property.

$$12x\left(\frac{3x-1}{4x}\right) + 12x\left(\frac{2}{3x}\right) = 12x\left(\frac{7}{6x}\right)$$

$$\frac{12x}{1}\left(\frac{3x-1}{4x}\right) + \frac{12x}{1}\left(\frac{2}{3x}\right) = \frac{12x}{1}\left(\frac{7}{6x}\right)$$

$$3(3x-1) + 4(2) = 2(7)$$

Solve for x.

$$9x - 3 + 8 = 14$$
$$9x + 5 = 14$$
$$9x = 9$$
$$x = 1$$

1 checks as a solution.

The solution is 1.

EXAMPLE 1 Solve: $\frac{4}{x} - \frac{x}{2} = \frac{7}{2}$

Solution

$$\frac{4}{x} - \frac{x}{2} = \frac{7}{2}$$
• The LCM of x and 2 is $2x$.

$$2x\left(\frac{4}{x} - \frac{x}{2}\right) = 2x\left(\frac{7}{2}\right)$$

$$\frac{2x}{1} \cdot \frac{4}{x} - \frac{2x}{1} \cdot \frac{x}{2} = \frac{2x}{1} \cdot \frac{7}{2}$$

$$8 - x^2 = 7x$$
• This is a quadratic equation.

$$0 = x^2 + 7x - 8$$

$$0 = (x + 8)(x - 1)$$

$$x + 8 = 0 \qquad x - 1 = 0$$

$$x = -8 \qquad x = 1$$

Both −8 and 1 check as solutions.

The solutions are −8 and 1.

PROBLEM 1 Solve: $x + \frac{1}{3} = \frac{4}{3x}$

Solution See page S21.

Occasionally, a value of a variable in a fractional equation makes one of the denominators zero. In this case, that value of the variable is not a solution of the equation.

Solve: $\frac{2x}{x-2} = 1 + \frac{4}{x-2}$

Find the LCM of the denominators.

The LCM is $x - 2$.

$$\frac{2x}{x-2} = 1 + \frac{4}{x-2}$$

Multiply each side of the equation by the LCM of the denominators.

$$(x-2)\frac{2x}{x-2} = (x-2)\left(1 + \frac{4}{x-2}\right)$$

Simplify using the Distributive Property.

$$(x-2)\left(\frac{2x}{x-2}\right) = (x-2) \cdot 1 + (x-2) \cdot \frac{4}{x-2}$$

Solve for x.

$$2x = x - 2 + 4$$

$$2x = x + 2$$

$$x = 2$$

When x is replaced by 2, the denominators of $\frac{2x}{x-2}$ and $\frac{4}{x-2}$ are zero. Therefore, 2 is not a solution of the equation.

The equation has no solution.

EXAMPLE 2 Solve: $\dfrac{3x}{x-4} = 5 + \dfrac{12}{x-4}$

Solution

$$\frac{3x}{x-4} = 5 + \frac{12}{x-4}$$ • The LCM is $x - 4$.

$$(x-4) \cdot \frac{3x}{x-4} = (x-4)\left(5 + \frac{12}{x-4}\right)$$

$$3x = (x-4)5 + 12$$

$$3x = 5x - 20 + 12$$

$$3x = 5x - 8$$

$$-2x = -8$$

$$x = 4$$

4 does not check as a solution.
The equation has no solution.

PROBLEM 2 Solve: $\dfrac{5x}{x+2} = 3 - \dfrac{10}{x+2}$

Solution See page S22.

OBJECTIVE 2 Solve proportions

Quantities such as 4 meters, 15 seconds, and 8 gallons are number quantities written with **units.** In these examples, the units are meters, seconds, and gallons.

A **ratio** is the quotient of two quantities that have the same unit.

The length of a living room is 16 ft, and the width is 12 ft. The ratio of the length to the width is written

$\dfrac{16\text{ ft}}{12\text{ ft}} = \dfrac{16}{12} = \dfrac{4}{3}$ A ratio is in simplest form when the two numbers do not have a common factor. Note that the units are not written.

A **rate** is the quotient of two quantities that have different units.

There are 2 lb of salt in 8 gal of water. The salt-to-water rate is

$\dfrac{2\text{ lb}}{8\text{ gal}} = \dfrac{1\text{ lb}}{4\text{ gal}}$ A rate is in simplest form when the two numbers do not have a common factor. The units are written as part of the rate.

A **proportion** is an equation that states the equality of two ratios or rates.

Examples of proportions are shown below.

$$\frac{30\text{ mi}}{4\text{ h}} = \frac{15\text{ mi}}{2\text{ h}} \qquad \frac{4}{6} = \frac{20}{30} \qquad \frac{3}{4} = \frac{x}{12}$$

Because a proportion is an equation containing fractions, the same method used to solve an equation containing fractions is used to solve a proportion. Multiply each side of the equation by the LCM of the denominators. Then solve for the variable.

Solve the proportion $\frac{4}{x} = \frac{2}{3}$.

$$\frac{4}{x} = \frac{2}{3}$$

Multiply each side of the proportion by the LCM of the denominators.

$$3x\left(\frac{4}{x}\right) = 3x\left(\frac{2}{3}\right)$$

$$12 = 2x$$

Solve the equation.

$$6 = x$$

The solution is 6.

EXAMPLE 3 Solve. **A.** $\frac{8}{x+3} = \frac{4}{x}$ **B.** $\frac{6}{x+4} = \frac{12}{5x-13}$

Solution **A.**

$$\frac{8}{x+3} = \frac{4}{x}$$

$$x(x+3)\frac{8}{x+3} = x(x+3)\frac{4}{x}$$

• **Multiply each side of the proportion by the LCM of the denominators.**

$$8x = (x+3)4$$

$$8x = 4x + 12$$

$$4x = 12$$

$$x = 3$$

• **Remember to check the solution because it is a fractional equation.**

The solution is 3.

B.

$$\frac{6}{x+4} = \frac{12}{5x-13}$$

$$(5x-13)(x+4)\frac{6}{x+4} = (5x-13)(x+4)\frac{12}{5x-13}$$

$$(5x-13)6 = (x+4)12$$

$$30x - 78 = 12x + 48$$

$$18x - 78 = 48$$

$$18x = 126$$

$$x = 7$$

The solution is 7.

PROBLEM 3 Solve. **A.** $\frac{2}{x+3} = \frac{6}{5x+5}$ **B.** $\frac{5}{2x-3} = \frac{10}{x+3}$

Solution See page S22.

OBJECTIVE 3 Applications of proportions

EXAMPLE 4 The monthly loan payment for a car is \$29.50 for each \$1000 borrowed. At this rate, find the monthly payment for a \$9000 car loan.

Take Note
It is also correct to write the proportion with the loan amounts in the numerators and the monthly payments in the denominators. The solution will be the same.

Strategy To find the monthly payment, write and solve a proportion using P to represent the monthly car payment.

Solution

$$\frac{29.50}{1000} = \frac{P}{9000}$$

• **The monthly payments are in the numerators. The loan amounts are in the denominators.**

$$9000\left(\frac{29.50}{1000}\right) = 9000\left(\frac{P}{9000}\right)$$

$$265.50 = P$$

The monthly payment is \$265.50.

PROBLEM 4 Nine ceramic tiles are required to tile a 4-square-foot area. At this rate, how many square feet can be tiled with 270 ceramic tiles?

Solution See page S22.

EXAMPLE 5 An investment of \$1200 earns \$96 each year. At the same rate, how much additional money must be invested to earn \$128 each year?

Take Note
It is also correct to write the proportion with the amounts earned in the numerators and the amounts invested in the denominators. The solution will be the same.

Strategy To find the additional amount of money that must be invested, write and solve a proportion using x to represent the additional money. Then $1200 + x$ is the total amount invested.

Solution

$$\frac{1200}{96} = \frac{1200 + x}{128}$$

• **The amounts invested are in the numerators. The amounts earned are in the denominators.**

$$\frac{25}{2} = \frac{1200 + x}{128}$$

• **Simplify $\frac{1200}{96}$.**

$$128\left(\frac{25}{2}\right) = 128\left(\frac{1200 + x}{128}\right)$$

$$1600 = 1200 + x$$

$$400 = x$$

An additional \$400 must be invested.

PROBLEM 5 Three ounces of a medication are required for a 120-pound adult. At the same rate, how many additional ounces of the medication are required for a 180-pound adult?

Solution See page S22.

OBJECTIVE 4 Problems involving similar triangles

Similar objects have the same shape but not necessarily the same size. A tennis ball is similar to a basketball. A model ship is similar to an actual ship.

Similar objects have corresponding parts; for example, the rudder on the model ship corresponds to the rudder on the actual ship. The relationship between the sizes of each of the corresponding parts can be written as a ratio, and each ratio will be the same. If the rudder on the model ship is $\frac{1}{100}$ the size of the rudder on the actual ship, then the model wheelhouse is $\frac{1}{100}$ the size of the actual wheelhouse, the width of the model is $\frac{1}{100}$ the width of the actual ship, and so on.

The two triangles ABC and DEF shown at the right are similar triangles. Side AB corresponds to DE, side BC corresponds to EF, and side AC corresponds to DF. The height CH corresponds to the height FK. The ratios of corresponding parts are equal.

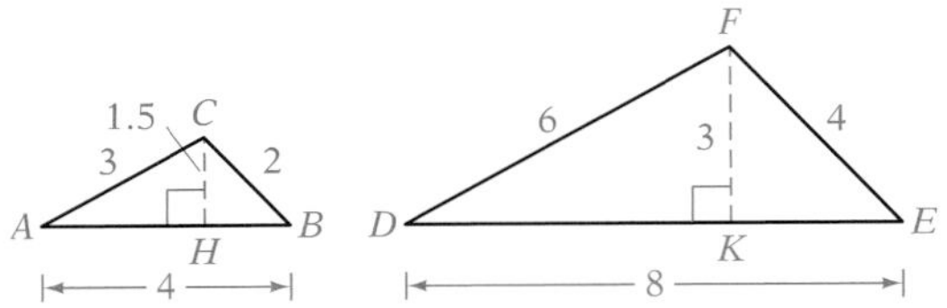

$$\frac{AB}{DE} = \frac{4}{8} = \frac{1}{2}, \quad \frac{AC}{DF} = \frac{3}{6} = \frac{1}{2}, \quad \frac{BC}{EF} = \frac{2}{4} = \frac{1}{2}, \quad \text{and} \quad \frac{CH}{FK} = \frac{1.5}{3} = \frac{1}{2}$$

Because the ratios of corresponding parts are equal, three proportions can be formed using the sides of the triangles.

$$\frac{AB}{DE} = \frac{AC}{DF}, \quad \frac{AB}{DE} = \frac{BC}{EF}, \quad \text{and} \quad \frac{AC}{DF} = \frac{BC}{EF}$$

Three proportions can also be formed by using the sides and heights of the triangles.

$$\frac{AB}{DE} = \frac{CH}{FK}, \quad \frac{AC}{DF} = \frac{CH}{FK}, \quad \text{and} \quad \frac{BC}{EF} = \frac{CH}{FK}$$

The corresponding angles in similar triangles are equal. Therefore,

$$\angle A = \angle D, \quad \angle B = \angle E, \quad \text{and} \quad \angle C = \angle F$$

Triangles ABC and DEF at the right are similar. Find the area of triangle ABC.

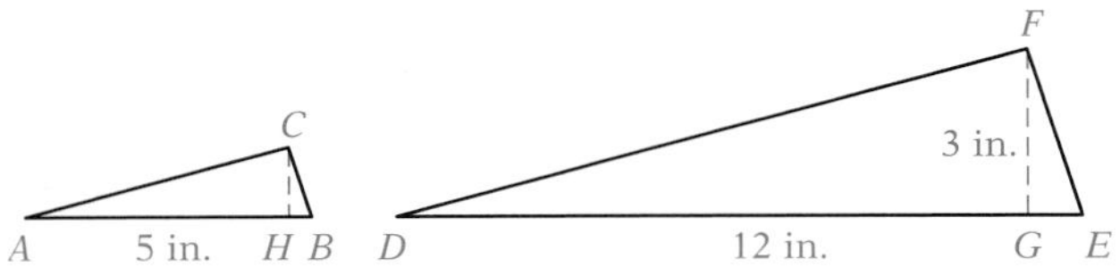

Solve a proportion to find the height of triangle ABC.

$$\frac{AB}{DE} = \frac{CH}{FG}$$

$$\frac{5}{12} = \frac{CH}{3}$$

$$12 \cdot \frac{5}{12} = 12 \cdot \frac{CH}{3}$$

$$5 = 4(CH)$$

$$1.25 = CH$$

The height is 1.25 in. The base is 5 in.

Use the formula for the area of a triangle.

$$A = \frac{1}{2}bh = \frac{1}{2}(5)(1.25) = 3.125$$

The area of triangle ABC is 3.125 in^2.

It is also true that if the three angles of one triangle are equal, respectively, to the three angles of another triangle, then the two triangles are similar.

Take Note

Vertical angles of intersecting lines, parallel lines, and angles of a triangle are discussed in the section on Geometry Problems in the chapter "Solving Equations and Inequalities: Applications."

A line segment $\overline{DE}$ is drawn parallel to the base AB in the triangle at the right. $\angle x = \angle m$ and $\angle y = \angle n$ because corresponding angles are equal. Because $\angle C = \angle C$, the three angles of triangle DEC are equal, respectively, to the three angles of triangle ABC. Triangle DEC is similar to triangle ABC.

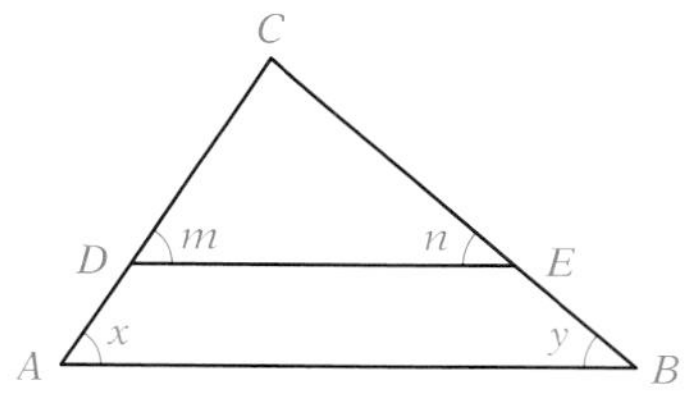

The sum of the three angles of a triangle is 180°. If two angles of one triangle are equal to two angles of another triangle, then the third angles must be equal. Thus we can say that if two angles of one triangle are equal to two angles of another triangle, then the two triangles are similar.

The line segments $\overline{AB}$ and $\overline{CD}$ intersect at point O in the figure at the right. Angles C and D are right angles. Find the length of DO.

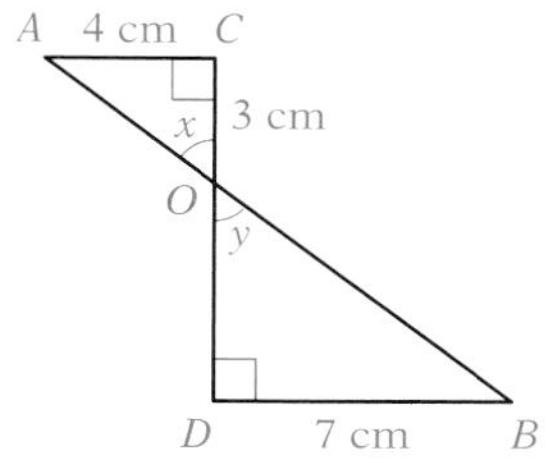

First determine whether triangle AOC is similar to triangle BOD.

Angle C = angle D because they are right angles. Angle x = angle y because they are vertical angles. Therefore, triangle AOC is similar to triangle BOD because two angles of one triangle are equal to two angles of the other triangle.

Use a proportion to find the length of the unknown side.

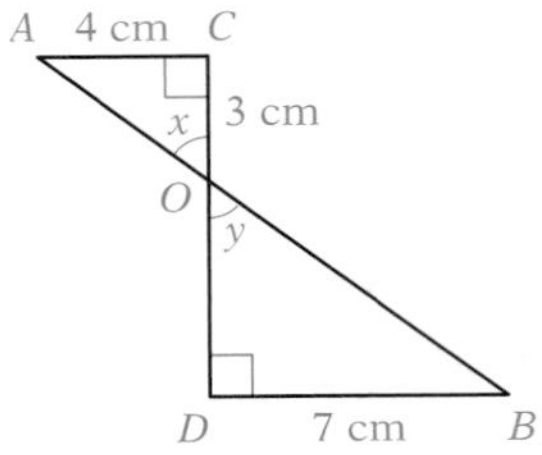

$$\frac{AC}{DB} = \frac{CO}{DO}$$
$$\frac{4}{7} = \frac{3}{DO}$$
$$7(DO)\frac{4}{7} = 7(DO)\frac{3}{DO}$$
$$4(DO) = 7(3)$$
$$4(DO) = 21$$
$$DO = 5.25$$

The length of DO is 5.25 cm.

EXAMPLE 6 In the figure at the right, $\overline{AB}$ is parallel to $\overline{DC}$, and angles B and D are right angles. $AB = 12$ m, $CD = 4$ m, and $AC = 18$ m. Find the length of CO.

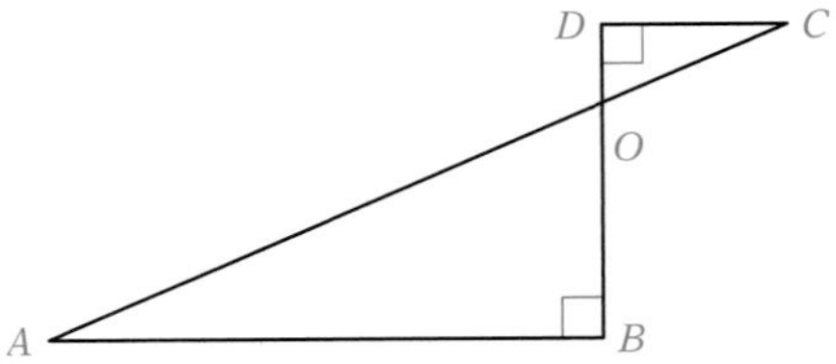

Strategy Triangle AOB is similar to triangle COD. Solve a proportion to find the length of CO. Let x represent the length of CO. Then $18 - x$ represents the length of AO.

Solution

$$\frac{CD}{AB} = \frac{CO}{AO}$$
$$\frac{4}{12} = \frac{x}{18 - x}$$
$$12(18 - x) \cdot \frac{4}{12} = 12(18 - x) \cdot \frac{x}{18 - x}$$
$$(18 - x)4 = 12x$$
$$72 - 4x = 12x$$
$$72 = 16x$$
$$4.5 = x$$

The length of CO is 4.5 m.

PROBLEM 6 In the figure at the right, $\overline{AB}$ is parallel to $\overline{DC}$, and angles A and D are right angles. $AB = 10$ cm, $CD = 4$ cm, and $DO = 3$ cm. Find the area of triangle AOB.

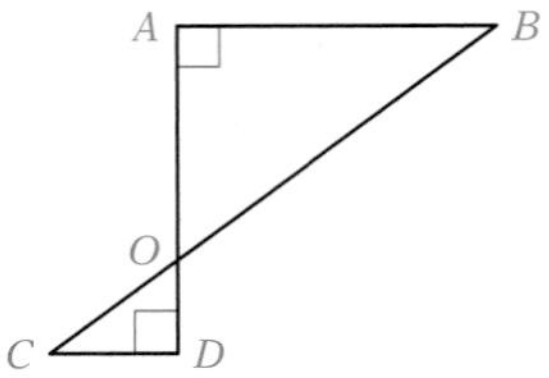

Solution See page S22.

9.5 Concept Review

Determine whether the statement is always true, sometimes true, or never true.

1. The process of clearing denominators in an equation containing fractions is an application of the Multiplication Property of Equations.

2. If the denominator of a fraction is $x + 3$, then $x \neq 3$ for that fraction.

3. The first step in solving an equation containing fractions is to find the LCM of the denominators.

4. The solutions to an equation containing rational expressions must be checked because a solution might make one of the denominators equal to zero.

5. Suppose, after the clearing of denominators, a fractional equation results in a quadratic equation. Then the equation has two solutions.

6. Both sides of an equation containing fractions can be multiplied by the same number without changing the solution of the equation.

7. To solve a proportion, multiply each side of the proportion by the LCM of the denominators.

9.5 Exercises

1 Solve equations containing fractions

1. In solving an equation containing fractions, why do we first multiply each side of the equation by the LCM of the denominators?

2. After solving an equation containing fractions, why must we check the solution?

For Exercises 3 to 6, use the equation $\frac{7}{x} = \frac{3}{x - 4}$.

3. The first step in solving the equation is to clear denominators by multiplying each side of the equation by the LCM of the denominators ___?___ and ___?___. The LCM is ___?___.

4. a. When you multiply the left side of the equation by the LCM $x(x - 4)$, the left side simplifies to ___?___.
   b. When you multiply the right side of the equation by the LCM $x(x - 4)$, the right side simplifies to ___?___.

5. Use your answers to Exercise 2 to write the equation that results from clearing the denominators: ___?___ = ___?___. The solution of this equation is ___?___.

6. The solution of a rational equation must be checked in the original equation. To check the solution you found in Exercise 3 in the original equation, substitute ___?___ for x in the original equation: $\frac{7}{7} = \frac{3}{7-4}$ simplifies to ___?___ = ___?___. The solution checks.

When a proposed solution of a rational equation does not check in the original equation, it is because it results in an expression involving division by zero. For each equation, state the values of x that would result in division by zero when substituted into the original equation.

7. $\frac{1}{x+5} = \frac{x}{x-3} + \frac{2}{x^2+2x-15}$

8. $\frac{3}{x-9} = \frac{1}{x^2-9x} + 2$

9. $\frac{6x}{x+1} - \frac{x}{x-2} = 4$

Solve.

10. $2 + \frac{5}{x} = 7$

11. $3 + \frac{8}{n} = 5$

12. $1 - \frac{9}{x} = 4$

13. $3 - \frac{12}{x} = 7$

14. $\frac{2}{y} + 5 = 9$

15. $\frac{6}{x} + 3 = 11$

16. $\frac{4x}{x-4} + 5 = \frac{5x}{x-4}$

17. $\frac{2x}{x+2} - 5 = \frac{7x}{x+2}$

18. $2 + \frac{3}{a-3} = \frac{a}{a-3}$

19. $\frac{x}{x+4} = 3 - \frac{4}{x+4}$

20. $\frac{x}{x-1} = \frac{8}{x+2}$

21. $\frac{x}{x+12} = \frac{1}{x+5}$

22. $\frac{2x}{x+4} = \frac{3}{x-1}$

23. $\frac{5}{3n-8} = \frac{n}{n+2}$

24. $x + \frac{6}{x-2} = \frac{3x}{x-2}$

25. $x - \frac{6}{x-3} = \frac{2x}{x-3}$

26. $\frac{x}{x+2} + \frac{2}{x-2} = \frac{x+6}{x^2-4}$

27. $\frac{x}{x+4} = \frac{11}{x^2-16} + 2$

28. $\frac{8}{y} = \frac{2}{y-2} + 1$

29. $\frac{8}{r} + \frac{3}{r-1} = 3$

2 Solve proportions

30. The quotient of two quantities that have the same unit is called a ___?___. The quotient of two quantities that have different units is called a ___?___.

31. An equation that states the equality of two ratios or rates is called a $\underline{\quad ? \quad}$.

Solve.

32. $\dfrac{x}{12} = \dfrac{3}{4}$

33. $\dfrac{6}{x} = \dfrac{2}{3}$

34. $\dfrac{4}{9} = \dfrac{x}{27}$

35. $\dfrac{16}{9} = \dfrac{64}{x}$

36. $\dfrac{x+3}{12} = \dfrac{5}{6}$

37. $\dfrac{3}{5} = \dfrac{x-4}{10}$

38. $\dfrac{18}{x+4} = \dfrac{9}{5}$

39. $\dfrac{2}{11} = \dfrac{20}{x-3}$

40. $\dfrac{2}{x} = \dfrac{4}{x+1}$

41. $\dfrac{16}{x-2} = \dfrac{8}{x}$

42. $\dfrac{x+3}{4} = \dfrac{x}{8}$

43. $\dfrac{x-6}{3} = \dfrac{x}{5}$

44. $\dfrac{2}{x-1} = \dfrac{6}{2x+1}$

45. $\dfrac{9}{x+2} = \dfrac{3}{x-2}$

46. $\dfrac{2x}{7} = \dfrac{x-2}{14}$

47. True or false? If $\dfrac{a}{b} = \dfrac{c}{d}$, then $\dfrac{d}{b} = \dfrac{c}{a}$.

48. True or false? If $\dfrac{a}{b} = \dfrac{c}{d}$, then $\dfrac{b}{a} = \dfrac{d}{c}$.

3 Applications of proportions

49. The scale on a map shows that a distance of 3 cm on the map represents an actual distance of 10 mi. This rate can be expressed as the quotient $\dfrac{\underline{\quad ? \quad}}{\underline{\quad ? \quad}}$ or as the quotient $\dfrac{\underline{\quad ? \quad}}{\underline{\quad ? \quad}}$.

50. Let x be the distance (in miles) represented by 12 cm on the map described in Exercise 49. Use a proportion to find x.

$\dfrac{10}{3} = \dfrac{\underline{\quad ? \quad}}{\underline{\quad ? \quad}}$ • **Write the proportion so that each side is the ratio of miles to centimeters.**

$(12)\left(\dfrac{10}{3}\right) = (12)\left(\dfrac{x}{12}\right)$ • **Multiply each side of the proportion by $\underline{\quad ? \quad}$, the LCM of the denominators.**

$\underline{\quad ? \quad} = x$ • **Simplify.**

12 cm on the map represents $\underline{\quad ? \quad}$ mi.

51. Could the proportion used in Exercise 50 have been written so that each side was the ratio of centimeters to miles, instead of miles to centimeters?

52. On the map described in Exercise 49, would a distance of 8 cm represent an actual distance that is greater than 30 mi or less than 30 mi?

53. **Elections** An exit poll showed that 4 out of every 7 voters cast a ballot in favor of an amendment to a city charter. At this rate, how many people voted in favor of the amendment if 35,000 people voted?

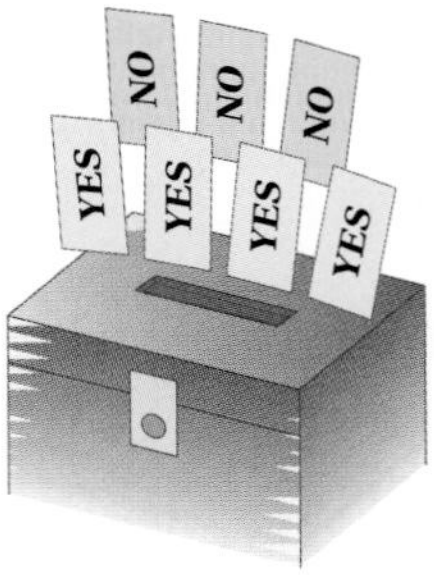

54. **Business** A quality control inspector found 3 defective transistors in a shipment of 500 transistors. At this rate, how many transistors would be defective in a shipment of 2000 transistors?

55. **Construction** An air conditioning specialist recommends 2 air vents for every 300 ft^2 of floor space. At this rate, how many air vents are required for an office building of 21,000 ft^2?

56. **Television** In a city of 25,000 homes, a survey was taken to determine the number with cable television. Of the 300 homes surveyed, 210 had cable television. Estimate the number of homes in the city that have cable television.

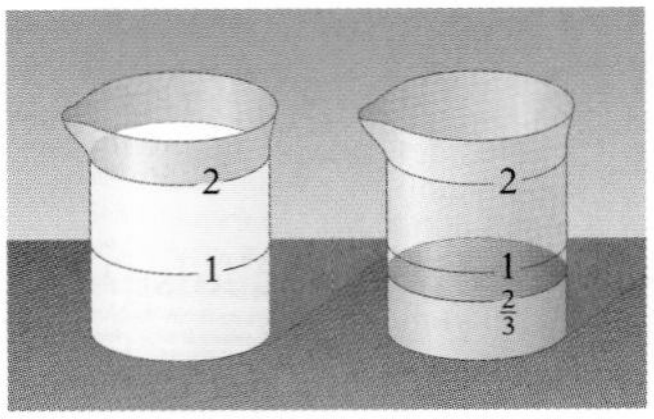

57. **Cooking** A simple syrup is made by dissolving 2 c of sugar in $\frac{2}{3}$ c of boiling water. At this rate, how many cups of sugar are required for 2 c of boiling water?

58. **Energy** The lighting for a billboard is provided by solar energy. If 3 energy panels generate 10 watts of power, how many panels are needed to provide 600 watts of power?

59. **Conservation** As part of a conservation effort for a lake, 40 fish were caught, tagged, and then released. Later, 80 fish were caught from the lake. Four of these 80 fish were found to have tags. Estimate the number of fish in the lake.

60. **Business** A company will accept a shipment of 10,000 computer disks if there are 2 or fewer defects in a sample of 100 randomly chosen disks. Assume that there are 300 defective disks in the shipment and that the rate of defective disks in the sample is the same as the rate in the shipment. Will the shipment be accepted?

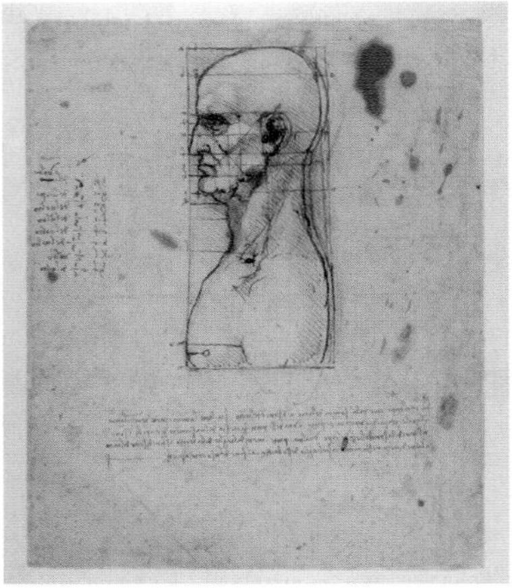

61. **Business** A company will accept a shipment of 20,000 precision bearings if there are 3 or fewer defects in a sample of 100 randomly chosen bearings. Assume that there are 400 defective bearings in the shipment and that the rate of defective bearings in the sample is the same as the rate in the shipment. Will the shipment be accepted?

62. **Art** Leonardo da Vinci measured various distances on the human body in order to make accurate drawings. He determined that in general, the ratio of the kneeling height of a person to his or her standing height is $\frac{3}{4}$. Using this ratio, determine the standing height of a person who has a kneeling height of 48 in.

63. **Art** In one of Leonardo da Vinci's notebooks, he wrote that ". . . from the top to the bottom of the chin is the sixth part of a face, and it is the fifty-fourth part of the man." Suppose the distance from the top to the bottom of a person's chin is 1.25 in. Using da Vinci's measurements, find the height of the person.

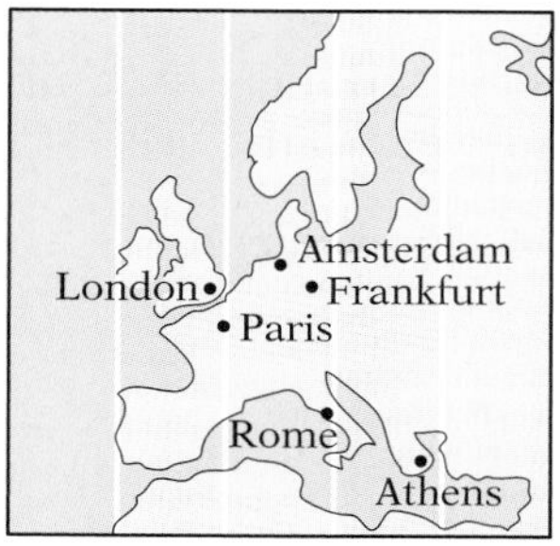

64. **Cartography** On a map, two cities are $2\frac{5}{8}$ in. apart. If $\frac{3}{8}$ in. on the map represents 25 mi, find the number of miles between the two cities.

65. **Cartography** On a map, two cities are $5\frac{5}{8}$ in. apart. If $\frac{3}{4}$ in. on the map represents 100 mi, find the number of miles between the two cities.

66. **Rocketry** The engine of a small rocket burns 170,000 lb of fuel in 1 min. At this rate, how many pounds of fuel does the rocket burn in 45 s?

67. **Construction** To conserve energy and still allow for as much natural lighting as possible, an architect suggests that the ratio of the area of a window to the area of the total wall surface be 5 to 12. Using this ratio, determine the recommended area of a window to be installed in a wall that measures 8 ft by 12 ft.

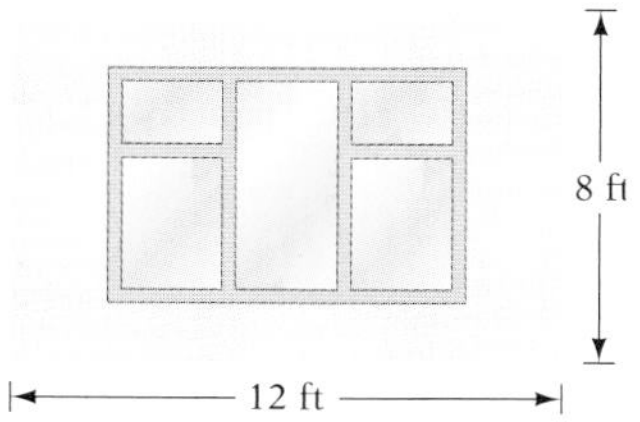

68. **Paint Mixtures** A green paint is created by mixing 3 parts of yellow with every 5 parts of blue. How many gallons of yellow paint are needed to make 60 gal of this green paint?

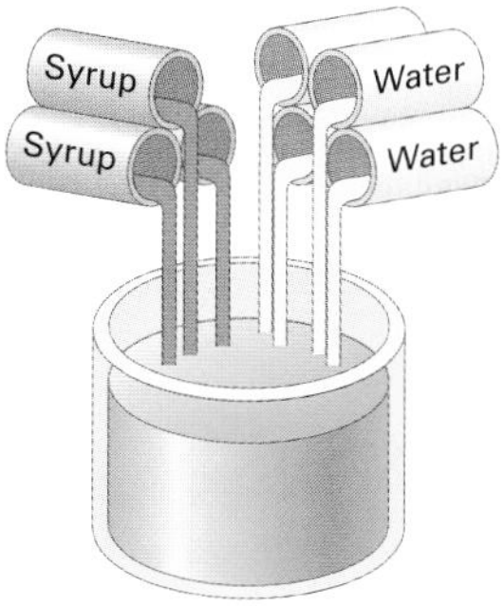

69. **Food Industry** A soft drink is made by mixing 4 parts of carbonated water with every 3 parts of syrup. How many milliliters of carbonated water are in 280 ml of soft drink?

70. **Redecorating** A painter estimates that 5 gal of paint will cover 1200 ft^2 of wall surface. How many additional gallons are required to cover 1680 ft^2?

71. **Agriculture** A 50-acre field yields 1100 bushels of wheat annually. How many additional acres must be planted so that the annual yield will be 1320 bushels?

72. **Taxes** The sales tax on a car that sold for \$12,000 is \$780. At the same rate, how much higher is the sales tax on a car that sells for \$13,500?

73. **Catering** A caterer estimates that 5 gal of coffee will serve 50 people. How much additional coffee is necessary to serve 70 people?

4 Problems involving similar triangles

For Exercises 74 and 75, use the pair of similar triangles shown at the right. Triangle PQR is similar to triangle XYZ.

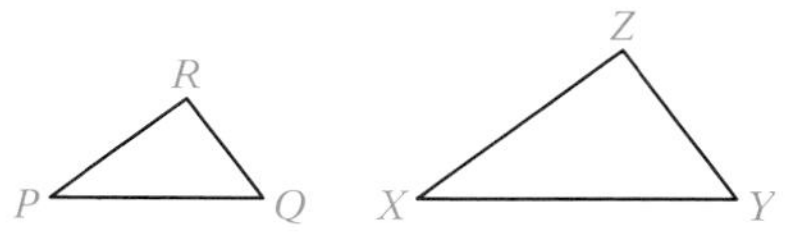

74. **a.** The corresponding part for side RP is ___?___.
b. The corresponding part for side YX is ___?___.
c. The corresponding part for $\angle X$ is ___?___.

75. **a.** Complete this proportion: $\dfrac{QR}{?} = \dfrac{PR}{XZ}$.

b. Complete this equality: $\angle Z = \underline{\quad ? \quad}$.

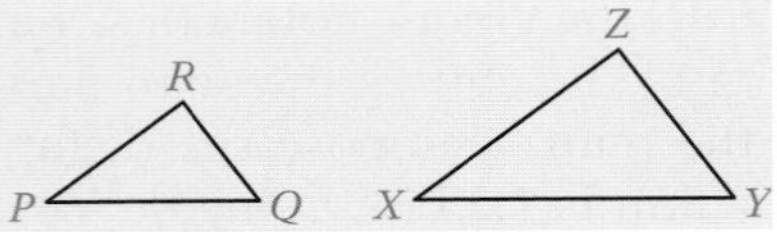

Solve. Triangles *ABC* and *DEF* in Exercises 76 to 83 are similar. Round answers to the nearest tenth.

76. Find side *AC*.

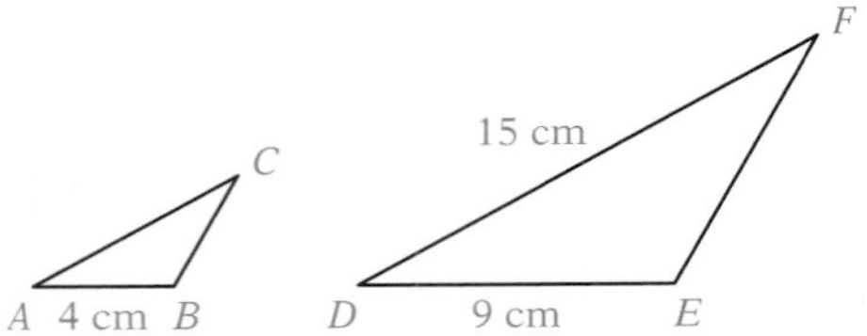

77. Find side *DE*.

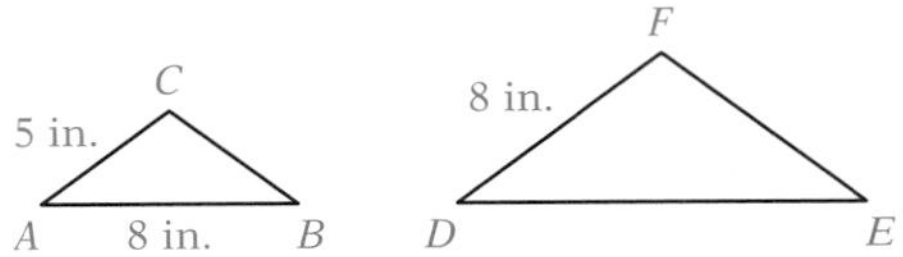

78. Find the height of triangle *ABC*.

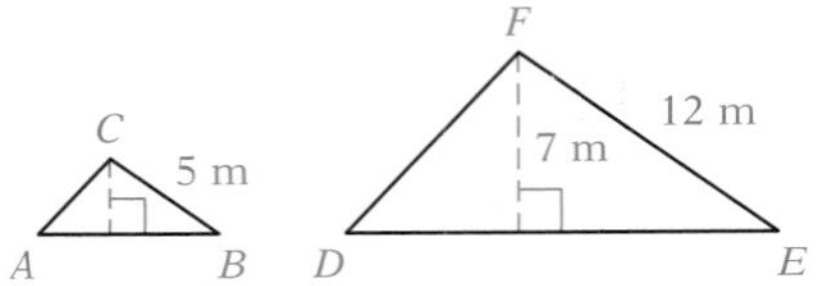

79. Find the height of triangle *DEF*.

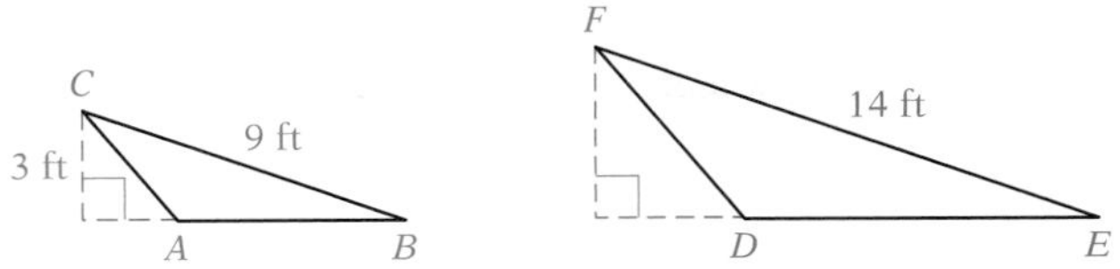

80. Find the perimeter of triangle *DEF*.

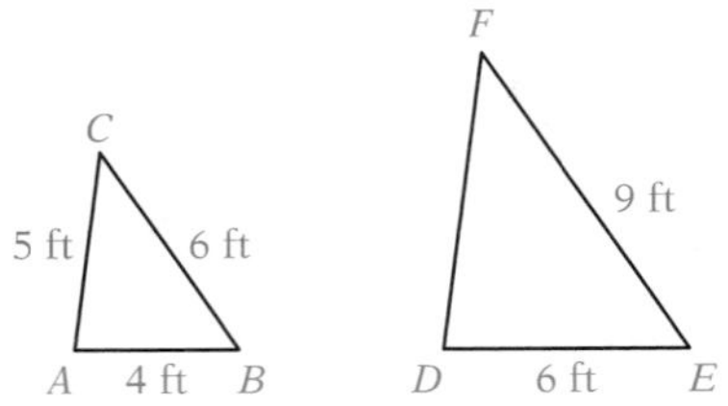

81. Find the perimeter of triangle *ABC*.

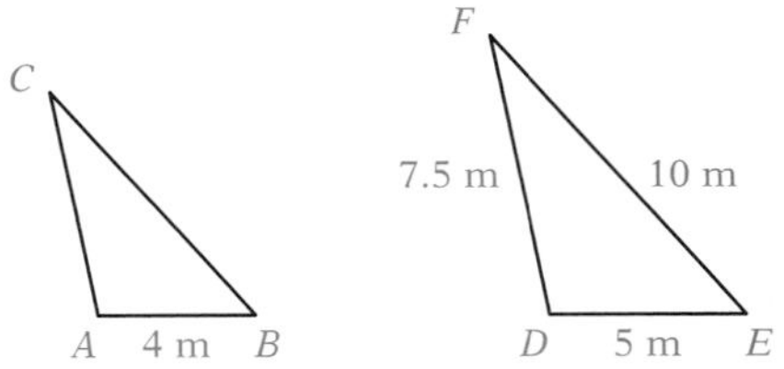

82. Find the area of triangle *ABC*.

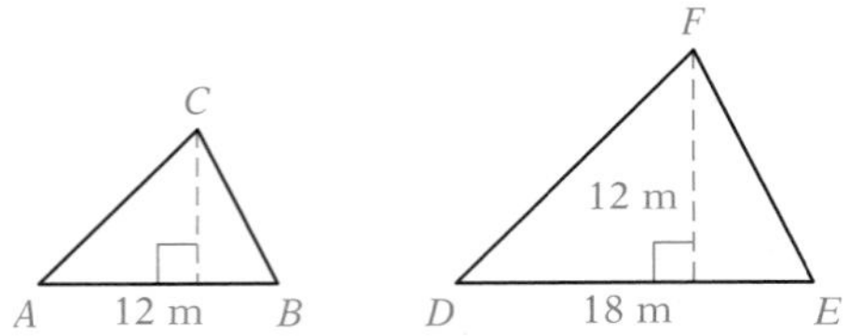

83. Find the area of triangle *ABC*.

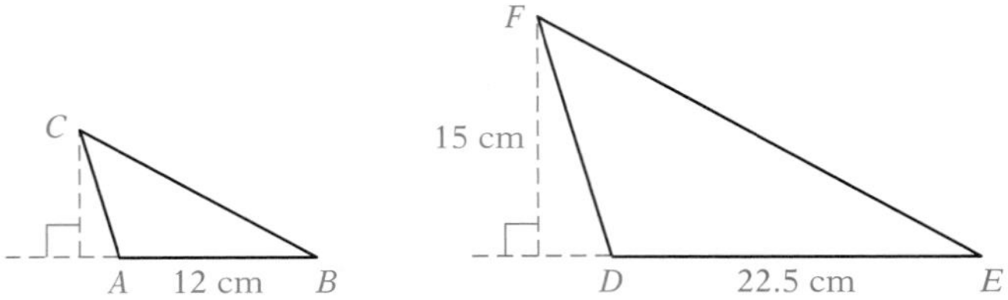

84. True or false? If the ratio of the corresponding sides of two similar triangles is $\frac{2}{3}$, the ratio of the perimeters of the two triangles is also $\frac{2}{3}$.

85. True or false? If the ratio of the corresponding sides of two similar triangles is $\frac{5}{4}$, the ratio of the areas of the two triangles is also $\frac{5}{4}$.

86. Look at the diagram in Exercise 88, in which *BD* is parallel to *AE*.
a. Triangle *CBD* is similar to triangle $\underline{\quad ? \quad}$.
b. Complete this proportion: $\dfrac{BD}{AE} = \dfrac{CD}{\underline{\quad ? \quad}}$.

87. Look at the diagram in Exercise 92.
a. Triangle *MNO* is similar to triangle $\underline{\quad ? \quad}$.
b. Complete this proportion: $\dfrac{OP}{\underline{\quad ? \quad}} = \dfrac{PQ}{NM}$.

88. Given $\overline{BD} \parallel \overline{AE}$, *BD* measures 5 cm, *AE* measures 8 cm, and *AC* measures 10 cm, find the length of *BC*.

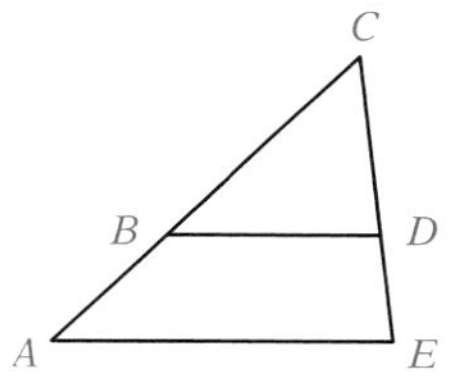

89. Given $\overline{AC} \parallel \overline{DE}$, *BD* measures 8 m, *AD* measures 12 m, and *BE* measures 6 m, find the length of *BC*.

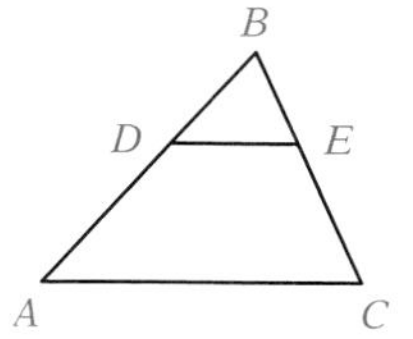

90. Given $\overline{DE} \parallel \overline{AC}$, *DE* measures 6 in., *AC* measures 10 in., and *AB* measures 15 in., find the length of *DA*.

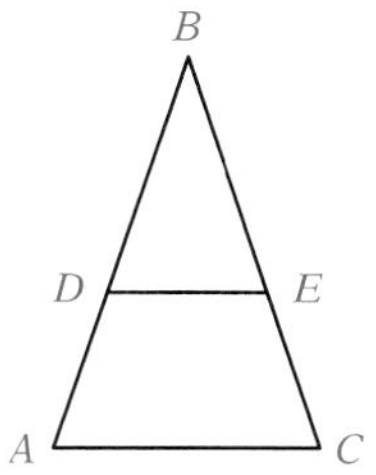

91. Given $\overline{MP}$ and $\overline{NQ}$ intersect at *O*, *NO* measures 25 ft, *MO* measures 20 ft, and *PO* measures 8 ft, find the length of *QO*.

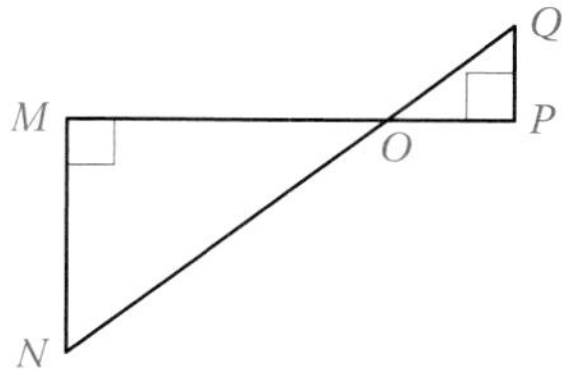

92. Given $\overline{MP}$ and $\overline{NQ}$ intersect at *O*, *NO* measures 24 cm, *MN* measures 10 cm, *MP* measures 39 cm, and *QO* measures 12 cm, find the length of *OP*.

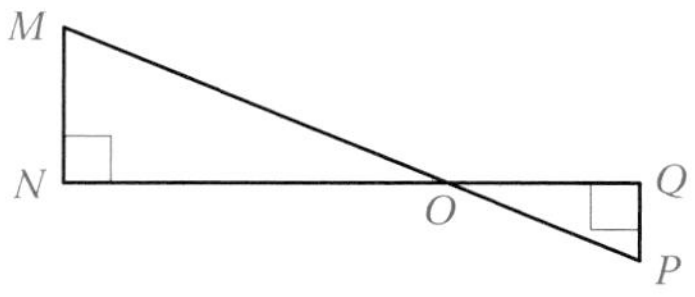

93. Given $\overline{MQ}$ and $\overline{NP}$ intersect at *O*, *NO* measures 12 m, *MN* measures 9 m, *PQ* measures 3 m, and *MQ* measures 20 m, find the perimeter of triangle *OPQ*.

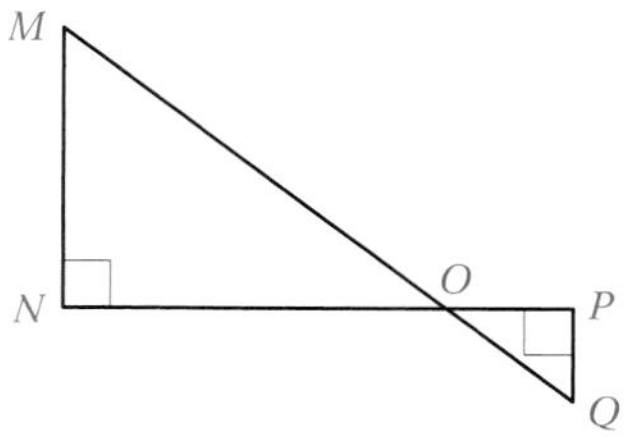

94. Similar triangles can be used as an indirect way to measure inaccessible distances. The diagram at the right represents a river of width DC. The triangles AOB and DOC are similar. The distances AB, BO, and OC can be measured. Find the width of the river.

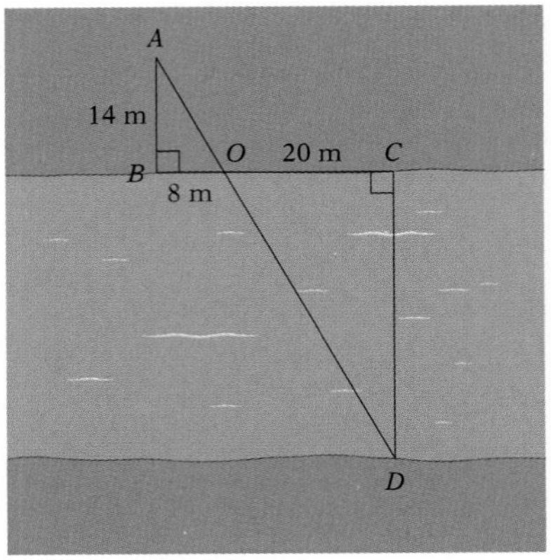

95. The sun's rays cast a shadow as shown in the diagram at the right. Find the height of the flagpole. Write the answer in terms of feet.

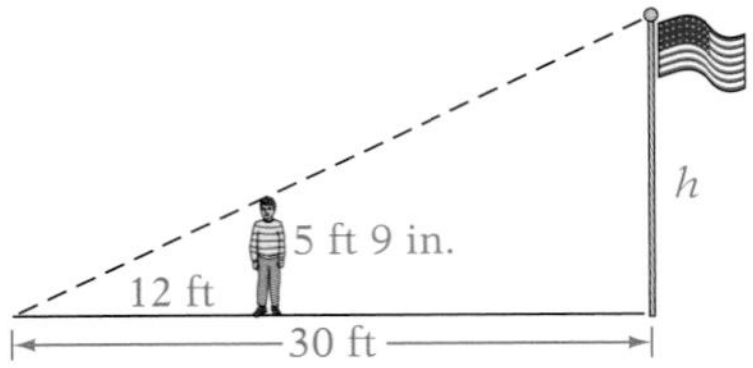

9.5 Applying Concepts

Solve.

96. $\frac{2}{3}(x+2) - \frac{x+1}{6} = \frac{1}{2}$

97. $\frac{3}{4}a = \frac{1}{2}(3-a) + \frac{a-2}{4}$

98. $\frac{x}{2x^2 - x - 1} = \frac{3}{x^2 - 1} + \frac{3}{2x+1}$

99. $\frac{x+1}{x^2+x-2} = \frac{x+2}{x^2-1} + \frac{3}{x+2}$

100. **Number Problem** The sum of a number and its reciprocal is $\frac{26}{5}$. Find the number.

101. **Number Problem** The sum of the multiplicative inverses of two consecutive integers is $-\frac{7}{12}$. Find the integers.

102. **Number Problem** The denominator of a fraction is 2 more than the numerator. If both the numerator and denominator of the fraction are increased by 3, the new fraction is $\frac{4}{5}$. Find the original fraction.

103. **Lotteries** Three people put their money together to buy lottery tickets. The first person put in \$25, the second person put in \$30, and the third person put in \$35. One of their tickets was a winning ticket. If they won \$4.5 million, what was the first person's share of the winnings?

104. Sports A basketball player has made 5 out of every 6 foul shots attempted. If 42 foul shots were missed in the player's career, how many foul shots were made in the player's career?

105. Photography The "sitting fee" for school pictures is \$4. If 10 photos cost \$10, including the sitting fee, what would 24 photos cost, including the sitting fee?

106. Fundraising No one belongs to both the Math Club and the Photography Club, but the two clubs join to hold a car wash. Ten members of the Math Club and 6 members of the Photography Club participate. The profits from the car wash are \$120. If each club's profits are proportional to the number of members participating, what share of the profits does the Math Club receive?

107. History Eratosthenes, the fifth librarian of Alexandria (230 B.C.), was familiar with certain astronomical data that enabled him to calculate the circumference of Earth by using a proportion. He knew that on a midsummer day, the sun was directly overhead at Syene, as shown in the diagram. At the same time, at Alexandria, the sun was at a 7.5° angle from the zenith. The distance from Syene to Alexandria was 5000 stadia, or about 520 mi. Eratosthenes reasoned that the ratio of the 7.5° angle to one revolution was equal to the ratio of the arc length of 520 mi to the circumference of Earth. From this, he wrote and solved a proportion.

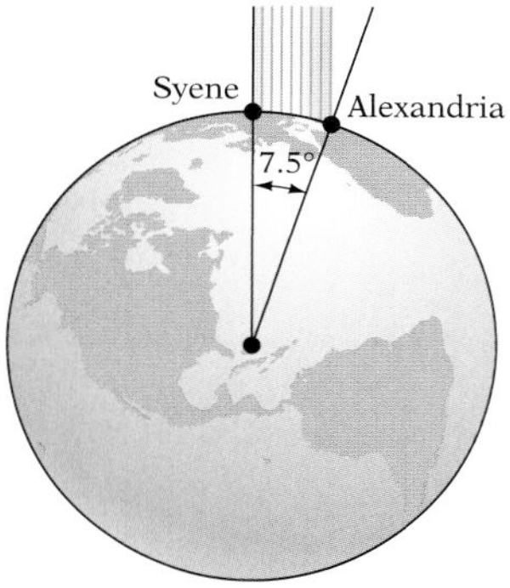

a. What did Eratosthenes calculate to be the circumference of Earth?

b. Find the difference between his calculation and the accepted value of 24,800 mi.

108. Population The table below shows the projected population of people age 65 and older and the projected total population of the United States each decade from 2010 to 2050.

Year	*Population 65+, in thousands*	*Total Population, in thousands*
2010	40,243	308,936
2020	54,632	335,805
2030	71,453	363,584
2040	80,049	391,948
2050	86,705	419,854

a. What is the percent increase, for each 10-year period, in the population of people age 65 and older? Round to the nearest tenth of a percent.

b. What is the percent increase, for each 10-year period, in the total population of the United States?

c. Are there any 10-year periods during which the total population of the United States is increasing more rapidly (at a faster rate) than the population of people age 65 and older?

d. Many people, as they age, need more medical care. The population of people in the 20-to-44-year age group who provide that care is given below. For each decade, find the ratio of the number of potential caregivers to the number of people in the 65 and older age group. Round to the nearest whole number.

Year	2010	2020	2030	2040	2050
Population 20–44, in millions	104,444	108,632	114,747	121,659	130,897

e. Write a sentence that explains the meaning of the ratios you found in part d. Are the ratios increasing or decreasing?

f. Write a few sentences that summarize the calculations in parts a through d.

9.6 Literal Equations

OBJECTIVE 1 Solve a literal equation for one of the variables

A **literal equation** is an equation that contains more than one variable. Examples of literal equations are shown at the right.

$$2x + 3y = 6$$
$$4w - 2x + z = 0$$

Formulas are used to express a relationship among physical quantities. A **formula** is a literal equation that states rules about measurements. Examples of formulas are shown below.

$$\frac{1}{R_1} + \frac{1}{R_2} = \frac{1}{R} \quad \text{(Physics)}$$
$$s = a + (n - 1)d \quad \text{(Mathematics)}$$
$$A = P + Prt \quad \text{(Business)}$$

The Addition and Multiplication Properties can be used to solve a literal equation for one of the variables. The goal is to rewrite the equation so that the letter being solved for is alone on one side of the equation and all numbers and other variables are on the other side.

Solve $A = P(1 + i)$ for i.

The goal is to rewrite the equation so that i is on one side of the equation and all other variables are on the other side.

$$A = P(1 + i)$$

Use the Distributive Property to remove parentheses.

$$A = P + Pi$$

Subtract P from each side of the equation.

$$A - P = P - P + Pi$$
$$A - P = Pi$$

Divide each side of the equation by P.

$$\frac{A - P}{P} = \frac{Pi}{P}$$
$$\frac{A - P}{P} = i$$

EXAMPLE 1 **A.** Solve $I = \dfrac{E}{R + r}$ for R. **B.** Solve $L = a(1 + ct)$ for c.

Solution **A.**

$$I = \frac{E}{R + r}$$
$$(R + r)I = (R + r)\frac{E}{R + r}$$
$$RI + rI = E$$
$$RI + rI - rI = E - rI$$
$$RI = E - rI$$
$$\frac{RI}{I} = \frac{E - rI}{I}$$
$$R = \frac{E - rI}{I}$$

B.

$$L = a(1 + ct)$$
$$L = a + act$$
$$L - a = a - a + act$$
$$L - a = act$$
$$\frac{L - a}{at} = \frac{act}{at}$$
$$\frac{L - a}{at} = c$$

PROBLEM 1 **A.** Solve $s = \dfrac{A + L}{2}$ for L. **B.** Solve $S = a + (n - 1)d$ for n.

Solution See page S22.

EXAMPLE 2 Solve $S = C - rC$ for C.

Solution

$$S = C - rC$$
$$S = C(1 - r)$$
• **Factor C from $C - rC$.**
$$\frac{S}{1 - r} = \frac{C(1 - r)}{1 - r}$$
• **Divide each side of the equation by $1 - r$.**
$$\frac{S}{1 - r} = C$$

PROBLEM 2 Solve $S = rS + C$ for S.

Solution See page S23.

9.6 Concept Review

Determine whether the statement is always true, sometimes true, or never true.

1. An equation that contains more than one variable is a literal equation.

2. The linear equation $y = 4x - 5$ is not a literal equation.

3. Literal equations are solved using the same properties of equations that are used to solve equations in one variable.

4. In solving a literal equation, the goal is to get the variable being solved for alone on one side of the equation and all numbers and other variables on the other side of the equation.

5. In solving $L = a(1 + ct)$ for c, you need to use the Distributive Property. In solving $S = C - rC$ for C, you need to factor.

6. We can divide both sides of a literal equation by the same nonzero expression.

9.6 Exercises

1 Solve a literal equation for one of the variables

Solve the formula for the variable given.

1. $A = \frac{1}{2}bh; h$ (Geometry)

2. $P = a + b + c; b$ (Geometry)

3. $d = rt; t$ (Physics)

4. $E = IR; R$ (Physics)

5. $PV = nRT; T$ (Chemistry)

6. $A = bh; h$ (Geometry)

7. $P = 2L + 2W; L$ (Geometry)

8. $\mathrm{F} = \frac{9}{5}\mathrm{C} + 32; \mathrm{C}$ (Temperature conversion)

9. $A = \frac{1}{2}h(b_1 + b_2); b_1$ (Geometry)

10. $\mathrm{C} = \frac{5}{9}(\mathrm{F} - 32); \mathrm{F}$ (Temperature conversion)

11. $V = \frac{1}{3}Ah; h$ (Geometry)

12. $P = R - C; C$ (Business)

13. $R = \frac{C - S}{t}; S$ (Business)

14. $P = \frac{R - C}{n}; R$ (Business)

15. $A = P + Prt; P$ (Business)

16. $T = fm - gm; m$ (Engineering)

17. $A = Sw + w; w$ (Physics)

18. $a = S - Sr; S$ (Mathematics)

19. When asked to solve $A = P(1 + i)$ for i, one student answered $i = \frac{A}{P} - 1$ and another student answered $i = \frac{A - P}{P}$. Are the two answers equivalent?

20. When asked to solve $A = P(1 + i)$ for i, one student answered $i = -\frac{P - A}{P}$ and another student answered $i = \frac{A - P}{P}$. Are the two answers equivalent?

9.6 Applying Concepts

Geometry The surface area of a right circular cylinder is given by the formula $S = 2\pi rh + 2\pi r^2$, where r is the radius of the base and h is the height of the cylinder.

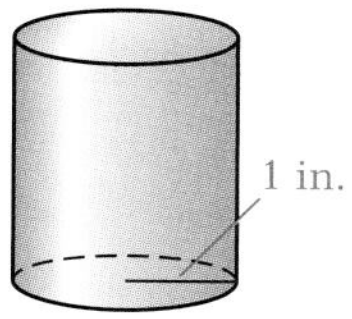

$S = 12\pi$ in^2

21. **a.** Solve the formula $S = 2\pi rh + 2\pi r^2$ for h.
  b. Use your answer to part a to find the height of a right circular cylinder when the surface area is 12π in^2 and the radius is 1 in.
  c. Use your answer to part a to find the height of a right circular cylinder when the surface area is 24π in^2 and the radius is 2 in.

Business Break-even analysis is a method used to determine the sales volume required for a company to break even, or experience neither a profit nor a loss, on the sale of its product. The break-even point represents the number of units that must be made and sold for income from sales to equal the cost of producing the product. The break-even point can be calculated using the formula $B = \frac{F}{S - V}$, where F is the fixed costs, S is the selling price per unit, and V is the variable costs per unit.

22. **a.** Solve the formula $B = \frac{F}{S - V}$ for S.
  b. Use your answer to part a to find the selling price per desk required for a company to break even. The fixed costs are \$40,000, the variable costs per desk are \$160, and the company plans to make and sell 200 desks.
  c. Use your answer to part a to find the selling price per camera required for a company to break even. The fixed costs are \$30,000, the variable costs per camera are \$100, and the company plans to make and sell 600 cameras.

Business When markup is based on selling price, the selling price of a product is given by the formula $S = C + rC$, where C is the cost of the product and r is the markup rate.

23. **a.** Solve the formula $S = C + rC$ for r.
  b. Use your answer to part a to find the markup rate on a tennis racket when the cost is \$108 and the selling price is \$180.
  c. Use your answer to part a to find the markup rate on a car radio when the cost is \$120 and the selling price is \$172.

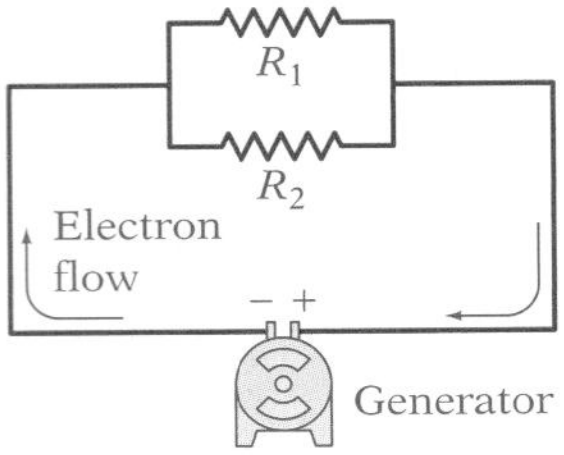

Electricity Resistors are used to control the flow of current. The total resistance of two resistors in a circuit can be given by the formula $R = \dfrac{1}{\dfrac{1}{R_1} + \dfrac{1}{R_2}}$, where R_1 and R_2 are the resistances of the two resistors in the circuit. Resistance is measured in ohms.

24. **a.** Solve the formula $R = \dfrac{1}{\dfrac{1}{R_1} + \dfrac{1}{R_2}}$ for R_1.

b. Use your answer to part a to find the resistance in R_1 if the resistance in R_2 is 30 ohms and the total resistance is 12 ohms.

c. Use your answer to part a to find the resistance in R_1 if the resistance in R_2 is 15 ohms and the total resistance is 6 ohms.

9.7 Application Problems

OBJECTIVE 1 Work problems

If a painter can paint a room in 4 h, then in 1 h the painter can paint $\frac{1}{4}$ of the room. The painter's rate of work is $\frac{1}{4}$ of the room each hour. The **rate of work** is that part of a task that is completed in 1 unit of time.

A pipe can fill a tank in 30 min. This pipe can fill $\frac{1}{30}$ of the tank in 1 min. The rate of work is $\frac{1}{30}$ of the tank each minute. If a second pipe can fill the tank in x min, the rate of work for the second pipe is $\frac{1}{x}$ of the tank each minute.

In solving a work problem, the goal is to determine the time it takes to complete a task. The basic equation that is used to solve work problems is

Rate of work · Time worked = Part of task completed

For example, if a faucet can fill a sink in 6 min, then in 5 min the faucet will fill $\frac{1}{6} \cdot 5 = \frac{5}{6}$ of the sink. In 5 min, the faucet completes $\frac{5}{6}$ of the task.

Solve: A painter can paint a ceiling in 60 min. The painter's apprentice can paint the same ceiling in 90 min. How long will it take them to paint the ceiling if they work together?

STRATEGY for solving a work problem

- For each person or machine, write a numerical or variable expression for the rate of work, the time worked, and the part of the task completed. The results can be recorded in a table.

Unknown time to paint the ceiling working together: t

Take Note

Use the information given in the problem to fill in the rate and time columns of the table. Fill in the part of task completed column by multiplying the two expressions you wrote in each row.

	Rate of work	·	Time worked	=	Part of task completed
Painter	$\frac{1}{60}$	·	t	=	$\frac{t}{60}$
Apprentice	$\frac{1}{90}$	·	t	=	$\frac{t}{90}$

▶ Determine how the parts of the task completed are related. Use the fact that the sum of the parts of the task completed must equal 1, the complete task.

$$\frac{t}{60} + \frac{t}{90} = 1$$

• **The part of the task completed by the painter plus the part of the task completed by the apprentice must equal 1.**

$$180\left(\frac{t}{60} + \frac{t}{90}\right) = 180 \cdot 1$$

• **Multiply each side of the equation by the LCM of 60 and 90.**

$$3t + 2t = 180$$
$$5t = 180$$
$$t = 36$$

Working together, they will paint the ceiling in 36 min.

EXAMPLE 1 A small water pipe takes four times longer to fill a tank than does a large water pipe. With both pipes open, it takes 3 h to fill the tank. Find the time it would take the small pipe, working alone, to fill the tank.

Strategy ▶ Time for large pipe to fill the tank: t

▶ Time for small pipe to fill the tank: $4t$

Fills tank in $4t$ hours — Fills tank in t hours

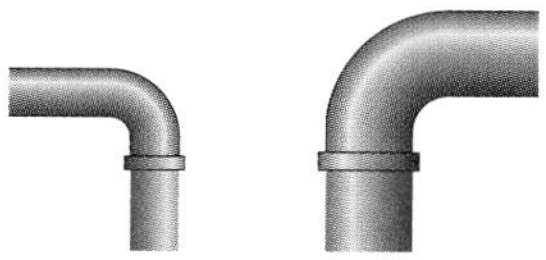

Fills $\frac{3}{4t}$ of the tank in 3 hours — Fills $\frac{3}{t}$ of the tank in 3 hours

	Rate	Time	Part
Small pipe	$\frac{1}{4t}$	3	$\frac{3}{4t}$
Large pipe	$\frac{1}{t}$	3	$\frac{3}{t}$

▶ The sum of the parts of the task completed must equal 1.

Solution

$$\frac{3}{4t} + \frac{3}{t} = 1$$

• **The part of the task completed by the small pipe plus the part of the task completed by the large pipe must equal 1.**

$$4t\left(\frac{3}{4t} + \frac{3}{t}\right) = 4t \cdot 1$$
$$3 + 12 = 4t$$

$$15 = 4t$$

$$\frac{15}{4} = t$$ • ***t* is the time for the large pipe to fill the tank.**

$$4t = 4\left(\frac{15}{4}\right) = 15$$ • **Substitute the value of *t* into the variable expression for the time for the small pipe to fill the tank.**

The small pipe, working alone, takes 15 h to fill the tank.

PROBLEM 1 Two computer printers that work at the same rate are working together to print the payroll checks for a corporation. After they work together for 3 h, one of the printers quits. The second requires 2 more hours to complete the checks. Find the time it would take one printer, working alone, to print the checks.

Solution See page S23.

OBJECTIVE 2 Uniform motion problems

A car that travels constantly in a straight line at 30 mph is in uniform motion. When an object is in **uniform motion,** its speed does not change.

The basic equation used to solve uniform motion problems is

$$\textbf{Distance} = \textbf{Rate} \cdot \textbf{Time}$$

An alternative form of this equation is written by solving the equation for time:

$$\frac{\textbf{Distance}}{\textbf{Rate}} = \textbf{Time}$$

This form of the equation is useful when the total time of travel for two objects is known or the times of travel for two objects are equal.

Solve: The speed of a boat in still water is 20 mph. The boat traveled 120 mi down a river in the same amount of time it took the boat to travel 80 mi up the river. Find the rate of the river's current.

STRATEGY for solving a uniform motion problem

▶ For each object, write a numerical or variable expression for the distance, rate, and time. The results can be recorded in a table.

The unknown rate of the river's current: r

Take Note

Use the information given in the problem to fill in the distance and rate columns of the table. Fill in the time column by dividing the two expressions you wrote in each row.

	Distance	÷	Rate	=	Time
Down river	120	÷	$20 + r$	=	$\frac{120}{20 + r}$
Up river	80	÷	$20 - r$	=	$\frac{80}{20 - r}$

▶ Determine how the times traveled by the two objects are related. For example, it may be known that the times are equal, or the total time may be known.

$$\frac{120}{20+r} = \frac{80}{20-r}$$

$$(20+r)(20-r)\frac{120}{20+r} = (20+r)(20-r)\frac{80}{20-r}$$

$$(20-r)120 = (20+r)80$$

$$2400 - 120r = 1600 + 80r$$

$$-200r = -800$$

$$r = 4$$

• **The time spent traveling down the river is equal to the time spent traveling up the river.**

The rate of the river's current is 4 mph.

EXAMPLE 2 A cyclist rode the first 20 mi of a trip at a constant rate. For the next 16 mi, the cyclist reduced the speed by 2 mph. The total time for the 36 mi was 4 h. Find the rate of the cyclist for each leg of the trip.

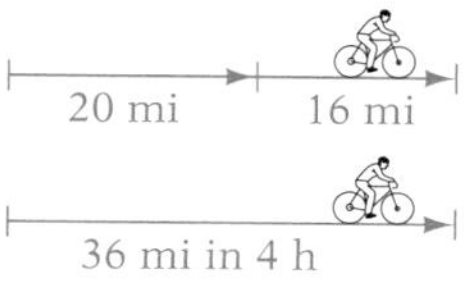

Strategy

▶ Rate for the first 20 mi: r

▶ Rate for the next 16 mi: $r - 2$

	Distance	Rate	Time
First 20 mi	20	r	$\frac{20}{r}$
Next 16 mi	16	$r - 2$	$\frac{16}{r-2}$

▶ The total time for the trip was 4 h.

Solution

$$\frac{20}{r} + \frac{16}{r-2} = 4$$

• **The time spent riding the first 20 mi plus the time spent riding the next 16 mi is equal to 4 h.**

$$r(r-2)\left[\frac{20}{r} + \frac{16}{r-2}\right] = r(r-2)\cdot 4$$

$$(r-2)20 + 16r = (r^2 - 2r)4$$

$$20r - 40 + 16r = 4r^2 - 8r$$

$$36r - 40 = 4r^2 - 8r$$

$$0 = 4r^2 - 44r + 40$$

• **This is a quadratic equation.**

$$0 = 4(r^2 - 11r + 10)$$

$$0 = r^2 - 11r + 10$$

• **Divide each side by 4.**

$$0 = (r-10)(r-1)$$

• **Solve by factoring.**

$$r - 10 = 0 \qquad r - 1 = 0$$

$$r = 10 \qquad r = 1$$

$$r - 2 = 10 - 2 \qquad r - 2 = 1 - 2$$
$$= 8 \qquad\qquad = -1$$

• **Find the rate for the last 16 mi. The solution $r = 1$ mph is not possible, because the rate on the last 16 mi would be -1 mph.**

10 mph was the rate for the first 20 mi.
8 mph was the rate for the next 16 mi.

PROBLEM 2 The total time for a sailboat to sail back and forth across a lake 6 km wide was 3 h. The rate sailing back was twice the rate sailing across the lake. Find the rate of the sailboat going across the lake.

Solution See page S23.

9.7 Concept Review

Determine whether the statement is always true, sometimes true, or never true.

1. The work problems in this section require use of the equation Rate of work · Time worked = 1.

2. If it takes a janitorial crew 5 h to clean a company's offices, then in x hours the crew has completed $\frac{x}{5}$ of the job.

3. If it takes an automotive crew x min to service a car, then the rate of work is $\frac{1}{x}$ of the job each minute.

4. If only two people worked on a job and together they completed it, and one person completed $\frac{t}{30}$ of the job and the other person completed $\frac{t}{20}$ of the job, then $\frac{t}{30} + \frac{t}{20} = 1$.

5. Uniform motion problems are based on the equation Distance · Rate = Time.

6. If a plane flies 300 mph in calm air and the rate of the wind is r mph, then the rate of the plane flying with the wind can be represented as $300 - r$, and the rate of the plane flying against the wind can be represented as $300 + r$.

9.7 Exercises

1 Work problems

1. Explain the meaning of the phrase "rate of work."

2. a. If $\frac{2}{5}$ of a room can be painted in 1 h, what is the rate of work?
   b. At the same rate, how long will it take to paint the entire room?

3. One electrician can do a wiring job in 10 h. It would take the electrician's assistant 12 h to complete the same wiring job. Let t represent the amont of time it would take the electrician and the assistant to complete the job if they worked together. Complete the following table.

	Rate of work	·	Time worked	=	Part of task completed
Electrician	?	·	?	=	?
Assistant	?	·	?	=	?

4. Refer to the situation presented in Exercise 3. When the wiring job is finished, the "part of task completed" is the whole task, so the sum of the parts completed by the electrician and the assistant is ___?___. Use this fact and the expressions in the table in Exercise 3 to write an equation that can be solved to find the amount of time it takes for the electrician and the assistant to complete the job together: ___?___ + ___?___ = ___?___.

5. A park has two sprinklers that are used to fill a fountain. One sprinkler can fill the fountain in 3 h, whereas the second sprinkler can fill the fountain in 6 h. How long will it take to fill the fountain with both sprinklers operating?

6. One grocery clerk can stock a shelf in 20 min. A second clerk requires 30 min to stock the same shelf. How long would it take to stock the shelf if the two clerks worked together?

7. One person with a skiploader requires 12 h to transfer a large quantity of earth. With a larger skiploader, the same amount of earth can be transferred in 4 h. How long would it take to transfer the earth if both skiploaders were operated together?

8. It takes Doug 6 days to reroof a house. If Doug's son helps him, the job can be completed in 4 days. How long would it take Doug's son, working alone, to do the job?

9. One computer can solve a complex prime factorization problem in 75 h. A second computer can solve the same problem in 50 h. How long would it take both computers, working together, to solve the problem?

10. A new machine makes 10,000 aluminum cans three times faster than an older machine. With both machines operating, it takes 9 h to make 10,000 cans. How long would it take the new machine, working alone, to make 10,000 cans?

11. A small air conditioner can cool a room 5°F in 60 min. A larger air conditioner can cool the room 5°F in 40 min. How long would it take to cool the room 5°F with both air conditioners working?

12. One printing press can print the first edition of a book in 55 min. A second printing press requires 66 min to print the same number of copies. How long would it take to print the first edition of the book with both presses operating?

13. Two welders working together can complete a job in 6 h. One of the welders, working alone, can complete the task in 10 h. How long would it take the second welder, working alone, to complete the task?

14. Working together, Pat and Chris can reseal a driveway in 6 h. Working alone, Pat can reseal the driveway in 15 h. How long would it take Chris, working alone, to reseal the driveway?

15. Two oil pipelines can fill a small tank in 30 min. Using one of the pipelines would require 45 min to fill the tank. How long would it take the second pipeline, working alone, to fill the tank?

16. A cement mason can construct a retaining wall in 8 h. A second mason requires 12 h to do the same job. After working alone for 4 h, the first mason quits. How long will it take the second mason to complete the wall?

17. With two reapers operating, a field can be harvested in 1 h. If only the newer reaper is used, the crop can be harvested in 1.5 h. How long would it take to harvest the field using only the older reaper?

18. A manufacturer of prefabricated homes has the company's employees work in teams. Team 1 can erect the Silvercrest model in 15 h. Team 2 can erect the same model in 10 h. How long would it take for Team 1 and Team 2, working together, to erect the Silvercrest model home?

19. One computer technician can wire a modem in 4 h. A second technician requires 6 h to do the same job. After working alone for 2 h, the first technician quits. How long will it take the second technician to complete the wiring?

20. A wallpaper hanger requires 2 h to hang the wallpaper on one wall of a room. A second wallpaper hanger requires 4 h to hang the same amount of wallpaper. The first wallpaper hanger works alone for 1 h and then quits. How long will it take the second hanger, working alone, to finish papering the wall?

21. A large heating unit and a small heating unit are being used to heat the water in a pool. The large unit, working alone, requires 8 h to heat the pool. After both units have been operating for 2 h, the large unit is turned off. The small unit requires 9 more hours to heat the pool. How long would it take the small unit, working alone, to heat the pool?

22. Two machines fill cereal boxes at the same rate. After the two machines work together for 7 h, one machine breaks down. The second machine requires 14 more hours to finish filling the boxes. How long would it have taken one of the machines, working alone, to fill the boxes?

23. Two welders who work at the same rate are riveting the girders of a building. After they work together for 10 h, one of the welders quits. The second welder requires 20 more hours to complete the welds. Find the time it would have taken one of the welders, working alone, to complete the welds.

24. A large drain and a small drain are opened to drain a pool. The large drain can empty the pool in 6 h. After both drains have been open 1 h, the large drain becomes clogged and is closed. The small drain remains open and requires 9 more hours to empty the pool. How long would it have taken the small drain, working alone, to empty the pool?

25. It takes Sam h hours to rake the yard and it takes Emma k hours to rake the yard, where $h > k$. Let t be the amount of time it takes Sam and Emma to rake the yard together. Is t less than k, between k and h, or greater than k?

26. Zachary and Eli picked a row of peas together in m minutes. It would have taken Zachary n minutes to pick the row of peas by himself. What fraction of the row of peas did Zachary pick? What fraction of the row of peas did Eli pick?

2 Uniform motion problems

27. a. A plane can fly 380 mph in calm air. In the time it takes the plane to fly 1440 mi against a headwind, it could fly 1600 mi if it were flying with the wind. Let r represent the rate of the wind. Complete the following table.

	Distance	÷	Rate	=	Time
Against the wind	?	÷	?	=	?
With the wind	?	÷	?	=	?

b. Use the relationship between the expressions in the last column of the table to write an equation that can be solved to find the rate of the wind: ___?___ = ___?___.

28. Use the equation from part b of Exercise 27. The first step in solving this equation is to multiply each side of the equation by ___?___.

29. A camper drove 80 mi to a recreational area and then hiked 4 mi into the woods. The rate of the camper while driving was ten times the rate while hiking. The time spent hiking and driving was 3 h. Find the rate at which the camper hiked.

30. The president of a company traveled 1800 mi by jet and 300 mi on a prop plane. The rate of the jet was four times the rate of the prop plane. The entire trip took 5 h. Find the rate of the jet plane.

31. To assess the damage done by a fire, a forest ranger traveled 1080 mi by jet and then an additional 180 mi by helicopter. The rate of the jet was four times the rate of the helicopter. The entire trip took 5 h. Find the rate of the jet.

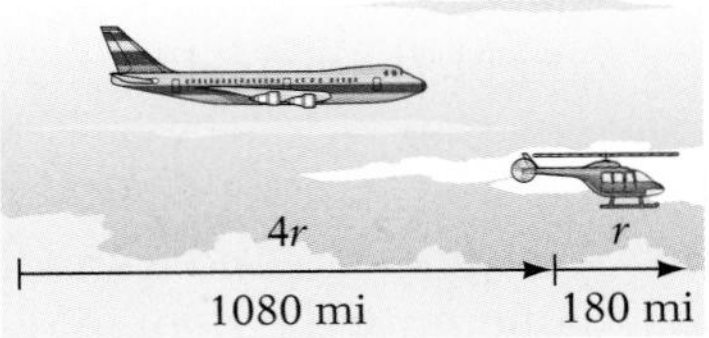

32. An engineer traveled 165 mi by car and then an additional 660 mi by plane. The rate of the plane was four times the rate of the car. The total trip took 6 h. Find the rate of the car.

33. After sailing 15 mi, a sailor changed direction and increased the boat's speed by 2 mph. An additional 19 mi was sailed at the increased speed. The total sailing time was 4 h. Find the rate of the boat for the first 15 mi.

34. On a recent trip, a trucker traveled 330 mi at a constant rate. Because of road conditions, the trucker then reduced the speed by 25 mph. An additional 30 mi was traveled at the reduced rate. The entire trip took 7 h. Find the rate of the trucker for the first 330 mi.

35. In calm water, the rate of a small rental motorboat is 15 mph. The rate of the current on the river is 3 mph. How far down the river can a family travel and still return the boat in 3 h?

36. The rate of a small aircraft in calm air is 125 mph. If the wind is currently blowing south at a rate of 15 mph, how far north can a pilot fly the plane and return it within 2 h?

37. Commuting from work to home, a lab technician traveled 10 mi at a constant rate through congested traffic. Upon reaching the expressway, the technician increased the speed by 20 mph. An additional 20 mi was traveled at the increased speed. The total time for the trip was 1 h. How fast did the technician travel through the congested traffic?

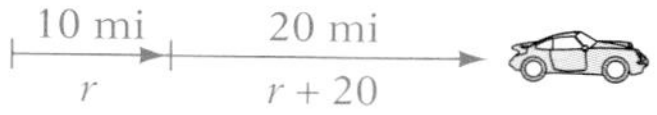

38. As part of a conditioning program, a jogger ran 8 mi in the same amount of time as it took a cyclist to ride 20 mi. The rate of the cyclist was 12 mph faster than the rate of the jogger. Find the rate of the jogger and the rate of the cyclist.

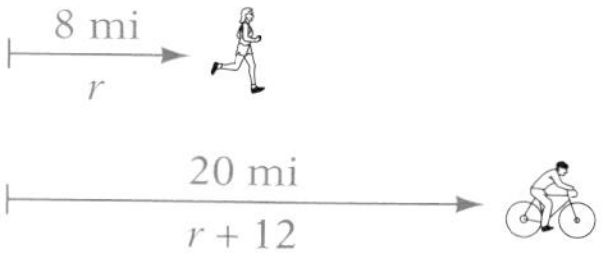

39. The speed of a boat in still water is 20 mph. The Jacksons traveled 75 mi down the Woodset River in the same amount of time as it took them to return 45 mi up the river. Find the rate of the river's current.

40. A backpacker hiking into a wilderness area walked 9 mi at a constant rate and then reduced this rate by 1 mph. Another 4 mi was hiked at this reduced rate. The time required to hike the 4 mi was 1 h less than the time required to walk the 9 mi. Find the rate at which the hiker walked the first 9 mi.

41. An express train traveled 600 mi in the same amount of time as it took a freight train to travel 360 mi. The rate of the express train was 20 mph faster than the rate of the freight train. Find the rate of each train.

42. A twin-engine plane flies 800 mi in the same amount of time as it takes a single-engine plane to fly 600 mi. The rate of the twin-engine plane is 50 mph faster than the rate of the single-engine plane. Find the rate of the twin-engine plane.

43. A car is traveling at a rate that is 36 mph faster than the rate of a cyclist. The car travels 384 mi in the same time as it takes the cyclist to travel 96 mi. Find the rate of the car.

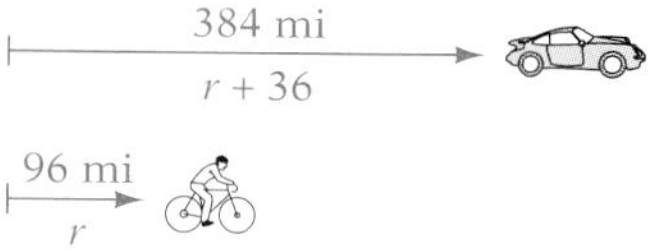

44. A small motor on a fishing boat can move the boat at a rate of 6 mph in calm water. Traveling with the current, the boat can travel 24 mi in the same amount of time as it takes to travel 12 mi against the current. Find the rate of the current.

45. A commercial jet can fly 550 mph in calm air. Traveling with the jet stream, the plane flew 2400 mi in the same amount of time as it takes to fly 2000 mi against the jet stream. Find the rate of the jet stream.

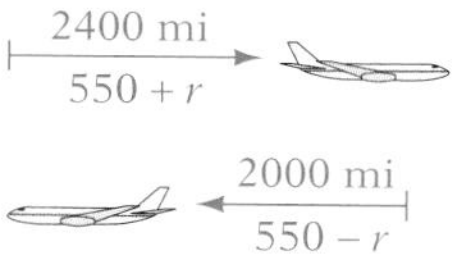

46. A cruise ship can sail 28 mph in calm water. Sailing with the Gulf Stream, the ship can sail 170 mi in the same amount of time as it takes to sail 110 mi against the Gulf Stream. Find the rate of the Gulf Stream.

47. Rowing with the current of a river, a rowing team can row 25 mi in the same amount of time as it takes to row 15 mi against the current. The rate of the rowing team in calm water is 20 mph. Find the rate of the current.

48. A plane can fly 180 mph in calm air. Flying with the wind, the plane can fly 600 mi in the same amount of time as it takes to fly 480 mi against the wind. Find the rate of the wind.

9.7 Applying Concepts

49. **Work Problem** One pipe can fill a tank in 2 h, a second pipe can fill the tank in 4 h, and a third pipe can fill the tank in 5 h. How long would it take to fill the tank with all three pipes operating?

50. **Work Problem** A mason can construct a retaining wall in 10 h. The mason's more experienced apprentice can do the same job in 15 h. How long would it take the mason's less experienced apprentice to do the job if, working together, all three can complete the wall in 5 h?

51. **Uniform Motion** An Outing Club traveled 18 mi by canoe and then hiked 3 mi. The rate by boat was three times the rate on foot. The time spent walking was 1 h less than the time spent canoeing. Find the amount of time spent traveling by canoe.

52. **Uniform Motion** A motorist drove 120 mi before running out of gas and walking 4 mi to a gas station. The rate of the motorist in the car was ten times the rate walking. The time spent walking was 2 h less than the time spent driving. How long did it take for the motorist to drive the 120 mi?

53. **Uniform Motion** Because of bad weather, a bus driver reduced the usual speed along a 150-mile bus route by 10 mph. The bus arrived only 30 min later than its usual arrival time. How fast does the bus usually travel?

Focus on Problem Solving

Calculators

A calculator is an important tool for problem solving. It can be used as an aide to guessing or estimating a solution to a problem. Here are a few problems to solve with a calculator.

1. Choose any positive integer less than 9. Multiply the number by 1507. Now multiply the result by 7519. What is the answer? Choose another positive single-digit number and again multiply by 1507 and 7519. What is the answer? What pattern do you see? Why does this work?

2. Are there enough people in the United States so that if they held hands in a line, they would stretch around the world at the equator? To answer this question, begin by determining what information you need. What assumptions must you make?

3. Which of the reciprocals of the first 16 natural numbers have a terminating decimal representation and which have a repeating decimal representation?

4. What is the largest natural number n for which $4^n > 1 \cdot 2 \cdot \cdots \cdot n$?

5. Calculate 15^2, 35^2, 65^2, and 85^2. Study the results. Make a conjecture about a relationship between a number ending in 5 and its square. Use your conjecture to find 75^2 and 95^2. Does your conjecture work for 125^2?

6. Find the sum of the first 1000 natural numbers. (*Hint:* You could just start adding $1 + 2 + 3 + 4 + \cdots$, but even if you performed one operation each second, it would take over 15 minutes to find the sum. Instead, try pairing the numbers and then adding the numbers in each pair. Pair 1 and 1000, 2 and 999, 3 and 998, and so on. What is the sum of each pair? How many pairs are there? Use this information to answer the original question.)

7. For a borrower to qualify for a home loan, a bank requires that the monthly mortgage payment be less than 25% of the borrower's monthly take-home income. A laboratory technician has deductions for taxes, insurance, and retirement that amount to 25% of the technician's monthly gross income. What minimum gross monthly income must this technician earn to receive a bank loan that has a mortgage payment of $1200 per month?

Projects & Group Activities

Scale Model of the Solar system

The table below lists the diameters of the sun and each of its nine planets, as well as the average distance of each planet from the sun.

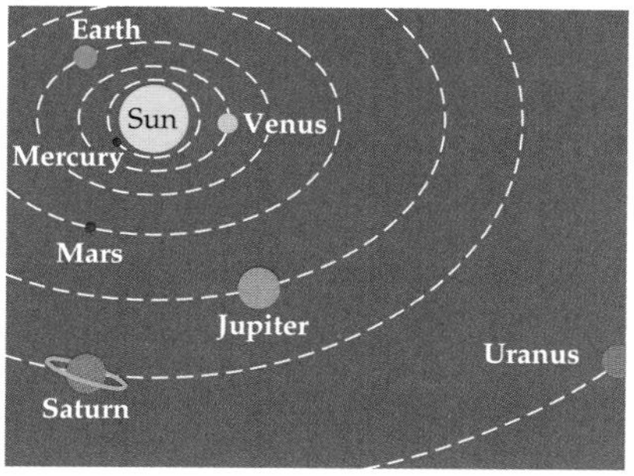

Body	*Body Diameter (in kilometers)*	*Average Distance from the Sun (in millions of kilometers)*
Sun	1,391,900	
Mercury	4,878	58.05
Venus	12,104	108.45
Earth	12,756	150.0
Mars	6,787	228.6
Jupiter	142,800	780.45
Saturn	120,660	1,430.85
Uranus	51,118	2,877.0
Neptune	49,528	4,509.0
Pluto	2,300	5,929.5

Source: http://pds.jpl.nasa.gov/planets/welcome

To make a scale model of our solar system, begin by choosing the diameter of the sun in the scale model. Use the chosen ratio to determine the diameters of the planets and the distances between the sun and each of the planets.

Chapter 9 Summary

Key Words

A **rational expression** is a fraction in which the numerator or denominator is a variable expression. A rational expression is in simplest form when the numerator and denominator have no common factors other than 1. [9.1.1, pp. 468–469]

Example: $\dfrac{x+4}{x-3}$ is a rational expression in simplest form.

The **reciprocal** of a fraction is that fraction with the numerator and denominator interchanged. [9.1.3, p. 471]

Example: The reciprocal of $\dfrac{x-7}{y}$ is $\dfrac{y}{x-7}$.

The **least common multiple** (LCM) of two or more numbers is the smallest number that contains the prime factorization of each number. [9.2.1, p. 479]

Example: The LCM of 8 and 12 is 24 because 24 is the smallest number that is a multiple of both 8 and 12.

A **complex fraction** is a fraction whose numerator or denominator contains one or more fractions. [9.4.1, p. 494]

Example: $\dfrac{x+\dfrac{1}{x}}{2-\dfrac{3}{x}}$ is a complex fraction.

A **ratio** is the quotient of two quantities that have the same unit. A **rate** is the quotient of two quantities that have different units. A **proportion** is an equation that states the equality of two ratios or rates. [9.5.2, p. 501]

Example: $\dfrac{3}{8}=\dfrac{15}{40}$ and $\dfrac{20\text{ m}}{5\text{ s}}=\dfrac{80\text{ m}}{20\text{ s}}$ are examples of proportions.

A **literal equation** is an equation that contains more than one variable. A **formula** is a literal equation that states rules about measurements. [9.6.1, p. 516]

Example: $2x+3y=6$ is an example of a literal equation. $A=\pi r^2$ is a literal equation that is also a formula.

Essential Rules and Procedures

Simplifying Rational Expressions
Factor the numerator and denominator. Divide by the common factors. [9.1.1, p. 469]

$$\frac{x^2-3x-10}{x^2-25}=\frac{(x+2)(x-5)}{(x+5)(x-5)}=\frac{x+2}{x+5}$$

Multiplying Rational Expressions
Multiply the numerators. Multiply the denominators. Write the answer in simplest form.
$\dfrac{a}{b}\cdot\dfrac{c}{d}=\dfrac{ac}{bd}$ [9.1.2, p. 470]

$$\frac{x^2-3x}{x^2+x}\cdot\frac{x^2+5x+4}{x^2-4x+3}$$
$$=\frac{x(x-3)}{x(x+1)}\cdot\frac{(x+4)(x+1)}{(x-3)(x-1)}$$
$$=\frac{x(x-3)(x+4)(x+1)}{x(x+1)(x-3)(x-1)}=\frac{x+4}{x-1}$$

Dividing Rational Expressions
To divide two fractions, multiply by the reciprocal of the divisor.
$\frac{a}{b} \div \frac{c}{d} = \frac{a}{b} \cdot \frac{d}{c} = \frac{ad}{bc}$ [9.1.3, p. 472]

$$\frac{3x^3y^2}{8a^4b^5} \div \frac{6x^4y}{4a^3b^2} = \frac{3x^3y^2}{8a^4b^5} \cdot \frac{4a^3b^2}{6x^4y} = \frac{3x^3y^2 \cdot 4a^3b^2}{8a^4b^5 \cdot 6x^4y} = \frac{y}{4ab^3x}$$

Adding and Subtracting Rational Expressions

1. Find the LCM of the denominators.
2. Write each fraction with the LCM as the denominator.
3. Add or subtract the numerators. The denominator of the sum or difference is the common denominator.
4. Write the answer in simplest form.

[9.3.2, p. 482]

$$\begin{aligned}\frac{4x-2}{3x+12} - \frac{x-2}{x+4} &= \frac{4x-2}{3(x+4)} - \frac{x-2}{x+4} \\ &= \frac{4x-2}{3(x+4)} - \frac{x-2}{x+4} \cdot \frac{3}{3} \\ &= \frac{4x-2}{3(x+4)} - \frac{3x-6}{3(x+4)} \\ &= \frac{4x-2-(3x-6)}{3(x+4)} \\ &= \frac{x+4}{3(x+4)} = \frac{1}{3}\end{aligned}$$

Simplifying Complex Fractions
Multiply the numerator and denominator of the complex fraction by the LCM of the denominators of the fractions in the numerator and denominator. [9.4.1, p. 494]

$$\frac{\frac{1}{x}+\frac{1}{y}}{\frac{1}{x}-\frac{1}{y}} = \frac{\frac{1}{x}+\frac{1}{y}}{\frac{1}{x}-\frac{1}{y}} \cdot \frac{xy}{xy} = \frac{\frac{1}{x}\cdot xy + \frac{1}{y}\cdot xy}{\frac{1}{x}\cdot xy - \frac{1}{y}\cdot xy} = \frac{y+x}{y-x}$$

Solving Equations Containing Fractions
Clear denominators by multiplying each side of the equation by the LCM of the denominators. Then solve for the variable. [9.5.1, p. 499]

$$\begin{aligned}\frac{1}{2a} &= \frac{2}{a} - \frac{3}{8} \\ 8a\left(\frac{1}{2a}\right) &= 8a\left(\frac{2}{a} - \frac{3}{8}\right) \\ 4 &= 16 - 3a \\ -12 &= -3a \\ 4 &= a\end{aligned}$$

Similar Triangles
Similar triangles have the same shape but not necessarily the same size. The ratios of corresponding sides of similar triangles are equal. The ratio of corresponding heights is equal to the ratio of corresponding sides. [9.5.4, p. 504]

Triangles ABC and DEF are similar triangles. The ratio of corresponding sides and of corresponding heights is $\frac{1}{3}$.

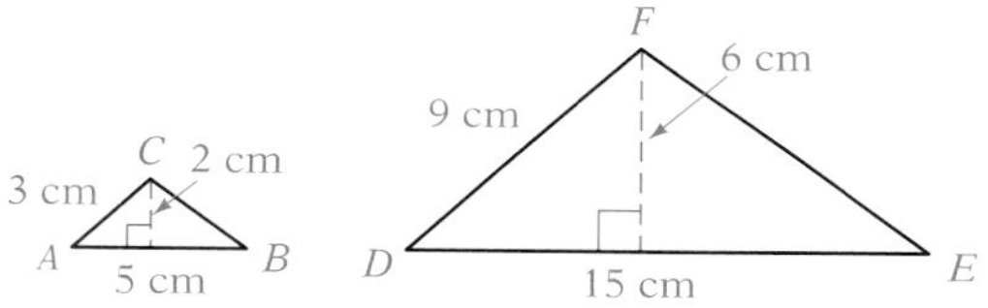

Solving Literal Equations
Rewrite the equation so that the letter being solved for is alone on one side of the equation and all numbers and other variables are on the other side. [9.6.1, p. 516]

Solve $A = \frac{1}{2}bh$ for b.

$$2(A) = 2\left(\frac{1}{2}bh\right)$$
$$2A = bh$$
$$\frac{2A}{h} = \frac{bh}{h}$$
$$\frac{2A}{h} = b$$

Work Problems
Rate of work · Time worked = Part of task completed [9.7.1, p. 520]

Pat can do a certain job in 3 h. Chris can do the same job in 5 h. How long would it take them, working together, to get the job done?

$$\frac{t}{3} + \frac{t}{5} = 1$$

Uniform Motion Problems
Distance ÷ Rate = Time [9.7.2, p. 522]

Train A's speed is 15 mph faster than Train B's speed. Train A travels 150 mi in the same amount of time as it takes Train B to travel 120 mi. Find the rate of Train B.

$$\frac{120}{r} = \frac{150}{r + 15}$$

Chapter 9 Review Exercises

1. Multiply: $\frac{8ab^2}{15x^3y} \cdot \frac{5xy^4}{16a^2b}$

2. Add: $\frac{5}{3x - 4} + \frac{4}{2x + 3}$

3. Solve $4x + 3y = 12$ for x.

4. Simplify: $\frac{16x^5y^3}{24xy^{10}}$

5. Divide: $\frac{20x^2 - 45x}{6x^3 + 4x^2} \div \frac{40x^3 - 90x^2}{12x^2 + 8x}$

6. Simplify: $\dfrac{x - \dfrac{16}{5x - 2}}{3x - 4 - \dfrac{88}{5x - 2}}$

7. Find the LCM of $24a^2b^5$ and $36a^3b$.

8. Subtract: $\frac{5x}{3x + 7} - \frac{x}{3x + 7}$

9. Write each fraction in terms of the LCM of the denominators.

$\frac{3}{16x}$; $\frac{5}{8x^2}$

10. Simplify: $\frac{2x^2 - 13x - 45}{2x^2 - x - 15}$

11. Divide: $\frac{x^2 - 5x - 14}{x^2 - 3x - 10} \div \frac{x^2 - 4x - 21}{x^2 - 9x + 20}$

12. Add: $\frac{2y}{5y - 7} + \frac{3}{7 - 5y}$

13. Multiply: $\frac{3x^3 + 10x^2}{10x - 2} \cdot \frac{20x - 4}{6x^4 + 20x^3}$

14. Subtract: $\frac{5x + 3}{2x^2 + 5x - 3} - \frac{3x + 4}{2x^2 + 5x - 3}$

15. Find the LCM of $5x^4(x - 7)^2$ and $15x(x - 7)$.

16. Solve: $\frac{6}{x - 7} = \frac{8}{x - 6}$

17. Solve: $\frac{x + 8}{x + 4} = 1 + \frac{5}{x + 4}$

18. Simplify: $\frac{12a^2b(4x - 7)}{15ab^2(7 - 4x)}$

19. Simplify: $\frac{5x - 1}{x^2 - 9} + \frac{4x - 3}{x^2 - 9} - \frac{8x - 1}{x^2 - 9}$

20. Triangles *ABC* and *DEF* below are similar. Find the perimeter of triangle *ABC*.

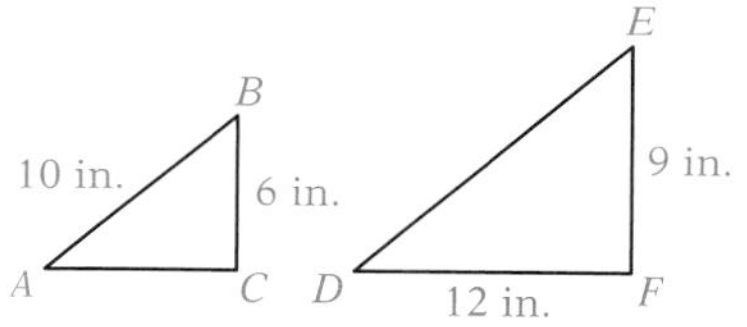

21. Solve: $\frac{20}{2x + 3} = \frac{17x}{2x + 3} - 5$

22. Simplify: $\dfrac{\frac{5}{x - 1} - \frac{3}{x + 3}}{\frac{6}{x + 3} + \frac{2}{x - 1}}$

23. Add: $\frac{x - 1}{x + 2} + \frac{3x - 2}{5 - x} + \frac{5x^2 + 15x - 11}{x^2 - 3x - 10}$

24. Divide: $\frac{18x^2 + 25x - 3}{9x^2 - 28x + 3} \div \frac{2x^2 + 9x + 9}{x^2 - 6x + 9}$

25. Simplify: $\frac{x^2 + x - 30}{15 + 2x - x^2}$

26. Solve: $\frac{5}{7} + \frac{x}{2} = 2 - \frac{x}{7}$

27. Simplify: $\dfrac{x + \frac{6}{x - 5}}{1 + \frac{2}{x - 5}}$

28. Multiply: $\frac{3x^2 + 4x - 15}{x^2 - 11x + 28} \cdot \frac{x^2 - 5x - 14}{3x^2 + x - 10}$

29. Solve: $\frac{x}{5} = \frac{x + 12}{9}$

30. Solve: $\frac{3}{20} = \frac{x}{80}$

31. Simplify: $\dfrac{1 - \dfrac{1}{x}}{1 - \dfrac{8x - 7}{x^2}}$

32. Solve $x - 2y = 15$ for x.

33. Add: $\dfrac{6}{a} + \dfrac{9}{b}$

34. Find the LCM of $10x^2 - 11x + 3$ and $20x^2 - 17x + 3$.

35. Solve $i = \dfrac{100m}{c}$ for c.

36. Solve: $\dfrac{15}{x} = \dfrac{3}{8}$

37. Solve: $\dfrac{22}{2x + 5} = 2$

38. Add: $\dfrac{x + 7}{15x} + \dfrac{x - 2}{20x}$

39. Multiply: $\dfrac{16a^2 - 9}{16a^2 - 24a + 9} \cdot \dfrac{8a^2 - 13a - 6}{4a^2 - 5a - 6}$

40. Write each fraction in terms of the LCM of the denominators.

$$\frac{x}{12x^2 + 16x - 3}; \frac{4x^2}{6x^2 + 7x - 3}$$

41. Add: $\dfrac{3}{4ab} + \dfrac{5}{4ab}$

42. Solve: $\dfrac{20}{x + 2} = \dfrac{5}{16}$

43. Solve: $\dfrac{5x}{3} - \dfrac{2}{5} = \dfrac{8x}{5}$

44. Divide: $\dfrac{6a^2b^7}{25x^3y} \div \dfrac{12a^3b^4}{5x^2y^2}$

45. **Masonry** A brick mason can construct a patio in 3 h. If the mason works with an apprentice, they can construct the patio in 2 h. How long would it take the apprentice, working alone, to construct the patio?

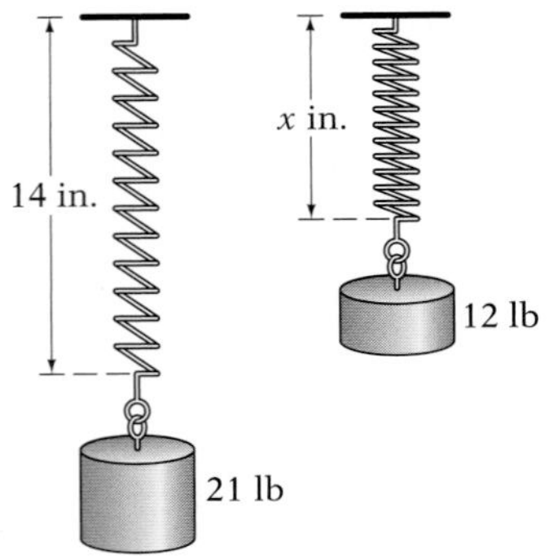

46. **Physics** A weight of 21 lb stretches a spring 14 in. At the same rate, how far would a weight of 12 lb stretch the spring?

47. **Uniform Motion** The rate of a jet is 400 mph in calm air. Traveling with the wind, the jet can fly 2100 mi in the same amount of time as it takes to fly 1900 mi against the wind. Find the rate of the wind.

48. **Gardening** A gardener uses 4 oz of insecticide to make 2 gal of garden spray. At this rate, how much additional insecticide is necessary to make 10 gal of the garden spray?

49. **Work Problem** One hose can fill a pool in 15 h. A second hose can fill the pool in 10 h. How long would it take to fill the pool using both hoses?

50. **Uniform Motion** A car travels 315 mi in the same amount of time as it takes a bus to travel 245 mi. The rate of the car is 10 mph faster than that of the bus. Find the rate of the car.

Chapter 9 Test

1. Divide: $\dfrac{x^2+3x+2}{x^2+5x+4} \div \dfrac{x^2-x-6}{x^2+2x-15}$

2. Subtract: $\dfrac{2x}{x^2+3x-10} - \dfrac{4}{x^2+3x-10}$

3. Find the LCM of $6x - 3$ and $2x^2 + x - 1$.

4. Solve: $\dfrac{3}{x+4} = \dfrac{5}{x+6}$

5. Multiply: $\dfrac{x^3y^4}{x^2-4x+4} \cdot \dfrac{x^2-x-2}{x^6y^4}$

6. Simplify: $\dfrac{1+\dfrac{1}{x}-\dfrac{12}{x^2}}{1+\dfrac{2}{x}-\dfrac{8}{x^2}}$

7. Write each fraction in terms of the LCM of the denominators.
$\dfrac{3}{x^2-2x}; \dfrac{x}{x^2-4}$

8. Solve $3x + 5y + 15 = 0$ for x.

9. Solve: $\dfrac{6}{x} - 2 = 1$

10. Subtract: $\dfrac{2}{2x-1} - \dfrac{3}{3x+1}$

11. Divide: $\dfrac{x^2-x-56}{x^2+8x+7} \div \dfrac{x^2-13x+40}{x^2-4x-5}$

12. Subtract: $\dfrac{3x}{x^2+5x-24} - \dfrac{9}{x^2+5x-24}$

13. Find the LCM of $3x^2 + 6x$ and $2x^2 + 8x + 8$.

14. Simplify: $\dfrac{x^2-7x+10}{25-x^2}$

15. Solve: $\dfrac{3x}{x-3} - 2 = \dfrac{10}{x-3}$

16. Solve $f = v + at$ for t.

17. Simplify: $\dfrac{12x^4y^2}{18xy^7}$

18. Subtract: $\dfrac{2}{2x-1} - \dfrac{1}{x+1}$

19. Solve: $\dfrac{2}{x-2} = \dfrac{12}{x+3}$

20. Multiply: $\dfrac{x^5y^3}{x^2-x-6} \cdot \dfrac{x^2-9}{x^2y^4}$

21. Write each fraction in terms of the LCM of the denominators.

$\dfrac{3y}{x(1-x)}; \dfrac{x}{(x+1)(x-1)}$

22. Simplify: $\dfrac{1-\dfrac{2}{x}-\dfrac{15}{x^2}}{1-\dfrac{25}{x^2}}$

23. **Mixture Problem** A salt solution is formed by mixing 4 lb of salt with 10 gal of water. At this rate, how many additional pounds of salt are required for 15 gal of water?

24. **Uniform Motion** A small plane can fly at 110 mph in calm air. Flying with the wind, the plane can fly 260 mi in the same amount of time as it takes to fly 180 mi against the wind. Find the rate of the wind.

25. **Work Problem** One pipe can fill a tank in 9 min. A second pipe requires 18 min to fill the tank. How long would it take both pipes, working together, to fill the tank?

Cumulative Review Exercises

1. Evaluate: $-|-17|$

2. Evaluate: $-\dfrac{3}{4} \cdot (2)^3$

3. Simplify: $\left(\dfrac{2}{3}\right)^2 \div \left(\dfrac{3}{2} - \dfrac{2}{3}\right) + \dfrac{1}{2}$

4. Evaluate $-a^2 + (a-b)^2$ when $a = -2$ and $b = 3$.

5. Simplify: $-2x - (-3y) + 7x - 5y$

6. Simplify: $2[3x - 7(x-3) - 8]$

7. Solve: $3 - \dfrac{1}{4}x = 8$

8. Solve: $3[x - 2(x-3)] = 2(3-2x)$

9. Find $16\frac{2}{3}\%$ of 60.

10. Solve: $\dfrac{5}{9}x < 1$

11. Solve: $x - 2 \geq 4x - 47$

12. Graph: $y = 2x - 1$

13. Graph: $f(x) = 3x + 2$

14. Graph: $x = 3$

15. Graph the solution set of $5x + 2y < 6$.

16. Find the range of the function given by the equation $f(x) = -2x + 11$ if the domain is $\{-8, -4, 0, 3, 7\}$.

17. Evaluate $f(x) = 4x - 3$ at $x = 10$.

18. Solve by substitution: $\begin{aligned} 6x - y &= 1 \\ y &= 3x + 1 \end{aligned}$

19. Solve by the addition method: $\begin{aligned} 2x - 3y &= 4 \\ 4x + y &= 1 \end{aligned}$

20. Multiply: $(3xy^4)(-2x^3y)$

21. Simplify: $(a^4b^3)^5$

22. Simplify: $\dfrac{a^2b^{-5}}{a^{-1}b^{-3}}$

23. Multiply: $(a - 3b)(a + 4b)$

24. Divide: $\dfrac{15b^4 - 5b^2 + 10b}{5b}$

25. Divide: $(x^3 - 8) \div (x - 2)$

26. Factor: $12x^2 - x - 1$

27. Factor: $y^2 - 7y + 6$

28. Factor: $2a^3 + 7a^2 - 15a$

29. Factor: $4b^2 - 100$

30. Solve: $(x + 3)(2x - 5) = 0$

31. Simplify: $\dfrac{x^2 + 3x - 28}{16 - x^2}$

32. Divide: $\dfrac{x^2 - 3x - 10}{x^2 - 4x - 12} \div \dfrac{x^2 - x - 20}{x^2 - 2x - 24}$

33. Subtract: $\dfrac{6}{3x - 1} - \dfrac{2}{x + 1}$

34. Solve: $\dfrac{4x}{x - 3} - 2 = \dfrac{8}{x - 3}$

35. Solve $f = v + at$ for a.

36. Translate "the difference between five times a number and eighteen is the opposite of three" into an equation and solve.

37. **Investments** An investment of \$5000 is made at an annual simple interest rate of 7%. How much additional money must be invested at an annual simple interest rate of 11% so that the total interest earned is 9% of the total investment?

38. **Metallurgy** A silversmith mixes 60 g of an alloy that is 40% silver with 120 g of another silver alloy. The resulting alloy is 60% silver. Find the percent of silver in the 120-gram alloy.

39. **Geometry** The length of the base of a triangle is 2 in. less than twice the height. The area of the triangle is 30 in^2. Find the base and height of the triangle.

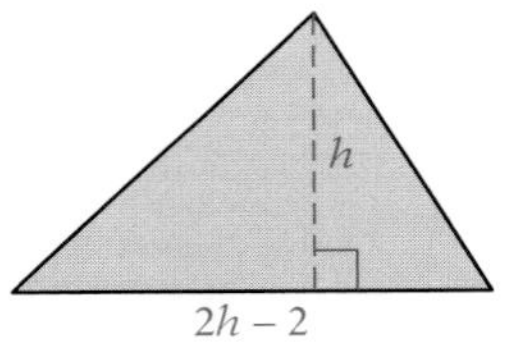

40. **Work Problem** One water pipe can fill a tank in 12 min. A second pipe requires 24 min to fill the tank. How long would it take both pipes, working together, to fill the tank?

CHAPTER

10 Radical Expressions

OBJECTIVES

10.1
1 Simplify numerical radical expressions
2 Simplify variable radical expressions

10.2
1 Add and subtract radical expressions

10.3
1 Multiply radical expressions
2 Divide radical expressions

10.4
1 Solve equations containing one or more radical expressions
2 Application problems

Civil engineers design expressways with efficiency and, most importantly, safety in mind. They have to take into account the speed of drivers entering and exiting these busy roadways. An on- or off-ramp cannot have too sharp a curve, or the drivers may be in danger of skidding off the road. However, a ramp with too wide a curve requires more building material, takes longer to travel, and uses more land. A radical equation is used to determine the maximum speed at which a car can travel around a curve without skidding. This equation is used in the **Projects & Group Activities on page 575.**

DVD SSM Online Study Center

Need help? For online student resources, such as section quizzes, visit the Online Study Center at college.hmco.com/pic/aufmannBAWA7e.

Prep Test

1. Evaluate $-|-14|$.

2. Simplify: $3x^2y - 4xy^2 - 5x^2y$

3. Solve: $1.5h = 21$

4. Solve: $3x - 2 = 5 - 2x$

5. Simplify: $x^3 \cdot x^3$

6. Simplify: $(x + y)^2$

7. Simplify: $(2x - 3)^2$

8. Simplify: $(a - 5)(a + 5)$

9. Simplify: $(2 - 3v)(2 + 3v)$

10. Simplify: $\dfrac{2x^4y^3}{18x^2y}$

10.1 Introduction to Radical Expressions

OBJECTIVE 1 Simplify numerical radical expressions

Point of Interest

The radical symbol was first used in 1525, when it was written as ⁄. Some historians suggest that the radical symbol also developed into the symbols for "less than" and "greater than." Because typesetters of that time did not want to make additional symbols, the radical was rotated to the position ↘ and used as a "greater than" symbol and rotated to ← and used for the "less than" symbol. Other evidence, however, suggests that the "less than" and "greater than" symbols were developed independently of the radical symbol.

A **square root** of a positive number x is a number whose square is x.

A square root of 16 is 4 because $4^2 = 16$.

A square root of 16 is -4 because $(-4)^2 = 16$.

Every positive number has two square roots, one a positive number and one a negative number. The symbol $\sqrt{}$, called a **radical sign,** is used to indicate the positive or **principal square root** of a number. For example, $\sqrt{16} = 4$ and $\sqrt{25} = 5$. The number or variable expression under the radical sign is called the **radicand.**

When the negative square root of a number is to be found, a negative sign is placed in front of the radical. For example, $-\sqrt{16} = -4$ and $-\sqrt{25} = -5$.

The square of an integer is a **perfect square.** 49, 81, and 144 are examples of perfect squares.

$7^2 = 49$
$9^2 = 81$
$12^2 = 144$

The principal square root of a perfect-square integer is a positive integer.

$$\sqrt{49} = 7$$
$$\sqrt{81} = 9$$
$$\sqrt{144} = 12$$

If an integer is not a perfect square, its square root can only be approximated. For example, 2 and 7 are not perfect squares. Thus their square roots can only be approximated. These numbers are **irrational numbers.** Their decimal representations never terminate or repeat.

$$\sqrt{2} \approx 1.4142135\ldots$$
$$\sqrt{7} \approx 2.6457513\ldots$$

The approximate square roots of numbers that are not perfect squares can be found using a calculator. The square roots can be rounded to any given place value.

Take Note

Recall that a factor of a number divides the number evenly. For example, 6 is a factor of 18. 9 is also a factor of 18. Note that 9 is a *perfect-square factor* of 18, whereas 6 is not a perfect-square factor of 18.

Radical expressions that contain radicands that are not perfect squares are generally written in *simplest form.* A radical expression is in **simplest form** when the radicand contains no factor greater than 1 that is a perfect square. For example, $\sqrt{50}$ is not in simplest form because 25 is a perfect-square factor of 50. The radical expression $\sqrt{15}$ is in simplest form because there is no perfect-square factor of 15 that is greater than 1.

The Product Property of Square Roots and a knowledge of perfect squares are used to simplify radical expressions.

The Product Property of Square Roots

If a and b are positive real numbers, then $\sqrt{ab} = \sqrt{a} \cdot \sqrt{b}$.

The chart below shows square roots of some perfect squares.

Square Roots of Perfect Squares

$\sqrt{1} = 1$	$\sqrt{16} = 4$	$\sqrt{49} = 7$	$\sqrt{100} = 10$
$\sqrt{4} = 2$	$\sqrt{25} = 5$	$\sqrt{64} = 8$	$\sqrt{121} = 11$
$\sqrt{9} = 3$	$\sqrt{36} = 6$	$\sqrt{81} = 9$	$\sqrt{144} = 12$

Simplify: $\sqrt{72}$

$\sqrt{72} = \sqrt{36 \cdot 2}$ • **Write the radicand as the product of a perfect square and a factor that does not contain a perfect square.**

$= \sqrt{36}\sqrt{2}$ • **Use the Product Property of Square Roots to write the expression as a product.**

$= 6\sqrt{2}$ • **Simplify $\sqrt{36}$.**

Note in the example on the previous page that 72 must be written as the product of a perfect square and *a factor that does not contain a perfect square.* Therefore, it would not be correct to rewrite $\sqrt{72}$ as $\sqrt{9 \cdot 8}$ and simplify the expression as shown at the right. Although 9 is a perfect-square factor of 72, 8 contains a perfect square ($8 = 4 \cdot 2$), and $\sqrt{4}$ can be simplified. Therefore, $\sqrt{8}$ is not in simplest form. Remember to find the *largest* perfect square that is a factor of the radicand.

$$\begin{aligned}\sqrt{72} &= \sqrt{9 \cdot 8}\\ &= \sqrt{9}\sqrt{8}\\ &= 3\sqrt{8}\end{aligned}$$

Not in simplest form

Simplify: $\sqrt{147}$

$\sqrt{147} = \sqrt{49 \cdot 3}$
- **Write the radicand as the product of a perfect square and a factor that does not contain a perfect square.**

$= \sqrt{49}\sqrt{3}$
- **Use the Product Property of Square Roots to write the expression as a product.**

$= 7\sqrt{3}$
- **Simplify $\sqrt{49}$.**

Simplify: $\sqrt{360}$

$\sqrt{360} = \sqrt{36 \cdot 10}$
- **Write the radicand as the product of a perfect square and a factor that does not contain a perfect square.**

$= \sqrt{36}\sqrt{10}$
- **Use the Product Property of Square Roots to write the expression as a product.**

$= 6\sqrt{10}$
- **Simplify $\sqrt{36}$.**

From the last example, note that $\sqrt{360} = 6\sqrt{10}$. The two expressions are different representations of the same number. Using a calculator, we find that $\sqrt{360} \approx 18.973666$ and $6\sqrt{10} \approx 6(3.1622777) = 18.973666$.

Simplify: $\sqrt{-16}$

Because the square of any real number is positive, there is no real number whose square is -16.

$\sqrt{-16}$ is not a real number.

EXAMPLE 1 Simplify: $3\sqrt{90}$

Solution $3\sqrt{90} = 3\sqrt{9 \cdot 10}$
- **Write the radicand as the product of a perfect square and a factor that does not contain a perfect square.**

$= 3\sqrt{9}\sqrt{10}$
- **Use the Product Property of Square Roots to write the expression as a product.**

$= 3 \cdot 3\sqrt{10}$
- **Simplify $\sqrt{9}$.**

$= 9\sqrt{10}$
- **Multiply $3 \cdot 3$.**

PROBLEM 1 Simplify: $-5\sqrt{32}$

Solution See page S23.

EXAMPLE 2 Simplify: $\sqrt{252}$

Solution $\sqrt{252} = \sqrt{36 \cdot 7}$ • **Write the radicand as the product of a perfect square and a factor that does not contain a perfect square.**

$= \sqrt{36}\,\sqrt{7}$ • **Use the Product Property of Square Roots to write the expression as a product.**

$= 6\sqrt{7}$ • **Simplify $\sqrt{36}$.**

PROBLEM 2 Simplify: $\sqrt{216}$

Solution See page S23.

OBJECTIVE 2 Simplify variable radical expressions

Variable expressions that contain radicals do not always represent real numbers.

The variable expression at the right does not represent a real number when x is a negative number, such as -4.

$\sqrt{x^3}$

$\sqrt{(-4)^3} = \sqrt{-64} \leftarrow$ Not a real number

Now consider the expression $\sqrt{x^2}$ and evaluate this expression for $x = -2$ and $x = 2$.

$\sqrt{x^2}$

$\sqrt{(-2)^2} = \sqrt{4} = 2 = |-2|$

$\sqrt{2^2} = \sqrt{4} = 2 = |2|$

This suggests the following.

The Square Root of a^2

For any real number a, $\sqrt{a^2} = |a|$.

If $a \geq 0$, then $\sqrt{a^2} = a$.

In order to avoid variable expressions that do not represent real numbers, and so that absolute value signs are not needed for certain expressions, the variables in this chapter will represent *positive* numbers unless otherwise stated.

A variable or a product of variables written in exponential form is a **perfect square** when each exponent is an even number.

To find the square root of a perfect square, remove the radical sign, and divide each exponent by 2.

Simplify: $\sqrt{a^6}$

Remove the radical sign, and divide the exponent by 2. $\sqrt{a^6} = a^3$

A variable radical expression is not in simplest form when the radicand contains a factor greater than 1 that is a perfect square.

Simplify: $\sqrt{x^7}$

Write x^7 as the product of x and a perfect square. $\sqrt{x^7} = \sqrt{x^6 \cdot x}$

Use the Product Property of Square Roots. $= \sqrt{x^6}\sqrt{x}$

Simplify the square root of the perfect square. $= x^3\sqrt{x}$

EXAMPLE 3 Simplify: $\sqrt{b^{15}}$

Solution $\sqrt{b^{15}} = \sqrt{b^{14} \cdot b} = \sqrt{b^{14}} \cdot \sqrt{b} = b^7\sqrt{b}$

PROBLEM 3 Simplify: $\sqrt{y^{19}}$

Solution See page S23.

Simplify: $3x\sqrt{8x^3y^{13}}$

Write the radicand as the product of a perfect square and factors that do not contain a perfect square. $3x\sqrt{8x^3y^{13}} = 3x\sqrt{4x^2y^{12}(2xy)}$

Use the Product Property of Square Roots. $= 3x\sqrt{4x^2y^{12}}\sqrt{2xy}$

Simplify. $= 3x \cdot 2xy^6\sqrt{2xy}$

$= 6x^2y^6\sqrt{2xy}$

EXAMPLE 4 Simplify. **A.** $\sqrt{24x^5}$ **B.** $2a\sqrt{18a^3b^{10}}$

Solution

A. $\sqrt{24x^5} = \sqrt{4x^4 \cdot 6x}$
$= \sqrt{4x^4}\sqrt{6x}$
$= 2x^2\sqrt{6x}$

B. $2a\sqrt{18a^3b^{10}} = 2a\sqrt{9a^2b^{10} \cdot 2a}$
$= 2a\sqrt{9a^2b^{10}}\sqrt{2a}$
$= 2a \cdot 3ab^5\sqrt{2a}$
$= 6a^2b^5\sqrt{2a}$

PROBLEM 4 Simplify. **A.** $\sqrt{45b^7}$ **B.** $3a\sqrt{28a^9b^{18}}$

Solution See page S23.

Simplify: $\sqrt{25(x+2)^2}$

25 is a perfect square. $(x+2)^2$ is a perfect square. $\sqrt{25(x+2)^2} = 5(x+2)$
$= 5x + 10$

EXAMPLE 5 Simplify: $\sqrt{16(x+5)^2}$

Solution $\sqrt{16(x+5)^2} = 4(x+5) = 4x + 20$

PROBLEM 5 Simplify: $\sqrt{25(a+3)^2}$

Solution See page S23.

10.1 Concept Review

Determine whether the statement is always true, sometimes true, or never true.

1. The square root of a positive number is a positive number, and the square root of a negative number is a negative number.

2. Every positive number has two square roots, one of which is the additive inverse of the other.

3. The square root of an integer that is not a perfect square is an irrational number.

4. If the radicand of a radical expression is evenly divisible by a perfect square greater than 1, then the radical expression is not in simplest form.

5. Suppose a and b are real numbers. Then $\sqrt{ab} = \sqrt{a} \cdot \sqrt{b}$.

6. When a perfect square is written in exponential form, the exponents are multiples of 2.

10.1 Exercises

1 Simplify numerical radical expressions

1. Show by example that a positive number has two square roots.

2. Why is the square root of a negative number not a real number?

3. Which of the numbers 2, 9, 20, 25, 50, 81, and 100 are *not* perfect squares?

4. Write down a number that has a perfect-square factor that is greater than 1.

5. Write a sentence or two that you could email a friend to explain the concept of a perfect-square factor.

6. Name the perfect-square factors of 540. What is the largest perfect-square factor of 540?

7. In the expression $\sqrt{a}$, the symbol $\sqrt{}$ is called the ___?___, and a is called the ___?___.

8. Simplify: $\sqrt{98}$

$\sqrt{98} = \sqrt{\underline{\quad ? \quad} \cdot 2}$ • **Write 98 as the product of a perfect-square factor and a factor that does not contain a perfect square.**

$= \sqrt{\underline{\quad ? \quad}}\sqrt{\underline{\quad ? \quad}}$ • **Use the Product Property of Radicals to write the expression as the product of two square roots.**

$= \underline{\quad ? \quad}\sqrt{2}$ • **Take the square root of the perfect square.**

Simplify.

9. $\sqrt{16}$ **10.** $\sqrt{64}$ **11.** $\sqrt{49}$ **12.** $\sqrt{144}$ **13.** $\sqrt{32}$ **14.** $\sqrt{50}$

15. $\sqrt{8}$ **16.** $\sqrt{12}$ **17.** $6\sqrt{18}$ **18.** $-3\sqrt{48}$ **19.** $5\sqrt{40}$ **20.** $2\sqrt{28}$

21. $\sqrt{15}$ **22.** $\sqrt{21}$ **23.** $\sqrt{29}$ **24.** $\sqrt{13}$ **25.** $-9\sqrt{72}$ **26.** $11\sqrt{80}$

27. $\sqrt{45}$ **28.** $\sqrt{225}$ **29.** $\sqrt{0}$ **30.** $\sqrt{210}$ **31.** $6\sqrt{128}$ **32.** $9\sqrt{288}$

33. $\sqrt{105}$ **34.** $\sqrt{55}$ **35.** $\sqrt{900}$ **36.** $\sqrt{300}$ **37.** $5\sqrt{180}$ **38.** $7\sqrt{98}$

39. $\sqrt{250}$ **40.** $\sqrt{120}$ **41.** $\sqrt{96}$ **42.** $\sqrt{160}$ **43.** $\sqrt{324}$ **44.** $\sqrt{444}$

Complete Exercises 45 and 46 without using a calculator.

45. Is the given number a rational number, an irrational number, or a number that is not a real number?

a. $\sqrt{0.16}$ **b.** $-\sqrt{18}$ **c.** $\sqrt{\sqrt{36}}$ **d.** $\sqrt{-25}$

46. Find consecutive integers m and n such that the given number is between m and n, or state that the given number is not a real number.

a. $-\sqrt{115}$ **b.** $-\sqrt{-90}$ **c.** $\sqrt{\sqrt{64}}$ **d.** $\sqrt{200}$

Find the decimal approximation to the nearest thousandth.

47. $\sqrt{240}$ **48.** $\sqrt{300}$ **49.** $\sqrt{288}$ **50.** $\sqrt{600}$

51. $\sqrt{245}$ **52.** $\sqrt{525}$ **53.** $\sqrt{352}$ **54.** $\sqrt{363}$

2 Simplify variable radical expressions

55. How can you tell whether a variable exponential expression is a perfect square?

56. When is a radical expression in simplest form?

57. $16x^6y^8$ is a perfect square because $16 = (\underline{\quad ? \quad})^2$, $x^6 = (\underline{\quad ? \quad})^2$, and $y^8 = (\underline{\quad ? \quad})^2$.

58. To simplify $\sqrt{75x^{15}}$, write $75x^{15}$ as the product of a perfect square and a factor that does not contain a perfect square. Then use the Product Property of Radicals and simplify:
$\sqrt{75x^{15}} = \sqrt{\underline{\quad ? \quad} \cdot 3x} = \sqrt{\underline{\quad ? \quad}}\,\sqrt{3x} = \underline{\quad ? \quad}\sqrt{3x}$

Simplify.

59. $\sqrt{x^6}$

60. $\sqrt{x^{12}}$

61. $\sqrt{y^{15}}$

62. $\sqrt{y^{11}}$

63. $\sqrt{a^{20}}$

64. $\sqrt{a^{16}}$

65. $\sqrt{x^4y^4}$

66. $\sqrt{x^{12}y^8}$

67. $\sqrt{4x^4}$

68. $\sqrt{25y^8}$

69. $\sqrt{24x^2}$

70. $\sqrt{x^3y^{15}}$

71. $\sqrt{x^3y^7}$

72. $\sqrt{a^{15}b^5}$

73. $\sqrt{a^3b^{11}}$

74. $\sqrt{24y^7}$

75. $\sqrt{60x^5}$

76. $\sqrt{72y^7}$

77. $\sqrt{49a^4b^8}$

78. $\sqrt{144x^2y^8}$

79. $\sqrt{18x^5y^7}$

80. $\sqrt{32a^5b^{15}}$

81. $\sqrt{40x^{11}y^7}$

82. $\sqrt{72x^9y^3}$

83. $\sqrt{80a^9b^{10}}$

84. $\sqrt{96a^5b^7}$

85. $2\sqrt{16a^2b^3}$

86. $5\sqrt{25a^4b^7}$

87. $x\sqrt{x^4y^2}$

88. $y\sqrt{x^3y^6}$

89. $4\sqrt{20a^4b^7}$

90. $5\sqrt{12a^3b^4}$

91. $3x\sqrt{12x^2y^7}$

92. $4y\sqrt{18x^5y^4}$

93. $2x^2\sqrt{8x^2y^3}$

94. $3y^2\sqrt{27x^4y^3}$

95. $\sqrt{25(a + 4)^2}$

96. $\sqrt{81(x + y)^4}$

97. $\sqrt{4(x + 2)^4}$

98. $\sqrt{9(x + 2)^2}$

99. $\sqrt{x^2 + 4x + 4}$

100. $\sqrt{b^2 + 8b + 16}$

101. $\sqrt{y^2 + 2y + 1}$

102. $\sqrt{a^2 + 6a + 9}$

For Exercises 103 to 106, a is a positive integer. State whether the expression represents a rational number or an irrational number.

103. $\sqrt{100a^6}$

104. $\sqrt{9a^9}$

105. $\sqrt{\sqrt{25a^{16}}}$

106. $\sqrt{\sqrt{81a^8}}$

10.1 Applying Concepts

107. **Traffic Safety** Traffic accident investigators can estimate the speed S, in miles per hour, of a car from the length of its skid mark by using the formula $S = \sqrt{30fl}$, where f is the coefficient of friction (which depends on the type of road surface) and l is the length of the skid mark in feet. Suppose the coefficient of friction is 1.2 and the length of a skid mark is 60 ft. Determine the speed of the car **a.** as a radical in simplest form and **b.** rounded to the nearest integer.

108. **Aviation** The distance a pilot in an airplane can see to the horizon can be approximated by the equation $d = 1.2\sqrt{h}$, where d is the distance to the horizon in miles and h is the height of the plane in feet. For a pilot flying at an altitude of 5000 ft, what is the distance to the horizon? Round to the nearest tenth.

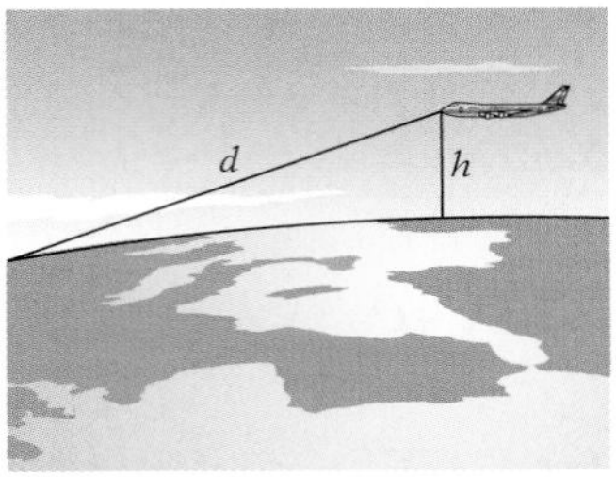

Simplify.

109. $\sqrt{0.0025a^3b^5}$

110. $-\frac{3y}{4}\sqrt{64x^4y^2}$

111. Given $f(x) = \sqrt{2x - 1}$, find each of the following. Write your answer in simplest form.
a. $f(1)$ **b.** $f(5)$ **c.** $f(14)$

112. Use the roster method to list the whole numbers between $\sqrt{8}$ and $\sqrt{90}$.

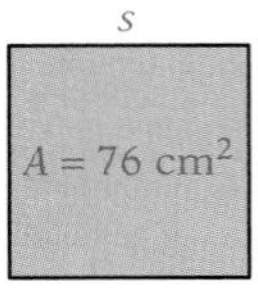

113. **Geometry** The area of a square is 76 cm^2. Find the length of a side of the square. Round to the nearest tenth.

Assuming x can be any real number, for what values of x is the radical expression a real number? Write the answer as an inequality or write "all real numbers."

114. $\sqrt{x}$

115. $\sqrt{4x}$

116. $\sqrt{x - 2}$

117. $\sqrt{x + 5}$

118. $\sqrt{6 - 4x}$

119. $\sqrt{5 - 2x}$

120. $\sqrt{x^2 + 7}$

121. $\sqrt{x^2 + 1}$

122.  Describe in your own words how to simplify a radical expression.

123.  Explain why $2\sqrt{2}$ is in simplest form and $\sqrt{8}$ is not in simplest form.

10.2 Addition and Subtraction of Radical Expressions

OBJECTIVE 1 Add and subtract radical expressions

The Distributive Property is used to simplify the sum or difference of radical expressions with the same radicand.

$$5\sqrt{2} + 3\sqrt{2} = (5+3)\sqrt{2} = 8\sqrt{2}$$
$$6\sqrt{2x} - 4\sqrt{2x} = (6-4)\sqrt{2x} = 2\sqrt{2x}$$

Radical expressions that are in simplest form and have different radicands cannot be simplified by the Distributive Property.

$2\sqrt{3} + 4\sqrt{2}$ cannot be simplified by the Distributive Property.

To simplify the sum or difference of radical expressions, simplify each term. Then use the Distributive Property.

Subtract: $4\sqrt{8} - 10\sqrt{2}$

Simplify each term.

$$\begin{aligned} 4\sqrt{8} - 10\sqrt{2} &= 4\sqrt{4\cdot 2} - 10\sqrt{2} \\ &= 4\sqrt{4}\sqrt{2} - 10\sqrt{2} \\ &= 4\cdot 2\sqrt{2} - 10\sqrt{2} \\ &= 8\sqrt{2} - 10\sqrt{2} \\ &= (8-10)\sqrt{2} \\ &= -2\sqrt{2} \end{aligned}$$

Subtract by using the Distributive Property.

EXAMPLE 1 Simplify. **A.** $5\sqrt{2} - 3\sqrt{2} + 12\sqrt{2}$ **B.** $3\sqrt{12} - 5\sqrt{27}$

Solution **A.** $5\sqrt{2} - 3\sqrt{2} + 12\sqrt{2}$
$= (5 - 3 + 12)\sqrt{2}$ • **Use the Distributive Property.**
$= 14\sqrt{2}$

B.
$$\begin{aligned} 3\sqrt{12} - 5\sqrt{27} &= 3\sqrt{4\cdot 3} - 5\sqrt{9\cdot 3} \\ &= 3\sqrt{4}\,\sqrt{3} - 5\sqrt{9}\,\sqrt{3} \\ &= 3\cdot 2\sqrt{3} - 5\cdot 3\sqrt{3} \\ &= 6\sqrt{3} - 15\sqrt{3} \\ &= -9\sqrt{3} \end{aligned}$$

PROBLEM 1 Simplify. **A.** $9\sqrt{3} + 3\sqrt{3} - 18\sqrt{3}$ **B.** $2\sqrt{50} - 5\sqrt{32}$

Solution See page S23.

Subtract: $8\sqrt{18x} - 2\sqrt{32x}$

Simplify each term.

$$\begin{aligned} 8\sqrt{18x} - 2\sqrt{32x} &= 8\sqrt{9}\,\sqrt{2x} - 2\sqrt{16}\,\sqrt{2x} \\ &= 8\cdot 3\sqrt{2x} - 2\cdot 4\sqrt{2x} \\ &= 24\sqrt{2x} - 8\sqrt{2x} \\ &= 16\sqrt{2x} \end{aligned}$$

Subtract the radical expressions.

EXAMPLE 2 Simplify.

A. $3\sqrt{12x^3} - 2x\sqrt{3x}$ **B.** $2x\sqrt{8y} - 3\sqrt{2x^2y} + 2\sqrt{32x^2y}$

Solution **A.**
$$\begin{aligned} 3\sqrt{12x^3} - 2x\sqrt{3x} &= 3\sqrt{4x^2}\sqrt{3x} - 2x\sqrt{3x} \\ &= 3 \cdot 2x\sqrt{3x} - 2x\sqrt{3x} \\ &= 6x\sqrt{3x} - 2x\sqrt{3x} \\ &= 4x\sqrt{3x} \end{aligned}$$

B.
$$\begin{aligned} &2x\sqrt{8y} - 3\sqrt{2x^2y} + 2\sqrt{32x^2y} \\ &= 2x\sqrt{4}\sqrt{2y} - 3\sqrt{x^2}\sqrt{2y} + 2\sqrt{16x^2}\sqrt{2y} \\ &= 2x \cdot 2\sqrt{2y} - 3 \cdot x\sqrt{2y} + 2 \cdot 4x\sqrt{2y} \\ &= 4x\sqrt{2y} - 3x\sqrt{2y} + 8x\sqrt{2y} \\ &= 9x\sqrt{2y} \end{aligned}$$

PROBLEM 2 Simplify.

A. $y\sqrt{28y} + 7\sqrt{63y^3}$ **B.** $2\sqrt{27a^5} - 4a\sqrt{12a^3} + a^2\sqrt{75a}$

Solution See page S24.

10.2 Concept Review

Determine whether the statement is always true, sometimes true, or never true.

1. $5\sqrt{2} + 6\sqrt{3} = 11\sqrt{5}$

2. The Distributive Property is used to add or subtract radical expressions with the same radicand.

3. $4\sqrt{7}$ and $\sqrt{7}$ are examples of like radical expressions.

4. The expressions $3\sqrt{12}$ and $5\sqrt{3}$ cannot be subtracted until $3\sqrt{12}$ is rewritten in simplest form.

5. $5\sqrt{32x} + 4\sqrt{18x} = 5(4\sqrt{2x}) + 4(3\sqrt{2x}) = 20\sqrt{2x} + 12\sqrt{2x} = 32\sqrt{2x}$

6. The expressions $9\sqrt{11}$ and $10\sqrt{13}$ can be added after each radical is written in simplest form.

10.2 Exercises

1 Add and subtract radical expressions

1. Simplify: $5\sqrt{5} - 8\sqrt{5}$

$5\sqrt{5} - 8\sqrt{5} = (\underline{\quad ? \quad} - \underline{\quad ? \quad})\sqrt{5}$ • **The radicands are the same. Use the Distributive Property.**

$= \underline{\quad ? \quad}\sqrt{5}$ • **Subtract.**

Simplify.

2. $2\sqrt{2} + \sqrt{2}$

3. $3\sqrt{5} + 8\sqrt{5}$

4. $-3\sqrt{7} + 2\sqrt{7}$

5. $4\sqrt{5} - 10\sqrt{5}$

6. $-3\sqrt{11} - 8\sqrt{11}$

7. $-3\sqrt{3} - 5\sqrt{3}$

8. $2\sqrt{x} + 8\sqrt{x}$

9. $3\sqrt{y} + 2\sqrt{y}$

10. $8\sqrt{y} - 10\sqrt{y}$

11. $-5\sqrt{2a} + 2\sqrt{2a}$

12. $-2\sqrt{3b} - 9\sqrt{3b}$

13. $-7\sqrt{5a} - 5\sqrt{5a}$

14. $3x\sqrt{2} - x\sqrt{2}$

15. $2y\sqrt{3} - 9y\sqrt{3}$

16. $2a\sqrt{3a} - 5a\sqrt{3a}$

17. $-5b\sqrt{3x} - 2b\sqrt{3x}$

18. $3\sqrt{xy} - 8\sqrt{xy}$

19. $-4\sqrt{xy} + 6\sqrt{xy}$

20. $\sqrt{45} + \sqrt{125}$

21. $\sqrt{32} - \sqrt{98}$

22. $2\sqrt{2} + 3\sqrt{8}$

23. $4\sqrt{128} - 3\sqrt{32}$

24. $5\sqrt{18} - 2\sqrt{75}$

25. $5\sqrt{75} - 2\sqrt{18}$

26. $5\sqrt{4x} - 3\sqrt{9x}$

27. $-3\sqrt{25y} + 8\sqrt{49y}$

28. Simplify: $3\sqrt{x^3} + 2x\sqrt{x}$

$3\sqrt{x^3} + 2x\sqrt{x} = 3\sqrt{\underline{\quad ? \quad}}\sqrt{x} + 2x\sqrt{x}$ • **Write $\sqrt{x^3}$ as the product of the square root of a perfect square and $\sqrt{x}$.**

$= 3\underline{\quad ? \quad}\sqrt{x} + 2x\sqrt{x}$ • **Simplify $\sqrt{x^2}$.**

$= (\underline{\quad ? \quad} + \underline{\quad ? \quad})\sqrt{x}$ • **Use the Distributive Property.**

$= \underline{\quad ? \quad}\sqrt{x}$ • **Add.**

29. $3\sqrt{3x^2} - 5\sqrt{27x^2}$

30. $-2\sqrt{8y^2} + 5\sqrt{32y^2}$

31. $2x\sqrt{xy^2} - 3y\sqrt{x^2y}$

32. $4a\sqrt{b^2a} - 3b\sqrt{a^2b}$

33. $3x\sqrt{12x} - 5\sqrt{27x^3}$

34. $2a\sqrt{50a} + 7\sqrt{32a^3}$

35. $4y\sqrt{8y^3} - 7\sqrt{18y^5}$

36. $2a\sqrt{8ab^2} - 2b\sqrt{2a^3}$

37. $b^2\sqrt{a^5b} + 3a^2\sqrt{ab^5}$

38. $y^2\sqrt{x^5y} + x\sqrt{x^3y^5}$

39. $4\sqrt{2} - 5\sqrt{2} + 8\sqrt{2}$

40. $3\sqrt{3} + 8\sqrt{3} - 16\sqrt{3}$

41. $5\sqrt{x} - 8\sqrt{x} + 9\sqrt{x}$

42. $\sqrt{x} - 7\sqrt{x} + 6\sqrt{x}$

43. $8\sqrt{2} - 3\sqrt{y} - 8\sqrt{2}$

44. $8\sqrt{3} - 5\sqrt{2} - 5\sqrt{3}$

45. $8\sqrt{8} - 4\sqrt{32} - 9\sqrt{50}$

46. $2\sqrt{12} - 4\sqrt{27} + \sqrt{75}$

47. $-2\sqrt{3} + 5\sqrt{27} - 4\sqrt{45}$

48. $-2\sqrt{8} - 3\sqrt{27} + 3\sqrt{50}$

49. $4\sqrt{75} + 3\sqrt{48} - \sqrt{99}$

50. $2\sqrt{75} - 5\sqrt{20} + 2\sqrt{45}$

51. $\sqrt{25x} - \sqrt{9x} + \sqrt{16x}$

52. $\sqrt{4x} - \sqrt{100x} - \sqrt{49x}$

53. $3\sqrt{3x} + \sqrt{27x} - 8\sqrt{75x}$

54. $5\sqrt{5x} + 2\sqrt{45x} - 3\sqrt{80x}$

55. $2a\sqrt{75b} - a\sqrt{20b} + 4a\sqrt{45b}$

56. $2b\sqrt{75a} - 5b\sqrt{27a} + 2b\sqrt{20a}$

57. $x\sqrt{3y^2} - 2y\sqrt{12x^2} + xy\sqrt{3}$

58. $a\sqrt{27b^2} + 3b\sqrt{147a^2} - ab\sqrt{3}$

59. $3\sqrt{ab^3} + 4a\sqrt{a^2b} - 5b\sqrt{4ab}$

60. $5\sqrt{a^3b} + a\sqrt{4ab} - 3\sqrt{49a^3b}$

61. $3a\sqrt{2ab^2} - \sqrt{a^2b^2} + 4b\sqrt{3a^2b}$

62. $2\sqrt{4a^2b^2} - 3a\sqrt{9ab^2} + 4b\sqrt{a^2b}$

63. Determine whether the statement is true or false.

a. $7x\sqrt{x} + x\sqrt{x} = 7x^2\sqrt{x}$

b. $\sqrt{10a} - \sqrt{a} = \sqrt{a}(\sqrt{10} - 1)$

c. $\sqrt{9 + y^2} = 3 + y$

d. $\sqrt{27x^4} + \sqrt{3} = \sqrt{3}(3x^2 + 1)$

64. Which expression is equivalent to $\sqrt{2ab} + \sqrt{2ab}$?

a. $2\sqrt{ab}$ b. $\sqrt{4ab}$ c. $2ab$ d. $\sqrt{8ab}$

10.2 Applying Concepts

Add or subtract.

65. $5\sqrt{x + 2} + 3\sqrt{x + 2}$

66. $8\sqrt{a + 5} - 4\sqrt{a + 5}$

67. $\frac{1}{2}\sqrt{8x^2y} + \frac{1}{3}\sqrt{18x^2y}$

68. $\frac{1}{4}\sqrt{48ab^2} + \frac{1}{5}\sqrt{75ab^2}$

69. $\frac{a}{3}\sqrt{54ab^3} + \frac{b}{4}\sqrt{96a^3b}$

70. $\frac{x}{6}\sqrt{72xy^5} + \frac{y}{7}\sqrt{98x^3y^3}$

71. $2\sqrt{8x + 4y} - 5\sqrt{18x + 9y}$

72. $3\sqrt{a^3 + a^2} + 5\sqrt{4a^3 + 4a^2}$

73. **Geometry** The lengths of the sides of a triangle are $4\sqrt{3}$ cm, $2\sqrt{3}$ cm, and $2\sqrt{15}$ cm. Find the perimeter of the triangle.

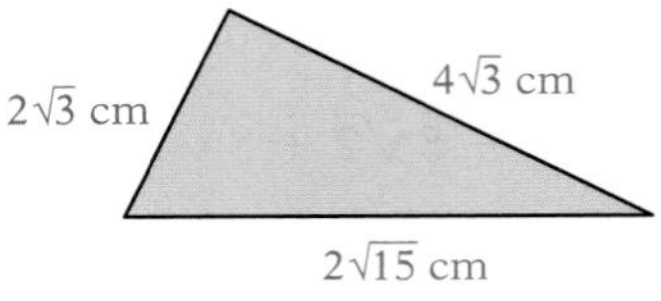

74. **Geometry** The length of a rectangle is $3\sqrt{2}$ cm. The width is $\sqrt{2}$ cm. Find the perimeter of the rectangle.

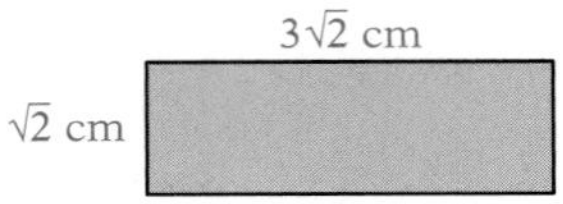

75. Geometry The length of a rectangle is $4\sqrt{5}$ cm. The width is $\sqrt{5}$ cm. Find the decimal approximation of the perimeter. Round to the nearest tenth.

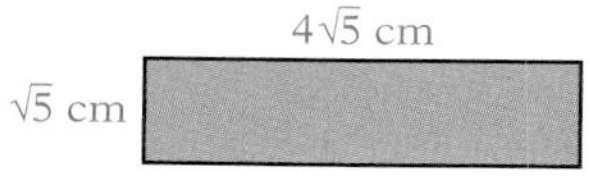

76. Given $G(x) = \sqrt{x+5} + \sqrt{5x+3}$, write $G(3)$ in simplest form.

77. Use complete sentences to explain the steps in simplifying the radical expression $a\sqrt{32ab^2} + b\sqrt{50a^3}$.

10.3 Multiplication and Division of Radical Expressions

OBJECTIVE 1 Multiply radical expressions

The Product Property of Square Roots is used to multiply variable radical expressions.

$$\sqrt{2x}\,\sqrt{3y} = \sqrt{2x \cdot 3y} = \sqrt{6xy}$$

Multiply: $\sqrt{2x^2}\,\sqrt{32x^5}$

Use the Product Property of Square Roots to multiply the radicands.

$$\sqrt{2x^2}\,\sqrt{32x^5} = \sqrt{2x^2 \cdot 32x^5} = \sqrt{64x^7}$$

Simplify.

$$= \sqrt{64x^6}\,\sqrt{x} = 8x^3\sqrt{x}$$

EXAMPLE 1 Multiply: $\sqrt{3x^4}\,\sqrt{2x^2y}\,\sqrt{6xy^2}$

Solution

$$\sqrt{3x^4}\,\sqrt{2x^2y}\,\sqrt{6xy^2} = \sqrt{3x^4 \cdot 2x^2y \cdot 6xy^2} = \sqrt{36x^7y^3} = \sqrt{36x^6y^2}\,\sqrt{xy} = 6x^3y\sqrt{xy}$$

PROBLEM 1 Multiply: $\sqrt{5a}\,\sqrt{15a^3b^4}\,\sqrt{3b^5}$

Solution See page S24.

When the expression $(\sqrt{x})^2$ is simplified by using the Product Property of Square Roots, the result is x.

$$(\sqrt{x})^2 = \sqrt{x}\,\sqrt{x} = \sqrt{x \cdot x} = \sqrt{x^2} = x$$

For $a > 0$, $(\sqrt{a})^2 = \sqrt{a^2} = a$.

Multiply: $\sqrt{2x}(x + \sqrt{2x})$

Use the Distributive Property to remove parentheses.

$$\sqrt{2x}(x + \sqrt{2x}) = \sqrt{2x}(x) + \sqrt{2x}\,\sqrt{2x} = x\sqrt{2x} + (\sqrt{2x})^2 = x\sqrt{2x} + 2x$$

EXAMPLE 2 Multiply: $\sqrt{3ab}(\sqrt{3a} + \sqrt{9b})$

Solution
$$\begin{aligned}\sqrt{3ab}(\sqrt{3a} + \sqrt{9b}) &= \sqrt{3ab}(\sqrt{3a}) + \sqrt{3ab}(\sqrt{9b})\\ &= \sqrt{9a^2b} + \sqrt{27ab^2}\\ &= \sqrt{9a^2}\sqrt{b} + \sqrt{9b^2}\sqrt{3a}\\ &= 3a\sqrt{b} + 3b\sqrt{3a}\end{aligned}$$

PROBLEM 2 Multiply: $\sqrt{5x}(\sqrt{5x} - \sqrt{25y})$

Solution See page S24.

To multiply $(\sqrt{2} - 3x)(\sqrt{2} + x)$, use the FOIL method.

$$\begin{aligned}(\sqrt{2} - 3x)(\sqrt{2} + x) &= (\sqrt{2})^2 + x\sqrt{2} - 3x\sqrt{2} - 3x^2\\ &= 2 + (x - 3x)\sqrt{2} - 3x^2\\ &= 2 - 2x\sqrt{2} - 3x^2\end{aligned}$$

EXAMPLE 3 Multiply: $(2\sqrt{x} - \sqrt{y})(5\sqrt{x} - 2\sqrt{y})$

Solution
$$\begin{aligned}&(2\sqrt{x} - \sqrt{y})(5\sqrt{x} - 2\sqrt{y})\\ &= 10(\sqrt{x})^2 - 4\sqrt{xy} - 5\sqrt{xy} + 2(\sqrt{y})^2\\ &= 10x - 9\sqrt{xy} + 2y\end{aligned}$$

PROBLEM 3 Multiply: $(3\sqrt{x} - \sqrt{y})(5\sqrt{x} - 2\sqrt{y})$

Solution See page S24.

The expressions $a + b$ and $a - b$, which are the sum and difference of two terms, are called **conjugates** of each other.

The product of conjugates is the difference of two squares.

$$\begin{aligned}&(a + b)(a - b) = a^2 - b^2\\ &(2 + \sqrt{7})(2 - \sqrt{7}) = 2^2 - (\sqrt{7})^2 = 4 - 7 = -3\\ &(3 + \sqrt{y})(3 - \sqrt{y}) = 3^2 - (\sqrt{y})^2 = 9 - y\end{aligned}$$

EXAMPLE 4 Multiply: $(\sqrt{a} - \sqrt{b})(\sqrt{a} + \sqrt{b})$

Solution $(\sqrt{a} - \sqrt{b})(\sqrt{a} + \sqrt{b}) = (\sqrt{a})^2 - (\sqrt{b})^2 = a - b$

PROBLEM 4 Multiply: $(2\sqrt{x} + 7)(2\sqrt{x} - 7)$

Solution See page S24.

OBJECTIVE 2 Divide radical expressions

The square root of a quotient is equal to the quotient of the square roots.

The Quotient Property of Square Roots

If a and b are positive real numbers, then $\sqrt{\dfrac{a}{b}} = \dfrac{\sqrt{a}}{\sqrt{b}}$.

Point of Interest

A radical expression that occurs in Einstein's Theory of Relativity is

$$\frac{1}{\sqrt{1-\frac{v^2}{c^2}}}$$

where v is the velocity of an object and c is the speed of light.

Simplify: $\sqrt{\dfrac{4x^2}{z^6}}$

Rewrite the radical expression as the quotient of the square roots.

Take the square roots of the perfect squares.

$$\sqrt{\frac{4x^2}{z^6}} = \frac{\sqrt{4x^2}}{\sqrt{z^6}} = \frac{2x}{z^3}$$

Simplify: $\sqrt{\dfrac{24x^3y^7}{3x^7y^2}}$

Simplify the radicand.

$$\sqrt{\frac{24x^3y^7}{3x^7y^2}} = \sqrt{\frac{8y^5}{x^4}}$$

Rewrite the radical expression as the quotient of the square roots.

$$= \frac{\sqrt{8y^5}}{\sqrt{x^4}}$$

Simplify.

$$= \frac{\sqrt{4y^4}\,\sqrt{2y}}{\sqrt{x^4}} = \frac{2y^2\sqrt{2y}}{x^2}$$

Simplify: $\dfrac{\sqrt{4x^2y}}{\sqrt{xy}}$

Use the Quotient Property of Square Roots.

$$\frac{\sqrt{4x^2y}}{\sqrt{xy}} = \sqrt{\frac{4x^2y}{xy}}$$

Simplify the radicand.

$$= \sqrt{4x}$$

Simplify the radical expression.

$$= \sqrt{4}\,\sqrt{x} = 2\sqrt{x}$$

A radical expression is not in simplest form if a radical remains in the denominator. The procedure used to remove a radical from the denominator is called **rationalizing the denominator.**

Simplify: $\dfrac{2}{\sqrt{3}}$

The expression $\dfrac{2}{\sqrt{3}}$ has a radical expression in the denominator. Multiply the expression by $\dfrac{\sqrt{3}}{\sqrt{3}}$, which equals 1.

$$\frac{2}{\sqrt{3}} = \frac{2}{\sqrt{3}} \cdot \frac{\sqrt{3}}{\sqrt{3}}$$

Simplify.

$$= \frac{2\sqrt{3}}{(\sqrt{3})^2} = \frac{2\sqrt{3}}{3}$$

Thus $\frac{2}{\sqrt{3}} = \frac{2\sqrt{3}}{3}$, but $\frac{2}{\sqrt{3}}$ is not in simplest form. Because no radical remains in the denominator and the radical in the numerator contains no perfect-square factors other than 1, $\frac{2\sqrt{3}}{3}$ is in simplest form.

When the denominator contains a radical expression with two terms, simplify the radical expression by multiplying the numerator and denominator by the conjugate of the denominator.

Simplify: $\frac{\sqrt{2y}}{\sqrt{y}+3}$

Multiply the numerator and denominator by $\sqrt{y} - 3$, the conjugate of $\sqrt{y} + 3$.

$$\frac{\sqrt{2y}}{\sqrt{y}+3} = \frac{\sqrt{2y}}{\sqrt{y}+3} \cdot \frac{\sqrt{y}-3}{\sqrt{y}-3}$$

Simplify.

$$= \frac{\sqrt{2y^2} - 3\sqrt{2y}}{(\sqrt{y})^2 - 3^2}$$

$$= \frac{y\sqrt{2} - 3\sqrt{2y}}{y - 9}$$

The following list summarizes the discussions about radical expressions in simplest form.

Radical Expressions in Simplest Form

A radical expression is in simplest form if:

1. The radicand contains no factor greater than 1 that is a perfect square.
2. There is no fraction under the radical sign.
3. There is no radical in the denominator of a fraction.

EXAMPLE 5 Simplify. **A.** $\frac{\sqrt{4x^2y^5}}{\sqrt{3x^4y}}$ **B.** $\frac{\sqrt{2}}{\sqrt{2}-\sqrt{x}}$ **C.** $\frac{3-\sqrt{5}}{2+3\sqrt{5}}$

Solution **A.** $\frac{\sqrt{4x^2y^5}}{\sqrt{3x^4y}} = \sqrt{\frac{4x^2y^5}{3x^4y}} = \sqrt{\frac{4y^4}{3x^2}} = \frac{\sqrt{4y^4}}{\sqrt{3x^2}} = \frac{2y^2}{x\sqrt{3}} \cdot \frac{\sqrt{3}}{\sqrt{3}} = \frac{2y^2\sqrt{3}}{3x}$

B. $\frac{\sqrt{2}}{\sqrt{2}-\sqrt{x}} = \frac{\sqrt{2}}{\sqrt{2}-\sqrt{x}} \cdot \frac{\sqrt{2}+\sqrt{x}}{\sqrt{2}+\sqrt{x}} = \frac{2+\sqrt{2x}}{2-x}$

C. $\frac{3-\sqrt{5}}{2+3\sqrt{5}} = \frac{3-\sqrt{5}}{2+3\sqrt{5}} \cdot \frac{2-3\sqrt{5}}{2-3\sqrt{5}}$

$$= \frac{6 - 9\sqrt{5} - 2\sqrt{5} + 3 \cdot 5}{4 - 9 \cdot 5}$$

$$= \frac{21 - 11\sqrt{5}}{-41}$$

$$= -\frac{21 - 11\sqrt{5}}{41}$$

PROBLEM 5 Simplify. **A.** $\dfrac{\sqrt{15x^6y^7}}{\sqrt{3x^7y^9}}$ **B.** $\dfrac{\sqrt{y}}{\sqrt{y}+3}$ **C.** $\dfrac{5+\sqrt{y}}{1-2\sqrt{y}}$

Solution See page S24.

10.3 Concept Review

Determine whether the statement is always true, sometimes true, or never true.

1. By the Product Property of Square Roots, if $a > 0$ and $b > 0$, then $\sqrt{a} \cdot \sqrt{b} = \sqrt{ab}$.
2. When we square a square root, the result is the radicand.
3. The procedure for rationalizing the denominator is used when a fraction has a radical expression in the denominator.
4. The square root of a fraction is equal to the square root of the numerator over the square root of the denominator.
5. A radical expression is in simplest form if the radicand contains no factor other than 1 that is a perfect square.
6. The conjugate of $5 - \sqrt{3}$ is $\sqrt{3} - 5$.

10.3 Exercises

1 Multiply radical expressions

1. $\sqrt{3} \cdot \sqrt{3} = \sqrt{\underline{\quad ? \quad}}$ • **Use the Product Property of Square Roots to multiply the radicands.**
   $= \underline{\quad ? \quad}$ • **Simplify.**

2. $\sqrt{3} \cdot \sqrt{15} = \sqrt{\underline{\quad ? \quad}}$ • **Use the Product Property of Square Roots to multiply the radicands.**
   $= \sqrt{9 \cdot \underline{\quad ? \quad}}$ • **Write the radicand as the product of a perfect square and a factor that does not contain a perfect square.**
   $= \sqrt{9}\sqrt{\underline{\quad ? \quad}}$ • **Use the Product Property of Square Roots.**
   $= \underline{\quad ? \quad}\sqrt{\underline{\quad ? \quad}}$ • **Simplify the square root of the perfect square.**

Multiply.

3. $\sqrt{5}\sqrt{5}$
4. $\sqrt{11}\sqrt{11}$
5. $\sqrt{3}\sqrt{12}$
6. $\sqrt{2}\sqrt{8}$

7. $\sqrt{x}\sqrt{x}$
8. $\sqrt{y}\sqrt{y}$
9. $\sqrt{xy^3}\sqrt{x^5y}$
10. $\sqrt{a^3b^5}\sqrt{ab^5}$

11. $\sqrt{3a^2b^5}\sqrt{6ab^7}$
12. $\sqrt{5x^3y}\sqrt{10x^2y}$
13. $\sqrt{6a^3b^2}\sqrt{24a^5b}$
14. $\sqrt{8ab^5}\sqrt{12a^7b}$

15. $\sqrt{2}(\sqrt{2} - \sqrt{3})$
16. $3(\sqrt{12} - \sqrt{3})$
17. $\sqrt{x}(\sqrt{x} - \sqrt{y})$
18. $\sqrt{b}(\sqrt{a} - \sqrt{b})$

19. $\sqrt{5}(\sqrt{10} - \sqrt{x})$
20. $\sqrt{6}(\sqrt{y} - \sqrt{18})$
21. $\sqrt{8}(\sqrt{2} - \sqrt{5})$
22. $\sqrt{10}(\sqrt{20} - \sqrt{a})$

23. $(\sqrt{x} - 3)^2$
24. $(2\sqrt{a} - y)^2$
25. $\sqrt{3a}(\sqrt{3a} - \sqrt{3b})$

26. $\sqrt{5x}(\sqrt{10x} - \sqrt{x})$
27. $\sqrt{2ac}\sqrt{5ab}\sqrt{10cb}$
28. $\sqrt{3xy}\sqrt{6x^3y}\sqrt{2y^2}$

29. $(3\sqrt{x} - 2y)(5\sqrt{x} - 4y)$
30. $(5\sqrt{x} + 2\sqrt{y})(3\sqrt{x} - \sqrt{y})$
31. $(\sqrt{x} - \sqrt{y})(\sqrt{x} + \sqrt{y})$

32. $(\sqrt{3x} + y)(\sqrt{3x} - y)$
33. $(2\sqrt{x} + \sqrt{y})(5\sqrt{x} + 4\sqrt{y})$
34. $(5\sqrt{x} - 2\sqrt{y})(3\sqrt{x} - 4\sqrt{y})$

35. For $a > 0$, is $(\sqrt{a} - 1)(\sqrt{a} + 1)$ less than, equal to, or greater than a?

36. For $a > 0$, is $\sqrt{a}(\sqrt{2a} - \sqrt{a})$ less than, equal to, or greater than a?

2 Divide radical expressions

37. Explain why $\frac{\sqrt{5}}{5}$ is in simplest form and $\frac{1}{\sqrt{5}}$ is not in simplest form.

38. Why can we multiply $\frac{1}{\sqrt{3}}$ by $\frac{\sqrt{3}}{\sqrt{3}}$ without changing the value of $\frac{1}{\sqrt{3}}$?

39. State whether the expression is in simplest form.

a. $\frac{a}{\sqrt{b}}$ **b.** $\frac{\sqrt{a}}{b}$ **c.** $\sqrt{\frac{a}{b}}$ **d.** $\frac{\sqrt{a}}{\sqrt{b}}$

40. By what expression should the numerator and denominator be multiplied in order to rationalize the denominator?

a. $\frac{2}{\sqrt{5}}$ **b.** $\frac{3}{\sqrt{y}}$ **c.** $\frac{14}{\sqrt{3xy}}$ **d.** $\frac{\sqrt{5}}{4\sqrt{6}}$

Simplify.

41. $\frac{\sqrt{32}}{\sqrt{2}}$

42. $\frac{\sqrt{45}}{\sqrt{5}}$

43. $\frac{\sqrt{98}}{\sqrt{2}}$

44. $\frac{\sqrt{48}}{\sqrt{3}}$

45. $\frac{\sqrt{27a}}{\sqrt{3a}}$

46. $\frac{\sqrt{72x^5}}{\sqrt{2x}}$

47. $\frac{\sqrt{15x^3y}}{\sqrt{3xy}}$

48. $\frac{\sqrt{40x^5y^2}}{\sqrt{5xy}}$

49. $\frac{\sqrt{2a^5b^4}}{\sqrt{98ab^4}}$

50. $\frac{\sqrt{48x^5y^2}}{\sqrt{3x^3y}}$

51. $\frac{1}{\sqrt{3}}$

52. $\frac{1}{\sqrt{8}}$

53. $\frac{15}{\sqrt{75}}$

54. $\frac{6}{\sqrt{72}}$

55. $\frac{6}{\sqrt{12x}}$

56. $\frac{14}{\sqrt{7y}}$

57. $\frac{8}{\sqrt{32x}}$

58. $\frac{15}{\sqrt{50x}}$

59. $\frac{3}{\sqrt{x}}$

60. $\frac{4}{\sqrt{2x}}$

61. $\frac{\sqrt{8x^2y}}{\sqrt{2x^4y^2}}$

62. $\frac{\sqrt{4x^2}}{\sqrt{9y}}$

63. $\frac{\sqrt{16a}}{\sqrt{49ab}}$

64. $\frac{5\sqrt{8}}{4\sqrt{50}}$

65. $\frac{5\sqrt{18}}{9\sqrt{27}}$

66. $\frac{\sqrt{12a^3b}}{\sqrt{24a^2b^2}}$

67. $\frac{\sqrt{3xy}}{\sqrt{27x^3y^2}}$

68. $\frac{\sqrt{9xy^2}}{\sqrt{27x}}$

69. $\frac{\sqrt{4x^2y}}{\sqrt{3xy^3}}$

70. $\frac{\sqrt{16x^3y^2}}{\sqrt{8x^3y}}$

71. $\frac{1}{\sqrt{2} - 3}$

72. $\frac{5}{\sqrt{7} - 3}$

73. $\frac{3}{5 + \sqrt{5}}$

74. $\frac{7}{\sqrt{2} - 7}$

75. $\frac{\sqrt{xy}}{\sqrt{x} - \sqrt{y}}$

76. $\frac{\sqrt{x}}{\sqrt{x} - \sqrt{y}}$

77. $\frac{5\sqrt{x^2y}}{\sqrt{75xy^2}}$

78. $\frac{3\sqrt{ab}}{a\sqrt{6b}}$

79. $\frac{\sqrt{2}}{\sqrt{2} - \sqrt{3}}$

80. $\frac{1 + \sqrt{2}}{1 - \sqrt{2}}$

81. $\frac{\sqrt{5}}{\sqrt{2} - \sqrt{5}}$

82. $\frac{\sqrt{6}}{\sqrt{3} - \sqrt{2}}$

83. $\frac{\sqrt{x}}{\sqrt{x} + 3}$

84. $\frac{\sqrt{y}}{2 - \sqrt{y}}$

85. $\frac{5\sqrt{3} - 7\sqrt{3}}{4\sqrt{3}}$

86. $\frac{10\sqrt{7} - 2\sqrt{7}}{2\sqrt{7}}$

87. $\frac{5\sqrt{8} - 3\sqrt{2}}{\sqrt{2}}$

88. $\frac{5\sqrt{12} - \sqrt{3}}{\sqrt{27}}$

89. $\frac{3\sqrt{2} - 8\sqrt{2}}{\sqrt{2}}$

90. $\frac{5\sqrt{3} - 2\sqrt{3}}{2\sqrt{3}}$

91. $\frac{2\sqrt{8} + 3\sqrt{2}}{\sqrt{32}}$

92. $\frac{3 - \sqrt{6}}{5 - 2\sqrt{6}}$

93. $\frac{6 - 2\sqrt{3}}{4 + 3\sqrt{3}}$

94. $\frac{\sqrt{2} + 2\sqrt{6}}{2\sqrt{2} - 3\sqrt{6}}$

95. $\dfrac{2\sqrt{3} - \sqrt{6}}{5\sqrt{3} + 2\sqrt{6}}$

96. $\dfrac{3 + \sqrt{x}}{2 - \sqrt{x}}$

97. $\dfrac{\sqrt{a} - 4}{2\sqrt{a} + 2}$

98. $\dfrac{3 + 2\sqrt{y}}{2 - \sqrt{y}}$

99. $\dfrac{2 + \sqrt{y}}{\sqrt{y} - 3}$

100. $\dfrac{\sqrt{x} + \sqrt{y}}{\sqrt{x} - \sqrt{y}}$

10.3 Applying Concepts

Simplify.

101. $-\sqrt{1.3}\,\sqrt{1.3}$

102. $\sqrt{\dfrac{5}{8}}\,\sqrt{\dfrac{5}{8}}$

103. $-\sqrt{\dfrac{16}{81}}$

104. $\sqrt{1\dfrac{9}{16}}$

105. $\sqrt{2\dfrac{1}{4}}$

106. $-\sqrt{6\dfrac{1}{4}}$

Geometry Find the area of the geometric figure. All dimensions are given in meters.

107.

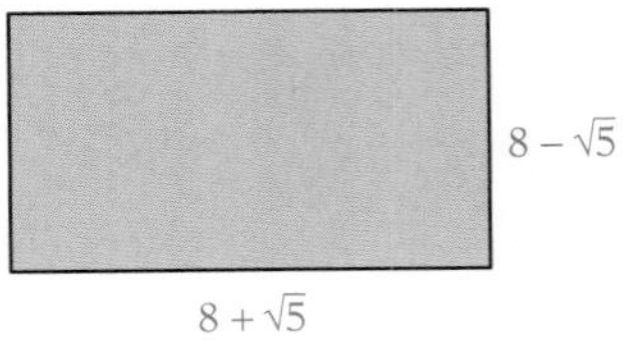

108.

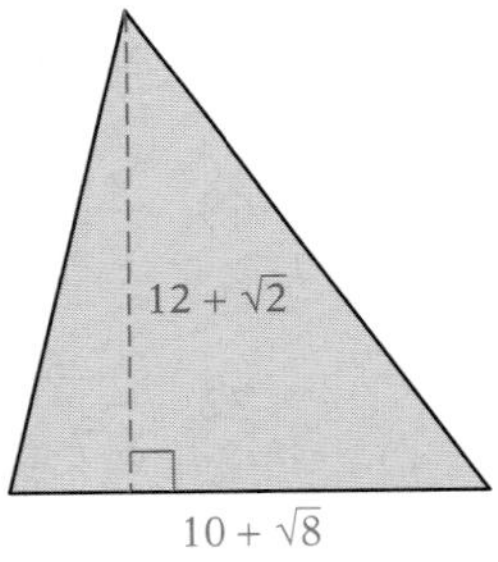

109. Is the equation true or false? If the equation is false, correct the right side.

a. $(\sqrt{y})^4 = y^2$

b. $(2\sqrt{x})^3 = 8x\sqrt{x}$

c. $(\sqrt{x} + 1)^2 = x + 1$

d. $\dfrac{1}{2 - \sqrt{3}} = 2 + \sqrt{3}$

110. Show that 2 is a solution of the equation $\sqrt{x + 2} + \sqrt{x - 1} = 3$.

111. Is 16 a solution of the equation $\sqrt{x} - \sqrt{x + 9} = 1$?

112. Show that $1 + \sqrt{6}$ and $1 - \sqrt{6}$ are solutions of the equation $x^2 - 2x - 5 = 0$.

113. In your own words, describe the process of rationalizing the denominator.

114. The number $\dfrac{\sqrt{5} + 1}{2}$ is called the golden ratio. Research the golden ratio and write a few paragraphs about this number and its applications.

10.4 Solving Equations Containing Radical Expressions

OBJECTIVE 1 Solve equations containing one or more radical expressions

An equation that contains a variable expression in a radicand is a **radical equation.**

$$\left.\begin{aligned}\sqrt{x} &= 4\\ \sqrt{x+2} &= \sqrt{x-7}\end{aligned}\right\}\text{ Radical equations}$$

The following property of equality states that if two numbers are equal, then the squares of the numbers are equal. This property is used to solve radical equations.

Property of Squaring Both Sides of an Equation

If a and b are real numbers and $\boldsymbol{a = b}$, then $\boldsymbol{a^2 = b^2}$.

Solve: $\sqrt{x-2} - 7 = 0$

Rewrite the equation with the radical on one side of the equation and the constant on the other side.

$$\sqrt{x-2} - 7 = 0$$
$$\sqrt{x-2} = 7$$

Square both sides of the equation.

$$(\sqrt{x-2})^2 = 7^2$$

Solve the resulting equation.

$$x - 2 = 49$$
$$x = 51$$

Take Note

Any time each side of an equation is squared, you must check the proposed solution of the equation.

Check the solution. When both sides of an equation are squared, the resulting equation may have a solution that is not a solution of the original equation.

Check: $\sqrt{x-2} - 7 = 0$

$\sqrt{51-2} - 7$	0
$\sqrt{49} - 7$	0
$7 - 7$	0

$0 = 0$

The solution is 51.

EXAMPLE 1 Solve: $\sqrt{3x} + 2 = 5$

Solution

$$\sqrt{3x} + 2 = 5$$
$$\sqrt{3x} = 3$$

- **Rewrite the equation so that the radical is alone on one side of the equation.**

$$(\sqrt{3x})^2 = 3^2$$

- **Square both sides of the equation.**

$$3x = 9$$
$$x = 3$$

- **Solve for *x*.**

Check $\sqrt{3x} + 2 = 5$

$\sqrt{3 \cdot 3} + 2$	5
$\sqrt{9} + 2$	5
$3 + 2$	5

- **Both sides of the equation were squared. The solution must be checked.**

$5 = 5$

- **This is a true equation. The solution checks.**

The solution is 3.

PROBLEM 1 Solve: $\sqrt{4x} + 3 = 7$

Solution See page S24.

EXAMPLE 2 Solve. **A.** $0 = 3 - \sqrt{2x - 3}$ **B.** $\sqrt{2x - 5} + 3 = 0$

Solution **A.**

$$0 = 3 - \sqrt{2x - 3}$$
$$\sqrt{2x - 3} = 3$$

- Rewrite the equation so that the radical is alone on one side of the equation.

$$\left(\sqrt{2x - 3}\right)^2 = 3^2$$

- Square both sides of the equation.

$$2x - 3 = 9$$
$$2x = 12$$
$$x = 6$$

Check

$0 = 3 - \sqrt{2x - 3}$	
0	$3 - \sqrt{2 \cdot 6 - 3}$
0	$3 - \sqrt{12 - 3}$
0	$3 - \sqrt{9}$
0	$3 - 3$

$0 = 0$

- This is a true equation. The solution checks.

The solution is 6.

B.

$$\sqrt{2x - 5} + 3 = 0$$
$$\sqrt{2x - 5} = -3$$

- Rewrite the equation so that the radical is alone on one side of the equation.

$$\left(\sqrt{2x - 5}\right)^2 = (-3)^2$$

- Square each side of the equation.

$$2x - 5 = 9$$

- Solve for *x*.

$$2x = 14$$
$$x = 7$$

Check

$\sqrt{2x - 5} + 3 = 0$	
$\sqrt{2 \cdot 7 - 5} + 3$	0
$\sqrt{14 - 5} + 3$	0
$\sqrt{9} + 3$	0
$3 + 3$	0

$6 \neq 0$

- This is not a true equation. The solution does not check.

There is no solution.

PROBLEM 2 Solve. **A.** $\sqrt{3x - 2} - 5 = 0$ **B.** $\sqrt{4x - 7} + 5 = 0$

Solution See page S24.

The following example illustrates the procedure for solving a radical equation containing two radical expressions. Note that the process of squaring both sides of the equation is perfomed twice.

Solve: $\sqrt{5+x} + \sqrt{x} = 5$

	$\sqrt{5+x} + \sqrt{x} = 5$
Solve for one of the radical expressions. Square each side.	$\sqrt{5+x} = 5 - \sqrt{x}$ $(\sqrt{5+x})^2 = (5 - \sqrt{x})^2$
Recall that $(a-b)^2 = a^2 - 2ab + b^2$.	$5 + x = 25 - 10\sqrt{x} + x$
Simplify.	$-20 = -10\sqrt{x}$
This is still a radical equation.	$2 = \sqrt{x}$
Square each side.	$2^2 = (\sqrt{x})^2$ $4 = x$
4 checks as the solution.	The solution is 4.

EXAMPLE 3 Solve: $\sqrt{x} - \sqrt{x-5} = 1$

Solution

$$\sqrt{x} - \sqrt{x-5} = 1$$

$$\sqrt{x} = 1 + \sqrt{x-5}$$ • **Solve for one of the radical expressions.**

$$(\sqrt{x})^2 = (1 + \sqrt{x-5})^2$$ • **Square each side.**

$$x = 1 + 2\sqrt{x-5} + (x-5)$$ • **Simplify.**

$$4 = 2\sqrt{x-5}$$

$$2 = \sqrt{x-5}$$ • **This is a radical equation.**

$$2^2 = (\sqrt{x-5})^2$$ • **Square each side.**

$$4 = x - 5$$ • **Simplify.**

$$9 = x$$

Check

$\sqrt{x} - \sqrt{x-5}$	$= 1$
$\sqrt{9} - \sqrt{9-5}$	1
$3 - \sqrt{4}$	1
$3 - 2$	1
$1 = 1$	

The solution is 9.

PROBLEM 3 Solve: $\sqrt{x} + \sqrt{x+9} = 9$

Solution See page S24.

OBJECTIVE 2 Application problems

Pythagoras (c. 580 B.C.–520 B.C.)

A **right triangle** contains one 90° angle. The side opposite the 90° angle is called the **hypotenuse.** The other two sides are called **legs.**

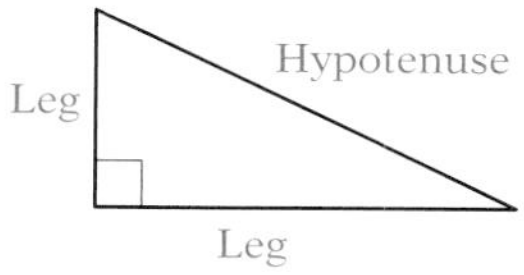

The angles in a right triangle are usually labeled with the capital letters A, B, and C, with C reserved for the right angle. The side opposite angle A is side a, the side opposite side B is side b, and c is the hypotenuse.

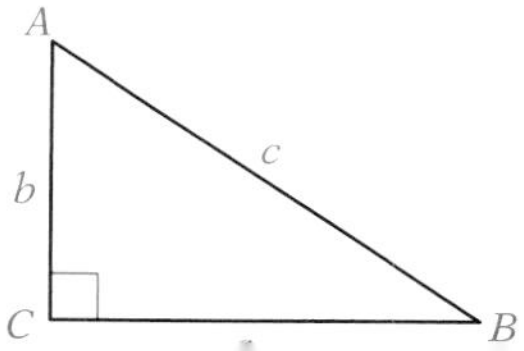

The Greek mathematician Pythagoras is generally credited with the discovery that the square of the hypotenuse of a right triangle is equal to the sum of the squares of the two legs. This is called the **Pythagorean Theorem.**

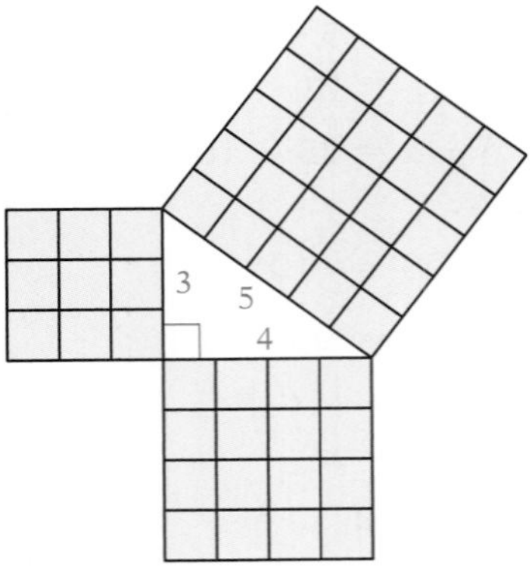

The figure at the left is a right triangle with legs measuring 3 units and 4 units and a hypotenuse measuring 5 units. Each side of the triangle is also the side of a square. The number of square units in the area of the largest square is equal to the sum of the numbers of square units in the areas of the smaller squares.

Square of the hypotenuse	=	Sum of the squares of the two legs

$$5^2 = 3^2 + 4^2$$
$$25 = 9 + 16$$
$$25 = 25$$

Point of Interest

The first known proof of this theorem occurs in a Chinese text, Arithmetic Classic, which was written around 600 B.C. (but there are no existing copies) and revised over a period of 500 years. The earliest known copy of this text dates from approximately 100 B.C.

Pythagorean Theorem

If a and b are the lengths of the legs of a right triangle and c is the length of the hypotenuse, then $\boldsymbol{c^2 = a^2 + b^2}$.

If the lengths of two sides of a right triangle are known, the Pythagorean Theorem can be used to find the length of the third side.

The Pythagorean Theorem is used to find the hypotenuse when the two legs are known.

$$\text{Hypotenuse} = \sqrt{(\text{leg})^2 + (\text{leg})^2}$$
$$c = \sqrt{a^2 + b^2}$$
$$c = \sqrt{(5)^2 + (12)^2}$$
$$c = \sqrt{25 + 144}$$
$$c = \sqrt{169}$$
$$c = 13$$

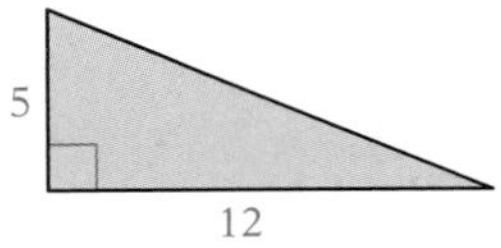

Take Note

If we let $a = 12$ and $b = 5$, the result is the same.

The Pythagorean Theorem is used to find the length of a leg when one leg and the hypotenuse are known.

$$\text{Leg} = \sqrt{(\text{hypotenuse})^2 - (\text{leg})^2}$$
$$a = \sqrt{c^2 - b^2}$$
$$a = \sqrt{(25)^2 - (20)^2}$$
$$a = \sqrt{625 - 400}$$
$$a = \sqrt{225}$$
$$a = 15$$

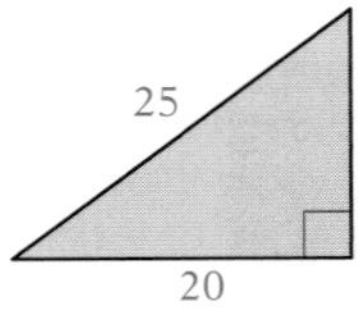

Example 4 and Problem 4 illustrate the use of the Pythagorean Theorem. Example 5 and Problem 5 illustrate other applications of radical equations.

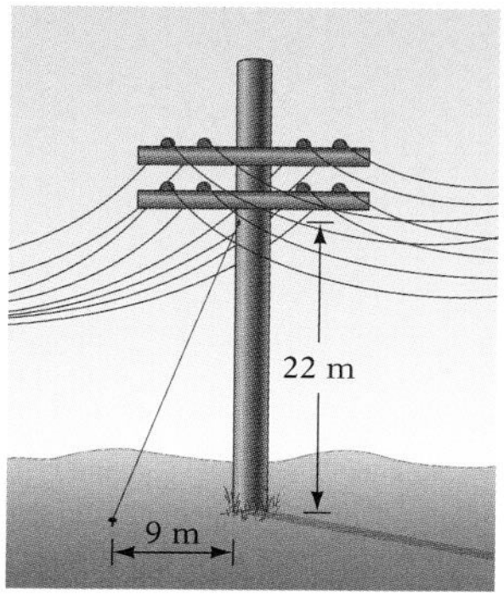

EXAMPLE 4 A guy wire is attached to a point 22 m above the ground on a telephone pole that is perpendicular to the ground. The wire is anchored to the ground at a point 9 m from the base of the pole. Find the length of the guy wire. Round to the nearest hundredth.

Strategy To find the length of the guy wire, use the Pythagorean Theorem. One leg is the distance from the bottom of the wire to the base of the telephone pole. The other leg is the distance from the top of the wire to the base of the telephone pole. The guy wire is the hypotenuse. Solve the Pythagorean Theorem for the hypotenuse.

Solution

$$c = \sqrt{a^2 + b^2}$$
$$c = \sqrt{(22)^2 + (9)^2}$$
$$c = \sqrt{484 + 81}$$
$$c = \sqrt{565}$$
$$c \approx 23.77$$

The guy wire has a length of 23.77 m.

PROBLEM 4 A ladder 12 ft long is resting against a building. How high on the building will the ladder reach when the bottom of the ladder is 5 ft from the building? Round to the nearest hundredth.

Solution See page S25.

EXAMPLE 5 How far would a submarine periscope have to be above the water for the lookout to locate a ship 5 mi away? The equation for the distance in miles that the lookout can see is $d = \sqrt{1.5h}$, where h is the height in feet above the surface of the water. Round to the nearest hundredth.

Strategy To find the height above water, replace d in the equation with the given value. Then solve for h.

Solution

$$d = \sqrt{1.5h}$$
$$5 = \sqrt{1.5h}$$
$$5^2 = \left(\sqrt{1.5h}\right)^2$$
$$25 = 1.5h$$
$$\frac{25}{1.5} = h$$
$$16.67 \approx h$$

The periscope must be 16.67 ft above the water.

PROBLEM 5 Find the length of a pendulum that makes one swing in 1.5 s. The equation for the time of one swing is $T = 2\pi\sqrt{\frac{L}{32}}$, where T is the time in seconds and L is the length in feet. Round to the nearest hundredth.

Solution See page S25.

10.4 Concept Review

Determine whether the statement is always true, sometimes true, or never true.

1. A radical equation is an equation that contains a radical.
2. We can square both sides of an equation without changing the solutions of the equation.
3. We use the Property of Squaring Both Sides of an Equation in order to eliminate a radical expression from an equation.
4. The first step in solving a radical equation is to square both sides of the equation.
5. Suppose $a^2 = b^2$. Then $a = b$.
6. The Pythagorean Theorem is used to find the length of a side of a triangle.

10.4 Exercises

1 Solve equations containing one or more radical expressions

1. Which of the following equations are radical equations?
   a. $8 = \sqrt{5} + x$
   b. $\sqrt{x - 7} = 9$
   c. $\sqrt{x} + 4 = 6$
   d. $12 = \sqrt{3x}$

2. What does the Property of Squaring Both Sides of an Equation state?

3. Solve: $\sqrt{x - 2} = 5$. You will check the solution in Exercise 4.

$\sqrt{x - 2} = 5$	• **The radical is alone on one side.**
$(\sqrt{x - 2})^{\underline{?}} = 5^{\underline{?}}$	• **Square each side of the equation.**
$\underline{\quad ? \quad} = \underline{\quad ? \quad}$	• **Simplify.**
$x = \underline{\quad ? \quad}$	• **Add** ___?___ **to each side of the equation.**

4. Check the solution of the equation $\sqrt{x - 2} = 5$ that you found in Exercise 3.

$\sqrt{x-2}$	$= 5$	
$\sqrt{27-2}$	5	• **Replace *x* with ___?___.**
$\sqrt{\underline{\quad ? \quad}}$	5	• **Subtract.**
$\underline{\quad ? \quad}$	$= 5$	• **Simplify the radical expression. This is a ___?___ equation. The solution checks.**

Solve and check.

5. $\sqrt{x} = 5$

6. $\sqrt{y} = 7$

7. $\sqrt{a} = 12$

8. $\sqrt{a} = 9$

9. $\sqrt{5x} = 5$

10. $\sqrt{3x} = 4$

11. $\sqrt{4x} = 8$

12. $\sqrt{6x} = 3$

13. $\sqrt{2x} - 4 = 0$

14. $3 - \sqrt{5x} = 0$

15. $\sqrt{4x} + 5 = 2$

16. $\sqrt{3x} + 9 = 4$

17. $\sqrt{3x - 2} = 4$

18. $\sqrt{5x + 6} = 1$

19. $\sqrt{2x + 1} = 7$

20. $\sqrt{5x + 4} = 3$

21. $0 = 2 - \sqrt{3 - x}$

22. $0 = 5 - \sqrt{10 + x}$

23. $\sqrt{5x + 2} = 0$

24. $\sqrt{3x - 7} = 0$

25. $\sqrt{3x} - 6 = -4$

26. $\sqrt{5x} + 8 = 23$

27. $0 = \sqrt{3x - 9} - 6$

28. $0 = \sqrt{2x + 7} - 3$

29. $\sqrt{5x - 1} = \sqrt{3x + 9}$

30. $\sqrt{3x + 4} = \sqrt{12x - 14}$

31. $\sqrt{5x - 3} = \sqrt{4x - 2}$

32. $\sqrt{5x - 9} = \sqrt{2x - 3}$

33. $\sqrt{x^2 - 5x + 6} = \sqrt{x^2 - 8x + 9}$

34. $\sqrt{x^2 - 2x + 4} = \sqrt{x^2 + 5x - 12}$

35. $\sqrt{x} = \sqrt{x + 3} - 1$

36. $\sqrt{x + 5} = \sqrt{x} + 1$

37. $\sqrt{2x + 5} = 5 - \sqrt{2x}$

38. $\sqrt{2x} + \sqrt{2x + 9} = 9$

39. $\sqrt{3x} - \sqrt{3x + 7} = 1$

40. $\sqrt{x} - \sqrt{x + 9} = 1$

41. Without actually solving the equations, identify which equation has no solution.

a. $-\sqrt{2x - 5} = -3$ **b.** $\sqrt{2x} - 5 = -3$ **c.** $\sqrt{2x - 5} = -3$

42. How many times will the Property of Squaring Both Sides of an Equation be used in the solving of each equation? Do not solve.

a. $\sqrt{x - 3} = \sqrt{4x - 7}$ **b.** $\sqrt{x - 6} = \sqrt{x} - 3$

2 Application problems

43. Integer Problem Five added to the square root of the product of four and a number is equal to seven. Find the number.

44. **Integer Problem** The product of a number and the square root of three is equal to the square root of twenty-seven. Find the number.

45. **Integer Problem** Two added to the square root of the sum of a number and five is equal to six. Find the number.

46. **Integer Problem** The product of a number and the square root of seven is equal to the square root of twenty-eight. Find the number.

47. In a right triangle, the hypotenuse is the side opposite the ___?___ angle. The other two sides are called ___?___.

48. Label the right triangle shown at the right. Include the right angle symbol, the three angles, the two legs, and the hypotenuse.

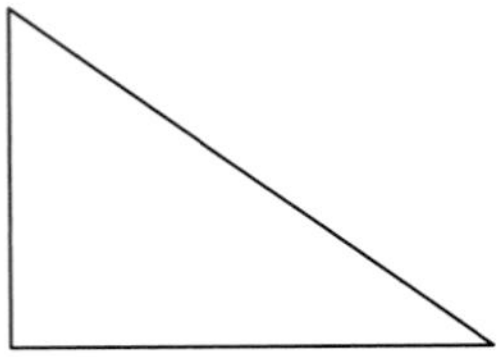

49. What does the Pythagorean Theorem state?

50. A 20-foot ladder leans against the side of a building with its bottom d foot from the building. The ladder reaches a height of h feet. Which of the following distances is not possible as a value for h?
a. 4 ft **b.** 10 ft **c.** 16 ft **d.** 22 ft

Solve. Round to the nearest hundredth.

51. **Geometry** The two legs of a right triangle measure 5 cm and 9 cm. Find the length of the hypotenuse.

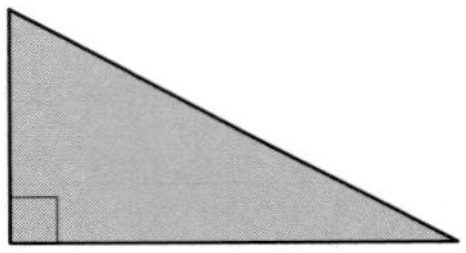

52. **Geometry** The two legs of a right triangle measure 8 in. and 4 in. Find the length of the hypotenuse.

53. **Geometry** The hypotenuse of a right triangle measures 12 ft. One leg of the triangle measures 7 ft. Find the length of the other leg of the triangle.

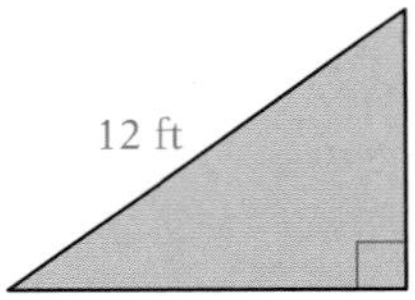

54. **Geometry** The hypotenuse of a right triangle measures 20 cm. One leg of the triangle measures 16 cm. Find the length of the other leg of the triangle.

55. **Geometry** The diagonal of a rectangle is a line drawn from one vertex to the opposite vertex. Find the length of the diagonal in the rectangle shown at the right. Round to the nearest tenth.

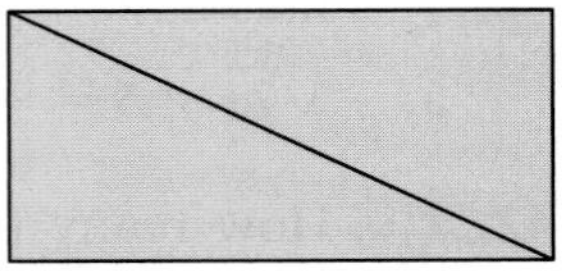

56. The equation $v = 4\sqrt{d}$ gives the speed, v, in feet per second, of a dropped object after the object has fallen d feet. A stone is dropped from a bridge. To find the distance the stone has fallen when it reaches a speed of 48 feet per second, replace ___?___ with 48 and solve for ___?___.

57. Is the equation equivalent to the equation $C = \sqrt{32H}$, given in Exercise 59? Assume C and H are positive.

a. $\dfrac{C^2}{H} = 32$ **b.** $C = 4\sqrt{2H}$ **c.** $\dfrac{C^2}{32} = H$ **d.** $\left(\dfrac{C}{4}\right)^2 = 2H$

58. **Education** One method used to "curve" the grades on an exam is to use the formula $R = 10\sqrt{O}$, where R is the revised score and O is the original score. Use this formula to find the original score on an exam that has a revised score of 75. Round to the nearest whole number.

59. **Physics** A formula used in the study of shallow-water wave motion is $C = \sqrt{32H}$, where C is the wave velocity in feet per second and H is the depth in feet. Use this formula to find the depth of the water when the wave velocity is 20 ft/s.

60. **Sports** The infield of a baseball diamond is a square. The distance between successive bases is 90 ft. The pitcher's mound is on the diagonal between home plate and second base at a distance of 60.5 ft from home plate. Is the pitcher's mound more or less than halfway between home plate and second base?

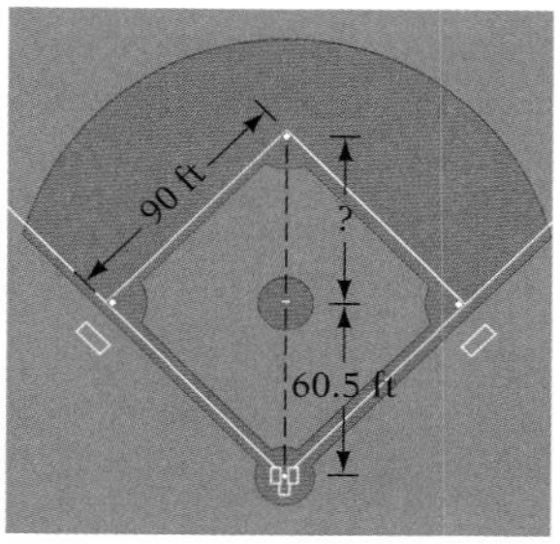

61. **Sports** The infield of a softball diamond is a square. The distance between successive bases is 60 ft. The pitcher's mound is on the diagonal between home plate and second base at a distance of 46 ft from home plate. Is the pitcher's mound more or less than halfway between home plate and second base?

62. **Communications** Marta Lightfoot leaves a dock in her sailboat and sails 2.5 mi due east. She then tacks and sails 4 mi due north. The walkie-talkie Marta has on board has a range of 5 mi. Will she be able to call a friend on the dock from her location using the walkie-talkie?

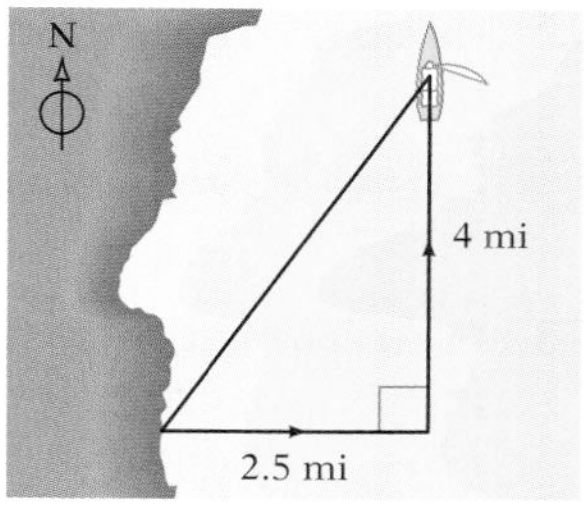

63. **Navigation** How far would a submarine periscope have to be above the water for the lookout to locate a ship 4 mi away? The equation for the distance in miles that the lookout can see is $d = \sqrt{1.5h}$, where h is the height in feet above the surface of the water.

64. **Navigation** How far would a submarine periscope have to be above the water for the lookout to locate a ship 7 mi away? The equation for the distance in miles that the lookout can see is $d = \sqrt{1.5h}$, where h is the height in feet above the surface of the water.

65. **Home Maintenance** Rick Wyman needs to clean the gutters of his home. The gutters are 24 ft above the ground. For safety, the distance a ladder reaches up a wall should be four times the distance from the bottom of the ladder to the base of the side of the house. Therefore, the bottom of the ladder must be 6 ft from the base of the house. Will a 25-foot ladder be long enough to reach the gutters?

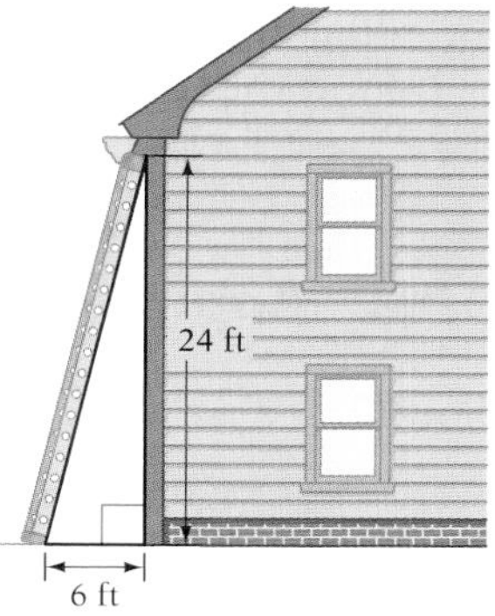

66. **Physics** The speed of a child riding a merry-go-round at a carnival is given by the equation $v = \sqrt{12r}$, where v is the speed in feet per second and r is the distance in feet from the center of the merry-go-round to the rider. If a child is moving at 15 ft/s, how far is the child from the center of the merry-go-round?

67. **Physics** Find the length of a pendulum that makes one swing in 3 s. The equation for the time of one swing is $T = 2\pi\sqrt{\frac{L}{32}}$, where T is the time in seconds and L is the length in feet.

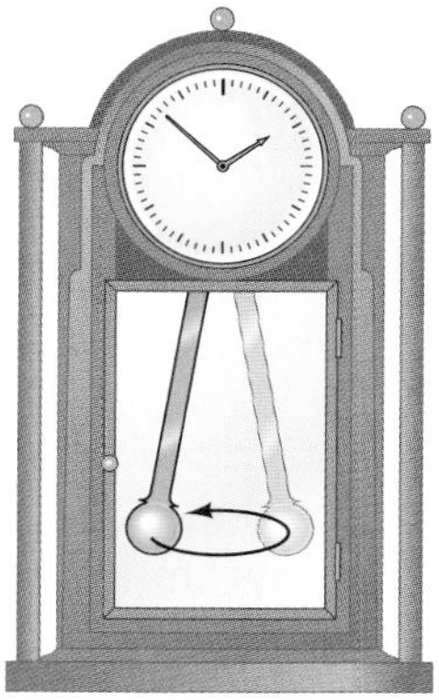

68. **Physics** Find the length of a pendulum that makes one swing in 2 s. The equation for the time of one swing is $T = 2\pi\sqrt{\frac{L}{32}}$, where T is the time in seconds and L is the length in feet.

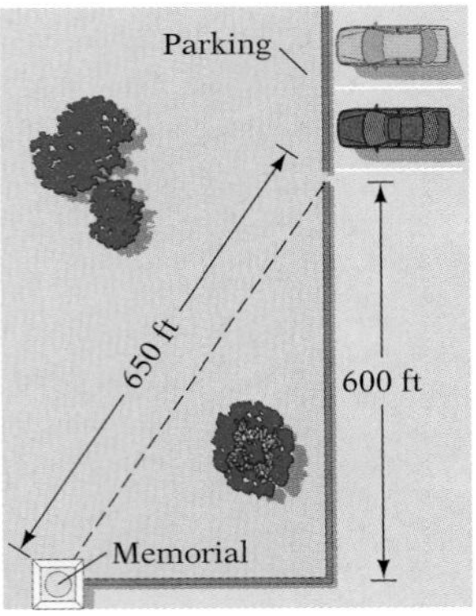

69. **Parks** An L-shaped sidewalk from the parking lot to a memorial is shown in the figure at the right. The distance directly across the grass to the memorial is 650 ft. The distance to the corner is 600 ft. Find the distance from the corner to the memorial.

70. **Aviation** A commuter plane leaves an airport traveling due south at 400 mph. Another plane leaving at the same time travels due east at 300 mph. Find the distance between the two planes after 2 h.

71. **Physics** A stone is dropped from a bridge and hits the water 2 s later. How high is the bridge? The equation for the distance an object falls in T seconds is $T = \sqrt{\frac{d}{16}}$, where d is the distance in feet.

72. **Physics** A stone is dropped into a mine shaft and hits the bottom 3.5 s later. How deep is the mine shaft? The equation for the distance an object falls in T seconds is $T = \sqrt{\frac{d}{16}}$, where d is the distance in feet.

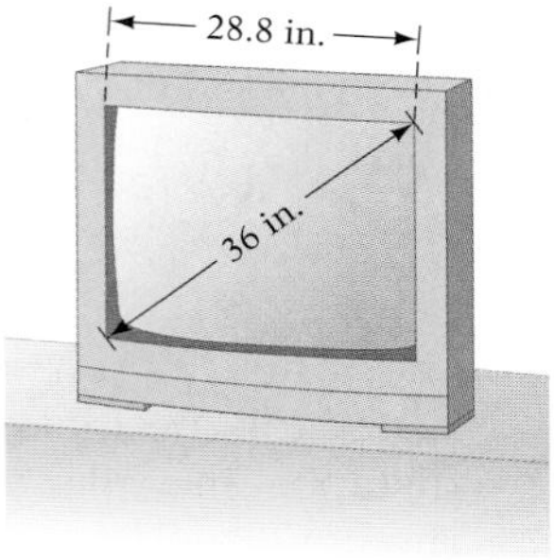

73. **Television** The measure of a television screen is given by the length of a diagonal across the screen. A 36-inch television has a width of 28.8 in. Find the height of the screen.

74. **Television** The measure of a television screen is given by the length of a diagonal across the screen. A 33-inch television has a width of 26.4 in. Find the height of the screen.

10.4 Applying Concepts

Solve.

75. $\sqrt{\frac{5y + 2}{3}} = 3$

76. $\sqrt{\frac{3y}{5}} - 1 = 2$

77. $\sqrt{9x^2 + 49} + 1 = 3x + 2$

78. **Geometry** In the coordinate plane, a triangle is formed by drawing lines between the points (0, 0) and (5, 0), (5, 0) and (5, 12), and (5, 12) and (0, 0). Find the number of units in the perimeter of the triangle.

79. **Geometry** The hypotenuse of a right triangle is $5\sqrt{2}$ cm, and the length of one leg is $4\sqrt{2}$ cm.
a. Find the perimeter of the triangle. **b.** Find the area of the triangle.

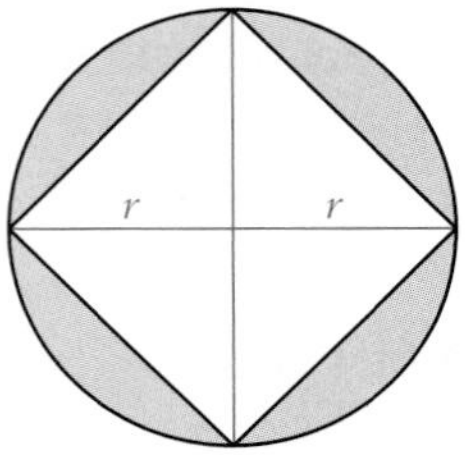

80. **Geometry** Write an expression in factored form for the shaded region in the diagram at the right.

81. **Geometry** A circular fountain is being designed for a triangular plaza in a cultural center. The fountain is placed so that each side of the triangle touches the fountain as shown in the diagram at the right. Find the area of the fountain. The formula for the radius of the circle is given by

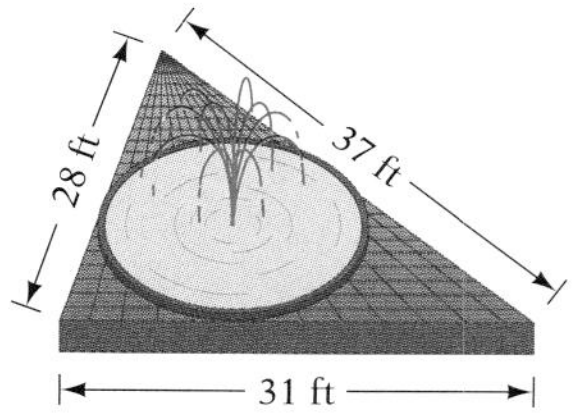

$$r = \sqrt{\frac{(s-a)(s-b)(s-c)}{s}}$$

where $s = \frac{1}{2}(a+b+c)$ and a, b, and c are the lengths of the sides of the triangle. Round to the nearest hundredth.

82. Can the Pythagorean Theorem be used to find the length of side c of the triangle at the right? If so, determine c. If not, explain why the theorem cannot be used.

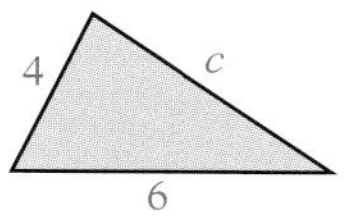

83. What is a Pythagorean triple? Provide at least three examples of Pythagorean triples.

84. Complete the statement using the symbol <, =, or >. Explain how you determined which symbol to use.

a. For an acute triangle with side c the longest side, $a^2 + b^2$ ______ c^2.
b. For a right triangle with side c the longest side, $a^2 + b^2$ ______ c^2.
c. For an obtuse triangle with side c the longest side, $a^2 + b^2$ ______ c^2.

Focus on Problem Solving

Deductive Reasoning

Deductive reasoning uses a rule or statement of fact to reach a conclusion. In the section Equations Containing Fractions in the "Rational Expressions" chapter, we established the rule that if two angles of one triangle are equal to two angles of another triangle, then the two triangles are similar. Thus any time we establish this fact about two triangles, we know that the triangles are similar. Two examples of deductive reasoning follow.

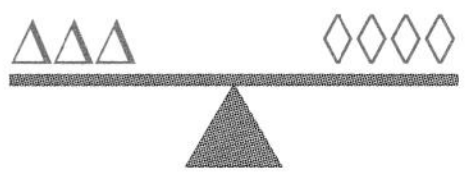

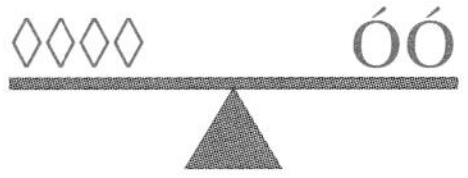

Given that ΔΔΔ = ◊◊◊◊ and ◊◊◊◊ = ÓÓ, then ΔΔΔΔΔΔ is equivalent to how many Ós?

Because 3 Δs = 4 ◊s and 4 ◊s = 2 Ós, 3 Δs = 2 Ós.

6 Δs is twice 3 Δs. We need to find twice 2 Ós, which is 4 Ós.

Therefore, ΔΔΔΔΔΔ = ÓÓÓÓ.

Lomax, Parish, Thorpe, and Wong are neighbors. Each drives a different type of vehicle: a compact car, a sedan, a sports car, or a station wagon. From the following statements, determine which type of vehicle each of the neighbors drives.

a. Although the vehicle owned by Lomax has more mileage on it than does either the sedan or the sports car, it does not have the highest mileage of all four cars. (Use Xa in the chart below to eliminate whatever possibilities this statement enables you to rule out.)

b. Wong and the owner of the sports car live on one side of the street, and Thorpe and the owner of the compact car live on the other side of the street. (Use Xb to eliminate possibilities that this statement rules out.)

c. Thorpe owns the vehicle with the most mileage on it. (Use Xc to eliminate possibilities that this statement rules out.)

	Compact	*Sedan*	*Sports Car*	*Wagon*
Lomax	✓	Xa	Xa	Xb
Parish	Xb	Xb	✓	Xb
Thorpe	Xb	Xc	Xb	✓
Wong	Xb	✓	Xb	

Take Note

To use the chart to solve this problem, write an X in a box to indicate that a possibility has been eliminated. Write a ✓ to show that a match has been found. When a row or column has 3 X's, a ✓ is written in the remaining open box in that row or column of the chart.

Lomax drives the compact car, Parish drives the sports car, Thorpe drives the station wagon, and Wong drives the sedan.

Try the following exercises.

1. Given that ‡‡ = ••••• and ••••• = ΔΔ, then ‡‡‡‡‡ = how many Δ's?

2. Given that ▽▽▽▽▽▽ = ◆◆◆◆ and ◆◆◆◆ = ⊕⊕, then ▽▽▽ = how many ⊕'s?

3. Given that ♣♣♣♣ = ⊗⊗⊗ and ⊗⊗⊗ = ♥♥, then ♥♥♥♥ = how many ♣'s?

4. Given that ◊◊◊◊◊ = ÓÓ and ÓÓ = ♠♠♠, then ♠♠♠♠♠♠ = how many ◊'s?

5. Anna, Kay, Megan, and Nicole decide to travel together during spring break, but they need to find a destination where each of them will be able to participate in her favorite sport (golf, horseback riding, sailing, or tennis). From the following statements, determine the favorite sport of each student.

a. Anna and the student whose favorite sport is sailing both like to swim, whereas Nicole and the student whose favorite sport is tennis would prefer to scuba dive.

b. Megan and the student whose favorite sport is sailing are roommates. Nicole and the student whose favorite sport is golf both live in a single.

6. Chang, Nick, Pablo, and Saul all take different forms of transportation (bus, car, subway, or taxi) from the office to the airport. From the following statements, determine which form of transportation each takes.

a. Chang spent more on transportation than the fellow who took the bus but less than the fellow who took the taxi.

b. Pablo, who did not travel by bus and who spent the least on transportation, arrived at the airport after Nick but before the fellow who took the subway.

c. Saul spent less on transportation than either Chang or Nick.

Projects & Group Activities

Expressway On-Ramp Curves

Highway engineers design expressway on-ramps with both efficiency and safety in mind. An on-ramp cannot be built with too sharp a curve, or the speed at which drivers take the curve will cause them to skid off the road. However, an on-ramp built with too wide a curve requires more building material, takes longer to travel, and uses more land. The following formula states the relationship between the maximum speed at which a car can travel around a curve without skidding: $v = \sqrt{2.5r}$. In this formula, v is speed in miles per hour and r is the radius, in feet, of an unbanked curve.

1. Use a graphing calculator to graph this equation. Use a window of Xmin = 0, Xmax = 2000, Ymin = 0, Ymax = 100. What do the values used for Xmin, Xmax, Ymin, and Ymax represent?
2. As the radius of the curve increases, does the maximum safe speed increase or decrease? Explain your answer on the basis of the graph of the equation.
3. Use the graph to approximate the maximum safe speed when the radius of the curve is 100 ft. Round to the nearest whole number.
4. Use the graph to approximate the radius of the curve for which the maximum safe speed is 40 mph. Round to the nearest whole number.
5. Dan Wheldon won the Indianapolis 500 in 2005 driving at an average speed of 157.603 mph. At this speed, should the radius of an unbanked curve be more or less than 1 mi?

Chapter 10 Summary

Key Words	*Examples*
A **square root** of a positive number x is a number whose square is x. The square root of a negative number is not a real number. [10.1.1, pp. 542, 544]	A square root of 25 is 5 because $5^2 = 25$. A square root of 25 is -5 because $(-5)^2 = 25$. $\sqrt{-9}$ is not a real number.
The **principal square root** of a number is the positive square root. The symbol $\sqrt{}$ is called a **radical sign** and is used to indicate the principal square root of a number. The negative square root of a number is indicated by placing a negative sign in front of the radical. The **radicand** is the expression under the radical symbol. [10.1.1, p. 542]	$\sqrt{25} = 5$ $-\sqrt{25} = -5$ In the expression $\sqrt{25}$, 25 is the radicand.

The square of an integer is a **perfect square.** If a number is not a perfect square, its square root can only be approximated. Such numbers are **irrational numbers.** Their decimal representations never terminate or repeat.
[10.1.1, pp. 542–543]

$2^2 = 4$, $3^2 = 9$, $4^2 = 16$, $5^2 = 25$, $6^2 = 36$, . . . 4, 9, 16, 25, 36, . . . are perfect squares.

5 is not a perfect square. $\sqrt{5}$ is an irrational number.

Conjugates are expressions with two terms that differ only in the sign of the second term. The expressions $a + b$ and $a - b$ are conjugates. [10.3.1, p. 556]

$3 + \sqrt{7}$ and $3 - \sqrt{7}$ are conjugates.

$\sqrt{x} + 2$ and $\sqrt{x} - 2$ are conjugates.

A **radical equation** is an equation that contains a variable expression in a radicand. [10.4.1, p. 563]

$\sqrt{2x} + 8 = 12$ is a radical equation.
$2x + \sqrt{8} = 12$ is not a radical equation.

Essential Rules and Procedures

The Product Property of Square Roots
If a and b are positive real numbers, then $\sqrt{ab} = \sqrt{a} \cdot \sqrt{b}$.
[10.1.1, p. 543]

$$\sqrt{12} = \sqrt{4 \cdot 3} = \sqrt{4}\sqrt{3} = 2\sqrt{3}$$

Adding and Subtracting Radical Expressions
The Distributive Property is used to simplify the sum or difference of like radical expressions. [10.2.1, p. 551]

$$\begin{aligned} 16\sqrt{3x} - 4\sqrt{3x} &= (16 - 4)\sqrt{3x} \\ &= 12\sqrt{3x} \end{aligned}$$

Multiplying Radical Expressions
The Product Property of Square Roots is used to multiply radical expressions.

$$\sqrt{5x}\sqrt{7y} = \sqrt{5x \cdot 7y} = \sqrt{35xy}$$

Use the Distributive Property to remove parentheses.

$$\sqrt{y}(2 + \sqrt{3x}) = 2\sqrt{y} + \sqrt{3xy}$$

Use the FOIL method to multiply radical expressions with two terms. [10.3.1, pp. 555–556]

$$\begin{aligned} &(5 - \sqrt{x})(11 + \sqrt{x}) \\ &= 55 + 5\sqrt{x} - 11\sqrt{x} - (\sqrt{x})^2 \\ &= 55 - 6\sqrt{x} - x \end{aligned}$$

The Quotient Property of Square Roots

If a and b are positive real numbers, then $\sqrt{\dfrac{a}{b}} = \dfrac{\sqrt{a}}{\sqrt{b}}$.

[10.3.2, p. 556]

$$\sqrt{\frac{9x^2}{y^8}} = \frac{\sqrt{9x^2}}{\sqrt{y^8}} = \frac{3x}{y^4}$$

Dividing Radical Expressions
The Quotient Property of Square Roots is used to divide radical expressions. [10.3.2, p. 557]

$$\begin{aligned} \frac{\sqrt{3x^5y}}{\sqrt{75xy^3}} &= \sqrt{\frac{3x^5y}{75xy^3}} = \sqrt{\frac{x^4}{25y^2}} \\ &= \frac{\sqrt{x^4}}{\sqrt{25y^2}} = \frac{x^2}{5y} \end{aligned}$$

Rationalizing the Denominator
A radical is not in simplest form if there is a radical in the denominator. The procedure used to remove a radical from the denominator is called rationalizing the denominator.
[10.3.2, p. 557]

$$\frac{5}{\sqrt{7}} = \frac{5}{\sqrt{7}} \cdot \frac{\sqrt{7}}{\sqrt{7}} = \frac{5\sqrt{7}}{7}$$

Radical Expressions in Simplest Form
A radical expression is in simplest form if:
1. The radicand contains no factor greater than 1 that is a perfect square.
2. There is no fraction under the radical sign.
3. There is no radical in the denominator of a fraction.

[10.3.2, p. 558]

$\sqrt{12}$, $\sqrt{\frac{3}{4}}$, and $\frac{1}{\sqrt{2}}$ are not in simplest form.

$2\sqrt{3}$, $\frac{\sqrt{3}}{2}$, and $\frac{\sqrt{2}}{2}$ are in simplest form.

Property of Squaring Both Sides of an Equation
If a and b are real numbers and $a = b$, then $a^2 = b^2$.
[10.4.1, p. 563]

$$\begin{aligned}\sqrt{x+3} &= 4\\ (\sqrt{x+3})^2 &= 4^2\\ x+3 &= 16\\ x &= 13\end{aligned}$$

Solving Radical Equations
When an equation contains one radical expression, write the equation with the radical alone on one side of the equation. Square both sides of the equation. Solve for the variable. Whenever both sides of an equation are squared, the solutions must be checked. [10.4.1, p. 563]

$$\begin{aligned}\sqrt{2x} - 1 &= 5\\ \sqrt{2x} &= 6\\ (\sqrt{2x})^2 &= 6^2\\ 2x &= 36\\ x &= 18 \quad \text{The solution checks.}\end{aligned}$$

Pythagorean Theorem
If a and b are the lengths of the legs of a right triangle and c is the length of the hypotenuse, then $c^2 = a^2 + b^2$.
[10.4.2, p. 566]

Two legs of a right triangle measure 4 cm and 7 cm. To find the length of the hypotenuse, use the equation

$$c = \sqrt{a^2 + b^2}$$
$$c = \sqrt{4^2 + 7^2} = \sqrt{16 + 49} = \sqrt{65}$$

The hypotenuse measures $\sqrt{65}$ cm.

Chapter 10 Review Exercises

1. Subtract: $5\sqrt{3} - 16\sqrt{3}$

2. Simplify: $\dfrac{2x}{\sqrt{3} - \sqrt{5}}$

3. Simplify: $\sqrt{x^2 + 16x + 64}$

4. Solve: $3 - \sqrt{7x} = 5$

5. Simplify: $\dfrac{5\sqrt{y} - 2\sqrt{y}}{3\sqrt{y}}$

6. Add: $6\sqrt{7} + \sqrt{7}$

7. Multiply: $(6\sqrt{a} + 5\sqrt{b})(2\sqrt{a} + 3\sqrt{b})$

8. Simplify: $\sqrt{49(x+3)^4}$

9. Simplify: $2\sqrt{36}$

10. Solve: $\sqrt{b} = 4$

11. Subtract: $9x\sqrt{5} - 5x\sqrt{5}$

12. Multiply: $(\sqrt{5ab} - \sqrt{7})(\sqrt{5ab} + \sqrt{7})$

13. Solve: $\sqrt{2x + 9} = \sqrt{8x - 9}$

14. Simplify: $\sqrt{35}$

15. Add: $2x\sqrt{60x^3y^3} + 3x^2y\sqrt{15xy}$

16. Simplify: $\dfrac{\sqrt{3x^3y}}{\sqrt{27xy^5}}$

17. Simplify: $(3\sqrt{x} - \sqrt{y})^2$

18. Simplify: $\sqrt{(a + 4)^2}$

19. Simplify: $5\sqrt{48}$

20. Add: $3\sqrt{12x} + 5\sqrt{48x}$

21. Simplify: $\dfrac{8}{\sqrt{x} - 3}$

22. Multiply: $\sqrt{6a}(\sqrt{3a} + \sqrt{2a})$

23. Simplify: $3\sqrt{18a^5b}$

24. Simplify: $-3\sqrt{120}$

25. Subtract: $\sqrt{20a^5b^9} - 2ab^2\sqrt{45a^3b^5}$

26. Simplify: $\dfrac{\sqrt{98x^7y^9}}{\sqrt{2x^3y}}$

27. Solve: $\sqrt{5x + 1} = \sqrt{20x - 8}$

28. Simplify: $\sqrt{c^{18}}$

29. Simplify: $\sqrt{450}$

30. Simplify: $6a\sqrt{80b} - \sqrt{180a^2b} + 5a\sqrt{b}$

31. Simplify: $\dfrac{16}{\sqrt{a}}$

32. Solve: $6 - \sqrt{2y} = 2$

33. Multiply: $\sqrt{a^3b^4c}\,\sqrt{a^7b^2c^3}$

34. Simplify: $7\sqrt{630}$

35. Simplify: $y\sqrt{24y^6}$

36. Simplify: $\dfrac{\sqrt{250}}{\sqrt{10}}$

37. Solve: $\sqrt{x^2 + 5x + 4} = \sqrt{x^2 + 7x - 6}$

38. Multiply: $(4\sqrt{y} - \sqrt{5})(2\sqrt{y} + 3\sqrt{5})$

39. Find the decimal approximation of $\sqrt{9900}$ to the nearest thousandth.

40. Multiply: $\sqrt{7}\,\sqrt{7}$

41. Simplify: $5x\sqrt{150x^7}$

42. Simplify: $2x^2\sqrt{18x^2y^5} + 6y\sqrt{2x^6y^3} - 9xy^2\sqrt{8x^4y}$

43. Simplify: $\dfrac{\sqrt{54a^3}}{\sqrt{6a}}$

44. Simplify: $4\sqrt{250}$

45. Solve: $\sqrt{5x} = 10$

46. Simplify: $\dfrac{3a\sqrt{3} + 2\sqrt{12a^2}}{\sqrt{27}}$

47. Multiply: $\sqrt{2}\,\sqrt{50}$

48. Simplify: $\sqrt{36x^4y^5}$

49. Simplify: $4y\sqrt{243x^{17}y^9}$

50. Solve: $\sqrt{x + 1} - \sqrt{x - 2} = 1$

51. Simplify: $\sqrt{400}$

52. Simplify: $-4\sqrt{8x} + 7\sqrt{18x} - 3\sqrt{50x}$

53. Solve: $0 = \sqrt{10x + 4} - 8$

54. Multiply: $\sqrt{3}(\sqrt{12} - \sqrt{3})$

55. **Integer Problem** The square root of the sum of two consecutive odd integers is equal to 10. Find the larger integer.

56. **Space Travel** The weight of an object is related to the object's distance from the surface of Earth. An equation for this relationship is $d = 4000\sqrt{\dfrac{W_0}{W_a}}$, where W_0 is the object's weight on the surface of Earth and W_a is the object's weight at a distance of d miles above Earth's surface. A space explorer weighs 36 lb when 8000 mi above Earth's surface. Find the explorer's weight on the surface of Earth.

57. **Geometry** The hypotenuse of a right triangle measures 18 cm. One leg of the triangle measures 11 cm. Find the length of the other leg of the triangle. Round to the nearest hundredth.

58. **Bicycling** A bicycle will overturn if it rounds a corner too sharply or too quickly. The equation for the maximum velocity at which a cyclist can turn a corner without tipping over is given by the equation $v = 4\sqrt{r}$, where v is the velocity of the bicycle in miles per hour and r is the radius of the corner in feet. Find the radius of the sharpest corner that a cyclist can safely turn when riding at a speed of 20 mph.

59. **Tsunamis** A tsunami is a great sea wave produced by underwater earthquakes or volcanic eruption. The velocity of a tsunami as it approaches land is approximated by the equation $v = 3\sqrt{d}$, where v is the velocity in feet per second and d is the depth of the water in feet. Find the depth of the water when the velocity of a tsunami is 30 ft/s.

60. **Guy Wires** A guy wire is attached to a point 25 ft above the ground on a telephone pole that is perpendicular to the ground. The wire is anchored to the ground at a point 8 ft from the base of the pole. Find the length of the guy wire. Round to the nearest hundredth.

Chapter 10 Test

1. Simplify: $\sqrt{121x^8y^2}$

2. Subtract: $5\sqrt{8} - 3\sqrt{50}$

3. Multiply: $\sqrt{3x^2y}\,\sqrt{6x^2}\,\sqrt{2x}$

4. Simplify: $\sqrt{45}$

5. Simplify: $\sqrt{72x^7y^2}$

6. Simplify: $3\sqrt{8y} - 2\sqrt{72x} + 5\sqrt{18x}$

7. Multiply: $(\sqrt{y} + 3)(\sqrt{y} + 5)$

8. Simplify: $\dfrac{4}{\sqrt{8}}$

9. Simplify: $\dfrac{\sqrt{162}}{\sqrt{2}}$

10. Solve: $\sqrt{5x - 6} = 7$

11. Find the decimal approximation of $\sqrt{500}$ to the nearest thousandth.

12. Simplify: $\sqrt{32a^5b^{11}}$

13. Multiply: $\sqrt{a}(\sqrt{a} - \sqrt{b})$

14. Multiply: $\sqrt{8x^3y}\,\sqrt{10xy^4}$

15. Simplify: $\dfrac{\sqrt{98a^6b^4}}{\sqrt{2a^3b^2}}$

16. Solve: $\sqrt{9x} + 3 = 18$

17. Simplify: $\sqrt{192x^{13}y^5}$

18. Simplify: $2a\sqrt{2ab^3} + b\sqrt{8a^3b} - 5ab\sqrt{ab}$

19. Multiply: $(\sqrt{a} - 2)(\sqrt{a} + 2)$

20. Simplify: $\dfrac{3}{2 - \sqrt{5}}$

21. Solve: $3 = 8 - \sqrt{5x}$

22. Multiply: $\sqrt{3}(\sqrt{6} - \sqrt{x^2})$

23. Subtract: $3\sqrt{a} - 9\sqrt{a}$

24. Simplify: $\sqrt{108}$

25. Find the decimal approximation of $\sqrt{63}$ to the nearest thousandth.

26. Simplify: $\dfrac{\sqrt{108a^7b^3}}{\sqrt{3a^4b}}$

27. Solve: $\sqrt{x} - \sqrt{x + 3} = 1$

28. **Integer Problem** The square root of the sum of two consecutive integers is equal to 9. Find the smaller integer.

29. **Physics** Find the length of a pendulum that makes one swing in 2.5 s. The equation for the time of one swing of a pendulum is $T = 2\pi\sqrt{\dfrac{L}{32}}$, where T is the time in seconds and L is the length in feet. Round to the nearest hundredth.

30. **Home Maintenance** A ladder 16 ft long is resting against a building. How high on the building will the ladder reach when the bottom of the ladder is 5 ft from the building? Round to the nearest tenth.

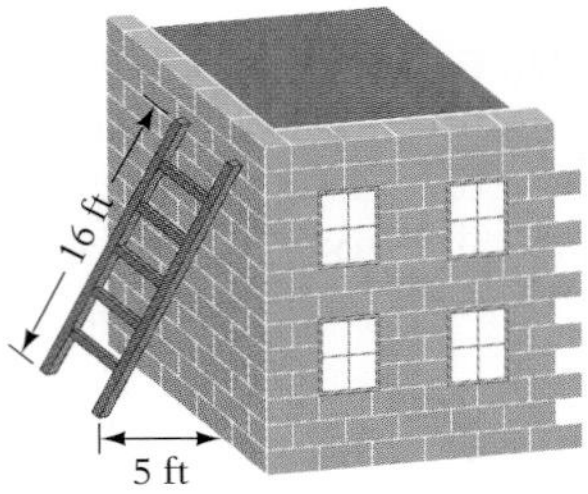

Cumulative Review Exercises

1. Simplify: $\left(\dfrac{2}{3}\right)^2\left(\dfrac{3}{4} - \dfrac{3}{2}\right) + \left(\dfrac{1}{2}\right)^2$

2. Simplify: $-3[x - 2(3 - 2x) - 5x] + 2x$

3. Solve: $2x - 4[3x - 2(1 - 3x)] = 2(3 - 4x)$

4. Solve: $3(x - 7) \geq 5x - 12$

5. Find the slope of the line that contains the points whose coordinates are $(2, -5)$ and $(-4, 3)$.

6. Find the equation of the line that contains the point whose coordinates are $(-2, -3)$ and has slope $\dfrac{1}{2}$.

7. Evaluate $f(x) = \frac{5}{2}x - 8$ at $x = -4$.

8. Graph: $f(x) = -4x + 2$

9. Graph the solution set of $2x + y < -2$.

10. Solve by graphing: $3x - 2y = 8$
$4x + 5y = 3$

11. Solve by substitution: $4x - 3y = 1$
$2x + y = 3$

12. Solve by the addition method: $5x + 4y = 7$
$3x - 2y = 13$

13. Simplify: $(-3x^2y)(-2x^3y^{-4})$

14. Simplify: $\dfrac{12b^4 - 6b^2 + 2}{-6b^2}$

15. Factor: $12x^3y^2 - 9x^2y^3$

16. Factor: $9b^2 + 3b - 20$

17. Factor: $2a^3 - 16a^2 + 30a$

18. Multiply: $\dfrac{3x^3 - 6x^2}{4x^2 + 4x} \cdot \dfrac{3x - 9}{9x^3 - 45x^2 + 54x}$

19. Simplify: $\dfrac{1 - \frac{2}{x} - \frac{15}{x^2}}{1 - \frac{9}{x^2}}$

20. Subtract: $\dfrac{x + 2}{x - 4} - \dfrac{6}{(x - 4)(x - 3)}$

21. Solve: $\dfrac{x}{2x - 5} - 2 = \dfrac{3x}{2x - 5}$

22. Simplify: $2\sqrt{27a} - 5\sqrt{49a} + 8\sqrt{48a}$

23. Simplify: $\dfrac{\sqrt{320}}{\sqrt{5}}$

24. Solve: $\sqrt{2x - 3} - 5 = 0$

25. **Integer Problem** Three-eighths of a number is less than negative twelve. Find the largest integer that satisfies the inequality.

26. **Markup** The selling price of a book is \$29.40. The markup rate used by the bookstore is 20% of the cost. Find the cost of the book.

27. **Mixture Problem** How many ounces of pure water must be added to 40 oz of a 12% salt solution to make a salt solution that is 5% salt?

28. **Integer Problem** The sum of two numbers is twenty-one. Three more than twice the smaller number is equal to the larger. Find the two numbers.

29. **Work Problem** A small water pipe takes twice as long to fill a tank as does a larger water pipe. With both pipes open, it takes 16 h to fill the tank. Find the time it would take the small pipe, working alone, to fill the tank.

30. **Integer Problem** The square root of the sum of two consecutive integers is equal to 7. Find the smaller integer.

CHAPTER

11 Quadratic Equations

OBJECTIVES

11.1
1 Solve quadratic equations by factoring
2 Solve quadratic equations by taking square roots

11.2
1 Solve quadratic equations by completing the square

11.3
1 Solve quadratic equations by using the quadratic formula

11.4
1 Simplify complex numbers
2 Add and subtract complex numbers
3 Multiply complex numbers
4 Divide complex numbers
5 Solve quadratic equations with complex number solutions

11.5
1 Graph a quadratic equation of the form $y = ax^2 + bx + c$

11.6
1 Application problems

Businesses take into account the cost of producing and selling their products, as well as the prices customers pay for them. Profit is the difference between a company's revenue (the total amount of money the company earns by selling its products or services) and its costs (the total amount of money the company spends doing business). Quadratic equations are used in the **Focus on Problem Solving on pages 635–636** to determine the maximum profit companies can earn. You will be asked to determine the maximum monthly profit for a company that sells guitars like the one being purchased in this photo.

DVD SSM *Online Study Center*

Need help? For online student resources, such as section quizzes, visit the Online Study Center at college.hmco.com/pic/aufmannBAWA7e.

Prep Test

1. Evaluate $b^2 - 4ac$ when $a = 2$, $b = -3$, and $c = -4$.
2. Solve: $5x + 4 = 3$
3. Factor: $x^2 + x - 12$
4. Factor: $4x^2 - 12x + 9$
5. Is $x^2 - 10x + 25$ a perfect square trinomial?
6. Solve: $\frac{5}{x-2} = \frac{15}{x}$
7. Graph: $y = -2x + 3$
8. Simplify: $\sqrt{28}$
9. If a is *any* real number, simplify $\sqrt{a^2}$.
10. Walking at a constant speed of 4.5 mph, Lucy and Sam walked from the beginning to the end of a hiking trail. When they reached the end, they immediately started back along the same path at a constant speed of 3 mph. If the round trip took 2 h, what is the length of the hiking trail?

11.1 Solving Quadratic Equations by Factoring or by Taking Square Roots

OBJECTIVE 1 Solve quadratic equations by factoring

In Section 5 of the chapter on factoring, we solved quadratic equations by factoring. In this section, we will review that material and then solve quadratic equations by taking square roots.

An equation of the form $ax^2 + bx + c = 0$, $a \neq 0$, is a **quadratic equation.**

$$4x^2 - 3x + 1 = 0, \qquad a = 4, b = -3, c = 1$$

$$3x^2 - 4 = 0, \qquad a = 3, b = 0, \quad c = -4$$

A quadratic equation is also called a **second-degree equation.**

A quadratic equation is in **standard form** when the polynomial is in descending order and equal to zero.

Recall that the Principle of Zero Products states that if the product of two factors is zero, then at least one of the factors must be zero.

If $a \cdot b = 0$, then $a = 0$ or $b = 0$.

The Principle of Zero Products can be used in solving quadratic equations.

Solve by factoring: $2x^2 - x = 1$

	$2x^2 - x = 1$	
Write the equation in standard form.	$2x^2 - x - 1 = 0$	
Factor the left side of the equation.	$(2x + 1)(x - 1) = 0$	
If $(2x + 1)(x - 1) = 0$, then either $2x + 1 = 0$ or $x - 1 = 0$.	$2x + 1 = 0$	$x - 1 = 0$
Solve each equation for x.	$2x = -1$	$x = 1$
	$x = -\frac{1}{2}$	

The solutions are $-\frac{1}{2}$ and 1.

A graphing calculator can be used to check the solutions of a quadratic equation. Consider the preceding example. The solutions appear to be $-\frac{1}{2}$ and 1. To check these solutions, store one value of x, $-\frac{1}{2}$, in the calculator. Note that after you store $-\frac{1}{2}$ in the calculator's memory, your calculator rewrites the fraction as the decimal -0.5. Evaluate the expression on the left side of the original equation: $2x^2 - x$. The result is 1, which is the number on the right side of the original equation. The solution -0.5 checks. Now store the other value of x, 1, in the calculator. Evaluate the expression on the left side of the original equation: $2x^2 - x$. The result is 1, which is the number on the right side of the equation. The solution 1 checks.

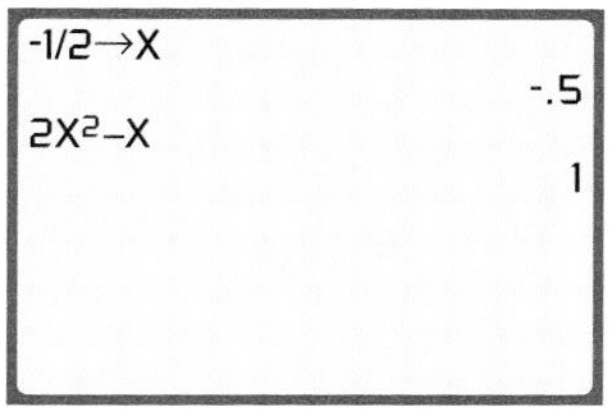

Solve by factoring: $x^2 = 10x - 25$

	$x^2 = 10x - 25$	
Write the equation in standard form.	$x^2 - 10x + 25 = 0$	
Factor the left side of the equation.	$(x - 5)(x - 5) = 0$	
Let each factor equal 0.	$x - 5 = 0$	$x - 5 = 0$
Solve each equation for x.	$x = 5$	$x = 5$

The factorization in this example produced two identical factors. Because $x - 5$ occurs twice in the factored form of the equation, 5 is a **double root** of the equation.

EXAMPLE 1 Solve by factoring: $\frac{z^2}{2} + \frac{z}{3} - \frac{1}{6} = 0$

Solution

$$\frac{z^2}{2} + \frac{z}{3} - \frac{1}{6} = 0$$

$$6\left(\frac{z^2}{2} + \frac{z}{3} - \frac{1}{6}\right) = 6(0)$$

• To eliminate the fractions, multiply each side of the equation by 6.

$$3z^2 + 2z - 1 = 0$$

• The quadratic equation is in standard form.

$$(3z - 1)(z + 1) = 0$$

• Factor the left side of the equation.

$$3z - 1 = 0 \qquad z + 1 = 0$$

• Let each factor equal zero.

$$3z = 1 \qquad z = -1$$

$$z = \frac{1}{3}$$

• Solve each equation for z.

The solutions are $\frac{1}{3}$ and -1.

• $\frac{1}{3}$ and -1 check as solutions.

PROBLEM 1 Solve by factoring: $\frac{3y^2}{2} + y - \frac{1}{2} = 0$

Solution See page S25.

OBJECTIVE 2 Solve quadratic equations by taking square roots

Consider a quadratic equation of the form $x^2 = a$. This equation can be solved by factoring.

$$x^2 = 25$$
$$x^2 - 25 = 0$$
$$(x + 5)(x - 5) = 0$$
$$x + 5 = 0 \qquad x - 5 = 0$$
$$x = -5 \qquad x = 5$$

The solutions are -5 and 5.

Take Note

Recall that the solution of the equation $|x| = 5$ is ± 5. This principle is used when solving an equation by taking square roots. Remember that $\sqrt{x^2} = |x|$. Therefore,

$$x^2 = 25$$
$$\sqrt{x^2} = \sqrt{25}$$
$$|x| = 5$$
$$x = \pm 5$$

• $\sqrt{x^2} = |x|$

• If $|x| = 5$, then $x = \pm 5$.

Solutions that are plus or minus the same number are frequently written using $\pm$. For the example above, this would be written: "The solutions are ± 5." Because the solutions ± 5 can be written as $\pm\sqrt{25}$, an alternative method of solving this equation is suggested.

Principle of Taking the Square Root of Each Side of an Equation

If $x^2 = a$, then $x = \pm\sqrt{a}$.

Solve by taking square roots: $x^2 = 25$

$$x^2 = 25$$

Take the square root of each side of the equation.

$$\sqrt{x^2} = \sqrt{25}$$

Simplify.

$$x = \pm\sqrt{25} = \pm 5$$

Write the solutions.

The solutions are 5 and -5.

Solve by taking square roots: $3x^2 = 36$

$$3x^2 = 36$$

Solve for x^2.

$$x^2 = 12$$

Take the square root of each side of the equation.

$$\sqrt{x^2} = \sqrt{12}$$

Simplify.

$$x = \pm\sqrt{12} = \pm 2\sqrt{3}$$

Check:

$3x^2 = 36$	
$3(2\sqrt{3})^2$	36
$3(12)$	36
$36 = 36$	

$3x^2 = 36$	
$3(-2\sqrt{3})^2$	36
$3(12)$	36
$36 = 36$	

These are true equations. The solutions check.

Write the solutions.

The solutions are $2\sqrt{3}$ and $-2\sqrt{3}$.

Take Note

You should always check your solutions by substituting them back into the *original* equation.

A graphing calculator can be used to check irrational solutions of a quadratic equation. Consider the preceding example; the solutions $2\sqrt{3}$ and $-2\sqrt{3}$ checked. To check these solutions on a calculator, store one value of x, $2\sqrt{3}$, in the calculator. Note that after you store this number in the calculator's memory, the calculator rewrites the expression as the decimal 3.464101615, which is an approximation of $2\sqrt{3}$. Evaluate the expression on the left side of the original equation. The result is 36, which is the number on the right side of the original equation. The solution $2\sqrt{3}$ checks. Now store the other value of x, $-2\sqrt{3}$, in the calculator. Note that after you store this number in the calculator's memory, the calculator rewrites the expression as the decimal -3.464101615, which is an approximation of $-2\sqrt{3}$. Evaluate the expression on the left side of the original equation. The result is 36, which is the number on the right side of the equation. The solution $-2\sqrt{3}$ checks.

```
-2√(3)→X
                -3.464101615
3X²
                          36
```

EXAMPLE 2 Solve by taking square roots.

A. $2x^2 - 72 = 0$ **B.** $x^2 + 16 = 0$

Solution **A.** $2x^2 - 72 = 0$

$$2x^2 = 72$$ • **Solve for x^2.**

$$x^2 = 36$$

$$\sqrt{x^2} = \sqrt{36}$$ • **Take the square root of each side of the equation.**

$$x = \pm\sqrt{36}$$

$$x = \pm 6$$

The solutions are 6 and -6.

B. $x^2 + 16 = 0$

$$x^2 = -16$$

$$\sqrt{x^2} = \sqrt{-16}$$ • **$\sqrt{-16}$ is not a real number.**

The equation has no real number solution.

PROBLEM 2 Solve by taking square roots.

A. $4x^2 - 96 = 0$ **B.** $x^2 + 81 = 0$

Solution See page S25.

An equation containing the square of a binomial can be solved by taking square roots.

Solve by taking square roots: $2(x - 1)^2 - 36 = 0$

$$2(x - 1)^2 - 36 = 0$$

Solve for $(x - 1)^2$.

$$2(x - 1)^2 = 36$$
$$(x - 1)^2 = 18$$

Take the square root of each side of the equation.

$$\sqrt{(x - 1)^2} = \sqrt{18}$$

Simplify.

$$x - 1 = \pm\sqrt{18}$$
$$x - 1 = \pm 3\sqrt{2}$$

Solve for x.

$$x - 1 = 3\sqrt{2} \qquad x - 1 = -3\sqrt{2}$$
$$x = 1 + 3\sqrt{2} \qquad x = 1 - 3\sqrt{2}$$

Check:

$2(x - 1)^2 - 36$	$= 0$
$2(1 + 3\sqrt{2} - 1)^2 - 36$	0
$2(3\sqrt{2})^2 - 36$	0
$2(18) - 36$	0
$36 - 36$	0
$0 = 0$	

$2(x - 1)^2 - 36$	$= 0$
$2(1 - 3\sqrt{2} - 1)^2 - 36$	0
$2(-3\sqrt{2})^2 - 36$	0
$2(18) - 36$	0
$36 - 36$	0
$0 = 0$	

Write the solutions. The solutions are $1 + 3\sqrt{2}$ and $1 - 3\sqrt{2}$.

EXAMPLE 3 Solve by taking square roots: $(x - 6)^2 = 12$

Solution

$$(x - 6)^2 = 12$$
$$\sqrt{(x - 6)^2} = \sqrt{12}$$
$$x - 6 = \pm\sqrt{12}$$
$$x - 6 = \pm 2\sqrt{3}$$

• **Take the square root of each side of the equation.**

$$x - 6 = 2\sqrt{3} \qquad x - 6 = -2\sqrt{3}$$
$$x = 6 + 2\sqrt{3} \qquad x = 6 - 2\sqrt{3}$$

• **Solve for x.**

The solutions are $6 + 2\sqrt{3}$ and $6 - 2\sqrt{3}$.

PROBLEM 3 Solve by taking square roots: $(x + 5)^2 = 20$

Solution See page S25.

11.1 Concept Review

Determine whether the statement is always true, sometimes true, or never true.

1. $2x^2 - 3x + 9$ is a quadratic equation.

2. By the Principle of Zero Products, if $(3x + 4)(x - 7) = 0$, then $3x + 4 = 0$ or $x - 7 = 0$.

3. A quadratic equation has two distinct solutions.

4. To solve the equation $3x^2 - 26x = 9$ by factoring, first write the equation in standard form.

5. To say that the solutions are ± 6 means that the solutions are 6 and -6.

6. If we take the square root of the square of a binomial, the result is the binomial.

11.1 Exercises

1 Solve quadratic equations by factoring

For the given quadratic equation, find the values of *a*, *b*, and *c*.

1. $3x^2 - 4x + 1 = 0$

2. $x^2 + 2x - 5 = 0$

3. $2x^2 - 5 = 0$

4. $4x^2 + 1 = 0$

5. $6x^2 - 3x = 0$

6. $-x^2 + 7x = 0$

Write the quadratic equation in standard form.

7. $x^2 - 8 = 3x$

8. $2x^2 = 4x - 1$

9. $x^2 = 16$

10. $x + 5 = x(x - 3)$

11. $2(x + 3)^2 = 5$

12. $4(x - 1)^2 = 3$

13. How does a quadratic equation differ from a linear equation?

14. What does the Principle of Zero Products state?

15. Explain why the equation $x(x + 5) = 12$ cannot be solved by saying $x = 12$ or $x + 5 = 12$.

16. What is a double root of a quadratic equation?

17. Solve: $x^2 - 36 = 0$

$x^2 - 36 = 0$		• **The equation is in __?__ form.**
(__?__)(__?__) = 0		• **Factor the difference of two squares.**
$x + 6 =$ __?__	$x - 6 =$ __?__	• **Use the Principle of __?__ to set each factor equal to 0.**
$x =$ __?__	$x =$ __?__	• **Solve each equation for *x*.**

18. Solve: $x^2 + 4x - 12 = 0$

$x^2 + 4x - 12 = 0$		• **The equation is in __?__ form.**
($x +$ __?__)($x -$ __?__) = 0		• **Factor the trinomial.**
__?__ = 0	__?__ = 0	• **Use the Principle of Zero Products to set each factor equal to 0.**
$x =$ __?__	$x =$ __?__	• **Solve each equation for *x*.**

Solve for x.

19. $(x + 3)(x - 5) = 0$

20. $(x - 9)(x + 11) = 0$

21. $x(x - 7) = 0$

22. $x(x + 10) = 0$

23. $(2x + 5)(3x - 1) = 0$

24. $(2x - 7)(3x + 4) = 0$

Solve by factoring.

25. $x^2 + 2x - 15 = 0$

26. $t^2 + 3t - 10 = 0$

27. $z^2 - 4z + 3 = 0$

28. $s^2 - 5s + 4 = 0$

29. $p^2 + 3p + 2 = 0$

30. $v^2 + 6v + 5 = 0$

31. $x^2 - 6x + 9 = 0$

32. $y^2 - 8y + 16 = 0$

33. $6x^2 - 9x = 0$

34. $12y^2 + 8y = 0$

35. $r^2 - 10 = 3r$

36. $t^2 - 12 = 4t$

37. $3v^2 - 5v + 2 = 0$

38. $2p^2 - 3p - 2 = 0$

39. $3s^2 + 8s = 3$

40. $3x^2 + 5x = 12$

41. $6r^2 = 12 - r$

42. $4t^2 = 4t + 3$

43. $5y^2 + 11y = 12$

44. $4v^2 - 4v + 1 = 0$

45. $9s^2 - 6s + 1 = 0$

46. $x^2 - 9 = 0$

47. $t^2 - 16 = 0$

48. $4y^2 - 1 = 0$

49. $9z^2 - 4 = 0$

50. $x + 15 = x(x - 1)$

51. $\dfrac{3x^2}{2} = 4x - 2$

52. $\dfrac{2x^2}{5} = 3x - 5$

53. $\dfrac{2x^2}{9} + x = 2$

54. $\dfrac{3x^2}{8} - x = 2$

55. $\dfrac{3}{4}z^2 - z = -\dfrac{1}{3}$

56. $\dfrac{r^2}{2} = 1 - \dfrac{r}{12}$

57. $p + 18 = p(p - 2)$

58. $r^2 - r - 2 = (2r - 1)(r - 3)$

59. $s^2 + 5s - 4 = (2s + 1)(s - 4)$

60. $x^2 + x + 5 = (3x + 2)(x - 4)$

61. $ax^2 + bx + c = 0$ is a quadratic equation that can be solved by factoring. For each case, state whether the equation has two positive solutions, two negative solutions, or one positive and one negative solution.
a. $a > 0, b < 0, c > 0$ **b.** $a > 0, b < 0, c < 0$ **c.** $a > 0, b > 0, c < 0$

62. Let a be a positive integer. Which equation has a positive double root?
a. $x^2 - a^2 = 0$ **b.** $x^2 + 2ax - a^2 = 0$
c. $x^2 + 2ax + a^2 = 0$ **d.** $x^2 - 2ax + a^2 = 0$

2 Solve quadratic equations by taking square roots

63. The notation $x = \pm 3$ means $x =$ ___?___ or $x =$ ___?___.

64. Solve by taking square roots: $4x^2 - 9 = 0$

$4x^2 - 9 = 0$

$4x^2 =$ ___?___ • **Add ___?___ to each side of the equation.**

$x^2 =$ ___?___ • **Divide each side of the equation by ___?___.**

$\sqrt{x^2} = \sqrt{\frac{9}{4}}$ • **Take the ___?___ of each side of the equation.**

$x =$ ___?___ $\sqrt{\frac{9}{4}}$ • **There are two square roots, one positive and one negative.**

$x = \pm$ ___?___ • **Simplify.**

Solve by taking square roots.

65. $x^2 = 36$ **66.** $y^2 = 49$ **67.** $v^2 - 1 = 0$ **68.** $z^2 - 64 = 0$

69. $4x^2 - 49 = 0$ **70.** $9w^2 - 64 = 0$ **71.** $9y^2 = 4$ **72.** $4z^2 = 25$

73. $16v^2 - 9 = 0$ **74.** $25x^2 - 64 = 0$ **75.** $y^2 + 81 = 0$ **76.** $z^2 + 49 = 0$

77. $w^2 - 24 = 0$ **78.** $v^2 - 48 = 0$ **79.** $(x - 1)^2 = 36$ **80.** $(y + 2)^2 = 49$

81. $2(x + 5)^2 = 8$ **82.** $4(z - 3)^2 = 100$ **83.** $2(x + 1)^2 = 50$

84. $3(x - 4)^2 = 27$ **85.** $4(x + 5)^2 = 64$ **86.** $9(x - 3)^2 = 81$

87. $2(x - 9)^2 = 98$ **88.** $5(x + 5)^2 = 125$ **89.** $12(x + 3)^2 = 27$

90. $8(x - 4)^2 = 50$ **91.** $9(x - 1)^2 - 16 = 0$ **92.** $4(y + 3)^2 - 81 = 0$

93. $49(v + 1)^2 - 25 = 0$ **94.** $81(y - 2)^2 - 64 = 0$ **95.** $(x - 4)^2 - 20 = 0$

96. $(y + 5)^2 - 50 = 0$

97. $(x + 1)^2 + 36 = 0$

98. $(y - 7)^2 + 49 = 0$

99. $2\left(z - \frac{1}{2}\right)^2 = 12$

100. $3\left(v + \frac{3}{4}\right)^2 = 36$

101. $4\left(x - \frac{2}{3}\right)^2 = 16$

For Exercises 102 to 105, a and b are both positive numbers. In each case, state how many solutions the equation has.

102. $(x + a)^2 = 0$

103. $ax^2 + b = 0$

104. $(x + a)^2 = b$

105. $ax^2 - b = 0$

11.1 Applying Concepts

106. Evaluate $2n^2 - 7n - 4$ given $n(n - 2) = 15$.

107. Evaluate $3y^2 + 5y - 2$ given $y(y + 3) = 28$.

Solve for x.

108. $(x^2 - 1)^2 = 9$

109. $(x^2 + 3)^2 = 25$

110. $(6x^2 - 5)^2 = 1$

111. $x^2 = x$

112. $ax^2 - bx = 0, a > 0$ and $b > 0$

113. $ax^2 - b = 0, a > 0$ and $b > 0$

114. **Investments** The value P of an initial investment of A dollars after 2 years is given by $P = A(1 + r)^2$, where r is the annual percentage rate earned by the investment. If an initial investment of \$1500 grew to a value of \$1782.15 in 2 years, what was the annual percentage rate?

115. **Energy** The kinetic energy of a moving body is given by $E = \frac{1}{2}mv^2$, where E is the kinetic energy in newton-meters, m is the mass in kilograms, and v is the speed in meters per second. What is the speed of a moving body whose mass is 5 kg and whose kinetic energy is 250 newton-meters?

116. **Automobiles** On a certain type of street surface, the equation $d = 0.055v^2$ can be used to approximate the distance d, in feet, a car traveling v miles per hour will slide when its brakes are applied. After applying the brakes, the owner of a car involved in an accident skidded 40 ft. Did the traffic officer investigating the accident issue the car owner a ticket for speeding if the speed limit was 30 mph?

11.2 Solving Quadratic Equations by Completing the Square

OBJECTIVE 1 Solve quadratic equations by completing the square

Recall that a perfect-square trinomial is the square of a binomial.

Perfect-square Trinomial		Square of a Binomial
$x^2 + 6x + 9$	$=$	$(x + 3)^2$
$x^2 - 10x + 25$	$=$	$(x - 5)^2$
$x^2 + 8x + 16$	$=$	$(x + 4)^2$

For each perfect-square trinomial above, the square of $\frac{1}{2}$ of the coefficient of x equals the constant term.

$x^2 + 6x + 9$, $\left(\frac{1}{2} \cdot 6\right)^2 = 9$

$x^2 - 10x + 25$, $\left[\frac{1}{2}(-10)\right]^2 = 25$ $\quad \left(\frac{1}{2}\textbf{ coefficient of } x\right)^2 = \textbf{Constant term}$

$x^2 + 8x + 16$, $\left(\frac{1}{2} \cdot 8\right)^2 = 16$

This relationship can be used to write the constant term for a perfect-square trinomial. Adding to a binomial the constant term that makes it a perfect-square trinomial is called **completing the square.**

Complete the square of $x^2 - 8x$. Write the resulting perfect-square trinomial as the square of a binomial.

$$x^2 - 8x$$

Find the constant term. $\left[\frac{1}{2}(-8)\right]^2 = 16$

Complete the square of $x^2 - 8x$ by adding the constant term. $x^2 - 8x + 16$

Write the resulting perfect-square trinomial as the square of a binomial. $x^2 - 8x + 16 = (x - 4)^2$

Complete the square of $y^2 + 5y$. Write the resulting perfect-square trinomial as the square of a binomial.

$$y^2 + 5y$$

Find the constant term. $\left(\frac{1}{2} \cdot 5\right)^2 = \left(\frac{5}{2}\right)^2 = \frac{25}{4}$

Complete the square of $y^2 + 5y$ by adding the constant term.

$$y + 5y + \frac{25}{4}$$

Write the resulting perfect-square trinomial as the square of a binomial.

$$y^2 + 5y + \frac{25}{4} = \left(y + \frac{5}{2}\right)^2$$

A quadratic equation of the form $x^2 + bx + c = 0$, $x \neq 0$, that cannot be solved by factoring can be solved by completing the square. The procedure is:

1. Write the equation in the form $x^2 + bx = c$.
2. Add to each side of the equation the term that completes the square on $x^2 + bx$.
3. Factor the perfect-square trinomial. Write it as the square of a binomial.
4. Take the square root of each side of the equation.
5. Solve for x.

Solve by completing the square: $x^2 - 6x - 3 = 0$

Add the opposite of the constant term to each side of the equation.

$$x^2 - 6x - 3 = 0$$
$$x^2 - 6x = 3$$

Find the constant term that completes the square of $x^2 - 6x$.

$$\left[\frac{1}{2}(-6)\right]^2 = 9$$

Add this term to each side of the equation.

$$x^2 - 6x + 9 = 3 + 9$$

Factor the perfect-square trinomial.

$$(x - 3)^2 = 12$$

Take the square root of each side of the equation.

$$\sqrt{(x - 3)^2} = \sqrt{12}$$

Simplify.

$$x - 3 = \pm\sqrt{12}$$
$$x - 3 = \pm 2\sqrt{3}$$

Solve for x.

$$x - 3 = 2\sqrt{3} \qquad x - 3 = -2\sqrt{3}$$
$$x = 3 + 2\sqrt{3} \qquad x = 3 - 2\sqrt{3}$$

Check:

$$\begin{array}{r|l} \multicolumn{2}{c}{x^2 - 6x - 3 = 0} \\ \hline (3 + 2\sqrt{3})^2 - 6(3 + 2\sqrt{3}) - 3 & 0 \\ 9 + 12\sqrt{3} + 12 - 18 - 12\sqrt{3} - 3 & 0 \\ 0 = 0 & \end{array}$$

$$\begin{array}{r|l} \multicolumn{2}{c}{x^2 - 6x - 3 = 0} \\ \hline (3 - 2\sqrt{3})^2 - 6(3 - 2\sqrt{3}) - 3 & 0 \\ 9 - 12\sqrt{3} + 12 - 18 + 12\sqrt{3} - 3 & 0 \\ 0 = 0 & \end{array}$$

Write the solutions.

The solutions are $3 + 2\sqrt{3}$ and $3 - 2\sqrt{3}$.

For the method of completing the square to be used, the coefficient of the x^2 term must be 1. If it is not 1, we must multiply each side of the equation by the reciprocal of the coefficient of x^2. This is illustrated in the example below.

Solve by completing the square: $2x^2 - x - 1 = 0$

Add the opposite of the constant term to each side of the equation.

$$2x^2 - x - 1 = 0$$
$$2x^2 - x = 1$$

The coefficient of the x^2 term must be 1. Multiply each side by the reciprocal of the coefficient of x^2.

$$\frac{1}{2}(2x^2 - x) = \frac{1}{2} \cdot 1$$
$$x^2 - \frac{1}{2}x = \frac{1}{2}$$

Find the constant term that completes the square of $x^2 - \frac{1}{2}x$.

$$\left[\frac{1}{2}\left(-\frac{1}{2}\right)\right]^2 = \left(-\frac{1}{4}\right)^2 = \frac{1}{16}$$

Add this term to each side of the equation.

$$x^2 - \frac{1}{2}x + \frac{1}{16} = \frac{1}{2} + \frac{1}{16}$$

Factor the perfect-square trinomial.

$$\left(x - \frac{1}{4}\right)^2 = \frac{9}{16}$$

Take the square root of each side of the equation.

$$\sqrt{\left(x - \frac{1}{4}\right)^2} = \sqrt{\frac{9}{16}}$$

Simplify.

$$x - \frac{1}{4} = \pm\sqrt{\frac{9}{16}}$$
$$x - \frac{1}{4} = \pm\frac{3}{4}$$

Solve for x.

$$x - \frac{1}{4} = \frac{3}{4} \qquad x - \frac{1}{4} = -\frac{3}{4}$$
$$x = 1 \qquad x = -\frac{1}{2}$$

Check:

$$2x^2 - x - 1 = 0$$

$2x^2 - x - 1$	0
$2(1)^2 - 1 - 1$	0
$2(1) - 1 - 1$	0
$2 - 1 - 1$	0

$$0 = 0$$

$$2x^2 - x - 1 = 0$$

$2x^2 - x - 1$	0
$2\left(-\frac{1}{2}\right)^2 - \left(-\frac{1}{2}\right) - 1$	0
$2\left(\frac{1}{4}\right) - \left(-\frac{1}{2}\right) - 1$	0
$\frac{1}{2} + \frac{1}{2} - 1$	0

$$0 = 0$$

Write the solutions.

The solutions are 1 and $-\frac{1}{2}$.

EXAMPLE 1 Solve by completing the square.

A. $2x^2 - 4x - 1 = 0$ **B.** $p^2 - 4p + 6 = 0$

Solution **A.** $2x^2 - 4x - 1 = 0$

$$2x^2 - 4x = 1$$

• Add the opposite of −1 to each side of the equation.

$$\frac{1}{2}(2x^2 - 4x) = \frac{1}{2} \cdot 1$$

• The coefficient of the x^2 term must be 1.

$$x^2 - 2x = \frac{1}{2}$$

$$x^2 - 2x + 1 = \frac{1}{2} + 1$$

• Complete the square of $x^2 - 2x$. Add 1 to each side of the equation.

$$(x - 1)^2 = \frac{3}{2}$$

• Factor the perfect-square trinomial.

$$\sqrt{(x - 1)^2} = \sqrt{\frac{3}{2}}$$

• Take the square root of each side of the equation.

$$x - 1 = \pm\sqrt{\frac{3}{2}}$$

$$x - 1 = \pm\frac{\sqrt{3}}{\sqrt{2}}$$

$$x - 1 = \pm\frac{\sqrt{6}}{2}$$

• Rationalize the denominator. $\frac{\sqrt{3}}{\sqrt{2}} = \frac{\sqrt{3}}{\sqrt{2}} \cdot \frac{\sqrt{2}}{\sqrt{2}} = \frac{\sqrt{6}}{2}$

$$x - 1 = \frac{\sqrt{6}}{2} \qquad x - 1 = -\frac{\sqrt{6}}{2}$$

$$x = 1 + \frac{\sqrt{6}}{2} \qquad x = 1 - \frac{\sqrt{6}}{2}$$

$$= \frac{2}{2} + \frac{\sqrt{6}}{2} \qquad = \frac{2}{2} - \frac{\sqrt{6}}{2}$$

$$= \frac{2 + \sqrt{6}}{2} \qquad = \frac{2 - \sqrt{6}}{2}$$

The solutions are $\frac{2 + \sqrt{6}}{2}$ and $\frac{2 - \sqrt{6}}{2}$.

B. $p^2 - 4p + 6 = 0$

$$p^2 - 4p = -6$$

• Add the opposite of the constant term to each side of the equation.

$$p^2 - 4p + 4 = -6 + 4$$

• Complete the square of $p^2 - 4p$. Add 4 to each side of the equation.

$$(p - 2)^2 = -2$$

• Factor the perfect-square trinomial.

$$\sqrt{(p - 2)^2} = \sqrt{-2}$$

• Take the square root of each side of the equation.

$\sqrt{-2}$ is not a real number.

The equation has no real number solution.

PROBLEM 1 Solve by completing the square.

A. $3x^2 - 6x - 2 = 0$ **B.** $y^2 - 6y + 10 = 0$

Solution See page S25.

EXAMPLE 2 Solve by completing the square: $x^2 + 6x + 4 = 0$
Approximate the solutions to the nearest thousandth.

Solution

$$x^2 + 6x + 4 = 0$$
$$x^2 + 6x = -4$$
$$x^2 + 6x + 9 = -4 + 9$$

• **Complete the square of $x^2 + 6x$. Add 9 to each side of the equation.**

$$(x + 3)^2 = 5$$
$$\sqrt{(x + 3)^2} = \sqrt{5}$$
$$x + 3 = \pm\sqrt{5}$$
$$x + 3 \approx \pm 2.2361$$

$$x + 3 \approx 2.2361 \qquad x + 3 \approx -2.2361$$
$$x \approx -3 + 2.2361 \qquad x \approx -3 - 2.2361$$
$$\approx -0.764 \qquad \approx -5.236$$

The solutions are approximately -0.764 and -5.236.

PROBLEM 2 Solve by completing the square: $x^2 + 8x + 8 = 0$
Approximate the solutions to the nearest thousandth.

Solution See page S26.

11.2 Concept Review

Determine whether the statement is always true, sometimes true, or never true.

1. When we square a binomial, the result is a perfect-square trinomial.

2. The constant term in a perfect-square trinomial is equal to the square of one-half the coefficient of x.

3. To "complete the square" means to add to $x^2 + bx$ the constant term that will make it a perfect-square trinomial.

4. To complete the square of $x^2 + 4x$, add 16 to it.

5. To complete the square of $3x^2 + 6x$, add 9 to it.

6. In solving a quadratic equation by completing the square, the next step after writing the equation in the form $(x + a)^2 = b$ is to take the square root of each side of the equation.

11.2 Exercises

1 Solve quadratic equations by completing the square

1. a. To complete the square of $x^2 + 18x$, find the constant c that makes $x^2 + 18x + c$ a __?__ trinomial.
The constant term c will be the square of half the coefficient of __?__, so $c = \left[\frac{1}{2}(\underline{\ ?\ })\right]^2 = \underline{\ ?\ }$.

b. Complete the square of $x^2 + 18x$ and write the result as the square of a binomial:
$x^2 + 18x + \underline{\quad ? \quad} = (\underline{\quad ? \quad})^2$

2. Rewrite the equation $5x^2 - 10x + 2 = 0$ in the form $(x - m)^2 = n$.

$5x^2 - 10x + 2 = 0$

$5x^2 - 10x = \underline{\quad ? \quad}$
- **Subtract 2 from each side of the equation.**

$x^2 - \underline{\quad ? \quad} x = \underline{\quad ? \quad}$
- **To make the coefficient of x^2 equal to 1, divide each side of the equation by 5.**

$x^2 - 2x + \underline{\quad ? \quad} = -\frac{2}{5} + \underline{\quad ? \quad}$
- **Add $\left[\frac{1}{2}(\underline{\quad ? \quad})\right]^2$ to each side of the equation.**

$(x - \underline{\quad ? \quad})^2 = \underline{\quad ? \quad}$
- **Factor the left side of the equation. Simplify the right side of the equation.**

Complete the square. Write the resulting perfect-square trinomial as the square of a binomial.

3. $x^2 + 12x$ **4.** $x^2 - 4x$ **5.** $x^2 + 10x$

6. $x^2 + 3x$ **7.** $x^2 - x$ **8.** $x^2 + 5x$

Solve by completing the square.

9. $x^2 + 2x - 3 = 0$ **10.** $y^2 + 4y - 5 = 0$ **11.** $v^2 + 4v + 1 = 0$ **12.** $y^2 - 2y - 5 = 0$

13. $v^2 - 6v + 13 = 0$ **14.** $x^2 + 4x + 13 = 0$ **15.** $x^2 + 6x = 5$ **16.** $w^2 - 8w = 3$

17. $x^2 = 4x - 4$ **18.** $z^2 = 8z - 16$ **19.** $z^2 = 2z + 1$ **20.** $y^2 = 10y - 20$

Solve. First try to solve the equation by factoring. If you are unable to solve the equation by factoring, solve the equation by completing the square.

21. $p^2 + 3p = 1$ **22.** $r^2 + 5r = 2$ **23.** $w^2 + 7w = 8$

24. $y^2 + 5y = -4$ **25.** $x^2 + 6x + 4 = 0$ **26.** $y^2 - 8y - 1 = 0$

27. $r^2 - 8r = -2$ **28.** $s^2 + 6s = 5$ **29.** $t^2 - 3t = -2$

30. $y^2 = 4y + 12$ **31.** $w^2 = 3w + 5$ **32.** $x^2 = 1 - 3x$

33. $x^2 - x - 1 = 0$

34. $x^2 - 7x = -3$

35. $y^2 - 5y + 3 = 0$

36. $z^2 - 5z = -2$

37. $v^2 + v - 3 = 0$

38. $x^2 - x = 1$

39. $y^2 = 7 - 10y$

40. $v^2 = 14 + 16v$

41. $s^2 + 3s = -1$

42. $r^2 - 3r = 5$

43. $t^2 - t = 4$

44. $y^2 + y - 4 = 0$

45. $x^2 - 3x + 5 = 0$

46. $z^2 + 5z + 7 = 0$

47. $2t^2 - 3t + 1 = 0$

48. $2x^2 - 7x + 3 = 0$

49. $2r^2 + 5r = 3$

50. $2y^2 - 3y = 9$

51. $4v^2 - 4v - 1 = 0$

52. $2s^2 - 4s - 1 = 0$

53. $4z^2 - 8z = 1$

54. $3r^2 - 2r = 2$

55. $3y - 5 = (y - 1)(y - 2)$

56. $4p + 2 = (p - 1)(p + 3)$

57. $\frac{x^2}{4} - \frac{x}{2} = 3$

58. $\frac{x^2}{6} - \frac{x}{3} = 1$

59. $\frac{2x^2}{3} = 2x + 3$

60. $\frac{3x^2}{2} = 3x + 2$

61. $\frac{x}{3} + \frac{3}{x} = \frac{8}{3}$

62. $\frac{x}{4} - \frac{2}{x} = \frac{3}{4}$

Complete Exercises 63 and 64 without using a calculator.

63. A quadratic equation has solutions $-3 \pm \sqrt{5}$. Are both of these solutions negative, are both positive, or is one negative and one positive?

64. A quadratic equation has solutions $2 \pm \sqrt{7}$. Are both of these solutions negative, are both positive, or is one negative and one positive?

Solve by completing the square. Approximate the solutions to the nearest thousandth.

65. $y^2 + 3y = 5$

66. $w^2 + 5w = 2$

67. $2z^2 - 3z = 7$

68. $2x^2 + 3x = 11$

69. $4x^2 + 6x - 1 = 0$

70. $4x^2 + 2x - 3 = 0$

11.2 Applying Concepts

71. Evaluate $2b^2$ given $b^2 - 6b + 7 = 0$.

72. Evaluate $2y^2$ given $y^2 - 2y - 7 = 0$.

Solve.

73. $\sqrt{2x + 7} - 4 = x$

74. $\dfrac{x+1}{2} + \dfrac{3}{x-1} = 4$

75. $\dfrac{x-2}{3} + \dfrac{2}{x+2} = 4$

76. Explain why the equation $(x - 2)^2 = -4$ does not have a real number solution.

11.3 Solving Quadratic Equations by Using the Quadratic Formula

OBJECTIVE 1 Solve quadratic equations by using the quadratic formula

Any quadratic equation can be solved by completing the square. Applying this method to the standard form of a quadratic equation produces a formula that can be used to solve any quadratic equation.

To solve $ax^2 + bx + c = 0$, $a \neq 0$, by completing the square, subtract the constant term from each side of the equation.

$$ax^2 + bx + c = 0$$
$$ax^2 + bx + c - c = 0 - c$$
$$ax^2 + bx = -c$$

Multiply each side of the equation by the reciprocal of a, the coefficient of x^2.

$$\frac{1}{a}(ax^2 + bx) = \frac{1}{a}(-c)$$
$$x^2 + \frac{b}{a}x = -\frac{c}{a}$$

Complete the square by adding $\left(\frac{1}{2} \cdot \frac{b}{a}\right)^2$ to each side of the equation.

$$x^2 + \frac{b}{a}x + \left(\frac{1}{2} \cdot \frac{b}{a}\right)^2 = \left(\frac{1}{2} \cdot \frac{b}{a}\right)^2 - \frac{c}{a}$$
$$x^2 + \frac{b}{a}x + \frac{b^2}{4a^2} = \frac{b^2}{4a^2} - \frac{c}{a}$$

Simplify the right side of the equation.

$$x^2 + \frac{b}{a}x + \frac{b^2}{4a^2} = \frac{b^2}{4a^2} - \left(\frac{c}{a} \cdot \frac{4a}{4a}\right)$$
$$x^2 + \frac{b}{a}x + \frac{b^2}{4a^2} = \frac{b^2}{4a^2} - \frac{4ac}{4a^2}$$
$$x^2 + \frac{b}{a}x + \frac{b^2}{4a^2} = \frac{b^2 - 4ac}{4a^2}$$

Factor the perfect-square trinomial on the left side of the equation.

$$\left(x + \frac{b}{2a}\right)^2 = \frac{b^2 - 4ac}{4a^2}$$

Take the square root of each side of the equation.

$$\sqrt{\left(x + \frac{b}{2a}\right)^2} = \sqrt{\frac{b^2 - 4ac}{4a^2}}$$

$$x + \frac{b}{2a} = \pm\frac{\sqrt{b^2 - 4ac}}{2a}$$

Solve for x.

$$x + \frac{b}{2a} = \frac{\sqrt{b^2 - 4ac}}{2a} \qquad x + \frac{b}{2a} = -\frac{\sqrt{b^2 - 4ac}}{2a}$$

$$x = -\frac{b}{2a} + \frac{\sqrt{b^2 - 4ac}}{2a} \qquad x = -\frac{b}{2a} - \frac{\sqrt{b^2 - 4ac}}{2a}$$

$$x = \frac{-b + \sqrt{b^2 - 4ac}}{2a} \qquad x = \frac{-b - \sqrt{b^2 - 4ac}}{2a}$$

The Quadratic Formula

The solution of $\boldsymbol{ax^2 + bx + c = 0, a \neq 0}$, is

$$\boldsymbol{x = \frac{-b + \sqrt{b^2 - 4ac}}{2a}} \quad \text{or} \quad \boldsymbol{x = \frac{-b - \sqrt{b^2 - 4ac}}{2a}}$$

The quadratic formula is frequently written in the form

$$\boldsymbol{x = \frac{-b \pm \sqrt{b^2 - 4ac}}{2a}}$$

Solve by using the quadratic formula: $2x^2 = 4x - 1$

$$2x^2 = 4x - 1$$

Write the equation in standard form. $a = 2$, $b = -4$, and $c = 1$.

$$2x^2 - 4x + 1 = 0$$

Replace a, b, and c in the quadratic formula by their values.

$$x = \frac{-b \pm \sqrt{b^2 - 4ac}}{2a}$$

$$= \frac{-(-4) \pm \sqrt{(-4)^2 - 4 \cdot 2 \cdot 1}}{2 \cdot 2}$$

Simplify.

$$= \frac{4 \pm \sqrt{16 - 8}}{4}$$

$$= \frac{4 \pm \sqrt{8}}{4}$$

$$= \frac{4 \pm 2\sqrt{2}}{4} = \frac{2(2 \pm \sqrt{2})}{2 \cdot 2} = \frac{2 \pm \sqrt{2}}{2}$$

Check:

$2x^2 = 4x - 1$	
$2\left(\frac{2+\sqrt{2}}{2}\right)^2$	$4\left(\frac{2+\sqrt{2}}{2}\right) - 1$
$2\left(\frac{4+4\sqrt{2}+2}{4}\right)$	$2(2+\sqrt{2}) - 1$
$2\left(\frac{6+4\sqrt{2}}{4}\right)$	$4 + 2\sqrt{2} - 1$
$\frac{6+4\sqrt{2}}{2}$	$3 + 2\sqrt{2}$

$3 + 2\sqrt{2} = 3 + 2\sqrt{2}$

$2x^2 = 4x - 1$	
$2\left(\frac{2-\sqrt{2}}{2}\right)^2$	$4\left(\frac{2-\sqrt{2}}{2}\right) - 1$
$2\left(\frac{4-4\sqrt{2}+2}{4}\right)$	$2(2-\sqrt{2}) - 1$
$2\left(\frac{6-4\sqrt{2}}{4}\right)$	$4 - 2\sqrt{2} - 1$
$\frac{6-4\sqrt{2}}{2}$	$3 - 2\sqrt{2}$

$3 - 2\sqrt{2} = 3 - 2\sqrt{2}$

Write the solutions. The solutions are $\frac{2+\sqrt{2}}{2}$ and $\frac{2-\sqrt{2}}{2}$.

EXAMPLE 1 Solve by using the quadratic formula.

A. $2x^2 - 3x + 1 = 0$ **B.** $2x^2 = 8x - 5$

C. $t^2 - 3t + 7 = 0$

Solution **A.** $2x^2 - 3x + 1 = 0$ • $a = 2, b = -3, c = 1$

$$x = \frac{-(-3) \pm \sqrt{(-3)^2 - 4(2)(1)}}{2 \cdot 2}$$

$$= \frac{3 \pm \sqrt{9-8}}{4} = \frac{3 \pm \sqrt{1}}{4} = \frac{3 \pm 1}{4}$$

$$x = \frac{3+1}{4} \qquad x = \frac{3-1}{4}$$

$$= \frac{4}{4} = 1 \qquad = \frac{2}{4} = \frac{1}{2}$$

The solutions are 1 and $\frac{1}{2}$.

B. $2x^2 = 8x - 5$

$2x^2 - 8x + 5 = 0$ • Write the equation in standard form. $a = 2, b = -8, c = 5$

$$x = \frac{-(-8) \pm \sqrt{(-8)^2 - 4(2)(5)}}{2 \cdot 2}$$

$$= \frac{8 \pm \sqrt{64 - 40}}{4}$$

$$= \frac{8 \pm \sqrt{24}}{4}$$

$$= \frac{8 \pm 2\sqrt{6}}{4}$$

$$= \frac{2(4 \pm \sqrt{6})}{2 \cdot 2} = \frac{4 \pm \sqrt{6}}{2}$$

The solutions are $\frac{4+\sqrt{6}}{2}$ and $\frac{4-\sqrt{6}}{2}$.

C. $t^2 - 3t + 7 = 0$ • $a = 1, b = -3, c = 7$

$$t = \frac{-(-3) \pm \sqrt{(-3)^2 - 4(1)(7)}}{2(1)}$$

$$= \frac{3 \pm \sqrt{9 - 28}}{2} = \frac{3 \pm \sqrt{-19}}{2}$$

$\sqrt{-19}$ is not a real number.

The equation has no real number solution.

PROBLEM 1 Solve by using the quadratic formula.

A. $3x^2 + 4x - 4 = 0$ **B.** $x^2 + 2x = 1$

C. $z^2 + 2z + 6 = 0$

Solution See page S26.

11.3 Concept Review

Determine whether the statement is always true, sometimes true, or never true.

1. Any quadratic equation can be solved by using the quadratic formula.

2. The solutions of a quadratic equation can be written as
$x = \dfrac{-b + \sqrt{b^2 - 4ac}}{2a}$ and $x = \dfrac{-b - \sqrt{b^2 - 4ac}}{2a}$.

3. The equation $4x^2 - 3x = 9$ is a quadratic equation in standard form.

4. In the quadratic formula $x = \dfrac{-b \pm \sqrt{b^2 - 4ac}}{2a}$, b is the coefficient of x^2.

5. $\dfrac{6 \pm 2\sqrt{3}}{2}$ simplifies to $3 \pm 2\sqrt{3}$.

11.3 Exercises

1 Solve quadratic equations by using the quadratic formula

1. Write the quadratic formula. Explain what each variable in the formula represents.

2. Explain what the quadratic formula is used for.

3. To write the equation $x^2 = 4x + 2$ in standard form, subtract $\underline{\quad ? \quad}$ and $\underline{\quad ? \quad}$ from each side of the equation. The resulting equation is $\underline{\quad ? \quad} = 0$. Then $a = \underline{\quad ? \quad}$, $b = \underline{\quad ? \quad}$, and $c = \underline{\quad ? \quad}$.

4. Use the values of a, b, and c that you found in Exercise 3 to evaluate the quadratic formula for the equation $x^2 = 4x + 2$.

$$x = \frac{-b \pm \sqrt{b^2 - 4ac}}{2a}$$

• **Write the ___?___ formula.**

$$= \frac{-(-4) \pm \sqrt{(-4)^2 - 4(1)(-2)}}{2(1)}$$

• **Replace b with ___?___, a with ___?___, and c with ___?___.**

$$= \frac{\underline{\quad ? \quad} \pm \sqrt{\underline{\quad ? \quad} + \underline{\quad ? \quad}}}{\underline{\quad ? \quad}}$$

• **Simplify.**

$$= \frac{4 \pm \sqrt{\underline{\quad ? \quad}}}{2}$$

• **Simplify the number under the radical sign.**

$$= \frac{4 \pm \underline{\quad ? \quad}\sqrt{\underline{\quad ? \quad}}}{2}$$

• **Simplify the radical.**

$$= \underline{\quad ? \quad} \pm \underline{\quad ? \quad}$$

• **Divide each term of the numerator by the 2 in the denominator.**

Solve by using the quadratic formula.

5. $z^2 + 6z - 7 = 0$

6. $s^2 + 3s - 10 = 0$

7. $w^2 = 3w + 18$

8. $r^2 = 5 - 4r$

9. $t^2 - 2t = 5$

10. $y^2 - 4y = 6$

11. $t^2 + 6t - 1 = 0$

12. $z^2 + 4z + 1 = 0$

13. $w^2 + 3w + 5 = 0$

14. $x^2 - 2x + 6 = 0$

15. $w^2 = 4w + 9$

16. $y^2 = 8y + 3$

Solve. First try to solve the equation by factoring. If you are unable to solve the equation by factoring, solve the equation by using the quadratic formula.

17. $p^2 - p = 0$

18. $2v^2 + v = 0$

19. $4t^2 - 4t - 1 = 0$

20. $4x^2 - 8x - 1 = 0$

21. $4t^2 - 9 = 0$

22. $4s^2 - 25 = 0$

23. $3x^2 - 6x + 2 = 0$

24. $5x^2 - 6x = 3$

25. $3t^2 = 2t + 3$

26. $4n^2 = 7n - 2$

27. $2x^2 + x + 1 = 0$

28. $3r^2 - r + 2 = 0$

29. $2y^2 + 3 = 8y$

30. $5x^2 - 1 = x$

31. $3t^2 = 7t + 6$

32. $3x^2 = 10x + 8$

33. $3y^2 - 4 = 5y$

34. $6x^2 - 5 = 3x$

35. $3x^2 = x + 3$

36. $2n^2 = 7 - 3n$

37. $5d^2 - 2d - 8 = 0$

38. $x^2 - 7x - 10 = 0$

39. $5z^2 + 11z = 12$

40. $4v^2 = v + 3$

41. $v^2 + 6v + 1 = 0$

42. $s^2 + 4s - 8 = 0$

43. $4t^2 - 12t - 15 = 0$

44. $4w^2 - 20w + 5 = 0$

45. $2x^2 = 4x - 5$

46. $3r^2 = 5r - 6$

47. $9y^2 + 6y - 1 = 0$

48. $9s^2 - 6s - 2 = 0$

49. $6s^2 - s - 2 = 0$

50. $6y^2 + 5y - 4 = 0$

51. $4p^2 + 16p = -11$

52. $4y^2 - 12y = -1$

53. $4x^2 = 4x + 11$

54. $4s^2 + 12s = 3$

55. $4p^2 = -12p - 9$

56. $3y^2 + 6y = -3$

57. $9v^2 = -30v - 23$

58. $9t^2 = 30t + 17$

59. $\dfrac{x^2}{2} - \dfrac{x}{3} = 1$

60. $\dfrac{x^2}{4} - \dfrac{x}{2} = 5$

61. $\dfrac{2x^2}{5} = x + 1$

62. $\dfrac{3x^2}{2} + 2x = 1$

63. $\dfrac{x}{5} + \dfrac{5}{x} = \dfrac{12}{5}$

64. $\dfrac{x}{4} + \dfrac{3}{x} = \dfrac{5}{2}$

65. True or false? If you solve $ax^2 + bx + c = 0$ by using the quadratic formula and the solutions are rational numbers, then the equation could have been solved by factoring.

66. True or false? If the value of $b^2 - 4ac$ in the quadratic formula is 0, then $ax^2 + bx + c = 0$ has one solution, a double root.

Solve by using the quadratic formula. Approximate the solutions to the nearest thousandth.

67. $x^2 - 2x - 21 = 0$

68. $y^2 + 4y - 11 = 0$

69. $s^2 - 6s - 13 = 0$

70. $w^2 + 8w - 15 = 0$

71. $2p^2 - 7p - 10 = 0$

72. $3t^2 - 8t - 1 = 0$

73. $4z^2 + 8z - 1 = 0$

74. $4x^2 + 7x + 1 = 0$

75. $5v^2 - v - 5 = 0$

11.3 Applying Concepts

Solve.

76. $\sqrt{x^2 + 2x + 1} = x - 1$

77. $\dfrac{x + 2}{3} - \dfrac{4}{x - 2} = 2$

78. $\dfrac{x + 1}{5} - \dfrac{3}{x - 1} = 2$

79. True or false?
- **a.** The equations $x = \sqrt{12 - x}$ and $x^2 = 12 - x$ have the same solution.
- **b.** If $\sqrt{a} + \sqrt{b} = c$, then $a + b = c^2$.
- **c.** $\sqrt{9} = \pm 3$
- **d.** $\sqrt{x^2} = |x|$

80. Factoring, completing the square, and using the quadratic formula are three methods of solving quadratic equations. Describe each method, and cite the advantages and disadvantages of using each.

81. Explain why the equation $0x^2 + 3x + 4 = 0$ cannot be solved by the quadratic formula.

11.4 Complex Numbers

OBJECTIVE 1

Simplify complex numbers

Point of Interest

It may seem strange to just invent new numbers, but that is how mathematics evolves. For instance, negative numbers were not an accepted part of mathematics until well into the 13th century. In fact, these numbers were often referred to as "fictitious numbers."

In the 17th century, René Descartes called square roots of negative numbers imaginary numbers, an unfortunate choice of words, and started using the letter i to denote these numbers. These numbers were subjected to the same skepticism as negative numbers.

Recall that $\sqrt{16} = 4$ because $4^2 = 16$. Now consider the expression $\sqrt{-16}$. To find $\sqrt{-16}$, we need to find a number n such that $n^2 = -16$. However, the square of any real number (except zero) is a *positive* number. To find a number n such that $n^2 = -16$, we introduce a new number.

Definition of *i*

The **imaginary unit,** designated by the letter i, is the number whose square is -1. Symbolically, this is written as follows:

$$i^2 = -1$$

Using this definition, we can now write that $\sqrt{-16} = 4i$ because

$(4i)^2 = 4^2 i^2$ • **Use the Rule for Simplifying Powers of Products.**

$= 16(-1)$ • $i^2 = -1$

$= -16$

The principal square root of a negative number is defined in terms of i.

Principal Square Root of a Negative Number

If a is a positive real number, then $\sqrt{-a} = \sqrt{a}i = i\sqrt{a}$. The number $i\sqrt{a}$ is called an **imaginary number.** When $a = 1$, we have $\sqrt{-1} = i$.

Examples of imaginary numbers are $-12i$, $\frac{3}{2}i$, and $i\sqrt{15}$. Note that we wrote $i\sqrt{15}$ rather than $\sqrt{15}i$. It is customary, when a radical occurs in an imaginary number, to write the i in front of the radical. This is done to avoid confusion of $\sqrt{15}i$ with $\sqrt{15i}$.

EXAMPLE 1 Write each expression in terms of i.

A. $\sqrt{-23}$ **B.** $\sqrt{-36}$ **C.** $\sqrt{-45}$ **D.** $5\sqrt{-27}$

Solution
A. $\sqrt{-23} = \sqrt{-1 \cdot 23} = \sqrt{-1}\sqrt{23} = i\sqrt{23}$

B. $\sqrt{-36} = \sqrt{-1 \cdot 36} = \sqrt{-1}\sqrt{36} = i\sqrt{36} = i \cdot 6 = 6i$

C. $\sqrt{-45} = \sqrt{-1 \cdot 45} = \sqrt{-1}\sqrt{45} = i\sqrt{45} = i\sqrt{9 \cdot 5}$
$= i\sqrt{9}\sqrt{5} = i \cdot 3\sqrt{5} = 3i\sqrt{5}$

D. $5\sqrt{-18} = 5\sqrt{-1 \cdot 18} = 5\sqrt{-1}\sqrt{18} = 5i\sqrt{18}$
$= 5i\sqrt{9 \cdot 2} = 5i\sqrt{9}\sqrt{2} = 5i \cdot 3\sqrt{2} = 15i\sqrt{2}$

PROBLEM 1 Write each expression in terms of i.

A. $\sqrt{-17}$ **B.** $\sqrt{-81}$ **C.** $\sqrt{-63}$ **D.** $4\sqrt{-50}$

Solution See page S26.

The real numbers and the imaginary numbers make up the *complex numbers*.

Complex Numbers

A **complex number** is a number of the form $a + bi$, where a and b are real numbers and $i = \sqrt{-1}$, the imaginary unit. The number a is the **real part of a complex number** and b is the **imaginary part of a complex number.**

Here are examples of complex numbers and their real and imaginary parts.

$-3 + 5i$	• **Real part: −3; imaginary part: 5**
$2 - 6i$	• **Real part: 2; imaginary part: −6. Note that $2 - 6i = 2 + (-6)i$.**
5	• **Real part: 5; imaginary part: 0. Note that $5 = 5 + 0i$.**
$7i$	• **Real part: 0; imaginary part: 7. Note that $7i = 0 + 7i$.**

From these examples, note that a real number, such as 5, is a complex number whose imaginary part is zero and that an imaginary number, such as $7i$, is a complex number whose real part is zero.

Although $3 + \sqrt{-4}$ is a complex number, the preferred form is $3 + 2i$. This is called the **standard form of a complex number.** If the imaginary part of a complex number is negative, such as $2 + (-5i)$, we normally write $2 - 5i$, for example, as the standard form of the complex number.

Write $7 - 2\sqrt{-20}$ in standard form.

$$7 - 2\sqrt{-20} = 7 - 2i\sqrt{20}$$ • $\sqrt{-20} = i\sqrt{20}$

$$= 7 - 2i\sqrt{4}\sqrt{5} = 7 - 2i \cdot 2\sqrt{5}$$ • **Simplify $\sqrt{20}$.**

$$= 7 - 4i\sqrt{5}$$ • **Multiply $2i$ times 2.**

EXAMPLE 2 Write $\dfrac{4 + 8\sqrt{-45}}{6}$ in standard form.

Solution

$$\frac{4 + 8\sqrt{-45}}{6} = \frac{4 + 8i\sqrt{45}}{6}$$ • $\sqrt{-45} = i\sqrt{45}$

$$= \frac{4 + 8i\sqrt{9}\sqrt{5}}{6} = \frac{4 + 24i\sqrt{5}}{6}$$

$$= \frac{4}{6} + \frac{24i\sqrt{5}}{6} = \frac{2}{3} + 4i\sqrt{5}$$

PROBLEM 2 Write $\dfrac{5 - 3\sqrt{-50}}{10}$ in standard form.

Solution See page S26.

OBJECTIVE 2 Add and subtract complex numbers

Operations on complex numbers can be related to operations on binomials. To add two complex numbers, add the real parts and add the imaginary parts. To subtract two complex numbers, subtract the real parts and subtract the imaginary parts.

EXAMPLE 3 Simplify.

A. $(-3 + 2i) + (5 - 6i)$ **B.** $(-9 + 4i) - (2 - 6i)$

Solution **A.** Add the real parts.

$$(-3 + 2i) + (5 - 6i) = (-3 + 5) + (2 + (-6))i$$

$$= 2 + (-4)i$$

Add the imaginary parts. $= 2 - 4i$

B. Subtract the real parts.

$$(-9 + 4i) - (2 - 6i) = (-9 - 2) + (4 - (-6))i$$

$$= -11 + 10i$$

Subtract the imaginary parts.

PROBLEM 3 Simplify.

A. $(7 - 3i) + (-8 + i)$ **B.** $(-5 + 4i) - (-3 - 7i)$

Solution See page S26.

OBJECTIVE 3 Multiply complex numbers

When multiplying complex numbers, recall that $i^2 = -1$. Here are some examples.

$$3i(5i) = 15i^2 = 15(-1) = -15$$
$$-2i(6i) = -12i^2 = -12(-1) = 12$$

EXAMPLE 4 Multiply: $3i(2 - 4i)$

Solution

$3i(2 - 4i) = 6i - 12i^2$ • **Use the Distributive Property to remove parentheses.**

$= 6i - 12(-1)$ • **Replace i^2 with -1.**

$= 6i + 12$

$= 12 + 6i$ • **Write the answer in the form $a + bi$.**

PROBLEM 4 Multiply: $5i(3 + 6i)$

Solution See page S26.

The product of two complex numbers of the form $a + bi$, $a \neq 0$, $b \neq 0$, can be found by using the FOIL method and the fact that $i^2 = -1$.

EXAMPLE 5 Multiply: $(5 - 4i)(2 + 3i)$

Solution

$(5 - 4i)(2 + 3i)$

$= 5(2) + 5(3i) + (-4i)2 + (-4i)3i$ • **Use the FOIL method.**

$= 10 + 15i - 8i - 12i^2$

$= 10 + 7i - 12i^2$ • **Combine like terms.**

$= 10 + 7i - 12(-1)$ • **Replace i^2 with -1.**

$= 10 + 7i + 12$

$= 22 + 7i$ • **Write the answer in the form $a + bi$.**

PROBLEM 5 Multiply: $(-1 + 5i)(2 - 3i)$

Solution See page S27.

The square of a complex number is found by using FOIL.

Write $(2 - 3i)^2$ in standard form.

$(2 - 3i)^2 = (2 - 3i)(2 - 3i)$ • **Multiply $2 - 3i$ times itself.**

$= 4 - 6i - 6i + 9i^2$ • **Use the FOIL method.**

$= 4 - 12i + 9i^2$ • **Combine like terms.**

$= 4 - 12i + 9(-1)$ • **Replace i^2 with -1.**

$= 4 - 12i - 9$

$= -5 - 12i$ • **Write in the form $a + bi$.**

The complex numbers $a + bi$ and $a - bi$ are called **complex conjugates** or **conjugates** of each other. Here are some examples.

Number	**Conjugate**
$2 + 5i$	$2 - 5i$
$-3 + 6i$	$-3 - 6i$
$5 - 4i$	$5 + 4i$

Consider the product of a complex number and its conjugate. For instance,

$$\begin{aligned}(2 + 5i)(2 - 5i) &= 4 - 10i + 10i - 25i^2 \\ &= 4 - 25i^2 \\ &= 4 - 25(-1) \\ &= 4 + 25 = 29\end{aligned}$$

Note that the product of complex conjugates is a *real* number. This is always true.

Product of Complex Conjugates

The product of a complex number and its conjugate is a real number. That is, $(a + bi)(a - bi) = a^2 + b^2$.

For instance, $(5 + 3i)(5 - 3i) = 5^2 + 3^2 = 25 + 9 = 34$.

EXAMPLE 6 Multiply: $(8 + 3i)(8 - 3i)$

Solution $(8 + 3i)(8 - 3i) = 8^2 + 3^2$ • $(a + bi)(a - bi) = a^2 + b^2$, $a = 8, b = 3$

$= 64 + 9$

$= 73$

PROBLEM 6 Multiply: $(-2 + 5i)(-2 - 5i)$

Solution See page S27.

OBJECTIVE 4 Divide complex numbers

Recall that the number $\frac{3}{\sqrt{2}}$ is not in simplest form because there is a radical expression in the denominator. Similarly, $\frac{3}{i}$ is not in simplest form because $i = \sqrt{-1}$. To write this expression in simplest form, multiply the numerator and denominator by i.

$$\frac{3}{i} \cdot \frac{i}{i} = \frac{3i}{i^2} = \frac{3i}{-1} = -3i$$

This process is used to divide a complex number by an imaginary number.

EXAMPLE 7 Divide: $\dfrac{3-6i}{2i}$

Solution $\dfrac{3-6i}{2i} = \dfrac{3-6i}{2i} \cdot \dfrac{i}{i}$ • **Multiply the numerator and denominator by *i*.**

$= \dfrac{3i-6i^2}{2i^2} = \dfrac{3i-6(-1)}{2(-1)}$ • $i^2 = -1$

$= \dfrac{3i+6}{-2} = \dfrac{3}{-2}i + \dfrac{6}{-2} = -3 - \dfrac{3}{2}i$ • **Write in the form *a* + *bi*.**

PROBLEM 7 Divide: $\dfrac{-12+8i}{-4i}$

Solution See page S27.

Recall that to simplify the quotient $\dfrac{2+\sqrt{3}}{5+2\sqrt{3}}$, multiply the numerator and denominator by the conjugate of $5+2\sqrt{3}$, which is $5-2\sqrt{3}$. In a similar manner, to simplify the quotient of the two complex numbers, multiply the numerator and denominator by the conjugate of the complex number in the denominator.

The next example shows how the quotient of two complex numbers is determined by using conjugates.

EXAMPLE 8 Divide: $\dfrac{3-6i}{4-3i}$

Solution $\dfrac{3-6i}{4-3i} = \dfrac{3-6i}{4-3i} \cdot \dfrac{4+3i}{4+3i}$ • **Multiply the numerator and denominator by the conjugate of the denominator.**

$= \dfrac{12+9i-24i-18i^2}{4^2+3^2}$

$= \dfrac{12-15i-18i^2}{16+9}$ • **Combine like terms in the numerator.**

$= \dfrac{12-15i-18(-1)}{25}$ • **Replace i^2 with −1.**

$= \dfrac{12-15i+18}{25}$

$= \dfrac{30-15i}{25}$

$= \dfrac{30}{25} - \dfrac{15}{25}i = \dfrac{6}{5} - \dfrac{3}{5}i$ • **Write in the form *a* + *bi*.**

PROBLEM 8 Divide: $\dfrac{16-11i}{5+2i}$

Solution See page S27.

OBJECTIVE 5 Solve quadratic equations with complex number solutions

Allowing complex numbers to be solutions of quadratic equations enables us to solve quadratic equations that in previous sections we stated have "no real number solutions."

Take Note

You should check these solutions. For instance, here is the check for $-8i$.

$2x^2 + 128 = 0$	
$2(-8i)^2 + 128$	0
$2(-8)^2i^2 + 128$	0
$2(64)(-1) + 128$	0
$-128 + 128$	0
$0 = 0$	

The solution $-8i$ checks. You should check that $8i$ is a solution.

Solve: $2x^2 + 128 = 0$

$2x^2 + 128 = 0$

$2x^2 = -128$ • **Subtract 128 from each side of the equation.**

$x^2 = -64$ • **Divide each side of the equation by 2.**

$\sqrt{x^2} = \sqrt{-64}$ • **Take the square root of each side of the equation.**

$x = \pm\sqrt{-64} = \pm i\sqrt{64}$ • **Rewrite $\sqrt{-64}$ as $i\sqrt{64}$.**

$x = \pm 8i$ • **Simplify $\sqrt{64}$.**

The solutions are $-8i$ and $8i$.

Solve $(x - 1)^2 + 9 = 1$ and check.

$(x - 1)^2 + 9 = 1$

$(x - 1)^2 = -8$ • **Subtract 9 from each side of the equation.**

$\sqrt{(x - 1)^2} = \sqrt{-8}$ • **Take the square root of each side of the equation.**

$x - 1 = \pm\sqrt{-8} = \pm i\sqrt{8}$ • **Rewrite $\sqrt{-8}$ as $i\sqrt{8}$.**

$x - 1 = \pm 2i\sqrt{2}$ • **Simplify $\sqrt{8}$.**

$x = 1 \pm 2i\sqrt{2}$ • **Add 1 to each side of the equation.**

Check:

$(x - 1)^2 + 9 = 1$	
$(1 + 2i\sqrt{2} - 1)^2 + 9$	1
$(2i\sqrt{2})^2 + 9$	1
$2^2(i^2)(\sqrt{2})^2 + 9$	1
$4(-1)(2) + 9$	1
$-8 + 9$	1
$1 = 1$	

$(x - 1)^2 + 9 = 1$	
$(1 - 2i\sqrt{2} - 1)^2 + 9$	1
$(-2i\sqrt{2})^2 + 9$	1
$(-2)^2(i^2)(\sqrt{2})^2 + 9$	1
$4(-1)(2) + 9$	1
$-8 + 9$	1
$1 = 1$	

The solutions are $1 + 2i\sqrt{2}$ and $1 - 2i\sqrt{2}$.

EXAMPLE 9 Solve $(2x + 1)^2 + 5 = 1$ and check.

Solution $(2x + 1)^2 + 5 = 1$

$(2x + 1)^2 = -4$ • **Subtract 5 from each side of the equation.**

$\sqrt{(2x + 1)^2} = \sqrt{-4}$ • **Take the square root of each side of the equation.**

$$2x + 1 = \pm 2i$$
• **Rewrite $\sqrt{-4}$ as $2i$.**

$$2x = -1 \pm 2i$$
• **Subtract 1 from each side of the equation.**

$$x = \frac{-1 \pm 2i}{2}$$
• **Divide each side of the equation by 2.**

$$x = -\frac{1}{2} \pm \frac{2i}{2}$$
• **Write the solution in standard form by dividing each term by 2.**

$$x = -\frac{1}{2} \pm i$$

Check

$(2x+1)^2 + 5 = 1$	
$\left(2\left(-\frac{1}{2} + i\right) + 1\right)^2 + 5$	1
$(-1 + 2i + 1)^2 + 5$	1
$(2i)^2 + 5$	1
$2^2i^2 + 5$	1
$4(-1) + 5$	1
$-4 + 5$	1
$1 = 1$	

$(2x+1)^2 + 5 = 1$	
$\left(2\left(-\frac{1}{2} - i\right) + 1\right)^2 + 5$	1
$(-1 - 2i + 1)^2 + 5$	1
$(-2i)^2 + 5$	1
$(-2)^2i^2 + 5$	1
$4(-1) + 5$	1
$-4 + 5$	1
$1 = 1$	

The solutions are $-\frac{1}{2} + i$ and $-\frac{1}{2} - i$.

PROBLEM 9 Solve: $8z^2 + 17 = -7$ and check.

Solution See page S27.

In Example 9 we were able to solve the equation by taking the square root of each side of the equation. In many instances, however, using the quadratic formula will be the best choice for solving a quadratic equation with complex number solutions. We restate the quadratic formula here for your reference.

The solutions of the quadratic equation $ax^2 + bx + c = 0$, $a \neq 0$, are given by

$$x = \frac{-b \pm \sqrt{b^2 - 4ac}}{2a}$$

Solve: $4x^2 - 4x + 2 = 0$

$$x = \frac{-b \pm \sqrt{b^2 - 4ac}}{2a}$$
• $a = 4, b = -4, c = 2$

$$x = \frac{-(-4) \pm \sqrt{(-4)^2 - 4(4)(2)}}{2(4)}$$

$$= \frac{4 \pm \sqrt{16 - 32}}{8} = \frac{4 \pm \sqrt{-16}}{8}$$

$$= \frac{4 \pm i\sqrt{16}}{8} = \frac{4 \pm 4i}{8}$$
• **Rewrite $\sqrt{-16}$ as $i\sqrt{16}$. $\sqrt{16} = 4$**

$$= \frac{4}{8} \pm \frac{4i}{8} = \frac{1}{2} \pm \frac{1}{2}i$$
• **Write the solution as a complex number in standard form.**

Check:

$$
\begin{array}{r|l}
4x^2 - 4x + 2 = 0 & \\
\hline
4\left(\frac{1}{2} + \frac{1}{2}i\right)^2 - 4\left(\frac{1}{2} + \frac{1}{2}i\right) + 2 & 0 \\
4\left(\frac{1}{4} + \frac{1}{4}i + \frac{1}{4}i + \frac{1}{4}i^2\right) - 2 - 2i + 2 & 0 \\
1 + i + i + i^2 - 2 - 2i + 2 & 0 \\
1 + 2i + (-1) - 2i & 0 \\
0 = 0 &
\end{array}
$$

$$
\begin{array}{r|l}
4x^2 - 4x + 2 = 0 & \\
\hline
4\left(\frac{1}{2} - \frac{1}{2}i\right)^2 - 4\left(\frac{1}{2} - \frac{1}{2}i\right) + 2 & 0 \\
4\left(\frac{1}{4} - \frac{1}{4}i - \frac{1}{4}i + \frac{1}{4}i^2\right) - 2 + 2i + 2 & 0 \\
1 - i - i + i^2 - 2 + 2i + 2 & 0 \\
1 - 2i + (-1) + 2i & 0 \\
0 = 0 &
\end{array}
$$

The solutions are $\frac{1}{2} + \frac{1}{2}i$ and $\frac{1}{2} - \frac{1}{2}i$.

EXAMPLE 10 Solve $x^2 + 4x + 6 = 0$ and check.

Solution

$$x = \frac{-b \pm \sqrt{b^2 - 4ac}}{2a}$$

$$= \frac{-4 \pm \sqrt{4^2 - 4(1)(6)}}{2(1)}$$

- $a = 1, b = 4, c = 6$

$$= \frac{-4 \pm \sqrt{16 - 24}}{2} = \frac{-4 \pm \sqrt{-8}}{2}$$

$$= \frac{-4 \pm i\sqrt{8}}{2} = \frac{-4 \pm 2i\sqrt{2}}{2}$$

- **Rewrite $\sqrt{-8}$ as $i\sqrt{8}$ and then rewrite $i\sqrt{8}$ as $2i\sqrt{2}$.**

$$= -\frac{4}{2} \pm \frac{2i\sqrt{2}}{2} = -2 \pm i\sqrt{2}$$

- **Write the solution as a complex number in standard form.**

Check

$$
\begin{array}{r|l}
x^2 + 4x + 6 = 0 & \\
\hline
(-2 + i\sqrt{2})^2 + 4(-2 + i\sqrt{2}) + 6 & 0 \\
4 - 2i\sqrt{2} - 2i\sqrt{2} + i^2(\sqrt{2})^2 - 8 + 4i\sqrt{2} + 6 & 0 \\
4 - 4i\sqrt{2} + (-1)2 - 8 + 4i\sqrt{2} + 6 & 0 \\
4 - 4i\sqrt{2} + (-2) - 8 + 4i\sqrt{2} + 6 & 0 \\
0 = 0 &
\end{array}
$$

$$
\begin{array}{r|l}
x^2 + 4x + 6 = 0 & \\
\hline
(-2 - i\sqrt{2})^2 + 4(-2 - i\sqrt{2}) + 6 & 0 \\
4 + 2i\sqrt{2} + 2i\sqrt{2} + i^2(\sqrt{2})^2 - 8 - 4i\sqrt{2} + 6 & 0 \\
4 + 4i\sqrt{2} + (-1)2 - 8 - 4i\sqrt{2} + 6 & 0 \\
4 + 4i\sqrt{2} + (-2) - 8 - 4i\sqrt{2} + 6 & 0 \\
0 = 0 &
\end{array}
$$

The solutions are $-2 + i\sqrt{2}$ and $-2 - i\sqrt{2}$.

PROBLEM 10 Solve $x^2 - 6x + 4 = -6$

Solution See page S27.

11.4 Concept Review

Determine whether each statement is always true, sometimes true, or never true.

1. Given that i is the imaginary unit, $i^2 = -1$.
2. All real numbers are complex numbers.
3. For the complex number $3 - 4i$, the real part is 3 and the imaginary part is 4.
4. The equation $\sqrt{-15} = i\sqrt{15}$ is a true equation.
5. The complex conjugate of $-3 + 4i$ is $3 - 4i$.
6. Quadratic equations have imaginary number solutions.

11.4 Exercises

1 Simplify complex numbers

1. a. The real part of the complex number $5 - 8i$ is __?__.
   b. The imaginary part of the complex number $5 - 8i$ is __?__.

2. a. If the complex number $a + bi$ is a real number, then __?__ $= 0$.
   b. If the complex number $a + bi$ is an imaginary number, then __?__ $= 0$.

3. Write $\sqrt{-100}$ in terms of i.

$\sqrt{-100} = \sqrt{\underline{\quad ? \quad} \cdot 100} = \sqrt{\underline{\quad ? \quad}}\sqrt{100} = \underline{\quad ? \quad}\sqrt{100} = \underline{\quad ? \quad}i$

4. Write $8 - 3\sqrt{-98}$ in standard form.

$8 - 3\sqrt{-98} = 8 - 3(\underline{\quad ? \quad})\sqrt{98}$ • **Write $\sqrt{-98}$ in terms of i.**

$= 8 - 3i\sqrt{\underline{\quad ? \quad}}\sqrt{2}$ • **Use the Product Property of Square Roots to simplify $\sqrt{98}$.**

$= 8 - 3i(\underline{\quad ? \quad})\sqrt{2}$ • **Take the square root of 49.**

$= 8 - \underline{\quad ? \quad}i\sqrt{2}$ • **Multiply 3 times 7.**

Write each expression in terms of i.

5. $\sqrt{-81}$ **6.** $\sqrt{-64}$ **7.** $5\sqrt{-49}$ **8.** $-3\sqrt{-16}$ **9.** $\sqrt{-13}$

10. $\sqrt{-26}$ **11.** $\sqrt{-75}$ **12.** $\sqrt{-90}$ **13.** $-4\sqrt{-54}$ **14.** $3\sqrt{-80}$

15. Let a and b be positive numbers. Is $a - bi$ equivalent to $a + \sqrt{-b^2}$ or to $a - \sqrt{-b^2}$?

16. Let a be a positive number. Which expression is equivalent to $\sqrt{a^2} + \sqrt{-a^2}$?

a. 0 **b.** $a + ai$ **c.** $a - ai$ **d.** $2ai$

Write each number in standard form.

17. $5 + \sqrt{-4}$ **18.** $-3 + \sqrt{-25}$ **19.** $-7 - 2\sqrt{-36}$ **20.** $5 - 3\sqrt{-100}$

21. $5 + 3\sqrt{-48}$ **22.** $2 - 2\sqrt{-50}$ **23.** $7 - 6\sqrt{-28}$ **24.** $-2 + 5\sqrt{-72}$

25. $\dfrac{6 + 5\sqrt{-4}}{2}$ **26.** $\dfrac{5 - 3\sqrt{-25}}{5}$ **27.** $\dfrac{-6 + 2\sqrt{-54}}{6}$

28. $\dfrac{-4 + 2\sqrt{-72}}{4}$ **29.** $\dfrac{-2 - 4\sqrt{-90}}{5}$ **30.** $\dfrac{4 - 5\sqrt{-63}}{6}$

2 Add and subtract complex numbers

31. Add: $(6 - 8i) + (-2 + 3i)$

$(6 - 8i) + (-2 + 3i)$

$= (6 + \underline{\quad ? \quad}) + (-8 + \underline{\quad ? \quad})i$ • **Add the real parts. Add the imaginary parts.**

$= \underline{\quad ? \quad}$ • **Simplify.**

32. Subtract: $10 - (8 - 7i)$

$10 - (8 - 7i) = (10 - \underline{\quad ? \quad}) - \underline{\quad ? \quad}i$ • **Subtract the real parts.**

$= \underline{\quad ? \quad}$ • **Simplify.**

Add or subtract.

33. $3i + 7i$

34. $-9i + 6i$

35. $-2i - 7i$

36. $5i - (-4i)$

37. $6i + (7 + 3i)$

38. $3 + (4 + 2i)$

39. $-2i - (8 - 9i)$

40. $5 - (7 + 6i)$

41. $(7 + 4i) + (6 - 2i)$

42. $(-2 + 12i) + (7 - 15i)$

43. $(5 - 8i) - (3 + 2i)$

44. $(-7 - i) - (6 - 2i)$

45. $(-10 + 4i) - (-2 + 6i)$

46. $(6 - 11i) + (-7 - i)$

47. $(8 + 4i) + (-2 - 4i)$

48. $(7 - 8i) + (-7 + 3i)$

49. $(-2 + 11i) - (-2 + 11i)$

50. $(3 - 13i) - (3 + 13i)$

For Exercises 51 to 54, use the complex numbers $m = a - bi$ and $n = c + di$.

51. True or false? If $a = c$ and $b = d$, then $m - n = 0$.

52. True or false? If $m - n$ is a real number, then b and d are opposites.

53. Suppose $b > 0$, $d > 0$, and $b > d$. Is the imaginary part of $m + n$ positive or negative?

54. Suppose $a > 0$, $c > 0$, and $a > c$. Is the real part of $m - n$ positive or negative?

3 Multiply complex numbers

55. Multiply: $-8i(1 + 7i)$

$-8i(1 + 7i) = (\underline{\quad ? \quad})(1) + (\underline{\quad ? \quad})(7i)$	• **Use the Distributive Property.**
$= \underline{\quad ? \quad} - (\underline{\quad ? \quad})i^2$	• **Simplify.**
$= -8i - 56(\underline{\quad ? \quad})$	• $i^2 = \underline{\quad ? \quad}$.
$= \underline{\quad ? \quad}$	• **Write the answer in the form $a + bi$.**

56. Multiply: $(1 + 9i)(2 - 3i)$

$(1 + 9i)(2 - 3i) = (1)(\underline{\quad ? \quad}) + (1)(\underline{\quad ? \quad}) + 9i(\underline{\quad ? \quad}) + 9i(\underline{\quad ? \quad})$	• **Use the FOIL method.**
$= \underline{\quad ? \quad} + \underline{\quad ? \quad} + \underline{\quad ? \quad} - \underline{\quad ? \quad}$	• **Simplify each term.**
$= 2 + \underline{\quad ? \quad} - 27i^2$	• **Combine like terms.**
$= 2 + 15i - 27(\underline{\quad ? \quad})$	• **Replace i^2 by $\underline{\quad ? \quad}$.**
$= 2 + 15i + \underline{\quad ? \quad}$	• **Simplify.**
$= \underline{\quad ? \quad}$	• **Write in the form $a + bi$.**

Multiply.

57. $4i \cdot 5i$

58. $6i \cdot 8i$

59. $(-2i)(9i)$

60. $6i(-9i)$

61. $5i(2 + 4i)$

62. $3i(2 - 7i)$

63. $(3 + 2i)(4 + 5i)$

64. $(4 - 3i)(2 + i)$

65. $(-3 + 2i)(1 + 3i)$

66. $(5 - 3i)(-2 + 4i)$

67. $(3 - 7i)(-2 - 5i)$

68. $(-5 - 3i)(4 - 6i)$

69. $(2 + 5i)^2$

70. $(-3 + 2i)^2$

71. $(1 - 2i)^2$

72. $(-4 - 3i)^2$

73. $(2 - 5i)(-5 + 2i)$

74. $(-1 + 3i)(3 - i)$

75. $(2 + 4i)(2 - 4i)$

76. $(-3 + 4i)(-3 - 4i)$

77. $(4 - i)(4 + i)$

78. True or false? For all nonzero real numbers a and b, the product $(a + bi)(a - bi)$ is a positive real number.

79. True or false? The product of two imaginary numbers is never a positive real number.

4 Divide complex numbers

80. Simplify: $\dfrac{2 - i}{-3i}$

$\dfrac{2 - i}{-3i} = \dfrac{2 - i}{-3i} \cdot \dfrac{\underline{\ ?\ }}{\underline{\ ?\ }}$ • **To remove i from the denominator, multiply the expression by 1 in the form $\frac{i}{i}$.**

$= \dfrac{2i - \underline{\ ?\ }}{-3i^2}$ • **Multiply the numerators. Multiply the denominators.**

$= \dfrac{2i - (\underline{\ ?\ })}{-3(\underline{\ ?\ })}$ • **Replace i^2 by -1.**

$= \dfrac{2i + \underline{\ ?\ }}{\underline{\ ?\ }}$ • **Simplify.**

$= \underline{\ ?\ } + \underline{\ ?\ }\, i$ • **Write the answer in the form $a + bi$.**

81. To simplify $\dfrac{3i}{1 - 4i}$, multiply the numerator and denominator by $\underline{\ ?\ }$.

Divide.

82. $\dfrac{2 + 3i}{i}$

83. $\dfrac{6 + i}{i}$

84. $\dfrac{3 - 5i}{i}$

85. $\dfrac{-2 + 7i}{-i}$

86. $\dfrac{-5 - 9i}{-i}$

87. $\dfrac{-9 + 15i}{3i}$

88. $\frac{6 - 4i}{2i}$

89. $\frac{6 + 12i}{8i}$

90. $\frac{4 - 10i}{6i}$

91. $\frac{-15 + 6i}{-9i}$

92. $\frac{4 - 15i}{-6i}$

93. $\frac{3}{1 + i}$

94. $\frac{-4}{1 - 2i}$

95. $\frac{-10i}{3 + i}$

96. $\frac{12i}{2 - 2i}$

97. $\frac{13 - i}{2 + i}$

98. $\frac{12 + i}{1 - 2i}$

99. $\frac{18 + 4i}{1 + 3i}$

100. $\frac{-18 + 13i}{1 + 4i}$

101. $\frac{8 - 14i}{-2 - 3i}$

102. $\frac{5 + 15i}{3 + 4i}$

103. True or false? The quotient of two imaginary numbers is a real number.

104. True or false? The reciprocal of an imaginary number is a real number.

5 Solve quadratic equations with complex number solutions

Solve.

105. $x^2 + 16 = 0$

106. $z^2 + 25 = 0$

107. $2z^2 + 49 = -49$

108. $3x^2 + 108 = 0$

109. $x^2 + 11 = -16$

110. $z^2 + 12 = -28$

111. $3z^2 + 16 = -20$

112. $4z^2 - 13 = -21$

113. $(x + 1)^2 + 36 = 0$

114. $(x - 3)^2 + 81 = 0$

115. $(x - 2)^2 + 12 = 0$

116. $(z + 4)^2 + 18 = 0$

117. $(z + 2)^2 + 27 = -23$

118. $(x - 5)^2 + 17 = 9$

119. $(2x + 3)^2 + 9 = 5$

120. $(2z - 1)^2 + 25 = 9$

121. $z^2 - 2z + 2 = 0$

122. $z^2 - 2z + 5 = 0$

123. $x^2 + 4x = -5$

124. $x^2 + 4x = -8$

125. $x^2 - 6x + 13 = 0$

126. $x^2 + 10 = 2x$

127. $x^2 - 2x + 3 = 0$

128. $x^2 + 2x + 13 = 0$

129. $4x^2 + 8x = -5$

130. $4x^2 + 12x + 25 = 0$

131. $4x^2 - 4x + 13 = 0$

For Exercises 132 and 133, a is a positive real number. State how many solutions the equation has and whether the solutions are real, imaginary, or complex numbers.

132. $x^2 + a = 0$

133. $(x + a)^2 = 0$

11.4 Applying Concepts

134. We can evaluate i^3 as $i^3 = (i \cdot i) \cdot i = i^2 \cdot i = (-1) \cdot i = -i$. Using a similar method, evaluate each of the following.
a. i^4 **b.** i^5 **c.** i^6 **d.** i^7

135. Using the fact that $i^9 = i$, find i^{18}.

Write each of the following in the form $a + bi$.

136. $(1 - i)(1 + i)(2 - 3i)$

137. $(2 - i)(2 + i)(1 + 5i)$

138. $(1 + i)^3$

139. $(2 - 3i)^3$

140. $(4 - 3i)(1 + 2i) + (3 - 2i)(2 - i)$

141. $(2 + 5i)(1 - 3i) - (3 + i)(4 - 2i)$

Solve.

142. $(x - 1)(x + 1) + 5 = 0$

143. $(x + 2)(x - 2) + 12 = 0$

144. $(x + 4)(x + 6) + 4 = 0$

145. $(x - 5)(x + 1) = -14$

146. $(x - 2)(x - 4) + 4 = 0$

147. $(x - 4)(x - 2) = -6$

11.5 Graphing Quadratic Equations in Two Variables

OBJECTIVE 1 Graph a quadratic equation of the form $y = ax^2 + bx + c$

An equation of the form $y = ax^2 + bx + c$, $a \neq 0$, is a **quadratic equation in two variables.** Examples of quadratic equations in two variables are shown at the right.

$$y = 3x^2 - x + 1$$
$$y = -x^2 - 3$$
$$y = 2x^2 - 5x$$

For these equations, y is a function of x, and we can write $f(x) = ax^2 + bx + c$. This equation represents a **quadratic function.**

Evaluate $f(x) = 2x^2 - 3x + 4$ when $x = -2$.

$$f(x) = 2x^2 - 3x + 4$$
$$f(-2) = 2(-2)^2 - 3(-2) + 4$$ • **Replace x with -2.**
$$= 2(4) - 3(-2) + 4$$ • **Simplify.**
$$= 8 + 6 + 4$$
$$= 18$$

The value of the function when $x = -2$ is 18.

The graph of $y = ax^2 + bx + c$ or $f(x) = ax^2 + bx + c$ is a **parabola.** The graph is ∪-shaped and opens up when a is positive and down when a is negative. The graphs of two parabolas are shown below.

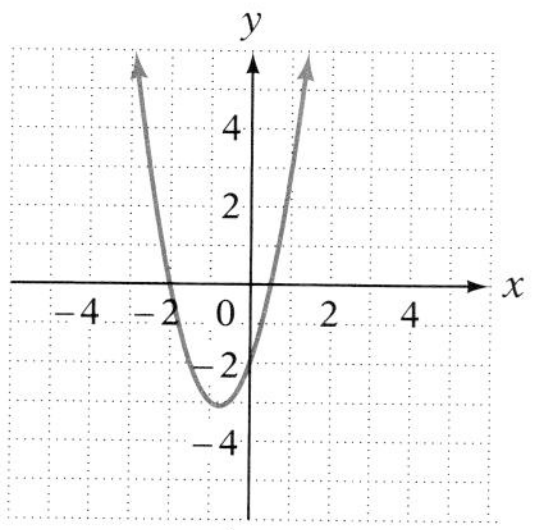

$y = 2x^2 + 3x - 2$
$a = 2$, a positive number
Parabola opens up

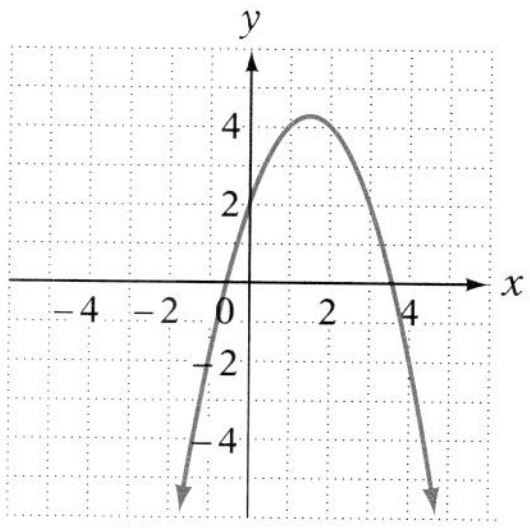

$f(x) = -x^2 + 3x + 2$
$a = -1$, a negative number
Parabola opens down

Graph $y = x^2 - 2x - 3$.

x	y
−2	5
−1	0
0	−3
1	−4
2	−3
3	0
4	5

• **Find several solutions of the equation. Because the graph is not a straight line, several solutions must be found in order to determine the ∪-shape. Record the ordered pairs in a table.**

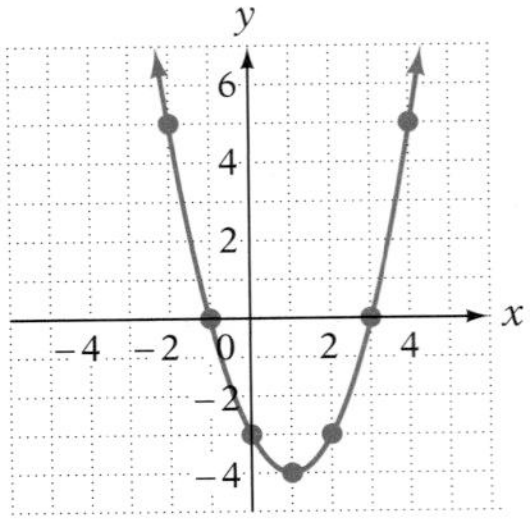

• Graph the ordered-pair solutions on a rectangular coordinate system. Draw a parabola through the points.

Note that the graph of $y = x^2 - 2x - 3$ crosses the x-axis at $(-1, 0)$ and at $(3, 0)$. These points are confirmed in the table of values. The x-intercepts of the graph are $(-1, 0)$ and $(3, 0)$.

The y-intercept is the point at which the graph crosses the y-axis. At this point, $x = 0$. From the graph or the table, we can see that the y-intercept is $(0, -3)$.

We can find the x-intercepts algebraically by letting $y = 0$ and solving for x.

$$y = x^2 - 2x - 3$$
$$0 = x^2 - 2x - 3$$
$$0 = (x + 1)(x - 3)$$

• Replace y with 0 and solve for x.
• This equation can be solved by factoring. However, it will be necessary to use the quadratic formula to solve some quadratic equations.

$$x + 1 = 0 \qquad x - 3 = 0$$
$$x = -1 \qquad x = 3$$

When $y = 0$, $x = -1$ or $x = 3$. The x-intercepts are $(-1, 0)$ and $(3, 0)$.

We can find the y-intercept algebraically by letting $x = 0$ and solving for y.

$$y = x^2 - 2x - 3$$
$$y = 0^2 - 2(0) - 3$$
$$y = 0 - 0 - 3$$
$$y = -3$$

• Replace x with 0 and simplify.

When $x = 0$, $y = -3$. The y-intercept is $(0, -3)$.

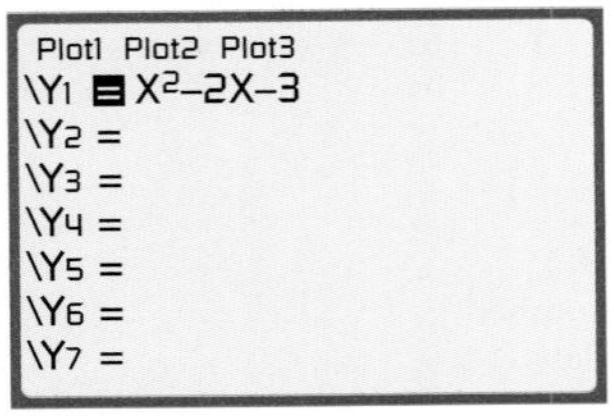

Using a graphing utility, enter the equation $y = x^2 - 2x - 3$ and verify the graph shown above. (Refer to the Appendix for instructions on using a graphing calculator to graph a quadratic equation.) Verify that $(-1, 0)$, $(3, 0)$, and $(0, -3)$ are coordinates of points on the graph.

The graph of $y = -2x^2 + 1$ is shown below.

x	y
0	1
1	−1
−1	−1
2	−7
−2	−7

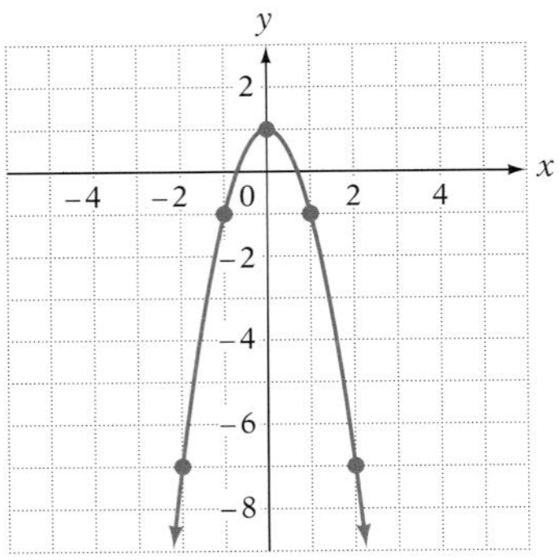

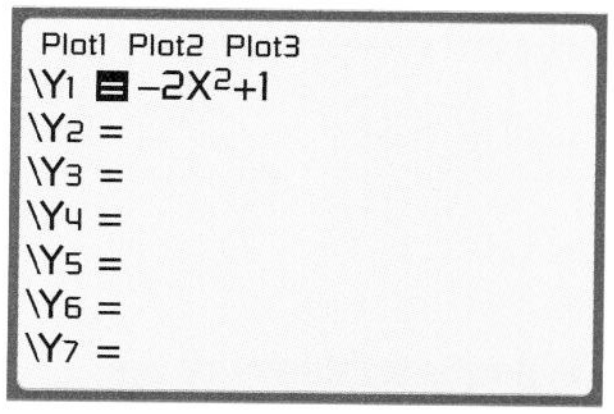

Use a graphing utility to verify the graph of $y = -2x^2 + 1$ shown at the bottom of the preceding page.

Note that the graph of $y = x^2 - 2x - 3$, shown on the previous page, opens up and that the coefficient of x^2 is positive. The graph of $y = -2x^2 + 1$ opens down, and the coefficient of x^2 is negative. As stated earlier, for any quadratic equation in two variables, the coefficient of x^2 determines whether the parabola opens up or down. When a is positive, the parabola opens up. When a is negative, the parabola opens down.

Point of Interest

Mirrors in some telescopes are ground into the shape of a parabola. The mirror at the Mount Palomar Observatory is 2 ft thick at the ends and weighs 14.75 tons. The mirror has been ground to a true paraboloid (the three-dimensional version of a parabola) to within 0.0000015 in.

Every parabola has an **axis of symmetry** and a **vertex** that is on the axis of symmetry. If the parabola opens up, the vertex is the lowest point on the graph. If the parabola opens down, the vertex is the highest point on the graph.

To understand the axis of symmetry, think of folding the paper along that axis. The two halves of the graph will match up.

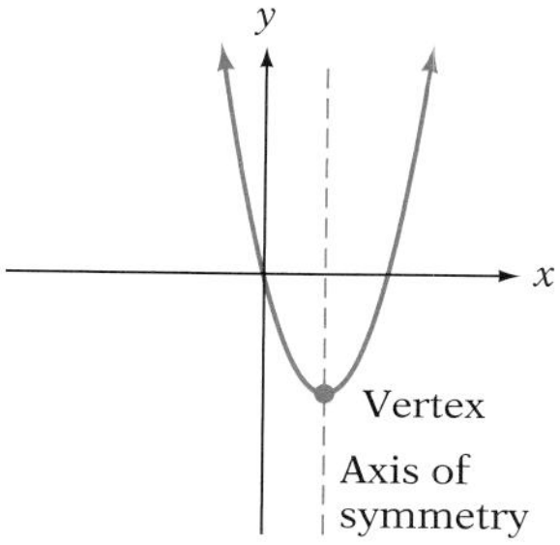

When graphing a quadratic equation in two variables, use the value of a to determine whether the parabola opens up or down. After graphing ordered-pair solutions of the equation, use symmetry to help you draw the parabola.

EXAMPLE 1 Graph. **A.** $y = x^2 - 2x$ **B.** $y = -x^2 + 4x - 4$

Solution **A.** $a = 1$. a is positive.
The parabola opens up.

x	y
0	0
1	−1
−1	3
2	0
3	3

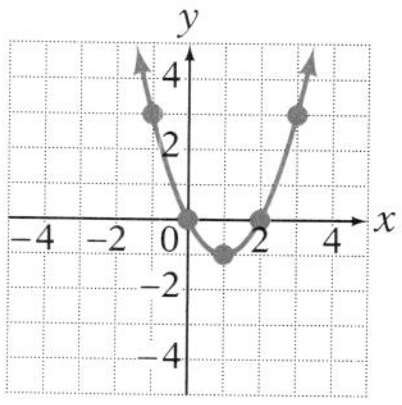

B. $a = -1$. a is negative.
The parabola opens down.

x	y
0	−4
1	−1
2	0
3	−1
4	−4

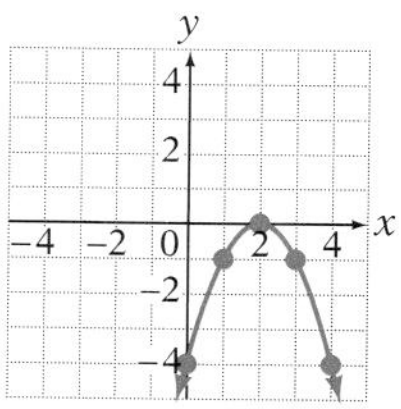

PROBLEM 1 Graph. **A.** $y = x^2 + 2$ **B.** $y = -x^2 - 2x + 3$

Solution See page S27.

EXAMPLE 2 Find the x- and y-intercepts of the graph of $y = x^2 - 2x - 5$.

Solution To find the x-intercepts, let $y = 0$ and solve for x.

$$y = x^2 - 2x - 5$$
$$0 = x^2 - 2x - 5$$
$$x = \frac{-b \pm \sqrt{b^2 - 4ac}}{2a}$$

• **$x^2 - 2x - 5$ is nonfactorable over the integers. Use the quadratic formula.**

$$= \frac{-(-2) \pm \sqrt{(-2)^2 - 4(1)(-5)}}{2(1)}$$
$$= \frac{2 \pm \sqrt{24}}{2} = \frac{2 \pm 2\sqrt{6}}{2} = 1 \pm \sqrt{6}$$

The x-intercepts are $(1 + \sqrt{6}, 0)$ and $(1 - \sqrt{6}, 0)$.

To find the y-intercept, let $x = 0$ and solve for y.

$$y = x^2 - 2x - 5$$
$$y = 0^2 - 2(0) - 5 = -5$$

The y-intercept is $(0, -5)$.

PROBLEM 2 Find the x- and y-intercepts of the graph of $y = x^2 - 6x + 9$.

Solution See page S28.

11.5 Concept Review

Determine whether the statement is always true, sometimes true, or never true.

1. The equation $y = 3x^2 - 2x + 1$ is an example of a quadratic equation in two variables.
2. The graph of an equation of the form $y = ax^2 + bx + c$, $a \neq 0$, is a parabola.
3. The graph of an equation of the form $y = ax^2 + c$, $a \neq 0$, is a straight line.
4. For the equation $y = -x^2 + 2x - 1$, when $x = 1$, $y = 2$.
5. The graph of the equation $y = -\frac{1}{2}x^2 + 5x$ is a parabola opening up.
6. If a parabola opens down, then the vertex is the highest point on the graph.

11.5 Exercises

1 Graph a quadratic equation of the form $y = ax^2 + bx + c$

1. What is a parabola?

2. Explain how you know whether the graph of the equation $y = -2x^2 + 3x + 4$ opens up or down.

3. Explain the axis of symmetry of a parabola.

4. What is the vertex of a parabola?

Determine whether the graph of the equation opens up or down.

5. $y = x^2 - 3$

6. $y = -x^2 + 4$

7. $y = \frac{1}{2}x^2 - 2$

8. $y = -\frac{1}{3}x^2 + 5$

9. $y = x^2 - 2x + 3$

10. $y = -x^2 + 4x - 1$

11. Use the quadratic equation $y = -x^2 + 9$.

a. The equation is in the standard form $y = ax^2 + bx + c$, where $a =$ ___?___, $b =$ ___?___, and $c =$ ___?___.

b. The graph of the equation is a ___?___. Because $a < 0$, the graph of the equation opens ___?___.

c. The equation can be written in function notation as $f(x) = -x^2 + 9$. To evaluate the function for $x = 2$, find $f(2) = -($___?___$)^2 + 9$ $=$ ___?___ $+ 9 =$ ___?___.

d. Use the results of part c to name one point on the graph of $y = -x^2 + 9$: (___?___, ___?___).

12. a. To find the x-intercepts of the graph of $y = x^2 - 3x - 4$, let ___?___ $= 0$ and solve for ___?___.

b. The equation $0 = x^2 - 3x - 4$ can be solved by factoring: $0 = (x -$ ___?___$)(x +$ ___?___$)$. The solutions are ___?___ and ___?___.

c. The x-intercepts of the graph of $y = x^2 - 3x - 4$ are (___?___, ___?___) and (___?___, ___?___).

Evaluate the function for the given value of x.

13. $f(x) = x^2 - 2x + 1; x = 3$

14. $f(x) = 2x^2 + x - 1; x = -2$

15. $f(x) = 4 - x^2; x = -3$

16. $f(x) = x^2 + 6x + 9; x = -3$

17. $f(x) = -x^2 + 5x - 6; x = -4$

18. $f(x) = -2x^2 + 2x - 1; x = -1$

Graph.

19. $y = x^2$

20. $y = -x^2$

21. $y = -x^2 + 1$

22. $y = x^2 - 1$

23. $y = 2x^2$

24. $y = \frac{1}{2}x^2$

25. $y = -\frac{1}{2}x^2 + 1$

26. $y = 2x^2 - 1$

27. $y = x^2 - 4x$

28. $y = x^2 + 4x$

29. $y = x^2 - 2x + 3$

30. $y = x^2 - 4x + 2$

31. $y = -x^2 + 2x + 3$

32. $y = x^2 + 2x + 1$

33. $y = -x^2 + 3x - 4$

34. $y = -x^2 + 6x - 9$

35. $y = 2x^2 + x - 3$

36. $y = -2x^2 - 3x + 3$

For Exercises 37 and 38, $y = ax^2 + bx + c$ is a quadratic equation whose graph is a parabola that has only one x-intercept, $(n, 0)$.

37. True or false? If $a < 0$, then for all real numbers x, $y \geq 0$.

38. True or false? The point on the parabola with x-coordinate $n - m$ has the same y-coordinate as the point on the parabola with x-coordinate $n + m$.

Determine the x- and y-intercepts of the graph of the equation.

39. $y = x^2 - 5x + 6$

40. $y = x^2 + 5x - 6$

41. $f(x) = 9 - x^2$

42. $f(x) = x^2 + 12x + 36$

43. $y = x^2 + 2x - 6$

44. $y = x^2 + 4x - 2$

45. $f(x) = 2x^2 - x - 3$

46. $f(x) = 2x^2 - 13x + 15$

47. $y = 4 - x - x^2$

48. $y = 2 - 3x - 3x^2$

Graph using a graphing utility. Verify that the graph is a graph of a parabola opening up if a is positive or opening down if a is negative.

49. $y = x^2 - 2$

50. $y = -x^2 + 3$

51. $y = x^2 + 2x$

52. $y = -2x^2 + 4x$

53. $y = \frac{1}{2}x^2 - x$

54. $y = -\frac{1}{2}x^2 + 2$

55. $y = x^2 - x - 2$

56. $y = x^2 - 3x + 2$

57. $y = 2x^2 - x - 5$

58. $y = -2x^2 - 3x + 2$

59. $y = -x^2 - 2x - 1$

60. $y = \frac{1}{2}x^2 - 2x - 1$

11.5 Applying Concepts

Show that the equation is a quadratic equation in two variables by writing it in the form $y = ax^2 + bx + c$.

61. $y + 1 = (x - 4)^2$

62. $y - 2 = 3(x + 1)^2$

63. $y - 4 = 2(x - 3)^2$

64. $y + 3 = 3(x - 1)^2$

Find the x-intercepts of the graph of the equation.

65. $y = x^3 - x^2 - 6x$

66. $y = x^3 - 4x^2 - 5x$

67. $y = x^3 + x^2 - 4x - 4$ (*Hint:* Factor by grouping.)

68. $y = x^3 + 3x^2 - x - 3$ (*Hint:* Factor by grouping.)

State whether the graph is the graph of a linear function, a quadratic function, or neither.

69.

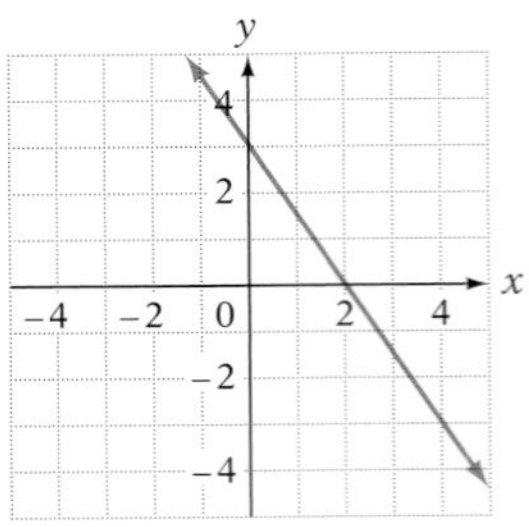

70.

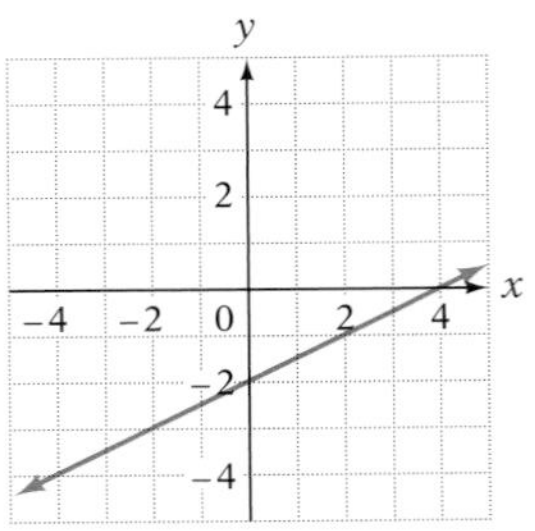

71.

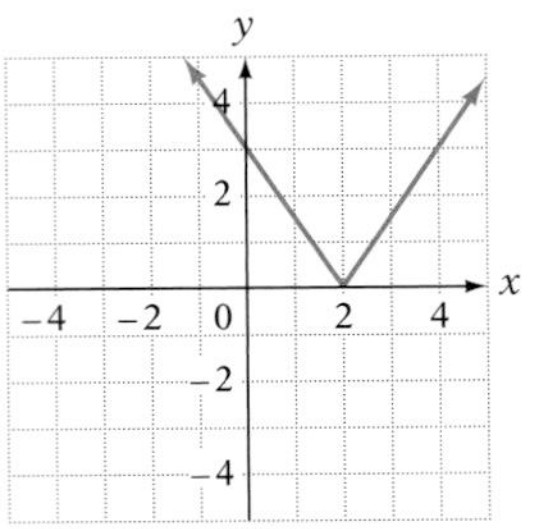

72.

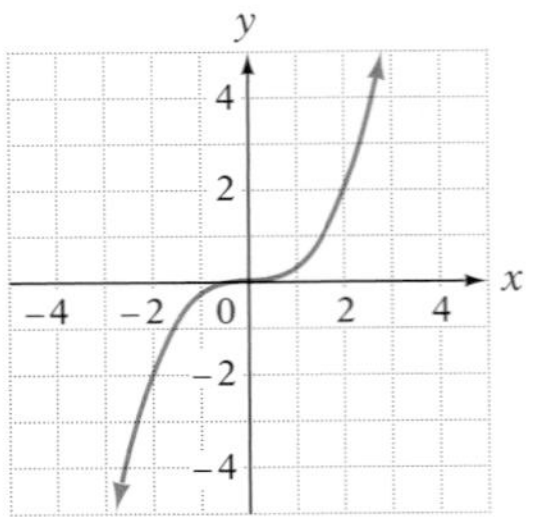

73.

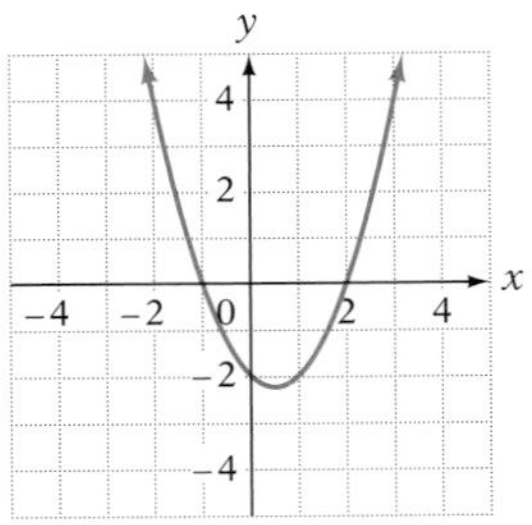

74.

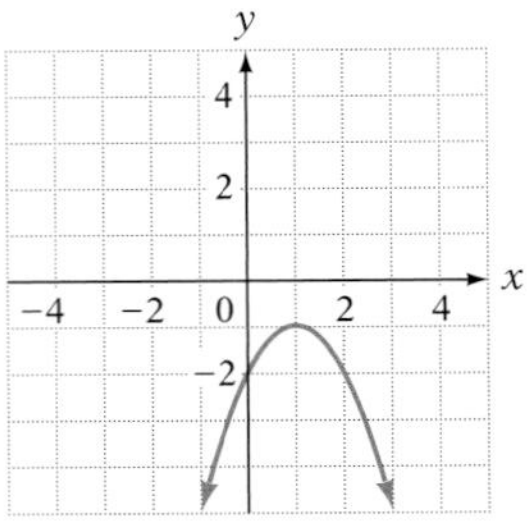

75. **The Postal Service** The graph below shows the cost of a first-class postage stamp from 1950 to 2006. A quadratic function that approximately models the data is $0.0034x^2 + 0.2509x - 24.7909$, where $x \geq 50$ and $x = 50$ for the year 1950, and y is the cost in cents of a first-class stamp. What does the model predict will be the cost of a first-class stamp in 2020? Round to the nearest cent.

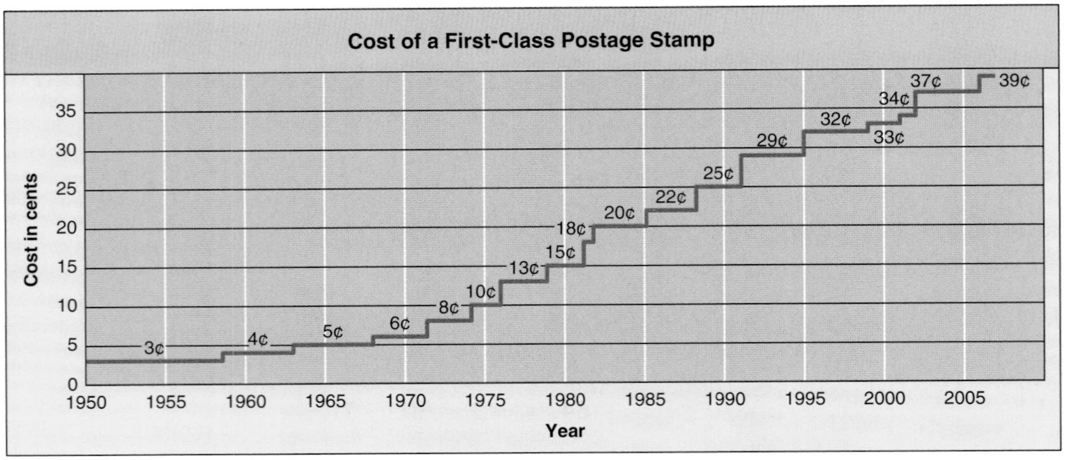

76. The point whose coordinates are (x_1, y_1) lies in quadrant I and is a point on the graph of the equation $y = 2x^2 - 2x + 1$. Given $y_1 = 13$, find x_1.

77. The point whose coordinates are (x_1, y_1) lies in quadrant II and is a point on the graph of the equation $y = 2x^2 - 3x - 2$. Given $y_1 = 12$, find x_1.

11.6 Application Problems

OBJECTIVE 1 Application problems

The application problems in this section are varieties of those problems solved earlier in the text. Each of the strategies for the problems in this section results in a quadratic equation.

Solve: It took a motorboat a total of 7 h to travel 48 mi down a river and then 48 mi back again. The rate of the current was 2 mph. Find the rate of the motorboat in calm water.

STRATEGY for solving an application problem

▶ Determine the type of problem. For example, is it a uniform motion problem, a geometry problem, or a work problem?

The problem is a uniform motion problem.

▶ Choose a variable to represent the unknown quantity. Write numerical or variable expressions for all the remaining quantities. These results can be recorded in a table.

The unknown rate of the motorboat: r

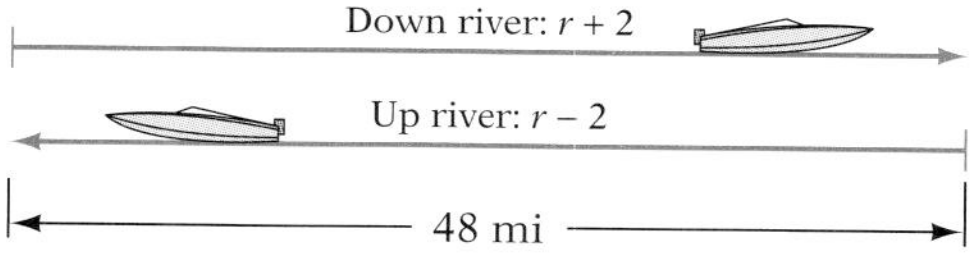

	Distance	÷	Rate	=	Time
Down river	48	÷	$r + 2$	=	$\frac{48}{r+2}$
Up river	48	÷	$r - 2$	=	$\frac{48}{r-2}$

▶ Determine how the quantities are related. If necessary, review the strategies presented in the chapter "Solving Equations and Inequalities: Applications."

The total time of the trip was 7 h.

$$\frac{48}{r+2} + \frac{48}{r-2} = 7$$

$$(r+2)(r-2)\left(\frac{48}{r+2} + \frac{48}{r-2}\right) = (r+2)(r-2)7$$

$$(r-2)48 + (r+2)48 = (r^2-4)7$$

$$48r - 96 + 48r + 96 = 7r^2 - 28$$

$$96r = 7r^2 - 28$$

$$0 = 7r^2 - 96r - 28$$

$$0 = (7r+2)(r-14)$$

$$7r + 2 = 0 \qquad r - 14 = 0$$

$$7r = -2 \qquad r = 14$$

$$r = -\frac{2}{7}$$

The solution $-\frac{2}{7}$ is not possible, because the rate cannot be negative.

The rate of the motorboat in calm water is 14 mph.

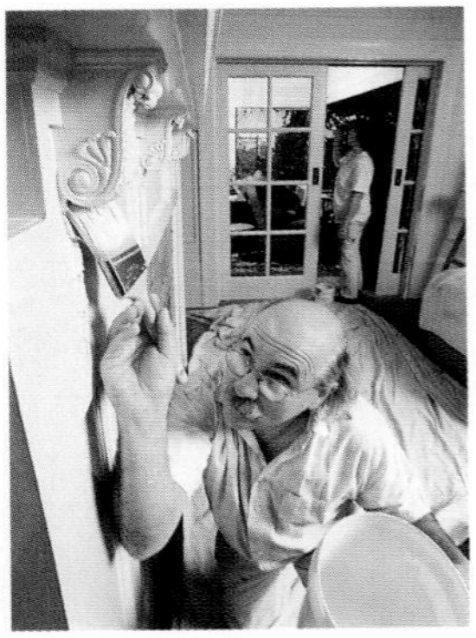

EXAMPLE 1 Working together, a painter and the painter's apprentice can paint a room in 4 h. Working alone, the apprentice requires 6 more hours to paint the room than the painter requires working alone. How long does it take the painter, working alone, to paint the room?

Strategy

▶ This is a work problem.

▶ Time for the painter to paint the room: t
Time for the apprentice to paint the room: $t + 6$

	Rate	Time	Part
Painter	$\frac{1}{t}$	4	$\frac{4}{t}$
Apprentice	$\frac{1}{t+6}$	4	$\frac{4}{t+6}$

▶ The sum of the parts of the task completed must equal 1.

Solution

$$\frac{4}{t} + \frac{4}{t+6} = 1$$

$$t(t+6)\left(\frac{4}{t} + \frac{4}{t+6}\right) = t(t+6) \cdot 1$$

$$(t+6)4 + t(4) = t(t+6)$$

$$4t + 24 + 4t = t^2 + 6t$$

$$0 = t^2 - 2t - 24$$

$$0 = (t-6)(t+4)$$

$$t - 6 = 0 \qquad t + 4 = 0$$

$$t = 6 \qquad t = -4$$

• **The solution $t = -4$ is not possible.**

Working alone, the painter requires 6 h to paint the room.

PROBLEM 1 The length of a rectangle is 3 m more than the width. The area is 40 m^2. Find the width.

Solution See page S28.

11.6 Concept Review

Determine whether the statement is always true, sometimes true, or never true.

1. If the length of a rectangle is three more than twice the width and the width is represented by W, then the length is represented by $3W + 2$.

2. The sum of the squares of two consecutive odd integers can be represented as $n^2 + (n + 1)^2$.

3. If it takes one pipe 15 min longer to fill a tank than it does a second pipe, then the rate of work for the second pipe can be represented by $\frac{1}{t}$ and the rate of work for the first pipe can be represented by $\frac{1}{t + 15}$.

4. If a plane's rate of speed is r and the rate of the wind is 30 mph, then the plane's rate of speed flying with the wind is $30 + r$ and the plane's rate of speed flying against the wind is $30 - r$.

5. The graph of the equation $h = 48t - 16t^2$ is the graph of a parabola opening down.

6. A number that is a solution to a quadratic equation may not be a possible answer to the application problem it models. Such a solution is disregarded.

11.6 Exercises

1 Application problems

1. The length of a rectangle is 2 ft less than twice the width. Let w be the width of the rectangle.
   a. In terms of w, the length of the rectangle is __?__.
   b. In terms of w, the area of the rectangle is __?__.
   c. The area of the rectangle is 84 ft^2. Use your answer to part b and the fact that the area of the rectangle is 84 ft^2 to write an equation that can be solved to find the width of the rectangle: __?__ = __?__.

2. a. Solve the equation that you wrote in part c of Exercise 1.

$w(2w - 2) = 84$	
$\underline{\quad ? \quad} - \underline{\quad ? \quad} = 84$	• **Use the Distributive Property.**
$2w^2 - 2w - 84 = 0$	• **Subtract** $\underline{\quad ? \quad}$ **from each side of the equation.**
$w^2 - w - 42 = 0$	• **Divide each side of the equation by** $\underline{\quad ? \quad}$.
$(w - \underline{\quad ? \quad})(w + \underline{\quad ? \quad}) = 0$	• **Factor the left side.**
$\underline{\quad ? \quad} = 0 \qquad \underline{\quad ? \quad} = 0$	• **Use the Principle of Zero Products.**
$w = \underline{\quad ? \quad} \qquad w = \underline{\quad ? \quad}$	• **Solve for *w*.**

b. Only one solution from part a makes sense as the width of the rectangle described in Exercise 1. The width of the rectangle is $\underline{\quad ? \quad}$. The length of the rectangle is $\underline{\quad ? \quad}$.

3. **Integer Problem** The sum of the squares of two positive consecutive odd integers is 130. Find the two integers.

4. **Integer Problem** The sum of two integers is 12. The product of the two integers is 35. Find the two integers.

5. **Integer Problem** The difference between two integers is 4. The product of the two integers is 60. Find the integers.

6. **Integer Problem** Twice an integer equals the square of the integer. Find the integer.

7. **Sports** The area of the batter's box on a major-league baseball field is 24 ft^2. The length of the batter's box is 2 ft more than the width. Find the length and width of the rectangular batter's box.

8. **Sports** The length of the batter's box on a softball field is 1 ft more than twice the width. The area of the batter's box is 21 ft^2. Find the length and width of the rectangular batter's box.

9. **Recreation** The length of a children's playground is twice the width. The area is 5000 ft^2. Find the length and width of the rectangular playground.

10. **Work Problem** A tank has two drains. One drain takes 16 min longer to empty the tank than does the second drain. With both drains open, the tank is emptied in 6 min. How long would it take each drain, working alone, to empty the tank?

11. **Work Problem** One computer takes 21 min longer than a second computer to calculate the value of a complex expression. Working together, these computers can complete the calculation in 10 min. How long would it take each computer, working alone, to calculate the value?

12. **Sports** The length of a singles tennis court is 24 ft more than twice the width. The area is 2106 ft^2. Find the length and width of the singles tennis court.

13. **Work Problem** It takes 6 h longer to cross a channel in a ferryboat when one engine of the boat is used alone than when a second engine is used alone. Using both engines, the ferryboat can make the crossing in 4 h. How long would it take each engine, working alone, to power the ferryboat across the channel?

14. **Work Problem** An apprentice mason takes 8 h longer than an experienced mason to build a small fireplace. Working together, they can build the fireplace in 3 h. How long would it take the experienced mason, working alone, to build the fireplace?

15. **Uniform Motion** It took a small plane 2 h longer to fly 375 mi against the wind than it took the plane to fly the same distance with the wind. The rate of the wind was 25 mph. Find the rate of the plane in calm air.

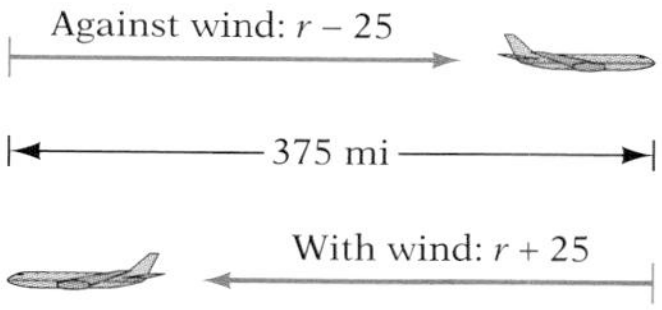

16. **Uniform Motion** It took a motorboat 1 h longer to travel 36 mi against the current than it took the boat to travel 36 mi with the current. The rate of the current was 3 mph. Find the rate of the boat in calm water.

17. **Uniform Motion** A motorcycle traveled 150 mi at a constant rate before its speed was decreased by 15 mph. Another 35 mi was driven at the decreased speed. The total time for the 185-mile trip was 4 h. Find the cyclist's rate during the first 150 mi.

18. **Uniform Motion** A cruise ship sailed through a 20-mile inland passageway at a constant rate before its speed was increased by 15 mph. Another 75 mi was traveled at the increased rate. The total time for the 95-mile trip was 5 h. Find the rate of the ship during the last 75 mi.

19. **Physics** An arrow is projected into the air with an initial velocity of 48 ft/s. At what times will the arrow be 32 ft above the ground? Use the equation $h = 48t - 16t^2$, where h is the height, in feet, above the ground after t seconds.

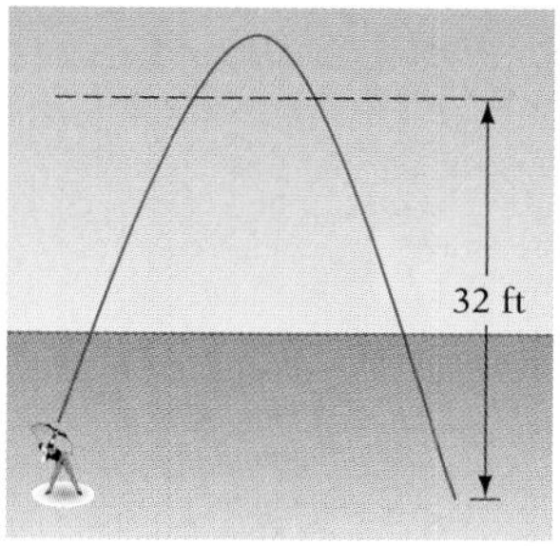

20. **Physics** A model rocket is launched with an initial velocity of 200 ft/s. The height, h, of the rocket t seconds after launch is given by $h = -16t^2 + 200t$. How many seconds after the launch will the rocket be 300 ft above the ground? Round to the nearest hundredth.

21. **Travel** In Germany there are no speed limits on some portions of the autobahn (highway). Other portions have a speed limit of 180 km/h (approximately 112 mph). The distance, d (in meters), required to stop a car traveling at v kilometers per hour is $d = 0.0056v^2 + 0.14v$. What is the maximum speed a driver can be traveling and still be able to stop within 150 m? Round to the nearest tenth.

German Autobahn System

22. **Sports** In a slow-pitch softball game, the height of the ball thrown by a pitcher can be modeled by the equation $h = -16t^2 + 24t + 4$, where h is the height of the ball in feet, and t is the time, in seconds, since it was released by the pitcher. If the batter hits the ball when it is 2 ft off the ground, how many seconds has the ball been in the air? Round to the nearest hundredth.

23. **Safety** The path of water from a hose on a fire tugboat can be modeled by the equation $y = -0.005x^2 + 1.2x + 10$, where y is the height in feet of the water above the ocean when it is x feet from the tugboat. At what distance from the tugboat is the water from the hose when the water from the hose is 5 ft above the ocean? Round to the nearest tenth.

24. **Sports** A baseball player hits a ball. The height, in feet, of the ball above the ground at time t, in seconds, can be approximated by the equation $h = -16t^2 + 76t + 5$. When will the ball hit the ground? Round to the nearest hundredth. (*Hint:* The ball strikes the ground when $h = 0$ ft.)

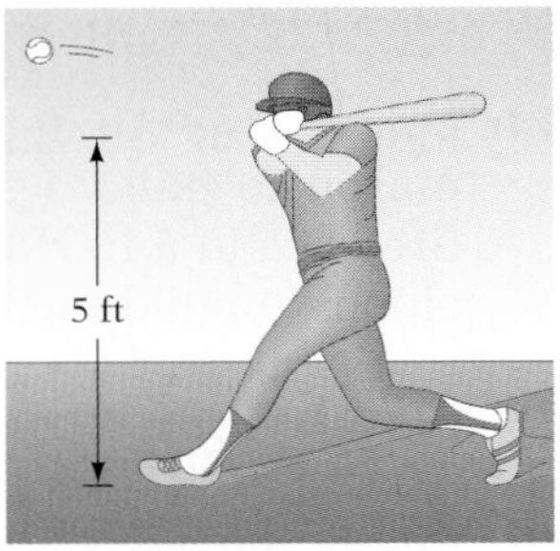

25. **Sports** A basketball player shoots at a basket 25 ft away. The height h, in feet, of the ball above the ground at time t, in seconds, is given by $h = -16t^2 + 32t + 6.5$. How many seconds after the ball is released does it hit the basket? Round to the nearest hundredth. (*Hint:* When it hits the basket, $h = 10$ ft.)

26. **Sports** The hang time of a football that is kicked on the opening kickoff is given by $s = -16t^2 + 88t + 1$, where s is the height, in feet, of the football t seconds after leaving the kicker's foot. What is the hang time of a kickoff that hits the ground without being caught? Round to the nearest tenth.

Complete Exercises 27 and 28 *without* writing and solving an equation. Use this situation: A small pipe takes 12 min longer to fill a tank than does a larger pipe. Working together, the pipes can fill the tank in 4 min.

27. True or false? The amount of time that it takes the larger pipe to fill the tank is less than 4 min.

28. True or false? The amount of time that it takes the small pipe to fill the tank is greater than 16 min.

11.6 Applying Concepts

29. **Geometry** A tin can has a volume of 1500 cm^3 and a height of 15 cm. Find the radius of the base of the tin can. Round to the nearest hundredth.

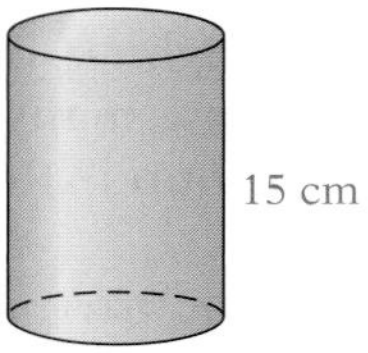

30. **Geometry** The hypotenuse of a right triangle measures $\sqrt{13}$ cm. One leg is 1 cm shorter than twice the length of the other leg. Find the lengths of the legs of the right triangle.

31. **Integer Problem** The sum of the squares of four consecutive integers is 86. Find the four integers.

32. **Geometry** Find the radius of a right circular cone that has a volume of 800 cm^3 and a height of 12 cm. Round to the nearest hundredth.

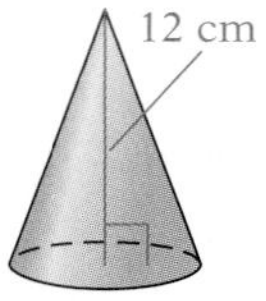

33. **Food Industry** The radius of a large pizza is 1 in. less than twice the radius of a small pizza. The difference between the areas of the two pizzas is 33π in^2. Find the radius of the large pizza.

34. **Gardening** The perimeter of a rectangular garden is 54 ft. The area of the garden is 180 ft^2. Find the length and width of the garden.

35. **Food Industry** A square piece of cardboard is to be formed into a box to transport pizzas. The box is formed by cutting 2-inch square corners from the cardboard and folding them up as shown in the figure at the right. If the volume of the box is 512 in^3, what are the dimensions of the cardboard?

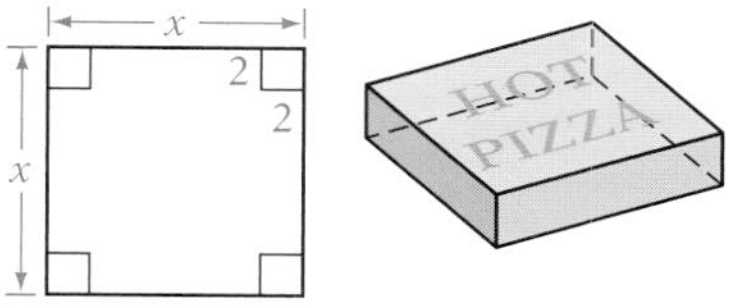

36. **Metalwork** A wire 8 ft long is cut into two pieces. A circle is formed from one piece and a square is formed from the other. The total area of both figures is given by $A = \frac{1}{16}(8 - x)^2 + \frac{x^2}{4\pi}$. What is the length of each piece of wire if the total area is 4.5 ft^2? Round to the nearest thousandth.

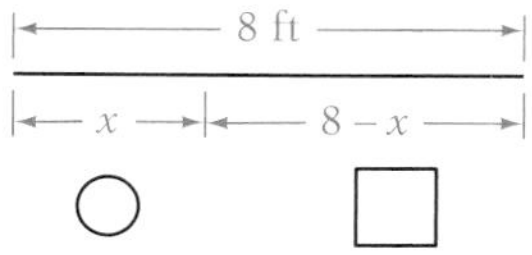

Focus on Problem Solving

Applying Algebraic Manipulation and Graphing Techniques to Business

Problem solving is often easier when we have both algebraic manipulation and graphing techniques at our disposal. Solving quadratic equations and graphing quadratic equations in two variables are used here to solve problems involving profit.

A company's **revenue,** R, is the total amount of money the company earned by selling its products. The **cost,** C, is the total amount of money the company spent to manufacture and sell its products. A company's **profit,** P, is the difference between the revenue and cost: $\boldsymbol{P = R - C}$. A company's revenue and cost may be represented by equations.

A company manufactures and sells wood stoves. The total monthly cost, in dollars, to produce n wood stoves is $C = 30n + 2000$. Write a variable expression for the company's monthly profit if the revenue, in dollars, obtained from selling all n wood stoves is $R = 150n - 0.4n^2$.

$$P = R - C$$
$$P = 150n - 0.4n^2 - (30n + 2000)$$
$$P = -0.4n^2 + 120n - 2000$$

- **Replace R by $150n - 0.4n^2$ and C by $30n + 2000$. Then simplify.**

The company's monthly profit is $P = -0.4n^2 + 120n - 2000$.

How many wood stoves must the company manufacture and sell in order to make a profit of \$6000 a month?

$$P = -0.4n^2 + 120n - 2000$$
$$6000 = -0.4n^2 + 120n - 2000$$
$$0 = -0.4n^2 + 120n - 8000$$
$$0 = n^2 - 300n + 20{,}000$$
$$0 = (n - 100)(n - 200)$$

- **Substitute 6000 for P.**
- **Write the equation in standard form.**
- **Divide each side of the equation by −0.4.**
- **Factor.**

$$n - 100 = 0 \qquad n - 200 = 0$$
$$n = 100 \qquad n = 200$$

- **Solve for n.**

The company will make a monthly profit of \$6000 if either 100 or 200 wood stoves are manufactured and sold.

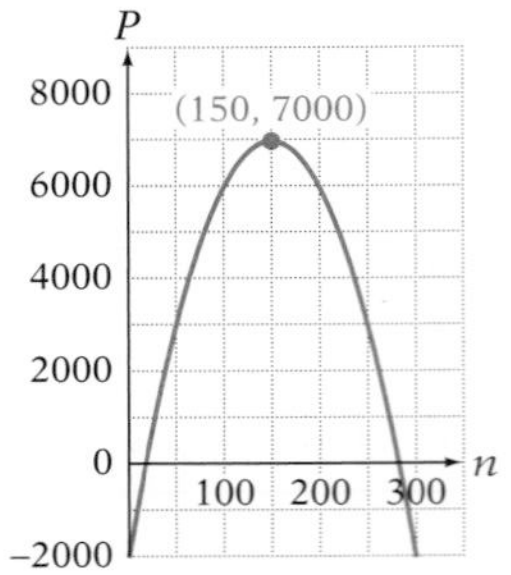

The graph of $P = -0.4n^2 + 120n - 2000$ is shown at the left. Note that when $P = 6000$, the values of n are 100 and 200.

Also note that the coordinates of the highest point on the graph are (150, 7000). This means that the company makes a *maximum* profit of \$7000 per month when 150 wood stoves are manufactured and sold.

1. The total cost, in dollars, for a company to produce and sell n guitars per month is $C = 240n + 1200$. The company's revenue, in dollars, from selling all n guitars is $R = 400n - 2n^2$.

a. How many guitars must the company produce and sell each month in order to make a monthly profit of \$1200?
b. Graph the profit equation. What is the maximum monthly profit the company can make?

2. A company's total monthly cost, in dollars, for manufacturing and selling n videotapes per month is $C = 35n + 2000$. The company's revenue, in dollars, from selling all n videotapes is $R = 175n - 0.2n^2$.

a. How many videotapes must be produced and sold each month in order for the company to make a monthly profit of \$18,000?
b. Graph the profit equation. How many videotapes must the company produce and sell in order to make the maximum monthly profit?

Projects & Group Activities

Graphical Solutions of Quadratic Equations

A real number x is called a **zero of a function** if the value of the function when evaluated at x is 0. That is, if $f(x) = 0$, then x is called a zero of the function. For instance, evaluating $f(x) = x^2 + x - 6$ at $x = -3$, we have

$$f(x) = x^2 + x - 6$$
$$f(-3) = (-3)^2 + (-3) - 6 \qquad \text{• Replace } x \text{ with } -3.$$
$$f(-3) = 9 - 3 - 6$$
$$f(-3) = 0$$

For this function, $f(-3) = 0$, so -3 is a zero of the function.

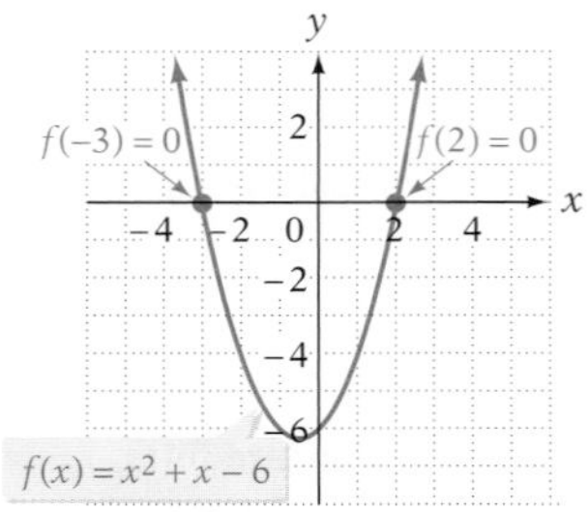

You can verify that 2 is also a zero of $f(x) = x^2 + x - 6$ by showing that $f(2) = 0$.

The graph of $y = x^2 + x - 6$ is shown at the left. Note that the graph crosses the x-axis at -3 and 2, the two zeros of the function. The points $(-3, 0)$ and $(2, 0)$ are x-intercepts of the graph.

Now consider the equation $0 = x^2 + x - 6$, which is $f(x) = x^2 + x - 6$ with $f(x)$ replaced with 0. Solving $0 = x^2 + x - 6$ for x, we have

$$0 = x^2 + x - 6$$
$$0 = (x + 3)(x - 2)$$

• **Solve by factoring and using the Principle of Zero Products.**

$$x + 3 = 0 \qquad x - 2 = 0$$
$$x = -3 \qquad x = 2$$

The solutions are −3 and 2.

Observe that the solutions of the equation are the zeros of the function. This important connection among the real zeros of a function, the x-intercepts of its graph, and the solutions of its equation is the basis for using a graphing calculator to solve an equation.

The following method of solving a quadratic equation using a graphing calculator is based on a TI-83/TI-83 Plus/TI-84 Plus calculator. Other calculators will require a slightly different approach.

Approximate the solutions of $x^2 + 4x = 6$ by using a graphing calculator.

a. Write the equation in standard form.

$$x^2 + 4x = 6$$
$$x^2 + 4x - 6 = 0$$

b. Press Y= and enter $x^2 + 4x - 6$ for Y1.

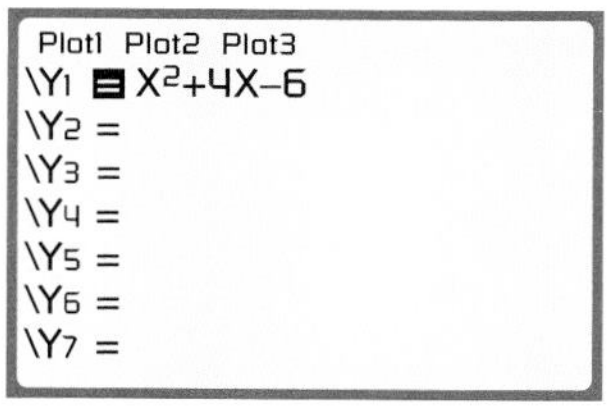

c. Press GRAPH. If the graph does not appear on the screen, press ZOOM 6.

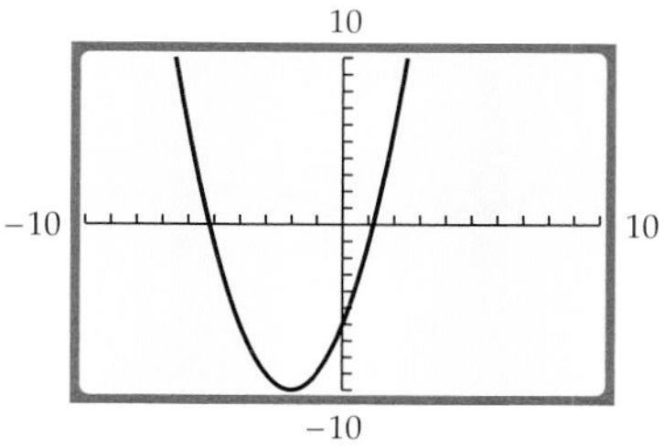

d. Press 2nd CALC 2. Note that the selection for 2 says zero. This will begin the calculation of the zeros of the function, which are the solutions of the equation.

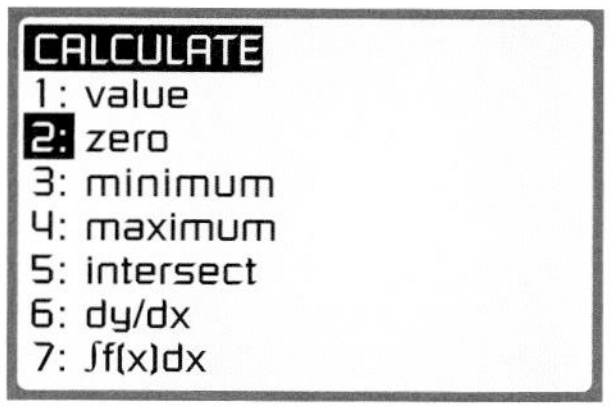

e. At the bottom of the screen you will see Left Bound? This is asking you to move the blinking cursor so that it is to the *left* of the first x-intercept. Use the left arrow key to move the cursor to the left of the first x-intercept. The values of x and y that appear on

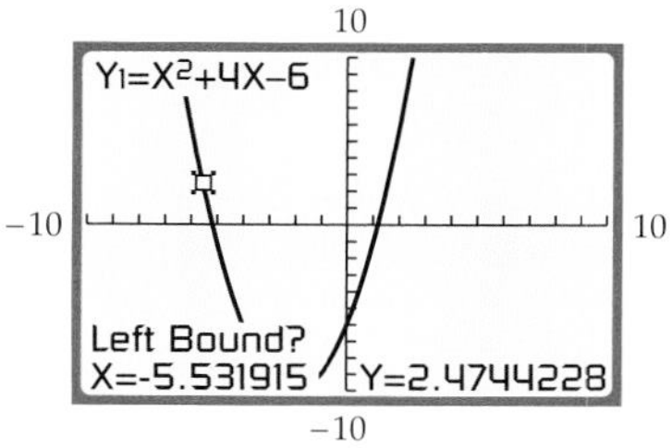

your calculator may be different from the ones shown here. Just be sure you are to the left of the x-intercept. When you have done that, press ENTER.

f. At the bottom of the screen you will see **Right Bound?** This is asking you to move the blinking cursor so that it is to the *right* of the x-intercept. Use the right arrow key to move the cursor to the right of the x-intercept. The values of x and y that appear on your calculator may be different from the ones shown here. Just be sure you are to the right of the x-intercept. When you have done that, press ENTER.

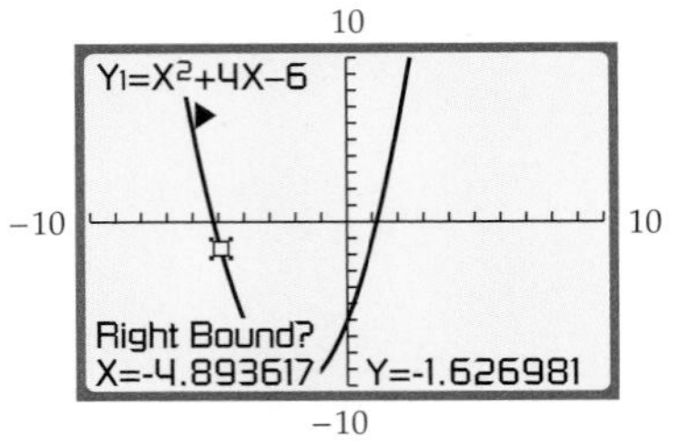

g. At the bottom of the screen you will see **Guess?** This is asking you to move the blinking cursor to the approximate x-intercept. Use the arrow keys to move the cursor to the approximate x-intercept. The values of x and y that appear on your calculator may be different from the ones shown here. When you have done that, press ENTER.

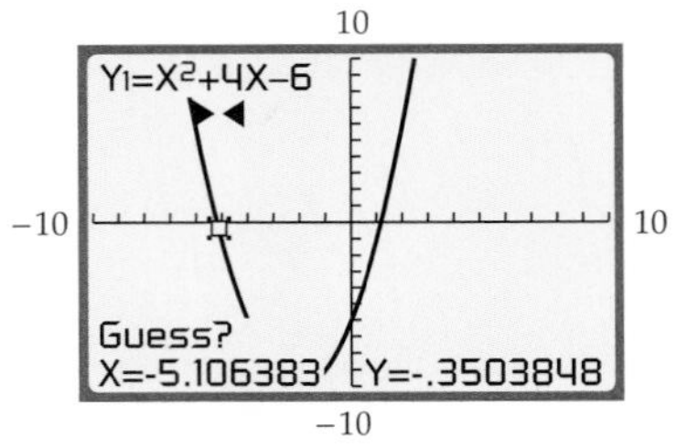

h. The zero of the function is approximately -5.162278. Thus one solution of $x^2 + 4x = 6$ is approximately -5.162278. Also note that the value of y is given as $Y = -1E{-}12$. This is the way the calculator writes a number in scientific notation. We would normally write $Y = -1.0 \times 10^{-12}$. This number is very close to zero.

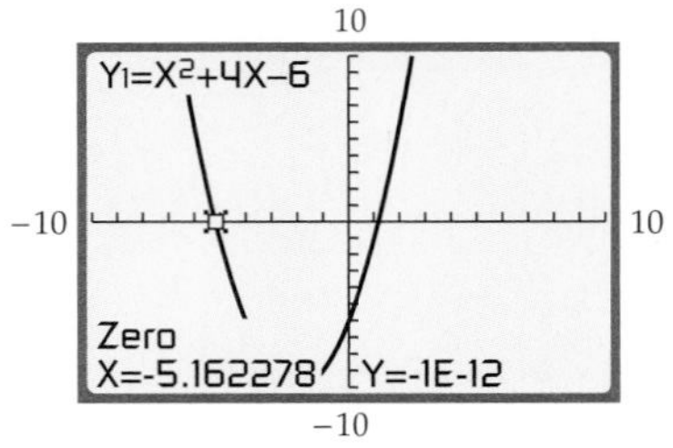

i. To find the other solution, repeat Steps d through g. The screens are shown below and at the top of the next page.

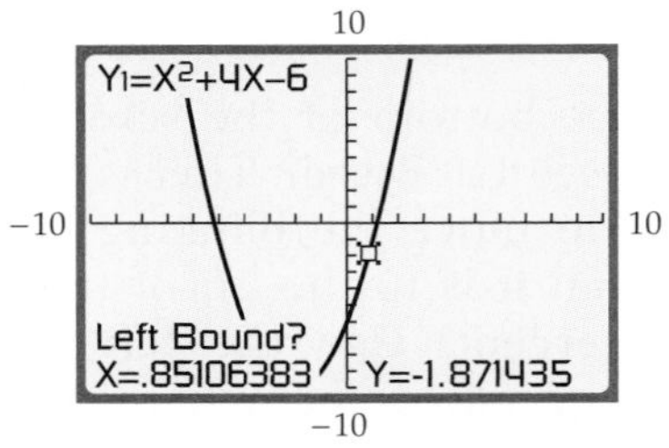

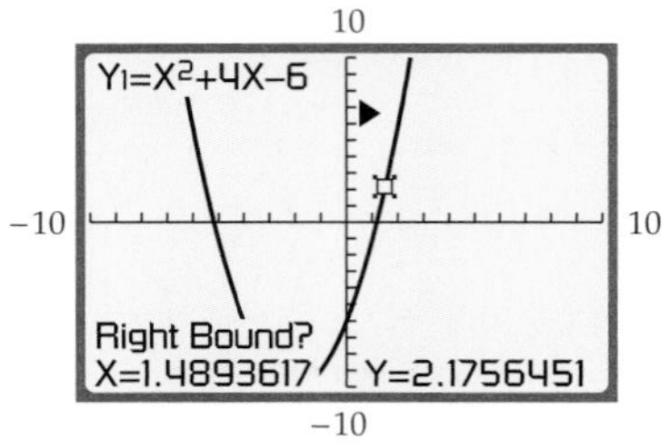

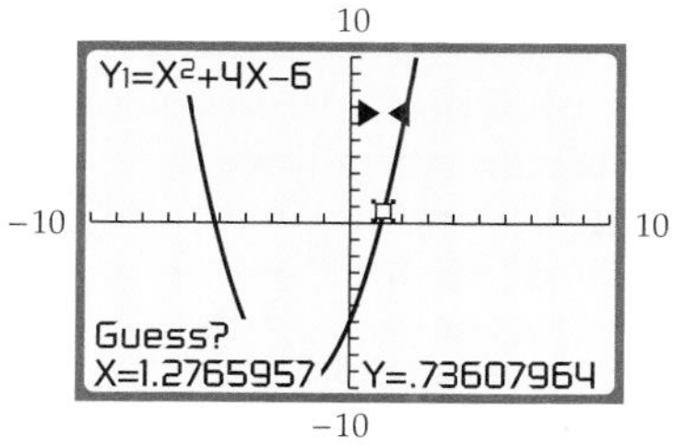

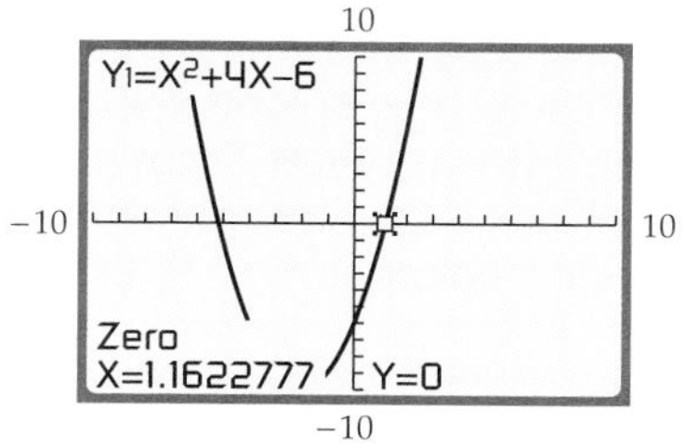

A second zero of the function is approximately 1.1622777.

Thus the two solutions of $x^2 + 4x = 6$ are approximately -5.162278 and 1.1622777.

Use a graphing calculator to approximate the solutions of the equation.

1. $x^2 + 3x - 4 = 0$

2. $2x^2 - 3x - 7 = 0$

3. $x^2 + 5x = 1$

4. $x^2 + 3.4x = 4.15$

5. $\pi x^2 - \sqrt{17}x - 2 = 0$

6. $\sqrt{2}x^2 + x = \sqrt{7}$

Chapter 11 Summary

Key Words	*Examples*
A **quadratic equation** is an equation that can be written in the form $ax^2 + bx + c = 0$, $a \neq 0$. A quadratic equation is also called a **second-degree equation.** [11.1.1, p. 584]	The equation $4x^2 - 3x + 6 = 0$ is a quadratic equation. In this equation, $a = 4$, $b = -3$, and $c = 6$.
A quadratic equation is in **standard form** when the polynomial is in descending order and equal to zero. [11.1.1, p. 584]	The quadratic equation $5x^2 + 3x - 1 = 0$ is in standard form.
Adding to a binomial the constant term that makes it a perfect-square trinomial is called **completing the square.** [11.2.1, p. 593]	Adding to $x^2 - 6x$ the constant term 9 results in a perfect-square trinomial: $x^2 - 6x + 9 = (x - 3)(x - 3) = (x - 3)^2$
A **complex number** is a number of the form $a + bi$, where a and b are real numbers and $i = \sqrt{-1}$. For the complex number $a + bi$, a is the **real part** of the complex number and b is the **imaginary part** of the complex number. [11.4.1, p. 607]	$5 + 2i$ is a complex number. 5 is the real part and 2 is the imaginary part of the complex number.

The graph of an equation of the form $y = ax^2 + bx + c$ is a **parabola**. The graph is ∪-shaped and opens up when a is positive and down when a is negative. The **vertex** is the lowest point on a parabola that opens up, or the highest point on a parabola that opens down. [11.5.1, pp. 621, 623]

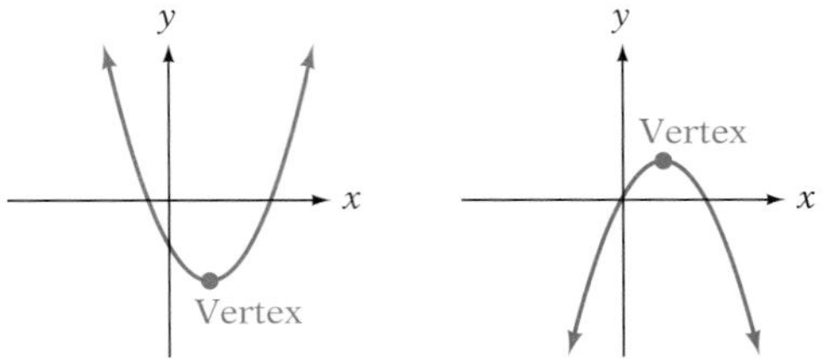

Parabola that opens up Parabola that opens down

Essential Rules and Procedures

Solving a Quadratic Equation by Factoring
Write the equation in standard form, factor the left side of the equation, apply the Principle of Zero Products, and solve for the variable. [11.1.1, p. 585]

$$x^2 + 2x = 15$$
$$x^2 + 2x - 15 = 0$$
$$(x - 3)(x + 5) = 0$$
$$x - 3 = 0 \qquad x + 5 = 0$$
$$x = 3 \qquad x = -5$$

Principle of Taking the Square Root of Each Side of an Equation
If $x^2 = a$, then $x = \pm\sqrt{a}$.

This principle is used to solve quadratic equations by taking square roots. [11.1.2, p. 586]

$$3x^2 - 48 = 0$$
$$3x^2 = 48$$
$$x^2 = 16$$
$$\sqrt{x^2} = \sqrt{16}$$
$$x = \pm\sqrt{16}$$
$$x = \pm 4$$

Solving a Quadratic Equation by Completing the Square
When the quadratic equation is in the form $x^2 + bx = c$, add to each side of the equation the term that completes the square of $x^2 + bx$. Factor the perfect-square trinomial, and write it as the square of a binomial. Take the square root of each side of the equation and solve for x. [11.2.1, p. 594]

$$x^2 + 6x = 5$$
$$x^2 + 6x + 9 = 5 + 9$$
$$(x + 3)^2 = 14$$
$$\sqrt{(x + 3)^2} = \sqrt{14}$$
$$x + 3 = \pm\sqrt{14}$$
$$x = -3 \pm \sqrt{14}$$

The Quadratic Formula
The solutions of $ax^2 + bx + c = 0$, $a \neq 0$, are

$x = \dfrac{-b \pm \sqrt{b^2 - 4ac}}{2a}$. [11.3.1, p. 601]

$$3x^2 = x + 5$$
$$3x^2 - x - 5 = 0$$
$$x = \frac{-b \pm \sqrt{b^2 - 4ac}}{2a}$$
$$= \frac{-(-1) \pm \sqrt{(-1)^2 - 4(3)(-5)}}{2(3)}$$
$$= \frac{1 \pm \sqrt{1 + 60}}{6} = \frac{1 \pm \sqrt{61}}{6}$$

Principal Square Root of a Negative Number
If a is a positive real number, then the **principal square root of negative** $\boldsymbol{a}$ is the imaginary number $i\sqrt{a}$: $\sqrt{-a} = i\sqrt{a}$. The number $i\sqrt{a}$ is called an **imaginary number.** When $a = 1$, we have $\sqrt{-1} = i$. [11.4.1, p. 607]

$$\sqrt{-8} = i\sqrt{8} = 2i\sqrt{2}$$

Addition and Subtraction of Complex Numbers
To add two complex numbers, add the real parts and add the imaginary parts. To subtract two complex numbers, subtract the real parts and subtract the imaginary parts. [11.4.2, p. 608]

$$(3 + 5i) + (2 + 4i) = (3 + 2) + (5 + 4)i$$
$$= 5 + 9i$$
$$(5 + 2i) - (8 + 4i) = (5 - 8) + (2 - 4)i$$
$$= -3 - 2i$$

Multiplication of Complex Numbers
The product of two complex numbers of the form $a + bi$, $a \neq 0$, $b \neq 0$, can be found by using the FOIL method and the fact that $i^2 = -1$. [11.4.3, p. 609]

$$(2 - 3i)(5 + 4i) = 10 + 8i - 15i - 12i^2$$
$$= 10 - 7i - 12(-1)$$
$$= 22 - 7i$$

Product of Complex Conjugates
$(a + bi)(a - bi) = a^2 + b^2$ [11.4.4, p. 611]

$$(3 + 5i)(3 - 5i) = 3^2 + 5^2$$
$$= 9 + 25$$
$$= 34$$

Graphing a Quadratic Equation in Two Variables
Find several solutions of the equation. Graph the ordered-pair solutions on a rectangular coordinate system. Draw a parabola through the points. [11.5.1, pp. 621–622]

To find the x-intercepts of the graph of a parabola, let $y = 0$ and solve for x. The x-intercepts of the graph at the right are $(-1, 0)$ and $(2, 0)$. To find the y-intercept, let $x = 0$ and solve for y. The y-intercept of the graph at the right is $(0, -2)$. [11.5.1, p. 622]

$y = x^2 - x - 2$

x	y
0	−2
1	−2
−1	0
2	0
−2	4
3	4

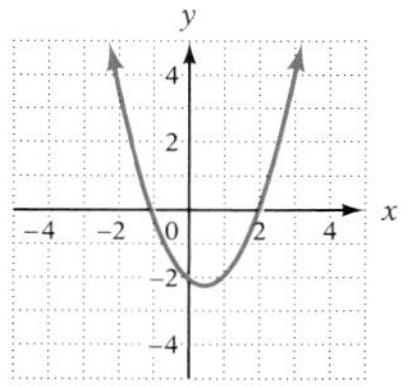

Chapter 11 Review Exercises

1. Solve: $b^2 - 16 = 0$

2. Solve: $x^2 - x - 3 = 0$

3. Solve: $x^2 - 3x - 5 = 0$

4. Solve: $49x^2 = 25$

5. Graph: $y = -\frac{1}{4}x^2$

6. Graph: $y = -3x^2$

7. Simplify: $3\sqrt{-28}$

8. Solve: $6x(x + 1) = x - 1$

9. Solve: $4y^2 + 9 = 0$

10. Solve: $5x^2 + 20x + 12 = 0$

11. Add: $(-4 + i) + (6 - 5i)$

12. Solve: $x^2 - x = 30$

13. Solve: $6x^2 + 13x - 28 = 0$

14. Solve: $x^2 = 40$

15. Subtract: $(-1 + 2i) - (2 - 3i)$

16. Solve: $x^2 - 2x - 10 = 0$

17. Solve: $x^2 - 12x + 27 = 0$

18. Solve: $(x - 7)^2 = 81$

19. Graph: $y = 2x^2 + 1$

20. Graph: $y = \frac{1}{2}x^2 - 1$

21. Solve: $(y + 4)^2 - 25 = 0$

22. Solve: $4x^2 + 16x = 7$

23. Solve: $24x^2 + 34x + 5 = 0$

24. Solve: $x^2 = 4x - 8$

25. Multiply: $4i(3 - 5i)$

26. Solve: $25(2x^2 - 2x + 1) = (x + 3)^2$

27. Solve: $\left(x - \frac{1}{2}\right)^2 = \frac{9}{4}$

28. Multiply: $(-2 + 4i)(3 - i)$

29. Solve: $x^2 + 7x = 3$

30. Solve: $12x^2 + 10 = 29x$

31. Solve: $4(x - 3)^2 = 20$

32. Solve: $x^2 + 8x - 3 = 0$

33. Graph: $y = x^2 - 3x$

34. Graph: $y = x^2 - 4x + 3$

35. Solve: $(x + 9)^2 = x + 11$

36. Divide: $\dfrac{3 - i}{2 - 4i}$

37. Solve: $x^2 + 6x + 12 = 0$

38. Solve: $x^2 + 6x - 2 = 0$

39. Solve: $18x^2 - 52x = 6$

40. Solve: $2x^2 + 5x = 1$

41. Graph: $y = -x^2 + 4x - 5$

42. Divide: $\dfrac{2 - 6i}{2i}$

43. Solve: $2x^2 + 5 = 7x$

44. Graph: $y = 4 - x^2$

45. **Uniform Motion** It took an air balloon 1 h longer to fly 60 mi against the wind than it took to fly 60 mi with the wind. The rate of the wind was 5 mph. Find the rate of the air balloon in calm air.

46. **Geometry** The height of a triangle is 2 m more than twice the length of the base. The area of the triangle is 20 m^2. Find the height of the triangle and the length of the base.

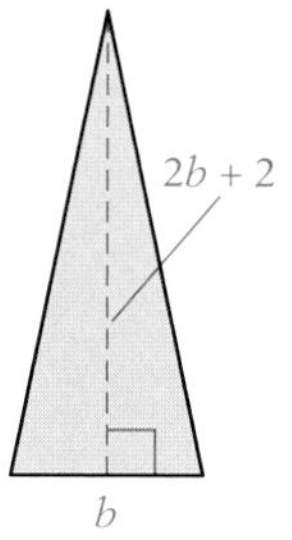

47. **Integer Problem** The sum of the squares of two consecutive positive odd integers is thirty-four. Find the two integers.

48. **Uniform Motion** In 5 h, two campers rowed 12 mi down a stream and then rowed back to their campsite. The rate of the stream's current was 1 mph. Find the rate of the boat in still water.

49. **Physics** An object is thrown into the air with an initial velocity of 32 ft/s. At what times will the object be 12 ft above the ground? Use the equation $h = 32t - 16t^2$, where h is the height, in feet, above the ground after t seconds.

50. **Work Problem** A smaller drain takes 8 h longer to empty a tank than does a larger drain. Working together, the drains can empty the tank in 3 h. How long would it take each drain, working alone, to empty the tank?

Chapter 11 Test

1. Solve: $3(x + 4)^2 - 60 = 0$

2. Solve: $2x^2 + 8x = 3$

3. Solve: $3x^2 + 7x = 20$

4. Simplify: $4\sqrt{-45}$

5. Solve: $x^2 + 4x - 16 = 0$

6. Graph: $y = x^2 + 2x - 4$

7. Solve: $x^2 + 4x + 2 = 0$

8. Subtract: $(-5 + 6i) - (3 - 7i)$

9. Solve: $2x^2 - 5x - 3 = 0$

10. Solve: $2x^2 - 6x + 1 = 0$

11. Multiply: $6i(5 - 4i)$

12. Solve: $2(x - 5)^2 = 36$

13. Solve: $x^2 - 6x - 5 = 0$

14. Multiply: $(-5 + 2i)(4 - i)$

15. Solve: $x^2 - 5x = 2$

16. Solve: $6x^2 - 17x = -5$

17. Solve: $x^2 + 3x - 7 = 0$

18. Divide: $\dfrac{3 - i}{2i}$

19. Solve: $x^2 - 8x + 17 = 0$

20. Graph: $y = x^2 - 2x - 3$

21. Divide: $\dfrac{4 - 2i}{1 - i}$

22. **Geometry** The length of a rectangle is 2 ft less than twice the width. The area of the rectangle is 40 ft^2. Find the length and width of the rectangle.

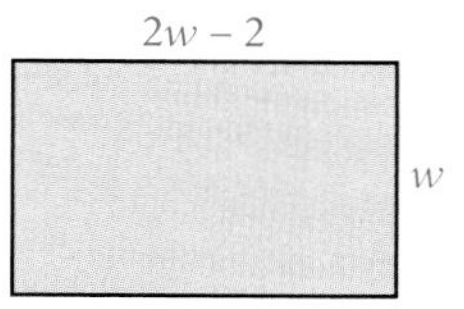

23. **Uniform Motion** It took a motorboat 1 h more to travel 60 mi against the current than it took to go 60 mi with the current. The rate of the current was 1 mph. Find the rate of the boat in calm water.

24. **Integer Problem** The sum of the squares of three consecutive odd integers is 83. Find the middle odd integer.

25. **Uniform Motion** A jogger ran 7 mi at a constant rate and then reduced the rate by 3 mph. An additional 8 mi was run at the reduced rate. The total time spent jogging the 15 mi was 3 h. Find the rate for the last 8 mi.

Cumulative Review Exercises

1. Simplify: $2x - 3[2x - 4(3 - 2x) + 2] - 3$

2. Solve: $-\frac{3}{5}x = -\frac{9}{10}$

3. Solve: $2x - 3(4x - 5) = -3x - 6$

4. Solve: $2x - 3(2 - 3x) > 2x - 5$

5. Find the x- and y-intercepts of the line $4x - 3y = 12$.

6. Find the equation of the line that contains the point whose coordinates are $(-3, 2)$ and has slope $-\frac{4}{3}$.

7. Find the domain and range of the relation $\{(-2, -8), (-1, -1), (0, 0), (1, 1), (2, 8)\}$. Is the relation a function?

8. Evaluate $f(x) = -3x + 10$ at $x = -9$.

9. Graph: $y = \frac{1}{4}x - 2$

10. Graph the solution set of $2x - 3y > 6$.

11. Solve by substitution: $\begin{aligned} 3x - y &= 5 \\ y &= 2x - 3 \end{aligned}$

12. Solve by the addition method: $\begin{aligned} 3x + 2y &= 2 \\ 5x - 2y &= 14 \end{aligned}$

13. Simplify: $\dfrac{(2a^{-2}b)^2}{-3a^{-5}b^4}$

14. Divide: $(x^2 - 8) \div (x - 2)$

15. Factor: $4y(x - 4) - 3(x - 4)$

16. Factor: $3x^3 + 2x^2 - 8x$

17. Divide: $\dfrac{3x^2 - 6x}{4x - 6} \div \dfrac{2x^2 + x - 6}{6x^2 - 24x}$

18. Subtract: $\dfrac{x}{2(x-1)} - \dfrac{1}{(x-1)(x+1)}$

19. Simplify: $\dfrac{1 - \dfrac{7}{x} + \dfrac{12}{x^2}}{2 - \dfrac{1}{x} - \dfrac{15}{x^2}}$

20. Solve: $\dfrac{x}{x+6} = \dfrac{3}{x}$

21. Multiply: $(\sqrt{a} - \sqrt{2})(\sqrt{a} + \sqrt{2})$

22. Solve: $3 = 8 - \sqrt{5x}$

23. Solve: $2x^2 - 7x = -3$

24. Solve: $3(x-2)^2 = 36$

25. Solve: $3x^2 - 4x - 5 = 0$

26. Graph: $y = x^2 - 3x - 2$

27. **Taxes** In a certain state, the sales tax is $7\frac{1}{4}\%$. The sales tax on a chemistry textbook is \$5.22. Find the cost of the textbook before the tax is added.

28. **Mixture Problem** Find the cost per pound of a mixture made from 20 lb of cashews that cost \$7 per pound and 50 lb of peanuts that cost \$3.50 per pound.

29. **Investments** A stock investment of 100 shares paid a dividend of \$215. At this rate, how many additional shares are required to earn a dividend of \$752.50?

30. **Uniform Motion** A 720-mile trip from one city to another takes 3 h when a plane is flying with the wind. The return trip, against the wind, takes 4.5 h. Find the rate of the plane in calm air and the rate of the wind.

31. **Test Scores** A student received a 70, a 91, an 85, and a 77 on four tests in a math class. What scores on the fifth test will enable the student to receive a minimum of 400 points?

32. **Guy Wires** A guy wire is attached to a point 30 m above the ground on a telephone pole that is perpendicular to the ground. The wire is anchored to the ground at a point 10 m from the base of the pole. Find the length of the guy wire. Round to the nearest hundredth.

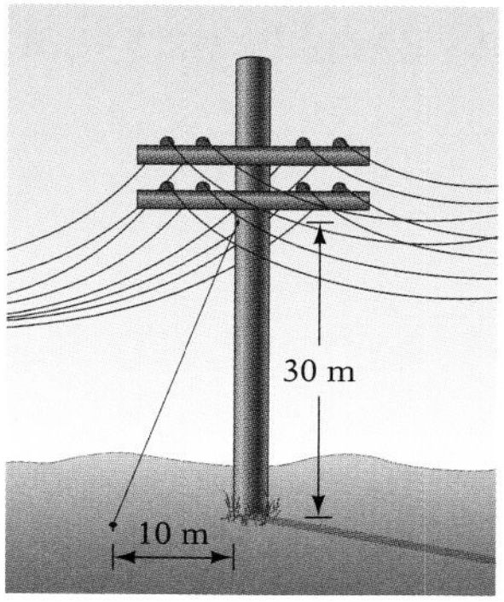

33. **Integer Problem** The sum of the squares of three consecutive odd integers is 155. Find the middle odd integer.

Final Exam

1. Evaluate: $-|-3|$

2. Subtract: $-15 - (-12) - 3$

3. Write $\frac{1}{8}$ as a percent.

4. Simplify: $-2^4 \cdot (-2)^4$

5. Simplify: $-7 - \frac{12 - 15}{2 - (-1)} \cdot (-4)$

6. Evaluate $\frac{a^2 - 3b}{2a - 2b^2}$ when $a = 3$ and $b = -2$.

7. Simplify: $6x - (-4y) - (-3x) + 2y$

8. Multiply: $(-15z)\left(-\frac{2}{5}\right)$

9. Simplify: $-2[5 - 3(2x - 7) - 2x]$

10. Solve: $20 = -\frac{2}{5}x$

11. Solve: $4 - 2(3x + 1) = 3(2 - x) + 5$

12. Find 19% of 80.

13. Solve: $4 - x \geq 7$

14. Solve: $2 - 2(y - 1) \leq 2y - 6$

15. Find the slope of the line that contains the points whose coordinates are $(-1, -3)$ and $(2, -1)$.

16. Find the equation of the line that contains the point whose coordinates are $(3, -4)$ and has slope $-\frac{2}{3}$.

17. Graph the line with slope $-\frac{1}{2}$ and y-intercept $(0, -3)$.

18. Graph: $f(x) = \frac{2}{3}x - 4$

19. Find the range of the function given by the equation $f(x) = -x + 5$ if the domain is $\{-6, -3, 0, 3, 6\}$.

20. Graph the solution set of $3x - 2y \geq 6$.

21. Solve by substitution: $\begin{aligned} y &= 4x - 7 \\ y &= 2x + 5 \end{aligned}$

22. Solve by the addition method: $\begin{aligned} 4x - 3y &= 11 \\ 2x + 5y &= -1 \end{aligned}$

23. Subtract: $(2x^2 - 5x + 1) - (5x^2 - 2x - 7)$

24. Simplify: $(-3xy^3)^4$

25. Multiply: $(3x^2 - x - 2)(2x + 3)$

26. Simplify: $\dfrac{(-2x^2y^3)^3}{(-4x^{-1}y^4)^2}$

27. Simplify: $(4x^{-2}y)^3(2xy^{-2})^{-2}$

28. Divide: $\dfrac{12x^3y^2 - 16x^2y^2 - 20y^2}{4xy^2}$

29. Divide: $(5x^2 - 2x - 1) \div (x + 2)$

30. Write 0.000000039 in scientific notation.

31. Factor: $2a(4 - x) - 6(x - 4)$

32. Factor: $x^2 - 5x - 6$

33. Factor: $2x^2 - x - 3$

34. Factor: $6x^2 - 5x - 6$

35. Factor: $8x^3 - 28x^2 + 12x$

36. Factor: $25x^2 - 16$

37. Factor: $75y - 12x^2y$

38. Solve: $2x^2 = 7x - 3$

39. Multiply: $\dfrac{2x^2 - 3x + 1}{4x^2 - 2x} \cdot \dfrac{4x^2 + 4x}{x^2 - 2x + 1}$

40. Subtract: $\dfrac{5}{x + 3} - \dfrac{3x}{2x - 5}$

41. Simplify: $\dfrac{x - \dfrac{3}{2x - 1}}{1 - \dfrac{2}{2x - 1}}$

42. Solve: $\dfrac{5x}{3x - 5} - 3 = \dfrac{7}{3x - 5}$

43. Solve $a = 3a - 2b$ for a.

44. Simplify: $\sqrt{49x^6}$

45. Add: $2\sqrt{27a} + 8\sqrt{48a}$

46. Simplify: $\dfrac{\sqrt{3}}{\sqrt{5} - 2}$

47. Solve: $\sqrt{x + 4} - \sqrt{x - 1} = 1$

48. Solve: $(x - 3)^2 = 7$

49. Solve: $4x^2 - 2x - 1 = 0$

50. Graph: $y = x^2 - 4x + 3$

51. Translate and simplify "the sum of twice a number and three times the difference between the number and two."

52. **Depreciation** Because of depreciation, the value of an office machine is now \$2400. This is 80% of its original value. Find the original value of the machine.

53. **Coins** A coin bank contains quarters and dimes. There are three times as many dimes as quarters. The total value of the coins in the bank is \$11. Find the number of dimes in the bank.

54. **Geometry** The measure of one angle of a triangle is 10° more than the measure of the second angle. The measure of the third angle is 10° more than the measure of the first angle. Find the measure of each angle of the triangle.

55. **Markup** The manufacturer's cost for a laser printer is \$900. The manufacturer sells the printer for \$1485. Find the markup rate.

56. **Investments** An investment of \$3000 is made at an annual simple interest rate of 8%. How much additional money must be invested at 11% so that the total interest earned is 10% of the total investment?

57. **Food Mixtures** A grocer mixes 4 lb of peanuts that cost \$2 per pound with 2 lb of walnuts that cost \$5 per pound. What is the cost per pound of the resulting mixture?

58. **Mixture Problem** A pharmacist mixes 20 L of a solution that is 60% acid with 30 L of a solution that is 20% acid. What is the percent concentration of acid in the resulting mixture?

59. **Uniform Motion** A small plane flew at a constant rate for 1 h. The pilot then doubled the plane's speed. An additional 1.5 h were flown at the increased speed. If the entire flight was 860 km, how far did the plane travel during the first hour?

60. **Uniform Motion** With the current, a motorboat travels 50 mi in 2.5 h. Against the current, it takes twice as long to travel 50 mi. Find the rate of the boat in calm water and the rate of the current.

61. **Geometry** The length of a rectangle is 5 m more than the width. The area of the rectangle is 50 m^2. Find the dimensions of the rectangle.

62. **Paint** A paint formula requires 2 oz of dye for every 15 oz of base paint. How many ounces of dye are required for 120 oz of base paint?

63. **Work Problem** It takes a chef 1 h to prepare a dinner. The chef's apprentice can prepare the same dinner in 1.5 h. How long would it take the chef and the apprentice, working together, to prepare the dinner?

64. **Geometry** The hypotenuse of a right triangle measures 14 cm. One leg of the triangle measures 8 cm. Find the length of the other leg of the triangle. Round to the nearest tenth.

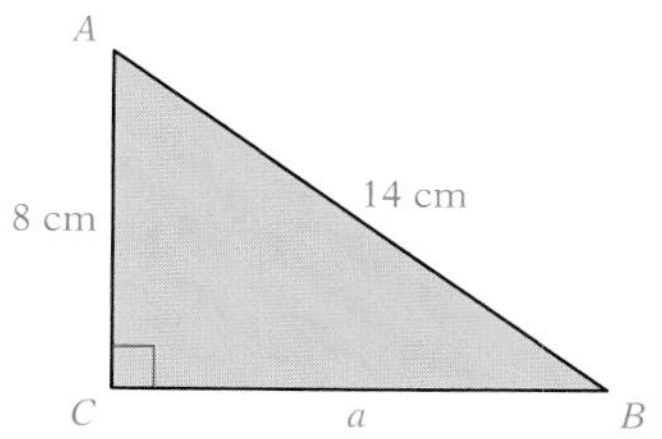

65. **Uniform Motion** It took a plane $\frac{1}{2}$ h more to fly 500 mi against the wind than it took to fly the same distance with the wind. The rate of the plane in calm air is 225 mph. Find the rate of the wind.

Appendix

Table of Properties

Properties of Real Numbers

The Associative Property of Addition
If a, b, and c are real numbers, then $(a + b) + c = a + (b + c)$.

The Commutative Property of Addition
If a and b are real numbers, then $a + b = b + a$.

The Addition Property of Zero
If a is a real number, then $a + 0 = 0 + a = a$.

The Multiplication Property of Zero
If a is a real number, then $a \cdot 0 = 0 \cdot a = 0$.

The Inverse Property of Addition
If a is a real number, then $a + (-a) = (-a) + a = 0$.

The Associative Property of Multiplication
If a, b, and c are real numbers, then $(a \cdot b) \cdot c = a \cdot (b \cdot c)$.

The Commutative Property of Multiplication
If a and b are real numbers, then $a \cdot b = b \cdot a$.

The Multiplication Property of One
If a is a real number, then $a \cdot 1 = 1 \cdot a = a$.

The Inverse Property of Multiplication
If a is a real number and $a \neq 0$, then $a \cdot \frac{1}{a} = \frac{1}{a} \cdot a = 1$.

Distributive Property
If a, b, and c are real numbers, then $a(b + c) = ab + ac$ or $(b + c)a = ba + ca$.

Properties of Equations

Addition Property of Equations
The same number or variable term can be added to each side of an equation without changing the solution of the equation.

Multiplication Property of Equations
Each side of an equation can be multiplied by the same nonzero number without changing the solution of the equation.

Properties of Inequalities

Addition Property of Inequalities
If $a > b$, then $a + c > b + c$.

If $a < b$, then $a + c < b + c$.

Multiplication Property of Inequalities
If $a > b$ and $c > 0$, then $ac > bc$.

If $a < b$ and $c > 0$, then $ac < bc$.

If $a > b$ and $c < 0$, then $ac < bc$.

If $a < b$ and $c < 0$, then $ac > bc$.

Table of Properties (*continued*)

Properties of Exponents

If m and n are integers, then $x^m \cdot x^n = x^{m+n}$.

If m and n are integers, then $(x^m)^n = x^{mn}$.

If $x \neq 0$, then $x^0 = 1$.

If m and n are integers and $x \neq 0$, then $\frac{x^m}{x^n} = x^{m-n}$.

If m, n, and p are integers, then $(x^m \cdot y^n)^p = x^{mp}y^{np}$.

If n is a positive integer and $x \neq 0$, then $x^{-n} = \frac{1}{x^n}$ and $\frac{1}{x^{-n}} = x^n$.

If m, n, and p are integers and $y \neq 0$, then $\left(\frac{x^m}{y^n}\right)^p = \frac{x^{mp}}{y^{np}}$.

Principle of Zero Products

If $a \cdot b = 0$, then $a = 0$ or $b = 0$.

Properties of Radical Expressions

If a and b are positive real numbers, then $\sqrt[n]{ab} = \sqrt[n]{a}\,\sqrt[n]{b}$.

If a and b are positive real numbers, then $\sqrt[n]{\frac{a}{b}} = \frac{\sqrt[n]{a}}{\sqrt[n]{b}}$.

Property of Squaring Both Sides of an Equation

If a and b are real numbers and $a = b$, then $a^2 = b^2$.

Keystroke Guide for the TI-83 and TI-83 Plus/TI-84 Plus

Basic Operations

Numerical calculations are performed on the **home screen.** You can always return to the home screen by pressing 2nd QUIT. Pressing CLEAR erases the home screen.

> **Take Note**
>
> The descriptions in the margins (for example, Basic Operations and Evaluating Functions) are the same as those used in the text and are arranged alphabetically.

To evaluate the expression $-2(3 + 5) - 8 \div 4$, use the following keystrokes.

(-) 2 (3 + 5) − 8 ÷ 4 ENTER

Note: There is a difference between the key to enter a negative number, (-), and the key for subtraction, −. You cannot use these keys interchangeably.

The 2nd key is used to access the commands in gold writing above a key. For instance, to evaluate the $\sqrt{49}$, press 2nd $\sqrt{\ }$ 49) ENTER.

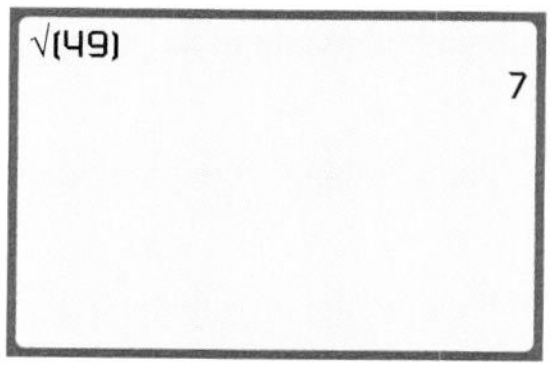

The ALPHA key is used to place a letter on the screen. One reason to do this is to store a value of a variable. The following keystrokes give A the value of 5.

5 STO▸ ALPHA A ENTER

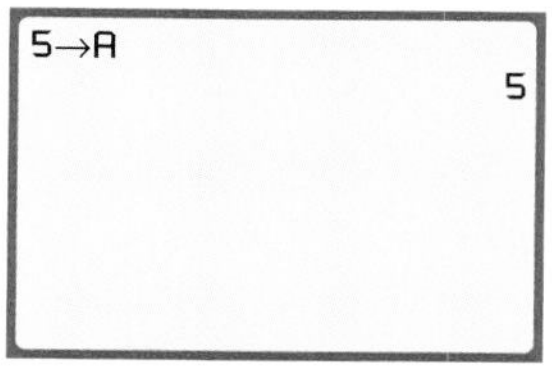

This value is now available in calculations. For instance, we can find the value of $3a^2$ by using the following keystrokes: 3 ALPHA A x^2. To display the value of the variable on the screen, press 2nd RCL ALPHA A.

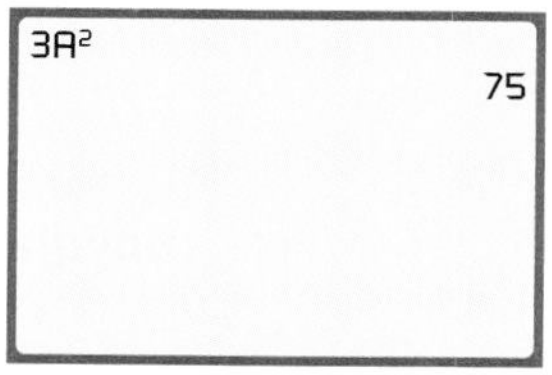

Note: When you use the ALPHA key, only capital letters are available on the TI calculators.

Evaluating Functions

There are various methods of evaluating a function, but all methods require that the expression be entered as one of the ten functions Y_1 to Y_0. To evaluate $f(x) = \frac{x^2}{x - 1}$ when $x = -3$, enter the expression into, for instance, Y_1, and then press VARS ▸ 1 1 ((-) 3 (ENTER.

> **Take Note**
>
> Use the down arrow key to scroll past Y_7 to see Y_8, Y_9, and Y_0.

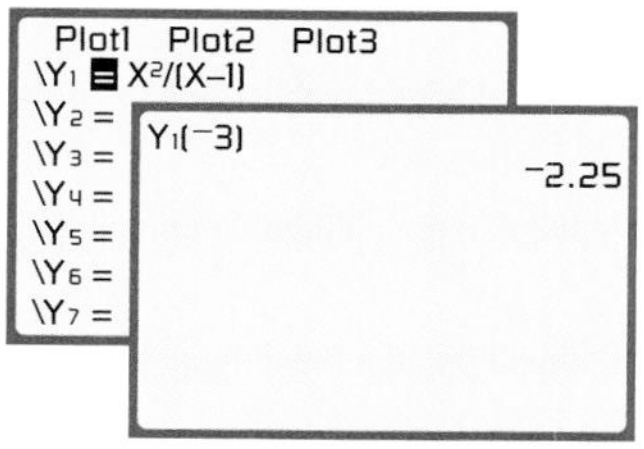

Note: If you try to evaluate a function at a number that is not in the domain of the function, you will get an error message. For instance, 1 is not in the domain of $f(x) = \frac{x^2}{x - 1}$. If we try to evaluate the function at 1, the error screen at the right appears.

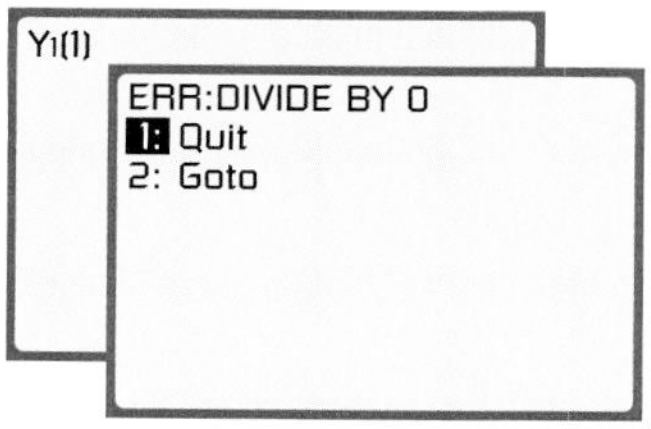

Evaluating Variable Expressions To evaluate a variable expression, first store the values of each variable. Then enter the variable expression. For instance, to evaluate $s^2 + 2sl$ when $s = 4$ and $l = 5$, use the following keystrokes.

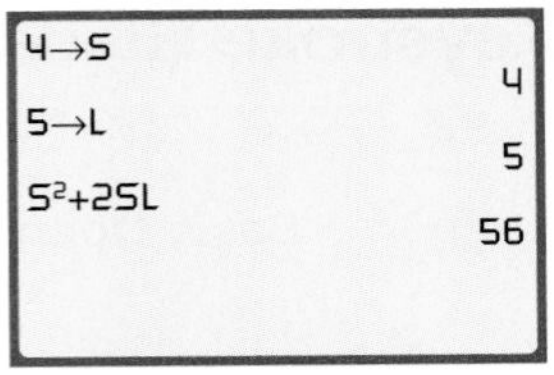

4 STO▸ ALPHA S ENTER 5 STO▸ ALPHA L ENTER ALPHA S x^2 + 2 ALPHA S ALPHA L ENTER

Graph To graph a function, use the Y= key to enter the expression for the function, select a suitable viewing window, and then press GRAPH. For instance, to graph $f(x) = 0.1x^3 - 2x - 1$ in the standard viewing window, use the following keystrokes.

Y= 0.1 X,T,θ,n ^ 3 − 2 X,T,θ,n − 1 ZOOM (scroll to 6) ENTER

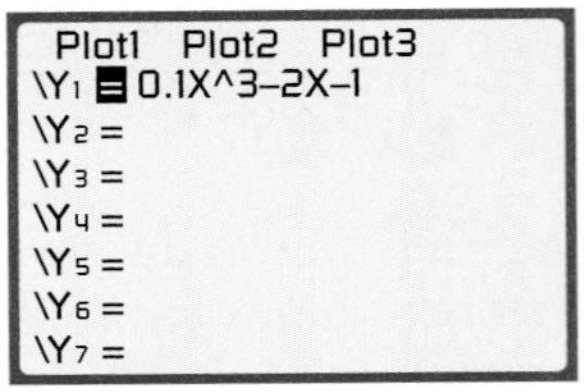

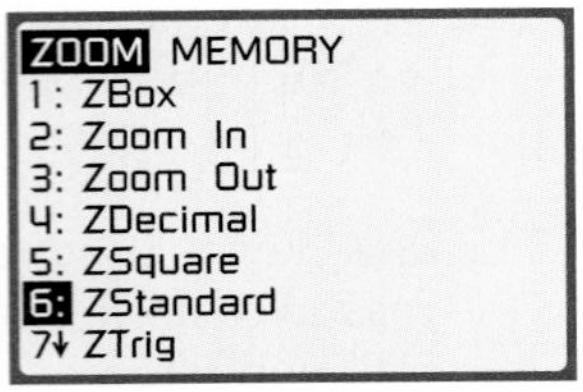

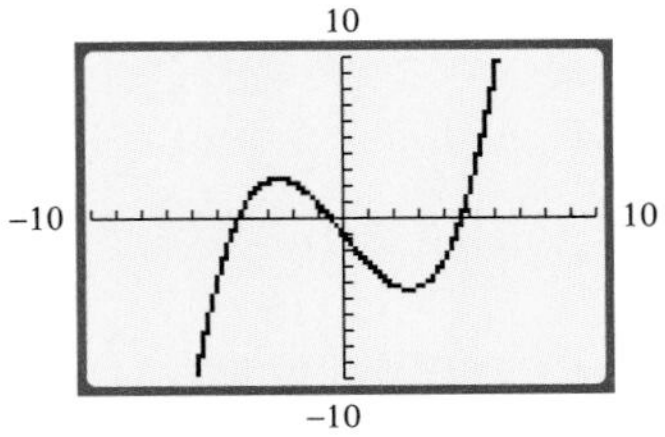

Note: For the keystrokes above, you do not have to scroll to 6. Alternatively, use ZOOM 6. This will select the standard viewing window and automatically start the graph. Use the WINDOW key to create a custom window for a graph.

Graphing Inequalities To illustrate this feature, we will graph $y \leq 2x - 1$. Enter $2x - 1$ into Y_1. Because $y \leq 2x - 1$, we want to shade below the graph. Move the cursor to the left of Y_1 and press ENTER three times. Press GRAPH.

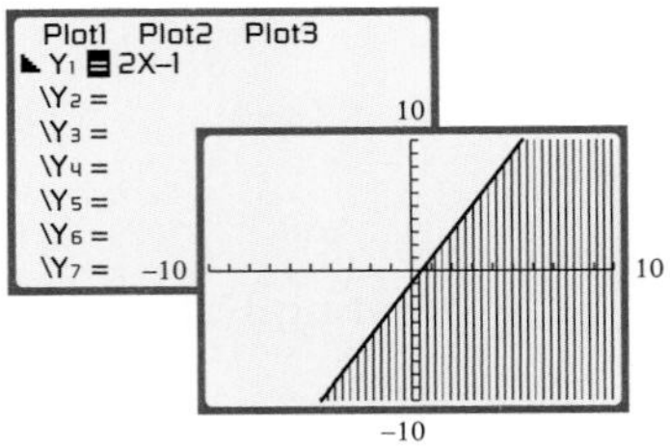

Note: To shade above the graph, move the cursor to the left of Y_1 and press ENTER two times. An inequality with the symbol $\leq$ or $\geq$ should be graphed with a solid line, and an inequality with the symbol $<$ or $>$ should be graphed with a dashed line. However, the graph of a linear inequality on a graphing calculator does not distinguish between a solid line and a dashed line.

To graph the solution set of a system of inequalities, solve each inequality for y and graph each inequality. The solution set is the intersection of the two inequalities. The solution set of $\begin{matrix} 3x + 2y > 10 \\ 4x - 3y \leq 5 \end{matrix}$ is shown at the right.

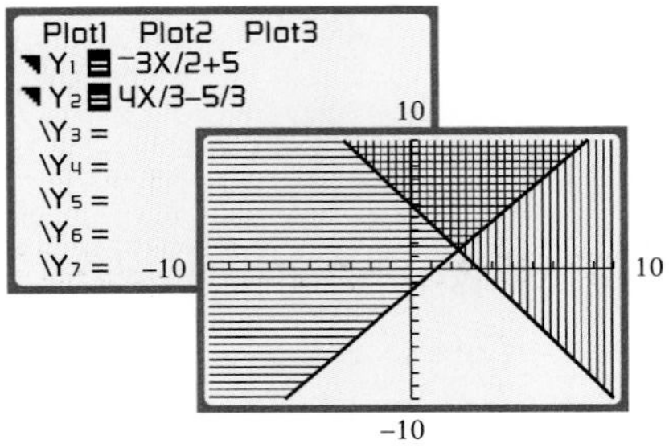

Intersect The INTERSECT feature is used to solve a system of equations. To illustrate this feature, we will use the system of equations $\begin{aligned} 2x - 3y &= 13 \\ 3x + 4y &= -6 \end{aligned}$.

Note: Some equations can be solved by this method. See the section "Solve an equation" below. Also, this method is used to find a number in the domain of a function for a given number in the range. See the section "Find a domain element."

Solve each of the equations in the system of equations for y. In this case, we have $y = \frac{2}{3}x - \frac{13}{3}$ and $y = -\frac{3}{4}x - \frac{3}{2}$.

Use the Y= editor to enter $\frac{2}{3}x - \frac{13}{3}$ into Y1 and $-\frac{3}{4}x - \frac{3}{2}$ into Y2. Graph the two functions in the standard viewing window. (If the window does not show the point of intersection of the two graphs, adjust the window until you can see the point of intersection.)

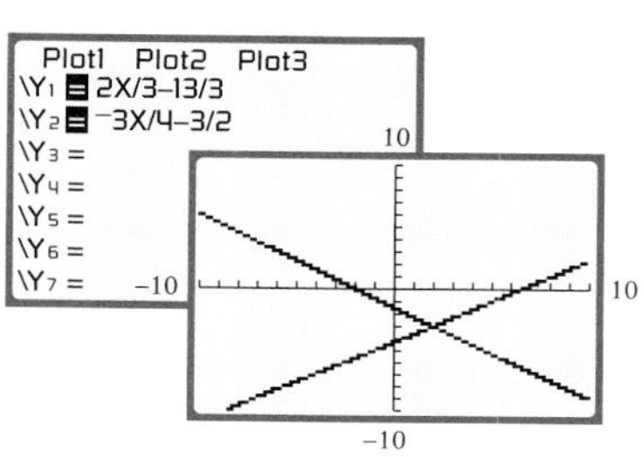

Press 2nd CALC (scroll to 5, intersect) ENTER.

Alternatively, you can just press 2nd CALC 5.

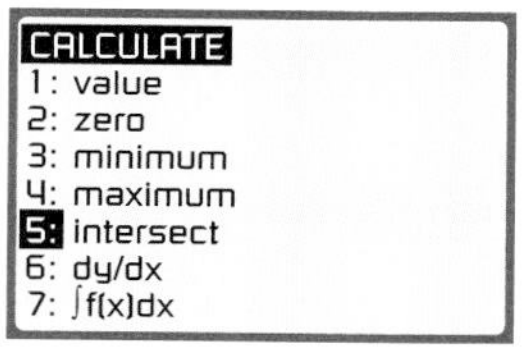

First curve? is shown at the bottom of the screen and identifies one of the two graphs on the screen. Press ENTER.

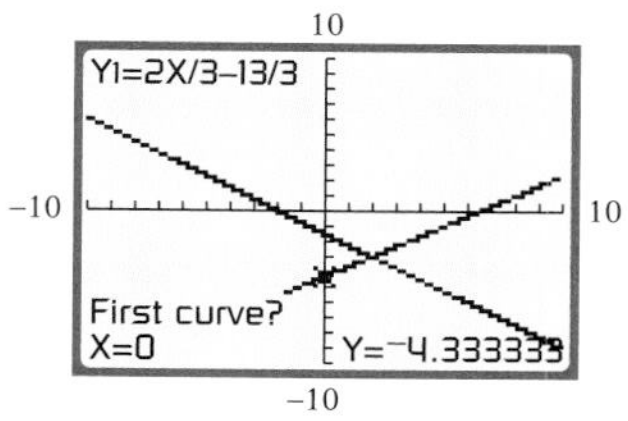

Second curve? is shown at the bottom of the screen and identifies the second of the two graphs on the screen. Press ENTER.

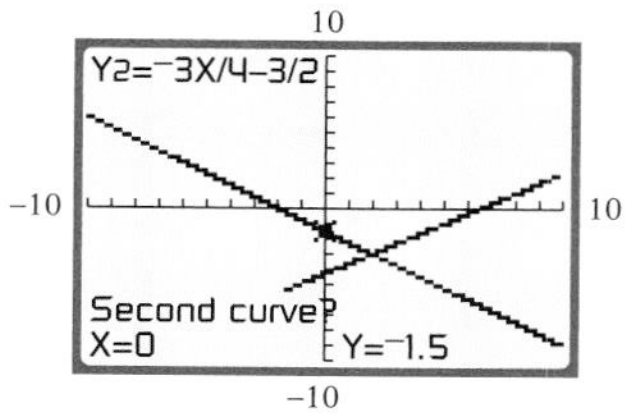

Guess? shown at the bottom of the screen asks you to use the left or right arrow key to move the cursor to the *approximate* location of the point of intersection. (If there are two or more points of intersection, it does not matter which one you choose first.) Press ENTER.

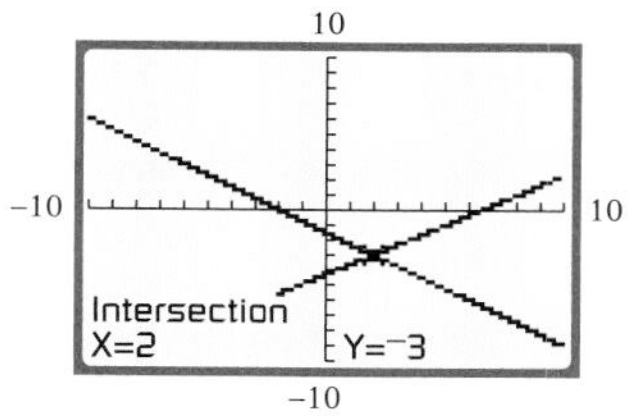

The solution of the system of equations is (2, −3).

Solve an equation To illustrate the steps involved, we will solve the equation $2x + 4 = -3x - 1$. The idea is to write the equation as the system of equations $\begin{array}{l} y = 2x + 4 \\ y = -3x - 1 \end{array}$ and then use the steps for solving a system of equations.

Use the Y= editor to enter the left and right sides of the equation into Y_1 and Y_2. Graph the two functions and then follow the steps for Intersect.

The solution is -1, the x-coordinate of the point of intersection.

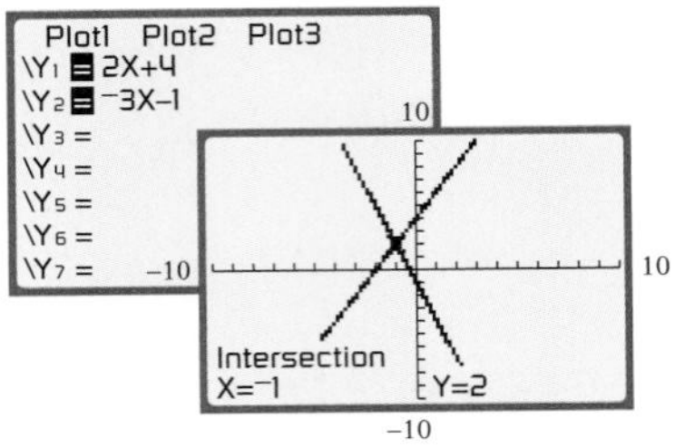

Find a domain element For this example, we will find a number in the domain of $f(x) = -\frac{2}{3}x + 2$ that corresponds to 4 in the range of the function. This is like solving the system of equations $y = -\frac{2}{3}x + 2$ and $y = 4$.

Use the Y= editor to enter the expression for the function in Y_1 and the desired output, 4, in Y_2. Graph the two functions and then follow the steps for Intersect.

The point of intersection is $(-3, 4)$. The number -3 in the domain of f produces an output of 4 in the range of f.

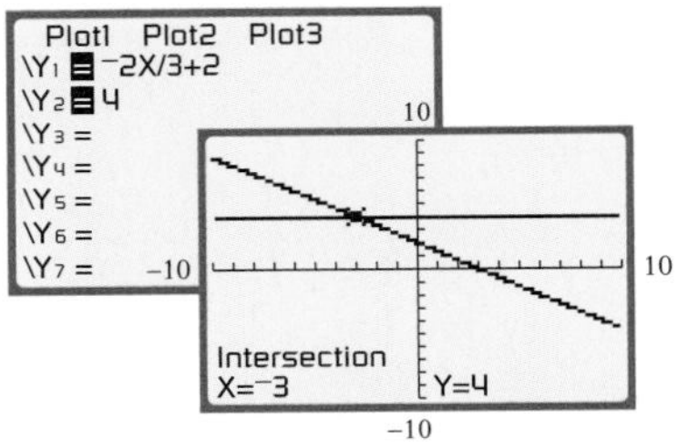

Math Pressing MATH gives you access to many built-in functions. The following keystrokes will convert 0.125 to a fraction: .125 MATH 1 ENTER.

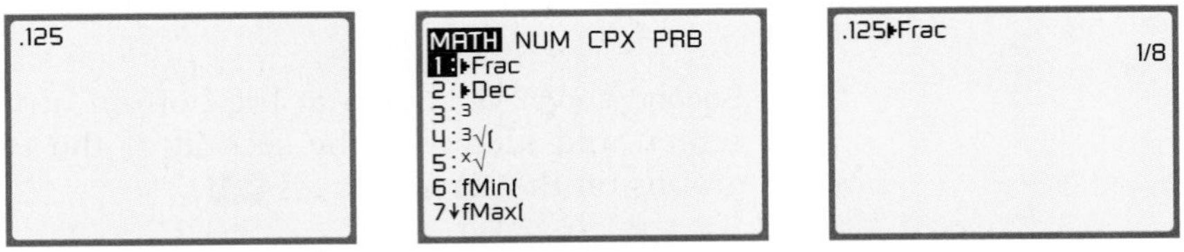

Additional built-in functions under MATH can be found by pressing MATH ▸. For instance, to evaluate $-|-25|$, press (−) MATH ▸ 1 (−) 25) ENTER.

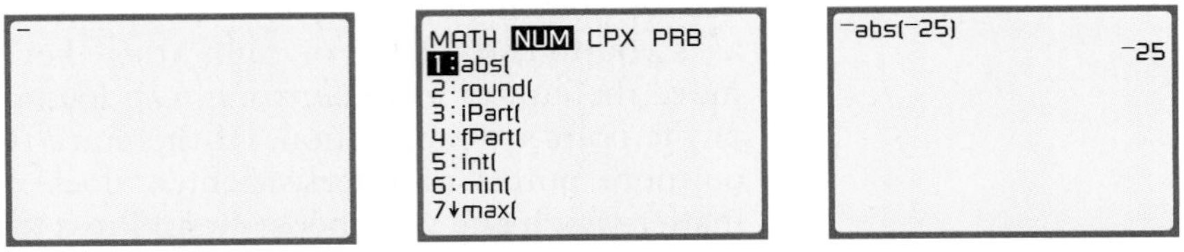

See your owner's manual for assistance with other functions under the MATH key.

Radical Expressions

To evaluate a square-root expression, press [2nd] [$\sqrt{\ }$].

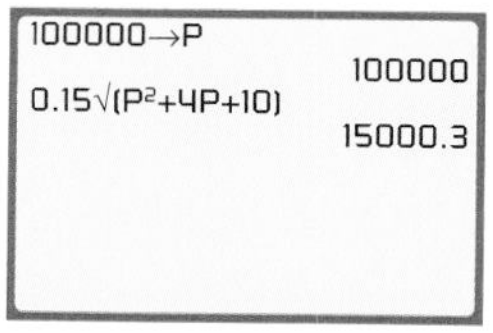

For instance, to evaluate $0.15\sqrt{p^2 + 4p + 10}$ when $p = 100{,}000$, first store 100,000 in P. Then press 0.15 [2nd] [$\sqrt{\ }$] [ALPHA] P [x^2] [+] 4 [ALPHA] P [+] 10 [)] [ENTER].

To evaluate a radical expression other than a square root, access $\sqrt[x]{\ }$ by pressing [MATH]. For instance, to evaluate $\sqrt[4]{67}$, press 4 (the index of the radical) [MATH] (scroll to 5) [ENTER] 67 [ENTER].

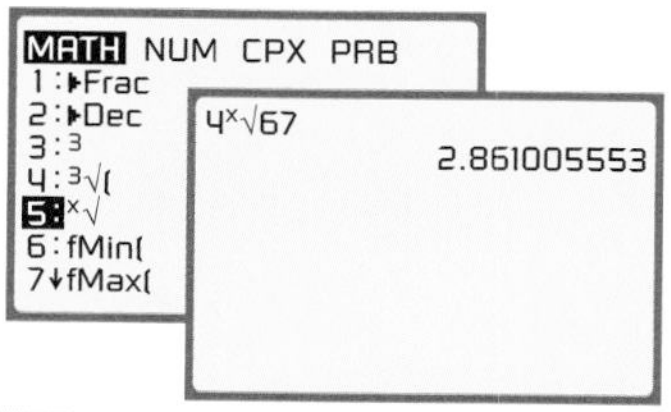

Scientific Notation

To enter a number in scientific notation, use [2nd] [EE]. For instance, to find $\dfrac{3.45 \times 10^{-12}}{1.5 \times 10^{25}}$, press 3.45 [2nd] [EE] [(-)] 12 [÷] 1.5 [2nd] [EE] 25 [ENTER]. The answer is 2.3×10^{-37}.

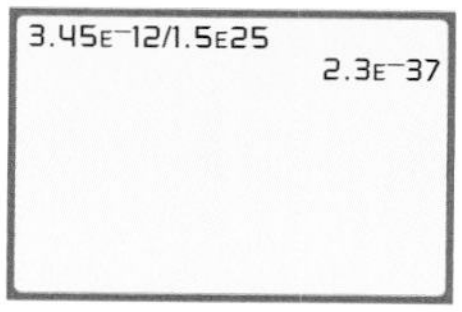

Table

There are three steps in creating an input/output table for a function. First use the [Y=] editor to input the function. The second step is setting up the table, and the third step is displaying the table.

To set up the table, press [2nd] [TBLSET]. TblStart is the first value of the independent variable in the input/output table. △Tbl is the difference between successive values. Setting this to 1 means that, for this table, the input values are $-2, -1, 0, 1, 2, \ldots$. If △Tbl $= 0.5$, then the input values are $-2, -1.5, -1, -0.5, 0, 0.5, \ldots$.

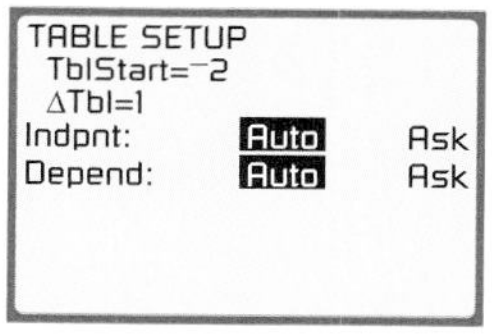

Indpnt is the independent variable. When this is set to Auto, values of the independent variable are automatically entered into the table. Depend is the dependent variable. When this is set to Auto, values of the dependent variable are automatically entered into the table.

To display the table, press [2nd] [TABLE]. An input/output table for $f(x) = x^2 - 1$ is shown at the right.

Once the table is on the screen, the up and down arrow keys can be used to display more values in the table. For the table at the right, we used the up arrow key to move to $x = -7$.

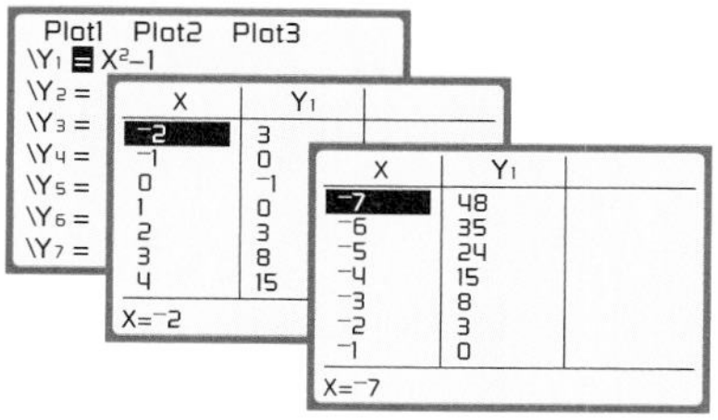

An input/output table for any given input can be created by selecting Ask for the independent variable. The table at the right shows an input/output table for $f(x) = \dfrac{4x}{x-2}$ for selected values of x. Note that the word ERROR or ERR: appeared when 2 was entered. This occurred because f is not defined when $x = 2$.

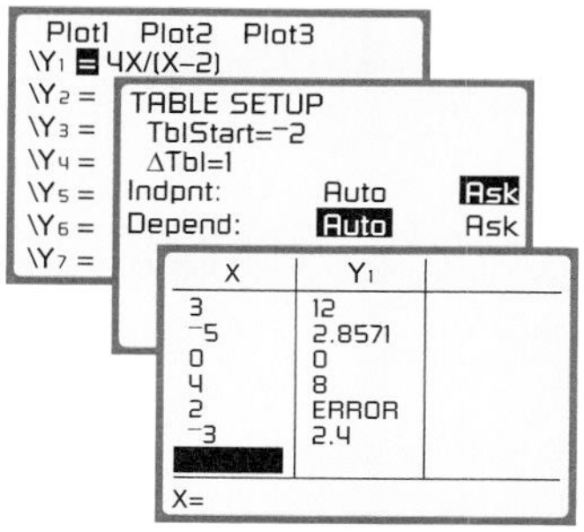

Note: Using the table feature in Ask mode is the same as evaluating a function for given values of the independent variable. For instance, from the table on the preceding page, we have $f(4) = 8$.

Test The TEST feature has many uses, one of which is to graph the solution set of a linear inequality in one variable. To illustrate this feature, we will graph the solution set of $x - 1 < 4$. Press Y= X,T,θ,n − 1 2nd TEST (scroll to 5) ENTER 4 GRAPH .

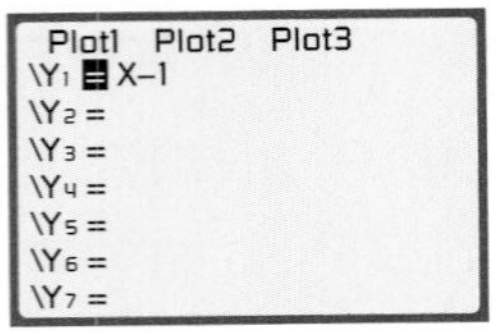

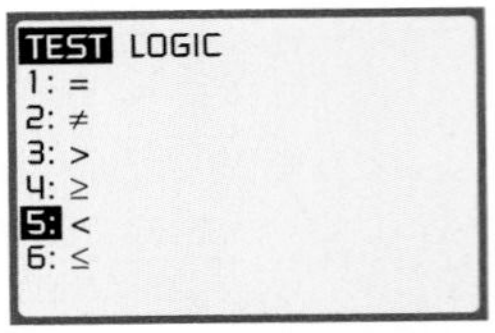

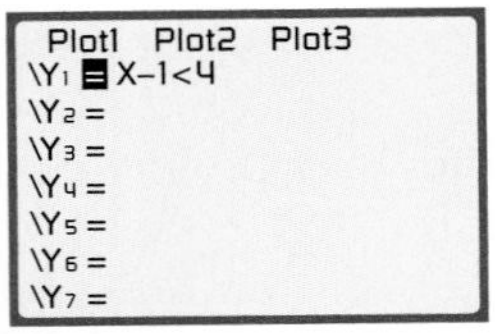

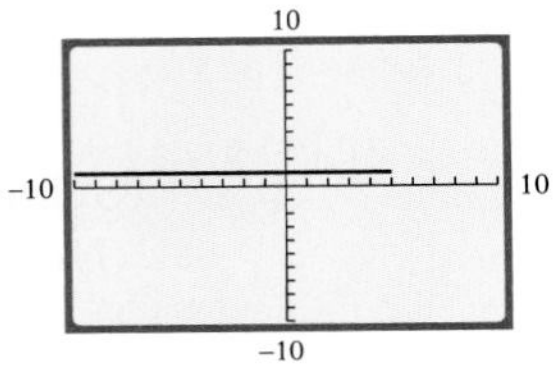

Trace Once a graph is drawn, pressing TRACE will place a cursor on the screen, and the coordinates of the point below the cursor are shown at the bottom of the screen. Use the left and right arrow keys to move the cursor along the graph. For the graph at the right, we have $f(4.8) = 3.4592$, where $f(x) = 0.1x^3 - 2x + 2$ is shown at the top left of the screen.

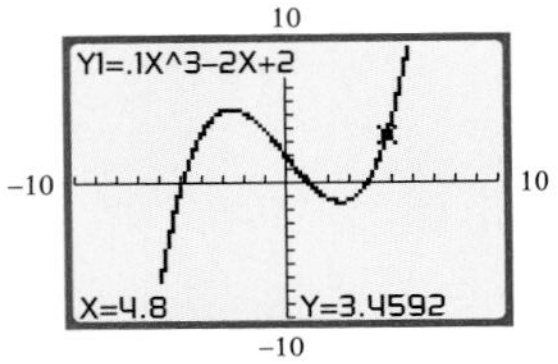

In TRACE mode, you can evaluate a function at any value of the independent variable that is within Xmin and Xmax. To do this, first graph the function. Now press TRACE (the value of x) ENTER . For the graph at the left below, we used $x = -3.5$. If a value of x is chosen outside the window, an error message is displayed.

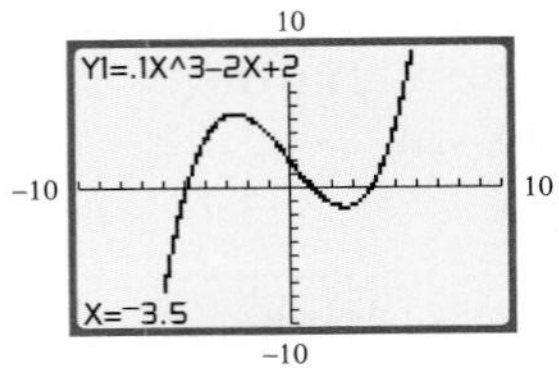

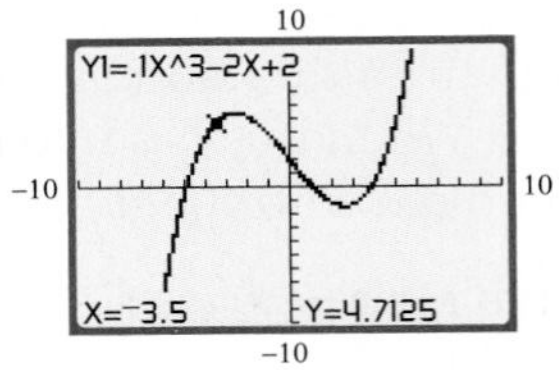

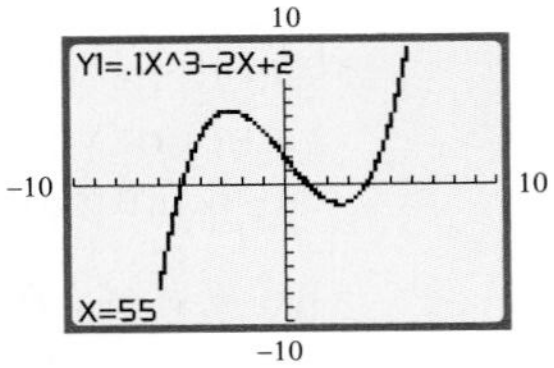

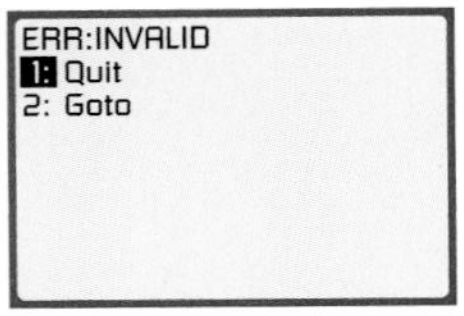

In the example above where we entered -3.5 for x, the value of the function was calculated as 4.7125. This means that $f(-3.5) = 4.7125$. The keystrokes 2nd QUIT VARS ▸ 11 MATH 1 ENTER will convert the decimal value to a fraction.

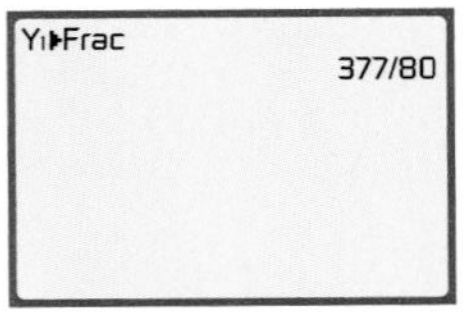

When the TRACE feature is used with two or more graphs, the up and down arrow keys are used to move between the graphs. The following two graphs are for the functions $f(x) = 0.1x^3 - 2x + 2$ and $g(x) = 2x - 3$. By using the up and down arrows, we can place the cursor on either graph. The right and left arrows are used to move along the graph.

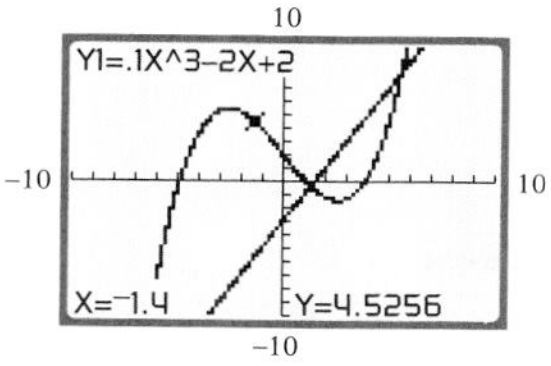

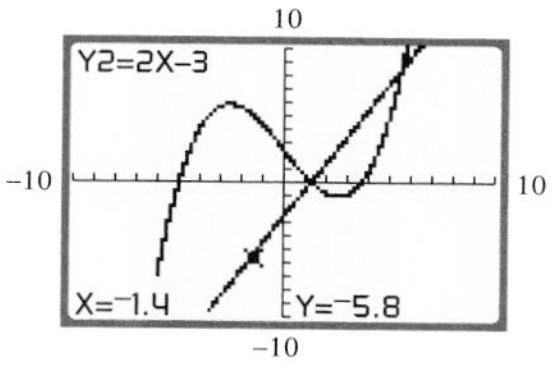

Window The viewing window for a graph is controlled by pressing [WINDOW]. Xmin and Xmax are the minimum value and maximum value, respectively, of the independent variable shown on the graph. Xscl is the distance between tick marks on the x-axis. Ymin and Ymax are the minimum value and maximum value, respectively, of the dependent variable shown on the graph. Yscl is the distance between tick marks on the y-axis. Leave Xres as 1.

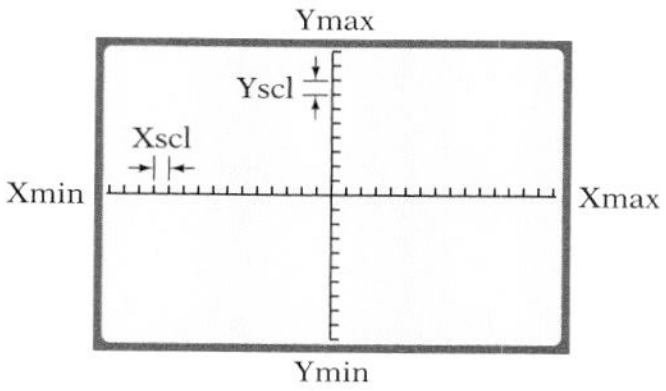

Note: In the standard viewing window, the distance between tick marks on the x-axis is different from the distance between tick marks on the y-axis. This will distort a graph. A more accurate picture of a graph can be created by using a square viewing window. See ZOOM.

[Y=] The [Y=] editor is used to enter the expression for a function. There are ten possible functions, labeled Y_1 to Y_0, that can be active at any one time. For instance, to enter $f(x) = x^2 + 3x - 2$ as Y_1, use the following keystrokes.

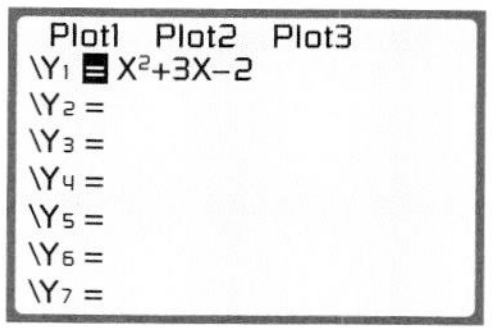

[Y=] [X,T,θ,n] [x^2] [+] 3 [X,T,θ,n] [−] 2

Note: If an expression is already entered for Y_1, place the cursor anywhere on that expression and press [CLEAR].

To enter $s = \dfrac{2v - 1}{v^3 - 3}$ into Y_2, place the cursor to the right of the equals sign for Y_2. Then press [(] 2 [X,T,θ,n] [−] 1 [)] [÷] [(] [X,T,θ,n] [^] 3 [−] 3 [)].

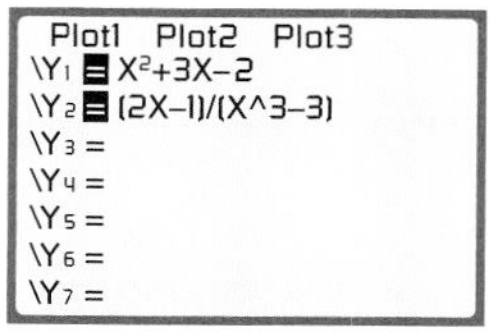

Note: When we enter an equation, the independent variable (v in the expression above) is entered using [X,T,θ,n]. The dependent variable (s in the expression above) is one of Y_1 to Y_0. Also note the use of parentheses to ensure the correct order of operations.

Observe the black rectangle that covers the equals sign for the two examples we have shown. This rectangle means that the function is "active." If we were to press [GRAPH], then the graph of both functions would appear. You can make a function inactive by using the arrow keys to move the cursor over the equals sign of that function and then pressing [ENTER]. This will remove the black rectangle. We have done that for Y_2, as shown at the right. Now if [GRAPH] is pressed, only Y_1 will be graphed.

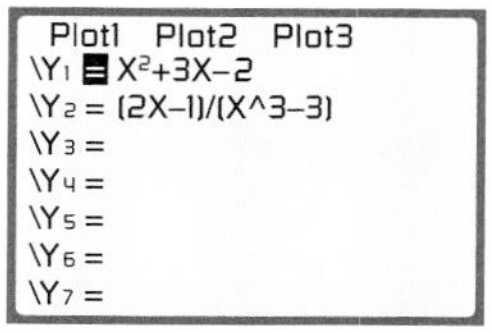

It is also possible to control the appearance of the graph by moving the cursor on the Y= screen to the left of any Y. With the cursor in this position, pressing ENTER will change the appearance of the graph. The options are shown at the right.

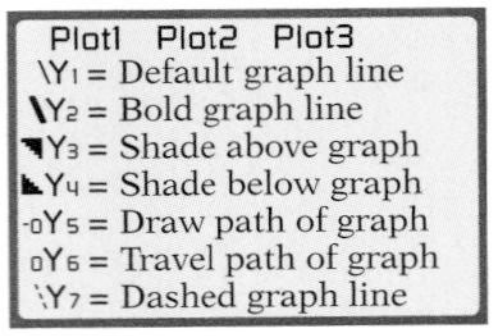

Zero The ZERO feature of a graphing calculator is used for various calculations: to find the x-intercepts of a function, to solve some equations, and to find the zero of a function.

***x*-intercepts** To illustrate the procedure for finding x-intercepts, we will use $f(x) = x^2 + x - 2$.

First, use the Y= editor to enter the expression for the function and then graph the function in the standard viewing window. (It may be necessary to adjust this window so that the intercepts are visible.) Once the graph is displayed, use the keystrokes below to find the x-intercepts of the graph of the function.

Press 2nd CALC (scroll to 2 for zero of the function) ENTER.

Alternatively, you can just press 2nd CALC 2.

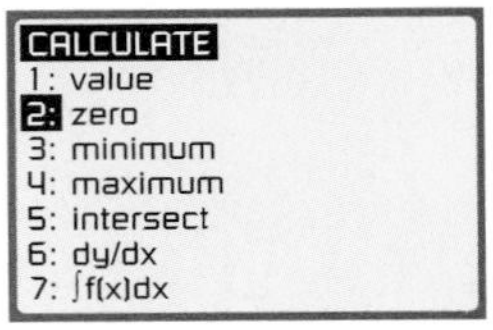

Left Bound? shown at the bottom of the screen asks you to use the left or right arrow key to move the cursor to the *left* of the desired x-intercept. Press ENTER.

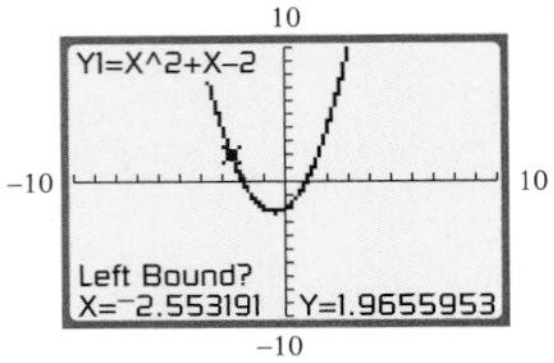

Right Bound? shown at the bottom of the screen asks you to use the left or right arrow key to move the cursor to the *right* of the desired x-intercept. Press ENTER.

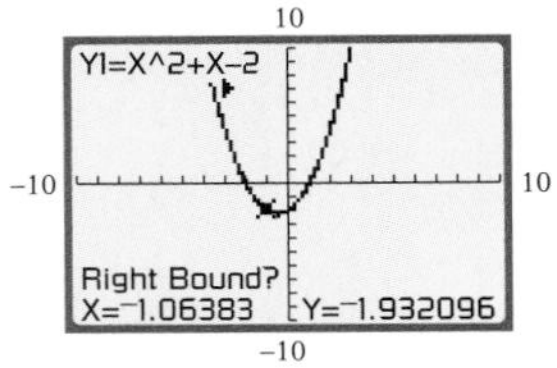

Guess? shown at the bottom of the screen asks you to use the left or right arrow key to move the cursor to the *approximate* location of the desired x-intercept. Press ENTER.

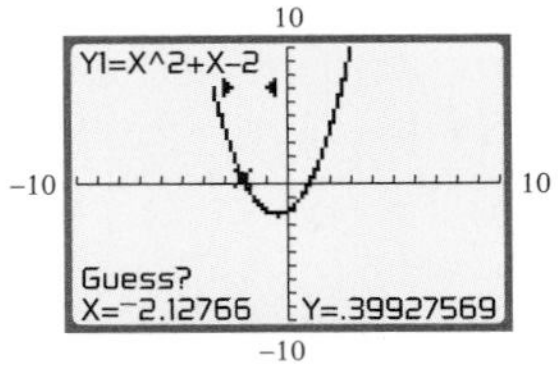

The x-coordinate of an x-intercept is -2. Therefore, an x-intercept is $(-2, 0)$.

To find the other x-intercept, follow the same steps as above. The screens for this calculation are shown at the top of the next page.

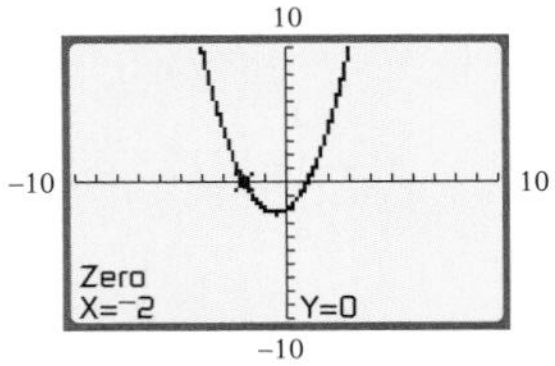

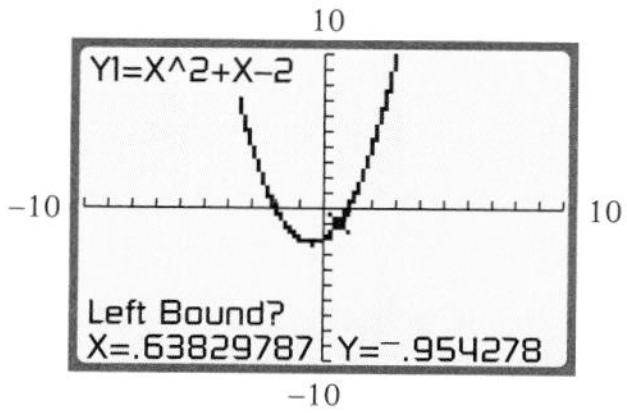

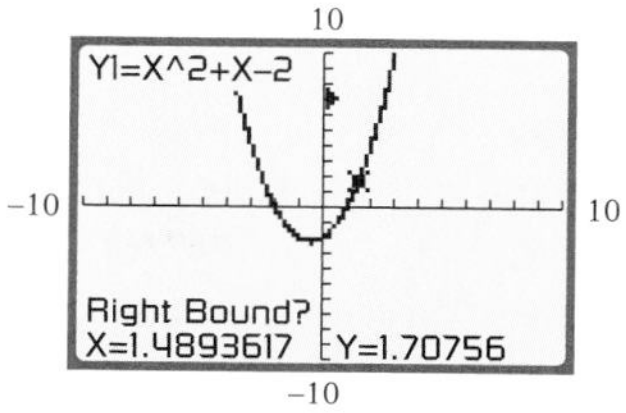

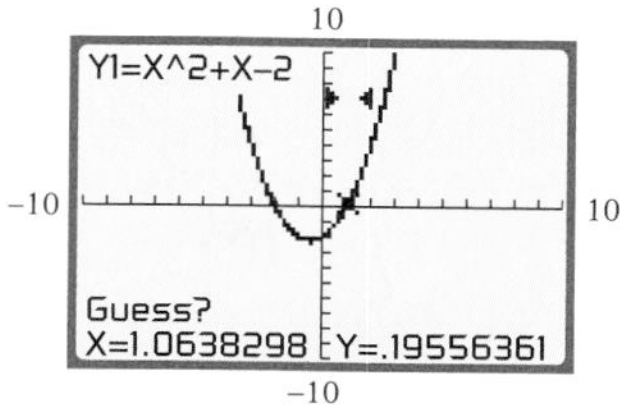

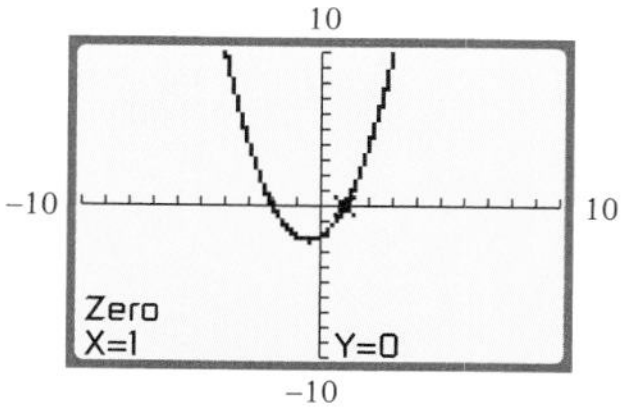

A second x-intercept is (1, 0).

Solve an equation To use the ZERO feature to solve an equation, first rewrite the equation with all terms on one side. For instance, one way to solve the equation $x^3 - x + 1 = -2x + 3$ is first to rewrite it as $x^3 + x - 2 = 0$. Enter $x^3 + x - 2$ into Y_1 and then follow the steps for finding x-intercepts.

Find the real zeros of a function To find the real zeros of a function, follow the steps for finding x-intercepts.

Zoom Pressing ZOOM allows you to select some preset viewing windows. This key also gives you access to ZBox, Zoom In, and Zoom Out. These functions enable you to redraw a selected portion of a graph in a new window. Some windows that are used frequently in this text are shown below.

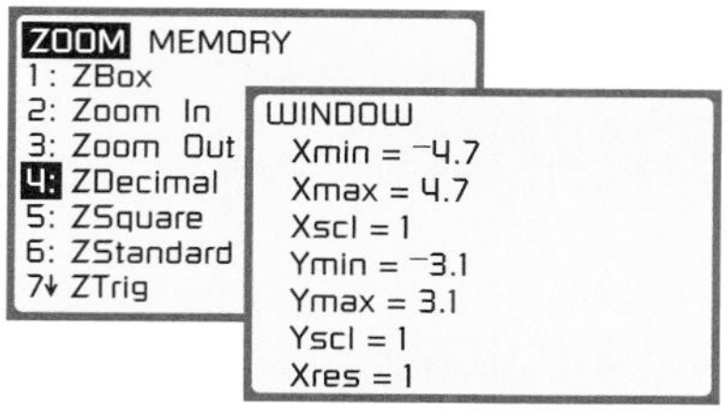

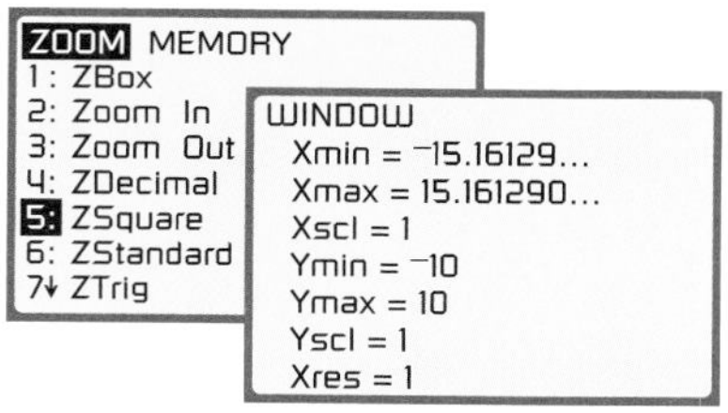

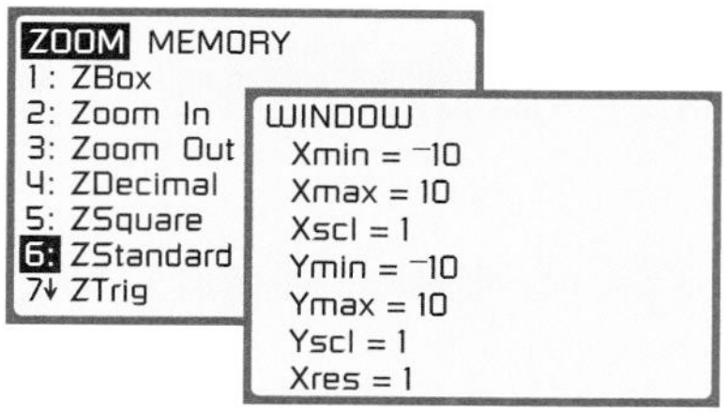

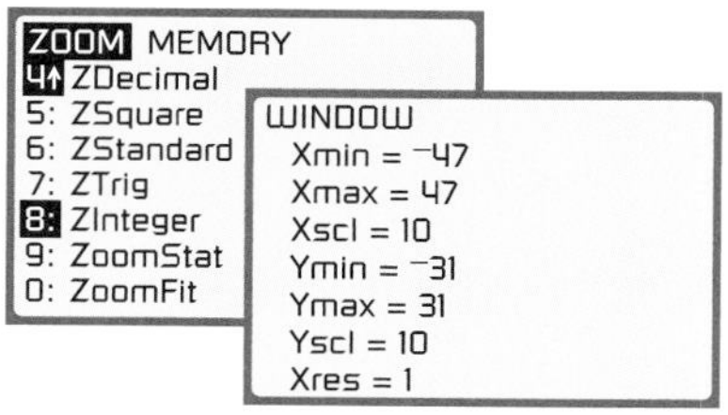

Photo Credits

p. 1 AP/Wide World Photos; *p. 21* Peter Arnold, Inc./Alamy; *p. 53* Royalty Free/CORBIS; *p. 54* Richard T. Nowitz/CORBIS; *p. 63* Frozen Images/The Image Works; *p. 65* Mary Steinbacher/PhotoEdit, Inc.; *p. 66* Dennis MacDonald/ PhotoEdit, Inc.; *p. 94* Lester V. Bergman/CORBIS; *p. 95* CORBIS; *p. 103* CORBIS; *p. 105* Ariel Skeeley/CORBIS; *p. 165* Elie Bernager/Getty Images; *p. 171 (top)* Paul Conklin/PhotoEdit, Inc., *(bottom)* AP/Wide World Photos; *p. 179* Courtesy of the US Postal Service via Getty Images; *p. 202* AP/Wide World Photos; *p. 204* Bill Freeman/PhotoEdit., Inc.; *p. 217* PhotoDisc/Getty Images; *p. 231* Paul Seheult/Eye Ubiquitous/CORBIS; *p. 241* Alan Schein Photography/CORBIS; *p. 246* AP/Wide World Photos; *p. 257* AP/Wide World Photos; *p. 287* Tony Freeman/PhotoEdit, Inc.; *p. 327* Philip Wallick/CORBIS; *p. 354* Eric and David Hosking/CORBIS; *p. 355* Bill Aron/PhotoEdit, Inc.; *p. 368* Royalty Free/CORBIS; *p. 399* Reuters/CORBIS; *p. 400* Will & Deni McIntyre/Stone/Getty Images; *p. 408* AP/Wide World Photos; *p. 417* AP/Wide World Photos; *p. 456* Sandor Szabo/EPA/Landov; *p. 467* Peter Pinnock/Getty Images; *p. 493* Stephen Frink/CORBIS; *p. 503* Paul Almasy/CORBIS; *p. 504* Clayton Sharrard/PhotoEdit, Inc.; *p. 510* Cameraphoto Arte, Venice/Art Resource, NY; *p. 515* AP/Wide World Photos; *p. 525* Tom Carter/PhotoEdit, Inc.; *p. 526 (top)* Koichi Kamoshida/Getty Images, *(bottom)* Mark Stephenson/ CORBIS; *p. 527* AP/Wide World Photos; *p. 529* Lee Cohen/CORBIS; *p. 541* Gary Gladstone Studio Inc./Getty Images; *p. 565* The Granger Collection; *p. 574* Robert Brenner/PhotoEdit, Inc.; *p. 583* © Royalty-Free/CORBIS; *p. 629* Grafton Marshall Smith/CORBIS; *p. 630* Billy Hustace/Stone/Getty Images; *p. 632* Robert Brenner/PhotoEdit, Inc.; *p. 633* David Young-Wolff/PhotoEdit, Inc.

Solutions to Chapter Problems

Solutions to Chapter 1 Problems

SECTION 1.1

Problem 1

$A = \{1, 2, 3, 4\}$

Problem 2

$-5 < -1$
$-1 = -1$
$5 > -1$

The element 5 is greater than -1.

Problem 3

A. 9 **B.** -62

Problem 4

A. $|-5| = 5$ **B.** $-|-9| = -9$

SECTION 1.2

Problem 1

A. $-162 + 98 = -64$

B. $-154 + (-37) = -191$

C. $-36 + 17 + (-21) = -19 + (-21) = -40$

Problem 2

$-8 - 14 = -8 + (-14) = -22$

Problem 3

$$\begin{aligned}&4 - (-3) - 12 - (-7) - 20\\ &= 4 + 3 + (-12) + 7 + (-20)\\ &= 7 + (-12) + 7 + (-20)\\ &= -5 + 7 + (-20)\\ &= 2 + (-20)\\ &= -18\end{aligned}$$

Problem 4

A. $-38 \cdot 51 = -1938$

B. $-7(-8)(9)(-2) = 56(9)(-2) = 504(-2) = -1008$

Problem 5

A. $(-135) \div (-9) = 15$

B. $\frac{84}{-6} = -14$

C. $-\frac{36}{-12} = -(-3) = 3$

Problem 6

Strategy To find the average daily high temperature:
- ▶ Add the seven temperature readings.
- ▶ Divide the sum by 7.

Solution
$$\begin{aligned}&-5 + (-6) + 3 + 0 + (-4) + (-7) + (-2)\\ &= -11 + 3 + 0 + (-4) + (-7) + (-2)\\ &= -8 + 0 + (-4) + (-7) + (-2)\\ &= -8 + (-4) + (-7) + (-2)\\ &= -12 + (-7) + (-2)\\ &= -19 + (-2)\\ &= -21\end{aligned}$$

$-21 \div 7 = -3$

The average daily high temperature was -3°C.

SECTION 1.3

Problem 1

$$\begin{array}{r} 0.16\\ 25\overline{)4.00}\\ -2\,5\\ \hline 1\,50\\ -1\,50\\ \hline 0\end{array}$$

$\frac{4}{25} = 0.16$

Problem 2

$$\begin{array}{r} 0.444\\ 9\overline{)4.000}\\ -3\,6\\ \hline 40\\ -36\\ \hline 40\\ -36\\ \hline 4\end{array}$$

$\frac{4}{9} = 0.\overline{4}$

Problem 3

$$-\frac{7}{12} \cdot \frac{9}{14} = -\frac{7 \cdot 9}{12 \cdot 14} = -\frac{\overset{1}{\cancel{7}} \cdot \overset{1}{\cancel{3}} \cdot 3}{2 \cdot 2 \cdot \underset{1}{\cancel{3}} \cdot 2 \cdot \underset{1}{\cancel{7}}} = -\frac{3}{8}$$

Problem 4

$$-\frac{3}{8} \div \left(-\frac{5}{12}\right) = \frac{3}{8} \cdot \frac{12}{5} = \frac{3 \cdot 12}{8 \cdot 5} = \frac{3 \cdot \overset{1}{\cancel{2}} \cdot \overset{1}{\cancel{2}} \cdot 3}{\underset{1}{\cancel{2}} \cdot \underset{1}{\cancel{2}} \cdot 2 \cdot 5} = \frac{9}{10}$$

Problem 5

$$\begin{array}{r} 5.44 \\ \times\quad 3.8 \\ \hline 4352 \\ 1632 \\ \hline 20.672 \end{array}$$

$(-5.44)(3.8) = -20.672$

Problem 6

$$\begin{array}{r} 0.231 \\ 1.7\overline{)0.3940} \\ -34 \\ \hline 54 \\ -51 \\ \hline 30 \\ -17 \\ \hline 13 \end{array}$$

$-0.394 \div 1.7 \approx -0.23$

Problem 7

Prime factorization of 9 and 12:

$9 = 3 \cdot 3 \qquad 12 = 2 \cdot 2 \cdot 3$

$\text{LCM} = 2 \cdot 2 \cdot 3 \cdot 3 = 36$

$$\frac{5}{9} - \frac{11}{12} = \frac{20}{36} - \frac{33}{36} = \frac{20}{36} + \frac{-33}{36}$$
$$= \frac{20 + (-33)}{36} = \frac{-13}{36} = -\frac{13}{36}$$

Problem 8

$$-\frac{7}{8} - \frac{5}{6} + \frac{1}{2} = -\frac{21}{24} - \frac{20}{24} + \frac{12}{24}$$
$$= \frac{-21}{24} + \frac{-20}{24} + \frac{12}{24}$$
$$= \frac{-21 + (-20) + 12}{24} = \frac{-29}{24} = -\frac{29}{24}$$

Problem 9

$$\begin{array}{r} 3.097 \\ 4.9 \\ +\ 3.09 \\ \hline 11.087 \end{array}$$

Problem 10

$$\begin{array}{r} 67.910 \\ -16.127 \\ \hline 51.783 \end{array}$$

$16.127 - 67.91 = -51.783$

Problem 11

$$125\% = 125\left(\frac{1}{100}\right) = \frac{125}{100} = 1\frac{1}{4}$$

$125\% = 125(0.01) = 1.25$

Problem 12

$$16\frac{2}{3}\% = 16\frac{2}{3}\left(\frac{1}{100}\right) = \frac{50}{3}\left(\frac{1}{100}\right) = \frac{1}{6}$$

Problem 13

$6.08\% = 6.08(0.01) = 0.0608$

Problem 14

A. $0.043 = 0.043(100\%) = 4.3\%$
B. $2.57 = 2.57(100\%) = 257\%$

Problem 15

$$\frac{5}{9} = \frac{5}{9}(100\%) = \frac{500}{9}\% \approx 55.6\%$$

Problem 16

$$\frac{9}{16} = \frac{9}{16}(100\%) = \frac{900}{16}\% = 56\frac{1}{4}\%$$

SECTION 1.4

Problem 1

$(-5)^3 = (-5)(-5)(-5) = 25(-5) = -125$
$-5^3 = -(5 \cdot 5 \cdot 5) = -(25 \cdot 5) = -125$

Problem 2

$(-3)^3 = (-3)(-3)(-3) = 9(-3) = -27$
$(-3)^4 = (-3)(-3)(-3)(-3)$
$\quad = 9(-3)(-3) = -27(-3) = 81$

Problem 3

$(3^3)(-2)^3 = (3)(3)(3) \cdot (-2)(-2)(-2)$
$\quad = 27 \cdot (-8) = -216$

$$\left(-\frac{2}{5}\right)^2 = \left(-\frac{2}{5}\right)\left(-\frac{2}{5}\right) = \frac{2 \cdot 2}{5 \cdot 5} = \frac{4}{25}$$

Problem 4

$36 \div (8 - 5)^2 - (-3)^2 \cdot 2$
$\quad = 36 \div (3)^2 - (-3)^2 \cdot 2$
$\quad = 36 \div 9 - 9 \cdot 2$
$\quad = 4 - 9 \cdot 2$
$\quad = 4 - 18$
$\quad = -14$

Problem 5

$27 \div 3^2 + (-3)^2 \cdot 4$
$\quad = 27 \div 9 + 9 \cdot 4$
$\quad = 3 + 9 \cdot 4$
$\quad = 3 + 36$
$\quad = 39$

Problem 6

$4 - 3[4 - 2(6 - 3)] \div 2$
$\quad = 4 - 3[4 - 2(3)] \div 2$
$\quad = 4 - 3[4 - 6] \div 2$
$\quad = 4 - 3(-2) \div 2$
$\quad = 4 - (-6) \div 2$
$\quad = 4 - (-3)$
$\quad = 7$

SECTION 1.5

Problem 1

To find the complement of 87°, subtract 87° from 90°.

$$90° - 87° = 3°$$

3° is the complement of 87°.

Problem 2

To find the supplement of 87°, subtract 87° from 180°.

$$180° - 87° = 93°$$

93° is the supplement of 87°.

Problem 3

$m\angle x$ is the sum of the measures of two angles.

$$m\angle x = 34° + 95° = 129°$$

Problem 4

$$\begin{aligned}\text{Perimeter} &= 4 \cdot \text{side}\\ &= 4 \cdot 4.2\text{ m} = 16.8\text{ m}\end{aligned}$$

Problem 5

$$\begin{aligned}\text{Circumference} &= \pi \cdot \text{diameter}\\ &\approx 3.14 \cdot 5\text{ in.}\\ &= 15.7\text{ in.}\end{aligned}$$

Problem 6

Strategy To find the cost of the metal strip:

- ▶ Find the circumference of the table in inches.
- ▶ Convert inches to feet.
- ▶ Multiply the circumference by the per-foot cost of the metal strip.

Solution

$$\begin{aligned}\text{Circumference} &= \pi \cdot \text{diameter}\\ &\approx 3.14 \cdot 36\text{ in.}\\ &= 113.04\text{ in.}\end{aligned}$$

$$\frac{113.04}{12} = 9.42\text{ ft}$$

Cost: $9.42(3.21) = 30.2382$

The cost is \$30.24.

Problem 7

$$\begin{aligned}\text{Area} &= \frac{1}{2} \cdot \text{base} \cdot \text{height}\\ &= \frac{1}{2} \cdot 5\text{ ft} \cdot 3\text{ ft} = 7.5\text{ ft}^2\end{aligned}$$

Problem 8

$$\begin{aligned}\text{Area} &= \pi \cdot (\text{radius})^2\\ &\approx 3.14 \cdot (6\text{ in.})^2\\ &= 113.04\text{ in}^2\end{aligned}$$

Problem 9

$$\begin{aligned}\text{Area} &= \text{base} \cdot \text{height}\\ &= 28\text{ in.} \cdot 15\text{ in.} = 420\text{ in}^2\end{aligned}$$

Problem 10

Strategy To find how much more expensive the wool rug is than the nylon rug:

- ▶ Find the area of the rug.
- ▶ Multiply the area of the rug by the per-square-foot cost of the wool rug.
- ▶ Multiply the area of the rug by the per-square-foot cost of the nylon rug.
- ▶ Find the difference between the two costs.

Solution

$$\begin{aligned}\text{Area} &= \text{length} \cdot \text{width}\\ &= 15\text{ ft} \cdot 4\text{ ft} = 60\text{ ft}^2\end{aligned}$$

Cost of wool rug = \$1.93 · 60 = \$115.80

Cost of nylon rug = \$1.25 · 60 = \$75

Difference in cost = \$115.80 − \$75 = \$40.80

The difference in cost is \$40.80.

Solutions to Chapter 2 Problems

SECTION 2.1

Problem 1

-4

Problem 2

$2xy + y^2$

$$\begin{aligned}2(-4)(2) + (2)^2 &= 2(-4)(2) + 4\\ &= -8(2) + 4\\ &= -16 + 4\\ &= -12\end{aligned}$$

Problem 3

$\dfrac{a^2 + b^2}{a + b}$

$$\begin{aligned}\frac{(5)^2 + (-3)^2}{5 + (-3)} &= \frac{25 + 9}{5 + (-3)}\\ &= \frac{34}{2}\\ &= 17\end{aligned}$$

Problem 4

$x^3 - 2(x + y) + z^2$

$$\begin{aligned}&(2)^3 - 2[2 + (-4)] + (-3)^2\\ &= (2)^3 - 2(-2) + (-3)^2\\ &= 8 - 2(-2) + 9\\ &= 8 + 4 + 9\\ &= 12 + 9\\ &= 21\end{aligned}$$

Problem 5

$$V = \frac{1}{3}\pi r^2 h$$

$$V = \frac{1}{3}\pi(4.5)^2(9.5) \qquad \bullet\ r = \frac{1}{2}d = \frac{1}{2}(9) = 4.5$$

$V = \frac{1}{3}\pi(20.25)(9.5)$

$V \approx 201.5$

The volume is approximately 201.5 cm^3.

SECTION 2.2

Problem 1

$7 + (-7) = 0$

Problem 2

The Associative Property of Addition

Problem 3

A. $9x + 6x = (9 + 6)x = 15x$

B. $-4y - 7y = [-4 + (-7)]y = -11y$

Problem 4

A. $3a - 2b + 5a = 3a + 5a - 2b$
$= (3a + 5a) - 2b$
$= 8a - 2b$

B. $x^2 - 7 + 9x^2 - 14$
$= x^2 + 9x^2 - 7 - 14$
$= (x^2 + 9x^2) + (-7 - 14)$
$= 10x^2 - 21$

Problem 5

A. $-7(-2a) = [-7(-2)]a$
$= 14a$

B. $-\frac{5}{6}(-30y^2) = \left[-\frac{5}{6}(-30)\right]y^2$
$= 25y^2$

C. $(-5x)(-2) = (-2)(-5x)$
$= [-2(-5)]x$
$= 10x$

Problem 6

A. $7(4 + 2y) = 7(4) + 7(2y)$
$= 28 + 14y$

B. $-(5x - 12) = -1(5x - 12)$
$= -1(5x) - (-1)(12)$
$= -5x + 12$

C. $(3a - 1)5 = (3a)(5) - (1)(5)$
$= 15a - 5$

D. $-3(6a^2 - 8a + 9)$
$= -3(6a^2) - (-3)(8a) + (-3)(9)$
$= -18a^2 + 24a - 27$

Problem 7

$7(x - 2y) - 3(-x - 2y)$
$= 7x - 14y + 3x + 6y$
$= 10x - 8y$

Problem 8

$3y - 2[x - 4(2 - 3y)]$
$= 3y - 2[x - 8 + 12y]$
$= 3y - 2x + 16 - 24y$
$= -2x - 21y + 16$

SECTION 2.3

Problem 1

A. eighteen less than the cube of x

$x^3 - 18$

B. y decreased by the sum of z and nine

$y - (z + 9)$

C. the difference between the square of q and the sum of r and t

$q^2 - (r + t)$

Problem 2

the unknown number: n
the square of the number: n^2
the product of five and the square of the number: $5n^2$

$5n^2 + n$

Problem 3

the unknown number: n
twice the number: $2n$
the sum of seven and twice the number: $7 + 2n$

$3(7 + 2n)$

Problem 4

the unknown number: n
twice the number: $2n$
the difference between twice the number and 17: $2n - 17$

$n - (2n - 17) = n - 2n + 17$
$= -n + 17$

Problem 5

the unknown number: n

three-fourths of the number: $\frac{3}{4}n$

one-fifth of the number: $\frac{1}{5}n$

$\frac{3}{4}n + \frac{1}{5}n = \frac{15}{20}n + \frac{4}{20}n$
$= \frac{19}{20}n$

Problem 6

the time required by the newer model: t
the time required by the older model is twice the time required for the newer model: $2t$

Problem 7

the length of one piece: L
the length of the second piece: $6 - L$

Solutions to Chapter 3 Problems

SECTION 3.1

Problem 1

$$\begin{array}{c|c} \multicolumn{2}{c}{5 - 4x = 8x + 2} \\ \hline 5 - 4\left(\frac{1}{4}\right) & 8\left(\frac{1}{4}\right) + 2 \\ 5 - 1 & 2 + 2 \\ \multicolumn{2}{c}{4 = 4} \end{array}$$

Yes, $\frac{1}{4}$ is a solution.

Problem 2

$$\begin{array}{c|c} \multicolumn{2}{c}{10x - x^2 = 3x - 10} \\ \hline 10(5) - (5)^2 & 3(5) - 10 \\ 50 - 25 & 15 - 10 \\ \multicolumn{2}{c}{25 \neq 5} \end{array}$$

No, 5 is not a solution.

Problem 3

$$\begin{aligned} x - \frac{1}{3} &= -\frac{3}{4} \\ x - \frac{1}{3} + \frac{1}{3} &= -\frac{3}{4} + \frac{1}{3} \\ x + 0 &= -\frac{9}{12} + \frac{4}{12} \\ x &= -\frac{5}{12} \end{aligned}$$

Check

$$\begin{array}{c|c} \multicolumn{2}{c}{x - \frac{1}{3} = -\frac{3}{4}} \\ \hline -\frac{5}{12} - \frac{1}{3} & -\frac{3}{4} \\ \multicolumn{2}{c}{-\frac{3}{4} = -\frac{3}{4}} \end{array}$$

The solution is $-\frac{5}{12}$.

Problem 4

$$\begin{aligned} -8 &= 5 + x \\ -8 - 5 &= 5 - 5 + x \\ -13 &= x \end{aligned}$$

The solution is -13.

Problem 5

$$\begin{aligned} -\frac{2x}{5} &= 6 \\ \left(-\frac{5}{2}\right)\left(-\frac{2}{5}x\right) &= \left(-\frac{5}{2}\right)(6) \\ 1x &= -15 \\ x &= -15 \end{aligned}$$

The solution is -15.

Problem 6

$$\begin{aligned} 6x &= 10 \\ \frac{6x}{6} &= \frac{10}{6} \\ x &= \frac{5}{3} \end{aligned}$$

Check

$$\begin{array}{c|c} \multicolumn{2}{c}{6x = 10} \\ \hline 6\left(\frac{5}{3}\right) & 10 \\ \multicolumn{2}{c}{10 = 10} \end{array}$$

The solution is $\frac{5}{3}$.

Problem 7

$$\begin{aligned} 4x - 8x &= 16 \\ -4x &= 16 \\ \frac{-4x}{-4} &= \frac{16}{-4} \\ x &= -4 \end{aligned}$$

The solution is -4.

Problem 8

Strategy The distance is 80 mi. Therefore, $d = 80$. The cyclists are moving in opposite directions, so the rate at which the distance between them is changing is the sum of the rates of the two cyclists. The rate is 18 mph + 14 mph = 32 mph. Therefore, $r = 32$. To find the time, solve the equation $d = rt$ for t.

Solution

$$\begin{aligned} d &= rt \\ 80 &= 32t \\ \frac{80}{32} &= \frac{32t}{32} \\ 2.5 &= t \end{aligned}$$

They will meet 2.5 h after they begin.

Problem 9

Strategy Because the plane is flying against the wind, the rate of the plane is its speed in calm air (250 mph) minus the speed of the headwind (25 mph): 250 mph − 25 mph = 225 mph. Therefore, $r = 225$. The time is 3 h, so $t = 3$. To find the distance, solve the equation $d = rt$ for d.

Solution

$$\begin{aligned} d &= rt \\ d &= 225(3) \\ d &= 675 \end{aligned}$$

The plane can fly 675 mi in 3 h.

Problem 10

$$PB = A$$
$$P(60) = 27$$
$$60P = 27$$
$$\frac{60P}{60} = \frac{27}{60}$$
$$P = 0.45$$

27 is 45% of 60.

Problem 11

Strategy To find the percent of the questions answered correctly, solve the basic percent equation using $B = 80$ and $A = 72$. The percent is unknown.

Solution
$$PB = A$$
$$P(80) = 72$$
$$80P = 72$$
$$\frac{80P}{80} = \frac{72}{80}$$
$$P = 0.9$$

90% of the questions were answered correctly.

Problem 12

Strategy To determine the sales tax, solve the basic percent equation using $B = 895$ and $P = 6\% = 0.06$. The amount is unknown.

Solution
$$PB = A$$
$$0.06(895) = A$$
$$53.7 = A$$

The sales tax is \$53.70.

Problem 13

Strategy To determine how much she must deposit into the bank account:

- ► Find the amount of interest earned on the municipal bond by solving the equation $I = Prt$ for I using $P = 1000$, $r = 6.4\% = 0.064$, and $t = 1$.
- ► Solve $I = Prt$ for P using the amount of interest earned on the municipal bond for I, $r = 8\% = 0.08$, and $t = 1$.

Solution
$$I = Prt$$
$$I = 1000(0.064)(1)$$
$$I = 64$$

The interest earned on the municipal bond is \$64.

$$I = Prt$$
$$64 = P(0.08)(1)$$
$$64 = 0.08P$$
$$\frac{64}{0.08} = \frac{0.08P}{0.08}$$
$$800 = P$$

Clarissa must deposit \$800 into the bank account.

Problem 14

Strategy To find the number of ounces of cereal in the bowl, solve the equation $Q = Ar$ for A using $Q = 2$ and $r = 25\% = 0.25$.

Solution
$$Q = Ar$$
$$2 = A(0.25)$$
$$\frac{2}{0.25} = \frac{A(0.25)}{0.25}$$
$$8 = A$$

The cereal bowl contains 8 oz of cereal.

SECTION 3.2

Problem 1

$$5x + 7 = 10$$
$$5x + 7 - 7 = 10 - 7$$
$$5x = 3$$
$$\frac{5x}{5} = \frac{3}{5}$$
$$x = \frac{3}{5}$$

The solution is $\frac{3}{5}$.

Problem 2

$$11 = 11 + 3x$$
$$11 - 11 = 11 - 11 + 3x$$
$$0 = 3x$$
$$\frac{0}{3} = \frac{3x}{3}$$
$$0 = x$$

The solution is 0.

Problem 3

$$\frac{5}{2} - \frac{2}{3}x = \frac{1}{2}$$
$$6\left(\frac{5}{2} - \frac{2}{3}x\right) = 6\left(\frac{1}{2}\right)$$
$$6\left(\frac{5}{2}\right) - 6\left(\frac{2}{3}x\right) = 3$$
$$15 - 4x = 3$$
$$15 - 15 - 4x = 3 - 15$$
$$-4x = -12$$
$$\frac{-4x}{-4} = \frac{-12}{-4}$$
$$x = 3$$

The solution is 3.

Problem 4

$$\begin{aligned} 5x + 4 &= 6 + 10x \\ 5x - 10x + 4 &= 6 + 10x - 10x \\ -5x + 4 &= 6 \\ -5x + 4 - 4 &= 6 - 4 \\ -5x &= 2 \\ \frac{-5x}{-5} &= \frac{2}{-5} \\ x &= -\frac{2}{5} \end{aligned}$$

The solution is $-\frac{2}{5}$.

Problem 5

$$\begin{aligned} 5x - 4(3 - 2x) &= 2(3x - 2) + 6 \\ 5x - 12 + 8x &= 6x - 4 + 6 \\ 13x - 12 &= 6x + 2 \\ 13x - 6x - 12 &= 6x - 6x + 2 \\ 7x - 12 &= 2 \\ 7x - 12 + 12 &= 2 + 12 \\ 7x &= 14 \\ \frac{7x}{7} &= \frac{14}{7} \\ x &= 2 \end{aligned}$$

The solution is 2.

Problem 6

$$\begin{aligned} -2[3x - 5(2x - 3)] &= 3x - 8 \\ -2[3x - 10x + 15] &= 3x - 8 \\ -2[-7x + 15] &= 3x - 8 \\ 14x - 30 &= 3x - 8 \\ 14x - 3x - 30 &= 3x - 3x - 8 \\ 11x - 30 &= -8 \\ 11x - 30 + 30 &= -8 + 30 \\ 11x &= 22 \\ \frac{11x}{11} &= \frac{22}{11} \\ x &= 2 \end{aligned}$$

The solution is 2.

Problem 7

Strategy To find the number of years, replace V with 10,200 in the given equation and solve for t.

Solution

$$\begin{aligned} V &= 450t + 7500 \\ 10{,}200 &= 450t + 7500 \\ 10{,}200 - 7500 &= 450t + 7500 - 7500 \\ 2700 &= 450t \\ \frac{2700}{450} &= \frac{450t}{450} \\ 6 &= t \end{aligned}$$

The value of the investment will be $10,200 in 6 years.

Problem 8

Strategy The lever is 14 ft long, so $d = 14$. One force is 6 ft from the fulcrum, so $x = 6$. The one force is 40 lb, so $F_1 = 40$. To find the other force when the system balances, replace the variables F_1, x, and d in the lever system equation with the given values, and solve for F_2.

Solution

$$\begin{aligned} F_1x &= F_2(d - x) \\ 40(6) &= F_2(14 - 6) \\ 240 &= F_2(8) \\ 240 &= 8F_2 \\ \frac{240}{8} &= \frac{8F_2}{8} \\ 30 &= F_2 \end{aligned}$$

A 30-pound force must be applied to the other end.

SECTION 3.3

Problem 1

The solution set is the numbers greater than −2.

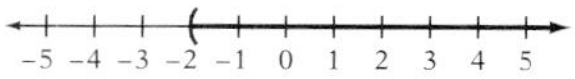

Problem 2

$$\begin{aligned} x + 2 &< -2 \\ x + 2 - 2 &< -2 - 2 \\ x &< -4 \end{aligned}$$

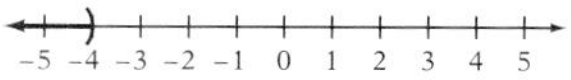

Problem 3

$$\begin{aligned} 5x + 3 &> 4x + 5 \\ 5x - 4x + 3 &> 4x - 4x + 5 \\ x + 3 &> 5 \\ x + 3 - 3 &> 5 - 3 \\ x &> 2 \end{aligned}$$

Problem 4

$$\begin{aligned} 3x &< 9 \\ \frac{3x}{3} &< \frac{9}{3} \\ x &< 3 \end{aligned}$$

Problem 5

$$\begin{aligned} -\frac{3}{4}x &\ge 18 \\ -\frac{4}{3}\left(-\frac{3}{4}x\right) &\le -\frac{4}{3}(18) \\ x &\le -24 \end{aligned}$$

Problem 6

$$\begin{aligned} 5 - 4x &> 9 - 8x \\ 5 - 4x + 8x &> 9 - 8x + 8x \\ 5 + 4x &> 9 \\ 5 - 5 + 4x &> 9 - 5 \\ 4x &> 4 \\ \frac{4x}{4} &> \frac{4}{4} \\ x &> 1 \end{aligned}$$

Problem 7

$$\begin{aligned} 8 - 4(3x + 5) &\le 6(x - 8) \\ 8 - 12x - 20 &\le 6x - 48 \\ -12 - 12x &\le 6x - 48 \\ -12 - 12x - 6x &\le 6x - 6x - 48 \\ -12 - 18x &\le -48 \\ -12 + 12 - 18x &\le -48 + 12 \\ -18x &\le -36 \\ \frac{-18x}{-18} &\ge \frac{-36}{-18} \\ x &\ge 2 \end{aligned}$$

Solutions to Chapter 4 Problems

SECTION 4.1

Problem 1

the unknown number: n

nine less than twice a number	is	five times the sum of the number and twelve

$$\begin{aligned} 2n - 9 &= 5(n + 12) \\ 2n - 9 &= 5n + 60 \\ 2n - 5n - 9 &= 5n - 5n + 60 \\ -3n - 9 &= 60 \\ -3n - 9 + 9 &= 60 + 9 \\ -3n &= 69 \\ \frac{-3n}{-3} &= \frac{69}{-3} \\ n &= -23 \end{aligned}$$

The number is -23.

Problem 2

Strategy To find the number of carbon atoms, write and solve an equation using n to represent the number of carbon atoms.

Solution

eight	represents	twice the number of carbon atoms

$$\begin{aligned} 8 &= 2n \\ \frac{8}{2} &= \frac{2n}{2} \\ 4 &= n \end{aligned}$$

There are 4 carbon atoms in a butane gas molecule.

Problem 3

Strategy To find the number of 10-speed bicycles made each day, write and solve an equation using n to represent the number of 10-speed bicycles and $160 - n$ to represent the number of 3-speed bicycles.

Solution

four times the number of 3-speed bicycles made	equals	30 less than the number of 10-speed bicycles made

$$\begin{aligned} 4(160 - n) &= n - 30 \\ 640 - 4n &= n - 30 \\ 640 - 4n - n &= n - n - 30 \\ 640 - 5n &= -30 \\ 640 - 640 - 5n &= -30 - 640 \\ -5n &= -670 \\ \frac{-5n}{-5} &= \frac{-670}{-5} \\ n &= 134 \end{aligned}$$

There are 134 10-speed bicycles made each day.

SECTION 4.2

Problem 1

Strategy ► First consecutive integer: n
Second consecutive integer: $n + 1$
Third consecutive integer: $n + 2$

► The sum of the three integers is -12.

Solution

$$\begin{aligned} n + (n + 1) + (n + 2) &= -12 \\ 3n + 3 &= -12 \\ 3n &= -15 \\ n &= -5 \end{aligned}$$

$n + 1 = -5 + 1 = -4$
$n + 2 = -5 + 2 = -3$

The three consecutive integers are -5, -4, and -3.

Problem 2

Strategy ► Number of dimes: x
Number of nickels: $5x$
Number of quarters: $x + 6$

Coin	Number	Value	Total value
Dime	x	10	$10x$
Nickel	$5x$	5	$5(5x)$
Quarter	$x + 6$	25	$25(x + 6)$

► The sum of the total values of the individual denominations of coins equals the total value of all the coins (630 cents).

Solution

$$10x + 5(5x) + 25(x + 6) = 630$$
$$10x + 25x + 25x + 150 = 630$$
$$60x + 150 = 630$$
$$60x = 480$$
$$x = 8$$

$5x = 5(8) = 40$
$x + 6 = 8 + 6 = 14$

The bank contains 8 dimes, 40 nickels, and 14 quarters.

SECTION 4.3

Problem 1

Strategy
- Each equal side: s
- Use the equation for the perimeter of a square.

Solution

$P = 4s$
$52 = 4s$
$13 = s$

The length of each side is 13 ft.

Problem 2

Strategy To find the supplement, let x represent the supplement of a 107° angle. Use the fact that supplementary angles are two angles whose sum is 180° to write an equation. Solve for x.

Solution

$107° + x = 180°$
$x = 73°$

The supplement of a 107° angle is a 73° angle.

Problem 3

Strategy The angles labeled are adjacent angles of intersecting lines and are therefore supplementary angles. To find x, write an equation and solve for x.

Solution

$$x + (3x + 20°) = 180°$$
$$4x + 20° = 180°$$
$$4x = 160°$$
$$x = 40°$$

Problem 4

Strategy $2x = y$ because alternate exterior angles have the same measure.

$y + (x + 15°) = 180°$ because adjacent angles of intersecting lines are supplementary angles. Substitute $2x$ for y and solve for x.

Solution

$$y + (x + 15°) = 180°$$
$$2x + (x + 15°) = 180°$$
$$3x + 15° = 180°$$
$$3x = 165°$$
$$x = 55°$$

Problem 5

Strategy
- To find the measure of $\angle a$, use the fact that $\angle a$ and $\angle y$ are vertical angles.
- To find the measure of $\angle b$, use the fact that the sum of the interior angles of a triangle is 180°.
- To find the measure of $\angle d$, use the fact that $\angle b$ and $\angle d$ are supplementary angles.

Solution

$\angle a = \angle y = 55°$

$$\angle a + \angle b + 90° = 180°$$
$$55° + \angle b + 90° = 180°$$
$$145° + \angle b = 180°$$
$$\angle b = 35°$$

$$\angle b + \angle d = 180°$$
$$35° + \angle d = 180°$$
$$\angle d = 145°$$

Problem 6

Strategy To find the measure of the third angle, use the fact that the sum of the measures of the interior angles of a triangle is 180°. Write an equation using x to represent the measure of the third angle. Solve the equation for x.

Solution

$$x + 90° + 27° = 180°$$
$$x + 117° = 180°$$
$$x = 63°$$

The measure of the third angle is 63°.

SECTION 4.4

Problem 1

Strategy Given: $C = \$120$
$S = \$180$
Unknown markup rate: r
Use the equation $S = C + rC$.

Solution

$S = C + rC$
$180 = 120 + 120r$
$60 = 120r$
$0.5 = r$

The markup rate is 50%.

Problem 2

Strategy Given: $r = 40\% = 0.40$
$S = \$266$
Unknown cost: C
Use the equation $S = C + rC$.

Solution

$S = C + rC$
$266 = C + 0.4C$
$266 = 1.40C$
$190 = C$

The cost is \$190.

Problem 3

Strategy Given: $R = \$39.80$
$S = \$29.85$
Unknown discount rate: r
Use the equation $S = R - rR$.

Solution
$$S = R - rR$$
$$29.85 = 39.80 - 39.80r$$
$$-9.95 = -39.80r$$
$$0.25 = r$$

The discount rate is 25%.

Problem 4

Strategy Given: $S = \$43.50$
$r = 25\% = 0.25$
Unknown regular price: R
Use the equation $S = R - rR$.

Solution
$$S = R - rR$$
$$43.50 = R - 0.25R$$
$$43.50 = 0.75R$$
$$58 = R$$

The regular price is $58.

SECTION 4.5

Problem 1

Strategy ► Additional amount: x

	Principal	·	Rate	=	Interest
Amount at 7%	2500	·	0.07	=	0.07(2500)
Amount at 10%	x	·	0.10	=	$0.10x$
Amount at 9%	$2500 + x$	·	0.09	=	$0.09(2500 + x)$

► The sum of the interest earned by the two investments equals the interest earned on the total investment.

Solution
$$0.07(2500) + 0.10x = 0.09(2500 + x)$$
$$175 + 0.10x = 225 + 0.09x$$
$$175 + 0.01x = 225$$
$$0.01x = 50$$
$$x = 5000$$

$5000 more must be invested at 10%.

SECTION 4.6

Problem 1

Strategy ► Pounds of $.75 fertilizer: x

	Amount	Cost	Value
$.90 fertilizer	20	0.90	0.90(20)
$.75 fertilizer	x	0.75	$0.75x$
$.85 fertilizer	$20 + x$	0.85	$0.85(20 + x)$

► The sum of the values before mixing equals the value after mixing.

Solution
$$0.90(20) + 0.75x = 0.85(20 + x)$$
$$18 + 0.75x = 17 + 0.85x$$
$$18 - 0.10x = 17$$
$$-0.10x = -1$$
$$x = 10$$

10 lb of the $.75 fertilizer must be added.

Problem 2

Strategy ► Pure orange juice is 100% orange juice.
100% = 1.00

Amount of pure orange juice: x

	Amount	Percent	Quantity
Pure orange juice	x	1.00	$1.00x$
Fruit drink	5	0.10	0.10(5)
Orange drink	$x + 5$	0.25	$0.25(x + 5)$

► The sum of the quantities before mixing is equal to the quantity after mixing.

Solution
$$1.00x + 0.10(5) = 0.25(x + 5)$$
$$1.00x + 0.5 = 0.25x + 1.25$$
$$0.75x + 0.5 = 1.25$$
$$0.75x = 0.75$$
$$x = 1$$

To make the orange drink, 1 qt of pure orange juice is added to the fruit drink.

SECTION 4.7

Problem 1

Strategy ► Rate of the first train: r
Rate of the second train: $2r$

	Rate	Time	Distance
First train	r	3	$3r$
Second train	$2r$	3	$3(2r)$

► The sum of the distances traveled by each train equals 306 mi.

Solution
$$3r + 3(2r) = 306$$
$$3r + 6r = 306$$
$$9r = 306$$
$$r = 34$$

$$2r = 2(34) = 68$$

The first train is traveling at 34 mph. The second train is traveling at 68 mph.

Problem 2

Strategy ▶ Time spent flying out: t
Time spent flying back: $7 - t$

	Rate	Time	Distance
Out	120	t	$120t$
Back	90	$7 - t$	$90(7 - t)$

▶ The distance out equals the distance back.

Solution
$$120t = 90(7 - t)$$
$$120t = 630 - 90t$$
$$210t = 630$$
$$t = 3 \quad \text{(The time out was 3 h.)}$$

Distance $= 120t = 120(3) = 360$ mi

The parcel of land was 360 mi away.

SECTION 4.8

Problem 1

Strategy To find the minimum selling price, write and solve an inequality using S to represent the selling price.

Solution
$$340 < 0.70S$$
$$\frac{340}{0.70} < \frac{0.70S}{0.70}$$
$$485.71429 < S$$

The minimum selling price is \$485.72.

Problem 2

Strategy To find the maximum number of miles:

- ▶ Write an expression for the cost of each car, using x to represent the number of miles driven during the week.
- ▶ Write and solve an inequality.

Solution

cost of a Company A car	is less than	cost of a Company B car

$$9(7) + 0.10x < 12(7) + 0.08x$$
$$63 + 0.10x < 84 + 0.08x$$
$$63 + 0.10x - 0.08x < 84 + 0.08x - 0.08x$$
$$63 + 0.02x < 84$$
$$63 - 63 + 0.02x < 84 - 63$$
$$0.02x < 21$$
$$\frac{0.02x}{0.02} < \frac{21}{0.02}$$
$$x < 1050$$

The maximum number of miles is 1049.

Solutions to Chapter 5 Problems

SECTION 5.1

Problem 1

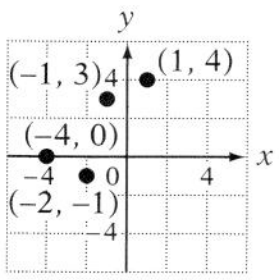

Problem 2

$A(4, 2)$, $B(-3, 4)$, $C(-3, 0)$, $D(0, 0)$

Problem 3

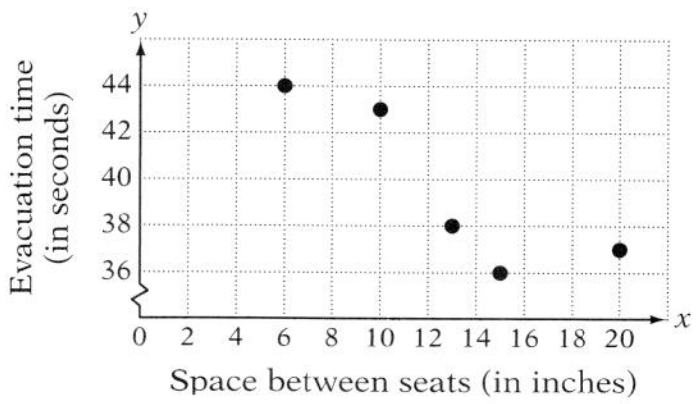

Problem 4

In 1900, the population was 76 million: (1900, 76)
In 2000, the population was 281 million: (2000, 281)

Average rate of change

$$= \frac{\text{change in } y}{\text{change in } x}$$
$$= \frac{\text{population in 2000} - \text{population in 1900}}{2000 - 1900}$$
$$= \frac{281 - 76}{2000 - 1900}$$
$$= \frac{205}{100} = 2.05$$

The average rate of change in the population was 2.05 million people per year.

Problem 5

28 weeks after conception, the weight is 3 lb: (28, 3)
38 weeks after conception, the weight is 7.5 lb: (38, 7.5)

Average rate of change

$$= \frac{\text{change in } y}{\text{change in } x}$$
$$= \frac{\text{weight after 38 weeks} - \text{weight after 28 weeks}}{38 - 28}$$
$$= \frac{7.5 - 3}{38 - 28}$$
$$= \frac{4.5}{10} = 0.45$$

The average rate of change in weight is 0.45 lb per week.

SECTION 5.2

Problem 1

$$y = -\frac{1}{2}x - 3$$

-4	$-\frac{1}{2}(2) - 3$
	$-1 - 3$
	-4

$-4 = -4$

Yes, $(2, -4)$ is a solution of $y = -\frac{1}{2}x - 3$.

Problem 2

$$y = -\frac{1}{4}x + 1$$
$$= -\frac{1}{4}(4) + 1$$
$$= -1 + 1$$
$$= 0$$

The ordered-pair solution is $(4, 0)$.

Problem 3

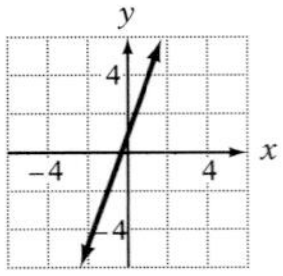

Problem 4

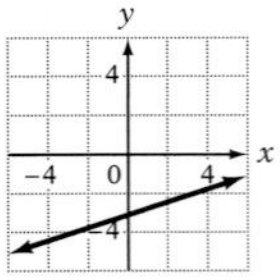

Problem 5

$$\begin{aligned} 5x - 2y &= 10 \\ 5x - 5x - 2y &= -5x + 10 \\ -2y &= -5x + 10 \\ \frac{-2y}{-2} &= \frac{-5x + 10}{-2} \\ y &= \frac{-5x}{-2} + \frac{10}{-2} \\ y &= \frac{5}{2}x - 5 \end{aligned}$$

Problem 6

A. $5x - 2y = 10$

$$-2y = -5x + 10$$
$$y = \frac{5}{2}x - 5$$

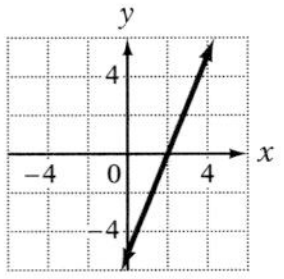

B. $x - 3y = 9$

$$-3y = -x + 9$$
$$y = \frac{1}{3}x - 3$$

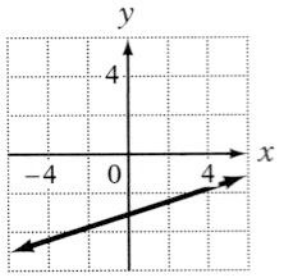

Problem 7

x-intercept:
$$\begin{aligned} 4x - y &= 4 \\ 4x - 0 &= 4 \\ 4x &= 4 \\ x &= 1 \end{aligned}$$

The x-intercept is $(1, 0)$.

y-intercept:
$$\begin{aligned} 4x - y &= 4 \\ 4(0) - y &= 4 \\ -y &= 4 \\ y &= -4 \end{aligned}$$

The y-intercept is $(0, -4)$.

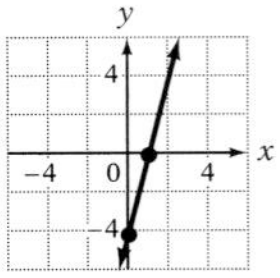

Problem 8

A.

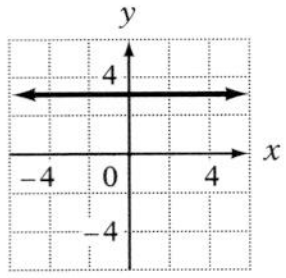

B.

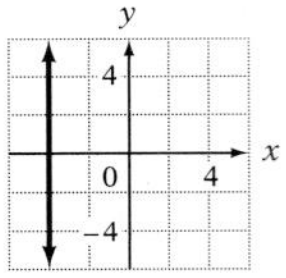

SECTION 5.3

Problem 1

A. $m = \frac{y_2 - y_1}{x_2 - x_1} = \frac{3 - 2}{1 - (-1)} = \frac{1}{2}$

The slope is $\frac{1}{2}$.

B. $m = \frac{y_2 - y_1}{x_2 - x_1} = \frac{-5 - 2}{4 - 1} = \frac{-7}{3}$

The slope is $-\frac{7}{3}$.

C. $m = \frac{y_2 - y_1}{x_2 - x_1} = \frac{7 - 3}{2 - 2} = \frac{4}{0}$

The slope is undefined.

D. $m = \frac{y_2 - y_1}{x_2 - x_1} = \frac{-3 - (-3)}{-5 - 1} = \frac{0}{-6} = 0$

The slope is 0.

Problem 2

Find the slope of the line through $(-2, -3)$ and $(7, 1)$.

$$m = \frac{y_2 - y_1}{x_2 - x_1} = \frac{1 - (-3)}{7 - (-2)} = \frac{4}{9}$$

Find the slope of the line through (1, 4) and (−5, 6).

$$m = \frac{y_2 - y_1}{x_2 - x_1} = \frac{6 - 4}{-5 - 1} = \frac{2}{-6} = -\frac{1}{3}$$

$$\frac{4}{9} \neq -\frac{1}{3}$$

The slopes are not equal.
The lines are not parallel.

Problem 3

$$m = \frac{8650 - 6100}{1 - 4} = \frac{2550}{-3} = -850$$

A slope of −850 means that the value of the car is decreasing at a rate of $850 per year.

Problem 4

y-intercept $= (0, b) = (0, -1)$

$$m = -\frac{1}{4}$$

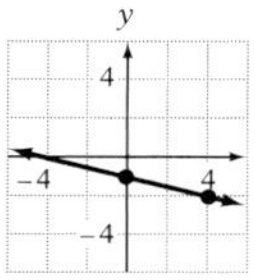

Problem 5

Solve the equation for y.

$$x - 2y = 4$$
$$-2y = -x + 4$$
$$y = \frac{1}{2}x - 2$$

y-intercept $= (0, b) = (0, -2)$

$$m = \frac{1}{2}$$

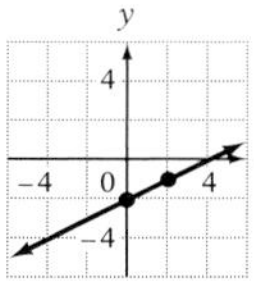

SECTION 5.4

Problem 1

$$y = \frac{3}{2}x + b$$
$$-2 = \frac{3}{2}(4) + b$$
$$-2 = 6 + b$$
$$-8 = b$$
$$y = \frac{3}{2}x - 8$$

Problem 2

$$m = \frac{2}{5} \quad (x_1, y_1) = (5, 4)$$
$$y - y_1 = m(x - x_1)$$
$$y - 4 = \frac{2}{5}(x - 5)$$
$$y - 4 = \frac{2}{5}x - 2$$
$$y = \frac{2}{5}x + 2$$

Problem 3

Let $(x_1, y_1) = (-3, -9)$ and $(x_2, y_2) = (1, -1)$.

$$m = \frac{y_2 - y_1}{x_2 - x_1} = \frac{-1 - (-9)}{1 - (-3)} = \frac{8}{4} = 2$$

$$y - y_1 = m(x - x_1)$$
$$y - (-9) = 2(x - (-3)) \qquad \bullet\ m = 2;\ (x_1, y_1) = (-3, -9)$$
$$y + 9 = 2(x + 3)$$
$$y + 9 = 2x + 6$$
$$y = 2x - 3$$

The equation of the line is $y = 2x - 3$.

SECTION 5.5

Problem 1

The domain is {1}.
The range is {0, 1, 2, 3, 4}.
There are ordered pairs with the same first coordinate and different second coordinates. The relation is not a function.

Problem 2

$$f(x) = -5x + 1$$
$$f(2) = -5(2) + 1$$
$$f(2) = -10 + 1$$
$$f(2) = -9$$

The ordered pair (2, −9) is an element of the function.

Problem 3

$$f(x) = 4x - 3$$
$$f(-5) = 4(-5) - 3 = -20 - 3 = -23$$
$$f(-3) = 4(-3) - 3 = -12 - 3 = -15$$
$$f(-1) = 4(-1) - 3 = -4 - 3 = -7$$
$$f(1) = 4(1) - 3 = 4 - 3 = 1$$

The range is {−23, −15, −7, 1}.
The ordered pairs (−5, −23), (−3, −15), (−1, −7), and (1, 1) belong to the function.

Problem 4

$$f(x) = -\frac{1}{2}x - 3$$
$$y = -\frac{1}{2}x - 3$$

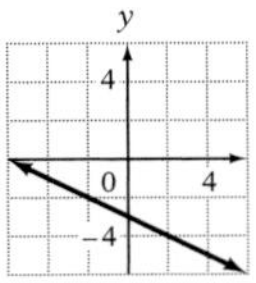

Problem 5

A. $d = 40t$
$f(t) = 40t$

B.

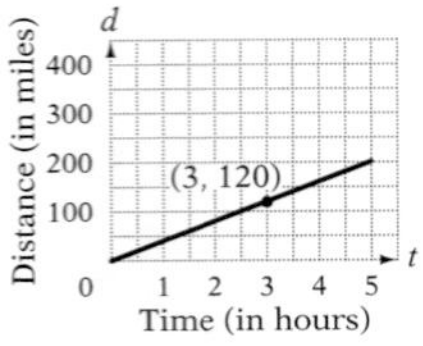

C. The ordered pair (3, 120) means that in 3 h, the car travels a distance of 120 mi.

SECTION 5.6

Problem 1

$$\begin{aligned} x - 3y &< 2 \\ x - x - 3y &< -x + 2 \\ -3y &< -x + 2 \\ \frac{-3y}{-3} &> \frac{-x + 2}{-3} \\ y &> \frac{1}{3}x - \frac{2}{3} \end{aligned}$$

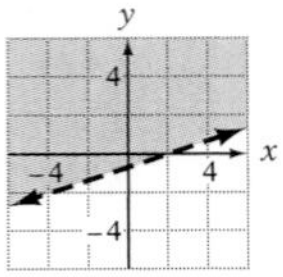

Problem 2

$x < 3$

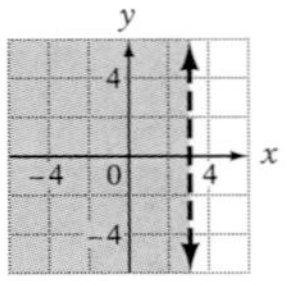

Solutions to Chapter 6 Problems

SECTION 6.1

Problem 1

$$\begin{array}{c|c} \multicolumn{2}{c}{2x - 5y = 8} \\ \hline 2(-1) - 5(-2) & 8 \\ -2 + 10 & 8 \\ 8 = 8 & \end{array} \qquad \begin{array}{c|c} \multicolumn{2}{c}{-x + 3y = -5} \\ \hline -(-1) + 3(-2) & -5 \\ 1 + (-6) & -5 \\ -5 = -5 & \end{array}$$

Yes, (−1, −2) is a solution of the system of equations.

Problem 2

A.

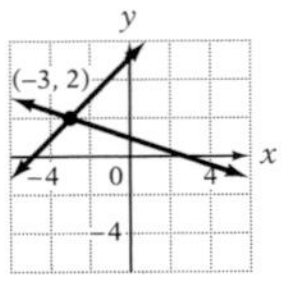

The solution is (−3, 2).

B.

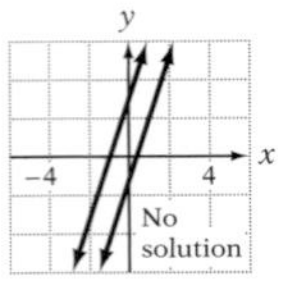

The lines are parallel and therefore do not intersect. The system of equations is inconsistent and has no solution.

SECTION 6.2

Problem 1

(1) $7x - y = 4$
(2) $3x + 2y = 9$

$$\begin{aligned} 7x - y &= 4 \\ -y &= -7x + 4 \\ y &= 7x - 4 \end{aligned}$$

• **Solve equation (1) for *y*.**

$$\begin{aligned} 3x + 2y &= 9 \\ 3x + 2(7x - 4) &= 9 \\ 3x + 14x - 8 &= 9 \\ 17x - 8 &= 9 \\ 17x &= 17 \\ x &= 1 \end{aligned}$$

• **Substitute $7x - 4$ for *y* in equation (2).**

$$\begin{aligned} 7x - y &= 4 \\ 7(1) - y &= 4 \\ 7 - y &= 4 \\ -y &= -3 \\ y &= 3 \end{aligned}$$

• **Substitute the value of *x* in equation (1).**

The solution is (1, 3).

Problem 2

$$\begin{aligned} 3x - y &= 4 \\ y &= 3x + 2 \end{aligned}$$

$$\begin{aligned} 3x - y &= 4 \\ 3x - (3x + 2) &= 4 \\ 3x - 3x - 2 &= 4 \\ -2 &= 4 \end{aligned}$$

The system of equations is inconsistent and has no solution.

Problem 3

$$\begin{aligned} y &= -2x + 1 \\ 6x + 3y &= 3 \end{aligned}$$

$$\begin{aligned} 6x + 3y &= 3 \\ 6x + 3(-2x + 1) &= 3 \\ 6x - 6x + 3 &= 3 \\ 3 &= 3 \end{aligned}$$

The system of equations is dependent. The solutions are the ordered pairs that satisfy the equation $y = -2x + 1$.

SECTION 6.3

Problem 1

(1) $x - 2y = 1$
(2) $2x + 4y = 0$

$$2(x - 2y) = 2 \cdot 1$$
$$2x + 4y = 0$$
• **Eliminate *y*.**

$$2x - 4y = 2$$
$$2x + 4y = 0$$
$$4x = 2$$
• **Add the equations.**

$$x = \frac{2}{4} = \frac{1}{2}$$

$$2x + 4y = 0$$
• **Replace *x* in equation (2).**

$$2\left(\frac{1}{2}\right) + 4y = 0$$
$$1 + 4y = 0$$
$$4y = -1$$
$$y = -\frac{1}{4}$$

The solution is $\left(\frac{1}{2}, -\frac{1}{4}\right)$.

Problem 2

(1) $2x - 3y = 4$
(2) $-4x + 6y = -8$

$$2(2x - 3y) = 2 \cdot 4$$
$$-4x + 6y = -8$$
• **Eliminate *y*.**

$$4x - 6y = 8$$
$$-4x + 6y = -8$$
$$0 + 0 = 0$$
• **Add the equations.**
$$0 = 0$$

The system of equations is dependent. The solutions are the ordered pairs that satisfy the equation $2x - 3y = 4$.

SECTION 6.4

Problem 1

Strategy ► Rate of the current: c
Rate of the canoeist in calm water: r

	Rate	Time	Distance
With current	$r + c$	3	$3(r + c)$
Against current	$r - c$	4	$4(r - c)$

► The distance traveled with the current is 24 mi.
The distance traveled against the current is 24 mi.

Solution

$$3(r + c) = 24 \longrightarrow \frac{3(r + c)}{3} = \frac{24}{3} \longrightarrow r + c = 8$$
$$4(r - c) = 24 \longrightarrow \frac{4(r - c)}{4} = \frac{24}{4} \longrightarrow r - c = 6$$
$$2r = 14$$
$$r = 7$$

$$r + c = 8$$
$$7 + c = 8$$
$$c = 1$$

The rate of the current is 1 mph.
The rate of the canoeist in calm water is 7 mph.

Problem 2

Strategy ► The number of dimes in the first bank: d
The number of quarters in the first bank: q

First bank

	Number	Value	Total value
Dimes	d	10	$10d$
Quarters	q	25	$25q$

Second bank

	Number	Value	Total value
Dimes	$2d$	10	$20d$
Quarters	$\frac{1}{2}q$	25	$\frac{25}{2}q$

► The total value of the coins in the first bank is \$3.90.
The total value of the coins in the second bank is \$3.30.

Solution

$$10d + 25q = 390 \qquad\qquad 10d + 25q = 390$$
$$20d + \frac{25}{2}q = 330 \qquad -2\left(20d + \frac{25}{2}q\right) = -2(330)$$

$$10d + 25q = 390$$
$$-40d - 25q = -660$$

$$-30d = -270$$
$$d = 9$$

$$10d + 25q = 390$$
$$10(9) + 25q = 390$$
$$90 + 25q = 390$$
$$25q = 300$$
$$q = 12$$

There are 9 dimes and 12 quarters in the first bank.

Solutions to Chapter 7 Problems

SECTION 7.1

Problem 1

$$\begin{array}{l} 2x^2 + 4x - 3 \\ \underline{5x^2 - 6x \phantom{{}-3}} \\ 7x^2 - 2x - 3 \end{array}$$

Problem 2

$(-4x^2 - 3xy + 2y^2) + (3x^2 - 4y^2)$
$= (-4x^2 + 3x^2) - 3xy + (2y^2 - 4y^2)$
$= -x^2 - 3xy - 2y^2$

Problem 3

The opposite of $2y^2 - xy + 5x^2$ is $-2y^2 + xy - 5x^2$.

$$\begin{array}{rrr} 8y^2 & - 4xy & + x^2 \\ -2y^2 & + xy & - 5x^2 \\ \hline 6y^2 & - 3xy & - 4x^2 \end{array}$$

Problem 4

$(-3a^2 - 4a + 2) - (5a^3 + 2a - 6)$
$= (-3a^2 - 4a + 2) + (-5a^3 - 2a + 6)$
$= -5a^3 - 3a^2 + (-4a - 2a) + (2 + 6)$
$= -5a^3 - 3a^2 - 6a + 8$

SECTION 7.2

Problem 1

$(3x^2)(6x^3) = (3 \cdot 6)(x^2 \cdot x^3) = 18x^5$

Problem 2

$(-3xy^2)(-4x^2y^3)$
$= [(-3)(-4)](x \cdot x^2)(y^2 \cdot y^3)$
$= 12x^3y^5$

Problem 3

$(3x)(2x^2y)^3 = (3x)(2^3x^6y^3) = (3x)(8x^6y^3)$
$= (3 \cdot 8)(x \cdot x^6)y^3 = 24x^7y^3$

SECTION 7.3

Problem 1

A. $(-2y + 3)(-4y) = 8y^2 - 12y$

B. $-a^2(3a^2 + 2a - 7) = -3a^4 - 2a^3 + 7a^2$

Problem 2

$$\begin{array}{rrrrr} & 2y^3 & + 2y^2 & & - 3 \\ & & & 3y & - 1 \\ \hline & -2y^3 & - 2y^2 & & + 3 \\ 6y^4 & + 6y^3 & & - 9y & \\ \hline 6y^4 & + 4y^3 & - 2y^2 & - 9y & + 3 \end{array}$$

Problem 3

$$\begin{array}{rrrrr} & 3x^3 & - 2x^2 & + x & - 3 \\ & & & 2x & + 5 \\ \hline & 15x^3 & - 10x^2 & + 5x & - 15 \\ 6x^4 & - 4x^3 & + 2x^2 & - 6x & \\ \hline 6x^4 & + 11x^3 & - 8x^2 & - x & - 15 \end{array}$$

Problem 4

$(4y - 5)(3y - 3)$
$= 12y^2 - 12y - 15y + 15$
$= 12y^2 - 27y + 15$

Problem 5

$(3a + 2b)(3a - 5b)$
$= 9a^2 - 15ab + 6ab - 10b^2$
$= 9a^2 - 9ab - 10b^2$

Problem 6

$(2a + 5c)(2a - 5c) = (2a)^2 - (5c)^2$
$= 4a^2 - 25c^2$

Problem 7

$(3x + 2y)^2 = (3x)^2 + 2(3x)(2y) + (2y)^2$
$= 9x^2 + 12xy + 4y^2$

Problem 8

$(6x - y)^2 = (6x)^2 + 2(6x)(-y) + (-y)^2$
$= 36x^2 - 12xy + y^2$

Problem 9

Strategy To find the area in terms of x, replace the variables L and W in the equation $A = LW$ with the given values, and solve for A.

Solution $A = LW$
$A = (x + 7)(x - 4)$
$A = x^2 - 4x + 7x - 28$
$A = x^2 + 3x - 28$

The area is $(x^2 + 3x - 28)$ m^2.

Problem 10

Strategy To find the area of the triangle in terms of x, replace the variables b and h in the equation $A = \frac{1}{2}bh$ with the given values, and solve for A.

Solution $A = \dfrac{1}{2}bh$

$A = \dfrac{1}{2}(x + 3)(4x - 6)$

$A = \dfrac{1}{2}(4x^2 + 6x - 18)$

$A = 2x^2 + 3x - 9$

The area is $(2x^2 + 3x - 9)$ cm^2.

SECTION 7.4

Problem 1

$\dfrac{2^{-2}}{2^3} = 2^{-2-3} = 2^{-5} = \dfrac{1}{2^5} = \dfrac{1}{32}$

Problem 2

$\dfrac{b^8}{a^{-5}b^6} = a^5b^{8-6} = a^5b^2$

Problem 3

A. $\dfrac{12x^{-8}y^4}{-16xy^{-3}} = -\dfrac{3x^{-9}y^7}{4} = -\dfrac{3y^7}{4x^9}$

B. $(-3ab)(2a^3b^{-2})^{-3} = (-3ab)(2^{-3}a^{-9}b^6)$

$= -\dfrac{3a^{-8}b^7}{2^3} = -\dfrac{3b^7}{8a^8}$

Problem 4

A. $57{,}000{,}000{,}000 = 5.7 \times 10^{10}$

B. $0.000000017 = 1.7 \times 10^{-8}$

Problem 5

A. $5 \times 10^{12} = 5{,}000{,}000{,}000{,}000$

B. $4.0162 \times 10^{-9} = 0.0000000040162$

Problem 6

A. $(2.4 \times 10^{-9})(1.6 \times 10^3) = 3.84 \times 10^{-6}$

B. $\dfrac{5.4 \times 10^{-2}}{1.8 \times 10^{-4}} = 3 \times 10^2$

SECTION 7.5

Problem 1

$$\frac{4x^3y + 8x^2y^2 - 4xy^3}{2xy} = \frac{4x^3y}{2xy} + \frac{8x^2y^2}{2xy} - \frac{4xy^3}{2xy}$$
$$= 2x^2 + 4xy - 2y^2$$

Problem 2

$$\frac{24x^2y^2 - 18xy + 6y}{6xy} = \frac{24x^2y^2}{6xy} - \frac{18xy}{6xy} + \frac{6y}{6xy}$$
$$= 4xy - 3 + \frac{1}{x}$$

Problem 3

$$\begin{array}{r}
x^2 + 2x + 2 \\
x - 2\overline{)x^3 + 0x^2 - 2x - 4} \\
\underline{x^3 - 2x^2} \\
2x^2 - 2x \\
\underline{2x^2 - 4x} \\
2x - 4 \\
\underline{2x - 4} \\
0
\end{array}$$

$(x^3 - 2x - 4) \div (x - 2) = x^2 + 2x + 2$

Solutions to Chapter 8 Problems

SECTION 8.1

Problem 1

$4x^6y = 2 \cdot 2 \cdot x^6 \cdot y$
$18x^2y^6 = 2 \cdot 3 \cdot 3 \cdot x^2 \cdot y^6$
$\text{GCF} = 2 \cdot x^2 \cdot y = 2x^2y$

Problem 2

A. $14a^2 = 2 \cdot 7 \cdot a^2$
$21a^4b = 3 \cdot 7 \cdot a^4 \cdot b$
The GCF is $7a^2$.

$14a^2 - 21a^4b = 7a^2(2) + 7a^2(-3a^2b)$
$= 7a^2(2 - 3a^2b)$

B. $6x^4y^2 = 2 \cdot 3 \cdot x^4 \cdot y^2$
$9x^3y^2 = 3 \cdot 3 \cdot x^3 \cdot y^2$
$12x^2y^4 = 2 \cdot 2 \cdot 3 \cdot x^2 \cdot y^4$
The GCF is $3x^2y^2$.

$6x^4y^2 - 9x^3y^2 + 12x^2y^4$
$= 3x^2y^2(2x^2) + 3x^2y^2(-3x) + 3x^2y^2(4y^2)$
$= 3x^2y^2(2x^2 - 3x + 4y^2)$

Problem 3

$a(b - 7) + b(b - 7) = (b - 7)(a + b)$

Problem 4

$3y(5x - 2) - 4(2 - 5x)$
$= 3y(5x - 2) + 4(5x - 2)$
$= (5x - 2)(3y + 4)$

Problem 5

$y^5 - 5y^3 + 4y^2 - 20$
$= (y^5 - 5y^3) + (4y^2 - 20)$
$= y^3(y^2 - 5) + 4(y^2 - 5)$
$= (y^2 - 5)(y^3 + 4)$

SECTION 8.2

Problem 1

Factors of 15	Sum
−1, −15	−16
−3, −5	−8

$x^2 - 8x + 15 = (x - 3)(x - 5)$

Problem 2

Factors of −18	Sum
1, −18	−17
−1, 18	17
2, −9	−7
−2, 9	7
3, −6	−3
−3, 6	3

$x^2 + 3x - 18 = (x + 6)(x - 3)$

Problem 3

The GCF is $3b$.

$3a^2b - 18ab - 81b = 3b(a^2 - 6a - 27)$

Factors of −27	Sum
1, −27	−26
−1, 27	26
3, −9	−6
−3, 9	6

$3a^2b - 18ab - 81b = 3b(a + 3)(a - 9)$

Problem 4

The GCF is 4.

$4x^2 - 40xy + 84y^2$
$= 4(x^2 - 10xy + 21y^2)$

Factors of 21	Sum
−1, −21	−22
−3, −7	−10

$4x^2 - 40xy + 84y^2 = 4(x - 3y)(x - 7y)$

SECTION 8.3

Problem 1

Factors of 6	Factors of 5
1, 6	−1, −5
2, 3	

Trial Factors	Middle Term
$(x - 1)(6x - 5)$	$-5x - 6x = -11x$

$6x^2 - 11x + 5 = (x - 1)(6x - 5)$

Problem 2

Factors of 8	Factors of −15
1, 8	1, −15
2, 4	−1, 15
	3, −5
	−3, 5

Trial Factors	Middle Term
$(x + 1)(8x - 15)$	$-15x + 8x = -7x$
$(x - 1)(8x + 15)$	$15x - 8x = 7x$
$(x + 3)(8x - 5)$	$-5x + 24x = 19x$
$(x - 3)(8x + 5)$	$5x - 24x = -19x$
$(2x + 1)(4x - 15)$	$-30x + 4x = -26x$
$(2x - 1)(4x + 15)$	$30x - 4x = 26x$
$(2x + 3)(4x - 5)$	$-10x + 12x = 2x$
$(2x - 3)(4x + 5)$	$10x - 12x = -2x$
$(8x + 1)(x - 15)$	$-120x + x = -119x$
$(8x - 1)(x + 15)$	$120x - x = 119x$
$(8x + 3)(x - 5)$	$-40x + 3x = -37x$
$(8x - 3)(x + 5)$	$40x - 3x = 37x$
$(4x + 1)(2x - 15)$	$-60x + 2x = -58x$
$(4x - 1)(2x + 15)$	$60x - 2x = 58x$
$(4x + 3)(2x - 5)$	$-20x + 6x = -14x$
$(4x - 3)(2x + 5)$	$20x - 6x = 14x$

$8x^2 + 14x - 15 = (4x - 3)(2x + 5)$

Problem 3

Factors of 24	Factors of −1
1, 24	1, −1
2, 12	
3, 8	
4, 6	

Trial Factors	Middle Term
$(1 - y)(24 + y)$	$y - 24y = -23y$
$(2 - y)(12 + y)$	$2y - 12y = -10y$
$(3 - y)(8 + y)$	$3y - 8y = -5y$
$(4 - y)(6 + y)$	$4y - 6y = -2y$

$24 - 2y - y^2 = (4 - y)(6 + y)$

Problem 4

The GCF is $2a^2$.

$4a^2b^2 - 30a^2b + 14a^2$
$= 2a^2(2b^2 - 15b + 7)$

Factors of 2	Factors of 7
1, 2	−1, −7

Trial Factors	Middle Term
$(b - 1)(2b - 7)$	$-7b - 2b = -9b$
$(b - 7)(2b - 1)$	$-b - 14b = -15b$

$4a^2b^2 - 30a^2b + 14a^2$
$= 2a^2(b - 7)(2b - 1)$

Problem 5

$a \cdot c = -14$
$-1(14) = -14, -1 + 14 = 13$

$2a^2 + 13a - 7$
$= 2a^2 - a + 14a - 7$
$= (2a^2 - a) + (14a - 7)$
$= a(2a - 1) + 7(2a - 1)$
$= (2a - 1)(a + 7)$

Problem 6

$a \cdot c = -12$
$1(-12) = -12, 1 - 12 = -11$

$4a^2 - 11a - 3$
$= 4a^2 + a - 12a - 3$
$= (4a^2 + a) - (12a + 3)$
$= a(4a + 1) - 3(4a + 1)$
$= (4a + 1)(a - 3)$

Problem 7

The GCF is $5x$.

$15x^3 + 40x^2 - 80x = 5x(3x^2 + 8x - 16)$
$3(-16) = -48$
$-4(12) = -48, -4 + 12 = 8$

$$\begin{aligned} &3x^2 + 8x - 16 \\ &= 3x^2 - 4x + 12x - 16 \\ &= (3x^2 - 4x) + (12x - 16) \\ &= x(3x - 4) + 4(3x - 4) \\ &= (3x - 4)(x + 4) \end{aligned}$$

$$\begin{aligned} 15x^3 + 40x^2 - 80x &= 5x(3x^2 + 8x - 16) \\ &= 5x(3x - 4)(x + 4) \end{aligned}$$

SECTION 8.4

Problem 1

A. $$\begin{aligned} 25a^2 - b^2 &= (5a)^2 - b^2 \\ &= (5a + b)(5a - b) \end{aligned}$$

B. $6x^2 - 1$ is nonfactorable over the integers.

C. $$\begin{aligned} n^8 - 36 &= (n^4)^2 - 6^2 \\ &= (n^4 + 6)(n^4 - 6) \end{aligned}$$

Problem 2

$$\begin{aligned} n^4 - 81 &= (n^2 + 9)(n^2 - 9) \\ &= (n^2 + 9)(n + 3)(n - 3) \end{aligned}$$

Problem 3

A. $16y^2 = (4y)^2, 1 = 1^2$

$$\begin{aligned} (4y + 1)^2 &= (4y)^2 + 2(4y)(1) + (1)^2 \\ &= 16y^2 + 8y + 1 \end{aligned}$$

$16y^2 + 8y + 1 = (4y + 1)^2$

B. $x^2 = (x)^2, 36 = 6^2$

$$\begin{aligned} (x + 6)^2 &= x^2 + 2(x)(6) + 6^2 \\ &= x^2 + 12x + 36 \end{aligned}$$

The polynomial is not a perfect square.

$x^2 + 14x + 36$ is nonfactorable over the integers.

Problem 4

A. $$\begin{aligned} 12x^3 - 75x &= 3x(4x^2 - 25) \\ &= 3x(2x + 5)(2x - 5) \end{aligned}$$

B. $$\begin{aligned} &a^2b - 7a^2 - b + 7 \\ &= (a^2b - 7a^2) - (b - 7) \\ &= a^2(b - 7) - (b - 7) \\ &= (b - 7)(a^2 - 1) \\ &= (b - 7)(a + 1)(a - 1) \end{aligned}$$

C. $$\begin{aligned} 4x^3 + 28x^2 - 120x &= 4x(x^2 + 7x - 30) \\ &= 4x(x + 10)(x - 3) \end{aligned}$$

SECTION 8.5

Problem 1

$$\begin{aligned} 2x^2 - 50 &= 0 \\ 2(x^2 - 25) &= 0 \\ x^2 - 25 &= 0 \quad \text{• Divide each side by 2.} \\ (x + 5)(x - 5) &= 0 \end{aligned}$$

$x + 5 = 0 \qquad x - 5 = 0$
$x = -5 \qquad x = 5$

The solutions are -5 and 5.

Problem 2

$$\begin{aligned} (x + 2)(x - 7) &= 52 \\ x^2 - 5x - 14 &= 52 \\ x^2 - 5x - 66 &= 0 \\ (x - 11)(x + 6) &= 0 \end{aligned}$$

$x - 11 = 0 \qquad x + 6 = 0$
$x = 11 \qquad x = -6$

The solutions are -6 and 11.

Problem 3

Strategy First positive integer: n
Second positive integer: $n + 1$
Square of the first positive integer: n^2
Square of the second positive integer: $(n + 1)^2$

The sum of the squares of the two integers is 85.

Solution

$$\begin{aligned} n^2 + (n + 1)^2 &= 85 \\ n^2 + n^2 + 2n + 1 &= 85 \\ 2n^2 + 2n - 84 &= 0 \\ 2(n^2 + n - 42) &= 0 \\ n^2 + n - 42 &= 0 \\ (n + 7)(n - 6) &= 0 \end{aligned}$$

$n + 7 = 0 \qquad n - 6 = 0$
$n = -7 \qquad n = 6$

-7 is not a positive integer.

$n + 1 = 6 + 1 = 7$

The two integers are 6 and 7.

Problem 4

Strategy Width $= W$
Length $= 2W + 3$

The area of the rectangle is 90 m^2.
Use the equation $A = LW$.

Solution

$$\begin{aligned} A &= LW \\ 90 &= (2W + 3)W \\ 90 &= 2W^2 + 3W \\ 0 &= 2W^2 + 3W - 90 \\ 0 &= (2W + 15)(W - 6) \end{aligned}$$

$2W + 15 = 0$ $\qquad$ $W - 6 = 0$

$2W = -15$ $\qquad$ $W = 6$

$W = -\frac{15}{2}$

The width cannot be a negative number.

$2W + 3 = 2(6) + 3 = 12 + 3 = 15$

The width is 6 m. The length is 15 m.

Solutions to Chapter 9 Problems

SECTION 9.1

Problem 1

A. $$\frac{6x^5y}{12x^2y^3} = \frac{\overset{1}{\cancel{2}} \cdot \overset{1}{\cancel{3}} \cdot x^5y}{\underset{1}{\cancel{2}} \cdot 2 \cdot \underset{1}{\cancel{3}} \cdot x^2y^3} = \frac{x^3}{2y^2}$$

B. $$\frac{x^2 + 2x - 24}{16 - x^2} = \frac{\overset{-1}{\cancel{(x - 4)}}(x + 6)}{\underset{1}{\cancel{(4 - x)}}(4 + x)} = -\frac{x + 6}{x + 4}$$

Problem 2

A. $$\frac{12x^2 + 3x}{10x - 15} \cdot \frac{8x - 12}{9x + 18}$$
$$= \frac{3x(4x + 1)}{5(2x - 3)} \cdot \frac{4(2x - 3)}{9(x + 2)}$$
$$= \frac{\overset{1}{\cancel{3}}x(4x + 1) \cdot 2 \cdot 2\overset{1}{\cancel{(2x - 3)}}}{5\underset{1}{\cancel{(2x - 3)}} \cdot \underset{1}{\cancel{3}} \cdot 3(x + 2)}$$
$$= \frac{4x(4x + 1)}{15(x + 2)}$$

B. $$\frac{x^2 + 2x - 15}{9 - x^2} \cdot \frac{x^2 - 3x - 18}{x^2 - 7x + 6}$$
$$= \frac{(x - 3)(x + 5)}{(3 - x)(3 + x)} \cdot \frac{(x + 3)(x - 6)}{(x - 1)(x - 6)}$$
$$= \frac{\overset{-1}{\cancel{(x - 3)}}(x + 5) \cdot \overset{1}{\cancel{(x + 3)}}\overset{1}{\cancel{(x - 6)}}}{\underset{1}{\cancel{(3 - x)}}\underset{1}{\cancel{(3 + x)}} \cdot (x - 1)\underset{1}{\cancel{(x - 6)}}}$$
$$= -\frac{x + 5}{x - 1}$$

Problem 3

A. $$\frac{a^2}{4bc^2 - 2b^2c} \div \frac{a}{6bc - 3b^2}$$
$$= \frac{a^2}{4bc^2 - 2b^2c} \cdot \frac{6bc - 3b^2}{a}$$
$$= \frac{a^2 \cdot 3b\overset{1}{\cancel{(2c - b)}}}{2bc\underset{1}{\cancel{(2c - b)}} \cdot a} = \frac{3a}{2c}$$

B. $$\frac{3x^2 + 26x + 16}{3x^2 - 7x - 6} \div \frac{2x^2 + 9x - 5}{x^2 + 2x - 15}$$
$$= \frac{3x^2 + 26x + 16}{3x^2 - 7x - 6} \cdot \frac{x^2 + 2x - 15}{2x^2 + 9x - 5}$$
$$= \frac{\overset{1}{\cancel{(3x + 2)}}(x + 8)}{\underset{1}{\cancel{(3x + 2)}}\underset{1}{\cancel{(x - 3)}}} \cdot \frac{\overset{1}{\cancel{(x + 5)}}\overset{1}{\cancel{(x - 3)}}}{(2x - 1)\underset{1}{\cancel{(x + 5)}}}$$
$$= \frac{x + 8}{2x - 1}$$

SECTION 9.2

Problem 1

$8uv^2 = 2 \cdot 2 \cdot 2 \cdot u \cdot v \cdot v$

$12uw = 2 \cdot 2 \cdot 3 \cdot u \cdot w$

$\text{LCM} = 2 \cdot 2 \cdot 2 \cdot 3 \cdot u \cdot v \cdot v \cdot w$

$= 24uv^2w$

Problem 2

$m^2 - 6m + 9 = (m - 3)(m - 3)$

$m^2 - 2m - 3 = (m + 1)(m - 3)$

$\text{LCM} = (m - 3)(m - 3)(m + 1)$

Problem 3

The LCM is $36xy^2z$.

$$\frac{x - 3}{4xy^2} = \frac{x - 3}{4xy^2} \cdot \frac{9z}{9z} = \frac{9xz - 27z}{36xy^2z}$$

$$\frac{2x + 1}{9y^2z} = \frac{2x + 1}{9y^2z} \cdot \frac{4x}{4x} = \frac{8x^2 + 4x}{36xy^2z}$$

Problem 4

$$\frac{2x}{25 - x^2} = \frac{2x}{-(x^2 - 25)} = -\frac{2x}{x^2 - 25}$$

The LCM is $(x + 2)(x - 5)(x + 5)$.

$$\frac{x + 4}{x^2 - 3x - 10} = \frac{x + 4}{(x + 2)(x - 5)} \cdot \frac{x + 5}{x + 5}$$
$$= \frac{x^2 + 9x + 20}{(x + 2)(x - 5)(x + 5)}$$

$$\frac{2x}{25 - x^2} = -\frac{2x}{(x - 5)(x + 5)} \cdot \frac{x + 2}{x + 2}$$
$$= -\frac{2x^2 + 4x}{(x + 2)(x - 5)(x + 5)}$$

SECTION 9.3

Problem 1

A. $$\frac{3}{xy} + \frac{12}{xy} = \frac{3 + 12}{xy} = \frac{15}{xy}$$

B. $\dfrac{2x^2}{x^2-x-12} - \dfrac{7x+4}{x^2-x-12} = \dfrac{2x^2-(7x+4)}{x^2-x-12}$

$= \dfrac{2x^2-7x-4}{x^2-x-12} = \dfrac{(2x+1)\overset{1}{\cancel{(x-4)}}}{(x+3)\underset{1}{\cancel{(x-4)}}} = \dfrac{2x+1}{x+3}$

Problem 2

A. The LCM of the denominators is $24y$.

$\dfrac{z}{8y} - \dfrac{4z}{3y} + \dfrac{5z}{4y} = \dfrac{z}{8y}\cdot\dfrac{3}{3} - \dfrac{4z}{3y}\cdot\dfrac{8}{8} + \dfrac{5z}{4y}\cdot\dfrac{6}{6}$

$= \dfrac{3z}{24y} - \dfrac{32z}{24y} + \dfrac{30z}{24y} = \dfrac{3z-32z+30z}{24y} = \dfrac{z}{24y}$

B. The LCM is $x-2$.

$\dfrac{5x}{x-2} - \dfrac{3}{2-x} = \dfrac{5x}{x-2} - \dfrac{3}{-(x-2)}\cdot\dfrac{-1}{-1}$

$= \dfrac{5x}{x-2} - \dfrac{-3}{x-2} = \dfrac{5x-(-3)}{x-2} = \dfrac{5x+3}{x-2}$

C. The LCM is $y-7$.

$y + \dfrac{5}{y-7} = \dfrac{y}{1} + \dfrac{5}{y-7} = \dfrac{y}{1}\cdot\dfrac{y-7}{y-7} + \dfrac{5}{y-7}$

$= \dfrac{y^2-7y}{y-7} + \dfrac{5}{y-7} = \dfrac{y^2-7y+5}{y-7}$

Problem 3

A. The LCM is $(3x-1)(x+4)$.

$\dfrac{4x}{3x-1} - \dfrac{9}{x+4}$

$= \dfrac{4x}{3x-1}\cdot\dfrac{x+4}{x+4} - \dfrac{9}{x+4}\cdot\dfrac{3x-1}{3x-1}$

$= \dfrac{4x^2+16x}{(3x-1)(x+4)} - \dfrac{27x-9}{(3x-1)(x+4)}$

$= \dfrac{(4x^2+16x)-(27x-9)}{(3x-1)(x+4)}$

$= \dfrac{4x^2+16x-27x+9}{(3x-1)(x+4)} = \dfrac{4x^2-11x+9}{(3x-1)(x+4)}$

B. The LCM is $(x+5)(x-5)$.

$\dfrac{2x-1}{x^2-25} + \dfrac{2}{5-x}$

$= \dfrac{2x-1}{(x+5)(x-5)} + \dfrac{2}{-(x-5)}\cdot\dfrac{-1(x+5)}{-1(x+5)}$

$= \dfrac{2x-1}{(x+5)(x-5)} + \dfrac{-2(x+5)}{(x+5)(x-5)}$

$= \dfrac{(2x-1)+(-2)(x+5)}{(x+5)(x-5)}$

$= \dfrac{2x-1-2x-10}{(x+5)(x-5)}$

$= \dfrac{-11}{(x+5)(x-5)} = -\dfrac{11}{(x+5)(x-5)}$

SECTION 9.4

Problem 1

A. The LCM of 3, x, 9, and x^2 is $9x^2$.

$\dfrac{\frac{1}{3}-\frac{1}{x}}{\frac{1}{9}-\frac{1}{x^2}} = \dfrac{\frac{1}{3}-\frac{1}{x}}{\frac{1}{9}-\frac{1}{x^2}}\cdot\dfrac{9x^2}{9x^2} = \dfrac{\frac{1}{3}\cdot 9x^2 - \frac{1}{x}\cdot 9x^2}{\frac{1}{9}\cdot 9x^2 - \frac{1}{x^2}\cdot 9x^2}$

$= \dfrac{3x^2-9x}{x^2-9} = \dfrac{3x\overset{1}{\cancel{(x-3)}}}{\underset{1}{\cancel{(x-3)}}(x+3)} = \dfrac{3x}{x+3}$

B. The LCM of x and x^2 is x^2.

$\dfrac{1+\frac{4}{x}+\frac{3}{x^2}}{1+\frac{10}{x}+\frac{21}{x^2}} = \dfrac{1+\frac{4}{x}+\frac{3}{x^2}}{1+\frac{10}{x}+\frac{21}{x^2}}\cdot\dfrac{x^2}{x^2}$

$= \dfrac{1\cdot x^2+\frac{4}{x}\cdot x^2+\frac{3}{x^2}\cdot x^2}{1\cdot x^2+\frac{10}{x}\cdot x^2+\frac{21}{x^2}\cdot x^2}$

$= \dfrac{x^2+4x+3}{x^2+10x+21}$

$= \dfrac{(x+1)\overset{1}{\cancel{(x+3)}}}{\underset{1}{\cancel{(x+3)}}(x+7)} = \dfrac{x+1}{x+7}$

SECTION 9.5

Problem 1

The LCM of 3 and $3x$ is $3x$.

$x + \dfrac{1}{3} = \dfrac{4}{3x}$

$3x\left(x+\dfrac{1}{3}\right) = 3x\left(\dfrac{4}{3x}\right)$

$3x\cdot x + \dfrac{3x}{1}\cdot\dfrac{1}{3} = \dfrac{3x}{1}\cdot\dfrac{4}{3x}$

$3x^2 + x = 4$

$3x^2 + x - 4 = 0$

$(3x+4)(x-1) = 0$

$3x+4=0 \qquad x-1=0$

$3x=-4 \qquad x=1$

$x=-\dfrac{4}{3}$

Both $-\dfrac{4}{3}$ and 1 check as solutions. The solutions are $-\dfrac{4}{3}$ and 1.

Problem 2

The LCM is $x + 2$.

$$\frac{5x}{x+2} = 3 - \frac{10}{x+2}$$
$$\frac{(x+2)}{1} \cdot \frac{5x}{x+2} = \frac{(x+2)}{1}\left(3 - \frac{10}{x+2}\right)$$
$$5x = (x+2)3 - 10$$
$$5x = 3x + 6 - 10$$
$$5x = 3x - 4$$
$$2x = -4$$
$$x = -2$$

-2 does not check as a solution. The equation has no solution.

Problem 3

A.
$$\frac{2}{x+3} = \frac{6}{5x+5}$$
$$(x+3)(5x+5)\frac{2}{x+3} = (x+3)(5x+5)\frac{6}{5x+5}$$
$$(5x+5)2 = (x+3)6$$
$$10x + 10 = 6x + 18$$
$$4x + 10 = 18$$
$$4x = 8$$
$$x = 2$$

The solution is 2.

B.
$$\frac{5}{2x-3} = \frac{10}{x+3}$$
$$(x+3)(2x-3)\frac{5}{2x-3} = (x+3)(2x-3)\frac{10}{x+3}$$
$$(x+3)5 = (2x-3)10$$
$$5x + 15 = 20x - 30$$
$$-15x + 15 = -30$$
$$-15x = -45$$
$$x = 3$$

The solution is 3.

Problem 4

Strategy To find the total area that 270 ceramic tiles will cover, write and solve a proportion using x to represent the number of square feet that 270 tiles will cover.

Solution
$$\frac{4}{9} = \frac{x}{270}$$
$$270\left(\frac{4}{9}\right) = 270\left(\frac{x}{270}\right)$$
$$120 = x$$

A 120-square-foot area can be tiled using 270 ceramic tiles.

Problem 5

Strategy To find the additional amount of medication required for a 180-pound adult, write and solve a proportion using x to represent the additional medication. Then $3 + x$ is the total amount required for a 180-pound adult.

Solution
$$\frac{120}{3} = \frac{180}{3+x}$$
$$\frac{40}{1} = \frac{180}{3+x}$$
$$(3+x)40 = (3+x)\frac{180}{3+x}$$
$$120 + 40x = 180$$
$$40x = 60$$
$$x = 1.5$$

1.5 additional ounces are required for a 180-pound adult.

Problem 6

Strategy Triangle AOB is similar to triangle DOC. Solve a proportion to find the length of AO. Then use the formula for the area of a triangle to find the area of triangle AOB.

Solution
$$\frac{CD}{AB} = \frac{DO}{AO}$$
$$\frac{4}{10} = \frac{3}{x}$$

• **Let x represent the length of AO.**

$$10x\left(\frac{4}{10}\right) = 10x\left(\frac{3}{x}\right)$$
$$4x = 30$$
$$x = 7.5$$

$$A = \frac{1}{2}bh$$
$$A = \frac{1}{2}(10)(7.5)$$
$$A = 37.5$$

The area of triangle AOB is 37.5 cm^2.

SECTION 9.6

Problem 1

A.
$$s = \frac{A+L}{2}$$
$$2 \cdot s = 2\left(\frac{A+L}{2}\right)$$
$$2s = A + L$$
$$2s - A = A - A + L$$
$$2s - A = L$$

B.
$$S = a + (n-1)d$$
$$S = a + nd - d$$
$$S - a = a - a + nd - d$$
$$S - a = nd - d$$
$$S - a + d = nd - d + d$$
$$S - a + d = nd$$

$$\frac{S - a + d}{d} = \frac{nd}{d}$$
$$\frac{S - a + d}{d} = n$$

Problem 2

$$S = rS + C$$
$$S - rS = C$$
$$S(1 - r) = C$$
$$S = \frac{C}{1 - r}$$

SECTION 9.7

Problem 1

Strategy ► Time for one printer to complete the job: t

	Rate	Time	Part
1st printer	$\frac{1}{t}$	3	$\frac{3}{t}$
2nd printer	$\frac{1}{t}$	5	$\frac{5}{t}$

► The sum of the parts of the task completed must equal 1.

Solution

$$\frac{3}{t} + \frac{5}{t} = 1$$
$$t\left(\frac{3}{t} + \frac{5}{t}\right) = t \cdot 1$$
$$3 + 5 = t$$
$$8 = t$$

Working alone, one printer takes 8 h to print the payroll.

Problem 2

Strategy ► Rate sailing across the lake: r
Rate sailing back: $2r$

	Distance	Rate	Time
Across	6	r	$\frac{6}{r}$
Back	6	$2r$	$\frac{6}{2r}$

► The total time for the trip was 3 h.

Solution

$$\frac{6}{r} + \frac{6}{2r} = 3$$
$$2r\left(\frac{6}{r} + \frac{6}{2r}\right) = 2r(3)$$
$$2r \cdot \frac{6}{r} + 2r \cdot \frac{6}{2r} = 6r$$
$$12 + 6 = 6r$$
$$18 = 6r$$
$$3 = r$$

The rate across the lake was 3 km/h.

Solutions to Chapter 10 Problems

SECTION 10.1

Problem 1

$$-5\sqrt{32} = -5\sqrt{16 \cdot 2}$$
$$= -5\sqrt{16}\sqrt{2}$$
$$= -5 \cdot 4\sqrt{2}$$
$$= -20\sqrt{2}$$

Problem 2

$$\sqrt{216} = \sqrt{36 \cdot 6}$$
$$= \sqrt{36}\sqrt{6}$$
$$= 6\sqrt{6}$$

Problem 3

$$\sqrt{y^{19}} = \sqrt{y^{18} \cdot y} = \sqrt{y^{18}}\sqrt{y} = y^9\sqrt{y}$$

Problem 4

A. $\sqrt{45b^7} = \sqrt{9b^6 \cdot 5b} = \sqrt{9b^6}\sqrt{5b} = 3b^3\sqrt{5b}$

B. $3a\sqrt{28a^9b^{18}} = 3a\sqrt{4a^8b^{18} \cdot 7a}$
$= 3a\sqrt{4a^8b^{18}}\sqrt{7a}$
$= 3a \cdot 2a^4b^9\sqrt{7a}$
$= 6a^5b^9\sqrt{7a}$

Problem 5

$$\sqrt{25(a + 3)^2} = 5(a + 3) = 5a + 15$$

SECTION 10.2

Problem 1

A. $9\sqrt{3} + 3\sqrt{3} - 18\sqrt{3}$
$= (9 + 3 - 18)\sqrt{3} = -6\sqrt{3}$

B. $2\sqrt{50} - 5\sqrt{32} = 2\sqrt{25 \cdot 2} - 5\sqrt{16 \cdot 2}$
$= 2\sqrt{25}\sqrt{2} - 5\sqrt{16}\sqrt{2}$
$= 2 \cdot 5\sqrt{2} - 5 \cdot 4\sqrt{2}$
$= 10\sqrt{2} - 20\sqrt{2} = -10\sqrt{2}$

Problem 2

A. $y\sqrt{28y} + 7\sqrt{63y^3}$
$= y\sqrt{4}\sqrt{7y} + 7\sqrt{9y^2}\sqrt{7y}$
$= y \cdot 2\sqrt{7y} + 7 \cdot 3y\sqrt{7y}$
$= 2y\sqrt{7y} + 21y\sqrt{7y} = 23y\sqrt{7y}$

B. $2\sqrt{27a^5} - 4a\sqrt{12a^3} + a^2\sqrt{75a}$
$= 2\sqrt{9a^4}\sqrt{3a} - 4a\sqrt{4a^2}\sqrt{3a} + a^2\sqrt{25}\sqrt{3a}$
$= 2 \cdot 3a^2\sqrt{3a} - 4a \cdot 2a\sqrt{3a} + a^2 \cdot 5\sqrt{3a}$
$= 6a^2\sqrt{3a} - 8a^2\sqrt{3a} + 5a^2\sqrt{3a} = 3a^2\sqrt{3a}$

SECTION 10.3

Problem 1

$$\begin{aligned}\sqrt{5a}\sqrt{15a^3b^4}\sqrt{3b^5} &= \sqrt{225a^4b^9}\\ &= \sqrt{225a^4b^8}\sqrt{b}\\ &= 15a^2b^4\sqrt{b}\end{aligned}$$

Problem 2

$\sqrt{5x}(\sqrt{5x} - \sqrt{25y}) = (\sqrt{5x})^2 - \sqrt{125xy}$
$= 5x - \sqrt{25}\sqrt{5xy} = 5x - 5\sqrt{5xy}$

Problem 3

$(3\sqrt{x} - \sqrt{y})(5\sqrt{x} - 2\sqrt{y})$
$= 15(\sqrt{x})^2 - 6\sqrt{xy} - 5\sqrt{xy} + 2(\sqrt{y})^2$
$= 15x - 11\sqrt{xy} + 2y$

Problem 4

$(2\sqrt{x} + 7)(2\sqrt{x} - 7)$
$= (2\sqrt{x})^2 - 7^2 = 4x - 49$

Problem 5

A. $\dfrac{\sqrt{15x^6y^7}}{\sqrt{3x^7y^9}} = \sqrt{\dfrac{15x^6y^7}{3x^7y^9}} = \sqrt{\dfrac{5}{xy^2}} = \dfrac{\sqrt{5}}{\sqrt{xy^2}}$
$= \dfrac{\sqrt{5}}{y\sqrt{x}} = \dfrac{\sqrt{5}}{y\sqrt{x}} \cdot \dfrac{\sqrt{x}}{\sqrt{x}} = \dfrac{\sqrt{5x}}{xy}$

B. $\dfrac{\sqrt{y}}{\sqrt{y} + 3} = \dfrac{\sqrt{y}}{\sqrt{y} + 3} \cdot \dfrac{\sqrt{y} - 3}{\sqrt{y} - 3} = \dfrac{y - 3\sqrt{y}}{y - 9}$

C. $\dfrac{5 + \sqrt{y}}{1 - 2\sqrt{y}} = \dfrac{5 + \sqrt{y}}{1 - 2\sqrt{y}} \cdot \dfrac{1 + 2\sqrt{y}}{1 + 2\sqrt{y}}$
$= \dfrac{5 + 10\sqrt{y} + \sqrt{y} + 2y}{1 - 4y}$
$= \dfrac{5 + 11\sqrt{y} + 2y}{1 - 4y}$

SECTION 10.4

Problem 1

$$\begin{aligned}\sqrt{4x} + 3 &= 7\\ \sqrt{4x} &= 4\\ (\sqrt{4x})^2 &= 4^2\\ 4x &= 16\\ x &= 4\end{aligned}$$

Check $\sqrt{4x} + 3 = 7$

$$\begin{array}{r|l} \sqrt{4 \cdot 4} + 3 & 7\\ \sqrt{16} + 3 & 7\\ 4 + 3 & 7\\ 7 = 7 & \end{array}$$

The solution is 4.

Problem 2

A.
$$\begin{aligned}\sqrt{3x - 2} - 5 &= 0\\ \sqrt{3x - 2} &= 5\\ (\sqrt{3x - 2})^2 &= 5^2\\ 3x - 2 &= 25\\ 3x &= 27\\ x &= 9\end{aligned}$$

Check $\sqrt{3x - 2} - 5 = 0$

$$\begin{array}{r|l} \sqrt{3 \cdot 9 - 2} - 5 & 0\\ \sqrt{27 - 2} - 5 & 0\\ \sqrt{25} - 5 & 0\\ 5 - 5 & 0\\ 0 = 0 & \end{array}$$

The solution is 9.

B.
$$\begin{aligned}\sqrt{4x - 7} + 5 &= 0\\ \sqrt{4x - 7} &= -5\\ (\sqrt{4x - 7})^2 &= (-5)^2\\ 4x - 7 &= 25\\ 4x &= 32\\ x &= 8\end{aligned}$$

Check $\sqrt{4x - 7} + 5 = 0$

$$\begin{array}{r|l} \sqrt{4 \cdot 8 - 7} + 5 & 0\\ \sqrt{32 - 7} + 5 & 0\\ \sqrt{25} + 5 & 0\\ 5 + 5 & 0\\ 10 \neq 0 & \end{array}$$

There is no solution.

Problem 3

$$\begin{aligned}\sqrt{x} + \sqrt{x + 9} &= 9\\ \sqrt{x} &= 9 - \sqrt{x + 9}\\ (\sqrt{x})^2 &= (9 - \sqrt{x + 9})^2\\ x &= 81 - 18\sqrt{x + 9} + (x + 9)\\ 18\sqrt{x + 9} &= 90\\ \sqrt{x + 9} &= 5\\ (\sqrt{x + 9})^2 &= 5^2\\ x + 9 &= 25\\ x &= 16\end{aligned}$$

Check $\sqrt{x} + \sqrt{x + 9} = 9$

$$\begin{array}{r|l} \sqrt{16} + \sqrt{16 + 9} & 9\\ 4 + \sqrt{25} & 9\\ 4 + 5 & 9\\ 9 = 9 & \end{array}$$

The solution is 16.

Problem 4

Strategy To find the distance, use the Pythagorean Theorem. The hypotenuse is the length of the ladder. One leg is the distance from the bottom of the ladder to the base of the building. The distance along the building from the ground to the top of the ladder is the unknown leg.

Solution

$$a = \sqrt{c^2 - b^2}$$
$$a = \sqrt{(12)^2 - (5)^2}$$
$$a = \sqrt{144 - 25}$$
$$a = \sqrt{119}$$
$$a \approx 10.91$$

The distance is 10.91 ft.

Problem 5

Strategy To find the length of the pendulum, replace T in the equation with the given value and solve for L.

Solution

$$T = 2\pi\sqrt{\frac{L}{32}}$$
$$1.5 = 2\pi\sqrt{\frac{L}{32}}$$
$$\frac{1.5}{2\pi} = \sqrt{\frac{L}{32}}$$
$$\left(\frac{1.5}{2\pi}\right)^2 = \left(\sqrt{\frac{L}{32}}\right)^2$$
$$\left(\frac{1.5}{2\pi}\right)^2 = \frac{L}{32}$$
$$32\left(\frac{1.5}{2\pi}\right)^2 = L \quad \text{• Use the } \pi \text{ key on your calculator.}$$
$$1.82 \approx L$$

The length of the pendulum is 1.82 ft.

Solutions to Chapter 11 Problems

SECTION 11.1

Problem 1

$$\frac{3y^2}{2} + y - \frac{1}{2} = 0$$
$$2\left(\frac{3y^2}{2} + y - \frac{1}{2}\right) = 2(0)$$
$$3y^2 + 2y - 1 = 0$$
$$(3y - 1)(y + 1) = 0$$

$$3y - 1 = 0 \qquad y + 1 = 0$$
$$3y = 1 \qquad y = -1$$
$$y = \frac{1}{3}$$

The solutions are $\frac{1}{3}$ and -1.

Problem 2

A. $4x^2 - 96 = 0$

$$4x^2 = 96$$
$$x^2 = 24$$
$$\sqrt{x^2} = \sqrt{24}$$
$$x = \pm\sqrt{24}$$
$$x = \pm 2\sqrt{6}$$

The solutions are $2\sqrt{6}$ and $-2\sqrt{6}$.

B. $x^2 + 81 = 0$

$$x^2 = -81$$
$$\sqrt{x^2} = \sqrt{-81} \quad \text{(not a real number)}$$

The equation has no real number solution.

Problem 3

$$(x + 5)^2 = 20$$
$$\sqrt{(x + 5)^2} = \sqrt{20}$$
$$x + 5 = \pm\sqrt{20}$$
$$x + 5 = \pm 2\sqrt{5}$$

$$x + 5 = 2\sqrt{5} \qquad x + 5 = -2\sqrt{5}$$
$$x = -5 + 2\sqrt{5} \qquad x = -5 - 2\sqrt{5}$$

The solutions are $-5 + 2\sqrt{5}$ and $-5 - 2\sqrt{5}$.

SECTION 11.2

Problem 1

A. $3x^2 - 6x - 2 = 0$

$$3x^2 - 6x = 2$$
$$\frac{1}{3}(3x^2 - 6x) = \frac{1}{3} \cdot 2$$
$$x^2 - 2x = \frac{2}{3}$$

Complete the square.

$$x^2 - 2x + 1 = \frac{2}{3} + 1$$
$$(x - 1)^2 = \frac{5}{3}$$
$$\sqrt{(x - 1)^2} = \sqrt{\frac{5}{3}}$$
$$x - 1 = \pm\sqrt{\frac{5}{3}}$$
$$x - 1 = \pm\frac{\sqrt{15}}{3}$$

$$x - 1 = \frac{\sqrt{15}}{3} \qquad x - 1 = -\frac{\sqrt{15}}{3}$$
$$x = 1 + \frac{\sqrt{15}}{3} \qquad x = 1 - \frac{\sqrt{15}}{3}$$
$$= \frac{3 + \sqrt{15}}{3} \qquad = \frac{3 - \sqrt{15}}{3}$$

The solutions are $\frac{3 + \sqrt{15}}{3}$ and $\frac{3 - \sqrt{15}}{3}$.

B. $y^2 - 6y + 10 = 0$

$y^2 - 6y = -10$

Complete the square.

$y^2 - 6y + 9 = -10 + 9$

$(y - 3)^2 = -1$

$\sqrt{(y - 3)^2} = \sqrt{-1}$

$\sqrt{-1}$ is not a real number.

The equation has no real number solution.

Problem 2

$x^2 + 8x + 8 = 0$

$x^2 + 8x = -8$

$x^2 + 8x + 16 = -8 + 16$

$(x + 4)^2 = 8$

$\sqrt{(x + 4)^2} = \sqrt{8}$

$x + 4 = \pm\sqrt{8}$

$x + 4 \approx \pm 2.828$

$x + 4 \approx 2.828$ $\qquad$ $x + 4 \approx -2.828$

$x \approx -4 + 2.828$ $\qquad$ $x \approx -4 - 2.828$

≈ -1.172 $\qquad$ ≈ -6.828

The solutions are approximately -1.172 and -6.828.

SECTION 11.3

Problem 1

A. $3x^2 + 4x - 4 = 0$

$a = 3, b = 4, c = -4$

$$x = \frac{-(4) \pm \sqrt{(4)^2 - 4(3)(-4)}}{2 \cdot 3} = \frac{-4 \pm \sqrt{16 + 48}}{6} = \frac{-4 \pm \sqrt{64}}{6} = \frac{-4 \pm 8}{6}$$

$$x = \frac{-4 + 8}{6} = \frac{4}{6} = \frac{2}{3} \qquad x = \frac{-4 - 8}{6} = \frac{-12}{6} = -2$$

The solutions are $\frac{2}{3}$ and -2.

B. $x^2 + 2x = 1$

$x^2 + 2x - 1 = 0$

$a = 1, b = 2, c = -1$

$$x = \frac{-(2) \pm \sqrt{(2)^2 - 4(1)(-1)}}{2 \cdot 1} = \frac{-2 \pm \sqrt{4 + 4}}{2} = \frac{-2 \pm \sqrt{8}}{2}$$

$$= \frac{-2 \pm 2\sqrt{2}}{2} = \frac{2(-1 \pm \sqrt{2})}{2} = -1 \pm \sqrt{2}$$

The solutions are $-1 + \sqrt{2}$ and $-1 - \sqrt{2}$.

C. $z^2 + 2z + 6 = 0$

$a = 1, b = 2, c = 6$

$$z = \frac{-(2) \pm \sqrt{2^2 - 4(1)(6)}}{2(1)} = \frac{-2 \pm \sqrt{4 - 24}}{2} = \frac{-2 \pm \sqrt{-20}}{2}$$

$\sqrt{-20}$ is not a real number.

The equation has no real number solution.

SECTION 11.4

Problem 1

A. $\sqrt{-17} = \sqrt{-1 \cdot 17} = \sqrt{-1}\sqrt{17} = i\sqrt{17}$

B. $\sqrt{-81} = \sqrt{-1 \cdot 81} = \sqrt{-1}\sqrt{81} = i\sqrt{81} = i \cdot 9 = 9i$

C. $\sqrt{-63} = \sqrt{-1 \cdot 63} = \sqrt{-1}\sqrt{63} = i\sqrt{63} = i\sqrt{9 \cdot 7}$
$= i\sqrt{9}\sqrt{7} = i \cdot 3\sqrt{7} = 3i\sqrt{7}$

D. $4\sqrt{-50} = 4\sqrt{-1 \cdot 50} = 4\sqrt{-1}\sqrt{50} = 4i\sqrt{50}$
$= 4i\sqrt{25 \cdot 2} = 4i\sqrt{25}\sqrt{2} = 4i \cdot 5\sqrt{2} = 20i\sqrt{2}$

Problem 2

$$\frac{5 - 3\sqrt{-50}}{10} = \frac{5 - 3i\sqrt{50}}{10}$$ • $\sqrt{-50} = i\sqrt{50}$

$$= \frac{5 - 3i\sqrt{25}\sqrt{2}}{10} = \frac{5 - 15i\sqrt{2}}{10}$$

$$= \frac{5}{10} - \frac{15i\sqrt{2}}{10} = \frac{1}{2} - \frac{3i\sqrt{2}}{2} = \frac{1}{2} - \frac{3\sqrt{2}}{2}i$$

Problem 3

A. $(7 - 3i) + (-8 + i) = (7 + (-8)) + (-3 + 1)i$
$= -1 - 2i$

B. $(-5 + 4i) - (-3 - 7i) = (-5 - (-3)) + (4 - (-7))i$
$= -2 + 11i$

Problem 4

$5i(3 + 6i) = 15i + 30i^2$ • **Use the Distributive Property to remove parentheses.**

$= 15i + 30(-1)$ • **Replace i^2 with -1.**

$= 15i + (-30)$ • **Write the answer in the form $a + bi$.**

$= -30 + 15i$

Problem 5

$(-1 + 5i)(2 - 3i)$

$= (-1)(2) + (-1)(-3i) + 5i(2) + 5i(-3i)$ • **Use the FOIL method.**

$= -2 + 3i + 10i - 15i^2$

$= -2 + 13i - 15i^2$ • **Combine like terms.**

$= -2 + 13i - 15(-1)$ • **Replace i^2 with -1.**

$= -2 + 13i + 15$ • **Write the answer in the form $a + bi$.**

$= 13 + 13i$

Problem 6

$(-2 + 5i)(-2 - 5i) = (-2)^2 + 5^2 = 4 + 25 = 29$

Problem 7

$\dfrac{-12 + 8i}{-4i} = \dfrac{-12 + 8i}{-4i} \cdot \dfrac{i}{i}$ • **Multiply the numerator and denominator by i.**

$= \dfrac{-12i + 8i^2}{-4i^2}$

$= \dfrac{-12i + 8(-1)}{(-4)(-1)}$ • **$i^2 = -1$**

$= \dfrac{-12i - 8}{4} = \dfrac{-12i}{4} - \dfrac{8}{4}$ • **Write in the form $a + bi$.**

$= -2 - 3i$

Problem 8

$\dfrac{16 - 11i}{5 + 2i} = \dfrac{16 - 11i}{5 + 2i} \cdot \dfrac{5 - 2i}{5 - 2i}$ • **Multiply the numerator and denominator by the conjugate of the denominator.**

$= \dfrac{80 - 32i - 55i + 22i^2}{5^2 + 2^2}$

$= \dfrac{80 - 87i + 22i^2}{25 + 4}$ • **Combine like terms.**

$= \dfrac{80 - 87i + 22(-1)}{29}$ • **$i^2 = -1$**

$= \dfrac{80 - 87i - 22}{29}$

$= \dfrac{58 - 87i}{29}$

$= \dfrac{58}{29} - \dfrac{87i}{29} = 2 - 3i$ • **Write in the form $a + bi$.**

Problem 9

$8z^2 + 17 = -7$

$8z^2 = -24$ • **Subtract 17 from each side of the equation.**

$z^2 = -3$ • **Divide each side of the equation by 8.**

$\sqrt{z^2} = \sqrt{-3}$ • **Take the square root of each side of the equation.**

$z = \pm\sqrt{-3}$

$= \pm i\sqrt{3}$ • **Rewrite $\sqrt{-3}$ as $i\sqrt{3}$.**

Check

$8z^2 + 17 = -7$	
$8(i\sqrt{3})^2 + 17$	-7
$8(i)^2(\sqrt{3})^2 + 17$	-7
$8(-1)3 + 17$	-7
$-7 = -7$	

$8z^2 + 17 = -7$	
$8(-i\sqrt{3})^2 + 17$	-7
$8(-i)^2(\sqrt{3})^2 + 17$	-7
$8(-1)3 + 17$	-7
$-7 = -7$	

The solutions are $i\sqrt{3}$ and $-i\sqrt{3}$.

Problem 10

$x^2 - 6x + 4 = -6$

$x^2 - 6x + 10 = 0$ • **Add 6 to each side of the equation.**

$x = \dfrac{-b \pm \sqrt{b^2 - 4ac}}{2a}$

$x = \dfrac{-(-6) \pm \sqrt{(-6)^2 - 4(1)(10)}}{2(1)}$ • **$a = 1, b = -6, c = 10$**

$= \dfrac{6 \pm \sqrt{36 - 40}}{2} = \dfrac{6 \pm \sqrt{-4}}{2}$

$= \dfrac{6 \pm i\sqrt{4}}{2} = \dfrac{6 \pm 2i}{2}$ • **Rewrite $\sqrt{-4}$ as $i\sqrt{4}$ and then rewrite $i\sqrt{4}$ as $2i$.**

$= \dfrac{6}{2} \pm \dfrac{2i}{2} = 3 \pm i$ • **Write as a complex number in standard form.**

Check

$x^2 - 6x + 4 = -6$	
$(3 + i)^2 - 6(3 + i) + 4$	-6
$9 + 6i + i^2 - 18 - 6i + 4$	-6
$9 + 6i + (-1) - 18 - 6i + 4$	-6
$-6 = -6$	

$x^2 - 6x + 4 = -6$	
$(3 - i)^2 - 6(3 - i) + 4$	-6
$9 - 6i + i^2 - 18 + 6i + 4$	-6
$9 - 6i + (-1) - 18 + 6i + 4$	-6
$-6 = -6$	

The solutions are $3 + i$ and $3 - i$.

SECTION 11.5

Problem 1

A. $y = x^2 + 2$

$a = 1$. a is positive.

The parabola opens up.

x	y
0	2
1	3
−1	3
2	6
−2	6

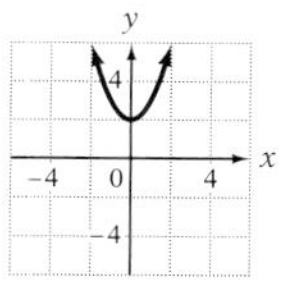

B. $y = -x^2 - 2x + 3$
$a = -1$. a is negative.
The parabola opens down.

x	y
0	3
1	0
−1	4
2	−5
−2	3
−3	0
−4	−5

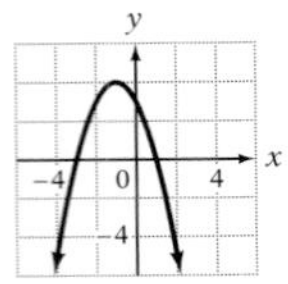

Problem 2

To find the x-intercepts, let $y = 0$ and solve for x.

$$y = x^2 - 6x + 9$$
$$0 = x^2 - 6x + 9$$
$$0 = (x - 3)(x - 3)$$

$x - 3 = 0$ $\qquad$ $x - 3 = 0$
$x = 3$ $\qquad$ $x = 3$

The x-intercept is (3, 0).

To find the y-intercept, let $x = 0$ and solve for y.

$$y = x^2 - 6x + 9$$
$$y = 0^2 - 6(0) + 9 = 9$$

The y-intercept is (0, 9).

SECTION 11.6

Problem 1

Strategy ▶ This is a geometry problem.

▶ Width of the rectangle: W
Length of the rectangle: $W + 3$

▶ Use the equation $A = LW$.

Solution $A = LW$

$$40 = (W + 3)W$$
$$40 = W^2 + 3W$$
$$0 = W^2 + 3W - 40$$
$$0 = (W + 8)(W - 5)$$

$W + 8 = 0$ $\qquad$ $W - 5 = 0$
$W = -8$ $\qquad$ $W = 5$

The solution −8 is not possible.
The width is 5 m.

Answers to Selected Exercises

Answers to Chapter 1 Selected Exercises

PREP TEST

1. 127.16 **2.** 49,743 **3.** 4517 **4.** 11,396 **5.** 24 **6.** 24 **7.** 4 **8.** $3 \cdot 7$ **9.** $\frac{2}{5}$

CONCEPT REVIEW 1.1

1. Sometimes true **3.** Never true **5.** Sometimes true **7.** Always true **9.** Always true

SECTION 1.1

3. natural **5.** is greater than or equal to **7.** $>$ **9.** $<$ **11.** $>$ **13.** $>$ **15.** $<$ **17.** $>$ **19.** $>$ **21.** $<$ **23.** a **25.** Yes **27.** $\{1, 2, 3, 4, 5, 6, 7, 8\}$ **29.** $\{1, 2, 3, 4, 5, 6, 7, 8\}$ **31.** $\{-6, -5, -4, -3, -2, -1\}$ **33.** 5 **35.** $-23, -18$ **37.** 21, 37 **39.** $-52, -46, 0$ **41.** $-17, 0, 4, 29$ **43.** 5, 6, 7, 8, 9 **45.** $-10, -9, -8, -7, -6, -5$ **49.** positive **51.** absolute value **53.** -22 **55.** 31 **57.** 168 **59.** -630 **61.** 18 **63.** -49 **65.** 16 **67.** 12 **69.** -29 **71.** -14 **73.** 0 **75.** -34 **77.** **a.** $8, 5, 2, -1, -3$ **b.** 8, 5, 2, 1, 3 **79.** True **81.** $>$ **83.** $<$ **85.** $>$ **87.** $<$ **89.** $-19, -|-8|, |-5|, 6$ **91.** $-22, -(-3), |-14|, |-25|$ **93.** **a.** 5°F with a 20 mph wind feels colder. **b.** -25°F with a 10 mph wind feels colder. **95.** $-4, 4$ **97.** $-3, 11$ **99.** Negative **101.** 0 **103.** True

CONCEPT REVIEW 1.2

1. Sometimes true **3.** Always true **5.** Always true **7.** Never true **9.** Never true

SECTION 1.2

3. 8; -3; 5 **5.** -11 **7.** -9 **9.** -3 **11.** 1 **13.** -5 **15.** -30 **17.** 9 **19.** 1 **21.** -10 **23.** -28 **25.** -392 **27.** Positive **31.** (-4); -14 **33.** 8 **35.** -7 **37.** 7 **39.** -2 **41.** -28 **43.** -13 **45.** 6 **47.** -9 **49.** 2 **51.** -138 **53.** -8 **55.** Negative **61.** -10; 7; -70 **63.** positive; 48 **65.** 42 **67.** -20 **69.** -16 **71.** 25 **73.** 0 **75.** -72 **77.** -102 **79.** 140 **81.** -70 **83.** 162 **85.** 120 **87.** 36 **89.** 192 **91.** -108 **93.** 0 **95.** Negative **97.** -15; 3 **99.** $3(-12) = -36$ **101.** $-5(11) = -55$ **103.** -2 **105.** 8 **107.** 0 **109.** -9 **111.** -9 **113.** 9 **115.** -24 **117.** -12 **119.** -13 **121.** -18 **123.** 19 **125.** 26 **127.** 11 **129.** -13 **131.** 13 **133.** Positive **135.** b **137.** The temperature is 3°C. **139.** The difference is 14°C. **141.** The difference is 399°C. **143.** The difference in elevation is 5662 m. **145.** The difference in elevation is 6028 m. **147.** The difference in elevation is 9244 m. **149.** The average daily high temperature is -3°C. **151.** The temperature dropped 100°F. **153.** The average temperature at 30,000 ft is 36°F colder than at 20,000 ft. **155.** The student's score is 93. **157.** The 5-day moving average for the Disney stock is $-24, -18, -2, 2, 8$. **159.** 17 **161.** 3 **163.** $-4, -9, -14$ **165.** $-16, 4, -1$ **167.** 5436 **169.** b **171.** a **173.** No. $10 - (-8) = 18$

CONCEPT REVIEW 1.3

1. Never true **3.** Sometimes true **5.** Always true **7.** Never true **9.** Always true

SECTION 1.3

1. 2; 3; repeating **3.** $0.\overline{3}$ **5.** 0.25 **7.** 0.4 **9.** $0.1\overline{6}$ **11.** 0.125 **13.** $0.\overline{2}$ **15.** $0.\overline{45}$ **17.** $0.58\overline{3}$ **19.** $0.2\overline{6}$ **21.** 0.4375 **23.** 0.24 **25.** 0.225 **27.** $0.\overline{681}$ **29.** $0.458\overline{3}$ **31.** $0.\overline{15}$ **33.** No **35.** 4 **37.** $-\frac{3}{8}$ **39.** $\frac{1}{10}$ **41.** $\frac{15}{64}$ **43.** $\frac{3}{2}$ **45.** $-\frac{8}{9}$ **47.** $\frac{2}{3}$ **49.** 4.164 **51.** 4.347 **53.** −4.028 **55.** −2.22 **57.** 12.26448 **59.** **a.** Less than one **b.** Greater than one **61.** 0.75 **63.** −2060.55 **65.** 0.09 **67.** 6 **69.** $\frac{1}{2}$ **71.** −1 **73.** $-\frac{25}{18}$ **75.** $\frac{1}{24}$ **77.** $\frac{17}{18}$ **79.** $-\frac{47}{48}$ **81.** $\frac{3}{8}$ **83.** $-\frac{7}{60}$ **85.** $-\frac{1}{16}$ **87.** $-\frac{7}{24}$ **89.** 7.29 **91.** −3.049 **93.** −1.06 **95.** −23.845 **97.** −10.7893 **99.** 11.56 **101.** −60.03 **103.** −34.99 **105.** 239.2351 **107.** **a.** 2 **b.** 0 **c.** 1 **d.** −1 **111.** $\frac{1}{100}; \frac{1}{100}; \frac{4}{5}$ **113.** 100%; 100%; 30% **115.** $\frac{3}{4}$, 0.75 **117.** $\frac{1}{2}$, 0.5 **119.** $\frac{16}{25}$, 0.64 **121.** $1\frac{3}{4}$, 1.75 **123.** $\frac{19}{100}$, 0.19 **125.** $\frac{1}{20}$, 0.05 **127.** $4\frac{1}{2}$, 4.5 **129.** $\frac{2}{25}$, 0.08 **131.** $\frac{1}{9}$ **133.** $\frac{5}{16}$ **135.** $\frac{1}{200}$ **137.** $\frac{1}{16}$ **139.** 0.073 **141.** 0.158 **143.** 0.0915 **145.** 0.1823 **147.** 15% **149.** 5% **151.** 17.5% **153.** 115% **155.** 0.8% **157.** 6.5% **159.** 54% **161.** 33.3% **163.** 44.4% **165.** 250% **167.** $37\frac{1}{2}\%$ **169.** $35\frac{5}{7}\%$ **171.** 125% **173.** $155\frac{5}{9}\%$ **175.** Greater than 100% **177.** $\frac{2}{5}$ of the respondents found their most recent jobs on the Internet. **179.** Less than one-quarter of the respondents found their most recent jobs through a newspaper ad. **181.** Natural number, integer, positive integer, rational number, real number **183.** Rational number, real number **185.** Irrational number, real number **187.** The cost is $1.35. **189.** The difference is $138.499 billion. **191.** The deficit in 1985 was 4 times greater than in 1975. **193.** The average deficit for the years 1995 through 2000 was −$4,579 million. **195.** The new fraction is greater than $\frac{2}{5}$. **197.** $1.06x$ **199.** 53¢ **201.** Yes. For example, $c = \frac{a+b}{2}$.

CONCEPT REVIEW 1.4

1. Never true **3.** Never true **5.** Always true **7.** Never true **9.** Never true

SECTION 1.4

1. base; exponent; −5; −5; 25 **3.** 36 **5.** −49 **7.** 9 **9.** 81 **11.** $\frac{1}{4}$ **13.** 0.09 **15.** 12 **17.** 0.216 **19.** −12 **21.** 16 **23.** −864 **25.** −1008 **27.** 3 **29.** −77,760 **31.** Positive **35.** −2; 4; 20; −17 **37.** 9 **39.** 12 **41.** 1 **43.** 7 **45.** −36 **47.** 13 **49.** 4 **51.** 15 **53.** −1 **55.** 4 **57.** 1.7 **59.** $\frac{17}{48}$ **61.** b **63.** $<$ **65.** $>$ **67.** 100 **69.** 120 **71.** It will take the computer 17 s. **73.** 6 **75.** 9

CONCEPT REVIEW 1.5

1. Never true **3.** Always true **5.** Never true

SECTION 1.5

1. 90° **3.** 90° **5.** Less than **7.** 28° **9.** 132° **11.** 83° **13.** 91° **15.** 132° **17.** 51° **19.** 77° **21.** 79° **23.** 292° **25.** triangle **27.** 9.71 cm **29.** 14 ft 2 in. **31.** 52 in. **33.** 131.88 cm **35.** 3.768 m **37.** The wood framing would cost $76.96. **39.** The cost of the binding is $19.78. **41.** 22 units **43.** width **45.** 32 ft^2 **47.** 378 cm^2 **49.** 50.24 in^2 **51.** 16.81 m^2 **53.** 52.5 cm^2 **55.** 226.865 in^2 **57.** 138.6 gal of water should be used. **59.** The cost to build the design is $172. **61.** The cost to plaster the room is $990.72. **63.** 4 times **65.** Perimeter: 265.6 m; area: 4056 m^2 **67.** Perimeter: 340 m; area: 1600 m^2 **69. a.** 39 in^2 **b.** 87 in^2

CHAPTER 1 REVIEW EXERCISES*

1. {1, 2, 3, 4, 5, 6} [1.1.1] **2.** 62.5% [1.3.4] **3.** −4 [1.1.2] **4.** 4 [1.2.2] **5.** 18 cm^2 [1.5.3] **6.** $0.\overline{7}$ [1.3.1] **7.** −5.3578 [1.3.2] **8.** 8 [1.4.2] **9.** 4 [1.1.2] **10.** −14 [1.2.2] **11.** 67.2% [1.3.4] **12.** $\frac{159}{200}$ [1.3.4] **13.** −9 [1.2.4] **14.** 0.85 [1.3.1] **15.** $-\frac{1}{2}$ [1.3.2] **16.** 9 [1.4.2] **17.** 37° [1.5.1] **18.** −16 [1.2.1] **19.** 90 [1.2.3] **20.** −6.881 [1.3.3] **21.** −5, −3 [1.1.1] **22.** 0.07 [1.3.4] **23.** 12 [1.4.1] **24.** > [1.1.1] **25.** −3 [1.2.1] **26.** 34° [1.5.1] **27.** $\frac{1}{15}$ [1.3.3] **28.** −108 [1.4.1] **29.** 277.8% [1.3.4] **30.** 2.4 [1.3.4] **31.** 152° [1.5.1] **32.** −8 [1.2.4] **33.** 28.26 m^2 [1.5.3] **34.** 12 [1.4.2] **35.** 3 [1.1.2] **36.** $288\frac{8}{9}\%$ [1.3.4] **37. a.** 12, 8, 1, −7 **b.** 12, 8, 1, 7 [1.1.2] **38.** $0.\overline{63}$ [1.3.1] **39.** −11.5 [1.3.2] **40.** 8 [1.4.2] **41.** −8 [1.2.1] **42.** $-\frac{11}{24}$ [1.3.3] **43.** −17, −9, 0, 4 [1.1.1] **44.** 0.2% [1.3.4] **45.** −4 [1.4.1] **46.** 3.561 [1.3.3] **47.** −17 [1.1.2] **48.** −27 [1.2.2] **49.** $-\frac{1}{10}$ [1.3.2] **50.** < [1.1.1] **51.** 44 in. [1.5.2] **52.** −128 [1.4.1] **53.** 7.5% [1.3.4] **54.** $54\frac{2}{7}\%$ [1.3.4] **55.** −18 [1.2.1] **56.** 0 [1.2.3] **57.** 9 [1.4.2] **58.** $\frac{7}{8}$ [1.3.3] **59.** 16 [1.2.4] **60.** < [1.1.1] **61.** −3 [1.4.1] **62.** −6 [1.2.1] **63.** 300 [1.2.3] **64.** {−3, −2, −1} [1.1.1] **65.** The cost is $240.96. [1.5.3] **66.** The temperature is 8°C. [1.2.5] **67.** The average low temperature was −2°C. [1.2.5] **68.** The difference is 106°F. [1.2.5] **69.** The temperature is −6°C. [1.2.5] **70.** The difference is 714°C. [1.2.5]

CHAPTER 1 TEST

1. $\frac{11}{20}$ [1.3.4] **2.** −6, −8 [1.1.1] **3.** 47° [1.5.1] **4.** 0.15 [1.3.1] **5.** $-\frac{1}{14}$ [1.3.2] **6.** −15 [1.2.4] **7.** $-\frac{8}{3}$ [1.4.1] **8.** 2 [1.2.1] **9.** {1, 2, 3, 4, 5, 6} [1.1.1] **10.** 159% [1.3.4]

*The numbers in brackets following the answers in the Chapter Review Exercises refer to the objective that corresponds to that problem. For example, the reference [1.2.1] stands for Section 1.2, Objective 1. This notation will be used for all Pretests, Chapter Review Exercises, Chapter Tests, and Cumulative Review Exercises throughout the text.

11. 29 [1.1.2] **12.** > [1.1.1] **13.** $-\frac{23}{18}$ [1.3.3] **14.** 90 cm^2 [1.5.3] **15.** 3 [1.4.2]
16. $\frac{5}{6}$ [1.3.2] **17.** 23.1% [1.3.4] **18.** 0.062 [1.3.4] **19.** 14 [1.2.2] **20.** $0.4\overline{3}$ [1.3.1]
21. −2.43 [1.3.2] **22.** 62° [1.5.1] **23.** 640 [1.4.1] **24.** −34 [1.1.2] **25.** 84.78 in. [1.5.2]
26. **a.** 17, 6, −5, −9 **b.** 17, 6, 5, 9 [1.1.2] **27.** $69\frac{13}{23}\%$ [1.3.4] **28.** −11.384 [1.3.3]
29. 160 [1.2.3] **30.** −2 [1.4.2] **31.** The temperature is 4°C. [1.2.5] **32.** The average is −48°F. [1.2.5] **33.** The cost is $4564. [1.5.3]

Answers to Chapter 2 Selected Exercises

PREP TEST

1. 3 [1.2.2] **2.** 4 [1.2.4] **3.** $\frac{1}{12}$ [1.3.3] **4.** $-\frac{4}{9}$ [1.3.2] **5.** $\frac{3}{10}$ [1.3.2]
6. −16 [1.4.1] **7.** $\frac{8}{27}$ [1.4.1] **8.** 48 [1.4.1] **9.** 1 [1.4.2] **10.** 12 [1.4.2]

CONCEPT REVIEW 2.1

1. Always true **3.** Sometimes true **5.** Always true

SECTION 2.1

1. $-4x$; -7; $3x^2$; $-4x$; -7 **3.** $2x^2$, $5x$, $\underline{-8}$ **5.** $-a^4$, $\underline{6}$ **7.** $7\underline{x^2y}$, $6\underline{xy^2}$ **9.** 1, −9 **11.** 1, −4, −1
15. 10 **17.** 32 **19.** 21 **21.** 16 **23.** −9 **25.** 3 **27.** −7 **29.** 13
31. −15 **33.** 41 **35.** 1 **37.** 5 **39.** 1 **41.** 57 **43.** 5 **45.** 12 **47.** 6
49. 10 **51.** 8 **53.** −3 **55.** −2 **57.** −22 **59.** 4 **61.** 20 **63.** 24
65. 4.96 **67.** −5.68 **69.** **a.** No, V cannot be a whole number. **b.** No, volume is not measured in square units. **71.** The volume is 25.8 in^3. **73.** The area is 93.7 cm^2. **75.** The volume is 484.9 m^3.
77. 41 **79.** 21 **81.** 24 **83.** $\frac{1}{2}$ **85.** 13 **87.** −1 **89.** 4 **91.** 81

CONCEPT REVIEW 2.2

1. Never true **3.** Always true **5.** Always true **7.** Never true

SECTION 2.2

1. Commutative **3.** reciprocal (or multiplicative inverse) **5.** 2 **7.** 5 **9.** 6 **11.** −8
13. −4 **15.** The Inverse Property of Addition **17.** The Commutative Property of Addition
19. The Associative Property of Addition **21.** The Commutative Property of Multiplication
23. The Associative Property of Multiplication **27.** $3x$, $5x$ **29.** $-8a$; Distributive; -3 **31.** $14x$
33. $5a$ **35.** $-6y$ **37.** $-3b - 7$ **39.** $5a$ **41.** $-2ab$ **43.** $5xy$ **45.** 0 **47.** $-\frac{5}{6}x$
49. $-\frac{1}{24}x^2$ **51.** $11x$ **53.** $7a$ **55.** $-14x^2$ **57.** $-x + 3y$ **59.** $17x - 3y$
61. $-2a - 6b$ **63.** $-3x - 8y$ **65.** $-4x^2 - 2x$ **67.** **a.** Negative **b.** Positive **c.** 0
69. Associative; $-48x$ **71.** $12x$ **73.** $-21a$ **75.** $6y$ **77.** $8x$ **79.** $-6a$ **81.** $12b$
83. $-15x^2$ **85.** x^2 **87.** x **89.** n **91.** x **93.** n **95.** $2x$ **97.** $-2x$

99. $-15a^2$ **101.** $6y$ **103.** $3y$ **105.** $-2x$ **107.** Less than one **109.** Distributive; -24; 16 **111.** $-x - 2$ **113.** $8x - 6$ **115.** $-2a - 14$ **117.** $-6y + 24$ **119.** $35 - 21b$ **121.** $-9 + 15x$ **123.** $15x^2 + 6x$ **125.** $2y - 18$ **127.** $-15x - 30$ **129.** $-6x^2 - 28$ **131.** $-6y^2 + 21$ **133.** $-6a^2 + 7b^2$ **135.** $4x^2 - 12x + 20$ **137.** $-3y^2 + 9y + 21$ **139.** $-12a^2 - 20a + 28$ **141.** $12x^2 - 9x + 12$ **143.** $10x^2 - 20xy - 5y^2$ **145.** $-8b^2 + 6b - 9$ **147.** 3 **149.** m; 3 **151.** $a - 7$ **153.** $-11x + 13$ **155.** $-4y - 4$ **157.** $-2x - 16$ **159.** $18y - 51$ **161.** $a + 7b$ **163.** $6x + 28$ **165.** $5x - 75$ **167.** $4x - 4$ **169.** $38x - 63$ **171.** b **173.** $20x + y$ **175.** b **177.** $-3x + y$ **179.** 0 **181.** $-a + b$ **183.** **a.** Yes **b.** No

CONCEPT REVIEW 2.3

1. Never true **3.** Never true **5.** Always true **7.** Never true

SECTION 2.3

1. Sum, times **3.** Total, divided by **5.** $19 - d$ **7.** $r - 12$ **9.** $28a$ **11.** $5(n - 7)$ **13.** $y - 3y$ **15.** $-6b$ **17.** $\frac{4}{p - 6}$ **19.** $\frac{x - 9}{2x}$ **21.** $-4s - 21$ **23.** $\frac{d + 8}{d}$ **25.** $\frac{3}{8}(t + 15)$ **27.** $w + \frac{7}{w}$ **29.** $d + (16d - 3)$ **31.** $\frac{n}{19}$ **33.** $n + 40$ **35.** $(n - 90)^2$ **37.** $\frac{4}{9}n + 20$ **39.** $n(n + 10)$ **41.** $7n + 14$ **43.** $\frac{12}{n + 2}$ **45.** $\frac{2}{n + 1}$ **47.** $60 - \frac{n}{50}$ **49.** $n^2 + 3n$ **51.** $(n + 3) + n^3$ **53.** $n - \frac{1}{4}n^2$ **55.** $n - \frac{7}{n}$ **57.** $n^3 - 12n$ **59.** c **61.** $\frac{1}{2}; \frac{3}{4}; \frac{5}{4}n$ **63.** $n + (n + 10)$; $2n + 10$ **65.** $n - (9 - n)$; $2n - 9$ **67.** $\frac{1}{5}n - \frac{3}{8}n$; $-\frac{7}{40}n$ **69.** $(n + 9) + 4$; $n + 13$ **71.** $2(3n + 40)$; $6n + 80$ **73.** $7(5n)$; $35n$ **75.** $17n + 2n$; $19n$ **77.** $n + 12n$; $13n$ **79.** $3(n^2 + 4)$; $3n^2 + 12$ **81.** $\frac{3}{4}(16n + 4)$; $12n + 3$ **83.** $16 - (n + 9)$; $-n + 7$ **85.** $\frac{4n}{2} + 5$; $2n + 5$ **87.** $6(n + 8)$; $6n + 48$ **89.** $7 - (n + 2)$; $-n + 5$ **91.** $\frac{1}{3}(n + 6n)$; $\frac{7n}{3}$ **93.** $(8 + n^3) + 2n^3$; $3n^3 + 8$ **95.** $(n - 6) + (n + 12)$; $2n + 6$ **97.** $(n - 20) + (n + 9)$; $2n - 11$ **99.** $14 + (n - 3)10$; $10n - 16$ **101.** $25 - x$ **103.** $\frac{1}{2}L$ **105.** Let x be one number; x and $18 - x$ **107.** Let G be the number of genes in the roundworm genome; $G + 11{,}000$ **109.** Let N be the total number of Americans; $\frac{3}{4}N$ **111.** Let s be the number of points awarded for a safety; $3s$ **113.** Let d be the diameter of Dione; $d + 253$ **115.** Let p be the pounds of pecans produced in Texas; $\frac{1}{2}p$ **117.** Let p be the world population in 1980; $2p$ **119.** Let L be the measure of the largest angle; $\frac{1}{2}L - 10$ **121.** Let n be either the number of nickels or the number of dimes; n and $35 - n$ **123.** Let h be the number of hours of overtime worked; $720 + 27h$ **125.** Let m be the number of minutes of phone calls; $19.95 + 0.08m$ **127.** $\frac{1}{4}x$

CHAPTER 2 REVIEW EXERCISES

1. y^2 [2.2.2] **2.** $3x$ [2.2.3] **3.** $-10a$ [2.2.3] **4.** $-4x + 8$ [2.2.4] **5.** $7x + 38$ [2.2.5] **6.** 16 [2.1.1] **7.** 9 [2.2.1] **8.** $36y$ [2.2.3] **9.** $6y - 18$ [2.2.4] **10.** $-3x + 21y$ [2.2.5] **11.** $-8x^2 + 12y^2$ [2.2.4] **12.** $5x$ [2.2.2] **13.** 22 [2.1.1] **14.** $2x$ [2.2.3] **15.** $15 - 35b$ [2.2.4] **16.** $-7x + 33$ [2.2.5] **17.** The Commutative Property of Multiplication [2.2.1] **18.** $24 - 6x$ [2.2.4] **19.** $5x^2$ [2.2.2] **20.** $-7x + 14$ [2.2.5] **21.** $-9y^2 + 9y + 21$ [2.2.4] **22.** $2x + y$ [2.2.5] **23.** 3 [2.1.1] **24.** $36y$ [2.2.3] **25.** $5x - 43$ [2.2.5] **26.** $2x$ [2.2.3] **27.** $-6x^2 + 21y^2$ [2.2.4] **28.** 6 [2.1.1] **29.** $-x + 6$ [2.2.5] **30.** $-5a - 2b$ [2.2.2] **31.** $-10x^2 + 15x - 30$ [2.2.4] **32.** $-9x - 7y$ [2.2.2] **33.** $6a$ [2.2.3] **34.** $17x - 24$ [2.2.5] **35.** $-2x - 5y$ [2.2.2] **36.** $30b$ [2.2.3] **37.** 21 [2.2.1] **38.** $-2x^2 + 4x$ [2.2.2] **39.** $-6x^2$ [2.2.3] **40.** $15x - 27$ [2.2.5] **41.** $-8a^2 + 3b^2$ [2.2.4] **42.** The Multiplication Property of Zero [2.2.1] **43.** $b - 7b$ [2.3.1] **44.** $n + 2n^2$ [2.3.1] **45.** $\frac{6}{n} - 3$ [2.3.1] **46.** $\frac{10}{y - 2}$ [2.3.1] **47.** $8\left(\frac{2n}{16}\right); n$ [2.3.2] **48.** $4(2 + 5n); 8 + 20n$ [2.3.2] **49.** Let h be the height of the triangle; $h + 15$ [2.3.3] **50.** Let b be the amount of either espresso beans or mocha java beans; b and $20 - b$ [2.3.3]

CHAPTER 2 TEST

1. $36y$ [2.2.3] **2.** $4x - 3y$ [2.2.2] **3.** $10n - 6$ [2.2.5] **4.** 2 [2.1.1] **5.** The Multiplication Property of One [2.2.1] **6.** $4x - 40$ [2.2.4] **7.** $\frac{1}{12}x^2$ [2.2.2] **8.** $4x$ [2.2.3] **9.** $-24y^2 + 48$ [2.2.4] **10.** 19 [2.2.1] **11.** 6 [2.1.1] **12.** $-3x + 13y$ [2.2.5] **13.** b [2.2.2] **14.** $78a$ [2.2.3] **15.** $3x^2 - 15x + 12$ [2.2.4] **16.** -32 [2.1.1] **17.** $37x - 5y$ [2.2.5] **18.** $\frac{n + 8}{17}$ [2.3.1] **19.** $(a + b) - b^2$ [2.3.1] **20.** $n^2 + 11n$ [2.3.1] **21.** $20(n + 9); 20n + 180$ [2.3.2] **22.** $(n - 3) + (n + 2); 2n - 1$ [2.3.2] **23.** $n - \frac{1}{4}(2n); \frac{1}{2}n$ [2.3.2] **24.** Let d be the distance from Earth to the sun; $30d$ [2.3.3] **25.** Let L be the length of one piece; L and $9 - L$ [2.3.3]

CUMULATIVE REVIEW EXERCISES

1. -7 [1.2.1] **2.** 5 [1.2.2] **3.** 24 [1.2.3] **4.** -5 [1.2.4] **5.** 1.25 [1.3.1] **6.** $\frac{3}{5}$, 0.60 [1.3.4] **7.** $\{-4, -3, -2, -1\}$ [1.1.1] **8.** 8% [1.3.4] **9.** $\frac{11}{48}$ [1.3.3] **10.** $\frac{5}{18}$ [1.3.2] **11.** $\frac{1}{4}$ [1.3.2] **12.** $\frac{8}{3}$ [1.4.1] **13.** -5 [1.4.2] **14.** $\frac{53}{48}$ [1.4.2] **15.** -8 [2.1.1] **16.** $5x^2$ [2.2.2] **17.** $-a - 12b$ [2.2.2] **18.** $3a$ [2.2.3] **19.** $20b$ [2.2.3] **20.** $20 - 10x$ [2.2.4] **21.** $6y - 21$ [2.2.4] **22.** $-6x^2 + 8y^2$ [2.2.4] **23.** $-8y^2 + 20y + 32$ [2.2.4] **24.** $-10x + 15$ [2.2.5] **25.** $5x - 17$ [2.2.5] **26.** $13x - 16$ [2.2.5] **27.** $6x + 29y$ [2.2.5] **28.** $6 - 12n$ [2.3.1] **29.** $5 + (n - 7); n - 2$ [2.3.2] **30.** Let s be the speed of the dial-up connection; $10s$ [2.3.3]

Answers to Chapter 3 Selected Exercises

PREP TEST

1. -4 [1.2.2] **2.** 1 [1.3.2] **3.** -10 [1.3.2] **4.** 0.9 [1.3.4] **5.** 75% [1.3.4] **6.** 63 [2.1.1] **7.** $10x - 5$ [2.2.2] **8.** -9 [2.2.2] **9.** $9x - 18$ [2.2.5]

CONCEPT REVIEW 3.1

1. Sometimes true **3.** Always true **5.** Always true **7.** Always true

SECTION 3.1

1. a. equation **b.** expression **3.** Yes **5.** No **7.** No **9.** Yes **11.** Yes **13.** Yes **15.** No **17.** No **19.** No **21.** Yes **23.** No **25.** No **29.** 30; 87 **33.** 2 **35.** 15 **37.** 6 **39.** -6 **41.** 3 **43.** 0 **45.** -2 **47.** -7 **49.** -7 **51.** -12 **53.** 2 **55.** -5 **57.** 15 **59.** 9 **61.** 14 **63.** -1 **65.** 1 **67.** $-\frac{1}{2}$ **69.** $-\frac{3}{4}$ **71.** $\frac{1}{12}$ **73.** $-\frac{7}{12}$ **75.** $-\frac{5}{7}$ **77.** $-\frac{1}{3}$ **79.** 1.869 **81.** 0.884 **85.** divide; 7 **89.** 7 **91.** -7 **93.** -4 **95.** 5 **97.** 9 **99.** -8 **101.** 0 **103.** -7 **105.** 8 **107.** 12 **109.** 12 **111.** -18 **113.** -18 **115.** 6 **117.** -12 **119.** 32 **121.** -12 **123.** 15 **125.** 25 **127.** $\frac{8}{7}$ **129.** 2 **131.** 3 **133.** -3 **135.** -22.62 **137.** 1.05 **139.** -3.4 **141.** No **143.** distance; rate; time **145.** $3t$; $2.5t$ **147. a.** Greater than **b.** Equal to **c.** 2 mi **149.** The train travels 245 mi in the 5-hour period. **151.** The dietician's average rate of speed is 30 mph. **153.** It will take 4 h to complete the trip. **155.** It would take 31.25 s to walk from one end of the moving sidewalk to the other. **157.** The two joggers will meet 40 min after they start. **159.** It will take her 0.5 h to travel 4 mi upstream. **163.** 24% **165.** 7.2 **167.** 400 **169.** 9 **171.** 25% **173.** 5 **175.** 200% **177.** 400 **179.** 7.7 **181.** 200 **183.** 400 **185.** 20 **187.** 80% **189.** 40% of 80 is equal to 80% of 40. **191.** unknown; 30; 24 **193.** unknown; 32; 0.1 **195.** 250 seats are reserved for wheelchair accessibility. **197.** In the average single-family home, 74 gal of water are used per person per day. **199.** 82.1% of the vacation cost is charged. **201.** There is insufficient information. **203.** 12% of the deaths were not attributed to motor vehicle accidents. **205.** In this country 96.1 billion kilowatt-hours of electricity are used for home lighting per year. **207. a.** 25% of the people watching the commercial would have to buy one can of the soft drink. **b.** 4.2% of the people watching the commercial would have to purchase one six-pack of the soft drink. **209.** The price of the less expensive model is \$1423.41. **211.** The annual simple interest rate is 9%. **213.** Sal earned \$240 in interest from the two accounts. **215.** Makana earned \$63 in one year. **217.** The interest rate on the combined investment is between 6% and 9%. **219.** The percent concentration of the hydrogen peroxide is 2%. **221.** Apple Dan's has the greater concentration of apple juice. **223.** 12.5 g of the cream are not glycerine. **225.** The percent concentration of salt in the remaining solution is 12.5%. **227.** -21 **229.** -27 **231.** 21 **233.** 22° **235.** The cost of the dinner was \$80. **237.** The new value is two times the original value. **239.** One possible answer is $5x = -10$.

CONCEPT REVIEW 3.2

1. Always true **3.** Never true **5.** Never true **7.** Sometimes true

SECTION 3.2

1. 5; 8 **3.** Negative **5.** 3 **7.** 6 **9.** -1 **11.** 1 **13.** -9 **15.** 3 **17.** 3

19. 3 **21.** 2 **23.** 2 **25.** 4 **27.** $\frac{6}{7}$ **29.** $\frac{2}{3}$ **31.** -1 **33.** $\frac{3}{4}$ **35.** $\frac{1}{3}$ **37.** $-\frac{3}{4}$ **39.** $\frac{1}{3}$ **41.** $-\frac{1}{6}$ **43.** 1 **45.** 0 **47.** $\frac{2}{5}$ **49.** $-\frac{3}{2}$ **51.** 18 **53.** 8 **55.** -16 **57.** 25 **59.** 21 **61.** 15 **63.** -16 **65.** $\frac{7}{6}$ **67.** $\frac{1}{8}$ **69.** $\frac{15}{2}$ **71.** $-\frac{18}{5}$ **73.** 2 **75.** 3 **77.** 1 **79.** 2 **81.** 3.95 **83.** -0.8 **85.** -11 **87.** 0 **89.** 12; 12; Distributive; 2; 84; $2x$; $2x$; 7; Divide; 7; -12 **91.** -2 **93.** 3 **95.** 8 **97.** 2 **99.** -2 **101.** -3 **103.** 2 **105.** -2 **107.** -2 **109.** -7 **111.** 0 **113.** -2 **115.** -2 **117.** 4 **119.** 10 **121.** 3 **123.** $\frac{3}{4}$ **125.** $\frac{2}{7}$ **127.** $-\frac{3}{4}$ **129.** 3 **131.** 10 **133.** $\frac{4}{3}$ **135.** 3 **137.** -14 **139.** 7 **141.** $3x$; 18 **143.** a, c **145.** 3 **147.** 4 **149.** 2 **151.** 2 **153.** 2 **155.** -7 **157.** $\frac{4}{7}$ **159.** $\frac{1}{2}$ **161.** $-\frac{1}{3}$ **163.** $\frac{10}{3}$ **165.** $-\frac{1}{4}$ **167.** 0.5 **169.** 0 **171.** -1 **173.** The car will slide 168 ft. **175.** The depth of the diver is 40 ft. **177.** The initial velocity is 8 ft/s. **179.** The height of the adult is approximately 182.5 cm. **181.** The passenger was driven 6 mi. **183.** He made 8 errors. **185.** The population is approximately 51,000 people. **187.** The break-even point is 350 television sets. **191.** 5 ft **193.** No **195.** No, the seesaw is not balanced. **197.** A force of 25 lb must be applied to the other end of the lever. **199.** The fulcrum must be placed 10 ft from the 128-pound acrobat. **201.** No solution **203.** $-\frac{11}{4}$ **205.** 62 **207.** One possible answer is $3x - 6 = 2x - 2$.

CONCEPT REVIEW 3.3

1. Always true **3.** Sometimes true **5.** Never true **7.** Always true **9.** Sometimes true

SECTION 3.3

1. includes; $\leq$ **3.** 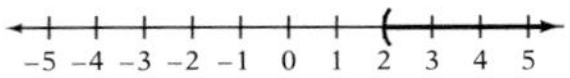
5. 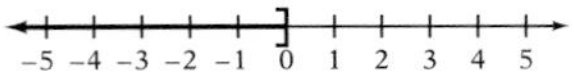
7. a, c **9.** $x < 2$ 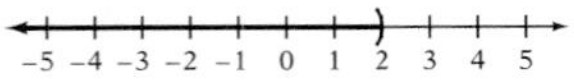
11. $x > 3$ 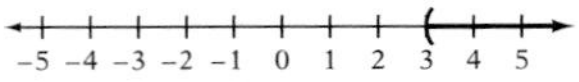
13. $n \geq 3$ 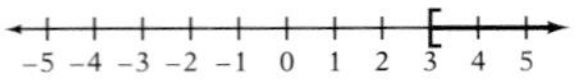
15. $x \leq -4$ 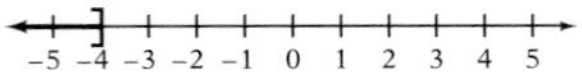
17. $x \geq -1$ 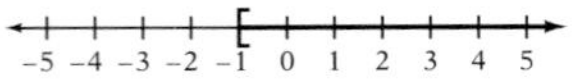
19. Only negative numbers **21.** Only positive numbers **23.** $y \geq -9$ **25.** $x < 12$ **27.** $x \geq 5$ **29.** $x < -11$ **31.** $x \leq 10$ **33.** $x \geq -6$ **35.** $x > 2$ **37.** $d < -\frac{1}{6}$ **39.** $x \geq -\frac{31}{24}$ **41.** $x < \frac{5}{4}$ **43.** $x > \frac{5}{24}$ **45.** $x \leq -1.2$ **47.** $x \leq 0.70$ **49.** $x < -7.3$ **51.** a, b, c **53.** is reversed **55.** $x \leq -3$ 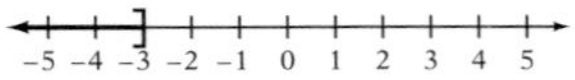
57. $x > -2$ 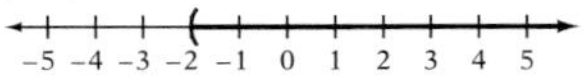
59. $x > 0$ 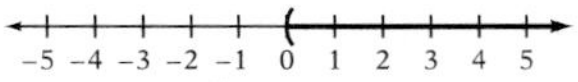
61. $n \geq 4$ 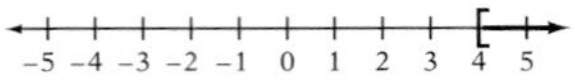
63. $x > -2$ 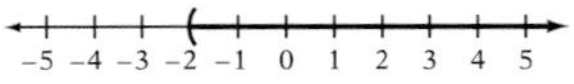
65. $x < \frac{5}{3}$ **67.** $x \geq 5$ **69.** $x > -\frac{5}{2}$ **71.** $x \leq -\frac{2}{3}$ **73.** $x < -18$ **75.** $x > -16$ **77.** $y \geq 6$ **79.** $x \geq -6$ **81.** $b \leq 33$ **83.** $n < \frac{3}{4}$ **85.** $x \leq -\frac{6}{7}$ **87.** $y \leq \frac{5}{6}$ **89.** $x \leq \frac{27}{28}$ **91.** $y > -\frac{3}{2}$ **93.** $x > -0.5$ **95.** $y \geq -0.8$ **97.** $x \leq 4.2$ **99.** $x \leq 5$ **101.** $x < -5.4$ **103.** d **107.** $2x$; $2x$; $3x$; 0; 9; $-3x$; -9, -3; $\leq$; -3; 3 **109.** $x < 4$ **111.** $x < -4$ **113.** $x \geq 1$

115. $x \le 5$ **117.** $x < 0$ **119.** $x < 20$ **121.** $x > 500$ **123.** $x > 2$ **125.** $x \le -5$

127. $y \le \frac{5}{2}$ **129.** $x < \frac{25}{11}$ **131.** $x > 11$ **133.** $n \le \frac{11}{18}$ **135.** $x \ge 6$ **137.** $x \le \frac{2}{5}$

139. $t < 1$ **141.** $n > \frac{7}{10}$ **143.** 3 **145.** c, d **147.** {1, 2} **149.** {1, 2, 3}

151. {3, 4, 5} **153.** {10, 11, 12, 13} **155.** 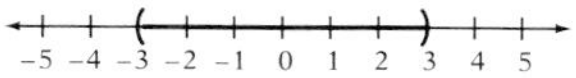 **157.** 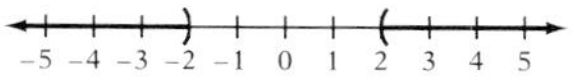

CHAPTER 3 REVIEW EXERCISES

1. No [3.1.1] **2.** 20 [3.1.2] **3.** −7 [3.1.3] **4.** 7 [3.2.1] **5.** 4 [3.2.2]

6. $-\frac{1}{5}$ [3.2.3] **7.** 405 [3.1.5] **8.** 25 [3.1.5] **9.** 67.5% [3.1.5]

10. 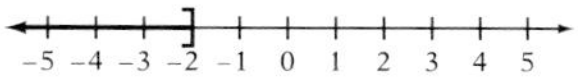 [3.3.1] **11.** $x > 2$ 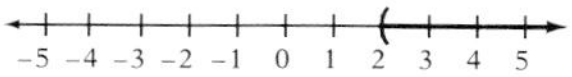 [3.3.1]

12. $x > -4$ 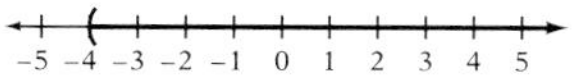 [3.3.2] **13.** $x \ge -4$ [3.3.3] **14.** $x \ge 4$ [3.3.3]

15. Yes [3.1.1] **16.** 2.5 [3.1.2] **17.** −49 [3.1.3] **18.** $\frac{1}{2}$ [3.2.1]

19. $\frac{1}{3}$ [3.2.2] **20.** 10 [3.2.3] **21.** 16 [3.1.5] **22.** 125 [3.1.5] **23.** $16\frac{2}{3}\%$ [3.1.5]

24. $x < -4$ 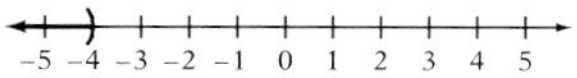 [3.3.1] **25.** $x \le -2$ 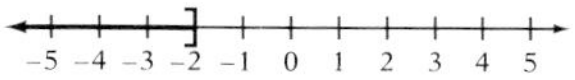 [3.3.2]

26. −2 [3.2.3] **27.** $\frac{5}{6}$ [3.1.2] **28.** 20 [3.1.3] **29.** 6 [3.2.1] **30.** 0 [3.2.3]

31. $x < 12$ [3.3.3] **32.** 15 [3.1.5] **33.** 5 [3.2.1] **34.** $x > 5$ [3.3.3] **35.** 4% [3.1.5]

36. $x > -18$ [3.3.3] **37.** $x < \frac{1}{2}$ [3.3.3] **38.** The measure of the third angle is 110°. [3.2.4]

39. A force of 24 lb must be applied to the other end of the lever. [3.2.4] **40.** The width is 6 ft. [3.2.4] **41.** The discount is $31.99. [3.2.4] **42.** Approximately 11,065 plants and animals are at risk of extinction on Earth. [3.1.5] **43.** The depth is 80 ft. [3.2.4] **44.** The fulcrum is 3 ft from the 25-pound force. [3.2.4] **45.** The length of the rectangle is 24 ft. [3.2.4] **46.** It will take the motorboat 1.5 h to travel 30 mi. [3.1.4] **47.** She must invest $625 in an account that earns an annual simple interest rate of 8%. [3.1.5] **48.** The percent concentration of hydrochloric acid is 6%. [3.1.5]

CHAPTER 3 TEST

1. −12 [3.1.3] **2.** $-\frac{1}{2}$ [3.2.2] **3.** −3 [3.2.1] **4.** No [3.1.1] **5.** $\frac{1}{8}$ [3.1.2]

6. $-\frac{1}{3}$ [3.2.3] **7.** 5 [3.2.1] **8.** $\frac{1}{2}$ [3.2.2] **9.** −5 [3.1.2] **10.** −5 [3.2.2]

11. $-\frac{40}{3}$ [3.1.3] **12.** $-\frac{22}{7}$ [3.2.3] **13.** 2 [3.2.3] **14.** $\frac{12}{11}$ [3.2.3] **15.** −3 [3.2.3]

16. 125% [3.1.5] **17.** 40 [3.1.5] **18.** 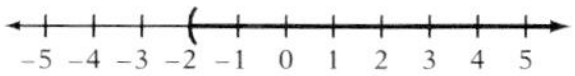 [3.3.1]

19. $x \le -1$ 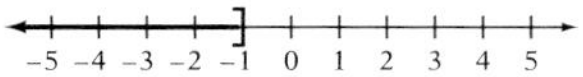 [3.3.1] **20.** $x > -2$ 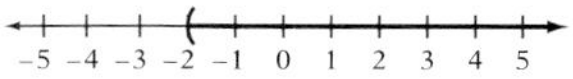 [3.3.2]

21. $x > \frac{1}{2}$ [3.3.1] **22.** $x \le -\frac{9}{2}$ [3.3.3] **23.** $x \ge -16$ [3.3.2] **24.** $x \le 2$ [3.3.3]

25. $x \le -3$ [3.3.3] **26.** $x > 2$ [3.3.3] **27.** 4 [3.2.2] **28.** 24 [3.1.5]

29. $x \ge 3$ 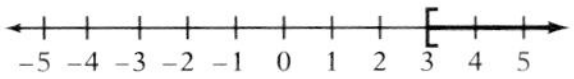 [3.3.2] **30.** Yes [3.1.1] **31.** The astronaut would weigh 30 lb on the moon. [3.1.5] **32.** The final temperature of the water after mixing is 60°C. [3.2.4] **33.** The number of calculators produced was 200. [3.2.4] **34.** They will meet 2 h after they begin. [3.1.4]

35. He must invest \$930 in the second account. [3.1.5] **36.** The percent concentration of chocolate syrup in the chocolate milk is 25%. [3.1.5]

CUMULATIVE REVIEW EXERCISES

1. 6 [1.2.2] **2.** −48 [1.2.3] **3.** $-\frac{19}{48}$ [1.3.3] **4.** −2 [1.3.2] **5.** 54 [1.4.1] **6.** 24 [1.4.2] **7.** 6 [2.1.1] **8.** $-17x$ [2.2.2] **9.** $-5a - 2b$ [2.2.2] **10.** $2x$ [2.2.3] **11.** $36y$ [2.2.3] **12.** $2x^2 + 6x - 4$ [2.2.4] **13.** $-4x + 14$ [2.2.5] **14.** $6x - 34$ [2.2.5] **15.** $\{-7, -6, -5, -4, -3, -2, -1\}$ [1.1.1] **16.** $87\frac{1}{2}\%$ [1.3.4] **17.** 3.42 [1.3.4] **18.** $\frac{5}{8}$ [1.3.4] **19.** Yes [3.1.1] **20.** −5 [3.1.2] **21.** −25 [3.1.3] **22.** 3 [3.2.1] **23.** −3 [3.2.2] **24.** 13 [3.2.3] **25.** $x < -\frac{8}{9}$ [3.3.2] **26.** $x \geq 12$ [3.3.3] **27.** $x > 9$ [3.3.3] **28.** $8 - \frac{n}{12}$ [2.3.1] **29.** $n + (n + 2)$; $2n + 2$ [2.3.2] **30.** b and $35 - b$ [2.3.3] **31.** Let L be the length of the longer piece; $3 - L$ [2.3.3] **32.** 17% of the computer programmer's salary is deducted for income tax. [3.1.5] **33.** The equation predicts that the first 4-minute mile was run in 1952. [3.2.4] **34.** The final temperature of the water after mixing is 60°C. [3.2.4] **35.** A force of 24 lb must be applied to the other end of the lever. [3.2.4]

Answers to Chapter 4 Selected Exercises

PREP TEST

1. $0.65R$ [2.2.2] **2.** $0.03x + 20$ [2.2.5] **3.** $3n + 6$ [2.2.2] **4.** $5 - 2x$ [2.3.1] **5.** 40% [1.3.4] **6.** 2 [3.2.3] **7.** 0.25 [3.2.1] **8.** $x < 4$ [3.3.3] **9.** $20 - n$ [2.3.3]

CONCEPT REVIEW 4.1

1. Always true **3.** Always true **5.** Never true

SECTION 4.1

1. equals **3.** $n - 15 = 7$; $n = 22$ **5.** $7n = -21$; $n = -3$ **7.** $3n - 4 = 5$; $n = 3$ **9.** $4(2n + 3) = 12$; $n = 0$ **11.** $12 = 6(n - 3)$; $n = 5$ **13.** $22 = 6n - 2$; $n = 4$ **15.** $4n + 7 = 2n + 3$; $n = -2$ **17.** $5n - 8 = 8n + 4$; $n = -4$ **19.** $2(n - 25) = 3n$; $n = -50$ **21.** $3n = 2(20 - n)$; 8 and 12 **23.** $3n + 2(18 - n) = 44$; 8 and 10 **25.** Answers may vary. For example: $n + n + 10 = 14$; $n + n - 10 = 14$ **27.** whole; low-fat **29.** The original value was \$16,000. **31.** There are 58 calories in a medium-size orange. **33.** The amount of mulch is 15 lb. **35.** The intensity of the sound is 140 decibels. **37.** The monthly payment is \$117.75. **39.** The length is 80 ft. The width is 50 ft. **41.** To replace the water pump, 5 h of labor were required. **43.** You are purchasing 9 tickets. **45.** The length of the patio is 15 ft. **47.** The union member worked 168 h during the month of March. **49.** The customer used the service for 11 min. **51.** One-third of the container is filled at 3:39 P.M. **53.** The package weighs more than 12 oz but not over 13 oz. **55.** There are 60 coins in the bank.

CONCEPT REVIEW 4.2

1. Always true **3.** Always true **5.** Never true

SECTION 4.2

1. consecutive **5.** The integers are 17, 18, and 19. **7.** The integers are 26, 28, and 30. **9.** The integers are 17, 19, and 21. **11.** The integers are 8 and 10. **13.** The integers are 7 and 9. **15.** The integers are −9, −8, and −7. **17.** The integers are 10, 12, and 14. **19.** No solution **21.** **b** **25.** Row 1: 5; $5n$; Row 2: $32 - n$; 10; $10(32 - n)$ **27.** **a.** $100d$ **b.** $20d$ **c.** $4d$ **29.** There are 12 dimes and 15 quarters in the bank. **31.** The executive bought eight 24¢ stamps and thirty-two 39¢ stamps. **33.** There are five 29¢ stamps in the drawer. **35.** There are 28 quarters in the bank. **37.** There are 20 one-dollar bills and 6 five-dollar bills in the cash box. **39.** There are 11 pennies in the bank. **41.** There are twenty-seven 22¢ stamps in the collection. **43.** There are thirteen 3¢ stamps, eighteen 7¢ stamps, and nine 12¢ stamps in the collection. **45.** There are eighteen 6¢ stamps, six 8¢ stamps, and twenty-four 15¢ stamps. **47.** The integers are −12, −10, −8, and −6. **49.** There is $6.70 in the bank. **51.** For any three consecutive odd integers, the sum of the first and third integers is twice the second integer.

CONCEPT REVIEW 4.3

1. Always true **3.** Always true **5.** Never true

SECTION 4.3

3. $2x - 3$ **5.** True **7.** The sides measure 50 ft, 50 ft, and 25 ft. **9.** The length is 13 m. The width is 8 m. **11.** The length is 40 ft. The width is 20 ft. **13.** The sides measure 40 cm, 20 cm, and 50 cm. **15.** The length is 130 ft. The width is 39 ft. **17.** The width is 12 ft. **19.** Each side measures 12 in. **21.** **a.** 90° **b.** 180° **c.** 360° **d.** between 0° and 90° **e.** between 90° and 180° **f.** 90° **g.** 180° **23.** 90; 37; 37° **25.** The complement of a 28° angle is 62°. **27.** The supplement of a 73° angle is 107°. **29.** 35° **31.** 20° **33.** 53° **35.** 121° **37.** 15° **39.** 18° **41.** 45° **43.** 49° **45.** 12° **47.** False **49.** True **51.** $\angle a = 122°$, $\angle b = 58°$ **53.** $\angle a = 44°$, $\angle b = 136°$ **55.** 20° **57.** 40° **59.** 128° **61.** Vertical; 180°; 50°; 85°; 135°; 45° **63.** $\angle x = 160°$, $\angle y = 145°$ **65.** $\angle a = 40°$, $\angle b = 140°$ **67.** $75° - x$ **69.** The measure of the third angle is 45°. **71.** The measure of the third angle is 73°. **73.** The measure of the third angle is 43°. **75.** The angles measure 38°, 38°, and 104°. **77.** The angles measure 60°, 30°, and 90°. **79.** True **81.** True **83.** The length is 9 cm. The width is 4 cm.

CONCEPT REVIEW 4.4

1. Always true **3.** Never true **5.** Always true

SECTION 4.4

3. 40; unknown; 0.25 **5.** The selling price is $56. **7.** The selling price is $565.64. **9.** The markup rate is 75%. **11.** The markup rate is 44.4%. **13.** The markup rate is 60%. **15.** The cost of the compact disc player is $120. **17.** The cost of the basketball is $59. **19.** The cost of the computer is $1750. **21.** True **25.** 318.75; 375; unknown **27.** The sale price is $101.25. **29.** The discount price is $218.50. **31.** The discount rate is 25%. **33.** The discount rate is 23.2%. **35.** The markdown rate is 38%. **37.** The regular price is $510. **39.** The regular price is $300. **41.** The regular price is $275. **43.** True **45.** The markup is $18. **47.** The markup rate is 40%. **49.** The cost of the camera is $230. **51.** The regular price is $80. **53.** No. The single discount that would give the same sale price is 28%.

CONCEPT REVIEW 4.5

1. Always true **3.** Always true **5.** Never true

SECTION 4.5

1. Row 1: 0.052; $0.052x$; Row 2: $x + 1000$; 0.072; $0.072(x + 1000)$ **3.** $9000 was invested at 7%, and $6000 was invested at 6.5%. **5.** $1500 was invested in the mutual fund. **7.** $200,000 was deposited at 10%, and $100,000 was deposited at 8.5%. **9.** Teresa has $3000 invested in bonds that earn 8% annual simple interest.

11. She has $2500 invested at 11%. **13.** $40,500 was invested at 8%, and $13,500 was invested at 12%. **15.** The total amount invested was $650,000. **17.** The total amount invested was $500,000. **19.** **a.** 3% and 5% **b.** $5000 **21.** The amount of the research consultant's investment is $45,000. **23.** The total annual interest received was $3040. **25.** The value of the investment in three years is $3831.87. **27.** **a.** By age 55, the couple should have $170,000 saved for retirement.

CONCEPT REVIEW 4.6

1. Always true **3.** Always true **5.** Never true **7.** Always true

SECTION 4.6

1. **a.** $10.50 **b.** $.36 **5.** The clinic should use 2 lb of dog food and 3 lb of vitamin supplement. **7.** The mixture costs $6.98 per pound. **9.** 56 oz of the $4.30 alloy and 144 oz of the $1.80 alloy were used. **11.** You can add 1 lb of blueberries. **13.** 10 kg of hard candy must be mixed with the jelly beans. **15.** To make the mixture, 3 lb of caramel are needed. **17.** To make the mixture, 300 lb of the $.80 meal are needed. **19.** 37 lb of almonds and 63 lb of walnuts were used. **21.** The cost per pound is $1.40. **23.** The cost per ounce is $3. **25.** **c, e,** and **f** **27.** 0.09; 225 **31.** The percent concentration is 24%. **33.** 20 gal of the 15% solution must be mixed with 5 gal of the 20% solution. **35.** 30 lb of 25% wool yarn is used. **37.** 6.25 gal of the plant food that is 9% nitrogen are combined with the plant food that is 25% nitrogen. **39.** The percent concentration is 19%. **41.** 30 oz of the potpourri that is 60% lavender are used. **43.** To make the solution, 100 ml of the 7% solution and 200 ml of the 4% solution are used. **45.** 150 oz of pure chocolate are added. **47.** The percent concentration is 12%. **49.** 1.2 oz of dried apricots must be added. **51.** False **53.** The cost is $3.65 per ounce. **55.** 10 oz of water evaporated from the solution. **57.** 75 g of pure water must be added. **59.** 85 adults and 35 children attended the performance.

CONCEPT REVIEW 4.7

1. Never true **3.** Never true **5.** Always true

SECTION 4.7

1. **a.** Row 1: $3r$; 5; $15r$; Row 2: 5; $5r$ **b.** $15r$; $5r$; 3520 **3.** **a** **5.** The speed of the first plane is 105 mph. The speed of the second plane is 130 mph. **7.** The second skater overtakes the first skater after 40 s. **9.** Michael's boat will be alongside the tour boat in 2 h. **11.** The airport is 120 mi from the corporate offices. **13.** The sailboat traveled 36 mi in the first 3 h. **15.** The passenger train is traveling at 50 mph. The freight train is traveling at 30 mph. **17.** It takes the second ship 1 h to catch up to the first ship. **19.** The two trains will pass each other in 4 h. **21.** The average speed on the winding road was 34 mph. **23.** The car overtakes the cyclist 48 mi from the starting point. **25.** The rate of the cyclist is 13 mph. **27.** The rate of the car is 60 mph. **29.** The joggers will meet at 7:48 A.M. **31.** The cyclist's average speed is $13\frac{1}{3}$ mph.

CONCEPT REVIEW 4.8

1. Never true **3.** Always true **5.** Never true

SECTION 4.8

1. $n \leq 50$ **3.** $500 > 0.12n$ **5.** The smallest integer is 2. **7.** The amount of income tax to be paid is $3150 or more. **9.** The organization must collect more than 440 lb. **11.** The student must score 78 or better. **13.** The dollar amount in sales must be more than $5714. **15.** The dollar amount the agent expects to sell is $20,000 or less. **17.** A person must use this service for more than 60 min. **19.** 8 ounces or less must be added. **21.** The ski area is more than 38 mi away. **23.** The maximum number of miles you can drive is 166. **25.** **b, c,** and **e** **27.** The integers are 1, 3, and 5 or 3, 5, or 7. **29.** The crew can prepare 8 to 12 aircraft in this period of time. **31.** The minimum number is 467 calendars.

CHAPTER 4 REVIEW EXERCISES

1. $2x - 7 = x$; 7 [4.1.1] **2.** The length of the shorter piece is 14 in. [4.1.2] **3.** The two numbers are 8 and 13. [4.1.2] **4.** $2x + 6 = 4(x - 2)$; 7 [4.1.1] **5.** The discount rate is $33\frac{1}{3}\%$. [4.4.2] **6.** \$8000 is invested at 6%, and \$7000 is invested at 7%. [4.5.1] **7.** The angles measure 65°, 65°, and 50°. [4.3.3] **8.** The rate of the motorcyclist is 45 mph. [4.7.1] **9.** The measures of the three angles are 16°, 82°, and 82°. [4.3.3] **10.** The markup rate is 80%. [4.4.1] **11.** The concentration of butterfat is 14%. [4.6.2] **12.** The length is 80 ft. The width is 20 ft. [4.3.1] **13.** A minimum of 1151 copies can be ordered. [4.8.1] **14.** The regular price is \$32. [4.4.2] **15.** 7 qt of cranberry juice and 3 qt of apple juice were used. [4.6.1] **16.** The cost is \$25.95. [4.4.1] **17.** The two numbers are 6 and 30. [4.1.2] **18.** \$5600 is deposited in the 12% account. [4.5.1] **19.** The cards are the 7 and 8 of hearts. [4.2.1] **20.** One liter of pure water should be added. [4.6.2] **21.** The lowest score the student can receive is 72. [4.8.1] **22.** $-7 = \frac{1}{2}x - 10$; 6 [4.1.1] **23.** The height is 1063 ft. [4.1.2] **24.** The measures of the three angles are 75°, 60°, and 45°. [4.3.3] **25.** There are 128 one-dollar bills. [4.2.2] **26.** The length of the longer piece is 7 ft. [4.1.2] **27.** The number of hours of consultation was 8. [4.1.2] **28.** There are 77 12¢ stamps and 37 17¢ stamps. [4.2.2] **29.** The cost is \$671.25. [4.4.1] **30.** They will meet after 4 min. [4.7.1] **31.** The measures of the three sides are 8 in., 12 in., and 15 in. [4.3.1] **32.** The integers are −17, −15, and −13. [4.2.1] **33.** The maximum width is 10 ft. [4.8.1] **34.** $\angle a = 138°$, $\angle b = 42°$ [4.3.2]

CHAPTER 4 TEST

1. $6n + 13 = 3n - 5$; $n = -6$ [4.1.1] **2.** $3n - 15 = 27$; $n = 14$ [4.1.1] **3.** The numbers are 8 and 10. [4.1.2] **4.** The lengths are 6 ft and 12 ft. [4.1.2] **5.** The cost is \$200. [4.4.1] **6.** The discount rate is 20%. [4.4.2] **7.** 20 gal of the 15% solution must be added. [4.6.2] **8.** The length is 14 m. The width is 5 m. [4.3.1] **9.** The integers are 5, 7, and 9. [4.2.1] **10.** Five or more residents are in the nursing home. [4.8.1] **11.** \$5000 is invested at 10%, and \$2000 is invested at 15%. [4.5.1] **12.** 8 lb of the \$7 coffee and 4 lb of the \$4 coffee should be used. [4.6.1] **13.** The rate of the first plane is 225 mph. The rate of the second plane is 125 mph. [4.7.1] **14.** The measures of the three angles are 48°, 33°, and 99°. [4.3.3] **15.** There are 15 nickels and 35 quarters in the bank. [4.2.2] **16.** The amounts to be deposited are \$1400 at 6.75% and \$1000 at 9.45%. [4.5.1] **17.** The minimum length is 24 ft. [4.8.1] **18.** The sale price is \$79.20. [4.4.2]

CUMULATIVE REVIEW EXERCISES

1. −12, −6 [1.1.1] **2.** 6 [1.2.2] **3.** $-\frac{1}{6}$ [1.4.1] **4.** $-\frac{11}{6}$ [1.4.2] **5.** −18 [1.1.2] **6.** −24 [2.1.1] **7.** $9x + 4y$ [2.2.2] **8.** $-12 + 8x + 20x^3$ [2.2.4] **9.** $4x + 4$ [2.2.5] **10.** $6x^2$ [2.2.2] **11.** No [3.1.1] **12.** −3 [3.2.1] **13.** −15 [3.1.3] **14.** 3 [3.2.1] **15.** −10 [3.2.3] **16.** $\frac{2}{5}$ [1.3.4] **17.** $x \geq 4$ 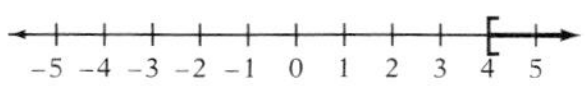

[3.3.2] **18.** $x \geq -3$ [3.3.2] **19.** $x > 18$ [3.3.3] **20.** $x \geq 4$ [3.3.3] **21.** 2.5% [1.3.4] **22.** 12% [1.3.4] **23.** 3 [3.1.5] **24.** 45 [3.1.5] **25.** $8n + 12 = 4n$; $n = -3$ [4.1.1] **26.** The area of the garage is 600 ft². [4.1.2] **27.** The number of hours of labor is 5. [4.1.2] **28.** 20% of the libraries had the reference book. [3.1.5] **29.** The amount of money deposited is \$2000. [4.5.1] **30.** The markup rate is 75%. [4.4.1] **31.** 60 g of the gold alloy must be used. [4.6.1] **32.** 30 oz of pure water must be added. [4.6.2] **33.** The measure of one of the equal angles is 47°. [4.3.3] **34.** The middle even integer is 14. [4.2.1] **35.** There are 7 dimes in the bank. [4.2.2]

Answers to Chapter 5 Selected Exercises

PREP TEST

1. −3 [1.4.2] **2.** −1 [2.1.1] **3.** $-3x + 12$ [2.2.4] **4.** −2 [3.2.1] **5.** 5 [3.2.1]
6. −2 [3.2.1] **7.** 13 [2.1.1] **8.** $\frac{3}{4}x - 4$ [2.2.4] **9.** **a, b, c** [3.3.1]

CONCEPT REVIEW 5.1

1. Always true **3.** Never true **5.** Never true **7.** Always true

SECTION 5.1

1. right; down **5.**

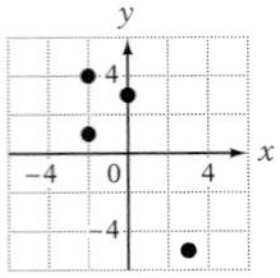

7.

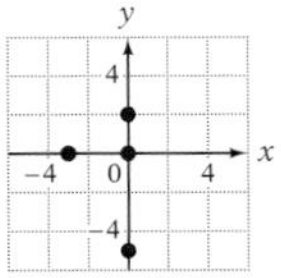

9.

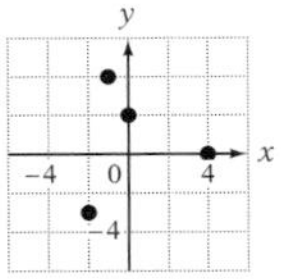

11. $A(2, 3), B(4, 0), C(-4, 1), D(-2, -2)$ **13.** $A(-2, 5), B(3, 4), C(0, 0), D(-3, -2)$ **15.** **a.** 2; −4 **b.** 1; −3 **17.** **a.** I **b.** II **c.** IV **d.** III **19.** 26; 60; 31; 56; 26; 60; 31; 56

21.

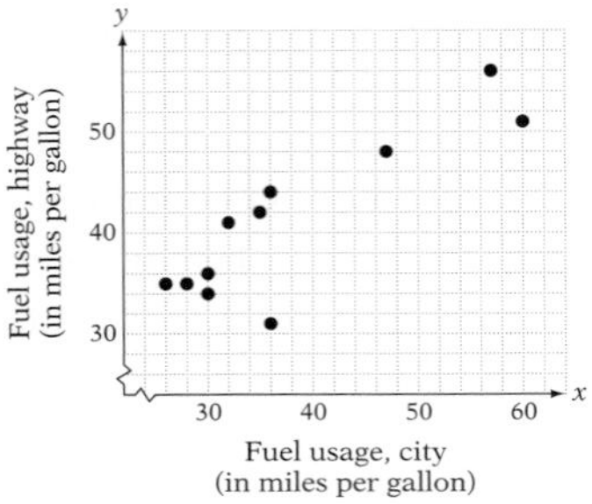

23.

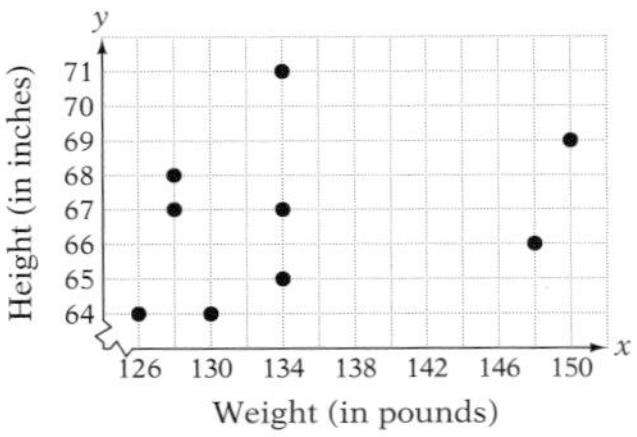

25.

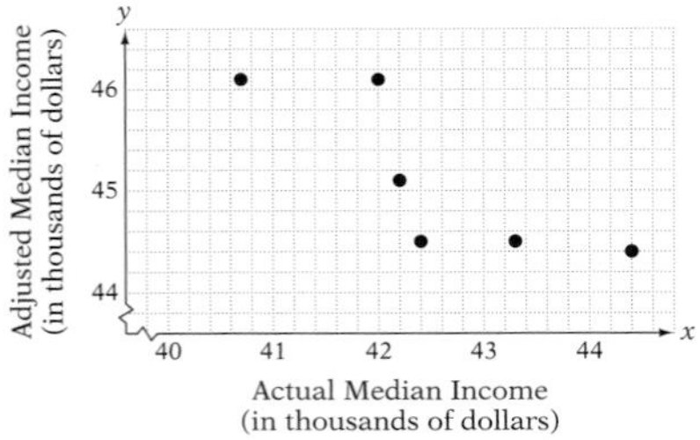

27. Denominator **29.** The average rate of change is 4° per hour.

31. **a.** 10.45 cents **b.** $9.7\overline{3}$ cents; less than **33.** **a.** The average rate of change is $-2.1\overline{3}$ million people per year. **b.** The average rate of change is −1.3 million people per year. **35.** **a.** −7.16 cents **b.** 1975–1980; 4.8 cents **37.** From 30 to 40 min **39.** 1 unit **41.** 0 units **43.** 1 unit **45.** (0, 0)

CONCEPT REVIEW 5.2

1. Never true **3.** Always true **5.** Never true **7.** Never true **9.** Always true

SECTION 5.2

1. x; y **3.** $m = 4, b = 1$ **5.** $m = \frac{5}{6}, b = \frac{1}{6}$ **7.** Yes **9.** No **11.** No **13.** Yes

15. No **17.** (3, 7) **19.** (6, 3) **21.** (0, 1) **23.** (−5, 0) **25.** **a.** 2 **b.** Negative

27. **a.** −7; −1; −7 **b.** −4; 0; −4 **c.** −1; 1; −1

29. 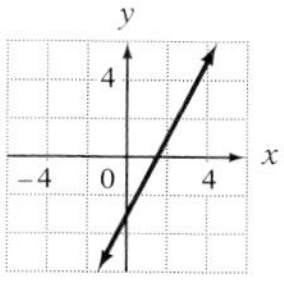

31. 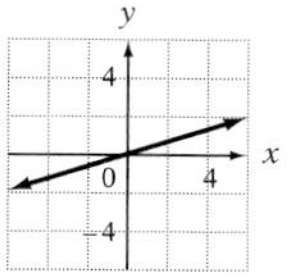

33. 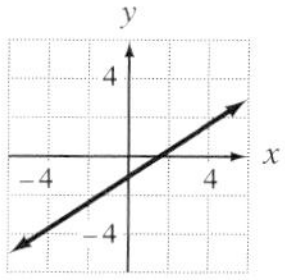

35. 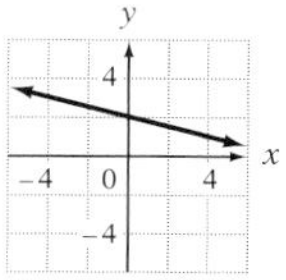

37. 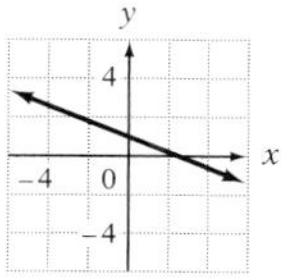

39. 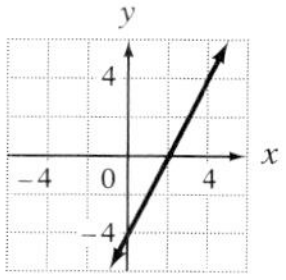

41. 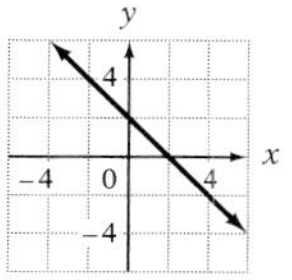

43. 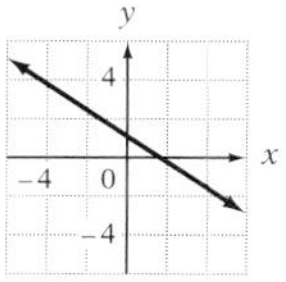

45. 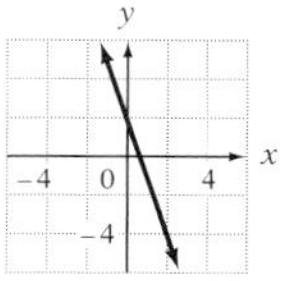

47. 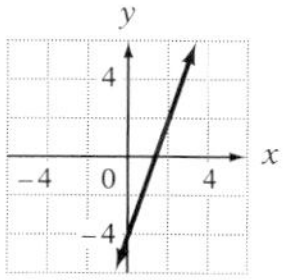

49. 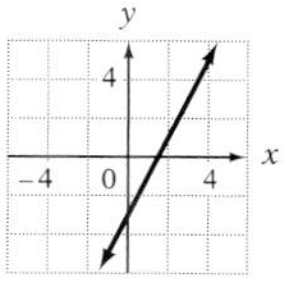

51. 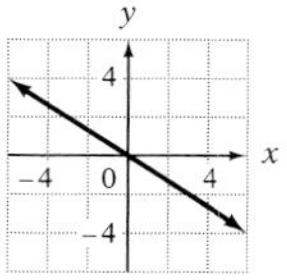

53. 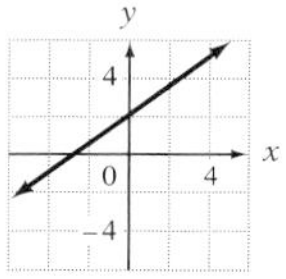

55. 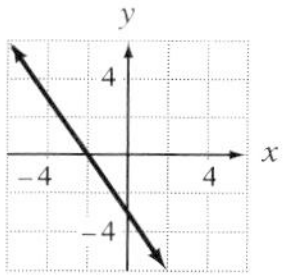

57. 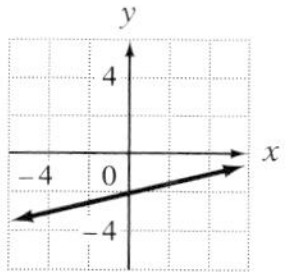

59. x; $-2y$; -2; $\frac{1}{2}$; 5 **61.** horizontal

63. $y = -3x + 10$ **65.** $y = 4x - 3$ **67.** $y = -\frac{3}{2}x + 3$ **69.** $y = \frac{2}{5}x - 2$ **71.** $y = -\frac{2}{7}x + 2$

73. $y = -\frac{1}{3}x + 2$

75. 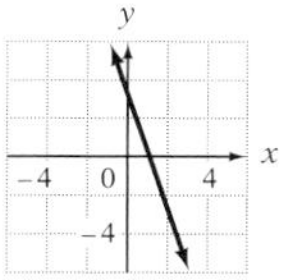

77. 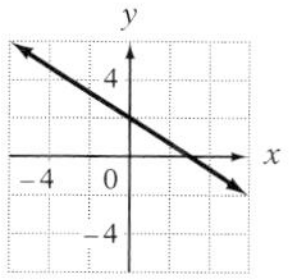

79. 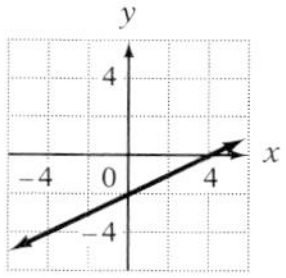

81. 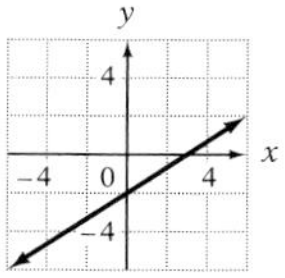

83. 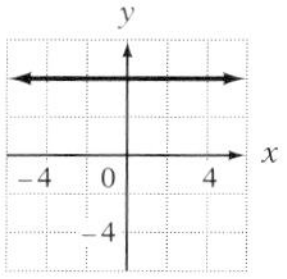

85. 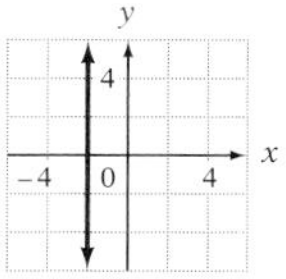

87. (3, 0), (0, −3) **89.** (3, 0), (0, −6) **91.** (10, 0), (0, −2)

93. (−4, 0), (0, 12) **95.** (0, 0), (0, 0) **97.** (−6, 0), (0, 3)

99. 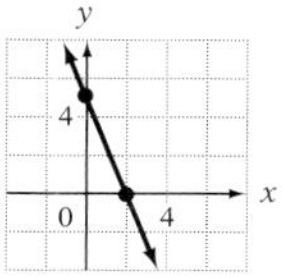

101. 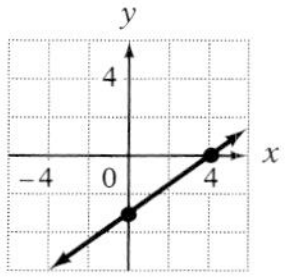

103. 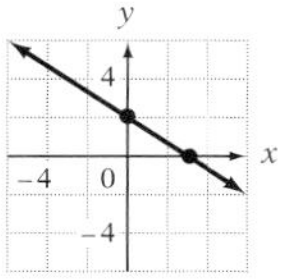

105. 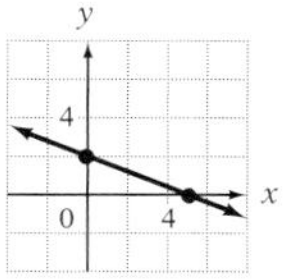

107. 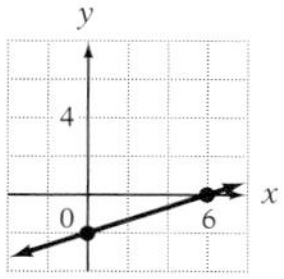

109. 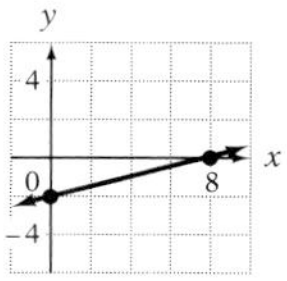

111. 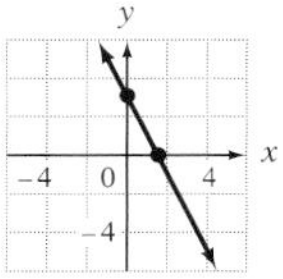

113. 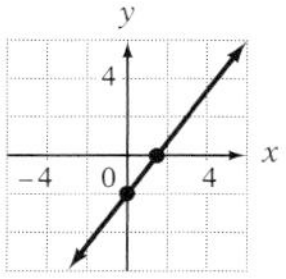

115. 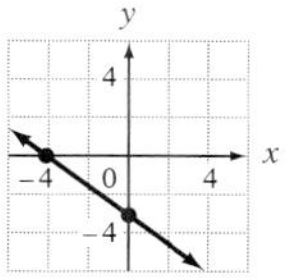

117. 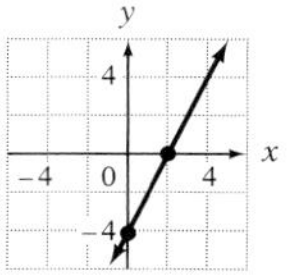

119. 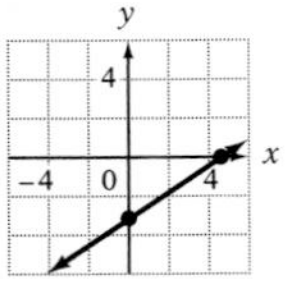
121. To the right **123. a.** $y = -\frac{1}{2}x - 5$ **b.** $(-2, -4)$ **125.** 1 unit

CONCEPT REVIEW 5.3

1. Always true **3.** Never true **5.** Never true

SECTION 5.3

3. 2; −4; 3; 1 **5.** −2 **7.** $\frac{1}{3}$ **9.** $-\frac{5}{2}$ **11.** $-\frac{1}{2}$ **13.** −1 **15.** Undefined **17.** 0
19. $-\frac{1}{3}$ **21.** 0 **23.** −5 **25.** Undefined **27.** $-\frac{2}{3}$ **29.** Yes **31.** No
33. $m = 50$. The electronic mail sorter sorts 50 pieces of mail per minute. **35.** $m = -0.02$. The car uses 0.02 gal of gasoline per mile driven. **37. a.** $a = c, b \neq d$ **b.** $b = d, a \neq c$ **c.** Downward to the right
39. 5; (0, −3)
41. 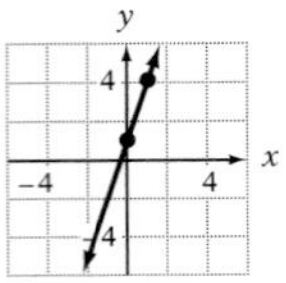
43. 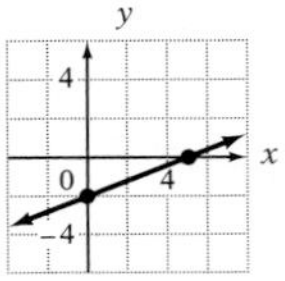
45. 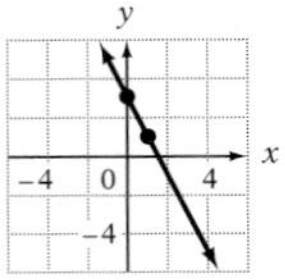
47. 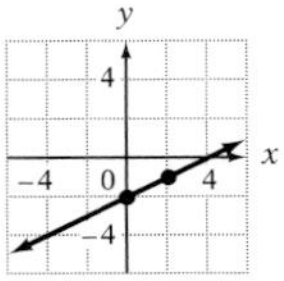
49. 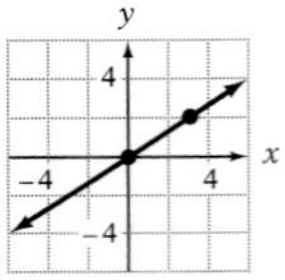
51. 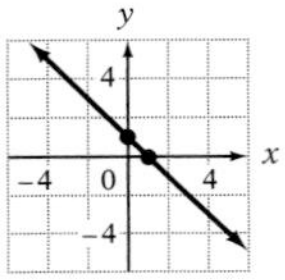
53. 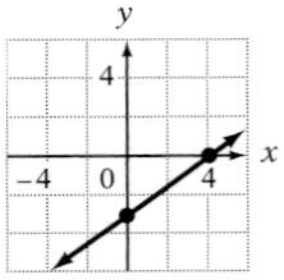
55. 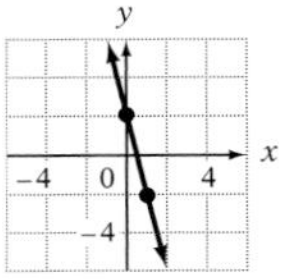
57. 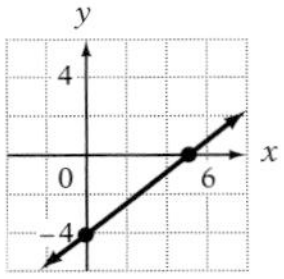
59. Above; downward to the right **61.** Increasing the coefficient of x increases the slope. **63.** Increasing the constant term increases the y-intercept. **65.** i and D; ii and C; iii and B; iv and F; v and E; vi and A
67. No, not all graphs of straight lines have a y-intercept. In general, vertical lines do not have a y-intercept. For example, $x = 2$ does not have a y-intercept.

CONCEPT REVIEW 5.4

1. Always true **3.** Sometimes true **5.** Always true

SECTION 5.4

1. 3; 1; $3x + 1$ **3.** $y = 2x + 2$ **5.** $y = -3x - 1$ **7.** $y = \frac{1}{3}x$ **9.** $y = \frac{3}{4}x - 5$ **11.** $y = -\frac{3}{5}x$
13. $y = \frac{1}{4}x + \frac{5}{2}$ **15.** $y = -\frac{2}{3}x - 7$ **19.** $y = 2x - 3$ **21.** $y = -2x - 3$ **23.** $y = \frac{2}{3}x$
25. $y = \frac{1}{2}x + 2$ **27.** $y = -\frac{3}{4}x - 2$ **29.** $y = \frac{3}{4}x + \frac{5}{2}$ **31.** $y = -\frac{4}{3}x - 9$
33. a. $y - b = m(x - 0)$ **b.** Yes **35.** $y = 3x + 4$ **37.** $y = -x - 4$ **39.** $y = -\frac{6}{5}x + 5$
41. $y = -\frac{2}{5}x - 7$ **43.** $y = 5$ **45.** $x = 5$ **47.** $y = \frac{4}{5}x + 8$ **49.** $y = -\frac{1}{2}x - 2$
51. $y = -\frac{4}{3}x - 3$ **53.** $y = 3x - 3$ **55.** $y = 3x$ **57.** $x = 3$ **59.** Yes; however, all of the points must be on the same line. **61.** Yes; $y = -x + 6$ **63.** No **65.** 7 **67.** −1

69. $F = \frac{9}{5}C + 32$ **71. a.** $y = 2.86x - 5438.4$ **b.** 324.5 million **c.** 0.9 million

CONCEPT REVIEW 5.5

1. Always true **3.** Never true **5.** Always true **7.** Always true

SECTION 5.5

1. ordered pairs; domain; range **3.** No
5. {(87.7, 91.0), (71.4, 84.0), (79.1, 84.5), (90.1, 91.6), (82.5, 94.3), (68.4, 74.5), (82.5, 80.2)}; no
7. {(4, 411), (5, 514), (6, 618), (7, 720), (8, 823)}; Yes **9.** {(55, 273), (65, 355), (75, 447), (85, 549)}; yes
11. Domain: {0, 2, 4, 6}; range: {0}; yes **13.** Domain: {2}; range: {2, 4, 6, 8}; no **15.** Domain: {0, 1, 2, 3}; range {0, 1, 2, 3}; yes **17.** Domain: {−3, −2, −1, 1, 2, 3}; range: {−3, 2, 3, 4}; yes **19.** 40; (10, 40)
21. −11; (−6, −11) **23.** 12; (−2, 12) **25.** $\frac{7}{2}$; $\left(\frac{1}{2}, \frac{7}{2}\right)$ **27.** 2; (−5, 2) **29.** 32; (−4, 32)
31. Range: {−19, −13, −7, −1, 5}; the ordered pairs (−5, −19), (−3, −13), (−1, −7), (1, −1), and (3, 5) belong to the function. **33.** Range: {1, 2, 3, 4, 5}; the ordered pairs (−4, 1), (−2, 2), (0, 3), (2, 4), and (4, 5) belong to the function. **35.** Range: {6, 7, 15}; the ordered pairs (−3, 15), (−1, 7), (0, 6), (1, 7), and (3, 15) belong to the function.
37. x; y; $f(x)$ **39.**

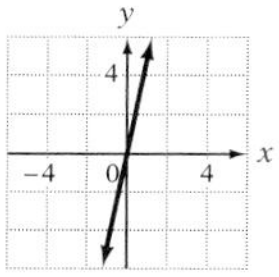

41.

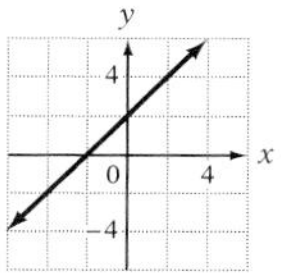

43.

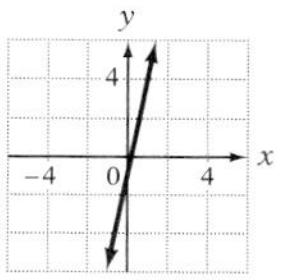

45.

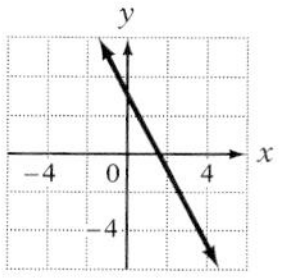

47.

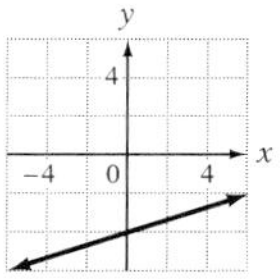

49.

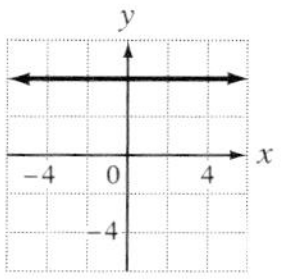

51.

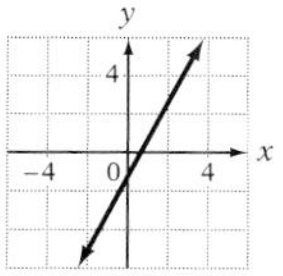

53.

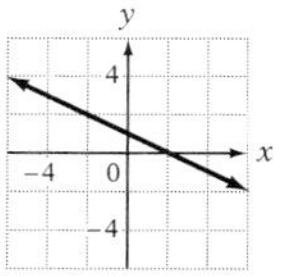

55.

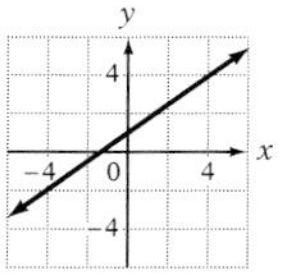

57.

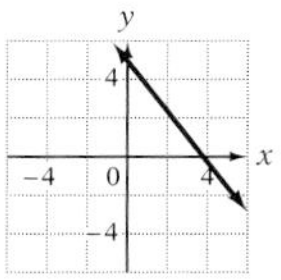

59.

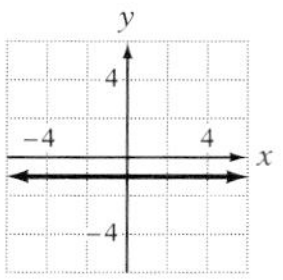

61. No **63. a.** $f(x) = 30{,}000 - 5000x$

b.

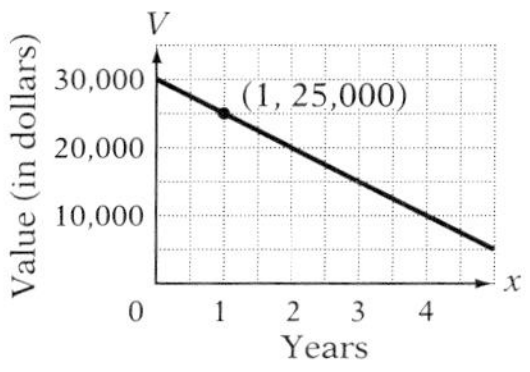

c. The value of the computer after 1 year is $25,000.

65. a. $f(m) = 0.18m + 50$ **b.**

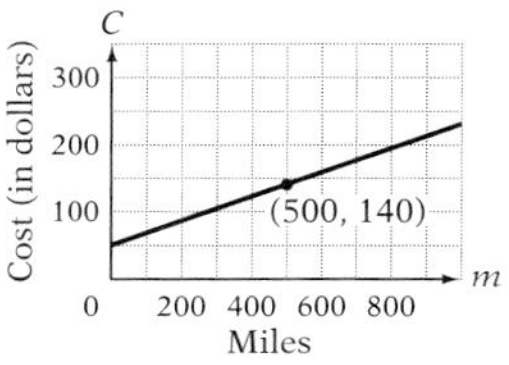

c. The cost to drive this car 500 mi is $140.

CONCEPT REVIEW 5.6

1. Never true **3.** Always true **5.** Always true

SECTION 5.6

3. 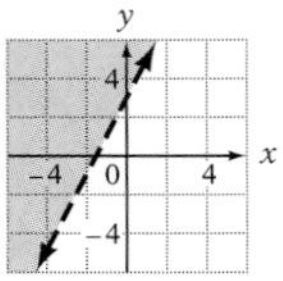

5. 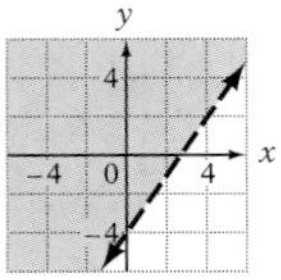

7. 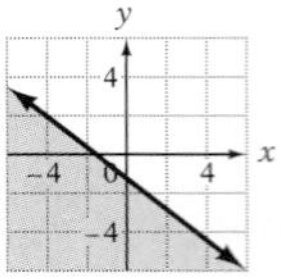

9. 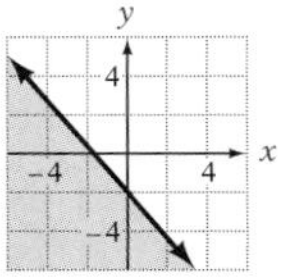

11. 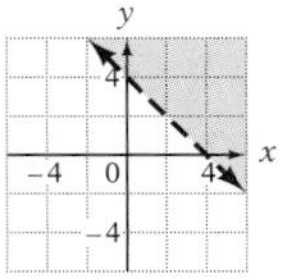

13. 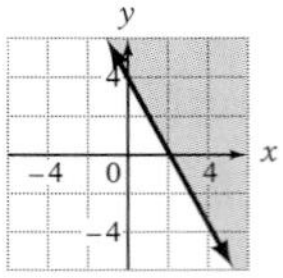

15. 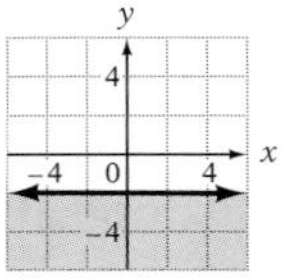

17. 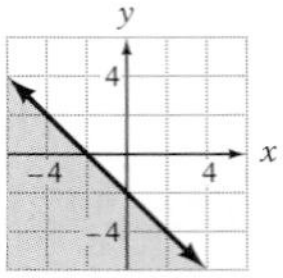

19. Negative

21. $y \geq 2x + 2$

23. $y > 2$

25. 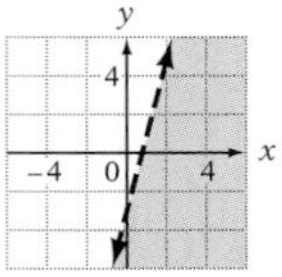

27. 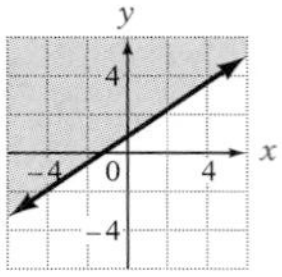

CHAPTER 5 REVIEW EXERCISES

1. (3, 0) [5.2.1]

2. $y = 3x - 1$ [5.4.1/5.4.2]

3. 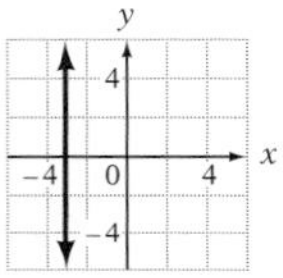 [5.2.3]

4. 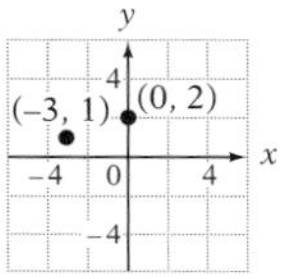

[5.1.1]

5. 79 [5.5.1]

6. 0 [5.3.1]

7. 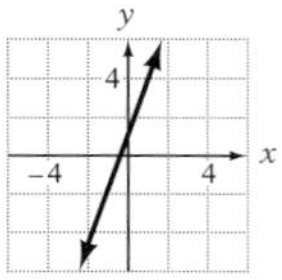 [5.2.2]

8. 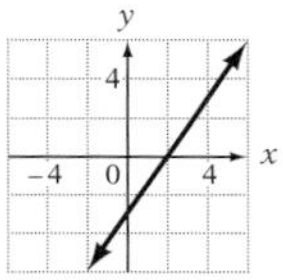 [5.2.3]

9. $y = -\frac{2}{3}x + \frac{4}{3}$ [5.4.1/5.4.2]

10. (2, 0), (0, −3) [5.2.3]

11. 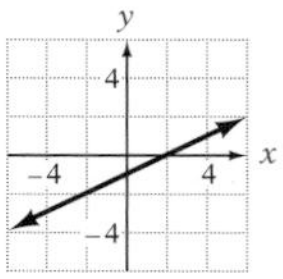 [5.3.2]

12. 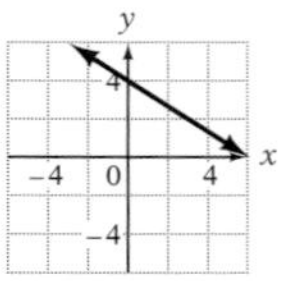 [5.5.2]

13. $y = \frac{2}{3}x + 3$ [5.4.1/5.4.2]

14. 2 [5.3.1]

15. −4 [5.5.1]

16. Domain: {−20, −10, 0, 10}; range: {−10, −5, 0, 5}; yes [5.5.1]

17. 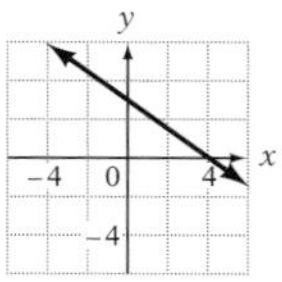 [5.2.2]

18. 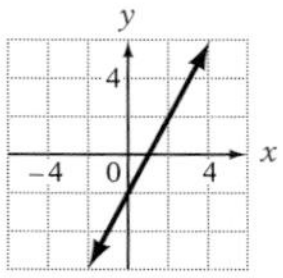 [5.3.2]

19. 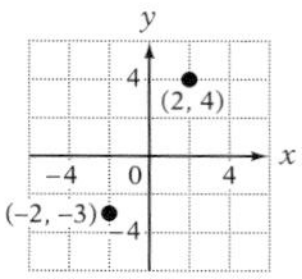

[5.1.1]

20. 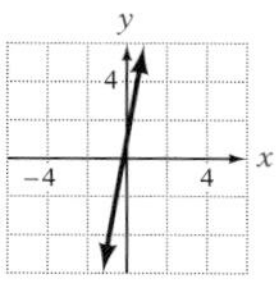 [5.5.2]

21. (6, 0), (0, −4) [5.2.3] **22.** $y = 2x + 2$ [5.4.1/5.4.2] **23.**

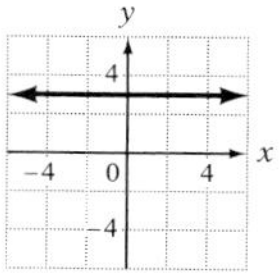

[5.2.3]

24.

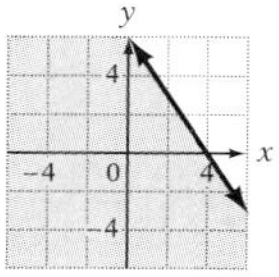

[5.6.1] **25.** Yes [5.3.1] **26.** $y = \frac{5}{4}x + 9$ [5.4.3] **27.**

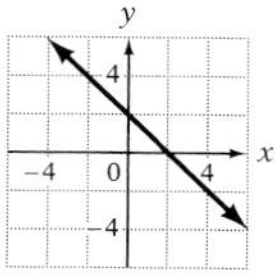

[5.3.2]

28.

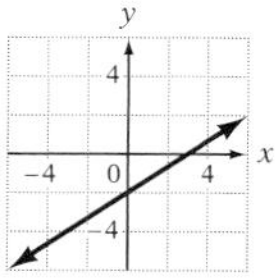

[5.2.3] **29.** (−2, −5) [5.2.1] **30.** $y = -3x + 2$ [5.4.1/5.4.2]

31.

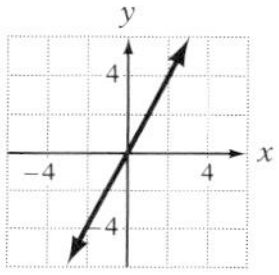

[5.5.2] **32.** 0 [5.5.1] **33.** $y = -\frac{1}{3}x - 2$ [5.4.3] **34.** $y = \frac{1}{2}x - 2$ [5.4.1/5.4.2]

35. Yes [5.2.1] **36.** (2, −1) [5.2.1] **37.** (0, 0); (0, 0) [5.2.3] **38.** $y = 3$ [5.4.1/5.4.2]

39.

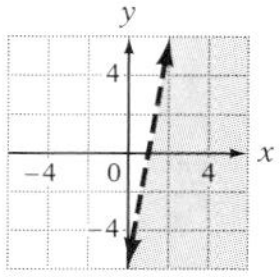

[5.6.1] **40.**

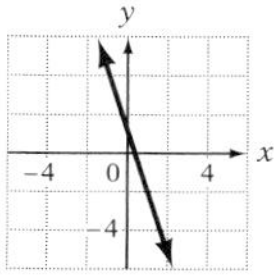

[5.3.2] **41.** $y = 3x - 4$ [5.4.1/5.4.2]

42.

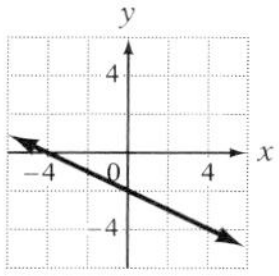

[5.2.3] **43.** Domain: {−10, −5, 5}; range {−5, 0}; no [5.5.1]

44. Range: {−53, −23, 7, 37, 67} [5.5.1] **45.** Range: {2, 3, 4, 5, 6} [5.5.1]

46.

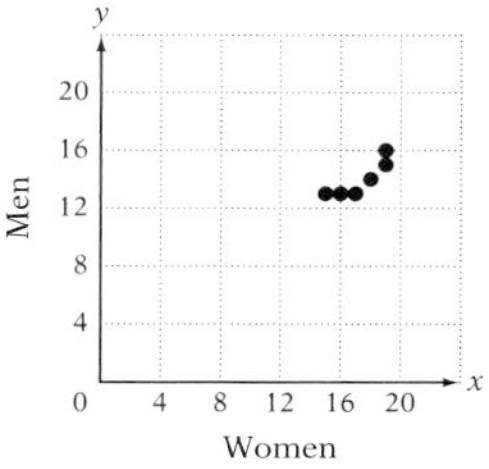

[5.1.2] **47.**

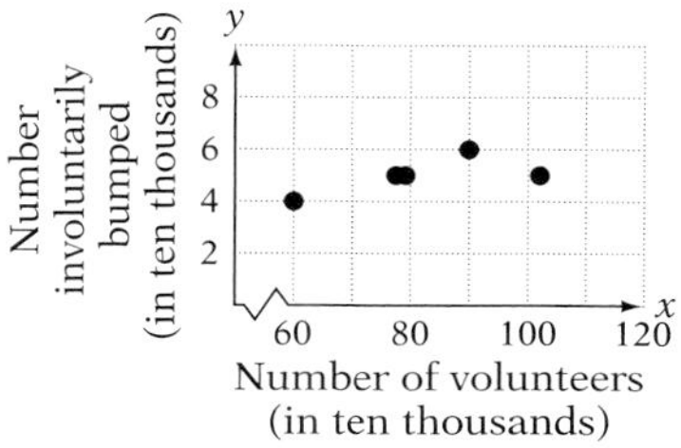

[5.1.2]

48. {(25, 4.8), (35, 3.5), (40, 2.1), (20, 5.5), (45, 1.0)}; yes [5.5.1]

49. **a.** $f(s) = 70s + 40{,}000$ **b.**

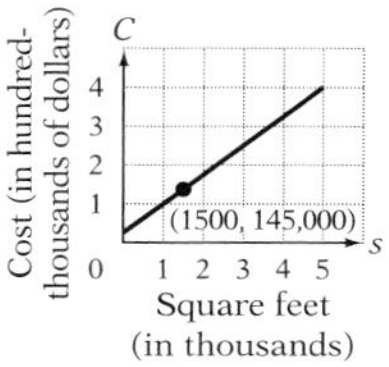

c. The contractor's cost to build a house of 1500 ft² is $145,000. [5.5.2]

50. The average hourly rate of change was 46 cents per year. [5.1.3]

CHAPTER 5 TEST

1. $y = -\frac{1}{3}x$ [5.4.1/5.4.2] **2.** $\frac{7}{11}$ [5.3.1] **3.** (8, 0); (0, −12) [5.2.3] **4.** (9, −13) [5.2.1]

5. 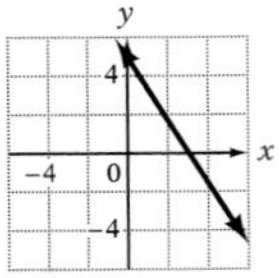 [5.2.3] **6.** 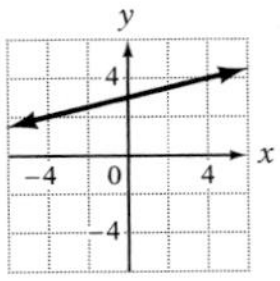 [5.2.2] **7.** 10 [5.5.1] **8.** No [5.2.1]

9. 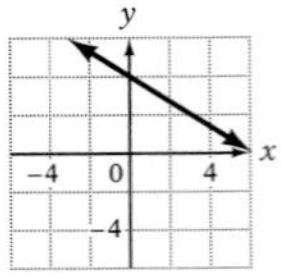 [5.3.2] **10.** 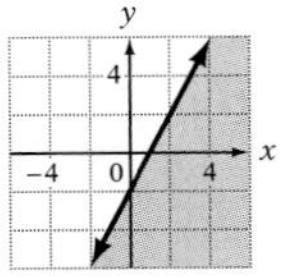 [5.6.1] **11.** 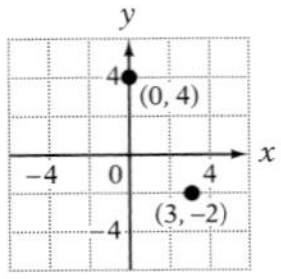

[5.1.1]

12. 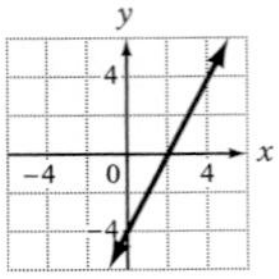 [5.3.2] **13.** $y = \frac{3}{5}x + 8$ [5.4.3] **14.** $y = -\frac{2}{5}x + 7$ [5.4.1/5.4.2]

15. $y = 4x - 7$ [5.4.1/5.4.2] **16.** 13 [5.5.1] **17.** 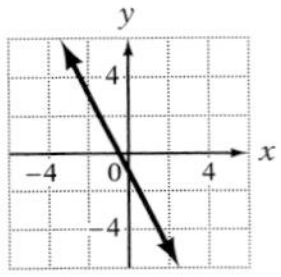 [5.2.2] **18.** 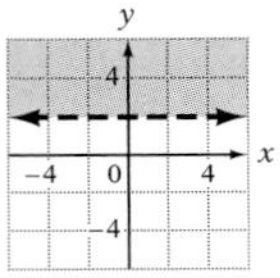 [5.6.1]

19. 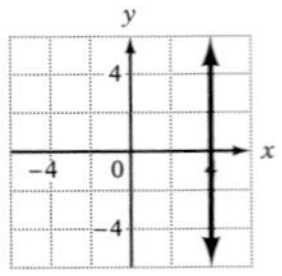 [5.2.3] **20.** 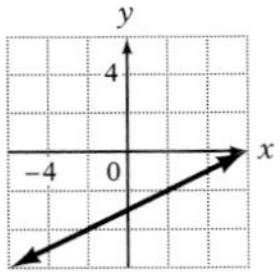 [5.3.2] **21.** 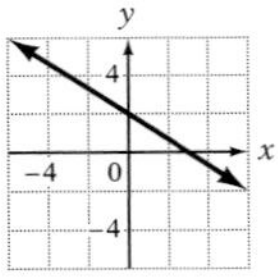 [5.5.2]

22. 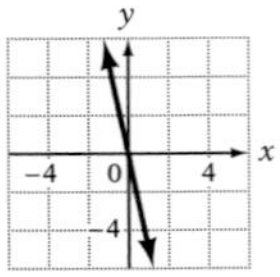 [5.5.2] **23.** 25 [5.5.1] **24.** {−22, −7, 5, 11, 26} [5.5.1] **25.** No [5.3.1]

26. The average annual rate of change was 0.5 million drivers per year. [5.1.3]

27. 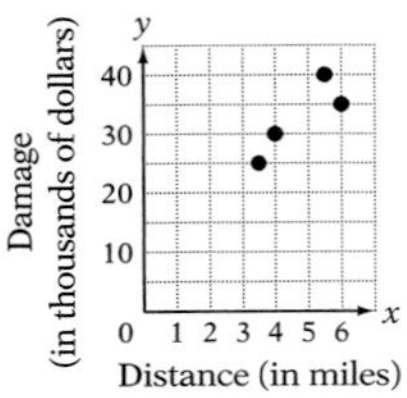

[5.1.2] **28. a.** $f(t) = 8t + 1000$ **b.** 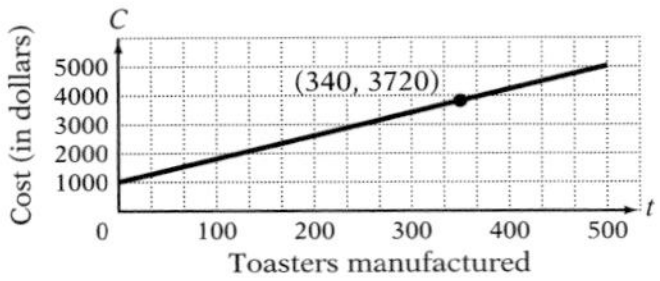

c. The cost to manufacture 340 toasters is $3720. [5.5.2]

29. {(8.5, 64), (9.4, 68), (10.1, 76), (11.4, 87), (12.0, 92)}; yes [5.5.1] **30.** The slope is 36. The cost of lumber has been increasing by $36 per month. [5.3.1]

CUMULATIVE REVIEW EXERCISES

1. −12 [1.4.2] **2.** $-\frac{5}{8}$ [2.1.1] **3.** $-17x + 28$ [2.2.5] **4.** $\frac{3}{2}$ [3.2.1] **5.** 1 [3.2.3]

6. $\frac{1}{15}$ [1.3.4] **7.** {1, 2, 3, 4, 5, 6, 7, 8} [1.1.1] **8.** −4, 0, 5 [1.1.1] **9.** $a \geq -1$ [3.3.3]

10. $y = \frac{4}{5}x - 3$ [5.2.3] **11.** $(-2, -7)$ [5.2.1] **12.** 0 [5.3.1] **13.** $(4, 0)$; $(0, 10)$ [5.2.3]
14. $y = -x + 5$ [5.4.1/5.4.2] **15.** 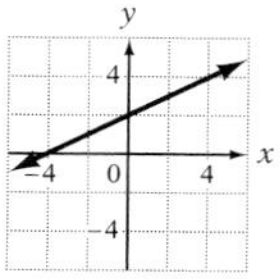 [5.2.2] **16.** 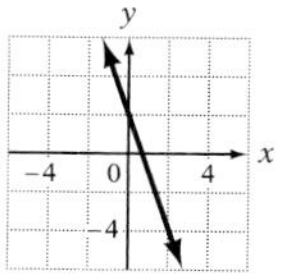 [5.2.3]

17. 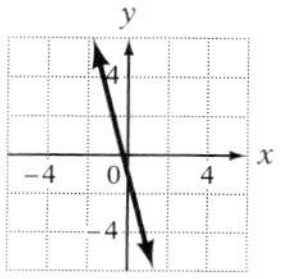 [5.5.2] **18.** 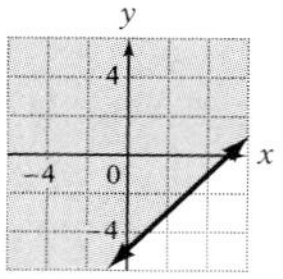 [5.6.1]

19. Domain: {0, 1, 2, 3, 4}; range: {0, 1, 2, 3, 4}; yes [5.5.1] **20.** −11 [5.5.1] **21.** {−7, −2, 3, 8, 13, 18} [5.5.1] **22.** 7 and 17 [4.1.2] **23.** The fulcrum is 7 ft from the 80-pound force. [3.2.4] **24.** The length of the first side is 22 ft. [4.3.1] **25.** The sale price is $62.30. [4.4.2]

Answers to Chapter 6 Selected Exercises

PREP TEST

1. $y = \frac{3}{4}x - 6$ [5.2.3] **2.** 1000 [3.2.3] **3.** $33y$ [2.2.5] **4.** $10x - 10$ [2.2.5] **5.** Yes [5.2.1]
6. $(4, 0)$ and $(0, -3)$ [5.2.3] **7.** Yes [5.3.1] **8.** 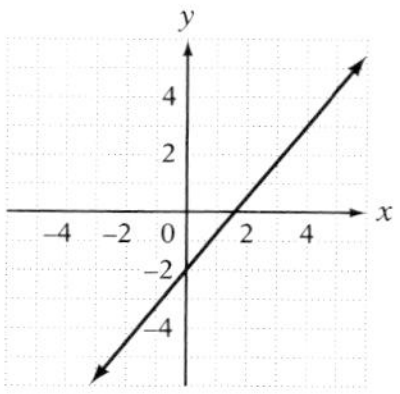 [5.2.2] **9.** 1.5 h [4.7.1]

CONCEPT REVIEW 6.1

1. Always true **3.** Sometimes true **5.** Never true

SECTION 6.1

3. Yes **5.** Yes **7.** No **9.** No **11.** No **13.** Yes **15.** Yes **19.** Independent **21.** Dependent **23.** Inconsistent **25.** $(2, -1)$ **27.** No solution **29.** $(-2, 4)$ **31.** $(4, 1)$ **33.** $(4, 1)$ **35.** $(4, 3)$ **37.** $(3, -2)$ **39.** $(2, -2)$ **41.** The system of equations is inconsistent and has no solution. **43.** The system of equations is dependent. The solutions are the ordered pairs that satisfy the equation $y = 2x - 2$. **45.** $(1, -4)$ **47.** $(0, 0)$ **49.** The system of equations is inconsistent and has no solution. **51.** $(0, -2)$ **53.** $(1, -1)$ **55.** $(2, 0)$ **57.** $(-3, -2)$
59. The system of equations is inconsistent and has no solution. **61.** Inconsistent
63. $y = 2$, $y = x + 4$ **65.** $y = x$, $y = -x + 2$ **67. a.** Always true **b.** Never true **c.** Always true

CONCEPT REVIEW 6.2

1. Always true **3.** Never true **5.** Never true

SECTION 6.2

1. 2; 1; 2; 1 **3.** $(2, 1)$ **5.** $(4, 1)$ **7.** $(-1, 1)$ **9.** $(3, 1)$ **11.** $(1, 1)$ **13.** $(-1, 1)$
15. The system of equations is inconsistent and has no solution. **17.** The system of equations is inconsistent

and has no solution. **19.** $\left(-\frac{3}{4}, -\frac{3}{4}\right)$ **21.** $\left(\frac{9}{5}, \frac{6}{5}\right)$ **23.** (−7, −23) **25.** (1, 1) **27.** (2, 0) **29.** (2, 1) **31.** $\left(\frac{9}{19}, -\frac{13}{19}\right)$ **33.** (5, 7) **35.** (1, 7) **37.** $\left(\frac{17}{5}, -\frac{7}{5}\right)$ **39.** $\left(-\frac{6}{11}, \frac{31}{11}\right)$ **41.** (2, 3) **43.** (0, 0) **45.** The system of equations is dependent. The solutions are the ordered pairs that satisfy the equation $3x + y = 4$. **47.** $\left(\frac{20}{17}, -\frac{15}{17}\right)$ **49.** (5, 2) **51.** (−17, −8) **53.** $\left(-\frac{5}{7}, \frac{13}{7}\right)$ **55.** (3, −2) **57.** Dependent **59.** $\left(-\frac{11}{20}, \frac{23}{40}\right)$ **61.** (3, −2) **63.** (1, 7) **65.** 2 **67.** 2

CONCEPT REVIEW 6.3

1. Always true **3.** Never true **5.** Never true

SECTION 6.3

1. **a** 3 **b** −4 **3.** (5, −1) **5.** (1, 3) **7.** (1, 1) **9.** (3, −2) **11.** The system of equations is dependent. The solutions are the ordered pairs that satisfy the equation $2x - y = 1$. **13.** (3, 1) **15.** The system of equations is inconsistent and has no solution. **17.** (1, 3) **19.** (2, 0) **21.** (0, 0) **23.** (5, −2) **25.** (−17, 7) **27.** (3, 4) **29.** (1, −1) **31.** The system of equations is dependent. The solutions are the ordered pairs that satisfy the equation $x + 3y = 4$. **33.** (3, 1) **35.** $\left(1, \frac{1}{3}\right)$ **37.** (1, 1) **39.** $\left(\frac{1}{2}, -\frac{1}{2}\right)$ **41.** $\left(\frac{2}{3}, \frac{1}{9}\right)$ **43.** $\left(\frac{7}{25}, -\frac{1}{25}\right)$ **45.** $\left(\frac{11}{12}, -\frac{7}{6}\right)$ **47.** (1, 4) **49.** (1, 2) **51.** $A = 3, B = -1$ **53.** $A = 2$ **55.** **a.** $k \neq 1$ **b.** $k \neq \frac{3}{2}$ **c.** $k \neq 4$

CONCEPT REVIEW 6.4

1. Always true **3.** Never true **5.** Never true

SECTION 6.4

1. Row 1: $b + c$; 2; $2(b + c)$; Row 2: $b - c$; 3; $3(b - c)$ **3.** Greater than **5.** The speed of the whale in calm water is 35 mph. The rate of the current is 5 mph. **7.** The team's rowing rate in calm water was 14 km/h. The rate of the current was 6 km/h. **9.** The rate of the boat in calm water was 7 mph. The rate of the current was 3 mph. **11.** The speed of the jet in calm air was 525 mph. The rate of the wind was 35 mph. **13.** The rate of the plane in calm air was 100 mph. The rate of the wind was 20 mph. **15.** The speed of the helicopter in calm air was 225 mph. The rate of the wind was 45 mph. **17.** Table 1: Row 1: 4; A; $4A$; Row 2: 2; C; $2C$; Table 2: Row 1: 2; A; $2A$; Row 2: 3; C; $3C$ **19.** Less than **21.** The cost is $245. **23.** The cost of the wheat is $.65 per pound. The cost of the rye is $.70 per pound. **25.** The daytime rate is $7 per hour. The nighttime rate is $9 per hour. **27.** The team scored 21 two-point baskets and 15 three-point baskets. **29.** There are 8 nickels and 10 quarters in the first bank. **31.** There are 8 dimes and 10 quarters in the bank. **33.** The two angles measure 55° and 125°. **35.** $6000 was invested in the 9% account, and $4000 was invested in the 8% account. **37.** There are 0 dimes and 5 nickels, or 1 dime and 3 nickels, or 2 dimes and 1 nickel in the bank.

CHAPTER 6 REVIEW EXERCISES

1. (−1, 1) [6.2.1] **2.** (2, −3) [6.1.1] **3.** (−3, 1) [6.3.1] **4.** (1, 6) [6.2.1] **5.** (1, 1) [6.1.1] **6.** (1, −5) [6.3.1] **7.** (3, 2) [6.2.1] **8.** The system of equations is dependent. The solutions are the ordered pairs that satisfy the equation $8x - y = 25$. [6.3.1] **9.** (3, −1) [6.3.1] **10.** (1, −3) [6.1.1] **11.** (−2, −7) [6.3.1] **12.** (4, 0) [6.2.1] **13.** Yes [6.1.1] **14.** $\left(-\frac{5}{6}, \frac{1}{2}\right)$ [6.3.1]

15. (−1, −2) [6.3.1] **16.** (3, −3) [6.1.1] **17.** The system of equations is inconsistent and has no solution. [6.3.1] **18.** $\left(-\frac{1}{3}, \frac{1}{6}\right)$ [6.2.1] **19.** The system of equations is dependent. The solutions are the ordered pairs that satisfy the equation $y = 2x - 4$. [6.1.1] **20.** The system of equations is dependent. The solutions are the ordered pairs that satisfy the equation $3x + y = -2$. [6.3.1] **21.** (−2, −13) [6.3.1] **22.** The system of equations is dependent. The solutions are the ordered pairs that satisfy the equation $4x + 3y = 12$. [6.2.1] **23.** (4, 2) [6.1.1] **24.** The system of equations is inconsistent and has no solution. [6.3.1] **25.** $\left(\frac{1}{2}, -1\right)$ [6.2.1] **26.** No [6.1.1] **27.** $\left(\frac{2}{3}, -\frac{1}{6}\right)$ [6.3.1] **28.** The system of equations is inconsistent and has no solution. [6.2.1] **29.** $\left(\frac{1}{3}, 6\right)$ [6.2.1] **30.** The system of equations is inconsistent and has no solution. [6.1.1] **31.** (0, −1) [6.3.1] **32.** (−1, −3) [6.2.1] **33.** (0, −2) [6.2.1] **34.** (2, 0) [6.3.1] **35.** (−4, 2) [6.3.1] **36.** (1, 6) [6.2.1] **37.** The rate of the plane in calm air is 180 mph. The rate of the wind is 20 mph. [6.4.1] **38.** There were 60 adult tickets and 140 children's tickets sold. [6.4.2] **39.** The rate of the canoeist in calm water was 8 mph. The rate of the current was 2 mph. [6.4.1] **40.** There were 130 mailings requiring 33¢ in postage. [6.4.2] **41.** The rate of the boat in calm water was 14 km/h. The rate of the current was 2 km/h. [6.4.1] **42.** The customer purchased 4 compact discs at $15 each and 6 at $10 each. [6.4.2] **43.** The rate of the plane in calm air was 125 km/h. The rate of the wind was 15 km/h. [6.4.1] **44.** The rate of the paddle boat in calm water was 3 mph. The rate of the current was 1 mph. [6.4.1] **45.** There are 350 bushels of lentils and 200 bushels of corn in the silo. [6.4.2] **46.** The rate of the plane in calm air was 105 mph. The rate of the wind was 15 mph. [6.4.1] **47.** There are 4 dimes in the coin purse. [6.4.2] **48.** The rate of the plane in calm air was 325 mph. The rate of the wind was 25 mph. [6.4.1] **49.** The investor bought 1300 of the $6 shares and 200 of the $25 shares. [6.4.2] **50.** The rate of the sculling team in calm water was 9 mph. The rate of the current was 3 mph. [6.4.1]

CHAPTER 6 TEST

1. (3, 1) [6.2.1] **2.** (2, 1) [6.3.1] **3.** Yes [6.1.1] **4.** (1, −1) [6.2.1] **5.** $\left(\frac{1}{2}, -1\right)$ [6.3.1] **6.** (−2, 6) [6.1.1] **7.** The system of equations is inconsistent and has no solution. [6.2.1] **8.** (2, −1) [6.2.1] **9.** (2, −1) [6.3.1] **10.** $\left(\frac{22}{7}, -\frac{5}{7}\right)$ [6.2.1] **11.** (1, −2) [6.3.1] **12.** No [6.1.1] **13.** (2, 1) [6.2.1] **14.** (2, −2) [6.3.1] **15.** (2, 0) [6.1.1] **16.** (4, 1) [6.2.1] **17.** (3, −2) [6.3.1] **18.** The system of equations is dependent. The solutions are the ordered pairs that satisfy the equation $3x + 6y = 2$. [6.1.1] **19.** (1, 1) [6.2.1] **20.** (4, −3) [6.3.1] **21.** (−6, 1) [6.2.1] **22.** (1, −4) [6.3.1] **23.** The rate of the plane in calm air is 100 mph. The rate of the wind is 20 mph. [6.4.1] **24.** The rate of the boat in calm water is 14 mph. The rate of the current is 2 mph. [6.4.1] **25.** There are 40 dimes and 30 nickels in the first bank. [6.4.2]

CUMULATIVE REVIEW EXERCISES

1. −8, −4 [1.1.1] **2.** {1, 2, 3, 4, 5, 6, 7, 8, 9, 10} [1.1.1] **3.** 10 [1.4.2] **4.** $40a - 28$ [2.2.5] **5.** $\frac{3}{2}$ [2.1.1] **6.** $-\frac{3}{2}$ [3.1.3] **7.** $-\frac{7}{2}$ [3.2.3] **8.** $-\frac{2}{9}$ [3.2.3] **9.** $x < -5$ [3.3.3] **10.** $x \le 3$ [3.3.3] **11.** 24% [3.1.5] **12.** (4, 0), (0, −2) [5.2.3] **13.** $-\frac{7}{5}$ [5.3.1]

14. $y = -\frac{3}{2}x$ [5.4.1/5.4.2] **15.** 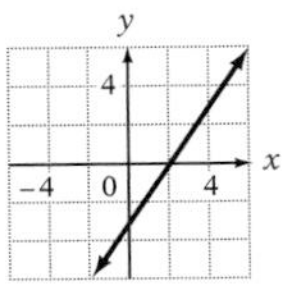 [5.2.3] **16.** 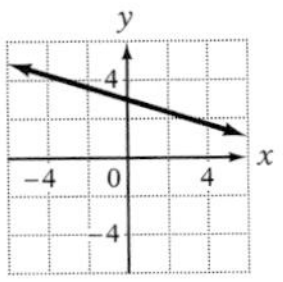 [5.2.2]

17. 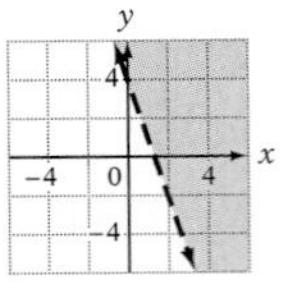 [5.6.1] **18.** 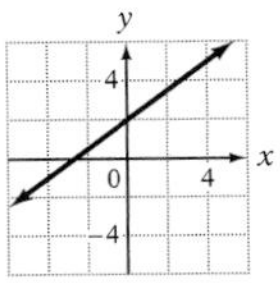 [5.5.2] **19.** Domain: {−5, 0, 1, 5}; range: {5}; yes [5.5.1]

20. 3 [5.5.1] **21.** Yes [6.1.1] **22.** (−2, 1) [6.2.1] **23.** (0, 2) [6.1.1] **24.** (2, 1) [6.3.1] **25.** {−22, −12, −2, 8, 18} [5.5.1] **26.** 200 cameras were produced during the month. [3.2.4] **27.** \$3750 should be invested at 9.6%, and \$5000 should be invested at 7.2%. [4.5.1] **28.** The rate of the plane is 160 mph. The rate of the wind is 30 mph. [6.4.1] **29.** The rate of the boat in calm water is 10 mph. [6.4.1] **30.** There are 40 dimes in the first bank. [6.4.2]

Answers to Chapter 7 Selected Exercises

PREP TEST

1. 1 [1.2.2] **2.** −18 [1.2.3] **3.** $\frac{2}{3}$ [1.2.4] **4.** 48 [2.1.1] **5.** 0 [1.2.4] **6.** No [2.2.2] **7.** $5x^2 - 9x - 6$ [2.2.2] **8.** 0 [2.2.2] **9.** $-6x + 24$ [2.2.4] **10.** $-7xy + 10y$ [2.2.5]

CONCEPT REVIEW 7.1

1. Always true **3.** Never true **5.** Always true

SECTION 7.1

1. Binomial **3.** Monomial **5.** No **7.** Yes **9.** Yes **11.** descending; like **13.** $-2x^2 + 3x$ **15.** $y^2 - 8$ **17.** $5x^2 + 7x + 20$ **19.** $x^3 + 2x^2 - 6x - 6$ **21.** $2a^3 - 3a^2 - 11a + 2$ **23.** $5x^2 + 8x$ **25.** $7x^2 + xy - 4y^2$ **27.** $3a^2 - 3a + 17$ **29.** $5x^3 + 10x^2 - x - 4$ **31.** $3r^3 + 2r^2 - 11r + 7$ **33.** $-2x^3 + 3x^2 + 10x + 11$ **35.** $Q + R$ **37.** $-7x^2 - 5x + 3$ **39.** $4x$ **41.** $3y^2 - 4y - 2$ **43.** $-7x - 7$ **45.** $4x^3 + 3x^2 + 3x + 1$ **47.** $y^3 - y^2 + 6y - 6$ **49.** $-y^2 - 13xy$ **51.** $2x^2 - 3x - 1$ **53.** $-2x^3 + x^2 + 2$ **55.** $3a^3 - 2$ **57.** $4y^3 - 2y^2 + 2y - 4$ **59. a.** Positive **b.** Negative **c.** Positive **61.** $-a^2 - 1$ **63.** $-4x^2 + 6x + 3$ **65.** $4x^2 - 6x + 3$ **67.** Yes. For example, $(3x^3 - 2x^2 + 3x - 4) - (3x^3 + 4x^2 - 6x + 5) = -6x^2 + 9x - 9$

CONCEPT REVIEW 7.2

1. Never true **3.** Always true **5.** Never true

SECTION 7.2

3. 2; a^5; b^3; 10; 6; 5; 1; 3; adding; 11; 4 **5.** $2x^2$ **7.** $12x^2$ **9.** $6a^7$ **11.** x^3y^5 **13.** $-10x^9y$ **15.** x^7y^8 **17.** $-6x^3y^5$ **19.** x^4y^5z **21.** $a^3b^5c^4$ **23.** $-a^5b^8$ **25.** $-6a^5b$ **27.** $40y^{10}z^6$ **29.** $-20a^2b^3$ **31.** $x^3y^5z^3$ **33.** $-12a^{10}b^7$ **37. a.** Power **b.** Product **39. a.** Product **b.** Power **41. a.** Yes **b.** No **c.** No **d.** Yes **43.** 64 **45.** 4 **47.** −64 **49.** x^9 **51.** x^{14} **53.** x^4 **55.** $4x^2$ **57.** $-8x^6$ **59.** x^4y^6 **61.** $9x^4y^2$ **63.** $27a^8$

65. $-8x^7$ **67.** x^8y^4 **69.** a^4b^6 **71.** $16x^{10}y^3$ **73.** $-18x^3y^4$ **75.** $-8a^7b^5$ **77.** $-54a^9b^3$ **79.** $-72a^5b^5$ **81.** $32x^3$ **83.** $-3a^3b^3$ **85.** $13x^5y^5$ **87.** $27a^5b^3$ **89.** $-5x^7y^4$ **91.** a^{2n} **93.** a^{2n} **95.** True **97.** False; $x^{2\cdot5} = x^{10}$ **99.** No; $2^{(3^2)}$ is larger. $(2^3)^2 = 8^2 = 64$, whereas $2^{(3^2)} = 2^9 = 512$. **101.** $x = y$ when n is odd.

CONCEPT REVIEW 7.3

1. Always true **3.** Sometimes true **5.** Always true **7.** Sometimes true

SECTION 7.3

1. $-3y$; $-3y$; Distributive; $-3y$; $-3y^2$; $21y$ **3.** $x^2 - 2x$ **5.** $-x^2 - 7x$ **7.** $3a^3 - 6a^2$ **9.** $-5x^4 + 5x^3$ **11.** $-3x^5 + 7x^3$ **13.** $12x^3 - 6x^2$ **15.** $6x^2 - 12x$ **17.** $-x^3y + xy^3$ **19.** $2x^4 - 3x^2 + 2x$ **21.** $2a^3 + 3a^2 + 2a$ **23.** $3x^6 - 3x^4 - 2x^2$ **25.** $-6y^4 - 12y^3 + 14y^2$ **27.** $-2a^3 - 6a^2 + 8a$ **29.** $6y^4 - 3y^3 + 6y^2$ **31.** $x^3y - 3x^2y^2 + xy^3$ **33.** **b** and **c** **35.** $x^3 + 4x^2 + 5x + 2$ **37.** $a^3 - 6a^2 + 13a - 12$ **39.** $-2b^3 + 7b^2 + 19b - 20$ **41.** $-6x^3 + 31x^2 - 41x + 10$ **43.** $x^4 - 4x^3 - 3x^2 + 14x - 8$ **45.** $15y^3 - 16y^2 - 70y + 16$ **47.** $5a^4 - 20a^3 - 15a^2 + 62a - 8$ **49.** $y^4 + 4y^3 + y^2 - 5y + 2$ **51. a.** 4 **b.** 5 **53.** $4x$; x; $4x$; 5; -3; x; -3; 5 **55. a.** $3d$; d **b.** $3d$; -1 **c.** 4; d **d.** 4; -1 **57.** $x^2 + 4x + 3$ **59.** $a^2 + a - 12$ **61.** $y^2 - 5y - 24$ **63.** $y^2 - 10y + 21$ **65.** $2x^2 + 15x + 7$ **67.** $3x^2 + 11x - 4$ **69.** $4x^2 - 31x + 21$ **71.** $3y^2 - 2y - 16$ **73.** $9x^2 + 54x + 77$ **75.** $21a^2 - 83a + 80$ **77.** $15b^2 + 47b - 78$ **79.** $2a^2 + 7ab + 3b^2$ **81.** $6a^2 + ab - 2b^2$ **83.** $2x^2 - 3xy - 2y^2$ **85.** $10x^2 + 29xy + 21y^2$ **87.** $6a^2 - 25ab + 14b^2$ **89.** $2a^2 - 11ab - 63b^2$ **91.** $100a^2 - 100ab + 21b^2$ **93.** $15x^2 + 56xy + 48y^2$ **95.** $14x^2 - 97xy - 60y^2$ **97.** $56x^2 - 61xy + 15y^2$ **99.** Positive **101.** $5x$; 1; $25x^2$; 1 **103.** $y^2 - 25$ **105.** $4x^2 - 9$ **107.** $x^2 + 2x + 1$ **109.** $9a^2 - 30a + 25$ **111.** $9x^2 - 49$ **113.** $4a^2 + 4ab + b^2$ **115.** $x^2 - 4xy + 4y^2$ **117.** $16 - 9y^2$ **119.** $25x^2 + 20xy + 4y^2$ **121.** Zero **123.** Positive **125.** $2x + 5$; $2x - 5$; $4x^2 - 25$ **127.** The area is $(10x^2 - 35x)$ ft^2. **129.** The area is $(18x^2 + 12x + 2)$ in^2. **131.** The area is $(4x^2 + 4x + 1)$ km^2. **133.** The area is $(4x^2 + 10x)$ m^2. **135.** The area is $(\pi x^2 + 8\pi x + 16\pi)$ cm^2. **137.** The area is $(90x + 2025)$ ft^2. **139.** $4ab$ **141.** $9a^4 - 24a^3 + 28a^2 - 16a + 4$ **143.** $24x^3 - 3x^2$ **145.** $x^{2n} + x^n$ **147.** $x^{2n} + 2x^n + 1$ **149.** $x^2 - 1$ **151.** $x^4 - 1$ **153.** $x^6 - 1$ **155.** 1024 **157.** $12x^2 - x - 20$ **159.** $7x^2 - 11x - 8$

CONCEPT REVIEW 7.4

1. Never true **3.** Always true **5.** Never true **7.** Never true

SECTION 7.4

1. $\frac{1}{25}$ **3.** 64 **5.** $\frac{1}{27}$ **7.** 1 **11.** 4; 10; 3; $4x^7$ **13.** y^4 **15.** a^3 **17.** p^4 **19.** $2x^3$ **21.** $2k$ **23.** m^5n^2 **25.** $\frac{3r^2}{2}$ **27.** $-\frac{2a}{3}$ **29.** $\frac{1}{x^2}$ **31.** a^6 **33.** $\frac{4}{x^7}$ **35.** $5b^8$ **37.** $\frac{x^2}{3}$ **39.** 1 **41.** $\frac{1}{y^5}$ **43.** $\frac{1}{a^6}$ **45.** $\frac{1}{3x^3}$ **47.** $\frac{2}{3x^5}$ **49.** $\frac{y^4}{x^2}$ **51.** $\frac{2}{5m^3n^8}$ **53.** $\frac{1}{p^3q}$ **55.** $\frac{1}{2y^3}$ **57.** $\frac{7xz}{8y^3}$ **59.** $\frac{p^2}{2m^3}$ **61.** $-\frac{8x^3}{y^6}$ **63.** $\frac{9}{x^2y^4}$ **65.** $\frac{2}{x^4}$ **67.** $-\frac{5}{a^8}$ **69.** $-\frac{a^5}{8b^4}$ **71.** $\frac{10y^3}{x^4}$ **73.** $\frac{1}{2x^3}$ **75.** $\frac{3}{x^3}$ **77.** $\frac{1}{2x^2y^6}$ **79.** $-\frac{1}{6x^3}$ **81. a.** False **b.** True **85.** 8; left; 8 **87.** No. 39.4 is not between 1 and 10.

89. No. 2.4 is not an integer. **91.** 2.37×10^6 **93.** 4.5×10^{-4} **95.** 3.09×10^5 **97.** 6.01×10^{-7} **99.** 710,000 **101.** 0.000043 **103.** 671,000,000 **105.** 0.00000713 **107.** 1×10^{21} **109.** 4×10^{-10} **111.** 1.2×10^{10} **113.** 2.45×10^9 **115.** 6.65×10^{19} **117.** 3.22×10^{-14} **119.** 3.6×10^5 **121.** 1.8×10^{-18} **123.** Less than **125.** $\frac{3}{64}$ **127.** For 2^x: $\frac{1}{4}, \frac{1}{2}$, 1, 2, 4. For 2^{-x}: 4, 2, 1, $\frac{1}{2}, \frac{1}{4}$. **129.** 0.0625 **131.** xy^2 **133.** $\frac{x^6z^6}{4y^5}$ **135.** 1 **137.** 0 **139.** False; $(2a)^{-3} = \frac{1}{8a^3}$ **141.** False; $(2 + 3)^{-1} = 5^{-1} = \frac{1}{5}$

CONCEPT REVIEW 7.5

1. Always true **3.** Never true

SECTION 7.5

1. $3y$; $3y$; $6y^4$; 1 **3.** $x + 1$ **5.** $2a - 5$ **7.** $3a + 2$ **9.** $4b^2 - 3$ **11.** $x - 2$ **13.** $-x + 2$ **15.** $x^2 + 3x - 5$ **17.** $x^4 - 3x^2 - 1$ **19.** $xy + 2$ **21.** $-3y^3 + 5$ **23.** $3x - 2 + \frac{1}{x}$ **25.** $-3x + 7 - \frac{6}{x}$ **27.** $4a - 5 + 6b$ **29.** $9x + 6 - 3y$ **31.** Multiply $4x$ and $2x^2 - 3x - 1$. $4x(2x^2 - 3x - 1) = 8x^3 - 12x^2 - 4x$ **33. a.** $3x^2$; x **b.** $3x$; $x - 2$ **c.** $-4x$; $-6x$ **d.** $3x + 2$; 11 **35.** $x + 2$ **37.** $2x + 1$ **39.** $2x - 4$ **41.** $x + 1 + \frac{2}{x - 1}$ **43.** $2x - 1 - \frac{2}{3x - 2}$ **45.** $5x + 12 + \frac{12}{x - 1}$ **47.** $a + 3 + \frac{4}{a + 2}$ **49.** $y - 6 + \frac{26}{2y + 3}$ **51.** $2x + 5 + \frac{8}{2x - 1}$ **53.** $5a - 6 + \frac{4}{3a + 2}$ **55.** $3x - 5$ **57.** $x^2 + 2x + 3$ **59.** $x^2 - 3$ **61.** False **63.** $(x + 2)$, $(x - 3)$ **65.** $3a^2$ **67.** $4x^2 - 6x + 3$

CHAPTER 7 REVIEW EXERCISES

1. $21y^2 + 4y - 1$ [7.1.1] **2.** $-20x^3y^5$ [7.2.1] **3.** $-8x^3 - 14x^2 + 18x$ [7.3.1] **4.** $10a^2 + 31a - 63$ [7.3.3] **5.** $6x^2 - 7x + 10$ [7.5.1] **6.** $2x^2 + 3x - 8$ [7.1.2] **7.** -729 [7.2.2] **8.** $x^3 - 6x^2 + 7x - 2$ [7.3.2] **9.** $a^2 - 49$ [7.3.4] **10.** 1296 [7.4.1] **11.** $x - 6$ [7.5.2] **12.** $2x^3 + 9x^2 - 3x - 12$ [7.1.1] **13.** $18a^8b^6$ [7.2.1] **14.** $3x^4y - 2x^3y + 12x^2y$ [7.3.1] **15.** $8b^2 - 2b - 15$ [7.3.3] **16.** $-4y + 8$ [7.5.1] **17.** $13y^3 - 12y^2 - 5y - 1$ [7.1.2] **18.** 64 [7.2.2] **19.** $6y^3 + 17y^2 - 2y - 21$ [7.3.2] **20.** $4b^2 - 81$ [7.3.4] **21.** $\frac{b^6c^2}{a^4}$ [7.4.1] **22.** $2y - 9$ [7.5.2] **23.** 3.97×10^{-6} [7.4.2] **24.** $x^4y^8z^4$ [7.2.1] **25.** $-12y^5 + 4y^4 - 18y^3$ [7.3.1] **26.** $18x^2 - 48x + 24$ [7.3.3] **27.** 0.0000623 [7.4.2] **28.** $-7a^2 - a + 4$ [7.1.2] **29.** $9x^4y^6$ [7.2.2] **30.** $12a^3 - 8a^2 - 9a + 6$ [7.3.3] **31.** $25y^2 - 70y + 49$ [7.3.4] **32.** $\frac{x^4y^6}{9}$ [7.4.1] **33.** $x + 5 + \frac{4}{x + 12}$ [7.5.2] **34.** 240,000 [7.4.2] **35.** $a^6b^{11}c^9$ [7.2.1] **36.** $8a^3b^3 - 4a^2b^4 + 6ab^5$ [7.3.1] **37.** $6x^2 - 7xy - 20y^2$ [7.3.3] **38.** $4b^4 + 12b^2 - 1$ [7.5.1] **39.** $-4b^2 - 13b + 28$ [7.1.2] **40.** $100a^{15}b^{13}$ [7.2.2] **41.** $12b^5 - 4b^4 - 6b^3 - 8b^2 + 5$ [7.3.2] **42.** $36 - 25x^2$ [7.3.4] **43.** $\frac{2y^3}{x^3}$ [7.4.1] **44.** $a^2 - 2a + 6$ [7.5.2] **45.** $4b^3 - 5b^2 - 9b + 7$ [7.1.1] **46.** $-54a^{13}b^5c^7$ [7.2.1] **47.** $-18x^4 - 27x^3 + 63x^2$ [7.3.1] **48.** $30y^2 - 109y + 30$ [7.3.3] **49.** 9.176×10^{12} [7.4.2] **50.** $-2y^2 + y - 5$ [7.1.2] **51.** $144x^{14}y^{18}z^{16}$ [7.2.2]

52. $-12x^4 - 17x^3 - 2x^2 - 33x - 27$ [7.3.2] **53.** $64a^2 + 16a + 1$ [7.3.4] **54.** $\frac{2}{ab^6}$ [7.4.1] **55.** $b^2 + 5b + 2 + \frac{7}{b - 7}$ [7.5.2] **56.** The area is $(20x^2 - 35x)$ m^2. [7.3.5] **57.** The area is $(25x^2 + 40x + 16)$ in^2. [7.3.5] **58.** The area is $(9x^2 - 4)$ ft^2. [7.3.5] **59.** The area is $(\pi x^2 - 12\pi x + 36\pi)$ cm^2. [7.3.5] **60.** The area is $(15x^2 - 28x - 32)$ mi^2. [7.3.5]

CHAPTER 7 TEST

1. $3x^3 + 6x^2 - 8x + 3$ [7.1.1] **2.** $-4x^4 + 8x^3 - 3x^2 - 14x + 21$ [7.3.2] **3.** $4x^3 - 6x^2$ [7.3.1] **4.** $-8a^6b^3$ [7.2.2] **5.** $-4x^6$ [7.4.1] **6.** $\frac{6b}{a}$ [7.4.1] **7.** $-5a^3 + 3a^2 - 4a + 3$ [7.1.2] **8.** $a^2 + 3ab - 10b^2$ [7.3.3] **9.** $4x^4 - 2x^2 + 5$ [7.5.1] **10.** $2x + 3 + \frac{2}{2x - 3}$ [7.5.2] **11.** $-6x^3y^6$ [7.2.1] **12.** $6y^4 - 9y^3 + 18y^2$ [7.3.1] **13.** $\frac{9}{x^3}$ [7.4.1] **14.** $4x^2 - 20x + 25$ [7.3.4] **15.** $10x^2 - 43xy + 28y^2$ [7.3.3] **16.** $x^3 - 7x^2 + 17x - 15$ [7.3.2] **17.** $\frac{a^4}{b^6}$ [7.4.1] **18.** 2.9×10^{-5} [7.4.2] **19.** $16y^2 - 9$ [7.3.4] **20.** $3y^3 + 2y^2 - 10y$ [7.1.2] **21.** $9a^6b^4$ [7.2.2] **22.** $10a^3 - 39a^2 + 20a - 21$ [7.3.2] **23.** $9b^2 + 12b + 4$ [7.3.4] **24.** $-\frac{1}{4a^2b^5}$ [7.4.1] **25.** $4x + 8 + \frac{21}{2x - 3}$ [7.5.2] **26.** a^3b^7 [7.2.1] **27.** $a^2 + ab - 12b^2$ [7.3.3] **28.** 0.000000035 [7.4.2] **29.** The area is $(4x^2 + 12x + 9)$ m^2. [7.3.5] **30.** The area is $(\pi x^2 - 10\pi x + 25\pi)$ in^2. [7.3.5]

CUMULATIVE REVIEW EXERCISES

1. $\frac{1}{144}$ [1.3.3] **2.** $\frac{25}{9}$ [1.4.1] **3.** $\frac{4}{5}$ [1.4.2] **4.** 87 [1.1.2] **5.** 0.775 [1.3.1] **6.** $-\frac{27}{4}$ [2.1.1] **7.** $-x - 4xy$ [2.2.2] **8.** $-12x$ [2.2.3] **9.** $-22x + 20$ [2.2.5] **10.** 8 [2.2.1] **11.** -18 [3.1.3] **12.** 16 [3.2.2] **13.** 12 [3.2.3] **14.** 80 [3.2.2] **15.** 24% [3.1.5] **16.** $x \geq -3$ [3.3.3] **17.** $-\frac{9}{5}$ [5.3.1] **18.** $y = -\frac{3}{2}x - \frac{3}{2}$ [5.4.1/5.4.2] **19.**

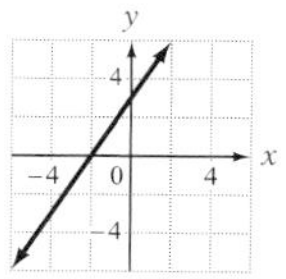

[5.2.3] **20.**

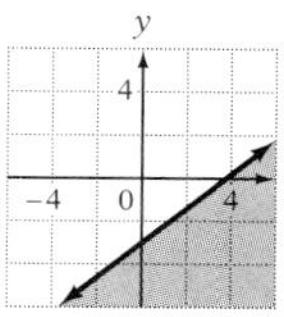

[5.6.1]

21. Domain: {−8, −6, −4, −2}; range: {−7, −5, −2, 0}; yes [5.5.1] **22.** −2 [5.5.1] **23.** (4, 1) [6.2.1] **24.** (1, −4) [6.3.1] **25.** $5b^3 - 7b^2 + 8b - 10$ [7.1.2] **26.** $15x^3 - 26x^2 + 11x - 4$ [7.3.2] **27.** $20b^2 - 47b + 24$ [7.3.3] **28.** $25b^2 + 30b + 9$ [7.3.4] **29.** $-\frac{b^4}{4a}$ [7.4.1] **30.** $5y - 4 + \frac{1}{y}$ [7.5.1] **31.** $a - 7$ [7.5.2] **32.** $\frac{9y^2}{x^6}$ [7.4.1] **33.** {1, 9, 17, 21, 25} [5.5.1] **34.** $5(n - 12)$; $5n - 60$ [2.3.2] **35.** $8n - 2n = 18$; $n = 3$ [4.1.1] **36.** The length is 15 m. The width is 6 m. [4.3.1] **37.** The selling price is $43.20. [4.4.1] **38.** The concentration of orange juice is 28%. [4.6.2] **39.** The car overtakes the cyclist 25 mi from the starting point. [4.7.1] **40.** The area is $(9x^2 + 12x + 4)$ ft^2. [7.3.5]

Answers to Chapter 8 Selected Exercises

PREP TEST

1. $2 \cdot 3 \cdot 5$ [1.3.3] **2.** $-12y + 15$ [2.2.4] **3.** $-a + b$ [2.2.4] **4.** $-3a + 3b$ [2.2.5]
5. 0 [3.1.3] **6.** $-\frac{1}{2}$ [3.2.1] **7.** $x^2 - 2x - 24$ [7.3.3] **8.** $6x^2 - 11x - 10$ [7.3.3]
9. x^3 [7.4.1] **10.** $3x^3y$ [7.4.1]

CONCEPT REVIEW 8.1

1. Always true **3.** Always true **5.** Never true **7.** Never true

SECTION 8.1

3. a. z **b.** 3 **c.** x **d.** y^2 **e.** $3xy^2$ **5.** x^3 **7.** xy^4 **9.** xy^4z^2 **11.** $7a^3$ **13.** 1
15. $3a^2b^2$ **17.** ab **19.** $2x$ **21.** $3x$ **23.** $5(a + 1)$ **25.** $8(2 - a^2)$ **27.** $4(2x + 3)$
29. $6(5a - 1)$ **31.** $x(7x - 3)$ **33.** $a^2(3 + 5a^3)$ **35.** $y(14y + 11)$ **37.** $2x(x^3 - 2)$
39. $2x^2(5x^2 - 6)$ **41.** $xy(x - y^2)$ **43.** $2a^5b + 3xy^3$ **45.** $6b^2(a^2b - 2)$ **47.** $2abc(3a + 2b)$
49. $9(2x^2y^2 - a^2b^2)$ **51.** $6x^3y^3(1 - 2x^3y^3)$ **53.** $x(x^2 - 3x - 1)$ **55.** $2(x^2 + 4x - 6)$
57. $b(b^2 - 5b - 7)$ **59.** $4(2y^2 - 3y + 8)$ **61.** $5y(y^2 - 4y + 2)$ **63.** $3y^2(y^2 - 3y - 2)$
65. $3y(y^2 - 3y + 8)$ **67.** $a^2(6a^3 - 3a - 2)$ **69.** $x^2(8y^2 - 4y + 1)$ **71.** $x^3y^3(4x^2y^2 - 8xy + 1)$
73. x^a **75. a.** $4(3x - 2)$; $3x - 2$ **b.** $5x$; 4 **77.** $(a + b)(x + 2)$ **79.** $(b + 2)(x - y)$
81. $(y - 4)(a - b)$ **83.** $a(x - 2) + b(x - 2)$ **85.** $b(a - 7) - 3(a - 7)$ **87.** $x(a - 2b) + y(a - 2b)$
89. $(x - 2)(a - 5)$ **91.** $(y - 3)(b - 3)$ **93.** $(x - y)(a + 2)$ **95.** $(c + 5)(z - 8)$
97. $(3x - 4)(w + 1)$ **99.** $(x + 4)(x^2 + 3)$ **101.** $(y + 2)(2y^2 + 3)$ **103.** $(a + 3)(b - 2)$
105. $(a - 2)(x^2 - 3)$ **107.** $(a - b)(3x - 2y)$ **109.** $(x - 3)(x + 4a)$ **111.** $(x - 5)(y - 2)$
113. $(7x + 2y)(3x - 7)$ **115.** $(2r + a)(a - 1)$ **117.** $(4x + 3y)(x - 4)$ **119.** $(2y - 3)(5xy + 3)$
121. II **123. a.** $(x + 3)(2x + 5)$ **b.** $(2x + 5)(x + 3)$ **125. a.** $(a - b)(2a - 3b)$
b. $(2a - 3b)(a - b)$ **127.** 28 **129.** P doubles

CONCEPT REVIEW 8.2

1. Never true **3.** Always true **5.** Never true

SECTION 8.2

1.

Factors of 18	Sum
1, 18	19
2, 9	11
3, 6	9

3.

Factors of −21	Sum
1, −21	−20
−1, 21	20
3, −7	−4
−3, 7	4

5.

Factors of −28	Sum
1, −28	−27
−1, 28	27
2, −14	−12
−2, 14	12
4, −7	−3
−4, 7	3

7. $(x + 1)(x + 2)$ **9.** $(x + 1)(x - 2)$ **11.** $(a + 4)(a - 3)$ **13.** $(a - 1)(a - 2)$ **15.** $(a + 2)(a - 1)$
17. $(b - 3)(b - 3)$ **19.** $(b + 8)(b - 1)$ **21.** $(y + 11)(y - 5)$ **23.** $(y - 2)(y - 3)$
25. $(z - 5)(z - 9)$ **27.** $(z + 8)(z - 20)$ **29.** $(p + 3)(p + 9)$ **31.** $(x + 10)(x + 10)$
33. $(b + 4)(b + 5)$ **35.** $(x + 3)(x - 14)$ **37.** $(b + 4)(b - 5)$ **39.** $(y + 3)(y - 17)$
41. $(p + 3)(p - 7)$ **43.** Nonfactorable over the integers **45.** $(x - 5)(x - 15)$ **47.** $(x - 7)(x - 8)$

49. $(x + 8)(x - 7)$ **51.** $(a + 3)(a - 24)$ **53.** $(a - 3)(a - 12)$ **55.** $(z + 8)(z - 17)$ **57.** $(c + 9)(c - 10)$ **59. a.** Positive **b.** Positive **61. a.** common **b.** 5 **c.** $x^2 - 2x - 8$ **d.** $x + 2; x - 4$ **63.** $2(x + 1)(x + 2)$ **65.** $3(a + 3)(a - 2)$ **67.** $a(b + 5)(b - 3)$ **69.** $x(y - 2)(y - 3)$ **71.** $z(z - 3)(z - 4)$ **73.** $3y(y - 2)(y - 3)$ **75.** $3(x + 4)(x - 3)$ **77.** $5(z + 4)(z - 7)$ **79.** $2a(a + 8)(a - 4)$ **81.** $(x - 2y)(x - 3y)$ **83.** $(a - 4b)(a - 5b)$ **85.** $(x + 4y)(x - 7y)$ **87.** Nonfactorable over the integers **89.** $z^2(z - 5)(z - 7)$ **91.** $b^2(b - 10)(b - 12)$ **93.** $2y^2(y + 3)(y - 16)$ **95.** $x^2(x + 8)(x - 1)$ **97.** $4y(x + 7)(x - 2)$ **99.** $8(y - 1)(y - 3)$ **101.** $c(c + 3)(c + 10)$ **103.** $3x(x - 3)(x - 9)$ **105.** $(x - 3y)(x - 5y)$ **107.** $(a - 6b)(a - 7b)$ **109.** $(y + z)(y + 7z)$ **111.** $3y(x + 21)(x - 1)$ **113.** $3x(x + 4)(x - 3)$ **115.** $4z(z + 11)(z - 3)$ **117. a.** Yes **b.** Yes **119.** $(c + 4)(c + 5)$ **121.** $a^2(b - 5)(b - 9)$ **123.** 36, 12, −12, −36 **125.** 22, 10, −10, −22 **127.** 3, 4 **129.** 5, 8, 9 **131.** 2

CONCEPT REVIEW 8.3

1. Never true **3.** Sometimes true **5.** Always true

SECTION 8.3

1. a. 2; −15; 15; −5; 5 **b.** $-29x$; $29x$; $-7x$; $7x$ **c.** $x - 5$; $2x + 3$ **3.** $(x + 1)(2x + 1)$ **5.** $(y + 3)(2y + 1)$ **7.** $(a - 1)(2a - 1)$ **9.** $(b - 5)(2b - 1)$ **11.** $(x + 1)(2x - 1)$ **13.** $(x - 3)(2x + 1)$ **15.** Nonfactorable over the integers **17.** $(2t - 1)(3t - 4)$ **19.** $(x + 4)(8x + 1)$ **21.** $(b - 4)(3b - 4)$ **23.** $(z - 14)(2z + 1)$ **25.** $(p + 8)(3p - 2)$ **27.** $(2x - 3)(3x - 4)$ **29.** $(b + 7)(5b - 2)$ **31.** $(2a - 3)(3a + 8)$ **33.** $(3t + 1)(6t - 5)$ **35.** $(3a + 7)(5a - 3)$ **37.** $(2y - 5)(4y - 3)$ **39.** $(2z + 3)(4z - 5)$ **41.** $(x + 5)(3x - 1)$ **43.** $(3x + 4)(4x + 3)$ **45.** Nonfactorable over the integers **47.** $(x + y)(3x - 2y)$ **49.** $(4 + z)(7 - z)$ **51.** $(1 - x)(8 + x)$ **53.** $3(x + 5)(3x - 4)$ **55.** $4(2x - 3)(3x - 2)$ **57.** $a^2(5a + 2)(7a - 1)$ **59.** $5(b - 7)(3b - 2)$ **61.** $2x(x + 1)(5x + 1)$ **63.** $2y(y - 4)(5y - 2)$ **65.** $yz(z + 2)(4z - 3)$ **67.** $b^2(4b + 5)(5b + 4)$ **69.** $xy(3x + 2)(3x + 2)$ **71.** m and p **73.** −18; −17; 18; 17; −9; −7; 9; 7; −6; −3; 6; 3 **75.** $(t + 2)(2t - 5)$ **77.** $(p - 5)(3p - 1)$ **79.** $(3y - 1)(4y - 1)$ **81.** Nonfactorable over the integers **83.** $(3y + 1)(4y + 5)$ **85.** $(a + 7)(7a - 2)$ **87.** $(z + 2)(4z + 3)$ **89.** $(2p + 5)(11p - 2)$ **91.** $(y + 1)(8y + 9)$ **93.** $(2b - 3)(3b - 2)$ **95.** $(3b + 5)(11b - 7)$ **97.** $(3y - 4)(6y - 5)$ **99.** Nonfactorable over the integers **101.** $(2z - 5)(5z - 2)$ **103.** $(6z + 5)(6z + 7)$ **105.** $(2y - 3)(7y - 4)$ **107.** $(x + 6)(6x - 1)$ **109.** $3(x + 3)(4x - 1)$ **111.** $10(y + 1)(3y - 2)$ **113.** $x(x + 1)(2x - 5)$ **115.** $(a - 3b)(2a - 3b)$ **117.** $(y + z)(2y + 5z)$ **119.** $(1 + x)(18 - x)$ **121.** $4(9y + 1)(10y - 1)$ **123.** $8(t + 4)(2t - 3)$ **125.** $p(2p + 1)(3p + 1)$ **127.** $3(2z - 5)(5z - 2)$ **129.** $3a(2a + 3)(7a - 3)$ **131.** $y(3x - 5y)(3x - 5y)$ **133.** $xy(3x - 4y)(3x - 4y)$ **135.** Two positive **137.** Two negative **139.** $2y(y - 3)(4y - 1)$ **141.** $ab(a + 4)(a - 6)$ **143.** $5t(3 + 2t)(4 - t)$ **145.** $(y + 3)(2y + 1)$ **147.** $(2x - 1)(5x + 7)$ **149.** 7, −7, 5, −5 **151.** 7, −7, 5, −5 **153.** 11, −11, 7, −7 **155.** $(x + 2)(x - 3)(x - 1)$

CONCEPT REVIEW 8.4

1. Never true **3.** Sometimes true **5.** Always true **7.** Never true

SECTION 8.4

1. a. $3x$; 2 **b.** $3x + 2$; $3x - 2$ **3.** Answers will vary. **a.** $x^2 - 16$ **b.** $(x + 7)(x - 7)$ **c.** $x^2 + 10x + 25$ **d.** $(x - 3)^2$ **e.** $x^2 + 36$ **5.** 4; $25x^6$; $100x^4y^4$ **7.** $(x + 2)(x - 2)$ **9.** $(a + 9)(a - 9)$ **11.** $(2x + 1)(2x - 1)$ **13.** $(y + 1)^2$ **15.** $(a - 1)^2$ **17.** Nonfactorable over the integers **19.** $(x^3 + 3)(x^3 - 3)$ **21.** $(5x + 1)(5x - 1)$ **23.** $(1 + 7x)(1 - 7x)$ **25.** $(x + y)^2$ **27.** $(2a + 1)^2$

29. $(8a - 1)^2$ **31.** Nonfactorable over the integers **33.** $(x^2 + y)(x^2 - y)$ **35.** $(3x + 4y)(3x - 4y)$ **37.** $(4b + 1)^2$ **39.** $(2b + 7)^2$ **41.** $(5a + 3b)^2$ **43.** $(xy + 2)(xy - 2)$ **45.** $(4 + xy)(4 - xy)$ **47.** $(2y - 9z)^2$ **49.** $(3ab - 1)^2$ **51.** $(m^2 + 16)(m + 4)(m - 4)$ **53.** $(x + 1)(9x + 4)$ **55.** $(y^4 + 9)(y^2 + 3)(y^2 - 3)$ **57.** **a and c** **59.** common **61.** $2(x + 3)(x - 3)$ **63.** $x^2(x + 7)(x - 5)$ **65.** $5(b + 3)(b + 12)$ **67.** Nonfactorable over the integers **69.** $2y(x + 11)(x - 3)$ **71.** $x(x^2 - 6x - 5)$ **73.** $3(y^2 - 12)$ **75.** $(2a + 1)(10a + 1)$ **77.** $y^2(x + 1)(x - 8)$ **79.** $5(a + b)(2a - 3b)$ **81.** $2(5 + x)(5 - x)$ **83.** $ab(3a - b)(4a + b)$ **85.** $2(x - 1)(a + b)$ **87.** $3a(2a - 1)^2$ **89.** $3(81 + a^2)$ **91.** $2a(2a - 5)(3a - 4)$ **93.** $(x - 2)(x + 1)(x - 1)$ **95.** $a(2a + 5)^2$ **97.** $3b(3a - 1)^2$ **99.** $6(4 + x)(2 - x)$ **101.** $(x + 2)(x - 2)(a + b)$ **103.** $x^2(x + y)(x - y)$ **105.** $2a(3a + 2)^2$ **107.** $b(2 - 3a)(1 + 2a)$ **109.** $(x - 5)(2 + x)(2 - x)$ **111.** $8x(3y + 1)^2$ **113.** $y^2(5 + x)(3 - x)$ **115.** $y(y + 3)(y - 3)$ **117.** $2x^2y^2(x + 1)(x - 1)$ **119.** $x^5(x^2 + 1)(x + 1)(x - 1)$ **121.** $2xy(3x - 2)(4x + 5)$ **123.** $x^2y^2(2x - 5)^2$ **125.** $(x - 2)^2(x + 2)$ **127.** $4xy^2(1 - x)(2 - 3x)$ **129.** $2ab(2a - 3b)(9a - 2b)$ **131.** $x^2y^2(1 - 3x)(5 + 4x)$ **133.** $(4x - 3 + y)(4x - 3 - y)$ **135.** $(x - 2 + y)(x - 2 - y)$ **137.** 4 **139.** 12, −12 **141.** 12, −12 **143.** 9 **145.** 1 **147.** 4 **149.** 3 **151.** $(x + 2)(x^2 - 2x + 4)$ **153.** $(y - 3)(y^2 + 3y + 9)$ **155.** $(y + 4)(y^2 - 4y + 16)$ **157.** $(2x - 1)(4x^2 + 2x + 1)$

CONCEPT REVIEW 8.5

1. Always true **3.** Always true **5.** Never true

SECTION 8.5

3. $0 = x^2 + x - 2$ **5.** −3, −2 **7.** 7, 3 **9.** 0, 5 **11.** 0, 9 **13.** $0, -\frac{3}{2}$ **15.** $0, \frac{2}{3}$ **17.** −2, 5 **19.** 9, −9 **21.** $\frac{7}{4}, -\frac{7}{4}$ **23.** 3, 5 **25.** 8, −9 **27.** $-\frac{1}{2}, 1$ **29.** $-\frac{2}{3}, -4$ **31.** −7, 3 **33.** 0, 7 **35.** −1, −4 **37.** 2, 3 **39.** $\frac{1}{2}, -4$ **41.** $\frac{1}{3}, 4$ **43.** 3, 9 **45.** 9, −2 **47.** −1, −2 **49.** 5, −9 **51.** 4, −7 **53.** −2, −3 **55.** −8, −5 **57.** 1, 3 **59.** −12, 5 **61.** 3, 4 **63.** $-\frac{1}{2}, -4$ **65.** Less than **67.** One **69.** $x + 1$; $x^2 + (x + 1)^2$; x^2; $(x + 1)^2$; 113 **71.** The number is 6. **73.** The numbers are 2 and 4. **75.** The integers are 4 and 5. **77.** The integers are 15 and 16. **79.** The base is 18 ft. The height is 6 ft. **81.** The length is 18 ft. The width is 8 ft. **83.** The length of a side of the original square is 4 m. **85.** The radius of the original circle is 3.81 in. **87.** The dimensions are 4 in. by 7 in. **89.** The object will hit the ground 10 s later. **91.** 12 consecutive natural numbers beginning with 1 will give a sum of 78. **93.** There are 8 teams in the league. **95.** The ball will be 16 ft above the ground 1 s after it hits home plate. **97.** $-\frac{3}{2}, -5$ **99.** 9, −3 **101.** 0, 9 **103.** −6, 3 **105.** 48 or 3 **107.** The length is 10 cm. The width is 7 cm.

CHAPTER 8 REVIEW EXERCISES

1. $7y^3(2y^6 - 7y^3 + 1)$ [8.1.1] **2.** $(a - 4)(3a + b)$ [8.1.2] **3.** $(c + 2)(c + 6)$ [8.2.1] **4.** $a(a - 2)(a - 3)$ [8.2.2] **5.** $(2x - 7)(3x - 4)$ [8.3.1/8.3.2] **6.** $(y + 6)(3y - 2)$ [8.3.1/8.3.2] **7.** $(3a + 2)(6a - 5)$ [8.3.1/8.3.2] **8.** $(ab + 1)(ab - 1)$ [8.4.1] **9.** $4(y - 2)^2$ [8.4.2]

10. $0, -\frac{1}{5}$ [8.5.1] **11.** $3ab(4a + b)$ [8.1.1] **12.** $(b - 3)(b - 10)$ [8.2.1] **13.** $(2x + 5)(5x + 2y)$ [8.1.2] **14.** $3(a + 2)(a - 7)$ [8.2.2] **15.** $n^2(n + 1)(n - 3)$ [8.2.2] **16.** Nonfactorable over the integers [8.3.1/8.3.2] **17.** $(2x - 1)(3x - 2)$ [8.3.1/8.3.2] **18.** Nonfactorable over the integers [8.4.1] **19.** $2, \frac{3}{2}$ [8.5.1] **20.** $7(x + 1)(x - 1)$ [8.4.2] **21.** $x^3(3x^2 - 9x - 4)$ [8.1.1] **22.** $(x - 3)(4x + 5)$ [8.1.2] **23.** $(a + 7)(a - 2)$ [8.2.1] **24.** $(y + 9)(y - 4)$ [8.2.1] **25.** $5(x - 12)(x + 2)$ [8.2.2] **26.** $-3, 7$ [8.5.1] **27.** $(a + 2)(7a + 3)$ [8.3.1/8.3.2] **28.** $(x + 20)(4x + 3)$ [8.3.1/8.3.2] **29.** $(3y^2 + 5z)(3y^2 - 5z)$ [8.4.1] **30.** $5(x + 2)(x - 3)$ [8.2.2] **31.** $-\frac{3}{2}, \frac{2}{3}$ [8.5.1] **32.** $2b(2b - 7)(3b - 4)$ [8.3.1/8.3.2] **33.** $5x(x^2 + 2x + 7)$ [8.1.1] **34.** $(x - 2)(x - 21)$ [8.2.1] **35.** $(3a + 2)(a - 7)$ [8.1.2] **36.** $(2x - 5)(4x - 9)$ [8.3.1/8.3.2] **37.** $10x(a - 4)(a - 9)$ [8.2.2] **38.** $(a - 12)(2a + 5)$ [8.3.1/8.3.2] **39.** $(3a - 5b)(7x + 2y)$ [8.1.2] **40.** $(a^3 + 10)(a^3 - 10)$ [8.4.1] **41.** $(4a + 1)^2$ [8.4.1] **42.** $\frac{1}{4}, -7$ [8.5.1] **43.** $10(a + 4)(2a - 7)$ [8.3.1/8.3.2] **44.** $6(x - 3)$ [8.1.1] **45.** $x^2y(3x^2 + 2x + 6)$ [8.1.1] **46.** $(d - 5)(d + 8)$ [8.2.1] **47.** $2(2x - y)(6x - 5)$ [8.4.2] **48.** $4x(x + 1)(x - 6)$ [8.2.2] **49.** $-2, 10$ [8.5.1] **50.** $(x - 5)(3x - 2)$ [8.3.1/8.3.2] **51.** $(2x - 11)(8x - 3)$ [8.3.1/8.3.2] **52.** $(3x - 5)^2$ [8.4.1] **53.** $(2y + 3)(6y - 1)$ [8.3.1/8.3.2] **54.** $3(x + 6)^2$ [8.4.2] **55.** The length is 100 yd. The width is 50 yd. [8.5.2] **56.** The length is 100 yd. The width is 60 yd. [8.5.2] **57.** The two integers are 4 and 5. [8.5.2] **58.** The distance is 20 ft. [8.5.2] **59.** The width of the larger rectangle is 15 ft. [8.5.2] **60.** The length of a side of the original square was 20 ft. [8.5.2]

CHAPTER 8 TEST

1. $3y^2(2x^2 + 3x + 4)$ [8.1.1] **2.** $2x(3x^2 - 4x + 5)$ [8.1.1] **3.** $(p + 2)(p + 3)$ [8.2.1] **4.** $(x - 2)(a - b)$ [8.1.2] **5.** $\frac{3}{2}, -7$ [8.5.1] **6.** $(a - 3)(a - 16)$ [8.2.1] **7.** $x(x + 5)(x - 3)$ [8.2.2] **8.** $4(x + 4)(2x - 3)$ [8.3.1/8.3.2] **9.** $(b + 6)(a - 3)$ [8.1.2] **10.** $\frac{1}{2}, -\frac{1}{2}$ [8.5.1] **11.** $(2x + 1)(3x + 8)$ [8.3.1/8.3.2] **12.** $(x + 3)(x - 12)$ [8.2.1] **13.** $2(b + 4)(b - 4)$ [8.4.2] **14.** $(2a - 3b)^2$ [8.4.1] **15.** $(p + 1)(x - 1)$ [8.1.2] **16.** $5(x^2 - 9x - 3)$ [8.1.1] **17.** Nonfactorable over the integers [8.3.1/8.3.2] **18.** $(2x + 7y)(2x - 7y)$ [8.4.1] **19.** $3, 5$ [8.5.1] **20.** $(p + 6)^2$ [8.4.1] **21.** $2(3x - 4y)^2$ [8.4.2] **22.** $2y^2(y + 1)(y - 8)$ [8.2.2] **23.** The length is 15 cm. The width is 6 cm. [8.5.2] **24.** The length of the base is 12 in. [8.5.2] **25.** The two integers are -13 and -12. [8.5.2]

CUMULATIVE REVIEW EXERCISES

1. -8 [1.2.2] **2.** -8.1 [1.3.2] **3.** 4 [1.4.2] **4.** -7 [2.1.1] **5.** The Associative Property of Addition [2.2.1] **6.** $18x^2$ [2.2.3] **7.** $-6x + 24$ [2.2.5] **8.** $\frac{2}{3}$ [3.1.3] **9.** 5 [3.2.3] **10.** $\frac{7}{4}$ [3.2.2] **11.** 3 [3.2.3] **12.** 35 [3.1.5] **13.** $x \le -3$ [3.3.3] **14.** $x < \frac{1}{5}$ [3.3.3]

15. 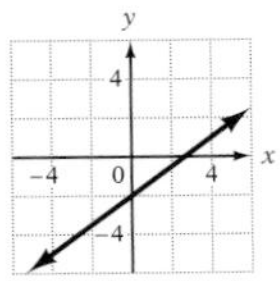 [5.2.2] **16.** 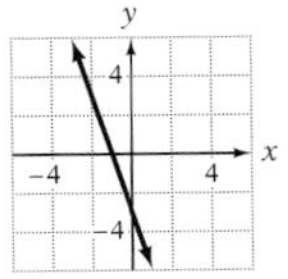 [5.5.2]

17. Domain: {−5, −3, −1, 1, 3}; range: {−4, −2, 0, 2, 4}; yes [5.5.1] **18.** 61 [5.5.1]

19. 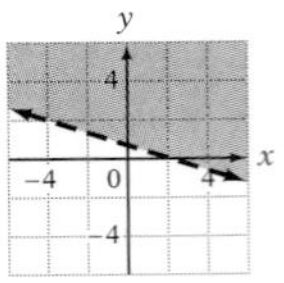 [5.6.1] **20.** (2, −5) [6.2.1] **21.** (1, 2) [6.3.1] **22.** $3y^3 - 3y^2 - 8y - 5$ [7.1.1]

23. $-27a^{12}b^6$ [7.2.2] **24.** $x^3 - 3x^2 - 6x + 8$ [7.3.2] **25.** $4x + 8 + \frac{21}{2x - 3}$ [7.5.2]

26. $\frac{y^6}{x^{12}}$ [7.4.1] **27.** $(a - b)(3 - x)$ [8.1.2] **28.** $(x + 5y)(x - 2y)$ [8.2.2]

29. $2a^2(3a + 2)(a + 3)$ [8.3.1/8.3.2] **30.** $(5a + 6b)(5a - 6b)$ [8.4.1] **31.** $3(2x - 3y)^2$ [8.4.2]

32. $\frac{4}{3}, -5$ [8.5.1] **33.** {−11, −7, −3, 1, 5} [5.5.1] **34.** The average daily high temperature was −3°C. [1.2.5] **35.** The length is 15 cm. The width is 6 cm. [4.3.1] **36.** The pieces measure 4 ft and 6 ft. [4.1.2] **37.** The maximum distance you can drive a Company A car is 359 mi. [4.8.1]

38. \$6500 must be invested at an annual simple interest rate of 11%. [4.5.1]

39. The discount rate is 40%. [4.4.2] **40.** The three integers are 10, 12, and 14. [4.2.1]

Answers to Chapter 9 Selected Exercises

PREP TEST

1. 36 [1.3.3] **2.** $\frac{3x}{y^3}$ [7.4.1] **3.** $-\frac{5}{36}$ [1.3.3] **4.** $-\frac{10}{11}$ [1.3.2] **5.** No. $\frac{0}{a} = 0$ but $\frac{a}{0}$ is undefined. [1.2.4] **6.** $\frac{19}{8}$ [3.2.1] **7.** 130° [4.3.2] **8.** $(x - 6)(x + 2)$ [8.2.1]

9. $(2x - 3)(x + 1)$ [8.3.1/8.3.2] **10.** Jean will catch up to Anthony at 9:40 A.M. [4.7.1]

CONCEPT REVIEW 9.1

1. Always true **3.** Never true **5.** Always true **7.** Never true

SECTION 9.1

5. a. $3; x^2; y^2$ **b.** $3y^3; x$ **7.** $\frac{3}{4x}$ **9.** $\frac{1}{x + 3}$ **11.** −1 **13.** $\frac{2}{3y}$ **15.** $-\frac{3}{4x}$ **17.** $\frac{a}{b}$

19. $-\frac{2}{x}$ **21.** $\frac{y - 2}{y - 3}$ **23.** $\frac{x + 5}{x + 4}$ **25.** $\frac{x + 4}{x - 3}$ **27.** $-\frac{x + 2}{x + 5}$ **29.** $\frac{2(x + 2)}{x + 3}$ **31.** $\frac{2x - 1}{2x + 3}$

33. False **35.** $\frac{2}{3xy}$ **37.** $\frac{8xy^2ab}{3}$ **39.** $\frac{2}{9}$ **41.** $\frac{y^2}{x}$ **43.** $\frac{y(x + 4)}{x(x + 1)}$ **45.** $\frac{x^3(x - 7)}{y^2(x - 4)}$

47. $-\frac{y}{x}$ **49.** $\frac{x + 3}{x + 1}$ **51.** $\frac{x - 5}{x + 3}$ **53.** $-\frac{x + 3}{x + 5}$ **55.** $\frac{12x^4}{(x + 1)(2x + 1)}$ **57.** $-\frac{x + 3}{x - 12}$

59. $\frac{x + 2}{x + 4}$ **61.** $\frac{2x - 5}{2x - 1}$ **63.** $\frac{3x - 4}{2x + 3}$ **65.** 1 **67.** x^d **69.** $a - 5; 5a$ **71.** $\frac{2xy^2ab^2}{9}$

73. $\frac{5}{12}$ **75.** $3x$ **77.** $\frac{y(x + 3)}{x(x + 1)}$ **79.** $\frac{x + 7}{x - 7}$ **81.** $-\frac{4ac}{y}$ **83.** $\frac{x - 5}{x - 6}$ **85.** 1

87. $-\frac{x+6}{x+5}$ **89.** $\frac{2x+3}{x-6}$ **91.** $\frac{4x+3}{2x-1}$ **93.** $\frac{(2x+5)(4x-1)}{(2x-1)(4x+5)}$ **95.** Yes **97.** Yes
99. $-6, 1$ **101.** $-1, 1$ **103.** $3, -2$ **105.** -3 **107.** $\frac{4}{3}, -\frac{1}{2}$ **109.** $\frac{4a}{3b}$ **111.** $\frac{8}{9}$
113. $\frac{x-4}{y^4}$ **115.** $\frac{(x-2)(x-2)}{(x-4)(x+4)}$ **117.** $\frac{x}{x+8}$

CONCEPT REVIEW 9.2

1. Always true **3.** Never true **5.** Always true

SECTION 9.2

1. a. 4; 5 **b.** 3; 4; 5; 60 **c.** $60x^4y^5$ **3.** $24x^3y^2$ **5.** $30x^4y^2$ **7.** $8x^2(x+2)$
9. $6x^2y(x+4)$ **11.** $40x^3(x-1)^2$ **13.** $4(x-3)^2$ **15.** $(2x-1)(2x+1)(x+4)$
17. $(x-7)^2(x+2)$ **19.** $(x+4)(x-3)$ **21.** $(x+5)(x-2)(x+7)$ **23.** $(x-7)(x-3)(x-5)$
25. $(x+2)(x+5)(x-5)$ **27.** $(2x-1)(x-3)(x+1)$ **29.** $(2x-5)(x-2)(x+3)$ **31.** $(x+3)(x-5)$
33. $(x+6)(x-3)$ **35. a.** One **b.** Zero **c.** Two **37.** $y(y-3)^2$ **39.** y
41. $\frac{4x}{x^2}; \frac{3}{x^2}$ **43.** $\frac{4x}{12y^2}; \frac{3yz}{12y^2}$ **45.** $\frac{xy}{x^2(x-3)}; \frac{6x-18}{x^2(x-3)}$ **47.** $\frac{9x}{x(x-1)^2}; \frac{6x-6}{x(x-1)^2}$
49. $\frac{3x}{x(x-3)}; \frac{5}{x(x-3)}$ **51.** $\frac{3}{(x-5)^2}; -\frac{2x-10}{(x-5)^2}$ **53.** $\frac{3x}{x^2(x+2)}; \frac{4x+8}{x^2(x+2)}$
55. $\frac{x^2-6x+8}{(x+3)(x-4)}; \frac{x^2+3x}{(x+3)(x-4)}$ **57.** $\frac{3}{(x+2)(x-1)}; \frac{x^2-x}{(x+2)(x-1)}$ **59.** $\frac{5}{(2x-5)(x-2)}; \frac{x^2-3x+2}{(2x-5)(x-2)}$
61. $\frac{x^2-3x}{(x+3)(x-3)(x-2)}; \frac{2x^2-4x}{(x+3)(x-3)(x-2)}$ **63.** $-\frac{x^2-3x}{(x-3)^2(x+3)}; \frac{x^2+2x-3}{(x-3)^2(x+3)}$
65. $\frac{3x^2+12x}{(x-5)(x+4)}; \frac{x^2-5x}{(x-5)(x+4)}; -\frac{3}{(x-5)(x+4)}$ **67.** $\frac{300}{10^4}; \frac{5}{10^4}$ **69.** $\frac{b^2}{b}; \frac{5}{b}$ **71.** $\frac{y-1}{y-1}; \frac{y}{y-1}$
73. $\frac{x^2+1}{(x-1)^3}; \frac{x^2-1}{(x-1)^3}; \frac{x^2-2x+1}{(x-1)^3}$ **75.** $\frac{2b}{8(a+b)(a-b)}; \frac{a^2+ab}{8(a+b)(a-b)}$
77. $\frac{x-2}{(x+y)(x+2)(x-2)}; \frac{x+2}{(x+y)(x+2)(x-2)}$

CONCEPT REVIEW 9.3

1. Never true **3.** Never true **5.** Always true

SECTION 9.3

1. numerators; $8a$; factors **3.** $\frac{11}{y^2}$ **5.** $-\frac{7}{x+4}$ **7.** $\frac{8x}{2x+3}$ **9.** $\frac{5x+7}{x-3}$ **11.** $\frac{2x-5}{x+9}$
13. $\frac{-3x-4}{2x+7}$ **15.** $\frac{1}{x+5}$ **17.** $\frac{1}{x-6}$ **19.** $\frac{3}{2y-1}$ **21.** $\frac{1}{x-5}$ **23.** common denominator; LCM **25.** False **27.** $\frac{4y+5x}{xy}$ **29.** $\frac{19}{2x}$ **31.** $\frac{5}{12x}$ **33.** $\frac{19x-12}{6x^2}$ **35.** $\frac{52y-35x}{20xy}$
37. $\frac{13x+2}{15x}$ **39.** $\frac{7}{24}$ **41.** $\frac{x+90}{45x}$ **43.** $\frac{x^2+2x+2}{2x^2}$ **45.** $\frac{2x^2+3x-10}{4x^2}$ **47.** $\frac{3y^2+8}{3y}$
49. $\frac{x^2+4x+4}{x+4}$ **51.** $\frac{4x+7}{x+1}$ **53.** $\frac{-3x^2+16x+2}{12x^2}$ **55.** $\frac{x^2-x+2}{x^2y}$
57. $\frac{16xy-12y+6x^2+3x}{12x^2y^2}$ **59.** $\frac{3xy-6y-2x^2-14x}{24x^2y}$ **61.** $\frac{9x+2}{(x-2)(x+3)}$ **63.** $\frac{2(x+23)}{(x-7)(x+3)}$

65. $\frac{2x^2 - 5x + 1}{(x + 1)(x - 3)}$ 67. $\frac{4x^2 - 34x + 5}{(2x - 1)(x - 6)}$ 69. $\frac{2a - 5}{a - 7}$ 71. $\frac{4x + 9}{(x + 3)(x - 3)}$ 73. $\frac{-x + 9}{(x + 2)(x - 3)}$
75. $\frac{14}{(x - 5)^2}$ 77. $\frac{-2(x + 7)}{(x + 6)(x - 7)}$ 79. $\frac{x - 2}{2x}$ 81. $\frac{x^2 + x + 4}{(x - 2)(x + 1)(x - 1)}$ 83. $\frac{x - 4}{x - 6}$
85. $\frac{2x + 1}{x - 1}$ 87. 2 89. $\frac{b^2 + b - 7}{b + 4}$ 91. $\frac{4n}{(n - 1)^2}$ 93. $-\frac{3(x^2 + 8x + 25)}{(x - 3)(x + 7)}$ 95. 1
97. $\frac{x^2 - x + 2}{(x + 5)(x + 1)}$ 99. $\frac{2}{3}; \frac{3}{4}; \frac{4}{5}; \frac{50}{51}; \frac{100}{101}; \frac{1000}{1001}$ 101. $\frac{6}{y} + \frac{7}{x}$ 103. $\frac{2}{m^2n} + \frac{8}{mn^2}$

CONCEPT REVIEW 9.4

1. Sometimes true 3. Never true 5. Always true

SECTION 9.4

1. $\frac{5}{x}; \frac{6}{x^2}; \frac{4}{x^2}; x^2$ 3. $x^2 - 4; x + 2; x - 2$ 5. $\frac{x}{x - 3}$ 7. $\frac{2}{3}$ 9. $\frac{y + 3}{y - 4}$ 11. $\frac{2(2x + 13)}{5x + 36}$
13. $\frac{3}{4}$ 15. $\frac{x - 2}{x + 2}$ 17. $\frac{x + 2}{x + 3}$ 19. $\frac{x - 6}{x + 5}$ 21. $-\frac{x - 2}{x + 1}$ 23. $x - 1$ 25. $\frac{1}{2x - 1}$
27. $\frac{x - 3}{x + 5}$ 29. $\frac{x - 7}{x - 8}$ 31. $\frac{2y - 1}{2y + 1}$ 33. $\frac{x - 2}{2x - 5}$ 35. $\frac{x - 2}{x + 1}$ 37. $\frac{x - 1}{x + 4}$ 39. $\frac{-x - 1}{4x - 3}$
41. $\frac{x + 1}{2(5x - 2)}$ 43. $\frac{b + 11}{4b - 21}$ 45. True 47. $\frac{5}{3}$ 49. $-\frac{1}{x - 1}$ 51. $\frac{ab}{b + a}$
53. $\frac{y + 4}{2(y - 2)}$

CONCEPT REVIEW 9.5

1. Always true 3. Always true 5. Sometimes true 7. Always true

SECTION 9.5

3. $x; x - 4; x(x - 4)$ 5. $7(x - 4); 3x; 7$ 7. $-5; 3$ 9. $-1; 2$ 11. 4 13. -3 15. $\frac{3}{4}$
17. -1 19. No solution 21. $-6; 2$ 23. $-\frac{2}{3}; 5$ 25. $6; -1$ 27. $-7; 3$ 29. $\frac{2}{3}; 4$
31. proportion 33. 9 35. 36 37. 10 39. 113 41. -2 43. 15 45. 4
47. True 49. 10 mi; 3 cm; 3 cm; 10 mi 51. Yes 53. 20,000 people voted in favor of the amendment. 55. The office building requires 140 air vents. 57. For 2 c of boiling water, 6 c of sugar are required. 59. There are about 800 fish in the lake. 61. Yes, the shipment will be accepted. 63. The person's height is 67.5 in. 65. The distance between the two cities is 750 mi. 67. The recommended area of a window is 40 ft^2. 69. There are 160 ml of carbonated water in 280 ml of soft drink. 71. For an annual yield of 1320 bushels, 10 additional acres must be planted. 73. To serve 70 people, 2 additional gallons are necessary. 75. a. *YZ* b. $\angle R$ 77. The measure of side *DE* is 12.8 in. 79. The height of triangle *DEF* is 4.7 ft. 81. The perimeter of triangle *ABC* is 18 m. 83. The area of triangle *ABC* is 48 cm^2. 85. False 87. a. *PQO* b. *OM* 89. The length of *BC* is 15 m. 91. The length of *QO* is 10 ft. 93. The perimeter of triangle *OPQ* is 12 m. 95. The height of the flagpole is 14.375 ft. 97. 1
99. $0; -\frac{2}{3}$ 101. -3 and -4 103. The first person's share of the winnings was $1.25 million.
105. The cost would be $18.40. 107. a. He calculated the circumference to be 24,960 mi.
b. The difference is 160 mi.

CONCEPT REVIEW 9.6

1. Always true **3.** Always true **5.** Always true

SECTION 9.6

1. $h = \frac{2A}{b}$ **3.** $t = \frac{d}{r}$ **5.** $T = \frac{PV}{nR}$ **7.** $L = \frac{P - 2W}{2}$ **9.** $b_1 = \frac{2A - hb_2}{h}$ **11.** $h = \frac{3V}{A}$ **13.** $S = C - Rt$ **15.** $P = \frac{A}{1 + rt}$ **17.** $w = \frac{A}{S + 1}$ **19.** Yes **21. a.** $h = \frac{S - 2\pi r^2}{2\pi r}$ **b.** 5 in. **c.** 4 in. **23. a.** $r = \frac{S - C}{C}$ **b.** $66.\overline{6}\%$ **c.** $43.\overline{3}\%$

CONCEPT REVIEW 9.7

1. Never true **3.** Always true **5.** Never true

SECTION 9.7

3. Row 1: $\frac{1}{10}$; t; $\frac{t}{10}$; Row 2: $\frac{1}{12}$; t; $\frac{t}{12}$ **5.** It will take 2 h to fill the fountain with both sprinklers operating. **7.** It would take 3 h to move the earth. **9.** It would take the computers 30 h. **11.** It would take 24 min to cool the room 5°F. **13.** It would take the second welder 15 h. **15.** It would take the second pipeline 90 min to fill the tank. **17.** It would take 3 h to harvest the field using only the older reaper. **19.** It will take the second technician 3 h. **21.** It would take the small unit $14\frac{2}{3}$ h. **23.** It would have taken one of the welders 40 h. **25.** Less than k **27. a.** Row 1: 1440; $380 - r$; $\frac{1440}{380 - r}$; Row 2: 1600; $380 + r$; $\frac{1600}{380 + r}$ **b.** $\frac{1440}{380 - r}$; $\frac{1600}{380 + r}$ **29.** The camper hiked at a rate of 4 mph. **31.** The rate of the jet was 360 mph. **33.** The rate of the boat for the first 15 mi was 7.5 mph. **35.** The family can travel 21.6 mi down the river. **37.** The technician traveled at a rate of 20 mph through the congested traffic. **39.** The rate of the river's current was 5 mph. **41.** The rate of the freight train was 30 mph. The rate of the express train was 50 mph. **43.** The rate of the car is 48 mph. **45.** The rate of the jet stream was 50 mph. **47.** The rate of the current is 5 mph. **49.** It would take $1\frac{1}{19}$ h to fill the tank. **51.** The amount of time spent traveling by canoe was 2 h. **53.** The bus usually travels at a rate of 60 mph.

CHAPTER 9 REVIEW EXERCISES

1. $\frac{by^3}{6ax^2}$ [9.1.2] **2.** $\frac{22x - 1}{(3x - 4)(2x + 3)}$ [9.3.2] **3.** $x = -\frac{3}{4}y + 3$ [9.6.1] **4.** $\frac{2x^4}{3y^7}$ [9.1.1] **5.** $\frac{1}{x^2}$ [9.1.3] **6.** $\frac{x - 2}{3x - 10}$ [9.4.1] **7.** $72a^3b^5$ [9.2.1] **8.** $\frac{4x}{3x + 7}$ [9.3.1] **9.** $\frac{3x}{16x^2}$; $\frac{10}{16x^2}$ [9.2.2] **10.** $\frac{x - 9}{x - 3}$ [9.1.1] **11.** $\frac{x - 4}{x + 3}$ [9.1.3] **12.** $\frac{2y - 3}{5y - 7}$ [9.3.2] **13.** $\frac{1}{x}$ [9.1.2] **14.** $\frac{1}{x + 3}$ [9.3.1] **15.** $15x^4(x - 7)^2$ [9.2.1] **16.** 10 [9.5.2] **17.** No solution [9.5.1] **18.** $-\frac{4a}{5b}$ [9.1.1] **19.** $\frac{1}{x + 3}$ [9.3.1] **20.** 24 in. [9.5.4] **21.** 5 [9.5.1] **22.** $\frac{x + 9}{4x}$ [9.4.1] **23.** $\frac{3x - 1}{x - 5}$ [9.3.2] **24.** $\frac{x - 3}{x + 3}$ [9.1.3]

25. $-\frac{x+6}{x+3}$ [9.1.1] **26.** 2 [9.5.1] **27.** $x - 2$ [9.4.1] **28.** $\frac{x+3}{x-4}$ [9.1.2] **29.** 15 [9.5.2] **30.** 12 [9.5.2] **31.** $\frac{x}{x-7}$ [9.4.1] **32.** $x = 2y + 15$ [9.6.1] **33.** $\frac{3(3a+2b)}{ab}$ [9.3.2] **34.** $(5x-3)(2x-1)(4x-1)$ [9.2.1] **35.** $c = \frac{100m}{i}$ [9.6.1] **36.** 40 [9.5.2] **37.** 3 [9.5.2] **38.** $\frac{7x+22}{60x}$ [9.3.2] **39.** $\frac{8a+3}{4a-3}$ [9.1.2] **40.** $\frac{3x^2-x}{(6x-1)(2x+3)(3x-1)}$; $\frac{24x^3-4x^2}{(6x-1)(2x+3)(3x-1)}$ [9.2.2] **41.** $\frac{2}{ab}$ [9.3.1] **42.** 62 [9.5.2] **43.** 6 [9.5.1] **44.** $\frac{b^3y}{10ax}$ [9.1.3] **45.** It would take the apprentice 6 h. [9.7.1] **46.** The spring would stretch 8 in. [9.5.3] **47.** The rate of the wind is 20 mph. [9.7.2] **48.** To make 10 gal of the garden spray will require 16 additional ounces. [9.5.3] **49.** Using both hoses, it would take 6 h to fill the pool. [9.7.1] **50.** The rate of the car is 45 mph. [9.7.2]

CHAPTER 9 TEST

1. $\frac{x+5}{x+4}$ [9.1.3] **2.** $\frac{2}{x+5}$ [9.3.1] **3.** $3(2x-1)(x+1)$ [9.2.1] **4.** -1 [9.5.2] **5.** $\frac{x+1}{x^3(x-2)}$ [9.1.2] **6.** $\frac{x-3}{x-2}$ [9.4.1] **7.** $\frac{3x+6}{x(x-2)(x+2)}$; $\frac{x^2}{x(x-2)(x+2)}$ [9.2.2] **8.** $x = -\frac{5}{3}y - 5$ [9.6.1] **9.** 2 [9.5.1] **10.** $\frac{5}{(2x-1)(3x+1)}$ [9.3.2] **11.** 1 [9.1.3] **12.** $\frac{3}{x+8}$ [9.3.1] **13.** $6x(x+2)^2$ [9.2.1] **14.** $-\frac{x-2}{x+5}$ [9.1.1] **15.** 4 [9.5.1] **16.** $t = \frac{f-v}{a}$ [9.6.1] **17.** $\frac{2x^3}{3y^5}$ [9.1.1] **18.** $\frac{3}{(2x-1)(x+1)}$ [9.3.2] **19.** 3 [9.5.2] **20.** $\frac{x^3(x+3)}{y(x+2)}$ [9.1.2] **21.** $-\frac{3xy+3y}{x(x+1)(x-1)}$; $\frac{x^2}{x(x+1)(x-1)}$ [9.2.2] **22.** $\frac{x+3}{x+5}$ [9.4.1] **23.** For 15 gal of water, 2 additional pounds of salt will be required. [9.5.3] **24.** The rate of the wind is 20 mph. [9.7.2] **25.** It would take both pipes 6 min to fill the tank. [9.7.1]

CUMULATIVE REVIEW EXERCISES

1. -17 [1.1.2] **2.** -6 [1.4.1] **3.** $\frac{31}{30}$ [1.4.2] **4.** 21 [2.1.1] **5.** $5x - 2y$ [2.2.2] **6.** $-8x + 26$ [2.2.5] **7.** -20 [3.2.1] **8.** -12 [3.2.3] **9.** 10 [3.1.5] **10.** $x < \frac{9}{5}$ [3.3.2] **11.** $x \le 15$ [3.3.3]

12.
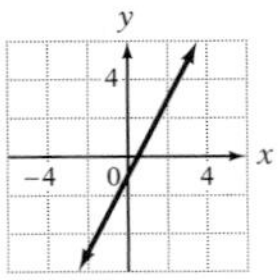

[5.2.2]

13.
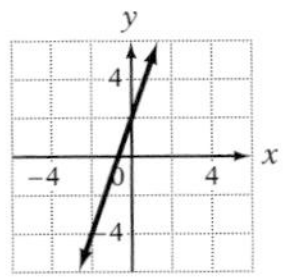

[5.5.2]

14.
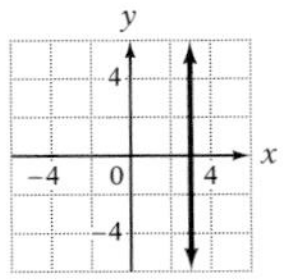

[5.2.3]

15.
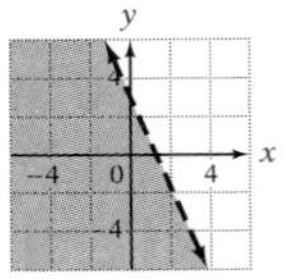

[5.6.1]

16. $\{-3, 5, 11, 19, 27\}$ [5.5.1] **17.** 37 [5.5.1] **18.** $\left(\frac{2}{3}, 3\right)$ [6.2.1] **19.** $\left(\frac{1}{2}, -1\right)$ [6.3.1] **20.** $-6x^4y^5$ [7.2.1] **21.** $a^{20}b^{15}$ [7.2.2] **22.** $\frac{a^3}{b^2}$ [7.4.1]

23. $a^2 + ab - 12b^2$ [7.3.3] **24.** $3b^3 - b + 2$ [7.5.1] **25.** $x^2 + 2x + 4$ [7.5.2]
26. $(4x + 1)(3x - 1)$ [8.3.1/8.3.2] **27.** $(y - 6)(y - 1)$ [8.2.1] **28.** $a(2a - 3)(a + 5)$ [8.3.1/8.3.2]
29. $4(b + 5)(b - 5)$ [8.4.2] **30.** -3 and $\frac{5}{2}$ [8.5.1] **31.** $-\frac{x + 7}{x + 4}$ [9.1.1] **32.** 1 [9.1.3]
33. $\frac{8}{(3x - 1)(x + 1)}$ [9.3.2] **34.** 1 [9.5.1] **35.** $a = \frac{f - v}{t}$ [9.6.1]
36. $5x - 18 = -3$; $x = 3$ [4.1.1] **37.** $5000 must be invested at an annual simple interest rate of 11%. [4.5.1]
38. There is 70% silver in the 120-gram alloy. [4.6.2] **39.** The base is 10 in. The height is 6 in. [8.5.2]
40. It would take both pipes 8 min to fill the tank. [9.7.1]

Answers to Chapter 10 Selected Exercises

PREP TEST

1. -14 [1.1.2] **2.** $-2x^2y - 4xy^2$ [2.2.2] **3.** 14 [3.1.3] **4.** $\frac{7}{5}$ [3.2.2] **5.** x^6 [7.2.1]
6. $x^2 + 2xy + y^2$ [7.3.4] **7.** $4x^2 - 12x + 9$ [7.3.4] **8.** $a^2 - 25$ [7.3.4] **9.** $4 - 9v^2$ [7.3.4]
10. $\frac{x^2y^2}{9}$ [7.4.1]

CONCEPT REVIEW 10.1

1. Never true **3.** Always true **5.** Sometimes true

SECTION 10.1

3. 2, 20, 50 **7.** radical sign; radicand **9.** 4 **11.** 7 **13.** $4\sqrt{2}$ **15.** $2\sqrt{2}$ **17.** $18\sqrt{2}$
19. $10\sqrt{10}$ **21.** $\sqrt{15}$ **23.** $\sqrt{29}$ **25.** $-54\sqrt{2}$ **27.** $3\sqrt{5}$ **29.** 0 **31.** $48\sqrt{2}$
33. $\sqrt{105}$ **35.** 30 **37.** $30\sqrt{5}$ **39.** $5\sqrt{10}$ **41.** $4\sqrt{6}$ **43.** 18 **45.** **a.** Rational
b. Irrational **c.** Irrational **d.** Not a real number **47.** 15.492 **49.** 16.971 **51.** 15.652
53. 18.762 **57.** 4; x^3; y^4 **59.** x^3 **61.** $y^7\sqrt{y}$ **63.** a^{10} **65.** x^2y^2 **67.** $2x^2$
69. $2x\sqrt{6}$ **71.** $xy^3\sqrt{xy}$ **73.** $ab^5\sqrt{ab}$ **75.** $2x^2\sqrt{15x}$ **77.** $7a^2b^4$ **79.** $3x^2y^3\sqrt{2xy}$
81. $2x^5y^3\sqrt{10xy}$ **83.** $4a^4b^5\sqrt{5a}$ **85.** $8ab\sqrt{b}$ **87.** x^3y **89.** $8a^2b^3\sqrt{5b}$ **91.** $6x^2y^3\sqrt{3y}$
93. $4x^3y\sqrt{2y}$ **95.** $5a + 20$ **97.** $2x^2 + 8x + 8$ **99.** $x + 2$ **101.** $y + 1$ **103.** Rational
105. Irrational **107.** **a.** The speed of the car is $12\sqrt{15}$ mph. **b.** The speed of the car is approximately 46 mph. **109.** $0.05ab^2\sqrt{ab}$ **111.** **a.** 1 **b.** 3 **c.** $3\sqrt{3}$ **113.** The length of a side of the square is 8.7 cm. **115.** $x \geq 0$ **117.** $x \geq -5$ **119.** $x \leq \frac{5}{2}$ **121.** All real numbers

CONCEPT REVIEW 10.2

1. Never true **3.** Always true **5.** Always true

SECTION 10.2

1. 5; 8; -3 **3.** $11\sqrt{5}$ **5.** $-6\sqrt{5}$ **7.** $-8\sqrt{3}$ **9.** $5\sqrt{y}$ **11.** $-3\sqrt{2a}$ **13.** $-12\sqrt{5a}$
15. $-7y\sqrt{3}$ **17.** $-7b\sqrt{3x}$ **19.** $2\sqrt{xy}$ **21.** $-3\sqrt{2}$ **23.** $20\sqrt{2}$ **25.** $25\sqrt{3} - 6\sqrt{2}$
27. $41\sqrt{y}$ **29.** $-12x\sqrt{3}$ **31.** $2xy\sqrt{x} - 3xy\sqrt{y}$ **33.** $-9x\sqrt{3x}$ **35.** $-13y^2\sqrt{2y}$
37. $4a^2b^2\sqrt{ab}$ **39.** $7\sqrt{2}$ **41.** $6\sqrt{x}$ **43.** $-3\sqrt{y}$ **45.** $-45\sqrt{2}$ **47.** $13\sqrt{3} - 12\sqrt{5}$
49. $32\sqrt{3} - 3\sqrt{11}$ **51.** $6\sqrt{x}$ **53.** $-34\sqrt{3x}$ **55.** $10a\sqrt{3b} + 10a\sqrt{5b}$ **57.** $-2xy\sqrt{3}$
59. $-7b\sqrt{ab} + 4a^2\sqrt{b}$ **61.** $3ab\sqrt{2a} - ab + 4ab\sqrt{3b}$ **63.** **a.** False **b.** True

c. False **d.** True **65.** $8\sqrt{x+2}$ **67.** $2x\sqrt{2y}$ **69.** $2ab\sqrt{6ab}$
71. $-11\sqrt{2x+y}$ **73.** The perimeter is $(6\sqrt{3}+2\sqrt{15})$ cm. **75.** The perimeter is 22.4 cm.

CONCEPT REVIEW 10.3

1. Always true **3.** Always true **5.** Sometimes true

SECTION 10.3

1. 9; 3 **3.** 5 **5.** 6 **7.** x **9.** x^3y^2 **11.** $3ab^6\sqrt{2a}$ **13.** $12a^4b\sqrt{b}$ **15.** $2-\sqrt{6}$
17. $x-\sqrt{xy}$ **19.** $5\sqrt{2}-\sqrt{5x}$ **21.** $4-2\sqrt{10}$ **23.** $x-6\sqrt{x}+9$ **25.** $3a-3\sqrt{ab}$
27. $10abc$ **29.** $15x-22y\sqrt{x}+8y^2$ **31.** $x-y$ **33.** $10x+13\sqrt{xy}+4y$ **35.** Less than
39. a. No **b.** Yes **c.** No **d.** No **41.** 4 **43.** 7 **45.** 3 **47.** $x\sqrt{5}$
49. $\frac{a^2}{7}$ **51.** $\frac{\sqrt{3}}{3}$ **53.** $\sqrt{3}$ **55.** $\frac{\sqrt{3x}}{x}$ **57.** $\frac{\sqrt{2x}}{x}$ **59.** $\frac{3\sqrt{x}}{x}$ **61.** $\frac{2\sqrt{y}}{xy}$
63. $\frac{4\sqrt{b}}{7b}$ **65.** $\frac{5\sqrt{6}}{27}$ **67.** $\frac{\sqrt{y}}{3xy}$ **69.** $\frac{2\sqrt{3x}}{3y}$ **71.** $-\frac{\sqrt{2}+3}{7}$ **73.** $\frac{15-3\sqrt{5}}{20}$
75. $\frac{x\sqrt{y}+y\sqrt{x}}{x-y}$ **77.** $\frac{\sqrt{3xy}}{3y}$ **79.** $-2-\sqrt{6}$ **81.** $-\frac{\sqrt{10}+5}{3}$ **83.** $\frac{x-3\sqrt{x}}{x-9}$ **85.** $-\frac{1}{2}$
87. 7 **89.** -5 **91.** $\frac{7}{4}$ **93.** $-\frac{42-26\sqrt{3}}{11}$ **95.** $\frac{14-9\sqrt{2}}{17}$ **97.** $\frac{a-5\sqrt{a}+4}{2a-2}$
99. $\frac{y+5\sqrt{y}+6}{y-9}$ **101.** -1.3 **103.** $-\frac{4}{9}$ **105.** $\frac{3}{2}$ **107.** The area is 59 m^2.
109. a. True **b.** True **c.** False; $x+2\sqrt{x}+1$ **d.** True **111.** No

CONCEPT REVIEW 10.4

1. Sometimes true **3.** Always true **5.** Sometimes true

SECTION 10.4

1. **b** and **c** **3.** 2; 2; $x-2$; 25; 27; 2 **5.** 25 **7.** 144 **9.** 5 **11.** 16 **13.** 8
15. No solution **17.** 6 **19.** 24 **21.** -1 **23.** $-\frac{2}{5}$ **25.** $\frac{4}{3}$ **27.** 15 **29.** 5
31. 1 **33.** 1 **35.** 1 **37.** 2 **39.** No solution **41.** **c** **43.** The number is 1.
45. The number is 11. **47.** 90°; legs **51.** The length of the hypotenuse is 10.30 cm. **53.** The length of the other leg of the triangle is 9.75 ft. **55.** The length of the diagonal is 12.1 mi. **57. a.** Yes **b.** Yes **c.** Yes **d.** Yes **59.** The depth of the water is 12.5 ft. **61.** The pitcher's mound is more than halfway between home plate and second base. **63.** The periscope has to be 10.67 ft above the water. **65.** Yes, the ladder will be long enough to reach the gutters. **67.** The length of the pendulum is 7.30 ft. **69.** The distance to the memorial is 250 ft. **71.** The bridge is 64 ft high. **73.** The height of the screen is 21.6 in. **75.** 5 **77.** 8 **79. a.** The perimeter is $12\sqrt{2}$ cm. **b.** The area is 12 cm^2.
81. The area is 244.78 ft^2.

CHAPTER 10 REVIEW EXERCISES

1. $-11\sqrt{3}$ [10.2.1] **2.** $-x\sqrt{3}-x\sqrt{5}$ [10.3.2] **3.** $x+8$ [10.1.2] **4.** No solution [10.4.1]
5. 1 [10.3.2] **6.** $7\sqrt{7}$ [10.2.1] **7.** $12a+28\sqrt{ab}+15b$ [10.3.1] **8.** $7x^2+42x+63$ [10.1.2]
9. 12 [10.1.1] **10.** 16 [10.4.1] **11.** $4x\sqrt{5}$ [10.2.1] **12.** $5ab-7$ [10.3.1]
13. 3 [10.4.1] **14.** $\sqrt{35}$ [10.1.1] **15.** $7x^2y\sqrt{15xy}$ [10.2.1] **16.** $\frac{x}{3y^2}$ [10.3.2]
17. $9x-6\sqrt{xy}+y$ [10.3.1] **18.** $a+4$ [10.1.2] **19.** $20\sqrt{3}$ [10.1.1] **20.** $26\sqrt{3x}$ [10.2.1]

21. $\frac{8\sqrt{x}+24}{x-9}$ [10.3.2] **22.** $3a\sqrt{2}+2a\sqrt{3}$ [10.3.1] **23.** $9a^2\sqrt{2ab}$ [10.1.2]
24. $-6\sqrt{30}$ [10.1.1] **25.** $-4a^2b^4\sqrt{5ab}$ [10.2.1] **26.** $7x^2y^4$ [10.3.2] **27.** $\frac{3}{5}$ [10.4.1]
28. c^9 [10.1.2] **29.** $15\sqrt{2}$ [10.1.1] **30.** $18a\sqrt{5b}+5a\sqrt{b}$ [10.2.1] **31.** $\frac{16\sqrt{a}}{a}$ [10.3.2]
32. 8 [10.4.1] **33.** $a^5b^3c^2$ [10.3.1] **34.** $21\sqrt{70}$ [10.1.1] **35.** $2y^4\sqrt{6}$ [10.1.2]
36. 5 [10.3.2] **37.** 5 [10.4.1] **38.** $8y+10\sqrt{5y}-15$ [10.3.1] **39.** 99.499 [10.1.1]
40. 7 [10.3.1] **41.** $25x^4\sqrt{6x}$ [10.1.2] **42.** $-6x^3y^2\sqrt{2y}$ [10.2.1] **43.** $3a$ [10.3.2]
44. $20\sqrt{10}$ [10.1.1] **45.** 20 [10.4.1] **46.** $\frac{7a}{3}$ [10.3.2] **47.** 10 [10.3.1]
48. $6x^2y^2\sqrt{y}$ [10.1.2] **49.** $36x^8y^5\sqrt{3xy}$ [10.1.2] **50.** 3 [10.4.1] **51.** 20 [10.1.1]
52. $-2\sqrt{2x}$ [10.2.1] **53.** 6 [10.4.1] **54.** 3 [10.3.1] **55.** The larger integer is 51. [10.4.2]
56. The explorer's weight on the surface of Earth is 144 lb. [10.4.2] **57.** The length of the other leg is 14.25 cm. [10.4.2] **58.** The radius of the sharpest corner is 25 ft. [10.4.2]
59. The depth is 100 ft. [10.4.2] **60.** The length of the guy wire is 26.25 ft. [10.4.2]

CHAPTER 10 TEST

1. $11x^4y$ [10.1.2] **2.** $-5\sqrt{2}$ [10.2.1] **3.** $6x^2\sqrt{xy}$ [10.3.1] **4.** $3\sqrt{5}$ [10.1.1]
5. $6x^3y\sqrt{2x}$ [10.1.2] **6.** $6\sqrt{2y}+3\sqrt{2x}$ [10.2.1] **7.** $y+8\sqrt{y}+15$ [10.3.1] **8.** $\sqrt{2}$ [10.3.2]
9. 9 [10.3.2] **10.** 11 [10.4.1] **11.** 22.361 [10.1.1] **12.** $4a^2b^5\sqrt{2ab}$ [10.1.2]
13. $a-\sqrt{ab}$ [10.3.1] **14.** $4x^2y^2\sqrt{5y}$ [10.3.1] **15.** $7ab\sqrt{a}$ [10.3.2] **16.** 25 [10.4.1]
17. $8x^6y^2\sqrt{3xy}$ [10.1.2] **18.** $4ab\sqrt{2ab}-5ab\sqrt{ab}$ [10.2.1] **19.** $a-4$ [10.3.1]
20. $-6-3\sqrt{5}$ [10.3.2] **21.** 5 [10.4.1] **22.** $3\sqrt{2}-x\sqrt{3}$ [10.3.1] **23.** $-6\sqrt{a}$ [10.2.1]
24. $6\sqrt{3}$ [10.1.1] **25.** 7.937 [10.1.1] **26.** $6ab\sqrt{a}$ [10.3.2] **27.** No solution [10.4.1]
28. The smaller integer is 40. [10.4.2] **29.** The length of the pendulum is 5.07 ft. [10.4.2]
30. The ladder reaches 15.2 ft high on the building. [10.4.2]

CUMULATIVE REVIEW EXERCISES

1. $-\frac{1}{12}$ [1.4.2] **2.** $2x+18$ [2.2.5] **3.** $\frac{1}{13}$ [3.2.3] **4.** $x \le -\frac{9}{2}$ [3.3.3] **5.** $-\frac{4}{3}$ [5.3.1]
6. $y=\frac{1}{2}x-2$ [5.4.1/5.4.2] **7.** -18 [5.5.1] **8.**

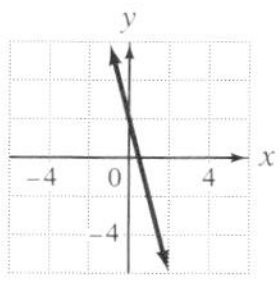

[5.5.2] **9.**

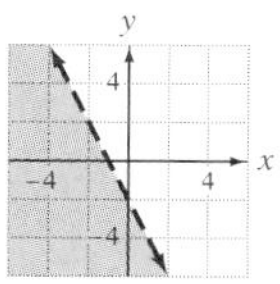

[5.6.1]

10. (2, −1) [6.1.1] **11.** (1, 1) [6.2.1] **12.** (3, −2) [6.3.1] **13.** $\frac{6x^5}{y^3}$ [7.4.1]
14. $-2b^2+1-\frac{1}{3b^2}$ [7.5.1] **15.** $3x^2y^2(4x-3y)$ [8.1.1] **16.** $(3b+5)(3b-4)$ [8.3.1/8.3.2]
17. $2a(a-3)(a-5)$ [8.2.2] **18.** $\frac{1}{4(x+1)}$ [9.1.2] **19.** $\frac{x-5}{x-3}$ [9.4.1] **20.** $\frac{x+3}{x-3}$ [9.3.2]
21. $\frac{5}{3}$ [9.5.1] **22.** $38\sqrt{3a}-35\sqrt{a}$ [10.2.1] **23.** 8 [10.3.2] **24.** 14 [10.4.1]
25. The largest integer that satisfies the inequality is −33. [4.8.1] **26.** The cost is $24.50. [4.4.1]
27. 56 oz of pure water must be added. [4.6.2] **28.** The two numbers are 6 and 15. [4.1.2]
29. It would take the small pipe 48 h to fill the tank. [9.7.1] **30.** The smaller integer is 24. [10.4.2]

Answers to Chapter 11 Selected Exercises

PREP TEST

1. 41 [2.1.1] **2.** $-\frac{1}{5}$ [3.2.1] **3.** $(x + 4)(x - 3)$ [8.2.1] **4.** $(2x - 3)^2$ [8.4.1]
5. Yes [8.4.1] **6.** 3 [9.5.2] **7.**

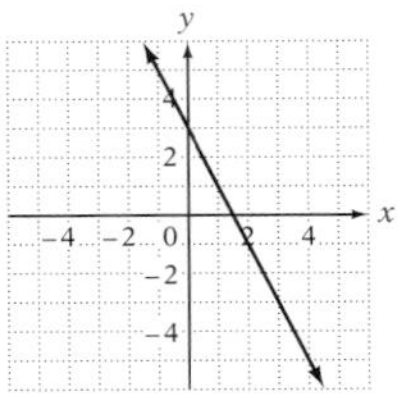

[5.2.2] **8.** $2\sqrt{7}$ [10.1.1]
9. $|a|$ [10.1.2] **10.** The hiking trail is 3.6 mi long. [9.7.2]

CONCEPT REVIEW 11.1

1. Never true **3.** Sometimes true **5.** Always true

SECTION 11.1

1. $a = 3, b = -4, c = 1$ **3.** $a = 2, b = 0, c = -5$ **5.** $a = 6, b = -3, c = 0$ **7.** $x^2 - 3x - 8 = 0$
9. $x^2 - 16 = 0$ **11.** $2x^2 + 12x + 13 = 0$ **17.** standard; $x + 6$; $x - 6$; 0; 0; Zero Products; -6; 6
19. -3 and 5 **21.** 0 and 7 **23.** $-\frac{5}{2}$ and $\frac{1}{3}$ **25.** -5 and 3 **27.** 1 and 3 **29.** -1 and -2
31. 3 **33.** 0 and $\frac{3}{2}$ **35.** -2 and 5 **37.** $\frac{2}{3}$ and 1 **39.** -3 and $\frac{1}{3}$ **41.** $-\frac{3}{2}$ and $\frac{4}{3}$
43. -3 and $\frac{4}{5}$ **45.** $\frac{1}{3}$ **47.** -4 and 4 **49.** $-\frac{2}{3}$ and $\frac{2}{3}$ **51.** $\frac{2}{3}$ and 2 **53.** -6 and $\frac{3}{2}$
55. $\frac{2}{3}$ **57.** -3 and 6 **59.** 0 and 12 **61. a.** Two positive **b.** One positive and one negative
c. One positive and one negative **63.** 3; -3 **65.** -6 and 6 **67.** -1 and 1 **69.** $-\frac{7}{2}$ and $\frac{7}{2}$
71. $-\frac{2}{3}$ and $\frac{2}{3}$ **73.** $-\frac{3}{4}$ and $\frac{3}{4}$ **75.** There is no real number solution. **77.** $2\sqrt{6}$ and $-2\sqrt{6}$
79. -5 and 7 **81.** -7 and -3 **83.** -6 and 4 **85.** -9 and -1 **87.** 2 and 16 **89.** $-\frac{9}{2}$ and $-\frac{3}{2}$ **91.** $-\frac{1}{3}$ and $\frac{7}{3}$ **93.** $-\frac{12}{7}$ and $-\frac{2}{7}$ **95.** $4 + 2\sqrt{5}$ and $4 - 2\sqrt{5}$ **97.** There is no real number solution. **99.** $\frac{1}{2} + \sqrt{6}$ and $\frac{1}{2} - \sqrt{6}$ **101.** $-\frac{4}{3}$ and $\frac{8}{3}$ **103.** Zero **105.** Two
107. 66 and 110 **109.** $\sqrt{2}$ and $-\sqrt{2}$ **111.** 0 and 1 **113.** $\frac{\sqrt{ab}}{a}$ and $-\frac{\sqrt{ab}}{a}$ **115.** The speed is 10 m/s.

CONCEPT REVIEW 11.2

1. Always true **3.** Always true **5.** Never true

SECTION 11.2

1. a. perfect-square; x; 18; 81 **b.** 81; $x + 9$ **3.** $x^2 + 12x + 36$; $(x + 6)^2$ **5.** $x^2 + 10x + 25$; $(x + 5)^2$
7. $x^2 - x + \frac{1}{4}$; $\left(x - \frac{1}{2}\right)^2$ **9.** -3 and 1 **11.** $-2 + \sqrt{3}$ and $-2 - \sqrt{3}$ **13.** There is no real number

solution. **15.** $-3 + \sqrt{14}$ and $-3 - \sqrt{14}$ **17.** 2 **19.** $1 + \sqrt{2}$ and $1 - \sqrt{2}$ **21.** $\frac{-3 + \sqrt{13}}{2}$ and $\frac{-3 - \sqrt{13}}{2}$ **23.** -8 and 1 **25.** $-3 + \sqrt{5}$ and $-3 - \sqrt{5}$ **27.** $4 + \sqrt{14}$ and $4 - \sqrt{14}$ **29.** 1 and 2 **31.** $\frac{3 + \sqrt{29}}{2}$ and $\frac{3 - \sqrt{29}}{2}$ **33.** $\frac{1 + \sqrt{5}}{2}$ and $\frac{1 - \sqrt{5}}{2}$ **35.** $\frac{5 + \sqrt{13}}{2}$ and $\frac{5 - \sqrt{13}}{2}$ **37.** $\frac{-1 + \sqrt{13}}{2}$ and $\frac{-1 - \sqrt{13}}{2}$ **39.** $-5 + 4\sqrt{2}$ and $-5 - 4\sqrt{2}$ **41.** $\frac{-3 + \sqrt{5}}{2}$ and $\frac{-3 - \sqrt{5}}{2}$ **43.** $\frac{1 + \sqrt{17}}{2}$ and $\frac{1 - \sqrt{17}}{2}$ **45.** There is no real number solution. **47.** $\frac{1}{2}$ and 1 **49.** -3 and $\frac{1}{2}$ **51.** $\frac{1 + \sqrt{2}}{2}$ and $\frac{1 - \sqrt{2}}{2}$ **53.** $\frac{2 + \sqrt{5}}{2}$ and $\frac{2 - \sqrt{5}}{2}$ **55.** $3 + \sqrt{2}$ and $3 - \sqrt{2}$ **57.** $1 + \sqrt{13}$ and $1 - \sqrt{13}$ **59.** $\frac{3 + 3\sqrt{3}}{2}$ and $\frac{3 - 3\sqrt{3}}{2}$ **61.** $4 + \sqrt{7}$ and $4 - \sqrt{7}$ **63.** Both negative **65.** 1.193 and -4.193 **67.** 2.766 and -1.266 **69.** 0.151 and -1.651 **71.** $22 + 12\sqrt{2}$ and $22 - 12\sqrt{2}$ **73.** -3 **75.** $6 + \sqrt{58}$ and $6 - \sqrt{58}$

CONCEPT REVIEW 11.3

1. Always true **3.** Never true **5.** Never true

SECTION 11.3

3. $4x$; 2; $x^2 - 4x - 2$; 1; -4; -2 **5.** -7 and 1 **7.** -3 and 6 **9.** $1 + \sqrt{6}$ and $1 - \sqrt{6}$ **11.** $-3 + \sqrt{10}$ and $-3 - \sqrt{10}$ **13.** There is no real number solution. **15.** $2 + \sqrt{13}$ and $2 - \sqrt{13}$ **17.** 0 and 1 **19.** $\frac{1 + \sqrt{2}}{2}$ and $\frac{1 - \sqrt{2}}{2}$ **21.** $-\frac{3}{2}$ and $\frac{3}{2}$ **23.** $\frac{3 + \sqrt{3}}{3}$ and $\frac{3 - \sqrt{3}}{3}$ **25.** $\frac{1 + \sqrt{10}}{3}$ and $\frac{1 - \sqrt{10}}{3}$ **27.** There is no real number solution. **29.** $\frac{4 + \sqrt{10}}{2}$ and $\frac{4 - \sqrt{10}}{2}$ **31.** $-\frac{2}{3}$ and 3 **33.** $\frac{5 + \sqrt{73}}{6}$ and $\frac{5 - \sqrt{73}}{6}$ **35.** $\frac{1 + \sqrt{37}}{6}$ and $\frac{1 - \sqrt{37}}{6}$ **37.** $\frac{1 + \sqrt{41}}{5}$ and $\frac{1 - \sqrt{41}}{5}$ **39.** -3 and $\frac{4}{5}$ **41.** $-3 + 2\sqrt{2}$ and $-3 - 2\sqrt{2}$ **43.** $\frac{3 + 2\sqrt{6}}{2}$ and $\frac{3 - 2\sqrt{6}}{2}$ **45.** There is no real number solution. **47.** $\frac{-1 + \sqrt{2}}{3}$ and $\frac{-1 - \sqrt{2}}{3}$ **49.** $-\frac{1}{2}$ and $\frac{2}{3}$ **51.** $\frac{-4 + \sqrt{5}}{2}$ and $\frac{-4 - \sqrt{5}}{2}$ **53.** $\frac{1 + 2\sqrt{3}}{2}$ and $\frac{1 - 2\sqrt{3}}{2}$ **55.** $-\frac{3}{2}$ **57.** $\frac{-5 + \sqrt{2}}{3}$ and $\frac{-5 - \sqrt{2}}{3}$ **59.** $\frac{1 + \sqrt{19}}{3}$ and $\frac{1 - \sqrt{19}}{3}$ **61.** $\frac{5 + \sqrt{65}}{4}$ and $\frac{5 - \sqrt{65}}{4}$ **63.** $6 + \sqrt{11}$ and $6 - \sqrt{11}$ **65.** True **67.** 5.690 and -3.690 **69.** 7.690 and -1.690 **71.** 4.589 and -1.089 **73.** 0.118 and -2.118 **75.** 1.105 and -0.905 **77.** $3 + \sqrt{13}$ and $3 - \sqrt{13}$ **79.** **a.** False **b.** False **c.** False **d.** True

CONCEPT REVIEW 11.4

1. Always true **3.** Never true **5.** Never true

SECTION 11.4

1. **a.** 5 **b.** -8 **3.** -1; -1; i; 10 **5.** $9i$ **7.** $35i$ **9.** $i\sqrt{13}$ **11.** $5i\sqrt{3}$ **13.** $-12i\sqrt{6}$ **15.** $a - \sqrt{-b^2}$ **17.** $5 + 2i$ **19.** $-7 - 12i$ **21.** $5 + 12i\sqrt{3}$ **23.** $7 - 12i\sqrt{7}$

25. $3 + 5i$ **27.** $-1 + i\sqrt{6}$ **29.** $-\frac{2}{5} - \frac{12\sqrt{10}}{5}i$ **31.** $-2; 3; 4 - 5i$ **33.** $10i$ **35.** $-9i$
37. $7 + 9i$ **39.** $-8 + 7i$ **41.** $13 + 2i$ **43.** $2 - 10i$ **45.** $-8 - 2i$ **47.** 6 **49.** 0
51. False **53.** Negative **55.** $-8i; -8i; -8i; 56; -1; -1; 56; -8i$ **57.** -20 **59.** 18
61. $-20 + 10i$ **63.** $2 + 23i$ **65.** $-9 - 7i$ **67.** $-41 - i$ **69.** $-21 + 20i$ **71.** $-3 - 4i$
73. $29i$ **75.** 20 **77.** 17 **79.** False **81.** $1 + 4i$ **83.** $1 - 6i$ **85.** $-7 - 2i$
87. $5 + 3i$ **89.** $\frac{3}{2} - \frac{3}{4}i$ **91.** $-\frac{2}{3} - \frac{5}{3}i$ **93.** $\frac{3}{2} - \frac{3}{2}i$ **95.** $-1 - 3i$ **97.** $5 - 3i$
99. $3 - 5i$ **101.** $2 + 4i$ **103.** True **105.** $4i, -4i$ **107.** $7i, -7i$ **109.** $3i\sqrt{3}, -3i\sqrt{3}$
111. $2i\sqrt{3}, -2i\sqrt{3}$ **113.** $-1 + 6i, -1 - 6i$ **115.** $2 + 2i\sqrt{3}, 2 - 2i\sqrt{3}$
117. $-2 + 5i\sqrt{2}, -2 - 5i\sqrt{2}$ **119.** $-\frac{3}{2} + i, -\frac{3}{2} - i$ **121.** $1 + i, 1 - i$ **123.** $-2 + i, -2 - i$
125. $3 + 2i, 3 - 2i$ **127.** $1 + i\sqrt{2}, 1 - i\sqrt{2}$ **129.** $-1 + \frac{1}{2}i, -1 - \frac{1}{2}i$ **131.** $\frac{1}{2} - i\sqrt{3}, \frac{1}{2} + i\sqrt{3}$
133. One real solution **135.** -1 **137.** $5 + 25i$ **139.** $-46 - 9i$ **141.** $3 + i$
143. $2i\sqrt{2}, -2i\sqrt{2}$ **145.** $2 + i\sqrt{5}, 2 - i\sqrt{5}$ **147.** $3 + i\sqrt{5}, 3 - i\sqrt{5}$

CONCEPT REVIEW 11.5

1. Always true **3.** Never true **5.** Never true

SECTION 11.5

5. Up **7.** Up **9.** Up **11.** **a.** $-1; 0; 9$ **b.** parabola; down **c.** $2; -4; 5$ **d.** $2; 5$
13. 4 **15.** -5 **17.** -42

19.
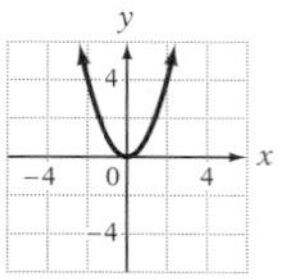

21.
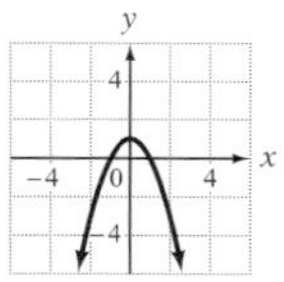

23.
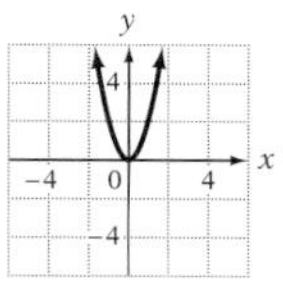

25.
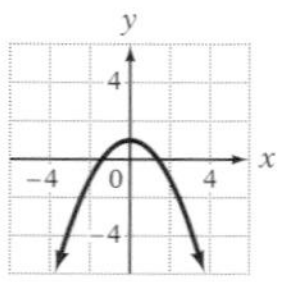

27.
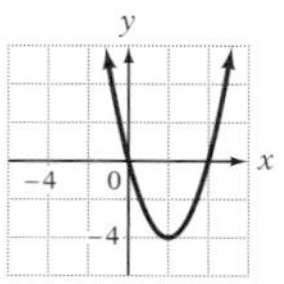

29.
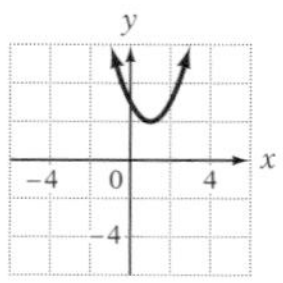

31.
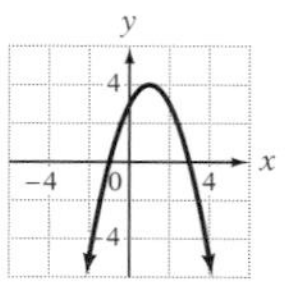

33.
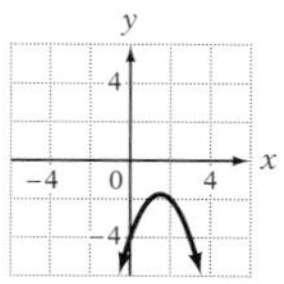

35.
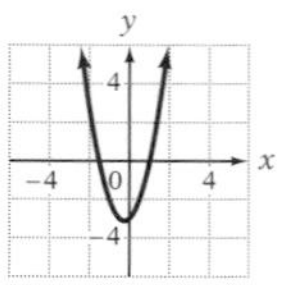

37. False **39.** The x-intercepts are (2, 0) and (3, 0). The y-intercept is (0, 6).

41. The x-intercepts are $(-3, 0)$ and $(3, 0)$. The y-intercept is (0, 9). **43.** The x-intercepts are $(-1 + \sqrt{7}, 0)$ and $(-1 - \sqrt{7}, 0)$. The y-intercept is $(0, -6)$. **45.** The x-intercepts are $\left(\frac{3}{2}, 0\right)$ and $(-1, 0)$. The y-intercept is $(0, -3)$.
47. The x-intercepts are $\left(\frac{1 + \sqrt{17}}{-2}, 0\right)$ and $\left(\frac{1 - \sqrt{17}}{-2}, 0\right)$. The y-intercept is (0, 4). **49.**
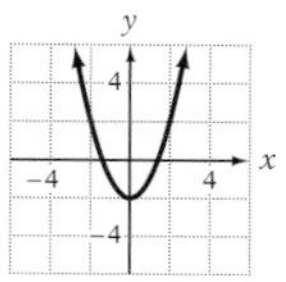

51. 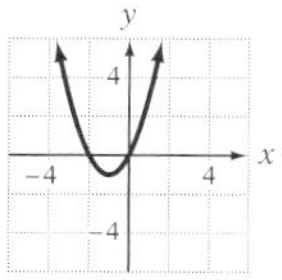

53. 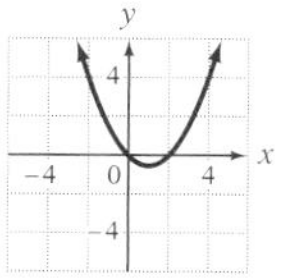

55. 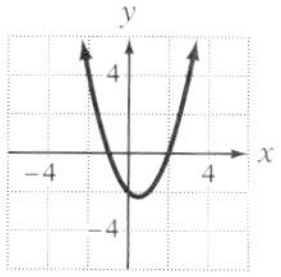

57. 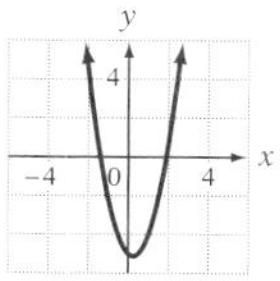

59. 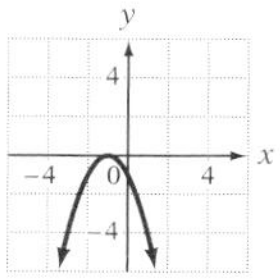

61. $y = x^2 - 8x + 15$ **63.** $y = 2x^2 - 12x + 22$ **65.** $(-2, 0)$, $(0, 0)$, and $(3, 0)$ **67.** $(-2, 0)$, $(-1, 0)$, and $(2, 0)$ **69.** Linear function **71.** Neither **73.** Quadratic function **75.** The model predicts the cost will be 54¢. **77.** -2

CONCEPT REVIEW 11.6

1. Never true **3.** Always true **5.** Always true

SECTION 11.6

1. **a.** $2w - 2$ **b.** $w(2w - 2)$ **c.** $w(2w - 2)$; 84 **3.** The two integers are 7 and 9. **5.** The integers are 6 and 10, or -10 and -6. **7.** The length is 6 ft. The width is 4 ft. **9.** The length is 100 ft. The width is 50 ft. **11.** It would take the first computer 35 min and the second computer 14 min. **13.** It would take the first engine 12 h and the second engine 6 h. **15.** The rate of the plane in calm air was 100 mph. **17.** The cyclist's rate during the first 150 mi was 50 mph. **19.** The arrow will be 32 ft above the ground at 1 s and at 2 s. **21.** The maximum speed is 151.6 km/h. **23.** The water from the hose is 244.1 ft from the tugboat. **25.** The ball hits the basket 1.88 s after it is released. **27.** False **29.** The radius of the base is 5.64 cm. **31.** The integers are -6, -5, -4, and -3, or 3, 4, 5, and 6. **33.** The radius of the large pizza is 7 in. **35.** The dimensions of the cardboard are 20 in. by 20 in.

CHAPTER 11 REVIEW EXERCISES

1. 4 and -4 [11.1.1/11.1.2] **2.** $\dfrac{1 + \sqrt{13}}{2}$ and $\dfrac{1 - \sqrt{13}}{2}$ [11.2.1/11.3.1] **3.** $\dfrac{3 + \sqrt{29}}{2}$ and $\dfrac{3 - \sqrt{29}}{2}$ [11.2.1/11.3.1] **4.** $\dfrac{5}{7}$ and $-\dfrac{5}{7}$ [11.1.1/11.1.2] **5.** 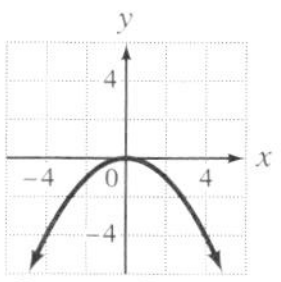

[11.5.1] **6.** 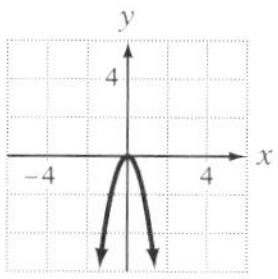

[11.5.1]

7. $6i\sqrt{7}$ [11.4.1] **8.** $-\dfrac{1}{2}$ and $-\dfrac{1}{3}$ [11.1.1] **9.** $\dfrac{3}{2}i$, $-\dfrac{3}{2}i$ [11.4.5]

10. $\dfrac{-10 + 2\sqrt{10}}{5}$ and $\dfrac{-10 - 2\sqrt{10}}{5}$ [11.2.1/11.3.1] **11.** $2 - 4i$ [11.4.2] **12.** 6 and -5 [11.1.1]

13. $\dfrac{4}{3}$ and $-\dfrac{7}{2}$ [11.1.1] **14.** $2\sqrt{10}$ and $-2\sqrt{10}$ [11.1.2] **15.** $-3 + 5i$ [11.4.2]

16. $1 + \sqrt{11}$ and $1 - \sqrt{11}$ [11.2.1/11.3.1] **17.** 3 and 9 [11.1.1] **18.** 16 and -2 [11.1.2]

19. 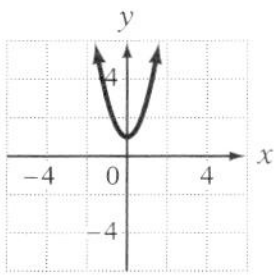

[11.5.1] **20.** 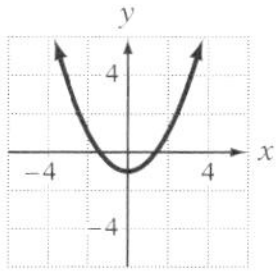

[11.5.1]

21. 1 and -9 [11.1.2] **22.** $\dfrac{-4 + \sqrt{23}}{2}$ and $\dfrac{-4 - \sqrt{23}}{2}$ [11.2.1/11.3.1] **23.** $-\dfrac{1}{6}$ and $-\dfrac{5}{4}$ [11.1.1]

24. $2 + 2i$ and $2 - 2i$ [11.4.5] **25.** $20 + 12i$ [11.4.3] **26.** $\frac{4}{7}$ [11.1.1] **27.** 2 and -1 [11.1.2] **28.** $-2 + 14i$ [11.4.3] **29.** $\frac{-7 + \sqrt{61}}{2}$ and $\frac{-7 - \sqrt{61}}{2}$ [11.2.1/11.3.1] **30.** 2 and $\frac{5}{12}$ [11.1.1] **31.** $3 + \sqrt{5}$ and $3 - \sqrt{5}$ [11.1.2] **32.** $-4 + \sqrt{19}$ and $-4 - \sqrt{19}$ [11.2.1/11.3.1]

33. 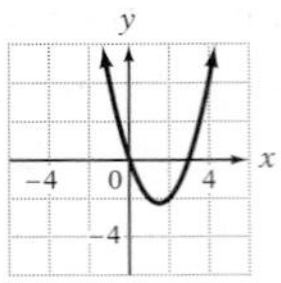

[11.5.1] **34.** 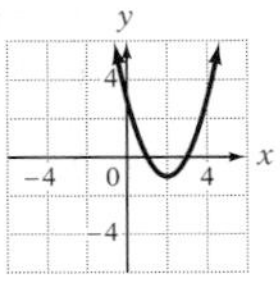

[11.5.1] **35.** -7 and -10 [11.1.1]

36. $\frac{1}{2} + \frac{1}{2}i$ [11.4.4] **37.** $-3 + i\sqrt{3}$ and $-3 - i\sqrt{3}$ [11.4.5] **38.** $-3 + \sqrt{11}$ and $-3 - \sqrt{11}$ [11.2.1/11.3.1] **39.** 3 and $-\frac{1}{9}$ [11.1.1] **40.** $\frac{-5 + \sqrt{33}}{4}$ and $\frac{-5 - \sqrt{33}}{4}$ [11.2.1/11.3.1] **41.** 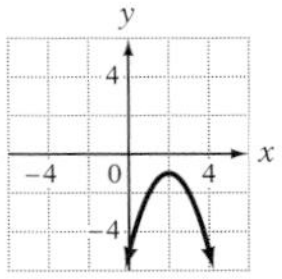

[11.5.1] **42.** $-3 - i$ [11.4.4] **43.** 1 and $\frac{5}{2}$ [11.1.1] **44.** 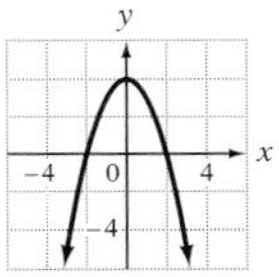

[11.5.1]

45. The rate of the air balloon is 25 mph. [11.6.1] **46.** The height is 10 m. The base is 4 m. [11.6.1] **47.** The two integers are 3 and 5. [11.6.1] **48.** The rate of the boat in still water is 5 mph. [11.6.1] **49.** The object will be12 ft above the ground at $\frac{1}{2}$ s and $1\frac{1}{2}$ s. [11.6.1] **50.** It would take the smaller drain 12 h and the larger drain 4 h. [11.6.1]

CHAPTER 11 TEST

1. $-4 + 2\sqrt{5}$ and $-4 - 2\sqrt{5}$ [11.1.2] **2.** $\frac{-4 + \sqrt{22}}{2}$ and $\frac{-4 - \sqrt{22}}{2}$ [11.2.1/11.3.1] **3.** -4 and $\frac{5}{3}$ [11.1.1] **4.** $12i\sqrt{5}$ [11.4.1] **5.** $-2 + 2\sqrt{5}$ and $-2 - 2\sqrt{5}$ [11.2.1/11.3.1]

6. 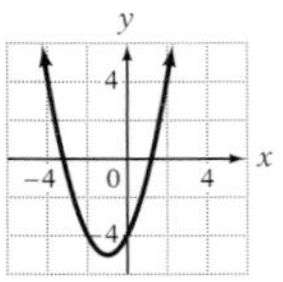

[11.5.1] **7.** $-2 + \sqrt{2}$ and $-2 - \sqrt{2}$ [11.2.1/11.3.1] **8.** $-8 + 13i$ [11.4.2]

9. $-\frac{1}{2}$ and 3 [11.1.1] **10.** $\frac{3 + \sqrt{7}}{2}$ and $\frac{3 - \sqrt{7}}{2}$ [11.2.1/11.3.1] **11.** $24 + 30i$ [11.4.3] **12.** $5 + 3\sqrt{2}$ and $5 - 3\sqrt{2}$ [11.1.2] **13.** $3 + \sqrt{14}$ and $3 - \sqrt{14}$ [11.2.1/11.3.1] **14.** $-18 + 13i$ [11.4.3] **15.** $\frac{5 + \sqrt{33}}{2}$ and $\frac{5 - \sqrt{33}}{2}$ [11.2.1/11.3.1] **16.** $\frac{5}{2}$ and $\frac{1}{3}$ [11.1.1] **17.** $\frac{-3 + \sqrt{37}}{2}$ and $\frac{-3 - \sqrt{37}}{2}$ [11.2.1/11.3.1] **18.** $-\frac{1}{2} - \frac{3}{2}i$ [11.4.4] **19.** $4 + i$ and $4 - i$ [11.4.5]

20. 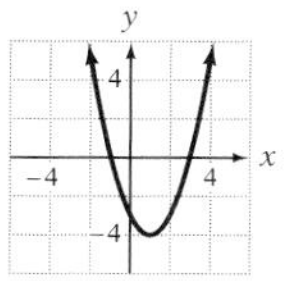

[11.5.1] **21.** $3 + i$ [11.4.4] **22.** The length is 8 ft. The width is 5 ft. [11.6.1]

23. The rate of the boat in calm water is 11 mph. [11.6.1] **24.** The middle odd integer is 5 or −5. [11.6.1]
25. The rate for the last 8 mi was 4 mph. [11.6.1]

CUMULATIVE REVIEW EXERCISES

1. $-28x + 27$ [2.2.5] **2.** $\frac{3}{2}$ [3.1.3] **3.** 3 [3.2.3] **4.** $x > \frac{1}{9}$ [3.3.3] **5.** (3, 0) and (0, −4) [5.2.3] **6.** $y = -\frac{4}{3}x - 2$ [5.4.1/5.4.2] **7.** Domain: {−2, −1, 0, 1, 2}; range: {−8, −1, 0, 1, 8}; yes [5.5.1]

8. 37 [5.5.1] **9.** 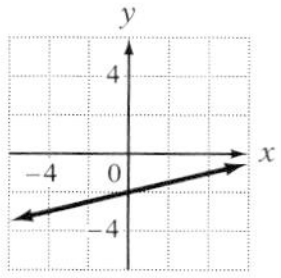

[5.2.2] **10.** 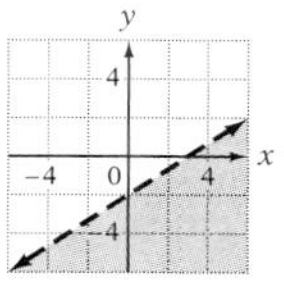

[5.6.1] **11.** (2, 1) [6.2.1]

12. (2, −2) [6.3.1] **13.** $-\frac{4a}{3b^2}$ [7.4.1] **14.** $x + 2 - \frac{4}{x - 2}$ [7.5.2] **15.** $(x - 4)(4y - 3)$ [8.1.2]

16. $x(3x - 4)(x + 2)$ [8.3.1/8.3.2] **17.** $\frac{9x^2(x - 2)(x - 4)}{(2x - 3)^2(x + 2)}$ [9.1.3] **18.** $\frac{x + 2}{2(x + 1)}$ [9.3.2]

19. $\frac{x - 4}{2x + 5}$ [9.4.1] **20.** −3 and 6 [9.5.2] **21.** $a - 2$ [10.3.1] **22.** 5 [10.4.1]

23. $\frac{1}{2}$ and 3 [11.1.1] **24.** $2 + 2\sqrt{3}$ and $2 - 2\sqrt{3}$ [11.1.2] **25.** $\frac{2 + \sqrt{19}}{3}$ and $\frac{2 - \sqrt{19}}{3}$ [11.2.1/11.3.1]

26. 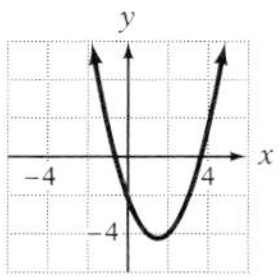

[11.5.1] **27.** The cost is $72. [3.1.5] **28.** The cost is $4.50 per pound. [4.6.1]

29. To earn a dividend of $752.50, 250 additional shares are required. [9.5.2] **30.** The rate of the plane in calm air is 200 mph. The rate of the wind is 40 mph. [6.4.1] **31.** The student must receive a score of 77 or better. [4.8.1] **32.** The length of the guy wire is 31.62 m. [10.4.2] **33.** The middle odd integer is −7 or 7. [11.6.1]

Answers to Final Exam

1. −3 [1.1.2] **2.** −6 [1.2.2] **3.** 12.5% [1.3.4] **4.** −256 [1.4.1] **5.** −11 [1.4.2]
6. $-\frac{15}{2}$ [2.1.1] **7.** $9x + 6y$ [2.2.2] **8.** $6z$ [2.2.3] **9.** $16x - 52$ [2.2.5] **10.** −50 [3.1.3]

11. −3 [3.2.3] **12.** 15.2 [3.1.5] **13.** $x \le -3$ [3.3.3] **14.** $y \ge \frac{5}{2}$ [3.3.3] **15.** $\frac{2}{3}$ [5.3.1]

16. $y = -\frac{2}{3}x - 2$ [5.4.1/5.4.2] **17.** 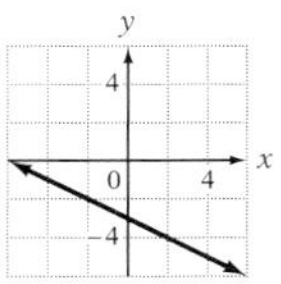

[5.3.2] **18.** 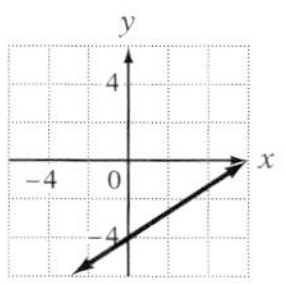

[5.5.2]

19. $\{-1, 2, 5, 8, 11\}$ [5.5.1] **20.**

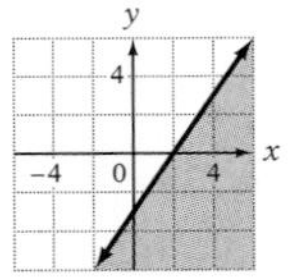

[5.6.1] **21.** (6, 17) [6.2.1] **22.** (2, −1) [6.3.1]

23. $-3x^2 - 3x + 8$ [7.1.2] **24.** $81x^4y^{12}$ [7.2.2] **25.** $6x^3 + 7x^2 - 7x - 6$ [7.3.2]

26. $-\frac{x^8y}{2}$ [7.4.1] **27.** $\frac{16y^7}{x^8}$ [7.4.1] **28.** $3x^2 - 4x - \frac{5}{x}$ [7.5.1] **29.** $5x - 12 + \frac{23}{x + 2}$ [7.5.2]

30. $3.9 \cdot 10^{-8}$ [7.4.2] **31.** $2(4 - x)(a + 3)$ [8.1.2] **32.** $(x - 6)(x + 1)$ [8.2.1]

33. $(2x - 3)(x + 1)$ [8.3.1/8.3.2] **34.** $(3x + 2)(2x - 3)$ [8.3.1/8.3.2] **35.** $4x(2x - 1)(x - 3)$ [8.3.1/8.3.2] **36.** $(5x + 4)(5x - 4)$ [8.4.1] **37.** $3y(5 + 2x)(5 - 2x)$ [8.4.2] **38.** $\frac{1}{2}$ and 3 [8.5.1/11.1.1] **39.** $\frac{2(x + 1)}{x - 1}$ [9.1.2] **40.** $\frac{-3x^2 + x - 25}{(2x - 5)(x + 3)}$ [9.3.2] **41.** $x + 1$ [9.4.1]

42. 2 [9.5.1] **43.** $a = b$ [9.6.1] **44.** $7x^3$ [10.1.2] **45.** $38\sqrt{3a}$ [10.2.1]

46. $\sqrt{15} + 2\sqrt{3}$ [10.3.2] **47.** 5 [10.4.1] **48.** $3 + \sqrt{7}$ and $3 - \sqrt{7}$ [11.1.2]

49. $\frac{1 + \sqrt{5}}{4}$ and $\frac{1 - \sqrt{5}}{4}$ [11.2.1/11.3.1] **50.**

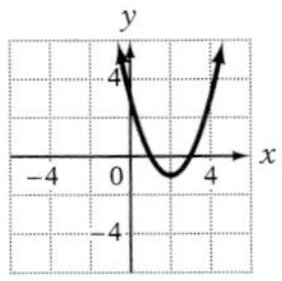

[11.5.1] **51.** $2x + 3(x - 2)$; $5x - 6$ [2.3.2]

52. The original value of the machine was $3000. [3.1.5] **53.** There are 60 dimes in the bank. [4.2.2] **54.** The angles measure 60°, 50°, and 70°. [4.3.3] **55.** The markup rate is 65%. [4.4.1] **56.** An additional $6000 must be invested at 11%. [4.5.1] **57.** The cost is $3 per pound. [4.6.1] **58.** The percent concentration is 36%. [4.6.2] **59.** The plane traveled 215 km during the first hour. [4.7.1] **60.** The rate of the boat is 15 mph. The rate of the current is 5 mph. [6.4.1] **61.** The length is 10 m. The width is 5 m. [8.5.2] **62.** 16 oz of dye are required. [9.5.3] **63.** It would take them 0.6 h to prepare the dinner. [9.7.1] **64.** The length of the other leg is 11.5 cm. [10.4.2] **65.** The rate of the wind is 25 mph. [11.6.1]

Glossary

abscissa The first number in an ordered pair. It measures a horizontal distance and is also called the first coordinate. (Sec. 5.1)

absolute value of a number The distance of the number from zero on the number line. (Sec. 1.1)

acute angle An angle whose measure is between 0° and 90°. (Sec. 4.3)

addend In addition, a number being added. (Sec. 1.2)

addition The process of finding the total of two numbers. (Sec. 1.2)

addition method An algebraic method of finding an exact solution of a system of linear equations. (Sec. 6.3)

additive inverses Numbers that are the same distance from zero on the number line, but on opposite sides; also called opposites. (Sec. 1.1, 2.2)

adjacent angles Two angles that share a common side. (Sec. 4.3)

alternate exterior angles Two nonadjacent angles that are on opposite sides of the transversal and outside the parallel lines. (Sec. 4.3)

alternate interior angles Two nonadjacent angles that are on opposite sides of the transversal and between the parallel lines. (Sec. 4.3)

analytic geometry Geometry in which a coordinate system is used to study the relationships between variables. (Sec. 5.1)

angle Figure formed when two rays start from the same point; it is measured in degrees. (Sec. 1.5)

area A measure of the amount of surface in a region. (Sec. 1.5)

arithmetic mean of values Average determined by calculating the sum of the values and then dividing that result by the number of values. (Sec. 1.2)

average of a set of numbers The sum of the numbers divided by the number of numbers in the set. (Sec. 1.2)

average rate of change The average rate of change of y with respect to x is the change in y divided by the change in x. (Sec. 5.1)

axes The two number lines that form a rectangular coordinate system; also called coordinate axes. (Sec. 5.1)

axis of symmetry of a parabola A line of symmetry that passes through the vertex of the parabola and is parallel to the y-axis for an equation of the form $y = ax^2 + bx + c$. (Sec. 11.5)

base In exponential notation, the factor that is multiplied the number of times shown by the exponent (Sec. 1.4)

base of a parallelogram One of the parallel sides of the parallelogram. (Sec. 1.5)

base of a triangle The side of a triangle that the triangle rests on. (Sec. 1.5)

binomial A polynomial of two terms. (Sec. 7.1)

binomial factor A factor that has two terms. (Sec. 8.1)

center of a circle The point from which all points on the circle are equidistant. (Sec. 1.5)

circle Plane figure in which all points are the same distance from its center. (Sec. 1.5)

circumference The distance around a circle. (Sec. 3.2)

clearing denominators Removing denominators from an equation that contains fractions by multiplying each side of the equation by the LCM of the denominators. (Sec. 3.2, 9.5)

coefficient The number part of a variable term. (Sec. 2.1)

combine like terms Use the Distributive Property to add the coefficients of like variable terms; add like terms of a variable expression. (Sec. 2.2)

complementary angles Two angles whose sum is 90°. (Sec. 1.5, 4.3)

complete the square Add to a binomial the constant term that makes it a perfect-square trinomial. (Sec. 11.2)

complex conjugates Complex numbers of the form $a + bi$ and $a - bi$. (Sec. 11.4)

complex fraction A fraction whose numerator or denominator contains one or more fractions. (Sec. 9.4)

complex number A number of the form $a + bi$, where a and b are real numbers and $i = \sqrt{-1}$. (Sec. 11.4)

conjugates Binomial expressions that differ only in the sign of a term. The expressions $a + b$ and $a - b$ are conjugates. (Sec. 10.3)

consecutive even integers Even integers that follow one another in order. (Sec. 4.2)

consecutive integers Integers that follow one another in order. (Sec. 4.2)

consecutive odd integers Odd integers that follow one another in order. (Sec. 4.2)

constant term A term that includes no variable part; also called a constant. (Sec. 2.1)

coordinate axes The two number lines that form a rectangular coordinate system; also simply called axes. (Sec. 5.1)

coordinates of a point The numbers in an ordered pair that is associated with a point. (Sec. 5.1)

corresponding angles Two angles that are on the same side of the transversal and are both acute angles or are both obtuse angles. (Sec. 4.3)

cost The price that a business pays for a product. (Sec. 4.4)

decimal notation Notation in which a number consists of a whole-number part, a decimal point, and a decimal part. (Sec. 1.3)

degree A unit used to measure angles. (Sec. 1.5, 4.3)

degree of a polynomial in one variable In a polynomial, the largest exponent that appears on the variable. (Sec. 7.1)

dependent system of equations A system of equations that has an infinite number of solutions. (Sec. 6.1)

dependent variable In a function, the variable whose value depends on the value of another variable known as the independent variable. (Sec. 5.5)

descending order The terms of a polynomial in one variable arranged so that the exponents on the variable decrease from left to right. The polynomial $9x^5 - 2x^4 + 7x^3 + x^2 - 8x + 1$ is in descending order. (Sec. 7.1)

diameter of a circle A line segment that has endpoints on the circle and goes through the circle's center. (Sec. 1.5)

difference of two squares A polynomial of the form $a^2 - b^2$. (Sec. 8.4)

discount The amount by which a retailer reduces the regular price of a product for a promotional sale. (Sec. 4.4)

discount rate The percent of the regular price that the discount represents. (Sec. 4.4)

domain The set of first coordinates of the ordered pairs in a relation. (Sec. 5.5)

double root The two equal roots of a quadratic equation. (Sec. 11.1)

element of a set One of the objects in a set. (Sec. 1.1)

equation A statement of the equality of two mathematical expressions. (Sec. 3.1)

equilateral triangle A triangle in which all three sides are of equal length. (Sec. 1.5, 4.3)

evaluate a function Replace x in $f(x)$ with some value and then simplify the numerical expression that results. (Sec. 5.5)

evaluate a variable expression Replace each variable by its value and then simplify the resulting numerical expression. (Sec. 2.1)

even integer An integer that is divisible by 2. (Sec. 4.2)

exponent In exponential notation, the elevated number that indicates how many times the base occurs in the multiplication. (Sec. 1.4)

exponential form The expression 2^5 is in exponential form. Compare *factored form.* (Sec. 1.4)

exterior angle of a triangle An angle adjacent to an interior angle of the triangle. (Sec. 4.3)

factor In multiplication, a number being multiplied. (Sec. 1.2)

factor a polynomial To write the polynomial as a product of other polynomials. (Sec. 8.1)

factor a trinomial of the form $ax^2 + bx + c$ To express the trinomial as the product of two binomials. (Sec. 8.3)

factor by grouping Group and factor terms in a polynomial in such a way that a common binomial factor is found. (Sec. 8.1)

factor completely Write a polynomial as a product of factors that are nonfactorable over the integers. (Sec. 8.2)

factored form The expression $2 \cdot 2 \cdot 2 \cdot 2 \cdot 2$ is in factored form. Compare *exponential form*. (Sec. 1.4)

FOIL method A method of finding the product of two binomials in which the sum of the products of the first terms, of the outer terms, of the inner terms, and of the last terms is found. (Sec. 7.3)

formula A literal equation that states rules about measurements. (Sec. 9.6)

simplest form of a fraction A fraction in which the numerator and denominator have no common factors other than 1. (Sec. 9.1)

function A relation in which no two ordered pairs that have the same first coordinate have different second coordinates. (Sec. 5.5)

function notation Notation used for those equations that define functions. (Sec. 5.5)

graph of a function A graph of the ordered pairs (x, y) of the function. (Sec. 5.5)

graph of a relation The graph of the ordered pairs that belong to the relation. (Sec. 5.5)

graph of an equation in two variables A graph of the ordered-pair solutions of the equation. (Sec. 5.2)

graph of an integer A heavy dot directly above that number on the number line. (Sec. 1.1)

graph of an ordered pair The dot drawn at the coordinates of the point in the plane. (Sec. 5.1)

graph a point in the plane Place a dot at the location given by the ordered pair; plot a point in the plane. (Sec. 5.1)

graph of $x = a$ A vertical line passing through the point whose coordinates are $(a, 0)$. (Sec. 5.2)

graph of $y = b$ A horizontal line passing through the point whose coordinates are $(0, b)$. (Sec. 5.2)

greater than A number a is greater than another number b, written $a > b$, if a is to the right of b on the number line. (Sec. 1.1)

greater than or equal to The symbol $\geq$ means "is greater than or equal to." (Sec. 1.1)

greatest common factor of two numbers The greatest number that is a factor of the two numbers. (Sec. 8.1)

greatest common factor of two monomials The product of the GCF of the coefficients of the monomials and the common variable factors. (Sec. 8.1)

half-plane The solution set of an inequality in two variables. (Sec. 5.6)

height of a triangle A line segment perpendicular to the base of the triangle from the opposite vertex. (Sec. 1.5)

height of a parallelogram The distance between the base of the parallelogram and the opposite parallel side. It is perpendicular to the base. (Sec. 1.5)

hypotenuse In a right triangle, the side opposite the 90° angle. (Sec. 10.4)

imaginary number A number of the form ai, where a is a real number and $i = \sqrt{-1}$. (Sec. 11.4)

imaginary part of a complex number For the complex number $a + bi$, b is the imaginary part. (Sec. 9.4)

imaginary unit The number whose square is -1, designated by the letter i. (Sec. 11.4)

inconsistent system of equations A system of equations that has no solution. (Sec. 6.1)

independent system of equations A system of equations that has one solution. (Sec. 6.1)

independent variable In a function, the variable that varies independently and whose value determines the value of the dependent variable. (Sec. 5.5)

inequality An expression that contains the symbol $>$, $<$, $\geq$ (is greater than or equal to), or $\leq$ (is less than or equal to). (Sec. 3.3)

integers The numbers $\ldots, -3, -2, -1, 0, 1, 2, 3, \ldots$. (Sec. 1.1)

interior angle of a triangle An angle within the region enclosed by the triangle. (Sec. 4.3)

intersecting lines Lines that cross at a point in the plane. (Sec. 1.5)

irrational number A number that cannot be written in the form a/b, where a and b are integers and b is not equal to zero. (Sec. 1.3, 10.1)

isosceles triangle A triangle that has two equal angles and two equal sides. (Sec. 1.5, 4.3)

least common multiple of two numbers The smallest number that contains the prime factorization of each number. (Sec. 1.3, 9.2)

least common multiple of two polynomials The polynomial of least degree that contains the factors of each polynomial. (Sec. 9.2)

legs In a right triangle, the sides opposite the acute angles, or the two shortest sides of the triangle. (Sec. 10.4)

legs than A number a is less than another number b, written $a < b$, if a is to the left of b on the number line. (Sec. 1.1)

less than or equal to The symbol $\leq$ means "is less than or equal to." (Sec. 1.1)

like terms Terms of a variable expression that have the same variable part. (Sec. 2.2)

line A line extends indefinitely in two directions in a plane; it has no width. (Sec. 1.5)

linear equation in two variables An equation of the form $y = mx + b$, where m is the coefficient of x and b is a constant; also called a linear function. (Sec. 5.2)

linear function An equation of the form $f(x) = mx + b$ or $y = mx + b$, where m is the coefficient of x and b is a constant; also called a linear equation in two variables. (Sec. 5.5)

line segment Part of a line; it has two endpoints. (Sec. 1.5)

literal equation An equation that contains more than one variable. (Sec. 9.6)

lowest common denominator The smallest number that is a multiple of each denominator in question. (Sec. 1.3)

markup The difference between selling price and cost. (Sec. 4.4)

markup rate The percent of a retailer's cost that the markup represents. (Sec. 4.4)

monomial A number, a variable, or a product of numbers and variables; a polynomial of one term. (Sec. 7.1)

multiplication The process of finding the product of two numbers. (Sec. 1.2)

multiplicative inverse of a number The reciprocal of the number. (Sec. 2.2)

natural numbers The numbers 1, 2, 3, ... (Sec. 1.1)

negative integers The numbers . . . , −4, −3, −2, −1. (Sec. 1.1)

negative slope A property of a line that slants downward to the right. (Sec. 5.3)

nonfactorable over the integers A description of a polynomial that does not factor when only integers are used. (Sec. 8.1)

numerical coefficient The number part of a variable term. When the numerical coefficient is 1 or −1, the 1 is usually not written. (Sec. 2.1)

obtuse angle An angle whose measure is between 90° and 180°. (Sec. 4.3)

odd integer An integer that is not divisible by 2. (Sec. 4.2)

opposite of a polynomial The polynomial created when the sign of each term of the original polynomial is changed. (Sec. 7.1)

opposites Numbers that are the same distance from zero on the number line, but on opposite sides; also called additive inverses. (Sec. 1.1)

ordered pair A pair of numbers, such as (a, b), that can be used to identify a point in the plane determined by the axes of a rectangular coordinate system. (Sec. 5.1)

Order of Operations Agreement A set of rules that tells us in what order to perform the operations that occur in a numerical expression. (Sec. 1.4)

ordinate The second number in an ordered pair. It measures a vertical distance and is also called the second coordinate. (Sec. 5.1)

origin The point of intersection of the two coordinate axes that form a rectangular coordinate system. (Sec. 5.1)

parabola The name given to the graph of a quadratic equation in two variables. (Sec. 11.4)

parallel lines Lines that never meet; the distance between them is always the same. (Sec. 1.5, 4.3)

parallelogram A four-sided plane figure with opposite sides parallel. (Sec. 1.5)

percent Parts of 100. (Sec. 1.3)

perfect cube The cube of an integer. (Sec. 8.4)

perfect square The square of an integer. (Sec. 10.1)

perfect-square trinomial A trinomial that is a product of a binomial and itself. (Sec. 8.4)

perimeter The distance around a plane geometric figure. (Sec. 1.5, 4.3)

perpendicular lines Intersecting lines that form right angles. (Sec. 1.5, 4.3)

plane Flat surface determined by the intersection of two lines. (Sec. 1.5)

plane figures Figures that lie entirely in a plane. (Sec. 1.5)

plot a point in the plane Place a dot at the location given by the ordered pair; graph a point in the plane. (Sec. 5.1)

point-slope formula If (x_1, y_1) is a point on a line with slope m, then $y - y_1 = m(x - x_1)$. (Sec. 5.4)

polynomial A variable expression in which the terms are monomials. (Sec. 7.1)

positive integers The integers 1, 2, 3, 4 . . . . (Sec. 1.1)

positive slope A property of a line that slants upward to the right. (Sec. 5.3)

principal square root The positive square root of a number. (Sec. 10.1)

product In multiplication, the result of multiplying two numbers. (Sec. 1.2)

proportion An equation that states the equality of two ratios or rates. (Sec. 9.5)

Pythagorean Theorem If a and b are the lengths of the legs of a right triangle and c is the length of the hypotenuse, then $c^2 = a^2 + b^2$. (Sec. 10.4)

quadrant One of the four regions into which the two axes of a rectangular coordinate system divide the plane. (Sec. 5.1)

quadratic equation An equation of the form $ax^2 + bx + c, a \neq 0$; also called a second-degree equation. (Sec. 8.5, 11.1)

quadratic equation in two variables An equation of the form $y = ax^2 + bx + c$, where a is not equal to zero. (Sec. 11.4)

quadratic function A function of the form $f(x) = ax^2 + bx + c$, where a is not equal to zero. (Sec. 11.4)

radical equation An equation that contains a variable expression in a radicand. (Sec. 10.4)

radical sign The symbol $\sqrt{\ }$, which is used to indicate the positive, or principal, square root of a number. (Sec. 10.1)

radicand In a radical expression, the expression under the radical sign. (Sec. 10.1)

radius of a circle A line segment from the center of a circle to a point on the circle. (Sec. 1.5)

range The set of second coordinates of the ordered pairs in a relation. (Sec. 5.5)

rate The quotient of two quantities that have different units. (Sec. 9.5)

rate of work That part of a task that is completed in one unit of time. (Sec. 9.7)

ratio The quotient of two quantities that have the same unit. (Sec. 9.5)

rational expression A fraction in which the numerator and denominator are polynomials. (Sec. 9.1)

rational number A number that can be written in the form a/b, where a and b are integers and b is not equal to zero. (Sec. 1.3)

rationalize the denominator Remove a radical from the denominator of a fraction. (Sec. 10.3)

ray A figure that starts at a point and extends indefinitely in one direction. (Sec. 1.5)

real numbers The rational numbers and the irrational numbers. (Sec. 1.3)

real part of a complex number For the complex number $a + bi$, a is the real part. (Sec. 11.4)

reciprocal of a fraction The fraction that results when the numerator and denominator of a fraction are interchanged. (Sec. 1.3, 2.2)

reciprocal of a rational expression The rational expression that results when the numerator and denominator of a rational expression are interchanged. (Sec. 9.1)

rectangle A parallelogram that has four right angles. (Sec. 1.5)

rectangular coordinate system System formed by two number lines, one horizontal and one vertical, that intersect at the zero point of each line. (Sec. 5.1)

relation Any set of ordered pairs. (Sec. 5.5)

repeating decimal A decimal formed when dividing the numerator of a fraction by its denominator, in which a digit or a sequence of digits in the decimal repeats infinitely. (Sec. 1.3)

right angle An angle whose measure is 90°. (Sec. 1.5, 4.3)

right triangle A triangle that contains a 90° angle. (Sec. 10.4)

roster method Method of writing a set by enclosing a list of the elements in braces. (Sec. 1.1)

scatter diagram A graph of collected data as points in a coordinate system. (Sec. 5.1)

scientific notation Notation in which a number is expressed as the product of two factors, one a number between 1 and 10 and the other a power of 10. (Sec. 7.4)

second-degree equation An equation of the form $ax^2 + bx + c = 0$, $a \neq 0$; also called a quadratic equation. (Sec. 11.1)

selling price The price for which a business sells a product to a customer. (Sec. 4.4)

set A collection of objects. (Sec. 1.1)

similar objects Objects that have the same shape but not necessarily the same size. (Sec. 9.5)

similar triangles Triangles that have the same shape but not necessarily the same size. (Sec. 9.5)

slope The measure of the slant of a line. The symbol for slope is m. (Sec. 5.3)

slope-intercept form The slope-intercept form of an equation of a straight line is $y = mx + b$. (Sec. 5.3)

solids Objects in space. (Sec. 1.5)

solution of a system of equations in two variables An ordered pair that is a solution of each equation of the system. (Sec. 6.1)

solution of an equation A number that, when substituted for the variable, results in a true equation. (Sec. 3.1)

solution of a linear equation in two variables An ordered pair whose coordinates make the equation a true statement. (Sec. 5.2)

solution set of an inequality A set of numbers, each element of which, when substituted for the variable, results in a true inequality. (Sec. 3.3)

solve an equation Find solutions of the equation. (Sec. 3.1)

square A rectangle that has four equal sides. (Sec. 1.5)

square root A square root of a positive number x is a number a for which $a^2 = x$. (Sec. 10.1)

standard form of a quadratic equation A quadratic equation written with the polynomial in descending order and equal to zero. $ax^2 + bx + c = 0$ is in standard form. (Sec. 8.5, 11.1)

straight angle An angle whose measure is 180°. (Sec. 1.5, 4.3)

substitution method An algebraic method of finding an exact solution of a system of equations. (Sec. 6.2)

subtraction The process of finding the difference between two numbers. (Sec. 1.2)

sum In addition, the total of two or more numbers. (Sec. 1.2)

supplementary angles Two angles whose sum is 180°. (Sec. 1.5, 4.3)

system of equations Equations that are considered together. (Sec. 6.1)

terminating decimal A decimal that is formed when dividing the numerator of its fractional counterpart by the denominator results in a remainder of zero. (Sec. 1.3)

terms of a variable expression The addends of the expression. (Sec. 2.1)

transversal A line intersecting two other lines at two different points. (Sec. 4.3)

triangle A three-sided closed figure. (Sec. 1.5, 4.3)

trinomial A polynomial of three terms. (Sec. 7.1)

undefined slope A property of a vertical line. (Sec. 5.3)

uniform motion The motion of a moving object whose speed and direction do not change. (Sec. 3.1, 4.7, 9.7)

value of a function The result of evaluating a variable expression, represented by the symbol $f(x)$. (Sec. 5.5)

variable A letter of the alphabet used to stand for a number that is unknown or that can change. (Sec. 1.1, 2.1)

variable expression An expression that contains one or more variables. (Sec. 2.1)

variable part In a variable term, the variable or variables and their exponents. (Sec. 2.1)

variable term A term composed of a numerical coefficient and a variable part. (Sec. 2.1)

vertex of an angle Point at which the two rays that form the angle meet. (Sec. 1.5)

vertex of a parabola The lowest point on the graph of a parabola if the parabola opens up. The highest point on the graph of a parabola if the parabola opens down. (Sec. 11.4)

vertical angles Two angles that are on opposite sides of the intersection of two lines. (Sec. 4.3)

whole numbers The whole numbers are 0, 1, 2, 3 . . . . (Sec. 1.1)

***x*-axis** The horizontal axis in an *xy*-coordinate system. (Sec. 5.1)

***x*-coordinate** The abscissa in an *xy*-coordinate system. (Sec. 5.1)

***x*-intercept** The point at which a graph crosses the *x*-axis. (Sec. 5.2)

***y*-axis** The vertical axis in an *xy*-coordinate system. (Sec. 5.1)

***y*-coordinate** The ordinate in an *xy*-coordinate system. (Sec. 5.1)

***y*-intercept** The point at which a graph crosses the *y*-axis. (Sec. 5.2)

zero slope A property of a horizontal line. (Sec. 5.3)

Index

Table of Equations and Formulas

Slope of a Straight Line

$$\text{Slope} = m = \frac{y_2 - y_1}{x_2 - x_1},\ x_1 \neq x_2$$

Slope-intercept Form of a Straight Line

$$y = mx + b$$

Point-slope Formula for a Line

$$y - y_1 = m(x - x_1)$$

Quadratic Formula

$$x = \frac{-b \pm \sqrt{b^2 - 4ac}}{2a}$$

Perimeter and Area of a Triangle, and Sum of the Measures of the Angles

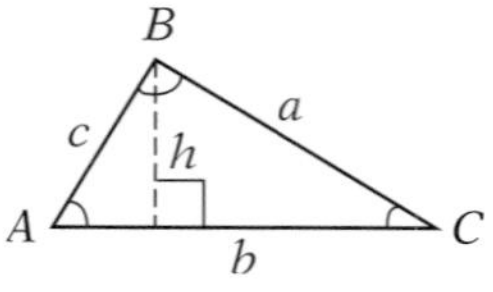

$$P = a + b + c$$

$$A = \frac{1}{2}bh$$

$$\angle A + \angle B + \angle C = 180°$$

Pythagorean Theorem

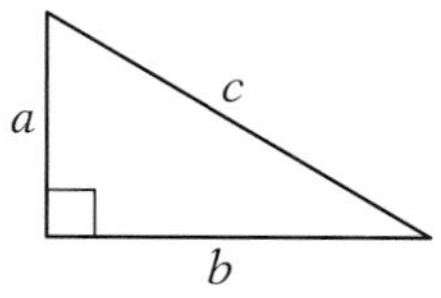

$$a^2 + b^2 = c^2$$

Perimeter and Area of a Rectangle

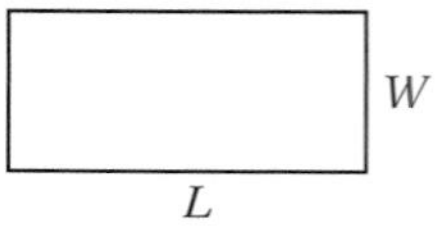

$$P = 2L + 2W$$

$$A = LW$$

Perimeter and Area of a Square

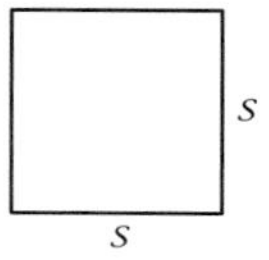

$$P = 4s$$

$$A = s^2$$

Circumference and Area of a Circle

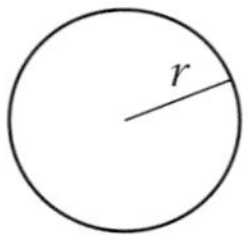

$C = 2\pi r$ or $C = \pi d$

$$A = \pi r^2$$

Area of a Trapezoid

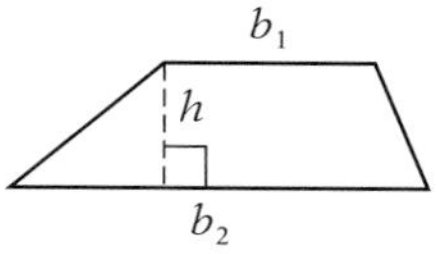

$$A = \frac{1}{2}h(b_1 + b_2)$$

Volume and Surface Area of a Rectangular Solid

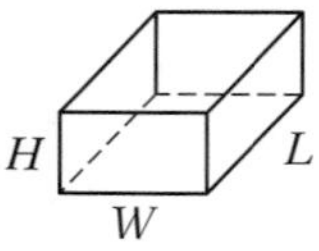

$$V = LWH$$

$$SA = 2LW + 2LH + 2WH$$

Volume and Surface Area of a Cube

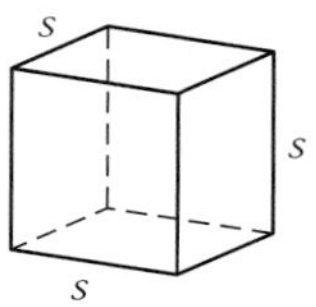

$$V = s^3$$

$$SA = 6s^2$$

Volume and Surface Area of a Right Circular Cylinder

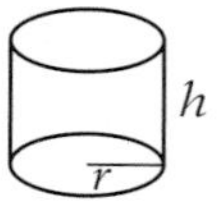

$$V = \pi r^2 h$$

$$SA = 2\pi r^2 + 2\pi rh$$

Volume and Surface Area of a Right Circular Cone

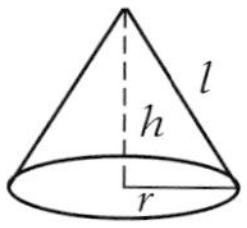

$$V = \frac{1}{3}\pi r^2 h$$

$$SA = \pi r^2 + \pi rl$$

Volume and Surface Area of a Sphere

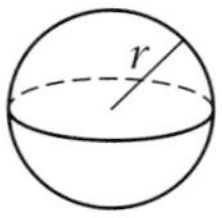

$$V = \frac{4}{3}\pi r^3$$

$$SA = 4\pi r^2$$

Table of Measurement Abbreviations

U.S. Customary System

Length		Capacity		Weight		Area	
in.	inches	oz	fluid ounces	oz	ounces	in^2	square inches
ft	feet	c	cups	lb	pounds	ft^2	square feet
yd	yards	qt	quarts				
mi	miles	gal	gallons				

Metric System

Length		Capacity		Weight/Mass		Area	
mm	millimeters (0.001 m)	ml	milliliters (0.001 L)	mg	milligrams (0.001 g)	cm^2	square centimeters
cm	centimeters (0.01 m)	cl	centiliters (0.01 L)	cg	centigrams (0.01 g)	m^2	square meters
dm	decimeters (0.1 m)	dl	deciliters (0.1 L)	dg	decigrams (0.1 g)		
m	meters	L	liters	g	grams		
dam	decameters (10 m)	dal	decaliters (10 L)	dag	decagrams (10 g)		
hm	hectometers (100 m)	hl	hectoliters (100 L)	hg	hectograms (100 g)		
km	kilometers (1000 m)	kl	kiloliters (1000 L)	kg	kilograms (1000 g)		

Time

h	hours	min	minutes	s	seconds

Table of Symbols

$+$	add
$-$	subtract
$\cdot$, $(a)(b)$	multiply
$\frac{a}{b}$, $\div$	divide
( )	parentheses, a grouping symbol
[ ]	brackets, a grouping symbol
π	pi, a number approximately equal to $\frac{22}{7}$ or 3.14
$-a$	the opposite, or additive inverse, of a
$\frac{1}{a}$	the reciprocal, or multiplicative inverse, of a
$=$	is equal to
$\approx$	is approximately equal to
$\neq$	is not equal to
$<$	is less than
$\leq$	is less than or equal to
$>$	is greater than
$\geq$	is greater than or equal to
(a, b)	an ordered pair whose first component is a and whose second component is b
$^\circ$	degree (for angles and temperature)
$\sqrt{a}$	the principal square root of a
$\lvert a \rvert$	the absolute value of a

TI-30X IIS

Access operations are lighter lines

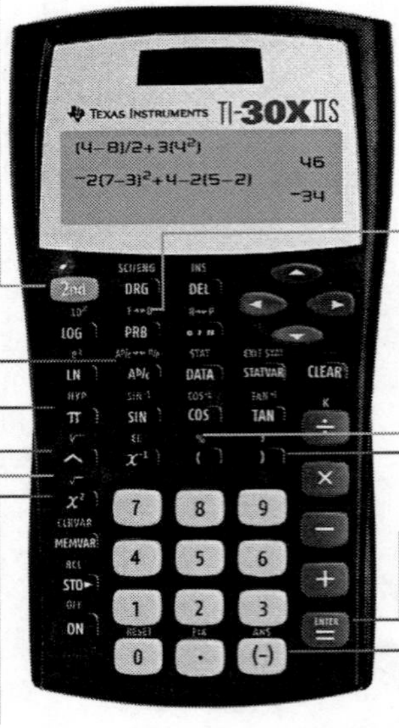

Photo courtesy of Texas Instruments Incorporated

6 [Ab/c] 2 [Ab/c] 3 [+] 3 [Ab/c] 4 [ENTER]

Operations on fractions $6\frac{2}{3} + \frac{3}{4} = 7\frac{5}{12}$

Display: 6⌴2⌟3+3⌟4 → 7⌴5/12

The value of π

Display: π → 3.141592654

13 [^] 4 [ENTER]

Power of a number (See Note 1 below.)

Display: 13^4 → 28561

[2nd] √36 [)] [ENTER]

Square root of a number

Display: √(36) → 6

7 [x^2] [ENTER]

Square a number

Display: 7² → 49

.4 [2nd] F◆D [ENTER]

Change decimal to fraction or fraction to decimal

Display: .4▸F◆D → 2/5

3 [+] 2 [(] 10 [−] 6 [)] [ENTER]

Operations with parentheses

Display: 3+2(10−6) → 11

11 [×] 25 [2nd] % [ENTER]

Operations with percent

Display: 11*25% → 2.75

Used to complete an operation

[(−)] 12 [÷] 6 [ENTER]

Enter a negative number (See Note 2 below.)

Display: −12/6 → −2

fx-300MS

Access operations are lighter lines

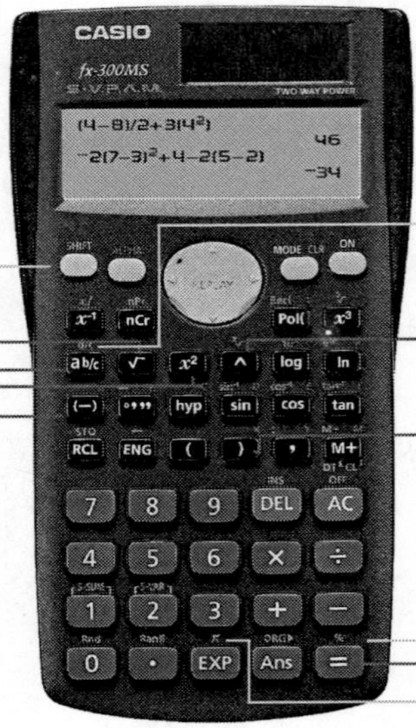

Photo courtesy of Casio, Inc.

[√] 36 [=]

Square root of a number

Display: √36 → 6

6 [ab/c] 2 [ab/c] 3 [+] 3 [ab/c] 4 [=]

Operations on fractions $6\frac{2}{3} + \frac{3}{4} = 7\frac{5}{12}$

Display: 6⌟2⌟3+3⌟4 → 7⌟5⌟12

7 [x^2] [=]

Square a number

Display: 7² → 49

Enter a negative number (See Note 2 below.)

[(−)] 12 [÷] 6 [=]

Display: −12÷6 → −2

.4 [=] SHIFT [ ] d/c

Change decimal to fraction

Display: .4 → 2⌟5

13 [^] 4 [=]

Power of a number (See Note 1 below.)

Display: 13^4 → 28561

3 [+] 2 [(] 10 [−] 6 [)] [=]

Operations with parentheses

Display: 3+2(10−6) → 11

11 [×] 25 SHIFT [ ] % [=]

Operations with percent

Display: 11x25% → 2.75

Used to complete an operation

SHIFT [ ] π [=]

The value of π

Display: π → 3.141592654

NOTE 1: Some calculators use the [y^x] key to calculate a power. For those calculators, enter 13 [y^x] 4 [=] to evaluate 13^4.

NOTE 2: Some calculators use the [+/−] key to enter a negative number. For those calculators, enter 12 [+/−] [÷] 6 [=] to calculate $-12 \div 6$.

TI-83 Plus/84 Plus*

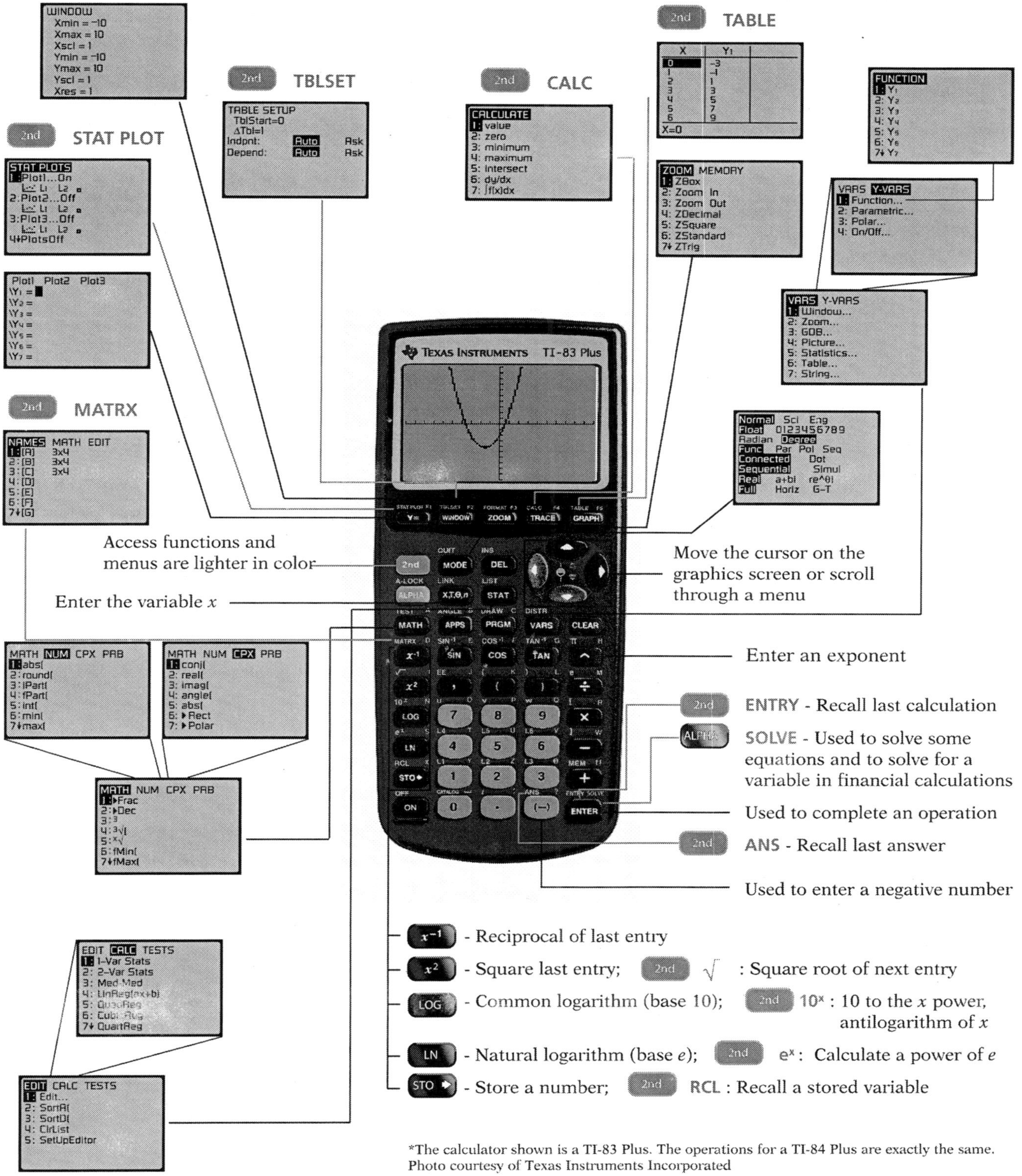

*The calculator shown is a TI-83 Plus. The operations for a TI-84 Plus are exactly the same.
Photo courtesy of Texas Instruments Incorporated

MATH STUDY SKILLS WORKBOOK

Third Edition

Paul D. Nolting, Ph.D.
Learning Specialist

Contents

Preface

Wouldn't it be nice if all we had to do was listen to a lecture on math and read the textbook in order to learn it? That would be paradise. However, most math courses take place on Earth, and students have to do much more than just take notes and read a textbook. They need a system of study skills that help them understand and master mathematics.

Many students in all levels of math courses have difficulty learning math because it is one of the most difficult subjects in college. First, many students who have struggled with math before going to college continue to struggle when they take their first college math courses, even developmental math courses. Second, some students who have done well in the past begin to struggle when they take upper-level math courses such as college algebra or calculus. They made As and Bs in previous math courses, but all of a sudden they are failing upper level math courses. These students probably lived off their intelligence until they took math courses that challenged them. Since they never had to study for math, they did not know where to begin to study. Students in all levels of math courses benefit from designing a system of study skills.

Does this sound far-fetched? Not really. I have watched calculus students read this workbook and improve their grades in order to be more competitive candidates for engineering programs. For example, I asked two calculus II students why they were taking my math study skills course. I thought they needed a one-credit-hour course to allow them to graduate, but I was wrong. Both students made a C in calculus I and said that they needed to make an A or B in calculus II because they were engineering majors. In most cases, students who make Cs in calculus are not admitted to engineering schools. Both students made an A in my course and a B in their calculus II course and went on to engineering school. Success for them!

Another success story belongs to a student who failed a beginning algebra course three times. Yes, three times. She came to my office ready to quit college altogether. I convinced her to focus on designing a system of study skills before taking the course one more time. She did. With her new system of study skills, she passed with a B and stayed in college. Success for her!

Earning better math grades doesn't have to be the only benefit from spending time developing a system for studying math. According to many students, they were able to take the math study skills and adapt them to their other courses. In fact, some students claim it is easier than adapting general study skills to learning math. They reported that their other course grades also went up. What a good experience!

So, what kind of assistance do most students want? Students want tips and procedures they can use to help them improve their math grades. The math study suggestions, however, have to be based on research and be statistically proven to improve student learning and grades. *Math Study Skills Workbook* is based on *Winning at Math: Your Guide to Learning Mathematics Through Successful Study Skills* (2002), which is the only math study skills text that can boast statistical evidence demonstrating an improvement in students' ability to learn math and make better grades. Learning and using these study skills techniques will improve your grades.

Math Study Skills Workbook is designed to supplement your math course or study skills course or to be used as part of a math anxiety workshop.

The workbook is designed for independent work or to be supplemented by lectures. To gain the most benefit, the workbook needs to be completed by midterm.

This workbook is designed to enhance learning by teaching math learning skills in small "chunks." After each section, you are required to recall the most important information by writing it down. The writing exercises are especially designed to help develop personalized learning techniques, such as the ten steps to better test taking. Each chapter review is designed to reinforce your learning and to help you immediately select and use the best learning strategy from that chapter. Lecture Notes pages have been added, where possible, to allow you to include your notes in this workbook.

Dan's Take is a new addition to each chapter. Dan recently graduated from college, so his experiences are fresh and relevant. His input at the end of each chapter helps each reader relate to the information in a more personal way. Make sure you read each Dan's Take.

As you adapt and practice each study skill, work it into a larger system for studying math. Decide which study skills will help with each of the following tasks you must perform when learning math:

1. Taking and reworking lecture notes
2. Learning vocabulary
3. Completing homework in a way that helps you learn and master the math
4. Mastering and memorizing the concepts
5. Preparing for tests
6. Taking tests
7. Managing any anxiety, whether math or text anxiety

Remember, to reap the most benefit, you need to complete this workbook and be using your system of study skills by midterm. Practice and master! Then, maybe we can use your success story in our next edition of the workbook!

1

What You Need to Know to Study Math

WHAT YOU WILL LEARN IN CHAPTER 1

- ❑ Why Learning Math Is Different from Learning Other Subjects
- ❑ The Differences between High School and College Math
- ❑ Why Your First Math Test Is Very Important

Mathematics courses are not like other courses. Because they are different, they require different study procedures. Passing most of your other courses requires only that you read, understand, and recall the subject material. To pass math, however, an extra step is required: you must use the information you have learned to solve math problems correctly.

Learning general study skills can help you pass most of your courses, but special math study skills are needed to help you learn more and get better grades in math.

Why Learning Math Is Different from Learning Other Subjects

In a math course, you must be able to do four things:

1. *Understand* the material
2. *Process* the material
3. *Apply* what you have learned to solve a problem correctly, and
4. *Remember* what you have learned in order to learn new material.

Of these four tasks, applying what you have learned to solve a problem correctly is the hardest.

> **Examples:** Political science courses require that you learn about politics and public service. But your instructor will not make you run for governor to pass the course. Psychology courses require you to understand the concepts of different psychology theories. But you will not have to help a patient overcome depression to pass the course. In math, however, you must be able to solve problems correctly to pass the course.

Sequential Learning Pattern

Another reason that learning math is different from learning other subjects is that it follows a *sequential learning pattern,* which simply means that the material learned on one day is used the next day and the next day, and so forth. This building-block approach to learning math is the reason it is difficult to catch up when you fall behind. All building blocks must be included to be successful in learning math. You can compare learning math to building a house. Like a house, which must be built foundation first, walls second, and roof last, math must be learned in a specific order. Just as you cannot build a house roof first, you cannot learn to solve complex problems without first learning to solve simple ones.

> **Example:** In a history class, if you study Chapters 1 and 2, do not understand Chapter 3, and end up studying and taking a test on Chapter 4, you *could* pass. Understanding Chapter 4 in history is not totally based on comprehending Chapters 1, 2, and 3. To succeed in math, however, each previous chapter has to be completely understood before you can continue to the next chapter.

Sequential learning also affects your ability to study for math tests. If you study Chapter 1 and understand it, study Chapter 2 and understand it, and study Chapter 3 and *do not* understand it, then when you study for a test on Chapter 4, you are not going to understand it either, and you probably will not do well on the test.

Remember

To learn the new math material for the test on Chapter 5, you must first go back and learn the material in Chapter 4. This means you will have to go back and learn Chapter 4 while learning Chapter 5. (The best of us can fall behind under these circumstances.) However, if you do not understand the material in Chapter 4, you will not understand the material in Chapter 5 either, and you will fail the test on Chapter 5. This is why the sequential learning of math concepts is so important.

The sequential learning pattern is also affected by:

- your previous math course grade,
- your math placement test scores, and
- the time elapsed since your last math course.

Sequential learning is influenced by how much math knowledge you have at the beginning of your course. Students who have forgotten or never acquired the necessary skills from their previous math courses will have difficulty with their current math courses. If you do not remember what you learned in your last math course, you will have to relearn

Copyright © Houghton Mifflin Company. All rights reserved.

the math concepts from the previous course as well as the new material for the current course. In most other courses, such as the humanities, previous course knowledge is not required. However, in math you must remember what the last course taught you so that you are prepared for the current course. Measuring previous course knowledge will be explained in Chapter 2, "How to Discover Your Math Learning Strengths and Challenges."

Math placement scores also affect sequential learning. If you barely scored high enough to be placed in a math course, then you will have math learning gaps. Learning problems will occur when new math material is based on one of your learning gaps. The age of the placement test score also affects sequential learning. Placement test scores are designed to measure your *current* math knowledge and are to be used immediately.

Sequential learning is interrupted if math courses are taken irregularly. Math courses are designed to be taken one after another. By taking math courses each semester, without semester breaks between courses, you are less likely to forget the concepts required for the next course. Research has shown that the more time between math courses, the more likely it is that a student will fail the current math course.

Now that you understand the "building-block" nature of math, think about your math history.

- What were your previous math grades?
- How well did you do on the math placement test at your college?
- How long has it been since you took a math course?
- When you look at your math history, were there semesters when you did not take math?

These questions are important because if there was too much time between your different math courses, you may have forgotten important math concepts that you need in your current class. To use the building-block analogy, the blocks may not be as strong any more.

Now that you understand how learning math is a building experience, what should you do? *First,* don't get anxious. Stay calm. *Second,* if your college has a diagnostic math inventory in the tutoring center or math lab, take it to see what math concepts you have forgotten. Then ask your instructor where you can go to relearn these math concepts. *Third,* take the time to follow through. Many students just give up too easily, or they think they will catch up a little at a time. Don't think that and don't give up. The energy put into your class at the beginning of the semester will be more productive than energy put into class at the end of the semester when you try to learn everything during the last week before the final exam. *Fourth,* study and really learn the math; don't just practice mimicking it. *Finally,* when it is time to register for the next semester, register immediately so you will be able to get into the math class you need. Why do all this? Because math is sequential!

Math as a Foreign Language

Another helpful technique for studying math is to consider it a foreign language. Looking at math as a foreign language can improve your study procedures. If you do not practice a foreign language, what happens? You forget it. If you do not practice math, what happens? You are likely to forget it, too.

Students who excel in a foreign language must practice it at least every other day. The same study skills apply to math, because it is considered a foreign language.

Like a foreign language, math has unfamiliar vocabulary words or terms that must be put in sentences called equations. Understanding and solving a math equation is similar to speaking and understanding a sentence in a foreign language.

> **Example:** Math sentences use symbols (which stand for spoken words), such as
>
> = (for which you *say,* "equals"),
>
> – (for which you *say,* "less"), and
>
> x (for which you *say,* "unknown").

Learning *how* to speak math as a language is the key to math success. Currently, most universities consider computer and statistics (a form

Copyright © Houghton Mifflin Company. All rights reserved.

of math) courses as foreign languages. Some universities now actually classify math as a foreign language.

Math as a Skill Subject

Math is a *skill subject,* which means you have to practice actively the skills involved to master it. Learning math is similar to learning to play a sport, learning to play a musical instrument, or learning auto mechanics skills. You can listen to and watch your coach or instructor all day, but unless you *practice* those skills yourself, you will not learn.

Examples: In basketball, the way to improve your free throws is to *see and understand* the correct shooting form and then *practice* the shots yourself. Practicing the shots improves your free-throw percentage. However, if you simply listen to your coach describe the correct form and see him demonstrate it, but you do not practice the correct form yourself, you will not increase your shooting percentage.

Let's say that you want to learn how to play the piano. You are thrilled when you manage to convince the best piano player in the world to be your instructor. During your first session, you intently stare at your teacher's hands as he moves his fingers across the keys, and you take note of every movement he makes and every note he plays. Now it is your turn. Is it plausible that just by watching him play, you will now be able to perform just as well as he did? No. You obviously cannot play the piano correctly just by watching someone, even if that person is the greatest player in the world. The only way to learn to play is to practice.

Learning math is no different from learning to play the piano. You can go to classes, listen to your professors, watch them demonstrate how to complete problems, and completely understand everything they are saying. But if you leave class and do not practice what you have learned, you simply will not learn math.

Many of your other courses can be learned by methods other than practicing. In social studies, for example, information can be learned by listening to your instructor, taking good notes, and participating in class discussions. Many students mistakenly believe that math can be learned the same way.

Remember

Math is different. If you want to learn math, you must practice. Practice not only means doing your homework but also means spending the time it takes to understand the reasons for each step in each problem.

Math as a Speed Subject

Math is a *speed subject,* which means that, in most cases, it is taught faster than your other subjects. Math instructors have a certain amount of material that must be covered each semester. They have to finish certain chapters because the next math course is based on the information taught in their courses. In many cases a common math department final exam is given to make sure you know the material for the next course. Instructors are under pressure to make sure you are ready for the final exam because it demonstrates how prepared you are for the next level in math. This is different from, let's say, a sociology course, in which an instructor's omission of the last chapter will not cause students too many problems in the next sociology or social science course. So don't complain to the math instructor about the speed of the course. Instead, improve your study skills so you can keep up!

Another way math is a speed subject is that most of the tests are timed, and many students think that they will run out of time. THIS CAUSES PANIC AND FEAR! This is different from most of your other courses, in which you generally have enough time to complete your tests, or in courses that have multiple-choice tests where you can start bubbling the responses on the scantron sheet if you start running out of time. Students not only must understand how to do the math problems but also

Copyright © Houghton Mifflin Company. All rights reserved.

must learn the math well enough to complete the problems with enough speed to finish the test.

What makes me curious is, if students feel that they don't have enough time to complete a math test, why are most of them gone before the test is over? Sure, students who have learned the math thoroughly may complete the test early. That makes sense. Some students, however, either leave because they don't know the material, or because they want to escape the anxious environment, or work through the test carelessly.

So, since speed is an issue in learning math, what should you do? *First,* to use an analogy, start a daily "workout" program to "stay in shape" mathematically. Review, review, review as you learn new material. *Second,* practice doing problems within a time constraint. Give yourself practice tests.

Remember

Passing math is your goal, regardless of your attitude.

Section Review

1. How does a sequential learning pattern affect math learning?

   ____

   ____

   ____

   Give two examples:

   Example 1: ______________________________

   Example 2: ______________________________

2. List two examples of how learning math is similar to learning a foreign language.

   Example 1: ______________________________

   ____

   Example 2: ______________________________

   ____

3. How is math similar to a skills subject? ______________________________

4. Why are math study skills important at all levels of math (see Preface)? ______________________________

   ____

5. Math study skills can help you in other subjects, but general study skills usually cannot improve math learning. Why is this statement important? (See Preface.)

   ____

   ____

Copyright © Houghton Mifflin Company. All rights reserved.

The Differences Between High School and College Math

College-level math courses, can be two to three times as difficult as high school math courses. There are many reasons for the increased difficulty: course class-time allowance, the amount of material covered in a course, the length of a course, and the college grading system.

The first important difference between high school and college math courses is the length of time devoted to instruction each week. Most college math instruction, for the fall and spring semesters, has been cut to three hours per week; high school math instruction is provided five hours per week. Additionally, college courses cover twice the material in the same time frame as do high school courses. What is learned in one year of high school math is learned in one semester (four months) of college math.

Simply put, in college math courses you are receiving less instructional time per week and covering twice the ground per course as you were in high school math courses. The responsibility for learning in college is the student's. As a result, most of your learning (and *practicing*) will have to occur outside of the college classroom.

College Summer Semester Versus Fall or Spring Semester and the Difference Between Night and Day

College math courses taught during summer semesters are more difficult than those taught during fall or spring. Furthermore, math taught during night courses is more difficult than math taught during day courses.

Students attending a six-week summer math session must learn the information—and master the skills—two and a half times faster than as students attending regular, full-semester math sessions. Although you receive the same amount of instructional classroom time, there is less time to understand and *practice the skills* between class sessions.

Summer classes are usually two hours per day, four days per week (nighttime summer classes are four hours per night, two nights per week).

> **Example:** If you do not understand the lecture on Monday, then you have only Monday night to learn the material before progressing to more difficult material on Tuesday. During a night course, you have to learn and understand the material before the break; after the break, you will move on to the more difficult material—*that night*.

Because math is a sequential learning experience, where every building block must be understood before proceeding to the next block, you can quickly fall behind, and you may never catch up. In fact, some students become lost during the first half of a math lecture and never understand the rest of the lecture (this can happen during just one session of night class). This is called "kamikaze" math because most students do not survive summer courses.

If you *must* take a summer math course, take a 10- or 12-week *daytime* session so that you will have more time to process the material between classes.

Course Grading System

The grading system for math is different in college than in high school.

> **Example:** While in high school, if you make a D or a borderline D/F, the teacher more than likely will give you a D, and you may continue to the next course. However, in some college math courses, a D is not considered a passing grade, or if a D is made, the course will not count toward graduation.

College instructors are more likely to give a grade of N (no grade), W (withdrawal from class), or F for barely knowing the material. This is because the instructor knows that you will be unable to pass the next course if you barely know the current one.

Most colleges require students to pass two college-level algebra courses to graduate. In most

Copyright © Houghton Mifflin Company. All rights reserved.

high schools, you may graduate by passing one to three math courses. In some college-degree programs, you may even have to take four math courses and make no worse than Cs in all of them to graduate.

The grading systems for math courses are very precise compared with the grading systems for humanities courses.

> **Example:** In a math course, if you have a 79 percent average and you need 80 percent to get a B, you will get a C in the course. But if you make a 79 percent in English class, you may be able to talk to your instructor and do extra credit work to earn a B.

Because math is an exact science and not as subjective as English, do not expect your math instructor to let you do extra work to earn a better grade. In college, there usually is no grade given for "daily work," as there often is in high school.

In fact, *your test scores may be the only grades that will count toward your final grade.* Therefore, you should not assume that you will be able to "make up" for a bad test score.

The Ordering of College Math Courses

College math courses should be taken, *in order,* from the fall semester to the spring semester. If at all possible, avoid taking math courses from the spring to fall semesters. There is less time between the fall and spring semesters for you to forget the information. During the summer break, you are more likely to forget important concepts required for the next course and therefore experience greater difficulty.

Section Review

1. Compare the amount of college class time to high school class time.

____

____

2. How do college summer math courses differ from courses offered in the spring or fall?

____

____

3. How can the order of taking math courses affect your learning?

____

____

Why Your First Math Test Is Very Important

Making a high grade on the first major math test is more important than making a high grade on the first major test in other subjects. The first major math test is the easiest and, most often, the one for which the student is least prepared.

Students often feel that the first major math test is mainly a review and that they can make a B or a C without much study. These students are overlooking an excellent opportunity to make an A on the easiest major math test of the semester. (Do not forget that this test counts the same as the more difficult math tests that are still to come.)

At the end of the semester, these students sometimes do not pass the math course or do not make an A because of their first major test grade. In other words, the first math test score was not

Copyright © Houghton Mifflin Company. All rights reserved.

high enough to "pull up" a low test score on one of the remaining major tests.

Studying hard for the first major math test and obtaining an A offers you several advantages:

- A high score on the first test can compensate for a low score on a more difficult fourth or fifth math test. All major tests have equal value in the final grade calculations.
- A high score on the first test can provide assurance that you have learned the basic math skills required to pass the course. This means you will not have to spend time relearning the misunderstood material covered on the first major test while learning new material for the next test.
- A high score on the first test can motivate you to do well. Improved motivation can cause you to increase your math study time, which will allow you to master the material.
- A high score on the first test can improve your confidence for higher test scores. With more confidence, you are more likely to work harder on the difficult math homework assignments, which will increase your chances of doing well in the course.

What happens if, after all your studying, you make a low score on your first math test? You can still use this test experience to help you improve your next grade or to help determine if you are in the right math course. Your first math test, no matter what you make on it, can be used as a diagnostic test. Your teacher can review your test with you to see which type of math problems you got right and which ones you need to learn how to solve. It may be that you missed only a few concepts that caused the low score, and you can learn how to do these problems by getting help from the teacher, a learning resource center, or the math lab. However, you need to learn how to do these problems immediately so that you don't fall behind in the course. After meeting with your teacher, ask for the best way you can learn the concepts that are the bases of the missed problems and how to prepare for the next test. Even students who made Bs on the first math test can benefit by seeing the teacher.

If you made below a 50 on your first math test, I suggest that it might be a good idea to drop back to a lower-level math course. Even though it might be beyond the first week of drop and add, many colleges/ universities will let you drop back to a lower math class after the first major math test. Students who drop back get a good foundation in mathematics that helps them in their next math courses. On the other hand, I have *seen* students who insisted on staying in the math course and repeated it several times before passing. Some of the students stopped taking the math course and dropped out of college. Dropping back to a lower-level math course and passing it is the smartest move. These students went on to become more successful in their math courses.

Remember

It does not matter where you start as long as you graduate. Discuss this option with your teacher.

A Bad Math "Attitude"

Students' attitudes about learning math are different from their attitudes about learning their other subjects. Many students who have had bad experiences with math do not like math and have a bad attitude about learning it. In fact, some students actually *hate* math, even though these same students have positive experiences with their other subjects and look forward to going to those classes.

Society as a whole reinforces students' negative attitudes about math. It has become socially acceptable not to do well in math. This negative attitude has become evident even in popular comic strips, such as *Peanuts*. The underlying message is that math should be feared and hated and that it is all right not to learn math.

This "popular" attitude toward math may reinforce your belief that it is all right to fail math. Such a belief is constantly being reinforced by others.

The bad math attitude is not a major problem, however. Many students who hate math pass it

Copyright © Houghton Mifflin Company. All rights reserved.

anyway, just as many students who hate history still pass it. The major problem concerning the bad math attitude is how you use this attitude. If a bad math attitude leads to poor class attendance, poor concentration, and poor study skills, then you have a bad math attitude *problem*.

Section Review

1. Why is your first math test supposed to be the easiest?

   ____

   ____

   ____

2. Give three reasons why your first math test is so important.

   First Reason: ______________________________

   ____

   Second Reason: ______________________________

   ____

   Third Reason: ______________________________

   ____

3. What do you do if you fail your first test?

   Option One: ______________________________

   ____

   Option Two: ______________________________

   ____

   Option Three: ______________________________

   ____

4. List three ways a bad math attitude could affect your mathematics learning.

   First Way: ______________________________

   ____

   Second Way: ______________________________

   ____

   Third Way: ______________________________

   ____

Copyright © Houghton Mifflin Company. All rights reserved.

Dan's Take

In high school, I was 6'4" tall and weighed 160 pounds. Being thin would not have been so bad, but I was the starting power forward for my school's basketball team and usually drew the biggest guy on the opposing team to guard. This left me at a disadvantage while playing basketball with guys who weighed 60 pounds more than me.

Since I was not very big, I had to look for other ways to improve. I knew there were other skills to focus on, and there were specific actions I could take to improve them. I ran up and down the driveway to improve my stamina. I spent hours shooting free throws in the gym before games. I took a basketball with me everywhere to improve my ball handling. If any of these things made me even slightly better, the hard work would be worth it to me.

Math, not unlike basketball, requires daily practice. For some of us, math does not come easily, and that is okay. The fact is, there are ways to improve our math success. The goal of this book is to help students focus on how they can improve. Whether one is an "A" student or a "wants to be an A" student, there is always something one can improve. Hopefully, this workbook will help us do just that.

Copyright © Houghton Mifflin Company. All rights reserved.

Name: ______________________________ Date: ______________

Chapter 1 Review

1. In a math course, you must be able to do four things. You must ____________ the material, ____________ the material, ____________ what you have learned to solve the problem, and ____________ what you have learned in order to learn new material.
2. Math requires ______________________, which means that one concept builds on the previous concept.
3. Placement test scores are designed to measure your ____________ math knowledge and are to be used ____________.
4. Like a foreign language, math has unfamiliar vocabulary words or terms that must be put in sentences called ____________.
5. Learning how to speak math as a ____________ ____________ is one key to math success.
6. Keeping a ____________ attitude about math will help you study more efficiently.
7. College math courses are ____________ to ____________ times as difficult as high school math courses.
8. Math courses are even more difficult than other courses because a grade of ____________ or better is usually required to take the next course.
9. Math grading is very precise; in many cases, you cannot do ____________ ____________ to improve your grade.
10. If you fail your first math test, you need to make an appointment with your ____________ to review your____________. Then you can decide if you should ____________ to a lower-level math course.

What is the most important information you learned from this chapter?

____

____

____

____

How can you immediately use it?

____

____

____

Copyright © Houghton Mifflin Company. All rights reserved.

Lecture Notes

Copyright © Houghton Mifflin Company. All rights reserved.

2

How to Discover Your Math Learning Strengths and Challenges

WHAT YOU WILL LEARN IN CHAPTER 2

- ❑ Variables Contributing to Student Academic Achievement
- ❑ Your "Learning Diagnostic" for Math Class
- ❑ Measuring Your Math Study Skills
- ❑ Reflecting on Your Affective Attributes
- ❑ How to Improve Your Math Knowledge

Students can improve their math grades when they take the time to understand their strengths and challenges in learning math. Then, if they enhance their strengths and find solutions to their challenges in learning math, they will see more success.

Just as a mechanic conducts a diagnostic test on a car before repairing it, you need to analyze your own learning in order to repair it and get it running smoothly. No one wants the mechanic to spend time working on something that doesn't need to be fixed. That doesn't make sense. Likewise, you want to work on the challenges you have when learning math, not on what you already do right when studying. This chapter guides students through a "learning" diagnostic so that they can improve some of their learning strategies for math and keep using the ones that already work.

Areas of math strengths and challenges include math knowledge, level of test anxiety, study skills, study attitudes, motivation, and test-taking skills. Before we start identifying your math strengths and challenges, you need to understand what contributes to math academic success.

Variables Contributing to Student Academic Achievement

Dr. Benjamin Bloom, a famous researcher in the field of educational learning, discovered that your IQ (intelligence) and your cognitive entry skills account for 50 percent of your course grade. See Figure 1.

Figure 1 Variables Contributing to Student Academic Achievement

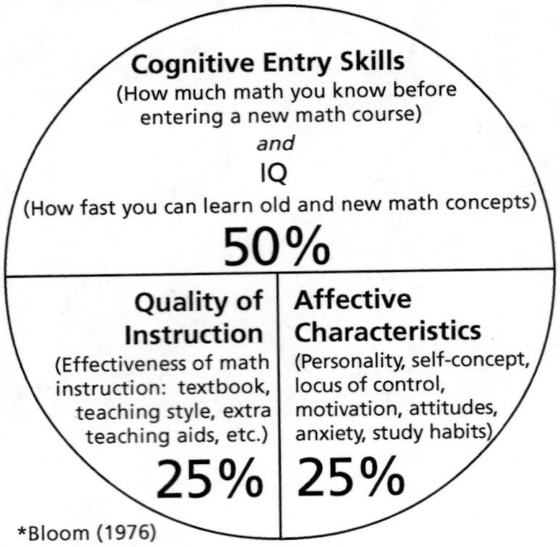

*Bloom (1976)

Quality of instruction represents 25 percent of your course grade, while affective student characteristics reflect the remaining 25 percent of your grade.

- *Intelligence* may be considered, for our purpose, how fast you can learn or relearn math concepts.
- *Cognitive entry skills* refer to how much math you already know the first day of your new class. For example, previous math knowledge can be based on previous math grades, the length of time since the last math course, the type of math courses completed (algebra I, algebra II, intermediate algebra), and placement test scores.
- *Quality of instruction* is concerned with the effectiveness of math instructors when presenting material to students in the classroom and math lab. This effectiveness depends on the course textbook, curriculum, teaching style, extra teaching aids (videos, audiocassettes), and other assistance. Quality of instruction may also include math lab resources, quality of tutoring based on tutor training and Supplemental Instruction.
- *Affective student characteristics* are characteristics you possess that affect your course grades—excluding how much math you knew before entering your math course. Some of these affective characteristics are anxiety, study skills, study attitudes, self-concept, motivation, and test-taking skills.

The following sections help students examine their own variables for success in math.

Cognitive Entry Skills

Poor math knowledge can cause low grades. A student placed in a math course that requires a more extensive math background than the student possesses will probably fail that course. Without the correct math background, you will fall behind and never catch up.

Placement Tests and Previous Course Grades

The math you need to know to enroll in a particular math course can be measured by a placement test (ACT, SAT) or by the grade received in the prerequisite math course. Some students are incorrectly placed in math courses on the basis of placement tests.

If, by the second class meeting, everything looks like Greek and you do not understand what is being explained, move to a lower-level course. In the lower-level math course you will have a better chance to understand the material and to pass the course. A false evaluation of math ability and knowledge can only lead to frustration, anxiety, and failure.

Requests by Students for Higher Placement

Some students try to encourage their instructors to move them to higher-level math courses because they believe their placement scores were wrong. Many students try to avoid noncredit math courses, while other students do not want to repeat courses

Copyright © Houghton Mifflin Company. All rights reserved.

that they have previously failed. These moves can also lead to failure.

Some older students imagine that their math skills are just as good as when they completed their last math course, which was five to ten years ago. If they have not been practicing their math skills, they are just fooling themselves. Still other students believe they do not need the math skills obtained in a prerequisite math course to pass the next course. This is also incorrect thinking. Research indicates that a student who was placed correctly in the prerequisite math course, and who subsequently failed it, will not pass the next math course.

What My Research Shows

I have conducted research on thousands of students who have either convinced their instructors to place them in higher-level math courses or have placed themselves in higher-level math courses. The results? These students failed their math courses many times before realizing they did not possess the prerequisite math knowledge needed to pass the course. Students who, without good reason, talk their instructors into moving them up a course level are setting themselves up to fail.

To be successful in a math course, you must have the appropriate math knowledge. If you think you may have difficulty passing a higher-level math course, you probably do not have an adequate math background. Even if you do pass the math course with a D or a C, research indicates that you will most likely fail the next higher math course.

It is better to be conservative and pass a lower-level math course with an A or a B instead of making a C or a D in a higher-level math course and failing the next course at a higher level.

This is evident when many students repeat a higher-level math course up to five times before repeating the lower-level math course that they barely passed. After repeating the lower-level math course with an A or a B, these students passed the higher-level math course.

How the Quality of Math Instruction Affects Your Grades

Quality of instruction accounts for 25 percent of a student's grade. Quality of instruction includes such things as classroom atmosphere, instructor's teaching style, lab instruction, and textbook content and format. All of these "quality" factors can affect a person's ability to learn in the math classroom.

Interestingly enough, probably the most important "quality" variable is the compatibility of an instructor's teaching style with your learning style. You need to discover your learning style and compare it with the instructional style. Noncompatibility can be best solved by finding an instructor who better matches your learning style. However, if you cannot find an instructor to match your learning style, improving your math study skills and using the math lab or learning resource center (LRC) can compensate for most of the mismatch.

Use of the math lab or LRC can dramatically improve the quality of instruction. With today's new technologies, students are able to select their best learning aids. These learning aids could be videotapes, CD-ROMs, computer programs, math study skills computer programs, math texts, and websites.

The quality of tutors is also a major factor in the math lab or LRC. A low student-to-tutor ratio and trained tutors are essential for good tutorial instruction. Otherwise, the result is just a math study hall with a few helpers.

The math textbook should be up to date with good examples and a solutions manual. This increases the amount of learning from the textbook compared with older, poorly designed texts.

The curriculum design affects the sequence of math courses, which could cause learning problems.

Some math courses have gaps between them that cause learning problems for all students.

How Affective Student Characteristics Affect Your Math Grades

Affective student characteristics account for about 25 percent of your grade. These affective characteristics include math study skills, test anxiety, motivation, locus of control, learning style, and other variables that affect your personal ability to learn math.

Most students do not have this 25 percent of the grade in their favor. In fact, most students have

Copyright © Houghton Mifflin Company. All rights reserved.

never been taught any study skills, let alone how to study math specifically. Students also do not know their best learning styles, which means they may study ineffectively by using their least effective learning styles. However, it is not your fault that you were not taught math study skills or made aware of your learning styles.

By working to improve your affective characteristics, you will reap the benefits by learning math more effectively and receiving higher grades. Thousands of students have improved their math affective characteristics and thereby their grades by using this workbook.

This section identified key factors that can determine a student's success in a math course. The next section focuses on your personal "learning diagnostic" for learning math.

Section Review

1. List and explain the three variables that contribute to your academic success.

   Variable 1: ______________________________

   ____

   ____

   ____

   Variable 2: ______________________________

   ____

   ____

   ____

   Variable 3: ______________________________

   ____

   ____

   ____

2. How does your placement test or previous math course grade affect your math learning?

   ____

   ____

   ____

   ____

3. How does the quality of math instructors affect your grade?

   ____

   ____

   ____

   ____

Copyright © Houghton Mifflin Company. All rights reserved.

4. How do your affective characteristics affect your grade?

____

____

____

____

Your "Learning Diagnostic" for Math Class

Research has shown that matching a student's best learning style with the instructional style improves learning. Research has also shown that students who understand their learning styles can improve their learning effectiveness. A learning disadvantage will occur for students who do not know or do not understand their learning styles. Students should talk to their instructors or counselors about taking one or more learning style inventories.

Measuring Previous Math Knowledge

Now it's time to measure your previous math knowledge. Your previous math knowledge is an excellent predictor of future math success.

Placement Test Scores

Visit your counselor or instructor to discuss your math placement test score. Ask your counselor or instructor how your placement score relates to the scores for the math courses below and above your course.

Find out if your score barely placed you in your course, if your score was in the middle, or if your score almost put you into the next course. If your placement score barely put you into your current math course, you will have difficulty learning the math required in that course.

A barely passing placement score means that you are missing some of the math knowledge you require to be successful, and you will really struggle to pass the course.

A middle placement score indicates that you probably have most of the math knowledge required for the course; however, you still may have difficulty passing the course. A high placement score means you have most of the math knowledge needed to pass and may have a good chance of passing the course. (Still, if you have poor math study skills and high test anxiety, you may not pass the course.)

Students who have low placement test scores need to improve their math knowledge as soon as possible. Students with middle placement scores should also consider improving their math knowledge.

Previous Grades

The best predictor of math success is your previous math grade (if taken within one year of your current course).

If you are taking your second math course, use your previous math course grade to determine your math knowledge. Your previous course grade is the best predictor of success in your next math course. (However, this is true only if your last math course was taken within the last year.)

A student who made an A or a B in the previous math course has a good chance of passing the next math course. However, a student who made a C in the previous math course has a poor chance of passing the next math course. A student who made less than a C or withdrew from the previous math course has virtually no chance of passing the next math course.

Copyright © Houghton Mifflin Company. All rights reserved.

The Amount of Time Since Your Last Math Course

Another indicator of math success can be the length of time since your last math course. The longer the time since your last math course, the less likely you will be to pass the current course. The exception to this rule is if you were practicing math while you were not taking math courses. Math is very easily forgotten if not practiced.

How long has it been since your last math course? If it has been two or more years since your last math class, your math may be similar to someone who has a low placement score or made a C or lower in the last math class. You can improve your math knowledge by following the same suggestions made for those students and applying the information in the next paragraph.

What level of math knowledge preparation do you possess right now for this course? If you have poor or good previous math knowledge, you need to build up those math concepts and skills as soon as possible. Go to your instructor and discuss how to build up your skills. Some suggestions are to review the chapters of the previous math text or ask your instructor about some websites that help students review math. Students with poor math knowledge have about three to four weeks to improve their math before it can become a major problem. Don't wait. Start now to review your math skills in order to improve your mathematics learning and grades. Additional information is presented in the section "How to Improve Your Math Knowledge."

Taking Stock of Your Learning Style

After examining your level of math knowledge and making any necessary accommodations, it is important to examine how you learn math best. There are many different learning styles, and no one style is necessarily better than another. Savvy students learn how to use their best learning styles and then learn how to use other learning style strategies, too. The first learning inventory you will take is a *Math Learning Modality Inventory*. It will measure how you take information in—visually, auditorily, or kinesthetically.

The Math Learning Modality Inventory

The Math Learning Modality Inventory measures how you best input new information when you are learning math. Some students understand new math better when they can see it worked out (**visual**), while others understand better when the math is explained using language (**auditory**). Still other students understand new math best when they have models or other tools that represent a math problem. They can use their hands to help them learn (**kinesthetic**). The word *modality* describes these different senses.

No one modality is necessarily better than the others. It is part of students' learning personalities. What is important, however, is to know your preferred learning modality and to design study strategies that use it. Even better, after learning how to use your preferred learning modality, learn how to use the other modalities when studying and learning in class, too. Why? Sometimes your instructor will teach in a way that is not your strongest way to learn. It is up to you to learn new strategies in that situation.

Cognitive Learning Styles

Cognitive learning styles describe how you process information, once you have heard, seen, or felt the information. Each individual has a unique system of doing this, but there are several general styles of what is called *cognitive processing*. Bernice McCarthy (1981) named four of these styles based on different ways to process information and make meaning from it: innovative learning, analytic learning, common sense learning, and dynamic learning.

First read through all the styles. Then read each style again, checking off the characteristics with which you identify.

What do these cognitive styles mean when it comes to learning math? First, each of these types of learners can learn math. Second, analytic and common sense learners tend to learn math using their natural ways to learn. Third, math teachers tend to be analytic and/or common sense learners and teachers. Fourth, dynamic and innovative

Copyright © Houghton Mifflin Company. All rights reserved.

Name: ______________________________ Date: ______________

LEARNING MODALITY INVENTORY FOR MATH STUDENTS

The following survey can help you discover how you best learn math. Answer the questions based on your personal learning characteristics. There are no right or wrong answers. The more you answer truthfully, the more you will be able to use the results to improve your study of math. A "1" means that the statement is hardly like you. A "4" means that the statement is really like you. Then, if you think the statement is somewhere in between, decide if it is a "2" or a "3."

Questions	Least like me 1	2	3	Most like me 4
1. Reading a math problem out loud helps me learn better when I am studying.	1	2	3	4
2. I learn math better if I can talk about it.	1	2	3	4
3. I select certain problems and memorize what they look like so I can use them to help me remember on a math test.	1	2	3	4
4. Making things with my hands helps me learn better.	1	2	3	4
5. Drawing a picture of a word problem helps me understand how to do it on a test.	1	2	3	4
6. Math makes more sense when I see it worked out on the board.	1	2	3	4
7. Moving around while studying helps me concentrate and learn more.	1	2	3	4
8. I understand written instructions better than ones told to me.	1	2	3	4
9. I memorize what a problem looks like so I can remember it better on a test or quiz.	1	2	3	4
10. I repeat the steps of a problem out loud or to myself in order to remember what I am supposed to do.	1	2	3	4
11. Watching someone complete a math problem helps me understand more than listening to someone tell me how to do it.	1	2	3	4
12. Talking about a math problem while learning in class helps me understand it better.	1	2	3	4
13. I learn math better when I watch someone do it.	1	2	3	4
14. When I take a test, I read the problems to myself softly.	1	2	3	4
15. When I solve a math problem on a test, I picture my notes in my head to help me remember how to solve it.	1	2	3	4
16. I enjoy making things with my hands for a hobby.	1	2	3	4
17. Math makes more sense to me when someone talks about it while doing it on the board rather than just doing it on the board.	1	2	3	4
18. Explaining a math problem to someone else helps me learn better when I am studying.	1	2	3	4
19. Looking at a picture from my notes or math book helps me understand a math problem.	1	2	3	4
20. Making study aids with my hands helps me learn better.	1	2	3	4
21. I understand instructions better when someone tells me what they are.	1	2	3	4
22. I memorize sentences or words I can say to myself to help me remember how to do problems on a test.	1	2	3	4
23. Pictures and charts help me see how all the parts of a word problem work together.	1	2	3	4
24. I enjoy putting things together.	1	2	3	4
25. When I solve a problem on a math test, I talk my way through it in my head or softly to myself.	1	2	3	4

Copyright © Houghton Mifflin Company. All rights reserved.

Scoring Your Results

Step One: Fill in each answer score next to the appropriate question number. Add the column totals. Divide column totals A and B by 2. Those numbers will be your final column totals. Leave column C total as is.

Column A	Column B	Column C
1. ______	3. ______	4. ______
2. ______	5. ______	7. ______
10. ______	6. ______	16. ______
12. ______	8. ______	20. ______
14. ______	9. ______	24. ______
17. ______	11. ______	
18. ______	13. ______	
21. ______	15. ______	
22. ______	19. ______	
25. ______	23. ______	
A Total ____/2 = _____ Column Total	B Total _____/2 = ______ Column Total	C Total ______ (Do not divide.)

Step Two: Fill in the number of squares to represent each column total. Any total greater than 12 indicates that modality style as a strength when you learn math. You can be strong in more than one modality. If none of the totals equals 12 squares, your highest score is your strongest modality. If you have a tie, pick the one that comes to mind as your strongest.

	Least Like Me																			Most Like Me
Modality	**1**				**5**					**10**					**15**					**20**
A = Auditory																				
B = Visual																				
C = Kinesthetic																				

This Learning Modality Inventory developed by Kimberly Nolting, ©.

Copyright © Houghton Mifflin Company. All rights reserved.

learners may need to learn how to think more analytically and use common sense, since it may not be their preferred way to learn math. They may grow impatient with all the details or feel that math is just not their subject when it really can be. Dynamic and innovative learners can be good mathematicians. They just may need to be more conscious of designing study strategies for math.

Chapter 6 suggests different study skills that will help you learn math through your preferred learning modality and style.

Remember

It is important to recognize that students who do not have learning styles that easily lend themselves to learning math can still learn math. Good study skills and awareness on the part of the math instructor and student can compensate for a mismatch of modality/ learning styles. Working together to find strategies to help improve the teaching and learning is most productive for everyone.

WHY? *Innovative learners* are imaginative thinkers with lots of ideas. They learn by thinking, listening, and sharing ideas. They want to make a personal connection to what they are learning, to the class, or to the instructors. They learn by bringing their own personal experiences into the process. They want to know "Why?" when they are learning. They solve problems by personally relating to them and using their feelings.

Innovative learners:

- ❑ work toward self-improvement
- ❑ tap into feelings to interpret what is going on
- ❑ listen and reflect
- ❑ like subjective tests
- ❑ strive for peace and harmony with people
- ❑ have concern for others
- ❑ listen and share
- ❑ favorite question: "Why?"
- ❑ are interested in people and their feelings
- ❑ personalize what they learn
- ❑ have lots of ideas

They like careers and majors in fields such as:

- ❑ counseling
- ❑ humanities
- ❑ social work
- ❑ education (in order to help others)
- ❑ English
- ❑ communications
- ❑ human resources
- ❑ other careers interacting with/or helping people

WHAT? *Analytic learners* put details together and use facts to understand ideas. They are more interested in ideas, facts, and theories than in people. They are uncomfortable with subjective topics and prefer logic. They learn best in traditional lecture classrooms when the instructor is the expert and provides the information. They want to know "What?" when they are learning. They solve problems by gathering information and using logic.

Analytic learners:

- ❑ use facts to interpret what is going on
- ❑ like lectures by experts
- ❑ usually prefer studying alone, and not in groups
- ❑ prefer objective tests
- ❑ are interested in ideas and facts more than in people
- ❑ enjoy research
- ❑ must have as much information as possible to make decisions
- ❑ favorite question: "What?"
- ❑ form theories from information they collect
- ❑ want to know what the experts think
- ❑ like problem solving

They like careers and majors in fields such as:

- ❑ mathematics
- ❑ education (in order to teach knowledge)
- ❑ sciences
- ❑ engineering or computer science
- ❑ accounting
- ❑ other careers that use logical reasoning

Copyright © Houghton Mifflin Company. All rights reserved.

HOW? ***Common sense learners*** want to know how they can use what they are learning immediately. They use facts to learn about concepts, and want to immediately use the information and see immediate application. (Analytic learners are satisfied with just coming up with the theories and concepts.) Common sense learners want to get right to the point when they are learning or studying. They want to know "How does this work?" They solve problems by knowing how something works.

Common sense learners:

- ❑ believe things should make common sense
- ❑ test theories with applications
- ❑ learn in math and science labs
- ❑ want to know how something applies immediately
- ❑ do not tolerate fuzzy ideas
- ❑ have a"light bulb" go on when applying new ideas
- ❑ are skills-oriented and like tinkering with things
- ❑ favorite question: "How?"
- ❑ want to get right to the point
- ❑ like objective tests
- ❑ like classes that are practical

They like careers and majors in fields such as:

- ❑ applied sciences
- ❑ engineering
- ❑ allied health sciences
- ❑ technologies
- ❑ computer science
- ❑ other fields in which they can take ideas and make practical applications

WHAT IF? ***Dynamic learners*** want to know what new possibilities exist for the concepts they are learning. They like learning to be more of a self-discovery process than a "listen to a lecture and discuss" approach. They like new things and can adapt to change. They learn by trial and error. They solve problems by looking at hidden possibilities. Their favorite question is "What if?"

Dynamic learners:

- ❑ adapt and even like change
- ❑ learn by trial and error
- ❑ learn best by independent self-instruction
- ❑ test new ideas through experiences
- ❑ get bored with routine in learning
- ❑ need to know what else can be done with new information
- ❑ are at ease with people
- ❑ favorite question: "What can this become?"
- ❑ favorite question: "What if?"
- ❑ like self-discovery learning
- ❑ often reach correct answers intuitively (using the "gut")
- ❑ are risk takers

They like careers and majors in fields such as:

- ❑ business
- ❑ administration (if innovation is allowed)
- ❑ marketing
- ❑ education (to help students learn to reach their goals)
- ❑ sales occupations
- ❑ roles/jobs in which they can get actions started and energize people

Section Review

1. My learning modality is ____________________ because ________________________________
____

2. My cognitive learning style is ____________________ because ____________________________
____

Copyright © Houghton Mifflin Company. All rights reserved.

Measuring Your Math Study Skills

Students have learning strengths and challenges that affect their math learning and course grades. They must identify and understand these strengths and challenges to know which strengths support them and which challenges to improve upon. After reading this section, you will be asked to complete the Math Learning Profile Sheet (Figure 2).

Examples: Having good math study skills is a *positive* math learning characteristic, whereas having high test anxiety is a *negative* math learning characteristic.

Math study skills comprise the main part of the affective characteristics that represent about 25 percent of your math grade. You can determine your math study skills expertise by taking the free Math Study Skills Evaluation at www.academicsuccess.com, or you can do a self-determination of your math study skills. If you take the online Math Study Skills Evaluation, the results will indicate your score. If you score below 70, you really need to focus on developing a set of study skills. A score between 70 and 80 means that you have average study skills, and a score above 90 means that you have good study skills. A self-determination can be made by asking yourself if you have ever

Figure 2 Math Learning Profile Sheet

After completing this profile, use your answers to select which areas you would like to improve first. If you have a serious problem with math or test anxiety, get help in this area immediately. Circle the X that best describes your belief.

	Strongly Disagree	Disagree	Agree	Strongly Agree
1. I have good math study skills.	X	X	X	X
2. Math tests don't make me anxious.	X	X	X	X
3. I have a strong basic knowledge of math to pass this class.	X	X	X	X
4. I have a positive attitude about learning math.	X	X	X	X
5. It has been less than a year since I took my last math class.	X	X	X	X
6. I have taken a math study skills course before this class.	X	X	X	X
7. I have good reading skills to be successful in this class.	X	X	X	X
8. I know if I improve my study habits, I can improve my math grades.	X	X	X	X

This informal survey is designed to help you decide what kind of shape you are in to do well in your course.

Which areas are strong and will help you do well in a math class?

____

____

Which areas keep you from doing the best you can in a math class? How can you change them?

____

____

Copyright © Houghton Mifflin Company. All rights reserved.

been taught math study skills. If you have, then you probably have either good or excellent math study skills. If you have not, then you most likely need to develop good math study skills.

Scoring low on the Math Study Skills Evaluation is not the end of the world. In fact, it might indicate that your problems with learning math may be due to your study habits instead of your math intelligence.

A low score on the Math Study Skills Evaluation means that most of your learning problems result from the fact that you have not been taught math study skills. This workbook can teach you math study skills. If you previously have gotten poor math grades, they were probably due to a lack of math study skills, and this was not your fault.

You can improve your math study skills and become a successful math student. If you have good math study skills, you can still improve them to make As in math. If you have excellent math study skills, you can still learn some additional math study skills that can help you in future courses.

Previous Study Skills Courses or Training

General study skills training that does not focus on math may help some students in time management, reading techniques, learning styles, and overcoming procrastination. Even though math requires specific study techniques, you can learn many other helpful general study skills and personal habits that will help you in math classes. If you have had no study skills training, then this workbook will help you in your math and other courses. Students with no past study skills training should also take advantage of any other opportunities to learn about college success skills in addition to learning from this workbook. Contact your learning centers, instructors, or counselors about study skills workshops and when they will be offered.

Previous/Current Required Reading Courses

College reading skills are also needed for success in math courses. This is especially true when you are trying to solve story or word problems.

At community colleges and some universities, there are three levels of reading courses. Usually, the first two levels are noncredit reading courses, and the third level is for college credit.

If you are enrolled in the lowest reading level, you will have difficulty reading and understanding the math text. Students who are enrolled in the second level may also have difficulty reading the text. Students who are not required to take a reading class or who are reading at grade level may still have some difficulty reading the math text.

Remember

Math texts are not written like English or history texts. Even students with college-level reading skills may experience difficulty understanding their math text.

Students not at college level reading can pass math courses; however, if you need help in reading, get that help as soon as possible. Or, many learning or study skills centers help students with reading skills for specific courses. Work with a learning specialist to design a system for reading your math textbook. If you do not know your reading level, ask to take a reading test. If in doubt about your reading level, take a reading class.

Reflecting on Your Affective Attributes

Determining Your Math Attitude

Math attitude can play a major part in your success in math courses. Some students who have a poor attitude toward math may not attend class as often as they should or may procrastinate in doing their homework. Other students avoid math until they have to take it. What is your math attitude—good, neutral, or negative? Remember, students with negative math attitudes can pass math. It depends on what you do with your attitude that counts. Don't let your negative attitude cause problems in your math course. Also, if you have a good math

Copyright © Houghton Mifflin Company. All rights reserved.

attitude, don't forget to study. A good math attitude can only get you so far!

Measuring Your Math Anxiety Level

It is also important to assess any math anxiety you might have, so that you can start managing it immediately. If you took the online Math Study Skills Evaluation, your score should indicate if you "seldom," "often," or "almost always" become anxious and forget important concepts during a test.

If you have medium or high math test anxiety, it can be reduced. This problem can be fixed if you follow the suggestions in the next chapter. This also means that some of your problems in learning math (if you have any) are due to anxiety instead of any intellectual inability to learn math.

If you have high text anxiety, then you will probably need to use the *How to Reduce Test Anxiety* CD. You can order this CD by going to www.academicsuccess.com.

Your Locus of Control

"Locus of control" is a concept that describes how much control you feel you have over both your life and your course grades. Some students feel they have a lot of control over their lives and learning, while other students feel they have very little control over their lives and grades. For example, when a student with external locus of control does poorly on a test, the blame is put on the instructor, when in reality the student did not study well enough. On the other hand, the student with internal locus of control admits that studying more and paying more attention in class would have helped. Students can improve their internal locus of control and be successful in mathematics at the same time.

Evaluating Your Findings

Now that you understand some of the general characteristics that help students be successful, complete the informal Math Learning Profile Sheet (Figure 2). When you look at your profile, think of it as similar to going to a fitness center for the first time. A professional trainer asks questions, runs you through equipment, analyzing your strengths and challenges, and then designs a program for you. You are doing the same thing here.

Section Review

1. List your strengths for learning math.

   ____

   ____

   ____

   ____

   ____

2. List three areas you will start improving right now.

   Area One: ______________________________________

   ____

   Area Two: ______________________________________

   ____

   Area Three: ____________________________________

   ____

Copyright © Houghton Mifflin Company. All rights reserved.

3. How will you improve these areas?

   Area One: ____
   ____

   Area Two: ____
   ____

   Area Three: ____
   ____

How to Improve Your Math Knowledge

Instructors always operate on the premise that you finished your previous math course just last week; they do not wait for you to catch up on current material. It does not matter if your previous math course was a month ago or five years ago. Instructors expect you to know the previous course material—period.

Review Your Previous Math Course Material and Tests

There are several ways to improve your math knowledge. Review your previous math course material before attending your present math course. Look closely at your final exam to determine your weak areas. Work on your weak areas as soon as possible so they can become building blocks (instead of stumbling blocks) for your current course.

If it has been some time since your last math course, visit the math lab or learning resource center to locate review material. Ask the instructor if there are any computer programs that will assess your math skills to determine your strengths and challenges for your course. Review math videotapes on the math course immediately below your level. Also review any computer software designed for the previous math course.

Another way to enhance learning is to review the previous math course text by taking all of the chapter review tests. If you score above 80 percent on one chapter review test, move on to the next chapter. A score below 80 percent means you need to work on that chapter before moving on to the next chapter. Get a tutor to help you with those chapters if you have trouble. Make sure you review all the chapters required in the previous course as soon as possible. If you wait more than two weeks to conclude this exercise, it may be too late to catch up (while learning new material at the same time).

Employ a Tutor

One last way to improve your cognitive entry skills is to employ a private tutor. If you have a history of not doing well in math courses, you may need to start tutorial sessions *the same week class begins.* This will give the tutor a better chance of helping you regain those old math skills.

You still need to work hard to relearn old math skills while continuing to learn the new material. If you wait four to five weeks to employ a tutor, it will probably be too late to catch up and do well or even pass the course.

Remember

Tutorial sessions work best when the sessions begin during the first two weeks of a math course.

Copyright © Houghton Mifflin Company. All rights reserved.

Schedule Math Courses "Back to Back"

Another way to maintain appropriate math knowledge is to take your math courses "back to back." It is better to take math courses every semester—even if you do not like math—so that you can maintain sequential (linear) learning.

I have known students who have made Bs or Cs in a math class and who then waited six months to a year to take the next math course. Inevitably, many failed. These students did not complete any preparatory math work before the math course and were lost after the second chapter. This is similar to having one semester of Spanish, not speaking it for a year, then visiting Spain and not understanding what is being said.

The only exception to taking math courses "back to back" is taking a six-week "kamikaze" math course (an ultracondensed version of a regular course), which should be avoided.

If you are one of the unfortunate many who are currently failing a math course, you need to ask yourself, "Am I currently learning any math or just becoming more confused?" If you are learning some math, stay in the course. If you are getting more confused, withdraw from the course. Improve your math knowledge prior to enrolling in a math course during the next semester.

> **Example:** You have withdrawn from a math course after midterm due to low grades. Instead of waiting until next semester, attend a math lab or seek a tutor and learn Chapters 1, 2, and 3 *to perfection*. Also use this time to improve your math study skills. You will enter the same math course next semester with excellent math knowledge and study skills. In fact, you can make an A on the first test and complete the course with a high grade. Does this sound far-fetched? It may, but I know hundreds of students who have used this learning procedure and passed their math course instead of failing it again and again.

Finding Your Best Instructor

Finding an instructor who best matches your learning style can be a difficult task. Your learning style is important; your learning style is how you best acquire information.

> **Example:** Auditory learners do better when hearing the information over and over again instead of carefully reading the information. If an auditory learner is taught by a visual-style instructor who prefers that students read materials on their own and who prefers working problems instead of describing them, the mismatch could cause the student to do worse than if the student were taught by an auditory instructor.

Most students are placed in their first math course by an academic advisor. Usually, academic advisors know who are the most popular and least popular math instructors. However, advisors can be reluctant to discuss teacher popularity. And unfortunately, students may want the counselor to devise a course schedule based on the student's time limits instead of teacher selection.

To learn who are the best math instructors, ask the academic advisor which math instructor's classes fill up first. This does not place the academic advisor in the position of making a value judgment; neither does it guarantee the best instructor. But it will increase the odds in your favor.

Another way to acquire a good math instructor is to ask your friends about their current and previous math instructors. However, if another student says that an instructor is excellent, make sure your learning style matches your friend's learning style. Ask your friend, "Exactly what makes that instructor so good?" Then compare the answer with how you learn best. If you have a different learning style than your friend, look for another instructor, or ask another friend whose learning style more closely matches your own.

To obtain the most from an instructor, discover your best learning style and match it to the instructor's teaching style. Most learning centers or student personnel offices will have counselors

Copyright © Houghton Mifflin Company. All rights reserved.

who can measure and explain your learning style. Interview or observe the instructor while the instructor is teaching. This process is time consuming, but it is well worth the effort!

Once you have found your best instructor, do not change. Remain with the same instructor for every math class whenever possible.

Remember

The first step in becoming a better math student is knowing your learning strengths and challenges. Now you can focus on what you need to improve.

Whether your learning styles are a natural fit for learning math or not, you still own the responsibility to be smart in selecting your study system for math class. You can be successful!

Section Review

1. Give four examples of how you can review math course materials.

Example 1: ______________________________

____

____

Example 2: ______________________________

____

____

Example 3: ______________________________

____

____

Example 4: ______________________________

____

____

2. What is the advantage of taking math courses back to back?

____

____

____

Copyright © Houghton Mifflin Company. All rights reserved.

3. Give two examples of how to find your best math instructor.

   Example 1: ____

   ____

   ____

   ____

   Example 2: ____

   ____

   ____

   ____

Dan's Take

Because I majored in journalism, I was required to take only one math course in order to graduate. I decided to put it off until the first semester of my senior year. I had not taken a math course since my junior year of high school, but I figured I could take the easiest math class in the course listings and cruise until graduation.

Wow, was I wrong.

Little did I know that I had to pass a math placement test, even though it had been more than four years since I had looked at a math textbook. Needless to say, I bombed. I was forced to take a remedial class before being allowed to take the course I needed to graduate.

My first mistake was waiting so long to take my math credit. I could have completed the course my freshman year when the information was still fresh in my head. Then I assumed that I knew the math. I never measured my math knowledge, and I went into the placement test in total ignorance.

After working in the remedial class for a couple of weeks, all of the math began to come back to me. It became very clear that I could have passed the placement test with just a little preparation. There were numerous online programs I could have used, and there were books I could have checked out from the library, but I went into the test completely unprepared.

The lesson to be learned here is that math is not a subject that should be put off. It is best to head into your new math course with the prerequisite knowledge freshly stored in your mind. By measuring what you know beforehand, you can avoid my situation.

Copyright © Houghton Mifflin Company. All rights reserved.

Name: ______________________________ Date: ______________

Chapter 2 Review

1. _______ _______ _______ refers to how much math you knew before entering your current math course.

2. _____ _______ _______ are the learning skills you possess that affect your grades.

3. Students who talk their instructors into moving them up a course level usually _____ that course.

4. The _____ of tutors is a major part of the math lab or learning resource center.

5. Affective student characteristics account for about _____ percent of your grade.

6. _____ learners look for facts and ask experts for their advice.

7. Hands-on learners are called _____ learners.

8. Assessing your math learning _____ and _____ will help you improve your studying and learning.

9. Students having previous difficulty in mathematics should start tutorial sessions the _____ week class begins.

10. Once you find your best math instructor, _____ _______ change instructors for your next math course.

11. What is the most important information you learned from this chapter?

____

12. How can you immediately use it?

____

Copyright © Houghton Mifflin Company. All rights reserved.

3

How to Reduce Math Test Anxiety

What You Will Learn in Chapter 3

- ❑ Understanding Math Anxiety
- ❑ How To Recognize Test Anxiety
- ❑ Causes of Test Anxiety
- ❑ Different Types of Test Anxiety
- ❑ How To Reduce Test Anxiety

In this chapter you will first learn about math anxiety and then explore test anxiety. They are different issues that can affect each other. It is best to learn about them as separate entities first.

Math anxiety is a common problem for many high school, college, and university students. It is especially difficult for students in developmental courses, who normally have more math anxiety than other students. However, there are students in higher-level math courses who also struggle with this problem. It is very common for students to have anxiety only about math and not in their other subjects.

Most students think that math anxiety affects them only when they are taking tests, but it also affects other areas. It can affect the way you do your homework, the way you learn in the classroom or through distance learning courses, and the way you choose a career. Students who have math anxiety may procrastinate in doing their homework or put off sitting down and completing an online lesson. This can lead to math failure. Students also select majors based on the amount of math that is required, which could lead to lower-paying or dissatisfying careers. However, most students with math anxiety meet it face to face during tests, experiencing test anxiety as well.

Mild test anxiety can be a motivational factor in that it can make students properly prepare for a test. However, high test anxiety can cause major problems in both learning and test taking, as students avoid studying for the test when anxiety begins to afflict their thought processes. Reducing test anxiety is the key for many students to become successful in math. Such students need to learn the causes of test anxiety and how to reduce the test anxiety that affects their learning and grades.

Several techniques have proven helpful in reducing both math anxiety and math test anxiety. However, reducing them does not guarantee good math grades. It must be coupled with effective study skills and a desire to do well in math.

Understanding Math Anxiety

Definitions of Math Anxiety

Math anxiety is a relatively new concept in education. During the 1970s, certain educators began referring to *mathophobia* or *mathemaphobia* as a possible cause for children's unwillingness to learn math. Math anxiety is an extreme emotional and/or physical reaction to a very negative attitude toward math. There is a strong relationship between low math confidence and high math test anxiety (Fox, 1977).

Math anxiety is the feeling of tension and anxiety that interferes with the manipulation of numbers and the solving of math problems during tests (Richardson and Suinn, 1973). Math anxiety is a state of panic, helplessness, paralysis, and mental disorganization that occurs in some students when they are required to solve math problems. This discomfort varies in intensity and is the outcome of numerous experiences students have had in their past learning situations (Tobias, 1978).

Today, math anxiety is accepted as one of the major problems students have in completing their math courses. It is real, but it can be overcome.

Types of Math Anxiety

Math anxiety can be divided into three separate anxieties: math test anxiety, numerical anxiety, and abstraction anxiety. Math test anxiety involves anticipation, completion, and feedback of math tests. Numerical anxiety refers to everyday situations requiring people to work with numbers and perform arithmetic calculations. Numerical anxiety can also include students who are trying to figure out the amount of a tip, thinking about mathematics, doing math homework, or listening to or seeing math instruction. Abstraction anxiety involves working with variables and mathematical concepts used to solve equations. Students can have all three math anxieties or only one anxiety. Most often, the students I have worked with have had math test anxiety and abstraction anxiety. These students don't have any anxiety working with numbers, but once they start learning algebra, they develop both conditions. This may have happened in high school or college.

> *Remember*
> **When people try to overcome anxiety of any kind, including math anxiety, they must seek advice and support. It is much easier with support!**

The Causes of Math Anxiety

Since math anxiety is a learned condition, its causes are unique to each student, but they are all rooted in individuals' past experiences. Bad experiences in elementary school are one of the most common sources of students' math anxiety: coming in last in math races at the blackboard, watching classmates finish problems twice as fast as they do, teachers saying, "That's okay, you just aren't good in math, you are better in English," and classmates and teachers calling them stupid. These words and experiences remain with people; they can still hear the words and eventually begin telling themselves the same thing. When these students walk into a classroom or open a math book, or take a test, these "mental tapes" play in their minds. When asked, many students indicate that they were made fun of when trying to solve math problems at the chalkboard. When they could not

Copyright © Houghton Mifflin Company. All rights reserved.

solve the problems, the teacher and/or students would call them "stupid."

Teacher and peer embarrassment and humiliation become the conditioning experiences that cause some students' math anxiety. Over the years, this math anxiety is reinforced and even increases in magnitude. In fact, many math-anxious students—now 30, 40, and 50 years old—still have extreme fear about working math problems on the board. One 56-year-old indicated that he had a great deal of fear that the instructor would call him to the board. Even if he knew how to do the problem, displaying that knowledge to his peers was very difficult. Some students have said that they absolutely refused to go to the board.

Being embarrassed by family members can also cause math anxiety. According to students who have been interviewed on the matter, their parents tried to help them with math and this sometimes led to serious trauma. These students claim that the tutoring from their guardians, mainly their fathers, often resulted in scolding when they were not able to complete the problems. One student reported that his father hit him every time he got a multiplication problem wrong. Brothers and sisters can also tease one another about being "dumb" in math. This is particularly true of boys telling girls that they cannot do math. When people hear these statements often enough, they may start to believe them and associate these bad feelings with the word *math*. So, for students many years later, just hearing the word "math" triggers a response of anxiety, consciously or unconsciously recalling the bad feelings, and becoming uneasy.

A good example of this is a student I worked with who had completed her B.S. degree 15 years ago at a college that did not require much math. She was returning to college to be an elementary school teacher, which required her to take math and a math placement test. As soon as I mentioned that she had to take math, she said, "I can't do math and I will have to wait a few days to get psychologically ready to take the math placement test." She indicated that her old feeling of not being able to do math rushed through her and she almost had an anxiety attack. This is an extreme case, but a true example, of math anxiety. In most cases, math anxiety is not this bad, but it is disruptive enough to cause learning and testing problems.

In order to overcome math anxiety, it is necessary to identify when it first started and what caused it. Math anxiety usually starts from one or a series of events in a student's past that were negative. Negative feelings were imbedded in memories and then anxiety started whenever the student was placed in similar situations.

Answer the questions on the Exploring Past Math Experiences Worksheet.

If some of the memories are tough ones, just make a short note of them right now. Don't dwell on them, because they are in the past. This can be frustrating for some students, but it is worth working through it. You will realize that math anxiety is usually a result of events, and does not occur because you are "dumb" or have other personal flaws.

If you have had a very positive experience in the past when you were studying math, brainstorm answers to the appropriate questions. You may want to keep in mind friends you know who struggle with math and think about the other questions.

This brainstorming will help you write your math autobiography assignment at the end of this chapter.

Some Facts to Remember

- Math anxiety is usually a result of past experiences that were negative. As a result of these experiences, any time a person is put in a similar situation, he/she gets anxious.
- Math anxiety is not related to how smart a person is.
- Math anxiety is a learned condition; therefore, in most cases, it can be unlearned or at least managed.
- A person must be willing to change and find strategies to practice continually that will help manage math anxiety.

Copyright © Houghton Mifflin Company. All rights reserved.

Exploring Past Math Experiences Worksheet

At the end of this chapter you will write a "Math Autobiography" to help you explore why you might have math anxiety. This knowledge is the first step in learning how to manage or overcome the anxiety. This worksheet will help you prepare for writing the autobiography. Answer the following questions. For some students, these questions will be easy to answer; for others, they will be more difficult because their past experiences are quite negative. The more honest you can be, the more you will be able to confront and work on any math anxiety.

1. When was the first time you were nervous or anxious about learning math? (Do not include taking tests.) Was it in elementary, middle, or high school? Can you recall a specific incident? If so, briefly describe it. It could have taken place in school or at home.

   Examples: Getting scolded by a teacher or parent for a poor homework grade. Losing a math race on the board. Going to recess late because you did not get your math work done in time. Older sibling always comparing math grades with you.

   ____

   ____

2. When was the last time you told yourself that you couldn't do math or were just not a math type?

   ____

   ____

3. Even though you might have math anxiety, there were probably some positive experiences associated with math in the past. Try to think of at least one of them.

   Examples: A good grade. Completing an assignment in class. A parent or teacher praising you for your math work.

   ____

   ____

4. If you have math anxiety, take heart. Most students can learn to minimize it and control it. Write a statement declaring that you will set a goal to learn to manage your math anxiety this semester.

   ____

   ____

How Math Anxiety Affects Learning

Math anxiety can cause learning problems in several ways. It can affect how you do your homework and your participation in the classroom and in study groups. Let's first start by looking at how math anxiety could affect your homework. Students with high math anxiety may have difficulty starting or completing their homework. Doing homework reminds some students of their learning problems in math. More specifically, it reminds them of their previous math failures, which causes further anxiety. This anxiety can lead to total avoidance of homework or "approach-avoidance" behavior.

Total homework avoidance is called *procrastination*. The very thought of doing their homework

Copyright © Houghton Mifflin Company. All rights reserved.

causes these students anxiety, which causes them to put off tackling their homework. This makes them feel better for a short amount of time—*until test day*.

Math anxiety can also affect your classroom participation and learning. Usually students with math anxiety are afraid to speak out in class and ask questions. They remember that in the past they were made fun of when they gave incorrect answers. They are also afraid of asking a question that others, including the teacher, will consider "dumb." So they sit in class fearful of being asked a question, looking like they understand the lecture so they will not be called on. They also take a lot of notes even though they don't understand them, in order to give the illusion of comprehension. If you are one of these students, these are hard habits to break. However, these habits may cause you to be unsuccessful in your math class. Here are some suggestions that may help you break these habits:

1. Make an appointment to talk to your math instructor. Math instructors want you to talk to them. When I do my consulting around the country, one of the major complaints I get from math instructors is that the students don't come and see them. Make an appointment to see your math instructor before the first major test to discuss your math history and to ask for learning suggestions. In most cases it is easier to talk to the instructor before you get your first grade.
2. Before class, ask the instructor to work one homework problem. You might want to write the problem on the board before the instructor arrives. This is less stressful because you are not asking the question in front of the whole class. In fact, one of my good friends, Dr. Mike Hamm, suggests that his students put the problems they do not know how to solve on the board before class. Other students go to the board and solve the problems. Dr. Hamm then solves the ones the students cannot solve.
3. Prepare one question from your homework and ask it within the first 15 minutes of class. Instructors are more likely to answer questions in the first part of class when they have time instead of the end of class when time is running out.
4. Ask a question to which you already know the answer. The question will begin discussion with the instructor and other students when you can contribute since you understand the problem. It will set you up for a positive experience.
5. Use email to send questions to your instructor. This way, you can still get the answer with very little anxiety.

By using these suggestions, you can reduce your math anxiety and learn more mathematics. A question unanswered could be a missed test question.

Remember

The instructor's job is to answer your questions, and you are paying for the course.

Math-anxious students sometimes avoid doing additional math outside of the classroom. They avoid study groups and supplemental instruction. It is like asking a person with hydrophobia (fear of water) to take a vacation at the beach. However, a person with hydrophobia can go to the beach and enjoy himself or herself and not get wet. In other words, students can still attend study groups and supplemental instruction and just listen. When they are ready to get their feet wet, they can ask a few questions. Don't let these great opportunities go by.

Math anxiety can affect how you learn mathematics. It can be overcome with your effort. You don't have to live in the past with your math fears. Today is a new day, and you can change how math affects you. The next step is to understand how test anxiety can affect your demonstration of math knowledge.

Copyright © Houghton Mifflin Company. All rights reserved.

Section Review

1. List and explain the three types of math anxiety.

   First Type: ______________________________

   Second Type: ______________________________

   Third Type: ______________________________

2. List and explain two causes of math anxiety.

   First Cause: ______________________________

   Second Cause: ______________________________

3. List three ways math anxiety can cause learning problems.

   First Way: ______________________________

   Second Way: ______________________________

   Third Way: ______________________________

4. List and explain three ways students can manage or avoid the effects of math anxiety.

   First Way: ______________________________

   Second Way: ______________________________

   Third Way: ______________________________

How to Recognize Test Anxiety

Test anxiety has existed for as long as tests have been used to evaluate student performance. Because it is so common and because it has survived the test of time, test anxiety has been carefully studied over the last 50 years. Pioneering studies indicate that test anxiety generally leads to low test scores. At the University of South Florida (Tampa), Dr. Charles Spielberger investigated the relationship between test anxiety and intellectual ability. The study results suggested that anxiety coupled with high ability can improve academic performance; but anxiety coupled with low or average ability can interfere with academic performance. That is:

Anxiety + high ability = improvement

Anxiety + low or average ability = no improvement

> **Example:** Students with average ability and low test anxiety had better performance and higher grades than did students with average ability and high test anxiety. However, there are students who make good grades, take calculus, and still have test anxiety.

Copyright © Houghton Mifflin Company. All rights reserved.

Test anxiety is a *learned* response; a person is not born with it. An environmental situation brings about test anxiety. The good news is that because it is a learned response, it can be *unlearned*. Test anxiety is a special kind of general stress. General stress is considered to be "strained exertion," which can lead to physical and psychological problems.

Math Test Anxiety

There are several definitions of test anxiety. One definition states, "Test anxiety is a conditioned emotional habit to either a single terrifying experience, recurring experience of high anxiety, or a continuous condition of anxiety" (Wolpe, 1958).

Another definition of test anxiety relates to the educational system. The educational system develops evaluations that measure one's mental performance, and this creates test anxiety. This definition suggests that test anxiety is the *anticipation* of some realistic or nonrealistic situational threat (Cattell, 1966). The "test" can be a research paper, an oral report, work at the chalkboard, a multiple-choice exam, a written essay, or a math test.

Math test anxiety is a relatively new concept in education. *Ms.* magazine published "Math Anxiety: Why Is a Smart Girl Like You Counting on Your Fingers?" (Tobias, 1976) and coined the phrase *math anxiety*. During the 1970s, other educators began referring to *mathophobia* or *mathemaphobia* as a possible cause of children's unwillingness to learn math. Additional studies on the graduate level discovered that math anxiety was common among adults as well as children.

One of my students once described math test anxiety as "being in a burning house with no way out." No matter how you define it, math test anxiety is real, and it affects millions of students.

Why Math Tests Create Anxiety

It has been shown that math anxiety exists among many students who usually do not suffer from other tensions. Counselors at a major university reported that one-third of the students who enrolled in behavior therapy programs offered through counseling centers had problems with math anxiety (Suinn, 1988).

Educators know that math anxiety is common among college students and is more prevalent in women than in men. They also know that math anxiety frequently occurs in students with poor high school math backgrounds. These students were found to have the greatest amount of anxiety.

Approximately half of the students in college prep math courses (designed for students with inadequate high school math backgrounds or low placement scores) could be considered to have math anxiety. However, math anxiety also occurs in students in high-level math courses, such as college algebra and calculus.

Educators investigating the relationship between anxiety and math have indicated that anxiety contributes to poor grades in math. They have also found that simply *reducing* math test anxiety does not guarantee higher math grades. Students often have other problems that affect their math grades, such as poor study skills, poor test-taking skills, or poor class attendance.

Section Review

1. What is your personal definition of test anxiety?

____

2. What type of student does math anxiety affect most?

____

Copyright © Houghton Mifflin Company. All rights reserved.

The Causes of Test Anxiety

The causes of test anxiety can be different for each student, but they can be explained by seven basic concepts. See Figure 3.

The causes of math test anxiety can be different for each student. It could possibly have first occurred in middle school or high school. However, for many students it first occurs in college when passing tests is the only way to pass the course. Homework and extra credit in most college courses don't count toward your grade. Now students must have a passing average and in some cases must pass the departmental final exam. Additional pressure also exists because not passing algebra means you won't graduate and you might not get the job you want. As you can see, there are more reasons to have math test anxiety in college than in high school.

If you have math test anxiety, I want you to try to remember the first time it surfaced. Was it in middle school, high school, or college? Can you recall a specific incident? Was it your first algebra test? Was it your first math test after being out of school for a long time? Was it after you decided to get serious about college? Was it a college algebra course that was required for your major? Was it an instructor who told you that if you didn't pass the next math test you would fail the course? Was it when you needed to pass the next math test to pass the course so you could keep your financial aid? Was it your children asking you why you failed your last math test? If you cannot remember a specific incident when you had test anxiety, do you expect to have any major anxiety on the next test you take?

Students with math test anxiety also have had positive experiences with taking math tests. Now try to remember your first positive experience with taking a math test. Was it in middle school, high school, or college? Was it after studying many hours for the test? Now think back to your last positive experience with a math test. How did it make you feel?

Since we have already explored your experiences with taking math tests, let's look at some of the direct causes of your math test anxiety. If you do have test anxiety, what is the main cause? If you don't know, then review the seven causes of test anxiety in Figure 3. Does one of these reasons fit you? If you don't have test anxiety, what would be a reason that could cause test anxiety?

Like you did before, brainstorm answers to the questions listed in the previous three paragraphs. You will also use this brainstorming to help you write your autobiography.

Remember

For some students, just writing about their previous math history helps them.

Figure 3 Causes of Test Anxiety

- Test anxiety can be a learned behavior resulting from the expectations of parents, teachers, or other significant people in the student's life.
- Test anxiety can be caused by the association between grades and a student's personal worth.
- Test anxiety develops from fear of alienating parents, family, or friends due to poor grades.
- Test anxiety can stem from a feeling of lack of control and an inability to change one's life situation.
- Test anxiety can be caused by a student's being embarrassed by the teacher or other students when trying to do math problems.
- Test anxiety can be caused by timed tests and the fear of not finishing the test, even if one can solve all the problems.
- Test anxiety can be caused by being put in math courses above one's level of competence.
- What is (are) the cause(s) of your *test* anxiety?

Copyright © Houghton Mifflin Company. All rights reserved.

Section Review

1. List and describe five causes of test anxiety.

   First Cause: ______________________________

   ____

   ____

   Second Cause: ______________________________

   ____

   ____

   Third Cause: ______________________________

   ____

   ____

   Fourth Cause: ______________________________

   ____

   ____

   Fifth Cause: ______________________________

   ____

   ____

2. Put into your own words your cause(s) of test anxiety. If you don't have test anxiety, list what you think is the major cause of test anxiety.

   ____

   ____

The Different Types of Test Anxiety

The two basic types of test anxiety are emotional anxiety (educators call this *somatic* anxiety) and worry anxiety (educators call this *cognitive* anxiety). Students with high test anxiety have *both* emotional and worry anxiety.

Signs of emotional anxiety are upset stomach; nausea; sweaty palms; pain in the neck; stiff shoulders; high blood pressure; rapid, shallow breathing; rapid heartbeat; and general feelings of nervousness. As anxiety increases, these feelings intensify. Some students even run to the bathroom to throw up or have diarrhea.

Even though these *feelings* are caused by anxiety, the physical response is real. These feelings and physical inconveniences can affect your concentration and your testing speed, and they can cause you to "draw a blank."

Worry anxiety causes the student to think about failing the test. These negative thoughts can happen either before or during the test. This negative "self-talk" causes students to focus on their anxiety instead of recalling math concepts.

Copyright © Houghton Mifflin Company. All rights reserved.

The effects of test anxiety range from a "mental block" on a test to avoiding homework. One of the most common side effects of test anxiety is getting the test and immediately forgetting information that you know. Some students describe this event as having a "mental block," "going blank," or finding that the test looks like a foreign language.

After five or ten minutes into the test, some of these students can refocus on the test and start working the problems. They have, however, lost valuable time. For other students, anxiety persists throughout the test and they cannot recall the needed math information. It is only after they walk out the door that they can remember how to work the problems.

Sometimes math anxiety does not cause students to "go blank" but slows down their mental processing speed. This means it takes longer to recall formulas and concepts and to work problems. The result is frustration and loss of time, leading to *more* anxiety. Since, in most cases, math tests are *speed* tests (those in which you have a certain amount of time to complete the test), you may not have enough time to work all the problems or to check the answers if you have mentally slowed down. The result is a lower test score, because even though you know the material, you do not complete all of the questions before test time runs out.

Not using all of the time allotted for the test is another problem caused by test anxiety. Students know that they should use all of the test time to check their answers. In fact, math is one of the few subjects in which you can check test problems to find out if your work is correct. However, most students do not use all of the test time, and this results in lower test scores. Why does this happen?

Students with high test anxiety do not want to stay in the classroom. This is especially true of students whose test anxiety increases as the test progresses. The test anxiety gets so bad that they would rather leave early and receive a lower grade than stay in that "burning house."

Students have another reason for leaving the test early: the fear of what the instructor and other students will think about them for being the last one to hand in the test. These students refuse to be the last ones to finish the test because they think that the instructor or other students will think they are "dumb." This is middle school thinking, but the feelings are still real — no matter what the age of the student. These students do not realize that some students who turn in their tests first fail, whereas many students who turn in their tests last make As and Bs.

Another effect of test anxiety relates to completing homework assignments. Students who have high test anxiety may have difficulty starting or completing their math homework. Doing homework reminds some students of their learning problems in math. More specifically, it reminds them of their previous math failures, which causes further anxiety. This anxiety can lead to total homework avoidance or "approach-avoidance" behavior.

Total homework avoidance is called *procrastination*. The very thought of doing their homework causes these students anxiety, which causes them to put off tackling their homework. This makes them feel better for a short amount of time—*until test day*.

> **Example:** Some students begin their homework and work some problems successfully. They then get stuck on a problem that causes them anxiety, so they take a break. During their break the anxiety disappears until they start doing their homework again. Continuing their homework causes more anxiety, which leads to another break. The breaks become more frequent. Finally, the student ends up taking one long break and not doing the homework. Quitting, to them, means *no more anxiety* until the next homework assignment.

The effects of math test anxiety can be different for each student. Students can have several of the mentioned characteristics that can interfere with math learning and test taking. However, there are certain myths about math that each student needs to know. Review Figure 4, The 12 Myths About Test Anxiety, to see which ones you believe. If you have test anxiety, which of the items listed is (are) true for you?

Copyright © Houghton Mifflin Company. All rights reserved.

Figure 4 The 12 Myths About Test Anxiety

1. Students are born with test anxiety.
2. Test anxiety is a mental illness.
3. Test anxiety cannot be reduced.
4. Any level of test anxiety is bad.
5. All students who are not prepared have test anxiety.
6. Students with test anxiety cannot learn math.
7. Students who are well prepared will not have test anxiety.
8. Very intelligent students and students taking high-level courses, such as calculus, do not have test anxiety.
9. Attending class and doing homework should reduce all test anxiety.
10. Being told to relax during a test will make a student relaxed.
11. Doing nothing about test anxiety will make it go away.
12. Reducing test anxiety will guarantee better grades.

Section Review

1. List and describe the two basic types of test anxiety.

   First Type: ____________________

   Second Type: ____________________

2. List two reasons students leave the test room early instead of checking their answers.

   First Reason: ____________________

   Second Reason: ____________________

3. List six of the twelve myths about test anxiety that you most believed.

   First Myth: ____________________

   Second Myth: ____________________

   Third Myth: ____________________

   Fourth Myth: ____________________

   Fifth Myth: ____________________

   Sixth Myth: ____________________

Copyright © Houghton Mifflin Company. All rights reserved.

How to Reduce Test Anxiety

To reduce math test anxiety, you need to understand both the relaxation response and how negative self-talk undermines your abilities.

Relaxation Techniques

The relaxation response is any technique or procedure that helps you to become relaxed. It will take the place of an anxiety response. Someone simply telling you to relax or even telling yourself to relax, however, does little to reduce your test anxiety. There are both short-term and long-term relaxation response techniques that help control emotional (somatic) math test anxiety. These techniques will also help reduce worry (cognitive) anxiety. Effective *short-term* techniques include the tensing and differential relaxation method, the palming method, and deep breathing.

Short-Term Relaxation Techniques

The Tensing and Differential Relaxation Method The tensing and differential relaxation method helps you relax by tensing and relaxing your muscles all at once. Follow these procedures while you are sitting at your desk before taking a test:

1. Put your feet flat on the floor.
2. With your hands, grab underneath the chair.
3. Push down with your feet and pull up on your chair at the same time for about five seconds.
4. Relax for five to ten seconds.
5. Repeat the procedure two or three times.
6. Relax all your muscles except the ones that are actually used to take the test.

The Palming Method The palming method is a visualization procedure used to reduce test anxiety. While you are at your desk before or during a test, follow these procedures:

1. Close and cover your eyes using the center of the palms of your hands.
2. Prevent your hands from touching your eyes by resting the lower parts of your palms on your cheekbones and placing your fingers on your forehead. Your eyeballs must not be touched, rubbed, or handled in any way.
3. Think of some real or imaginary relaxing scene. Mentally visualize this scene. Picture the scene as if you were actually there, looking through your own eyes.
4. Visualize this relaxing scene for one to two minutes.
5. Open your eyes and wait about two minutes and visualize the scene again. This time also imagine any sounds or smells that can enhance your scene. For example, if you are imagining a beach scene, imagine the sound of the waves on the beach and the smell of the salty air. This technique can also be completed without having your hands over your eyes by just closing your eyes.

Practice visualizing this scene for several days before taking a test and the effectiveness of this relaxation procedure will improve.

Deep Breathing Deep breathing is another short-term relaxation technique that can help you relax. Proper breathing is a way to reduce stress and decrease test anxiety. When you are breathing properly, enough oxygen gets into your bloodstream to nourish your body and mind. A lack of oxygen in your blood contributes to an anxiety state that makes it more difficult to react to stress. Proper deep breathing can help you control your test anxiety.

Deep breathing can replace the rapid, shallow breathing that sometimes accompanies test anxiety, or it can prevent test anxiety. Here are the steps in the deep breathing technique:

1. Sit straight up in your chair in a good posture position.
2. Slowly inhale through your nose.
3. As you inhale, first fill the lower section of your lungs and work your way up to the upper part of your lungs.

Copyright © Houghton Mifflin Company. All rights reserved.

4. Hold your breath for a few seconds.
5. Exhale slowly through your mouth.
6. Wait a few seconds and repeat the cycle.
7. Keep doing this exercise for four or five minutes. This should involve going through about ten breathing cycles. Remember to take two normal breaths between cycles. If you start to feel lightheaded during this exercise, stop for 30 to 45 seconds and then start again.
8. Throughout the entire exercise, make sure you keep breathing smoothly and in a regular rhythm without gulping air or suddenly exhaling.
9. As an extra way to improve your relaxation, say "relax" or "be calm" to yourself as you exhale. This can start a conditioned response that can trigger relaxation when you repeat the words during anxious situations. As you keep practicing, this conditioned response will strengthen. Practice is the key to success.

You need to practice this breathing exercise for several weeks before using the technique during tests. If you don't practice this technique, it will not work. After taking your first test, keep doing the exercise several times a week to strengthen the relaxation response.

The CD *How to Reduce Test Anxiety* further explains test anxiety and discusses these and other short-term relaxation response techniques. Short-term relaxation techniques can be learned quickly but are not as successful as the long-term relaxation technique. Short-term techniques are intended to be used while learning the long-term technique.

Long-Term Relaxation Technique

The cue-controlled relaxation response technique is the best long-term relaxation technique. It is presented on the CD *How To Reduce Test Anxiety*. Cue-controlled relaxation means you can induce your own relaxation based on repeating certain cue words to yourself. In essence, you are taught to relax and then silently repeat cue words, such as "I am relaxed." After enough practice, you can relax during math tests. The cue-controlled relaxation technique has worked with thousands of students. For a better understanding of test anxiety and how to reduce it, listen to *How to Reduce Test Anxiety*.

Negative Self-Talk

According to cognitive psychologists, self-talk is what we say to ourselves as a response to an event or situation. This self-talk determines our feelings about that event or situation. Sometimes we say it so quickly and automatically that we don't even hear ourselves. We then think it is the situation that causes the feeling, but in reality it is our interactions or thoughts about the experience that are controlling our emotions. This sequence of events can be represented by the following timeline:

External Events
(Math test)

⇩

Interpretation of Events and Self-Talk
(How you feel about the test
and what you are telling yourself)

⇩

Feelings and Emotions
(Happy, glad, angry, mad, upset)

In most cases this means that you are responsible for how and what you feel. You can engage in positive self-talk or negative self-talk about taking a math test. Yes, some students practice positive self-talk about math tests and see each test as a challenge and something to accomplish that makes them feel good, while others see it as an upsetting event that leads to anger and anxiety. In other words, you are what you tell yourself.

Negative self-talk is a form of worry (cognitive) anxiety. This type of worrying can interfere with your test preparation and can keep you from concentrating on the test. Worrying can motivate you to study, but too much worrying may prevent you from studying at all.

Copyright © Houghton Mifflin Company. All rights reserved.

Negative self-talk is defined as the negative statements you tell yourself before and during tests. Negative self-talk causes students to lose confidence and to give up on tests. Furthermore, it can give you an inappropriate excuse for failing math and cause you to give up on learning math.

Examples of Negative Self-Talk

"It doesn't matter how hard I work. I am going to fail the class no matter what."

"I have already failed this class before. There is no way I can pass it this time, either."

"I do not get these problems. I am going to fail this test and flunk the course."

"I knew how to do these problems not 15 minutes ago, and now ... nothing! What is up with me, I always do this when I take math tests."

"If I can't even pass this easy test, how can I expect to pass the math classes I need to graduate?"

Students who have test anxiety are prone to negative self-talk. Test anxiety can be generated or heightened by repeatedly making statements to yourself that usually begin with "What if." For example, "What if I fail the test?" or "What if I fail this class again?" These "what if" statements generate more anxiety that can cause students to feel sick. These statements tell them to be anxious. Some other aspects of self-talk are:

- Self-talk can be in telegraphic form with short words or images.
- Self-talk can be illogical, but at the time, the person believes it.
- Negative self-talk can lead to avoidance such as not taking a test or skipping classes.
- Negative self-talk can cause more anxiety.
- Negative self-talk can lead to depression and a feeling of helplessness.
- Negative self-talk is a bad habit that can be changed.

There are different types of negative self-talk. If you have negative self-talk, then review the types below and see which one fits you best. You may use a combination of them.

1. *The Critic* is the person inside us who is always trying to put us down. It constantly judges our behaviors and finds fault even if there is none. It jumps on any mistake and exaggerates it to cause more anxiety. The Critic puts us down for mistakes on tests and blames us for not controlling our anxiety. The Critic reminds us of previous comments from real people who have criticized us. It compares us with other students who are doing better in the class. It loves to say, "That was a stupid mistake!" or "You are a total disappointment. You can't pass this math class like everyone else can!" The Critic's goal is to promote low self-esteem.
2. *The Worrier* is the person inside us who looks at the worst-case scenario. It wants to scare us with ideas of disaster and complete failure. When it sees the first sign of anxiety, it "blows it out of proportion" to the extent that we will not remember anything and totally fail the test. The Worrier creates more anxiety than normal. The Worrier anticipates the worst, underestimates our ability, and sees us not only failing the test but also "failing life." The Worrier loves to ask "What if?" For example, "What if I fail the math test and don't graduate?" or "What if I can't control my anxiety and throw up in math class?" The goal of the Worrier is to cause more anxiety so we will quit.
3. *The Victim* is the person inside us who wants us to feel helpless or hopeless. It wants us to believe that no matter what we do, we will not be successful in math. The Victim does not blame other events (poor schooling) or people (bad teachers) for our math failures. It blames us. It dooms us and puts us into a learned helpless mode, meaning that if we try to learn math, we will fail, or if we don't try to learn math, we will fail. So why try? The Victim likes to say, "I can't

Copyright © Houghton Mifflin Company. All rights reserved.

learn math." The goal of the Victim is to cause depression and make us stop trying.

4. *The Perfectionist* is similar to the Critic, but is the opposite of the Victim. It wants us to do the best we can and will guide us into doing better. It tells us that we are not studying enough for math tests and that a B is not good enough and that we must make an A. In fact, sometimes an A is not good enough unless it is a score of 100 percent. So, if we make a B on a test, the Perfectionist says, "An A or a B is just like making an F." The Perfectionist is the hard-driving part of us that wants the best but cannot stand mistakes or poor grades. It can drive us to mental and physical exhaustion to make that perfect grade. It is not interested in self-worth, just perfect grades. Students driven by the Perfectionist often drop a math course because they only have a B average. The Perfectionist loves to repeat, "I should have ..." or "I must ..." The goal of the Perfectionist is to cause chronic anxiety that leads to burnout.

Review these types of personalities to see which one may fit you best. We may have a little of each one in us, but what is the dominant one for you in math? Now we can look at how to stop these negative thoughts.

Managing Negative Self-Talk

Students need to change their negative self-talk to positive self-talk without making unrealistic statements.

Positive self-statements can improve your studying and test preparation. During tests, positive self-talk can build confidence and decrease your test anxiety. These positive statements (see examples) can help reduce your test anxiety and improve your grades. Some more examples of positive self-statements are on the CD *How to Reduce Test Anxiety*. Before each test, make up some positive statements to tell yourself.

There are several ways to counter and control negative self-talk. Students can replace negative self-talk with positive statements and questions that make them think in a realistic way about the situation. Another way is to develop thought-stopping techniques to reduce or eliminate the negative thoughts. Try each way or a combination to see what works best for you.

Countering self-talk involves writing down and practicing positive statements that can replace negative statements. Students can develop their own positive statements. Some rules for writing positive statements are:

1. Use the first person present tense. For example, "I can control my anxiety and relax myself."
2. Don't use negatives in the statement. For example, don't say, "I am not going to have anxiety." Instead, say, "I will be calm during the test."
3. Have a positive and realistic belief in the statement. For example, say, "I am going to pass this test," instead of saying, "I am going to make an A on this test" when you have not made an A on any of the tests.

The statements used to counter negative thoughts can be based on the type of negative self-talk we tend to engage in. The Critic who puts us down by saying, "Your test anxiety is going to cause you to fail the test" can be countered with, "I have test anxiety, but I am learning to control it." The Worrier who asks, "What if I fail the test?" can be countered with "So what? I will do better on the next test." The Victim who thinks things are hopeless and says, "I will never be able to pass math" can be countered with, "I have studied differently for this test, and I can pass the math course." The Perfectionist who says, "I need to make an A on the test or I will drop out of school" can be countered with, " I don't need to make an A to please anyone. All I need is to pass the math course to get the career I want." These are some of the examples of positive statements that can control anxiety.

Examples of Positive Self-Talk

"I might have failed the course last semester, but things are going to be different this time now that I have learned how to study math."

Copyright © Houghton Mifflin Company. All rights reserved.

"Now that I know how to fight off test anxiety, there is no way I will panic during an exam like I did before."

"Just because I haven't had perfect results in the past doesn't mean that I am bad at math. This time, I know how to study math, so this course should not be a problem."

"If I put in the work, then I will pass with flying colors."

"I have done everything I needed to do to prepare for this test. If I can keep my composure during the test, and not get frustrated if I don't understand one or two problems, I should do all right."

"I will not let this one problem bother me. I have answered all the other problems correctly, so I cannot let this one make me miss the rest of the questions on the test."

"I will not hurry in order to be the first person to finish this test. I can go ahead and take my time to make sure I don't make any careless mistakes."

Thought-Stopping Technique

Some students have difficulty stopping their negative self-talk. These students cannot just tell themselves to eliminate those thoughts. These students need to use a thought-stopping technique to overcome their worry and become relaxed.

Thought stopping involves focusing on the unwanted thoughts and, after a few seconds, suddenly stopping those thoughts by emptying your mind. Using the command "Stop!" or a loud noise like clapping your hands can effectively interrupt the negative self-talk. In a homework situation, you may be able to use a loud noise to stop your thoughts, but don't use it during a test.

To stop your thoughts in the classroom or during a test, silently shout to yourself "Stop!" or "Stop thinking about that!" After your silent shout, either relax yourself or repeat one of your positive self-talk statements. You may have to shout to yourself several times during a test or while doing homework to control negative self-talk. After every shout, use a different relaxation technique/scene or positive self-talk statement.

Thought stopping works because it interrupts the worry response before it can cause high negative emotions. During that interruption, you can replace the negative self-talk with positive statements or relaxation. However, students with high worry anxiety should practice this technique for three days to one week before taking a test. Contact your counselor if you have additional questions about the thought-stopping technique.

Writing Your Math Autobiography

An autobiography relates how you remember and feel about your past experiences. In addition, many autobiographies explore how these past feelings and experiences shape current life. While some people write autobiographies so that others can learn about their lives, many people write private autobiographies in order to understand what is going on in their lives.

Use the Appendix as a guide to writing your math autobiography. Your final product will be a typed (or handwritten if your instructor approves) paper that summarizes your experiences learning math, how you feel about these experiences, and how they shape your current perspective on learning math.

Section Review

1. Describe your best short-term relaxation technique.

____

Copyright © Houghton Mifflin Company. All rights reserved.

2. You can use the palming method by closing your eyes and visualizing a scene without putting your hands to your face. Describe a very relaxing scene that you could visualize. Make sure to include some sounds and visual images in your scene.

____

____

____

____

3. Practice your relaxation scene for three to five minutes for the next five days. List the times and dates you practiced your scene.

Date: ____________________ Time: ____________________

Date: ____________________ Time: ____________________

Date: ____________________ Time: ____________________

Date: ____________________ Time: ____________________

Date: ____________________ Time: ____________________

4. How does negative self-talk cause you to have text anxiety?

____

____

____

____

5. Make up three positive self-talk statements that are not listed in this text.

Statement 1: ____________________________________

Statement 2: ____________________________________

Statement 3: ____________________________________

6. Describe the thought-stopping technique in your own words.

____

7. What word or words will you use as your silent shout?

____

8. What will you do after your silent shout?

____

9. How does the thought-stopping technique work?

____

Copyright © Houghton Mifflin Company. All rights reserved.

Dan's Take

In 10th grade, I achieved the lowest test score of my life. The class: trigonometry. The grade: you could count my score on one hand.

But before you judge me, let's follow my thought process before the exam:

1. I am bad at math. I do not get it.
2. This test is the third in the semester and I have already failed the previous two.
3. If I failed the other tests, what are the chances that I'll pass the third?
4. Conclusion: there is absolutely no point in studying. I can't possibly do any worse, right?

I was wrong. Horribly wrong. I *could* do worse ... and I did.

At the time, I was looking for an excuse to cover up the real issue behind my poor math grades: math anxiety. I convinced myself that I was just bad at math. This fear made me "draw blanks" during my exams and I would wind up failing. By thinking these thoughts, I set myself up to fail from the very beginning.

It was not until I went to a tutor that I realized that I could get over these fears. I had to stop using the excuse "I am just bad at math." With a little help, I pulled my grade up to a C. It turned out I was not bad at math at all—I was merely afraid of it!

Copyright © Houghton Mifflin Company. All rights reserved.

Name: ______________________________ Date: ______________

Chapter 3 Review

1. Reducing math test anxiety ________ ________ guarantee good math grades.
2. Test anxiety is a ________________ response; a person is not ________________ with it.
3. Math test anxiety involves ________________, ________________, and ________________ of math tests.
4. One cause of test anxiety is that a student goes to the board to work a problem but is called ________________ when he or she cannot work the problem.
5. The two basic types of test anxiety are ________________ and ________________.
6. The effects of test anxiety range from a "____________ ______________" on a test to ________________ homework.
7. The ________________ and ________________ ________________ method helps you relax by tensing and relaxing your muscles all at once.
8. The palming method is a ________________ procedure used to reduce text anxiety.
9. Negative self-talk is a form of ________________ anxiety.
10. Thought stopping works because it interrupts the ________________ response before it can cause ________________ emotions.

What is the most important information you learned from this chapter?

____

____

____

How can you immediately use it?

____

____

____

Copyright © Houghton Mifflin Company. All rights reserved.

Lecture Notes

Copyright © Houghton Mifflin Company. All rights reserved.

4

How to Improve Your Listening and Note-Taking Skills

WHAT YOU WILL LEARN IN CHAPTER 4

- ❏ How to Become an Effective Listener
- ❏ How to Become a Good Note Taker
- ❏ The Seven Steps to Math Note Taking
- ❏ How to Rework Your Notes

Listening and note-taking skills in a math class are very important, since most students either do not read the math text or have difficulty understanding it. In most of your other classes, if you do not understand the lecture, you can read the text and get almost all the information. In math class, however, the instructor can usually explain the textbook better than the students can read and understand it.

Students who do not have good listening skills or note-taking skills will be at a disadvantage in learning math. Most math understanding takes place in the classroom. Students must learn how to take advantage of learning math in the classroom by becoming effective listeners, calculator users, and note takers.

How to Become an Effective Listener

Becoming an effective listener is the foundation for good note taking. You can become an effective listener using a set of skills that you can learn and practice. To become an effective listener, you must prepare yourself both physically and mentally.

Sitting in the Golden Triangle

The physical preparation for becoming an effective listener involves *where you sit* in the classroom. Sit in the best area to obtain high grades, that is, in "the golden triangle of success." The golden triangle of success begins with seats in the front row facing the instructor's desk (see Figure 5).

Figure 5 The Golden Triangle of Success

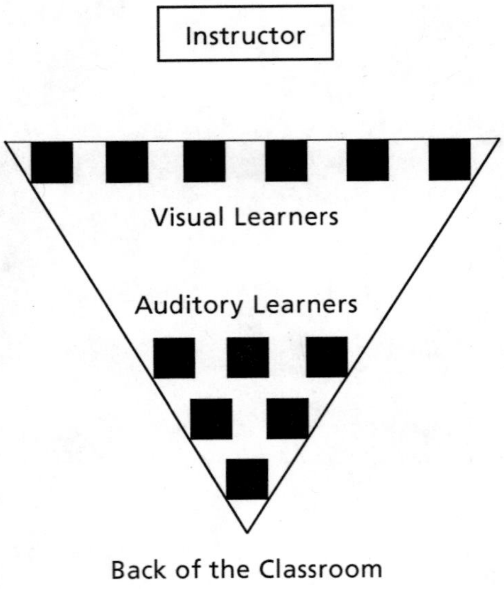

Students seated in this area (especially in the front row) directly face the teacher and are most likely to pay attention to the lecture. This is a great seating location for visual learners. There is also less tendency for them to be distracted by activities outside the classroom or by students making noise within the classroom.

The middle seat in the back row is another point in the golden triangle for students to sit, especially those who are auditory (hearing) learners. You can hear the instructor better because the instructor's voice is projected to that point. This means that there is less chance of misunderstanding the instructor, and you can hear well enough to ask appropriate questions.

By sitting in the golden triangle of success, you can force yourself to pay more attention during class and be less distracted by other students. This is very important for math students, because math instructors usually go over a point once and continue on to the next point. If you miss that point in the lesson, then you could be lost for the remainder of the class.

This may seem obvious, but I know too many students who do the following if they have early morning classes. They roll out of bed, put on the closest clothes to them, brush their hair, maybe their teeth, and race to class. Don't do this. You won't wake up until the end of your class! Train yourself to be somewhere on campus to review your notes at least 15 minutes before class starts and follow some of the other strategies suggested in the next section. So, another physical way to be ready is to be awake and nourished!

Warming Up for Math Class

The mental preparation for note-taking involves "warming up" before class begins and becoming an active listener. Just as an athlete must warm up before a game begins, you must warm up before taking notes. Warm up by:

- reviewing the previous day's notes,
- reviewing the reading material,
- reviewing the homework,
- preparing questions,
- working one or two unassigned homework problems.

This mental warm-up before the lecture allows you to refresh your memory and prepare pertinent questions, making it easier to learn the new lecture material.

Copyright © Houghton Mifflin Company. All rights reserved.

How to Become an Active Listener

Becoming an active listener is the second part of the mental preparation for note taking.

Do not anticipate what the instructor is going to say or immediately judge the instructor's information before the point is made. This will distract you from learning the information.

> **Examples:** Watch the speaker, listen for main ideas, and nod your head or say to yourself, "I understand" when agreeing with the instructor.

Expend energy looking for interesting topics in the lecture. When the instructor discusses information that you need to know, immediately repeat it to yourself to begin the learning process.

You can practice this exercise by viewing math videotapes and repeating important information. This is an especially good learning technique for auditory learners.

Ask appropriate questions when you have them. Sometimes if you are so confused you do not know what question to ask, still let the instructor know you are confused. Also, mark your notes where you got lost so that if the instructor doesn't have time to answer your question, you can visit during office hours to get an answer.

Remember

Class time is an intense study period that should not be wasted.

Listening and Learning

Some students think that listening to the instructor and taking notes are a waste of valuable time. Students too often sit in class and use only a fraction of their learning ability. Class time should be considered a valuable study period where you can listen, take notes, and learn at the same time. One way to do this is by memorizing important facts when the instructor is talking about material you already know. Another technique is to repeat to yourself the important concepts right after the instructor discusses them in class. Using class time to learn math is an efficient learning system.

Section Review

1. Explain how sitting in the golden triangle of success makes you a better listener.

 ____

 ____

 ____

2. List five ways you can warm up before math class begins.

 First Way: ______________________________

 Second Way: ______________________________

 Third Way: ______________________________

 Fourth Way: ______________________________

 Fifth Way: ______________________________

Copyright © Houghton Mifflin Company. All rights reserved.

3. Select your best warm-up process and try it before your next math class. What was your warm-up process, and how did it help you?

____

____

____

____

4. How can you listen and learn at the same time?

____

____

____

____

How to Become a Good Notetaker

Becoming a good note taker requires two basic strategies. One strategy is to be specific in detail. In other words, *copy* the problems down, step by step. The second strategy is to *understand* the general principles, general concepts, and general ideas.

Copying from the Board

While taking math notes, you need to copy each and every step of each problem even though you may already know every step. While in the classroom, you might understand each step, but a week later you might not remember how to do the problem unless you have written down all the steps. In addition, as you write down each step, you are memorizing it. Make sure to copy every step of each problem written on the board.

There will be times when you will get lost while listening to a lecture. Nevertheless, you should keep taking notes, even though you do not understand the problem. This will provide you with a reference point for further study. Put a question mark by each step that you do not understand; then, after class, review the steps you did not understand with the instructor, your tutor, or another student.

If you seem to think that many other students are lost, too, ask questions or let the instructor know.

Taking Notes

The goal of note taking is to take the least amount of notes and get the greatest amount of information on your paper. This could be the opposite of what most instructors have told you. Some instructors tell you to take down everything. This is not necessarily a good note-taking system, since it is very difficult to take precise, specific notes while trying to understand the instructor.

What you need to develop is a note-taking system in which you write the least amount possible and get the most information down while still understanding what the instructor is saying.

Developing an Abbreviation List

To reduce the amount of written notes, an abbreviation system is needed. An abbreviation system is your own system of reducing long words to shorter versions that you still can understand. By writing less, you can listen more and gain a better understanding of the material.

Copyright © Houghton Mifflin Company. All rights reserved.

> **Example:** When the instructor starts explaining the Commutative Property, you need to write "Commutative Property" out the first time. After that, use "Com." You should develop abbreviations for all the most commonly used words in math.

Figure 6 provides a list of abbreviations. Add your own abbreviations to this list. By using abbreviations as much as possible, you can obtain the same meaning from your notes and have more time to listen to the instructor.

When to Take Notes

To become a better note taker, you must know when to take notes and when not to take notes. The instructor will give cues that indicate which material is important. These cues include:

- Presenting facts or ideas
- Writing on the board
- Summarizing
- Pausing
- Repeating statements
- Enumerating, such as "1, 2, 3" or "A, B, C"
- Working several examples of the same type of problem on the chalkboard
- Saying "This is a tricky problem"
- Saying "This is the most difficult step in the problem"
- Indicating that certain types of problems will be on the test, such as coin or age problems
- Explaining boldface words.

You must learn the cues your instructor gives to indicate important material. If you are in doubt about the importance of the class material, do not hesitate to ask the instructor about its importance.

While taking notes, you may become confused about math material. At that point, take as many notes as possible, and do not give up on note taking. One thing you shouldn't do—bother the student next to you for an explanation. This can be annoying, and both of you will miss important information while you are talking.

Figure 6 Abbreviations

E.G.	(for example)
CF.	(compare, remember in context)
N.B.	(note well, this is important)
\	(therefore)
∴	(because)
É	(implies, it follows from this)
>	(greater than)
<	(less than)
=	(equals, is the same)
≠	(does not equal, is not the same)
()	(parentheses in the margin, around a sentence or group of sentences, indicates an important idea)
?	(used to indicate that you do not understand the material)
O	(a circle around a word may indicate that you are not familiar with it; look it up)
E	(marks important materials likely to be used in an exam)
1, 2, 3	(to indicate a series of facts)
D	(shows disagreement with a statement or passage)
REF	(reference)
et al.	(and others)
bk	(book)
p	(page)
etc.	(and so forth)
V	(see)
VS	(see above)
SC	(namely)
SQ	(the following)
Com.	(Commutative)
Dis.	(Distributive)
APA	(Associative Property of Addition)
AI	(Additive Inverse)
IPM	(Identity Property of Multiplication)

Copyright © Houghton Mifflin Company. All rights reserved.

As you take notes on confusing problem steps, leave extra space; then go back and fill in information that clarifies your misunderstanding of the steps in question. Ask your tutor or instructor for help with the uncompleted problem steps, and write down the reasons for each step in the space provided.

Another procedure for saving time while taking notes is to stop writing complete sentences. Write your main thoughts in phrases. Phrases are easier to jot down and easier to memorize.

Section Review

1. Note taking requires two basic strategies: ______________________ and ______________________

2. List five abbreviations (and their meanings) that you use in your math class (one abbreviation and meaning per line).
____
____
____
____
____

3. List five cues that your instructor gives that indicate which material is important (one cue per line).
____
____
____
____
____

The Seven Steps in Math Note Taking

No matter what format you use to take notes, a good set of notes contains:

- examples of problems,
- explanations of how to complete the problems, and
- appropriate math vocabulary and rules that are used for each problem.

In addition, it is wise to make your notes as organized as possible. It may get on your nerves for a while, but when you see that organized notes save time when you are studying, you will be more willing to take the time to organize them.

Many successful math students, whether in developmental math courses or calculus, use a form of the three-column note-taking system. It organizes the information, making it easy to review. While creating the three-column system, students are also learning the math, so it is not busywork.

Copyright © Houghton Mifflin Company. All rights reserved.

It takes a few weeks to feel comfortable with this system, but it is worth sticking with it. Many students have adopted this system and improved the efficiency of their study time.

The seven steps lead you through several important stages in the learning process. Steps 1 to 3 help you *record the information* accurately, completely, and in an organized fashion. Steps 4 to 7 help you *rehearse and understand the information.* These steps also help you learn to *recall the information,* thus helping you prepare for tests.

To prepare for taking notes this way, get a good chunk of paper ready. Here are some choices:

- Use regular paper, portrait or landscape style, and draw two lines to create three columns. See Appendix 127–128 for sample pages, or Figure 7, for a completed example.
- Some students purchase graph paper because it helps them keep numbers lined up correctly.
- Other students design the page on a computer and print out copies.
- Choose two columns next to each other to be the "Examples" and the "Explanations" columns. Label them as such. These are the two columns you will use all the time during class.
- Label the other column "Key Words/Rules." You might fill this column in during class but will probably complete it outside of class.

If you do this ahead of time, you do not have to draw lines frantically while the instructor is talking. If you forget or run out of paper, it might be quicker to fold the paper into three columns.

Draw a line dividing the end of one problem from the beginning of the next. Or, do one problem per page to leave plenty of room for notes. Graph paper can help students keep numbers and words lined up. Some students like to turn the graph paper sideways and then organize their notes in three columns.

During class you will use two columns most of the time—the "Examples" and the "Explanations" columns. Sometimes, when instructors really want their students to use this method, they will organize

Figure 7 Three-Column Note Taking System

Key Words/Rules	Examples	Explanations
Solve a linear equation	$4(x + 4) + 3(x - 4) = 2(x - 1)$	Have to get x on one side of the = and numbers on the other side of the =.
Distributive Property	$4x + 16 + 3x - 12 = 2x - 2$	Multiply numbers to the left of the ( ) by each variable and number in the ( ).
Commutative Property	$4x + 3x + 16 - 12 = 2x - 2$	Regroup numbers and variables.
Combine like terms	$7x + 4 = 2x - 2$	
Additive Inverse Property	$7x - 2x + 4 = 2x - 2x - 2$ $5x + 4 = -2$	Subtract 2x from both sides in order to get variables all on the right side of the =.
Additive Inverse Property	$5x + 4 - 4 = -2 - 4$ $5x = -6$	Subtract 4 from both sides to getnumbers all on the right side of the =.
Mulitiplicative Inverse Property	$\frac{5x}{5} = \frac{-6}{5}$	Divide both sides by 5 to get x by itself on the left side of the =.
Simplify	$x = -1\frac{1}{5}$	Write as a whole number and fraction.
	Insert new problem.	

Copyright © Houghton Mifflin Company. All rights reserved.

their board work to reflect what the notes should look like. Most of the time, however, this does not happen.

The "Examples" column is where you will place the examples the instructor uses during class.

The "Explanations" column is where you will put the instructor's verbal explanations of the examples. If the instructor tends to explain by just doing the problem without talking about it, ask questions that will force the instructor to explain the problem verbally.

When the instructor simply explains a vocabulary word or rule, write the vocabulary word or a phrase naming the rule in the "Key Words/Rules" column. Write the explanation in the "Explanations" column. If the instructor provides an example, obviously it goes in the "Examples" column. If no example is provided, ask for one. Then if your wish is not granted, look one up in the textbook after class.

Here are the seven steps in math note taking. Remember that these are the basic steps. You can adapt them to work for you.

Step 1 *Record the instructor's example problems in the "Examples" column.*

Step 2 *Record the reasons for each step in the "Explanations" column.* After completing a problem, draw a horizontal line, separating it from the next problem.

If you get lost during the lecture, place a question mark in this column and move on.

Step 3 *If possible, record the key words and rules in the first column.* Here is an opportunity for you to ask what rules are being used if the instructor is assuming that the class knows them and you do not. Otherwise, you will need to refer to the textbook, work with a tutor, or use online resources after class to complete this column.

It is important to understand the vocabulary words, rules, and concepts when learning how to complete a math problem. You will be able to figure out other problems that may be slightly different.

Step 4 *In order to keep everything in your head, use the notes to review.* Cover up the "Examples" and "Explanations" columns and quiz yourself on the vocabulary and rules. Or, fold back the "Key Words/Rules" column, look at the examples and explanations, and choose the correct key words and rules used to complete the examples.

Step 5 *Place a check mark by the key words and concepts that you did not know.*

Step 6 *Review the information that you checked until you understand and remember it.*

Step 7 *Develop a glossary of the math terms and rules that are difficult for you to remember.*

For a while you might spend more time organizing this system outside of class. Some students still have to depend on their current process, concentrating on getting the information down. Then they transfer the information into the three-column method. However, it is best to learn how to do most of the process during math class.

Remember the learning modalities and learning styles? This process can use all of them!

- *Kinesthetic:* Writing out the notes
- *Auditory:* Saying information out loud
- *Visual:* Looking at the notes and thinking; color-code each column with highlighters, making sure you do not smear the pencil writing
- *Group:* Working on the notes with one or two other people to make sure they are complete and accurate
- *Individual:* Reading the notes to yourself while waiting to meet someone.

Current research is discovering that using language (vocabulary, discussion) to learn math helps students understand the concepts more deeply.

Copyright © Houghton Mifflin Company. All rights reserved.

Then completing many problems helps them master the skills and increase the speed that are important in preparing for tests. These notes will help you understand the math so that it will stick with you. You will remember more information. Homework will help you master the skills and increase the speed at which you can complete problems.

A Math Glossary

A math glossary is created to define math vocabulary in your own words. Since math is considered a foreign language, understanding the math vocabulary becomes the key to comprehending math. Creating a glossary for each chapter of your textbook will help you understand math.

Your glossary should include all words printed in boldface in the text and any words you do not understand. If you cannot explain the math vocabulary in your own words, ask your instructor or tutor for help. You may want to use the last pages in your notebook to develop a math glossary for each chapter in your textbook. Some students use note cards. Review your math glossary before each test.

Section Review

1. List and describe the seven steps in math note taking.

   First Step: ____________________

   Second Step: ____________________

   Third Step: ____________________

   Fourth Step: ____________________

   Fifth Step: ____________________

   Sixth Step: ____________________

   Seventh Step: ____________________

2. Make several copies of the modified three-column note-taking system, and take notes using this system in your next math class. Or develop the modified three-column note-taking system in your own notebook.

3. List two benefits of creating a math glossary.

   Benefit 1: ____________________

   Benefit 2: ____________________

4. From your current math chapter, list and define five words that you can put in your math glossary.

   Word 1: ____________________

   Word 2: ____________________

Copyright © Houghton Mifflin Company. All rights reserved.

Word 3: ____

Word 4: ____

Word 5: ____

How to Rework Your Notes

The note-taking system does not stop when you leave the classroom. As soon as possible after class, rework your notes. You can rework the notes between classes or as soon as you get home. By reworking your notes as soon as possible, you can decrease the amount of information you forget. This is an excellent procedure for transferring math information from short-term memory to long-term memory.

Remember

Most forgetting occurs right after the material is learned. You need to rework your notes as soon as possible. Waiting means that you probably will not understand what was written.

Here are six important steps in reworking your notes:

Step 1 *Rewrite the material you cannot read or will not be able to understand a few weeks later.* If you do not rework your notes, you will be frustrated when studying for a test if you come across notes you cannot read. Another benefit of rewriting the notes is that you immediately learn the new material. Waiting means it will take more time to learn the material.

Step 2 *Fill in the gaps.* Most of the time, when you are listening to a lecture, you cannot write down everything. It is almost impossible to write down everything, even if you know shorthand. Locate the portions of your notes that are incomplete. Fill in the concepts that were left out. In the future, skip two or three lines in your notebook page for anticipated lecture gaps.

Step 3 *Add additional key words and rules in the "Key Words/Rules" column.* These key words and rules are the ones that were not recorded during the lecture.

Example: You did not know that you should add the *opposite* of 18 to solve a particular problem, and you incorrectly added 18. Put additional important key words and ideas (such as "opposite" and "negative of") in the notes; these are the words that will improve your understanding of math.

Step 4 *Make a problem log of those problems that the teacher worked in class.* The problem log is a separate section of your notebook that contains a listing of the problems (without explanations—just the problems) that your teacher worked in class. If your teacher chose those problems to work in class, you can bet that they are considered important. The problems in this log can be used as a practice test for the next exam. Your regular class notes will contain not only the solutions but also all the steps involved in arriving at those solutions and can be used as a reference when you take your practice test.

Write the problem on the left half of the page. Then save some room

Copyright © Houghton Mifflin Company. All rights reserved.

on the right side for writing out what the test instructions might be for the problem. Sometimes we forget what the test instructions are, and we miss points on the test by following the directions incorrectly. Skip several lines to complete the problem when you use the problem log as a practice test.

Step 5 *Make a calculator handbook and put in it your keystroke sequences.* The calculator handbook can be a spiral-bound set of note cards or a separate section of your notebook that holds only calculator-related information. Your handbook should also include an explanation of when that particular set of keystrokes is to be used.

Step 6 *Reflection and synthesis.* Once you have finished going over your notes, review the major points in your mind. Combine your new notes with your previous knowledge to gain a better understanding of what you have learned today.

If you are a group learner and even if you are not, it helps to review and reflect with other students.

Use a Tape Recorder

If you have a math class during which you cannot get all the information down while listening to the lecture, ask your instructor about using a tape recorder. To ensure success, the tape recorder must have a tape counter and must be voice-activated.

The tape counter displays a number indicating the amount of tape to which you have listened. When you find you are in an area of confusing information, write the beginning and ending tape counter numbers in the left margin of your notes. When reviewing your notes, the tape count number will be a reference point for obtaining information to work the problem. You can also reduce the time it takes to listen to the tape by using the pause button to stop the recording of unnecessary material.

Ask Questions

To obtain the most from a lecture, you must ask questions in class. By asking questions, you improve your understanding of the material and decrease your homework time. By not asking questions, you create for yourself unnecessary confusion during the remainder of the class period. Also, it is much easier to ask questions in class about potential homework problems than it is to spend hours trying to figure out the problems on your own at a later time.

If you are shy about asking questions in class, write down the questions and read them to your instructor. If the instructor seems confused about the questions, tell him or her that you will discuss the problem after class. To encourage yourself to ask questions, remember the following:

- You have paid for the instructor's help.
- Five other students probably have the same question.
- The instructor needs feedback on his or her teaching to help the class learn the material.
- There is no such thing as a "stupid" question.

Record Each Problem Step

The final suggestion on note taking is to record each step of every problem written or verbally explained. By recording each problem step, you begin over-learning how to work the problems. This will increase your problem-solving speed during future tests. If you get stuck on the homework, you will also have complete examples to review.

The major reason for recording every step of a problem is to understand how to do the problem while the instructor is explaining it instead of trying to remember unwritten steps later. Although it may seem time consuming, it pays off during homework and test time.

Copyright © Houghton Mifflin Company. All rights reserved.

Section Review

1. List and describe the six steps in reworking your notes.

   First Step: ____________________

   Second Step: ____________________

   Third Step: ____________________

   Fourth Step: ____________________

   Fifth Step: ____________________

   Sixth Step: ____________________

2. How can using a tape recorder in class improve your learning?

   ____

3. List three reasons for asking questions in class.

   First Reason: ____________________

   Second Reason: ____________________

   Third Reason: ____________________

4. What is the major reason for recording each problem step?

   ____

Dan's Take

My university became an "e-campus" my freshman year. Gone were the days of pencil and paper. Now they gave us laptops. The tapping of computer keys became a common soundtrack during class, as students tried to type the last words of a PowerPoint slide into their notes before the professor hit the "next slide" button—or as they instant messaged their friends across campus.

Students today have more distractions in the classroom than ever before. More campuses are using computers in the classroom, making paying attention nearly impossible.

But math teachers can rejoice. It is very difficult to write math problems using a computer. Even when using online math courses, all of the work has to be done on paper. This means there is no time for distraction.

The note-taking methods described in this chapter are invaluable. They really help you keep an organized notebook. It is important to be able to reference your notes easily during homework and remember which information is needed to answer each type of problem.

Copyright © Houghton Mifflin Company. All rights reserved.

Name: ______________________________ Date: ______________

Chapter 4 Review

1. Sitting in the golden triangle of success can help you pay more __________ during class.
2. Class time is an intense ____________________ that should not be wasted.
3. Auditory learners should review the math videotape and __________ back the important information.
4. The goal of note taking is to take the __________ amount of notes and get the __________ amount of information.
5. Using abbreviations can help you write __________ and listen __________.
6. Your __________ should include any words you don't know and their explanations.
7. Rework your notes to transfer information from __________-__________ memory to __________-__________ memory.
8. A __________ __________ is a separate section in your notebook that contains problems that your teacher worked in class.
9. Asking __________ in class will improve your understanding and decrease your homework time.
10. __________ each step of the problem will increase your problem-solving speed and memory.

What is the most important information you learned from this chapter?

____

____

____

____

How can you immediately use it?

____

____

____

____

Copyright © Houghton Mifflin Company. All rights reserved.

Lecture Notes

Copyright © Houghton Mifflin Company. All rights reserved.

5

How to Improve Your Reading, Homework, and Study Techniques

What You Will Learn in Chapter 5

- ❏ How to Read a Math Textbook
- ❏ How to Do Your Homework
- ❏ How to Solve Word Problems
- ❏ How to Work with a Study Buddy
- ❏ Using Online/Computer Resources to Support Learning

Reading a math textbook is more difficult than reading other textbooks. Math textbooks are written differently than your English and social science textbooks. Math textbooks contain condensed material and therefore take longer to read.

Mathematicians can reduce a page of writing to one paragraph using math formulas and symbols. To make sure you understood that same information, an English instructor would take that original page of writing and expand it into two pages. Mathematicians pride themselves on how little they can write and still cover the concept. This is one reason it may take you two to three times as long to read your math text as it would any other text.

Remember

Reading your math text will take longer than reading your other texts.

Math students are expected to know how to do their homework; however, most math students do not have a homework system. Most students begin their homework by going directly to the problems and trying to work them. When they get stuck, they usually quit. This is not a good homework system.

A good homework system will improve your homework success and math learning at the same time.

How to Read a Math Textbook

The way you read a math textbook is different from the traditional way students are taught to read textbooks in high school and college. Students are taught to read quickly or skim the material. If you do not understand a word, you are supposed to keep on reading. Instructors of other courses want students to continue to read so they can pick up the unknown words and their meanings from context.

This reading technique may work with your other classes, but using it in your math course will be totally confusing. If you skip some major concept words or boldface words, you will not understand the math textbook or be able to do the homework. Reading a math textbook takes more time and concentration than reading your other textbooks.

If you have a reading problem, it would be wise to take a developmental reading course before taking math. This is especially true with reform math courses, where reading and writing are emphasized.

Reform math classes deal more with word problems than traditional math courses do. If you cannot take the developmental reading course before taking math, then take it during the same semester as the math course.

Ten Steps in Understanding Reading Materials

There are several appropriate steps in reading a math textbook:

Step 1 *Skim the assigned reading material.* Skim the material to get a general idea about the major topics. Read the chapter introduction and each section summary. You do not want to learn the material at this time; you simply want to get an overview of the assignment. Then think about similar math topics that you already know.

Example: Skimming will allow you to see if problems presented in one chapter section are further explained in later chapter sections.

Step 2 *As you skim the chapter, circle (using a pencil) the new words that you do not understand.* If you do not understand these new words after reading the assignment, ask the instructor for help. Skimming the reading assignments should take only five to ten minutes.

Step 3 *Put all your concentration into reading.* While reading the textbook, highlight the material that is important to you. However, do not highlight more than 50 percent of any page, because doing so will not sufficiently narrow the material for future study. Especially highlight the material that is also discussed in the lecture. Material discussed in both the textbook and the lecture will usually appear on the test. The purpose of highlighting is to emphasize the important material for future study. Do not skip reading assignments.

Remember

Reading a math textbook is very difficult. It might take you half an hour to read and understand just one page.

Step 4 *When you get to the examples, go through each step.* If the example skips any steps, make sure you write down each one of those skipped steps in the textbook for better understanding. Later on, when you go back and review, the steps will already be filled in. You will understand how each step was completed. Also, by filling in the extra steps, you will start to overlearn the material for better recall on future tests.

Step 5 *Mark the concepts and words that you do not know.* Maybe you marked

Copyright © Houghton Mifflin Company. All rights reserved.

them the first time while skimming. If you understand them now, erase the marks. If you do not understand the words or concepts, then reread the page or look them up in the glossary. Try not to read any further until you understand all the words and concepts.

Step 6 *If you do not clearly understand some words or concepts, add these words to the note-taking glossary in the back of your notebook.* Your glossary will contain the boldface words that you do not understand. If you have difficulty understanding the boldface words, ask the instructor for a better explanation. You should know all the words and concepts in your notebook's glossary before taking the test.

Step 7 *If you do not understand the material, follow these eight points, one after the other, until you do understand the material:*

Point 1—Go back to the previous page and reread the information to maintain a train of thought.

Point 2—Read ahead to the next page to discover if any additional information better explains the misunderstood material.

Point 3—Locate and review any diagrams, examples, or rules that explain the misunderstood material.

Point 4—Read the misunderstood paragraph(s) several times aloud to better understand their meaning.

Point 5—Refer to your math notes for a better explanation of the misunderstood material.

Point 6—Refer to another math textbook, computer software program, or videotape that expands the explanation of the misunderstood material.

Point 7—Define exactly what you do not understand and call your study buddy for help.

Point 8—Contact your math tutor or math instructor for help in understanding the material.

Step 8 *Recall important material.* Try to recall some of the important concepts and rules. If you have difficulty recalling this information, look at the highlighted areas of the text, boldface words, or formulas. If you are a visual learner, write down these words several times on a separate sheet of paper. If you are an auditory learner, repeat these words several times out loud.

If you are a kinesthetic (hands on) learner, write out the formulas twice on two separate cards. Cut one of them up into puzzle pieces. Mix up the parts of the puzzle. Turn over the other formula card so you cannot see it. Put the puzzle back together. Do this several times.

For boldface words, write the word on one card and its explanation twice on two other separate cards. Make another puzzle. Mix up the pieces of the explanation and put them back together.

Then add these words and formulas to your note-taking glossary. Recalling important material right after you read it improves you ability to remember that information.

Step 9 *Reflect on what you have read.* Combine what you already know with the new information that you just read. Think about how this new information enhances your math knowledge. Prepare questions for your instructor on the confusing information. Ask those questions at the next class meeting.

Copyright © Houghton Mifflin Company. All rights reserved.

Step 10 *Write anticipated test questions.* Research has noted that students have about 80 percent accuracy in predicting test questions. Think about what is the most important concept you just read and what problems the instructor could give you that would test the knowledge of that concept. Make up three to five problems and add them to your problem log (this was part of your note-taking system). Indicate in the log that these are your questions, not the instructor's.

By using this reading technique, you narrow down the important material to be learned. You skim the textbook to get an overview of the assignment. You carefully read the material and highlight the important parts. You then add unfamiliar words or concepts to your note-taking glossary.

Remember
You should review the highlighted material before doing the homework problems, and you should learn 100 percent of the glossary before taking the test.

How Reading Ahead Can Help

Reading ahead is another way to improve learning. If you read ahead, do not expect to understand everything. Read ahead two or three sections and put question marks (in pencil) by the material you do not understand.

When the instructor starts discussing that material, have your questions prepared and take good notes. Also, if the lecture is about to end, ask the instructor to explain the confusing material in the textbook. Reading ahead will take more time and effort, but it will better prepare you for the lectures.

How to Establish Study Period Goals

Before beginning your homework, establish goals for the study period. Do not just do the homework problems.

Ask yourself this question: "What am I going to do tonight to become more successful in math?"

By setting up short-term homework goals and reaching them, you will feel more confident about math. This also improves your self-esteem and helps you become a more internally motivated student. Set up homework tasks that you can complete. Be realistic.

Study period goals are set up either on a time-line basis or an item-line basis. Studying on a time-line basis is studying math for a certain amount of time.

> **Example:** You may want to study math for an hour, then switch to another subject. You, will be studying on a time-line basis.

Studying on an item-line basis means you will study your math until you have completed a certain number of homework problems.

> **Example:** You might set a goal to study math until you have completed all the odd-numbered problems in the chapter review. The odd-numbered problems are the most important problems to work, because, in most texts, they are answered in the answer section in the back of the book. Such problems provide the opportunity to recheck your work if you do not get the answer correct. Once you have completed these problems, do the even-numbered problems.

No matter what homework system you use, remember this important rule: Always finish a homework session by understanding a concept or doing a homework problem correctly.

Do not end a homework session with a problem you cannot complete. You will lose confidence, since all you will think about is the last problem you could not solve instead of the 50 problems you solved correctly. If you do quit on a problem you cannot solve, rework some of the problems you have done correctly.

Remember
Do not end your study period with a problem you cannot complete.

Copyright © Houghton Mifflin Company. All rights reserved.

Section Review

1. List and describe the ten steps in reading a math textbook.

   First Step: ____________________

   Second Step: ____________________

   Third Step: ____________________

   Fourth Step: ____________________

   Fifth Step: ____________________

   Sixth Step: ____________________

   Seventh Step: ____________________

   Eighth Step: ____________________

   Ninth Step: ____________________

   Tenth Step: ____________________

2. After trying each of the ten steps, make up, your own condensed version of these steps.

   First Step: ____________________

   Second Step: ____________________

   Third Step: ____________________

   Fourth Step: ____________________

   Fifth Step: ____________________

   Sixth Step: ____________________

   Seventh Step: ____________________

   Eighth Step: ____________________

   Ninth Step: ____________________

   Tenth Step: ____________________

3. List two reasons why reading ahead can improve your learning.

   First Reason: ____________________

   Second Reason: ____________________

Copyright © Houghton Mifflin Company. All rights reserved.

4. Describe the two types of study period goals. Which one do you use?

   First Type: ____

   ____

   Second Type: ____

   ____

How to Do Your Homework

Doing your homework can be frustrating or rewarding. Most students jump right into their homework, become frustrated, and stop studying. These students usually go directly to the math problems and start working them without any preparation. When they get stuck on one problem, they flip to the back of the text for the answer. Then they either try to work the problem backward to understand the problem steps or they just copy down the answer.

Other students go to the solution guide and just copy the steps. After getting stuck several times, these students will inevitably quit doing their homework. Their homework becomes a frustrating experience, and they may even quit doing their math homework altogether.

Ten Steps in Doing Your Homework

To improve your homework success and learning, refer to these ten steps:

Step 1 *Review the textbook material that relates to the homework.* A proper review will increase your chances of successfully completing your homework. If you get stuck on a problem, you will have a better chance of finding similar problems. If you do not review prior to doing your homework, you could get stuck and not know where to find help in the textbook.

Remember

To be successful in learning the material and in completing homework assignments, you must first review your textbook.

Step 2 *Review your lecture notes that relate to the homework.* If you cannot understand the explanation in the textbook on how to complete the homework assignment, then review your notes.

Remember

Reviewing your notes will give you a better idea about how to complete your homework assignment.

Step 3 *Do your homework as neatly as possible.* Doing your homework neatly has several benefits. When approaching your instructor about problems with your homework, he or she will be able to understand your previous attempts to solve the problem. The instructor will easily locate the mistakes and show you how to correct the steps without having to decipher your handwriting. Another benefit is that when you review for midterm or final exams, you can quickly relearn the homework material without having to decipher your own writing.

Copyright © Houghton Mifflin Company. All rights reserved.

Remember
Neatly prepared homework can help you now and in the future.

Step 4 *When doing your homework, write down every step of the problem.* Even if you can do the step in your head, write it down anyway. This will increase the amount of homework time, but you will be overlearning how to solve problems, which improves your memory. Writing down every step is an easy way to memorize and understand the material. Another advantage is that when you rework the problems you did wrong, it is easy to review each step and to find your mistake.

Remember
In the long run, writing down every step of your homework problems will save you time and frustration.

Step 5 *Understand the reasons for each problem step and check your answers.* Do not get into the bad habit of memorizing how to do problems without knowing the reasons for each step. Many students are smart enough to memorize the procedures required to complete a set of homework problems. However, when similar homework problems are presented on a test, some of these students cannot solve them. To avoid this dilemma, keep reminding yourself about the rules, laws, or properties used to solve problems.

Example: *Problem:* $2(a + 5) = 0$. What property allows you to change this equation to $2a + 10 = 0$? *Answer:* The Distributive Property.

Once you know the correct reason for going from one step to another in solving a math problem, you can solve any problem requiring that property. Students who simply memorize how to do problems instead of understanding the reasons for correctly working the steps are more likely to fail their math course.

Checking your homework answers should be part of your homework duties. Checking your answers can improve your learning and help you prepare for tests.

Check the answers of the problems for which solutions are not given. These may be the even-numbered or odd-numbered problems or the problems not answered in the solutions manual.

First, check each answer by estimating the correct answer.

Example: If you are multiplying 2.234 by 5.102, remember that 2 times 5 is 10. The answer should be a little over 10.

You can also check your answers by substituting the answer back into the equation or doing the opposite function required to answer the question. The more answers you check, the faster you will become. This is very important because increasing your answer-checking speed can help you catch more careless errors on future tests.

Step 6 *If you do not understand how to do a problem, refer to the following points:*

Point 1—Review the textbook material that relates to the problem.

Point 2—Review the lecture notes that relate to the problem.

Point 3—Review any similar problems, diagrams, examples, or rules that explain the misunderstood material.

Point 4—Refer to another math textbook, solutions guide, math computer program software, or videotape to obtain a better understanding of the material.

Point 5—Call your study buddy.

Point 6—Skip the problem and ask your tutor or math instructor for help as soon as possible.

Copyright © Houghton Mifflin Company. All rights reserved.

Step 7 *Always finish your homework by successfully completing problems.* Even if you get stuck, go back and successfully complete previous problems before quitting. You want to end your homework assignment with feelings of success.

Step 8 *After finishing your homework assignment, recall to yourself or write down the most important concepts you have learned.* Recalling this information will increase your ability to learn these new concepts. Additional information about Step 8 will be presented later in this chapter.

Step 9 *Make up note cards containing hard-to-remember problems or concepts.* Note cards are an excellent way to review material for a test. More information on the use of note cards as learning tools is presented later in this chapter.

Step 10 *Do not fall behind.* As mentioned in Chapter 1, learning math is a sequential process. If you get behind, it is difficult to catch up because each topic builds on the previous topic. Falling behind in math is like going to Spanish class without learning the last set of vocabulary words. The teacher will be talking to you using the new vocabulary, but you will not understand what is being said.

Do Not Fall Behind

To keep up with your homework, it is recommended that you work on it every school day and even on weekends. Working on your homework for one-half hour each day for two days in a row is better than working on it for one hour every other day.

If you have to get behind in one of your courses, *make sure it is not math.* Fall behind in a course that does not require a sequential learning process, such as psychology or history. After using the ten steps in doing your homework, you may be able to combine two steps into one. Find your best combination of homework steps and use them.

Remember

Getting behind in math homework is the fastest way to fail the course.

Section Review

1. List the ten steps you should follow in doing your math homework.

First Step: ____________________

Second Step: ____________________

Third Step: ____________________

Fourth Step: ____________________

Fifth Step: ____________________

Sixth Step: ____________________

Copyright © Houghton Mifflin Company. All rights reserved.

Seventh Step: ______________________________

Eighth Step: ______________________________

Ninth Step: ______________________________

Tenth Step: ______________________________

2. After trying each of the ten steps, make up your own condensed version of these steps.

   First Step: ______________________________

   Second Step: ______________________________

   Third Step: ______________________________

   Fourth Step: ______________________________

   Fifth Step: ______________________________

   Sixth Step: ______________________________

   Seventh Step: ______________________________

   Eighth Step: ______________________________

   Ninth Step: ______________________________

   Tenth Step: ______________________________

3. How will reviewing your notes or your math text help you complete your homework more successfully?

   ____

   ____

   ____

4. List two ways you can check your homework answers.

   First Way: ______________________________

   Second Way: ______________________________

5. What happens to students who fall behind in their math homework?

   ____

   ____

   ____

Copyright © Houghton Mifflin Company. All rights reserved.

How to Solve Word Problems

The most difficult homework assignment for most math students is working story/word problems. Solving word problems requires excellent reading comprehension and translating skills.

Students often have difficulty substituting algebraic symbols and equations for English terms. But once an equation is written, it is usually easily solved. To help you solve word problems, follow these ten steps:

Step 1 *Read the problem three times.* Read the problem quickly the first time as a scanning procedure. As you are reading the problem the second time, answer these three questions:

1. *What is this problem asking me?* (This is usually at the end of the problem.)
2. *What is this problem telling me that is useful?* (Cross out unneeded information.)
3. *What is this problem implying?* (This is usually something you have been told to remember.) Now read the problem a third time to make sure that you fully understand its meaning.

Step 2 *Draw a simple picture of the problem to make it more real to you* (e.g., a circle with an arrow can represent travel in any form—by train, by boat, by plane, by car, or by foot).

Step 3 *Make a table of information and leave a blank space for the information you are not told.*

Step 4 *Use as few unknowns in your table as possible.* If you can represent all the unknown information in terms of a single letter, do so! When using more than one unknown, use letters that remind you of each unknown. Then write down what each unknown represents. This eliminates the problem of assigning the right answer to the wrong unknown. Remember that you have to create as many separate equations as you have unknowns.

Step 5 *Translate the word problem into an algebraic equation using the lists of terms in Figures 8 and 9 on the next page.* Remember, English terms are sometimes stated in a different order than the corresponding algebraic terms.

Step 6 *Immediately retranslate the equation, as you now have it, back into words.* The translation may not sound like a normal word problem, but the meaning should be the same as the original problem. If the meaning is not the same, the equation is incorrect and needs to be rewritten. Rewrite the equation until it means the same as the word problem.

Step 7 *Review the equation to see if it is similar to equations from your homework and if it makes sense.* Some formulas dealing with specific word problems may need to be rewritten. Distance problems, for example, may need to be written solving for each of the other variables in the formula. Distance = rate x time; therefore, time = distance/rate, and rate = distance/ time. Usually, a distance problem will identify the specific variable to be solved.

Step 8 *Solve the equation using the rules of algebra.*

Remember

Whatever is done to one side of the equation must be done to the other side of the equation. The unknown must end up on one side of the equation, by itself. If you have more than one unknown, then use the substitution method or the elimination method to solve the equations.

Copyright © Houghton Mifflin Company. All rights reserved.

Figure 8 Translating English Words and Phrases into Algebraic Symbols

English Word or Phrase	Algebraic Symbol
Sum	+
Add	+
In addition	+
More than	+
Increased	+
In excess	+
Greater	+
Decreased by	−
Less than	−
Subtract	−
Difference	−
Diminished	−
Reduced	−
Remainder	−
Times as much	×
Percent of	×
Product	×
Interest on	×
Per	÷
Divide	÷
Quotient	÷
Quantity	( )
Is	=
Was	=
Equal	=
Will be	=
Results	=
Greater than	>
Greater than or equal to	≥
Less than	<
Less than or equal to	≤

Figure 9 Translating English Phrases into Algebraic Expressions

English Phrases	Algebraic Expression
Ten more than *x*	$x + 10$
A number added to 5	$5 + x$
A number increased by 13	$x + 13$
Five less than 10	$10 - 5$
A number decreased by 7	$x - 7$
Difference between *x* and 3	$x - 3$
Difference between 3 and *x*	$3 - x$
Twice a number	$2x$
Ten percent of *x*	$0.10x$
Ten times *x*	$10x$
Quotient of *x* and 3	$x/3$
Quotient of 3 and *x*	$3/x$
Five is 3 more than a number	$5 = x + 3$
The product of 2 and a number is 10	$2x = 10$
One-half of a number is 10	$x/2 = 10$
Five times the sum of *x* and 2	$5(x + 2)$
Seven is greater than *x*	$7 > x$
Five times the difference of a number and 4	$5(x - 4)$
Ten subtracted from 10 times a number is that number plus 5	$10x - 10 = x + 5$
The sum of 5*x* and 10 is equal to the product of *x* and 15	$5x + 10 = 15x$
The sum of two consecutive integers	$(x) + (x + 1)$
The sum of two consecutive even integers	$(x) + (x + 2)$
The sum of two consecutive odd integers	$(x) + (x + 2)$

Step 9 *Look at your answer to see if it makes sense.*

Example: If tax is added to an item, it should cost more; if a discount is applied to an item, it should cost less. Is there more than one answer? Does your answer match the original question? Does your answer have the correct units?

Step 10 *Substitute your answer back into the original equation to see if it is correct.* If one side of the equation equals the other side of the equation, then you have the correct answer. If you do not have the correct answer, go back to Step 5.

Copyright © Houghton Mifflin Company. All rights reserved.

The most difficult part of solving word problems is translating part of a sentence into algebraic symbols and then into algebraic expressions. Review Figure 8 (Translating English Words and Phrases into Algebraic Symbols) and Figure 9 (Translating English Phrases into Algebraic Expressions), both on the previous page.

How to Recall What You Have Learned

After completing your homework problems, a good visual learning technique is to make note cards. Note cards are 3" x 5" index cards on which you place information that is difficult to learn or material you think will be on a test.

On the front of each note card, write a math problem or information that you need to know. Color-code the important information in red or blue. On the back of the note card, write how to work the problem or explain important information.

> **Example:** If you are having difficulty remembering the rules for multiplying positive and negative numbers, write some examples on the front of a note card and write the answers on the back.

Make note cards on important information you might forget. Every time you have five spare minutes, pull out your note cards and review them. You can glance at the front of the card, repeat the answer to yourself, and check it by looking at the back of the card. If you are correct and know the information on the card, do not put it back in the deck. Mix up the cards you do not know and pick another card. Keep doing this until there are no cards left in the deck.

If you are an auditory learner, use a tape recorder instead of note cards. Record the important information as you would on the front of a note card. Then leave a blank space on the recording before recording the answer. Play the tape back. When you hear the silence, put the tape on pause. Then say the answer out loud to yourself. Take the tape player off pause and see if you were correct.

Review What You Have Learned

After finishing your homework, close the textbook and try to remember what you have learned. Ask yourself these questions: "What major concepts did I learn tonight?" and "What test questions might the instructor ask on this material?"

Recall for about three to four minutes the major points of the assignment, especially the areas you had difficulty understanding. Write down questions for the instructor or tutor. Since most forgetting occurs right after the material is learned, this short review will help you retain the new material.

Section Review

1. List the ten steps in solving word problems.

   First Step: ____________________

   Second Step: ____________________

   Third Step: ____________________

   Fourth Step: ____________________

   Fifth Step: ____________________

   Sixth Step: ____________________

   Seventh Step: ____________________

Copyright © Houghton Mifflin Company. All rights reserved.

Eighth Step: ____________________

Ninth Step: ____________________

Tenth Step: ____________________

2. What is your best way to recall what you have learned?

____

____

____

3. How does reviewing right after doing your homework help you remember?

____

____

____

How to Work with a Study Buddy

You need to have a study buddy when you miss class or when you do your homework. A study buddy is a friend or classmate who is taking the same course. You can find a study buddy by talking to your classmates or making friends in the math lab. Try to find a study buddy who knows more about math than you do. Tell the class instructor that you are trying to find a study buddy and ask which students make the best grades. Meet with your study buddy several times a week to work on problems and to discuss math. If you miss class, get the notes from your study buddy so you will not fall behind.

Call your study buddy when you get stuck on your homework. You can solve math problems over the phone. Do not sit for half an hour or an hour trying to work one problem; that will destroy your confidence, waste valuable time, and possibly alienate your study buddy. Think how much you could have learned by trying the problem for 15 minutes and then calling your study buddy for help. Spend, at the maximum, 15 minutes on one problem before going on to the next problem or calling your study buddy.

Remember

A study buddy can improve your learning while helping you complete your homework assignments. Just do not overuse your study buddy or expect your study buddy to do your homework for you.

Section Review

1. How do you select a study buddy? ____________________

2. How can a study buddy help you learn math? ____________________

3. Who is your study buddy? ____________________

Copyright © Houghton Mifflin Company. All rights reserved.

The Benefits of Study Breaks

Psychologists have discovered that learning decreases if you do not take study breaks. Therefore, take a break after studying math for 45 minutes to one hour.

If you have studied for only 15 or 20 minutes and feel you are not retaining the information or your mind is wandering, take a break. If you continue to force yourself to study, you will not learn the material. After taking a break, return to studying.

If you still cannot study after taking a break, review your purpose for studying and your educational goals. Think about what is required to graduate. It will probably come down to the fact that you will have to pass math. Think about how studying math today will help you pass the next test; this will increase your chances of passing the course and of graduating.

Write on an index card three positive statements about yourself and three positive statements about studying. Look at this index card every time you have a study problem. Use every opportunity available to reinforce your study habits.

Section Review

1. How can study breaks improve your learning?

____

____

____

____

2. What do you do when you don't want to study? How do you get started?

____

____

____

____

Using Online/Computer Resources to Support Learning

Many math textbooks include CDs and access to online websites that provide further practice and learning. There are even online homework programs that offer instant feedback and help. While these resources may seem unfamiliar or difficult to use at first, online support and CDs can improve some student learning and are worth a try.

What are Online/Computer Resources?

Computer and web resources come in a variety of formats. Some math texts have CDs that can provide additional practice exercises and suggestions to improve learning. Other books come with passwords to websites that contain online tutorials and extra practice problems. Other publishers provide live tutorial help, such as *Smarthinking*®, which is offered by Houghton Mifflin, and provides 24-hour-a-day support for students. There are even math

Copyright © Houghton Mifflin Company. All rights reserved.

tutorial sites that are not meant for use with your textbook—just Google "math" and see what comes up! Finally, your own math department, math lab, or learning resource center may have other CDs, computer programs, or websites that can help you. Find out what online/computer resources are available to supplement your math learning.

Computer Technology Requirements

It is important to find out if the computer you use on a regular basis will support the online/computer program resources for further math learning. Check the operating or installation instructions for any program or website you want to use to make sure that your computer meets the minimum hardware and Internet connection requirements.

If your own computer is inadequate, do not despair and decide not to try the online or CD resources. Most campuses provide excellent computer and online access for students, but remember that most computers in the lab may not let you save your work on their hard drives. Be sure to bring your own disk or recordable CD so you can save your work.

After finding a computer that is adequate for the program's technical requirements, do a trial run. It is helpful if you can do this in a lab or library that has technical assistants in case you run into problems during installation or setup. Once the math program or website comes up, explore the different aspects of that program. If you have difficulty running the programs or need input on which program may be best for you, don't hesitate to ask your instructor for help. If your instructor is not available, then ask the lab learning assistants or a tutor. If they are not available, then ask your fellow students for help.

During the Semester

Using online/computer resources can help in various ways. First, try each online/computer resource available to you and see which ones work best for you. Some students like the drill and practice that is provided by an online quiz, while other students want more in-depth knowledge on the reason for doing each step and prefer interactive tutorials. Second, try using the online/computer resources both before and after your class or tutoring session to see which schedule helps you most. Some students like to use these resources as a preview to a math lesson or as a review after the lesson. Sometimes it might help to use the resources before *and* after the lesson.

Overcoming Technophobia

If you are experiencing technophobia (fear of technology, including computers), this is a wonderful time to overcome it. You can start with these strategies:

- Get in touch with the benefits of technology. Being comfortable with computers can give you an edge in almost every aspect of being a student, from doing library research to planning your career. In the eyes of many employers, experience with computers is sometimes a necessity and almost always a plus.
- Sign up for a computer class for beginners.
- Ask questions. When it comes to computers, there truly aren't any "dumb" questions.
- Find a competent teacher—someone who remembers what it was like to know nothing about computers.
- Just experiment. Sit down, do something, and see what happens. Short of dropping a computer or hitting it with a hammer, you can't hurt the thing.
- Remember that computers are not always user-friendly—at least not yet. Learning how to use them takes patience and time. Knowing this up front can put you at ease and prepare you for the cyberspace adventures ahead.
- Also remind yourself of past successes in making transitions. As far as technology is concerned, this includes everything from writing with a pen to driving a car. You're already mastering a major life change—the transition to higher education. In doing so, you've shown that you have what it takes to tame any technology that enters your life.

Dave Ellis, *Becoming a Master Student,* Eleventh Edition. Copyright © 2006 by Houghton Mifflin Company. Reprinted with permission.

Copyright © Houghton Mifflin Company. All rights reserved.

Treat the time you spend using the resources as if it were class or lab time. First, set up a time and place to use the online/computer resources. Try to use the resources at the same place and same time. For example, if you have an hour between classes, go to the lab and practice, or practice right when you get home. This is a good way to develop excellent study habits. Second, keep a log for several weeks on which resources you used and how much time you spent on them. If it is obvious that certain times, places, or programs work best for you, keep the same study system. If your system is not working for you, adjust and revise it. Ask a lab assistant or instructor for advice.

Learning Styles and Online/ Computer Learning

Your learning modality style may determine how helpful online/computer learning may be for you. Visual learners who like to learn by themselves usually work well with these types of resources, while auditory learners who need to hear the information may not like the resources unless they are also auditorily enhanced. Also, hands-on learners may not benefit from these programs unless there is some type of movement with the learning. Nevertheless, these programs are worth a try no matter what the learning style. Why? We all learn visually to some extent, and auditory and hands-on learners can adjust these resources to be more auditory or hands-on. For instance, students can read the screens out loud as they are using them, or can work with partners. Learning styles are just preferred ways to learn. Productive students learn how to use all available modalities when learning math.

Evaluate the Experience

After trying these programs for several weeks, evaluate whether they are helping you improve your learning or your grades. Evaluate each program. Take into consideration how much time you spent with each program. Look through your log to remind yourself of these details. You may have to wait until the next major test to see if your grades improve. Ask yourself, "Did the resources improve my learning?" and "Did the resources improve my test scores?" If the answer to either of these questions is "Yes," then keep on using them!

Section Review

1. Look in the preface of your math textbook and list some of the online/computer resources that are included with your book. ______________________________

____

____

2. Which resource listed sounds as if it would be the most helpful to you? Why?

____

____

____

3. Remember your learning modality style from Chapter 2. How could you use one of the online/ computer resources so that it worked with your personal learning modality?

____

____

Copyright © Houghton Mifflin Company. All rights reserved.

Dan's Take

College students are busy people. With hours of work and multiple deadlines, procrastination seems very appealing. Why suffer every night when you can put things off?

This type of logic stayed with me most of the way through college, and to be honest, it worked fairly well. Then I took my first college math course.

In this class, homework was going to be collected only four times during the semester. I thought I would need to spend only four nights the entire semester doing math homework.

I went to class every day and took very good notes. Then I went home at night and let them gather dust. By the time the first test rolled around, I had not done a single math problem. The night before the exam I sat down, opened my book, and looked at the homework assignment list. There were *ten chapters* due! I worked the whole night, and got a low C on my first test.

When I actually thought about it, I got really mad at myself. The homework was the easiest way to earn points. All I had to do was complete the work and I would have been given full credit. I also didn't realize that taking good notes was not enough to succeed in a college-level math course. By putting the homework off, I forgot how to do the math and had to relearn it all in one night.

Math is totally different from other courses such as science, history, and literature. Putting off homework can cause you to fall far behind, and catching up is very difficult. It's much easier to do a little bit every day than to try to cram an entire semester's worth of material into one night!

Copyright © Houghton Mifflin Company. All rights reserved.

Name: ______________________________ Date: ______________

Chapter 5 Review

1. Reading one page of a math text might take you ______________________
______________________ ______________________.

2. After reading your textbooks, ______________________ important material can improve your ability to remember that information.

3. Write anticipated test questions in your ______________________ and indicate that they are your questions.

4. Checking your homework answers can improve your ______________________ and help you prepare for ______________________.

5. Matching:

(For students in pre-algebra class)

______ Product	A. +
______ Increased	B. –
______ Sum	C. ×
______ Per	D. ÷
______ Is	E. =
______ Reduced	
______ Remainder	

(For students taking elementary algebra or a higher-level math course)

______ Difference between x and 3	A. $10x$
______ Quotient of x and 3	B. $x/3$
______ Five times the sum of x and 2	C. $5(x - 4)$
______ A number added to 5	D. $5(x + 2)$
______ Five less than 10	E. $5 = x + 3$
______ Ten times x	F. $5 + x$
______ Five is 3 more than a number	G. $10 - 5$
______ Five times the difference of a number and 4	H. $x - 3$

Copyright © Houghton Mifflin Company. All rights reserved.

6. Make sure you finish your homework by working problems you ____________________ do.
7. Using ____________________ ____________________ is a visual way to recall what you learned in math.
8. Using a ____________________ ____________________ is an auditory way to recall what you learned in math.
9. Most ____________________ occurs right after learning; a short review will help you ____________________ the new material.
10. A ____________________ ____________________ can improve your learning while helping you complete your homework assignments.

What is the most important information you learned from this chapter?

____

____

____

____

How can you immediately use it?

____

____

____

____

Copyright © Houghton Mifflin Company. All rights reserved.

Lecture Notes

Copyright © Houghton Mifflin Company. All rights reserved.

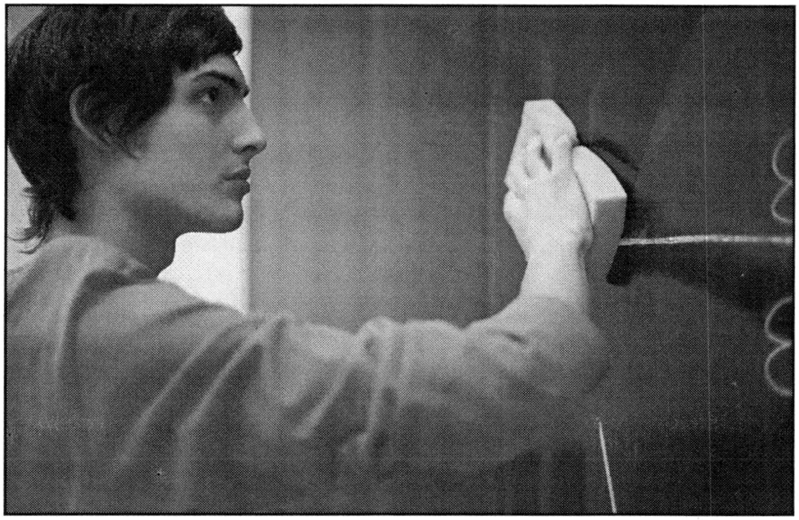

6

How to Remember What You Have Learned

WHAT YOU WILL LEARN IN CHAPTER 6

- ❑ How You Learn
- ❑ How to Use Learning Styles to Improve Memory
- ❑ How to Use Memory Techniques
- ❑ How to Develop Practice Tests
- ❑ How to Use Number Sense

To understand the learning process, you must understand how your memory works. You learn by conditioning and thinking. But memorization is different from learning. For memorization, your brain must perform several tasks, including receiving the information, storing the information, and recalling the information.

By understanding how your memory works, you will be better able to learn at which point your memory is failing you. Most students usually experience memory trouble between the time their brain receives the information and the time the information is stored.

There are many techniques for learning information that can help you receive and store information without losing it in the process. Some of these techniques may be more successful than others, depending on how you learn best.

How You Learn

Educators tell us that learning is the process of "achieving competency." More simply put, it is how you become good at something. The three ways of learning are by conditioning, by thinking, and by a combination of conditioning and thinking.

Learning by Conditioning and Thinking

Conditioning is learning things with a maximum of physical and emotional reaction and a minimum of thinking.

> **Examples:** Repeating the word *pi* to yourself and practicing finding its symbol on a calculator are two forms of conditioned learning. You are learning using by your voice and your eye-hand coordination (physical activities), and you are doing very little thinking.

Thinking is defined as learning with a maximum of thought and a minimum of emotional and physical reaction.

> **Example:** Learning about *pi* by thinking is different from learning about it by conditioning. To learn *pi* by thinking, you would have to do the calculations necessary to arrive at the numeric value that the word *pi* represents. You are learning *by using your mind* (thought activities), and you are using very little emotional or physical energy to learn *pi* in this way.

The most successful way to learn is to combine thinking and conditioning. The best learning combination is to learn by thinking first and by conditioning second.

Learning by thinking means that you learn by

- observing
- processing, and
- understanding the information.

How Your Memory Works

In order to remember information, we must receive and store it in a way that allows us to retrieve it. It is important to understand the process we must use to remember, because it can help us design more productive and time-efficient learning strategies. Briefly put, the memory process includes the following stages:

1. We receive information through our five senses: hearing, seeing, tasting, touching and smelling (**sensory input**).

2. Then, we briefly hold the image or sound of each sensory experience until it can be processed (**sensory register**).

3. After registering each sensory experience, we store the information that passes through the sensory register in **short-term memory.** We store small pieces of information in short-term memory for only a few seconds. Short-term memory is the ability to recall information immediately after it is given. If we do not do anything with it, such as put it in notes or learn it immediately, we lose this information. We can't put it into long-term memory.

4. Next, we use information we have stored in long-term memory along with new information that we have just processed to learn how to do math (**working memory**). Working memory is the ability to think about and use many pieces of information at the same time. It is like a mental chalkboard. It is also like the RAM in a computer, determining how many tasks can be done at the same time to produce an end product—understanding new math concepts. We also use reasoning skills to understand new concepts. **Reasoning** is thinking about these memories stored in long-term memory and comprehending what they mean. We also use reasoning and **long-term memory** to help us understand new concepts.

Copyright © Houghton Mifflin Company. All rights reserved.

The goal of all the steps above is to get new information into long term memory. Long-term memory is a storehouse of information that is remembered for long periods of time.

5. The final goal for math students is to be able to show what they have learned—**memory output.** We recall what we have put into long-term memory and express this knowledge. It is the ability to go into the "storehouse of information," the long-term memory, and find what we need to complete a math problem.

Here is a story that describes the memory process.

On the second day of math class, Claudia, determined to start off strong, arrived at class early, enabling her to claim a desk where she could hear and make eye contact with the instructor. She wanted to make sure she caught everything he said. It worked. As the instructor began to discuss order of operations, she heard every word, and saw everything he wrote on the board (sensory input and sensory register). Since she was able to pick up easily on what he was saying and writing, she was able to remember all the information until she could record it in her notes (short-term memory). Also going for her was the fact that she had attended a review workshop before the semester started, which helped her review everything from the course she had taken the previous semester. Her long-term memory was strong as a result. So, she was able to use her working memory and reasoning in class to understand the math, not just record the information in her notes. At the end of class, the instructor gave the students a practice quiz to see what they had learned during the past hour. She aced the quiz using her memory output.

What did Claudia do to make sure she worked through each stage of the memory process? You should take the same steps to improve your memory! Try the following suggestions provided in the table.

Memory Process	Strategies
Sensory input and sensory register	Sit where you can easily hear the professor and see what the professor writes on the board.
Short-term memory	Make sure you have a good system of taking notes. Get plenty of sleep so that you are alert.
Working Memory	Make sure you complete all homework before going to class. Learn while you are doing your homework; do not just hurry through to get it done. Read the textbook before class to familiarize yourself with the vocabulary. You do not have to understand it all, but it will help your learning during class.
Long-term memory and reasoning	Whenever you are studying math, take time to memorize what you are learning and thinking. Use the study strategies mentioned later in this chapter to help you understand and memorize math concepts. Make mental cheat sheets to review constantly.
Memory Output	Practice, practice, practice. Ask your instructor for practice tests. Rehearse the "Ten Steps to Better Test Taking" in Chapter 7. Get with a group of students, and make up practice test questions.

Copyright © Houghton Mifflin Company. All rights reserved.

The consequences of something interfering with any one of these stages are substantial. Here are some possible consequences.

If you do not input and register the information:	There is nothing to work with. The rest of the class is confusing, as is your homework.
If you do not hold information in short-term memory long enough to record it in your notes:	You end up reteaching yourself when working on homework. Sometimes, you have to take more time and go to a tutor.
If you do not spend quality time doing homework, which limits your working memory that helps you understand the math:	You will not remember what you spent time doing. The information will not remain in long-term memory. You won't get a good grasp on what is going on.
If you do not spend time memorizing what you are learning:	You will forget and have to relearn and rememorize the night before the test. You won't do as well on the math tests. Learning new material will always be harder for you.
If you freeze up when trying to answer math problems (memory output):	You can't show what you really know. You get a lower score than you think you deserve.

It is important to take a few moments to talk more about memory output. Many students struggle with this. They know the information going into the test, but they forget it once the test is on their desks. Memory output can be blocked by three things:

1. **Insufficient processing of information into long-term memory.** For most students, this is a result of not studying correctly throughout the math unit. It is easier to fix than other memory blocks.
2. **Poor test-taking skills.** Most students have not mastered a system for taking tests. That is why an entire chapter is devoted to test taking. Once again, this is not difficult to fix.
3. **Test anxiety.** Test anxiety is a learned behavior that blocks memory. Students with test anxiety usually need to learn some strategies to help them manage their anxiety, as well as learn good test-taking strategies.

Many students who have trouble taking tests wait too late to get help. If you have a pattern of test anxiety in your past, get assistance before the first test. Success on the first test will help you overcome anxiety. Failure on the first test will only feed it. Be proactive and set up a plan for taking your first test.

What is great about our memory is that we can learn strategies to improve it. The next section will describe ways in which you can improve the memory process by practicing learning strategies based on your learning modalities and learning styles.

Remember

Locating where your memory breaks down and compensating for those weaknesses will improve your math learning.

Copyright © Houghton Mifflin Company. All rights reserved.

Section Review

1. Label the boxes in Figure 10 with the stages of memory.

Figure 10 Stages of Memory

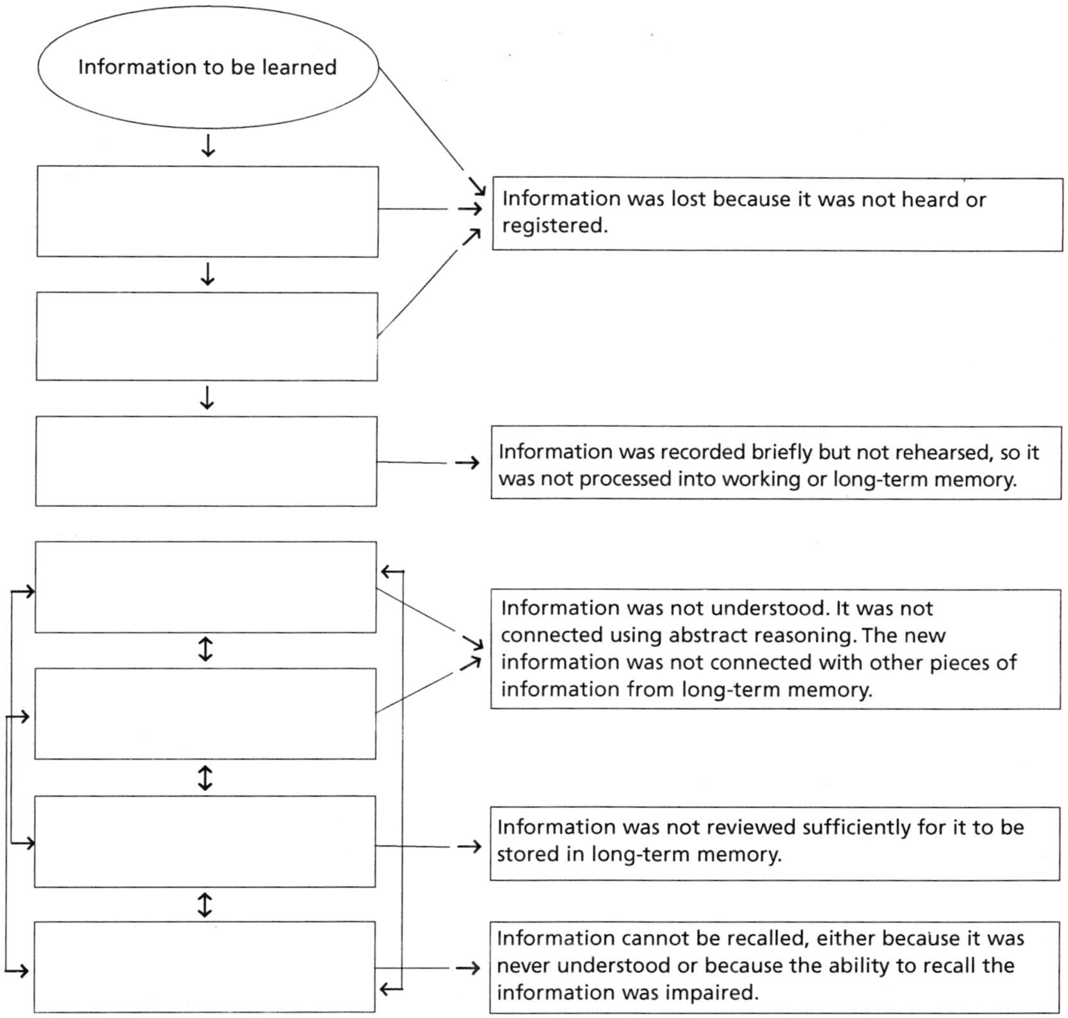

Copyright © Houghton Mifflin Company. All rights reserved.

2. List, define, and give examples of each stage of memory.

   Stage One: ______

   Example: ______

   Stage Two: ______

   Example: ______

   Stage Three: ______

   Example: ______

   Stage Four: ______

   Example: ______

   Stage Five: ______

   Example: ______

   Stage Six: ______

   Example: ______

   Stage Seven: ______

   Example: ______

3. What are three conditions that can block your memory output?

   First Condition: ______

   Second Condition: ______

   Third Condition: ______

4. Review the stages of memory and list the stages at which *your* memory breaks down. For each stage of breakdown, state how you can prevent it.

   Stage: ______

   Prevention: ______

   ______

   Stage: ______

   Prevention: ______

   ______

   Stage: ______

   Prevention: ______

   ______

Copyright © Houghton Mifflin Company. All rights reserved.

How to Use Learning Styles to Improve Memory

There are many different techniques that can help you store information in your long-term memory and reasoning. Using your learning sense or learning style and decreasing distractions while studying are very efficient ways to learn. Using your best *learning sense* (what educators call your "predominant learning modality") can improve how well you learn and enhance the transfer of knowledge into long-term memory/reasoning. Your learning senses are vision, hearing, touching, etc. Ask yourself if you learn best by watching (vision), listening (hearing), or touching (feeling).

> *Remember*
> **Learning styles are neither good nor bad and are based on genetics and environment. Knowing your best learning styles and using them effectively can dramatically improve your math learning and grades.**

Visual (Watching) Learner

Knowing that you are a *visual math learner* can help you select the memory technique that will work best for you. Repeatedly reading and writing down math materials being studied is the best way for a visual learner to study.

Based on the Learning Styles Inventory, students who learn math best by seeing it written are *visual numerical learners*. If you are a visual numerical learner you will learn best by following the ten suggestions in Figure 11. Try as many of these suggestions as possible and then select and practice those that are most helpful.

A visual way to decrease distractions is by using the "my mind is full" concept. Imagine that your mind is completely filled with thoughts of learning math, and other distracting thoughts cannot enter. Your mind has one-way input and output, which responds only to thinking about math when you are doing homework or studying.

Figure 11 Visual Numerical Learners

1. Study a variety of written materials, such as additional handouts and math texts.
2. Play games with, and get involved in activities with, visible printed number problems.
3. Use visually orientated computer programs, CD-ROMs, and math websites.
4. Rework your notes using suggestions from this workbook.
5. Visualize numbers and formulas in detail.
6. Check out videocassette tapes from the math lab or learning resource center on campus.
7. Make 3" x 5" note (flash) cards, in color.
8. Use different colors of ink to emphasize different parts of each math formula.
9. Ask your tutor to ***show*** you how to do the problems instead of ***telling*** you how to do the problems.
10. Write down each problem step the tutor tells you to do. Highlight the important steps or concepts, that cause you difficulty.

Auditory (Hearing) Learner

If you are an *auditory learner* (one who learns best by hearing the information), then learning formulas is best accomplished by repeating them back to yourself, or recording them on a tape recorder and listening to them. Reading out loud is one of the best auditory ways to get important information into long-term memory. Stating facts and ideas out loud improves your ability to think and remember. If you cannot recite out loud, recite the material to yourself, emphasizing the key words.

Based on the Learning Styles Inventory, students who learn math best by hearing it are *auditory numerical learners*. If you are an auditory numerical learner you may learn best by following the ten suggestions in Figure 12 on the next page. Try as many of these suggestions as possible and then select and practice those that are most helpful.

Copyright © Houghton Mifflin Company. All rights reserved.

Figure 12 Auditory Numerical Learners

1. Say numbers to yourself or move your lips as you read problems.
2. Tape-record your class and play it back while reading your notes.
3. Read aloud any written explanations.
4. Explain to your tutor how to work math problems.
5. Make sure all important facts are spoken aloud with auditory repetition.
6. Remember important facts by auditory repetition.
7. Read math problems aloud and try solutions verbally and subverbally as you talk yourself through the problems.
8. Record directions to difficult math problems on audiotape and refer to them when solving those specific types of problems.
9. Have your tutor explain how to work problems instead of just showing you how to solve them.
10. Record math laws and rules in your own words, by chapters, and listen to them every other day (auditory highlighting).

Figure 13 The FOIL Method

F (a) (c)
O (a) (d)
I (b) (c)
L (b) (d)

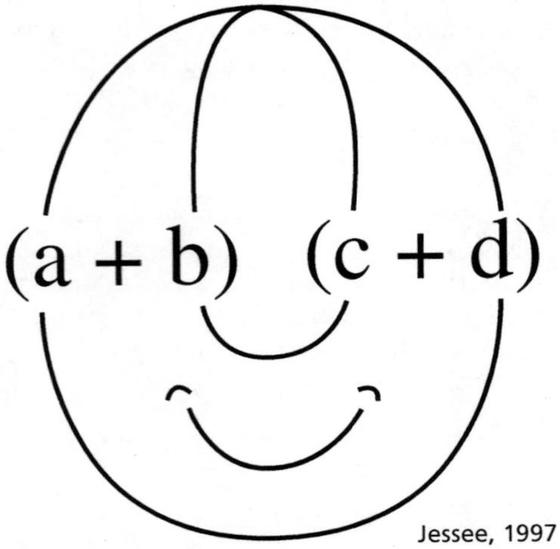

Jessee, 1997

The FOIL Method is used to remember the procedure for multiplying two binomials. The letters in FOIL stand for First, Outside, Inside, and Last. To use the FOIL Method, multiply

- the First terms ((a) (c)),
- the Outside terms ((a) (d)),
- the Inside terms ((b) (c)),
- the Last terms ((b) (d)),
- and then combine the four products.

To learn the FOIL Method, trace your finger along the FOIL route.

An auditory way to improve your concentration is to become aware of your distractions and tell yourself to concentrate. If you are in a location where talking out loud will cause a disturbance, mouth the words "start concentrating" as you say them in your mind. Your concentration periods should increase.

Tactile/Concrete (Touching) Learner

A *tactile/concrete learner* needs to feel and touch the material to learn it. Tactile/concrete learners, who are also called *kinesthetic learners*, tend to learn best when they can concretely manipulate the information to be learned. Unfortunately, most math instructors do not use this learning sense. As a result, students who depend heavily on feeling and touching for learning will usually have the most difficulty developing effective math learning techniques. This learning style creates a problem with math learning because math is more abstract than concrete. Also, most math instructors are visual abstract learners and have difficulty teaching

Copyright © Houghton Mifflin Company. All rights reserved.

math tactilely. Ask for the math instructors and tutors who give the most practical examples and who may even "act out" the math problems.

As mentioned before, a tactile/concrete learner will probably learn most efficiently by hands-on learning. For example, if you want to learn the FOIL Method, you would take your fingers and trace the "face" to remember the steps. See Figure 13 (The FOIL Method). Also, learning is most effective when physical involvement with manipulation is combined with sight and sound. For example, as you trace the face you also say the words out loud.

Based on the Learning Styles Inventory, tactile/concrete learners best learn math by manipulating the information that is to be taught. If you are a tactile/concrete learner, you may learn best by following the ten suggestions in Figure 14. Try as many of these suggestions as possible and then select and practice the ones that help the most. If you do not have these manipulatives or don't know how to use them, ask the math lab supervisor or instructor if they have any manipulative materials or models. If the math lab does not have any manipulative materials, you may have to ask for help to develop your own.

Tactile/concrete learners can also use graphing calculators to improve their learning. Entering the keystrokes makes it easier to remember how to solve the problems. This practice is also an excellent way to remember how to solve the problem when using a calculator while taking a test.

Another way tactile/concrete learners can learn is to trace graphs with their fingers when they appear on the calculator. They should read out loud and trace every equation to "feel" how the graph changes for different equations. For example, if you add 2 to one side of an equation, move your finger to where the graph changed and say out loud how much it moved.

A tactile/concrete way to improve your study concentration is by counting the number of distractions during each study session. Place a sheet of paper by your book when doing homework. When you catch yourself not concentrating, write the letter C on the sheet of paper. This will remind you to concentrate and get back to work. After each study period, count up the number of Cs and watch the number decrease over time.

Figure 14 Tactile/Concrete Learners

1. Cut up a paper plate to represent fractions of a whole.
2. Fold a piece of paper several times and cut along the fold marks to represent fractions of a whole.
3. In order to understand math concepts, ask to be shown how to use algebra tiles as manipulatives.
4. Try to use your hands and body to "act out" a solution. For example, you may "become" the car in a rate-and-distance word problem.
5. Obtain diagrams, objects, or manipulatives and incorporate activities such as drawing and writing into your study time. You may also enhance your learning by doing some type of physical activity such as walking.
6. Try to get involved with at least one other student, a tutor, or an instructor who uses manipulatives to help you learn math.
7. Ask to use the Hands-on Equations Learning System, which uses manipulatives, to learn basic algebra. You can go to their website (www.Borenson.com) to learn more about this system and other systems that can help you learn math.
8. Go to one of the "learning stores" in shopping malls to see if they have manipulatives.
9. Go to a K–12 learning resource store to see if they have manipulatives, such as magnetic boards with letters and numbers.
10. Talk to the coordinator of students with disabilities to see if they use manipulatives when tutoring their students.

Social Individual Learner

If you are a *social individual learner,* you may learn math best by learning it individually. You may learn best by yourself, working with computer programs and an individual tutor. In some cases, social individual learners may have to meet in groups to develop practice tests but leave socializing to a minimum. If you are a social individual learner

Copyright © Houghton Mifflin Company. All rights reserved.

and a visual learner, the computer may be one of the best learning tools available. If you are a social individual learner, based on the Learning Styles Inventory, you may learn best by following the eight suggestions in Figure 15. Try as many of these suggestions as possible and then select those that are most helpful.

A problem that social individual learners may encounter is working too long on problems for which they could have received help. Social individual learners must understand that getting help is okay, especially if it saves study time and makes their studying more efficient.

Figure 15 Social Individual Learners

1. Study math, English, and your other subjects alone.
2. Utilize videocassette tapes or auditory tapes to learn by yourself.
3. Prepare individual questions for your tutor or instructor.
4. Obtain individual help from the math lab or hire your own tutor.
5. Set up a study schedule and a study area so that other people will not bother you.
6. Study in a library or in some other private, quiet place.
7. Use group study times only as a way to ask questions, obtain information, and take pretests on your subject material.
8. Use math websites to help you learn.

Social Group Learners

If you are a *social group learner* (one who best learns in a group), then learning math may best be done in study groups and in math classes that offer collaborative learning (group learning). Social group learners may learn best by discussing information. They can usually develop their own study groups and discuss how to solve problems over the phone. If you are a social group learner and an auditory learner, then you definitely learn best by talking to people. If you are a social group learner, based on the Learning Styles Inventory, you may learn best by following the eight suggestions in Figure 16. Try as many of these suggestions as possible and then select and practice those that are most helpful.

A learning problem that a social group learner may have is talking too much about other subjects when in a study group. This is called being off task. You may want to have a group member serve as a discussion monitor and let the other students know when they need to get back on task. Also, social group learners need to know that they still must study math individually to be successful. During these individual study sessions, they should prepare questions for the group.

Figure 16 Social Group Learners

1. Study math, English, and your other subjects in a study group.
2. Sign up for math course sections that offer cooperative learning (learning in small groups).
3. Review your notes with a small group.
4. Obtain help in the math lab or other labs where you can work in group situations.
5. Watch math videocassette tapes with a group and discuss the subject matter.
6. Listen to audiocassette tapes on the lecture and discuss them with the group.
7. Obtain several "study buddies" so you can discuss with them the steps to solving math problems.
8. Form a study group. Each member should bring ten test questions with explanations on the back. The group should complete all the test questions.

Multiple Senses

If you have difficulty learning material through one sense (learning style), you might want to try learning material through two or three senses. Involving two or more senses in learning improves your

Copyright © Houghton Mifflin Company. All rights reserved.

learning and remembering. Review the figures in this section on learning styles and whenever possible combine two or more learning styles.

If your primary sense is visual and your secondary sense is auditory, you may want to write down equations while saying them out loud to yourself. Writing and reciting the material at the same time combines visual, auditory, and (to some extent) tactile/concrete styles of learning.

Studying with a pen or highlighter is a visual as well as a tactile/concrete way to improve your concentration. Placing the pen or highlighter in your hand and using it will force you to concentrate more on what you are reading. After you write and recite the material back to yourself, do it five or ten more times to overlearn it.

Section Review

1. List five ways visual learners can improve their memory.

   First Way: ______________________

   Second Way: ______________________

   Third Way: ______________________

   Fourth Way: ______________________

   Fifth Way: ______________________

2. List five ways auditory learners can improve their memory.

   First Way: ______________________

   Second Way: ______________________

   Third Way: ______________________

   Fourth Way: ______________________

   Fifth Way: ______________________

3. List five ways tactile/concrete learners can improve their memory.

   First Way: ______________________

   Second Way: ______________________

   Third Way: ______________________

   Fourth Way: ______________________

   Fifth Way: ______________________

Copyright © Houghton Mifflin Company. All rights reserved.

4. List three ways social individual learners can improve their memory.

   First Way: ______________________________

   Second Way: ______________________________

   Third Way: ______________________________

5. List three ways social group learners can improve their memory.

   First Way: ______________________________

   Second Way: ______________________________

   Third Way: ______________________________

6. What is your best modality learning style for math? Visual, auditory, or tactile/concrete?

   ____

   ____

7. What is your second-best modality learning style for math?

   ____

8. Are you more of an individual or a group learner? Why?

   ____

   ____

   ____

9. How can you use multiple senses to improve your memory?

   ____

   ____

   ____

10. What is your best combination of learning styles to learn math? ______________

    ____

    ____

    Give an example of how you can combine your learning styles to learn a math concept. (If you cannot think of a concept, ask your instructor for one.)

    ____

    ____

    ____

Copyright © Houghton Mifflin Company. All rights reserved.

How to Use Memory Techniques

There are many different techniques that can help you store information in your long-term memory: a positive attitude about studying, selective learning, organization, visual imagery, mnemonic devices, and acronyms.

A Good Study/Math Attitude

A positive attitude about studying will help you concentrate and improve your retention of information. This means that you should have at least a neutral math attitude (you neither like nor dislike it) and should reserve the right to learn to like math. If you still don't like math, just pretend that you do while studying it. View studying as an opportunity to learn rather than an unpleasant task. Tell yourself that you can learn the material, and it will help you pass the course and graduate.

Be a Selective Learner

Being selective in your math learning will improve your memory. Prioritize the materials you are studying; decide which facts you need to know and which ones you can ignore. Narrow down information into laws and principles that can be generalized. Learn the laws and principles 100 percent.

> **Example:** If you have been given a list of math principles and laws to learn for a test, put each one on an index card. As you go through them, create two piles: an "I already know this" pile and an "I don't know this" pile. Then study *only* the cards in the "I don't know this" pile. Study the principles on these cards until you have memorized them and understand them completely.

Become an Organizer

Organizing your math material into idea/fact clusters or groups will help you learn and memorize it. Grouping similar material in a problem log or calculator log is an example of categorizing information. Do not learn isolated facts; always try to connect them with other similar material.

Use Visual Imagery

Using mental pictures or diagrams to help you learn the material is especially helpful for visual learners and for students who are right-hemisphere dominant (who tend to learn best by visual and spatial methods). Mental pictures and actual diagrams involve 100 percent of your brain power. Picturing solution steps can help you solve difficult math problems in your mind.

> **Example:** Use the FOIL Method (see Figure 13 on page 94) to learn visually how to multiply binomials. Memorize the face until you can sketch it from memory. If you need to use it during a test, you can sketch the face on your scratch paper and refer to it.

Make Associations

Association learning can help you remember better. Find a link between new facts and some well-established old facts and study them together. The recalling of old facts will help you remember the new facts and strengthen a mental connection between the two. Make up your own associations to remember math properties and laws.

> *Remember*
> **The more ridiculous the association, the more likely you are to remember it.**

> **Examples:** When learning the *Commutative Property,* remember that the word *commutative* sounds like the word *community*. A community is made up of different types of people who could be divided into an *a* group and a *b* group. However, in a community of a people and b people, it does not matter if we count the a people first or the b people first; we still have the

Copyright © Houghton Mifflin Company. All rights reserved.

same total number of people in the community. Thus, $a + b = b + a$.

When learning the *Distributive Law of Multiplication Over Addition,* such as $a(b + c)$, remember that "distributive" sounds like "distributor," which is associated with giving out a product. The distributor a is giving its products to b and c.

Use Mnemonic Devices

The use of mnemonic devices is another way to help you remember. Mnemonic devices are easily remembered words, phrases, or rhymes associated with difficult-to-remember principles or facts.

Example: Many students become confused by the order of operations. These students mix up the order of the steps in solving a problem, such as dividing before adding the numbers in parentheses. A mnemonic device that can help you remember the order of operations is "Please Excuse My Dear Aunt Sally." The first letter in each of these words represents the math function to be completed from the first to the last. Thus, the order of operations is Parentheses (***P**lease*), Exponents (***E**xcuse*), Multiplication (***M**y*), Division (***D**ear*), Addition (***A**unt*), and Subtraction (***S**ally*). Remember to multiply and/or divide whatever comes first, from left to right. Also, add or subtract whatever comes first, from left to right.

Use Acronyms

Acronyms are another memory device that can help you learn math. Acronyms are word forms created from the first letters of a series of words.

Example: FOIL is one of the most common math acronyms. FOIL is used to remember the procedure for multiplying two binomials. Each letter in the word *FOIL* represents a math operation. **FOIL** stands for **F**irst, **O**utside, **I**nside, and **L**ast, as it applies to multiplication of two binomials such as $(2x + 3)(x + 7)$. The **F**irst quantities are $2x$ (in the first expression) and x (in the second expression). The **O**utside quantities are $2x$ (in the first expression) and 7 (in the second expression). The **I**nside quantities are 3 (in the first expression) and x (in the second expression). The **L**ast quantities are 3 (in the first expression) and 7 (in the second expression). This results in

F $(2x)(x)$ + **O** $(2x)(7)$ + **I** $(3)(x)$ + **L** $(3)(7)$.

Do the multiplication to get $2x^2 + 14x + 3x + 21$, which adds up to $2x^2 + 17x + 21$. See Figure 13 (the FOIL Method).

Section Review

1. How can a good math attitude help you learn?

____

____

2. Give an example of being a selective learner in your math class.

____

____

3. From your current math lessons, make up and explain one association remembering device that is not in this workbook.

____

____

Copyright © Houghton Mifflin Company. All rights reserved.

4. For your next major math test, make up and explain one mnemonic device that is not in this workbook.

____

____

5. For your next major math test, make up and explain one acronym that is not in this workbook.

____

____

How to Develop Practice Tests

Developing a practice test is one of the best ways to evaluate your memory and math skills before taking a real test. You want to find out what you do not know *before* the real test instead of *during* the test. Practice tests should be as real as possible and should include time constraints.

You can create a practice test by reworking all the problems that you have recorded in your problem log since your last test. Another practice test can be developed using every other problem in the textbook chapter tests. Further, you can use the solutions manual to generate other problems with which to test yourself. You can also use old exams from the previous semester. Check to see if your math lab/LRC or library has tests on file from previous semesters, or ask your instructor for other tests. For some students, a better way to prepare for a test is the group method.

> **Example:** Hold a group study session several days before the test. Have each student prepare a test with ten questions. On the back of the test, have the answers listed, worked out step by step. Have each member of the study group exchange his or her test with another member of the group. Once all the tests have been completed, have the author of each test discuss with the group the procedures used to solve the problems in his or her test.

If group work improves your learning, you may want to hold a group study session at least once a week. Make sure the individual or group test is completed at least three days before the real test.

Completing practice math tests will help you increase your testing skills. It will also reveal your test problem weaknesses in enough time for you to learn how to solve the problems before the real test. If you have difficulty with any of the problems during class or after taking the practice test, be sure to see your tutor or instructor.

After taking the practice test(s), you should know what types of problems you do not understand (and need to study) and what is likely to be on the actual test. Put this valuable information on one sheet of paper. This information needs to be understood and memorized. It may include formulas, rules, or steps in solving problems.

Use the learning strategies discussed in this chapter to remember this information. A good example of how this information should look is what students might call a mental "cheat sheet." Obviously, you cannot use the written form of this sheet during the real test.

If you cannot take a practice test, put down on your mental cheat sheet the valuable information you will need for the test. Work to understand and memorize your mental cheat sheet. Chapter 7, "How to Improve Your Math Test-Taking Skills," will discuss how to use the information on the mental cheat sheet—*without cheating.*

Copyright © Houghton Mifflin Company. All rights reserved.

Section Review

1. List three different ways you can make up a practice test.

   First Way: ____________________

   Second Way: ____________________

   Third Way: ____________________

2. List ten different problems you would put on your practice test for the next exam.

   First Problem: ____________________

   Second Problem: ____________________

   Third Problem: ____________________

   Fourth Problem: ____________________

   Fifth Problem: ____________________

   Sixth Problem: ____________________

   Seventh Problem: ____________________

   Eighth Problem: ____________________

   Ninth Problem: ____________________

   Tenth Problem: ____________________

3. Give these ten problems to your study buddy and get ten problems from him or her. Compare your answers with those of your study buddy. How many did you get right? __________ How can you correct the wrong answers?

   ____

   ____

   ____

   ____

How to Use Number Sense

When taking your practice tests, you should use "number sense," or estimations, to make sure your answers are reasonable. Number sense is common sense applied to math. Number sense is the ability to see if your answer makes sense without using algorithms. (Algorithms are the sequential math steps used to solve problems.) The following examples demonstrate solving a math problem (from a national math test given to high school students) using algorithms and number sense.

Copyright © Houghton Mifflin Company. All rights reserved.

Example: Solve 3.04 x 5.3. Students used algorithms to solve this problem by multiplying the number 3.04 by 5.3, in sequence. Seventy-two percent of the students answered the problem correctly using algorithms.

Example: Estimate the product 3.04 x 5.3, and choose from the following answers.

(A) 1.6 (C) 160
(B) 16 (D) 1600

Only 15 percent of the students chose B, which is the correct answer. Twenty-eight percent of the students chose A. Using *estimation* to solve the answer, a whopping 85 percent of the students got the problem wrong.

These students were incorrectly using their "mental chalkboard" instead of using number sense. In using number sense, you would multiply the numbers to the left of the decimal point in each number to estimate the answer. To estimate the answer, then, you would multiply 3 (the number to the left of the decimal in 3.04) by 5 (the number to the left of the decimal in 5.3) and expect the answer to be a little larger than 15.

It appears that the students' procedural processing (the use of algorithms) was good, but when asked to solve a nonroutine problem using estimation (which is easier than using algorithms), the results were disappointing.

Another example of using number sense, or estimation, is "rounding off."

Taking the time to estimate the answer to a math problem is a good way to check your answer. Another way to check your answer is to see if it is reasonable. Many students forget this important step and get the answer wrong. This is especially true of word or story problems.

Example: Solve 48 + 48 by rounding off. Rounding off means mentally changing the number (up or down) to make it more manageable to you, without using algorithms. By rounding off, 48 becomes 50 (which is easier to work with). 50 + 50 = 100. If the choices for answers were 104, 100, 98, and 96, you would then subtract 4 from 100 (since each number was rounded up by 2) and you would get 96.

Also, when dealing with an equation, make sure to substitute the answer back into the equation to see if one side of the equation equals the other. If the two sides are not equal, you have the wrong answer. If you have extra time after you have completed a test, you should check answers using this method.

Examples: When solving a rate-and-distance problem, use your common sense to realize that a car cannot go 500 miles per hour to catch another car. However, the car can go 50 miles per hour.

The same common sense rule applies to age problems, where the age of a person cannot be 150 years, but it can be 15 years.

Furthermore, in solving equations that are not word problems, x is *usually* a number that is less than 20. When you solve a problem for x and get 50, then this isn't reasonable, and you should recheck your calculations.

Example: In solving the equation $x + 3 = 9$, you calculated that $x = 5$. To check your answer, substitute 5 for x and see if the problem works out correctly. 5 + 3 does not equal 9, so you know you have made a mistake and need to recalculate the problem. The correct answer, of course, is $x = 6$.

Remember

Number sense is a way to get more math problems correct by estimating your answer to determine if it is reasonable.

Copyright © Houghton Mifflin Company. All rights reserved.

Section Review

1. Give an explanation of number sense.

____

____

2. How does number sense compare with common sense?

____

____

3. Give an example of a recent math problem you failed to solve correctly as a result of number sense.

____

____

4. List two ways you can improve your number sense.

First Way: ____

Second Way: ____

Dan's Take

Have you ever known someone who could learn something right away and then remember it perfectly forever? I had a friend like this in college. He could sit in on a lecture and remember the speech two years later without missing a beat.

Needless to say, most of us aren't like this. Most of our brains aren't strong enough to keep up with it all, so we hold onto the information we care about and filter the rest out of our minds.

This process makes learning math, a sequential learning subject, more demanding than most other subjects. It's important when learning a step in a math problem to remember it for the rest of your college career.

So how do you remember math? I had this problem throughout high school and college. I eventually realized that the answer to this problem was simple: to remember math, you simply need to do math every day. I noticed that by breaking up my math homework and doing a little bit of it every day, I was able to keep the information fresh in my head.

For the majority of us, remembering something takes effort. For me, remembering how to do math took a little bit of daily effort, and in the end it paid off.

Copyright © Houghton Mifflin Company. All rights reserved.

Name: ______________________________ Date: ______________

Chapter 6 Review

1. The way you receive information is through your five senses, which are ____________, ____________, ____________, ____________, and ____________.
2. The main problem most students have is converting learned material into ____________ ____________ and ____________ it.
3. Repeatedly reading and writing math material is one of the best ways for a ____________ learner to study.
4. Reading ____________ ____________ is one of the best auditory ways to learn material.
5. A ____________/ ____________ learner needs to feel and touch material to learn it.
6. Being a selective learner means ____________ the material to study and learning the laws and principles ____________ percent.
7. Mnemonic devices are easy-to-remember ____________, ____________, or ____________ associated with difficult-to-remember principles or facts.
8. ____________ are word forms created from the first letters of a series of words.
9. The reason to develop a practice test is to find out what you do not know ____________ the test instead of ____________ the test.
10. Social group learners benefit from forming ____________ ____________.

What is the most important information you learned from this chapter?

____

____

____

How can you immediately use it?

____

____

____

Copyright © Houghton Mifflin Company. All rights reserved.

Lecture Notes

Copyright © Houghton Mifflin Company. All rights reserved.

7

How to Improve Your Math Test-Taking Skills

What You Will Learn in Chapter 7

- ❑ Why Attending Class and Doing Your Homework May Not Be Enough to Pass
- ❑ The Ten Steps to Better Test Taking
- ❑ The Six Types of Test-Taking Errors
- ❑ How to Prepare for the Final Exam

Taking a math test is different from taking tests in other subjects. Math tests require you not only to recall the information, but also to apply the information. Multiple-choice tests, for example, usually test you on recall, and if you do not know the answers, you can guess.

Math tests build on each other, whereas history tests often do not test you on previous material. Most math tests are speed tests, where the faster you are, the better grade you can receive; most social science tests are designed for everyone to finish.

Math test preparation and test-taking skills are different from preparation and skills needed for other tests. You need to have a test-taking plan and a test analysis plan to demonstrate your total knowledge on math tests. Students with these plans make better grades compared with students without them. Math instructors want to measure your math knowledge, not your test-taking skills.

Why Attending Class and Doing Your Homework May Not Be Enough to Pass

Most students and some instructors believe that attending class and doing all the homework ensures an A or a B on tests. This is far from true. Doing all the homework and getting the correct answers is very different in many ways from taking tests:

1. While doing homework, there is little anxiety. A test situation is just the opposite.
2. You are not under a time constraint while doing your homework; you may have to complete a test in 55 minutes or less.
3. If you get stuck on a homework problem, your textbook and notes are there to assist you. This is not true for most tests.
4. Once you learn how to do several problems in a homework assignment, the rest are similar. In a test, the problems may be in random order.
5. In doing homework, you have the answers to at least half the problems in the back of the text and answers to all the problems in the solutions guide. This is not true for tests.
6. While doing homework, you have time to figure out how to use your calculator. During the test, you can waste valuable time figuring out how to use your calculator.
7. When doing homework, you can call your study buddy or ask the tutor for help, something you cannot do during the test.
8. While doing your homework, you can go to websites for online tutoring to help you solve problems you do not understand.

Do not develop a false sense of security by believing you can make an A or a B by just doing your homework. Tests measure more than just your math knowledge.

The General Pretest Rules

General rules are important when taking any type of test:

1. *Get a good night's sleep before taking a test.* This is true for the ACT, the SAT, and your math tests. If you imagine you are going to cram all night and perform well on your test with three to four hours of sleep, you are wrong. It would be better to get seven or eight hours of sleep and be fresh enough to use your memory to recall information needed to answer the questions.
2. *Start studying for the test at least three days ahead of time.* Make sure you take a practice test to find out, before the test, what you do not know. Review your problem log and work the problems. Review the concept errors you made on the last test. (How to identify and correct your concept errors will be discussed later in this chapter.) Meet with your instructor or tutor for help on those questions you cannot solve.
3. *Review only the material you have already learned the night before a test.*
4. *Make sure you know all the information on your mental cheat sheet.* Review your notebook and glossary to make sure you understand the concepts. Work a few problems and recall the information on your mental cheat sheet right before you go to bed. Go directly to bed; do not watch television, listen to the radio, or party. While you are asleep, your mind will work on and remember the last thing you did before you went to sleep.
5. *Get up in the morning at your usual time and review your notes and problem log.* Do not do any new problems, but make sure your calculator is working.

Copyright © Houghton Mifflin Company. All rights reserved.

Section Review

1. List three reasons why only attending class and doing your homework may not be enough to pass your math course.

   First Reason: ______________________________

   Second Reason: ______________________________

   Third Reason: ______________________________

2. List and explain three general pretest rules that best apply to you.

   First Rule: ______________________________

   Second Rule: ______________________________

   Third Rule: ______________________________

Copyright © Houghton Mifflin Company. All rights reserved.

Pretest Checkoff List

Just like a pilot who conducts a preflight check list, you can do a pretest check list in order take off safely and not "crash" on your test. Complete as many of the items on the checkoff list as you can two days or more ***before*** the test.

Reducing Test Anxiety

Students who have test anxiety need to practice the relaxation techniques that they will use before and during the test. Reducing test anxiety can help students recall information for the test.

I have practiced my best short-term relaxation technique. *Yes* ____ *No* ____ *Don't have test anxiety* ____

Students with test anxiety usually say very negative statements to themselves, which intensifies their test anxiety further.

What I usually say to myself during a test is not positive. *Yes* ___ *No* ____

What are these negative statements?

1. ______________________________
2. ______________________________
3. ______________________________

I have written and practiced saying positive statements to replace the negative ones. *Yes* ____ *No* ____

What are these positive statements?

1. ______________________________
2. ______________________________
3. ______________________________

Reviewing Notes and Problem Log

Understanding math vocabulary is key to learning math. Talking about the meaning and uses for vocabulary words helps to review the key concepts you must remember for a test. To review math vocabulary, use your math glossary and/or the key words in your note-taking system.

I have reviewed my math glossary or key words at least three or four times a week. *Yes* ____ *No* ____ *Did not develop a glossary or set of key words* _____

I reviewed my math glossary or key words at least once a day starting two days before the test. *Yes* ____ *No* ____ *Did not develop a glossary or set of key words* _____

Reviewing all your notes before the test is a good strategy to help you remember math concepts and how to do math problems.

I have reviewed all my notes two days before the test. *Yes* ____ *No* ____ *Did not take notes* _____

Reviewing your problem log of instructor examples is another way to understand math concepts and problem-solving strategies.

I have reviewed my problem log examples by two days before the test. *Yes* ____ *No* ____ *Did not develop a problem log* _____

Reviewing the Textbook

Reviewing the examples in the textbook is another way to refresh your math skills.

I have reviewed the examples in the textbook two days before the test. *Yes* ____ *No* ____

One of the strategies of reading a textbook is to develop anticipated test questions.

I reviewed my anticipated test questions. *Yes* ____ *No* ____ *Did not develop anticipated test questions* ____

Copyright © Houghton Mifflin Company. All rights reserved.

Reviewing Homework

Reviewing your homework problems is a good way to help remember how to do the problems.

I reviewed homework problems two days before the test. *Yes* ____ *No* ____
Did not do the homework problems ____

To study productively, it is important to identify the problems and concepts you do not know well. Instead of repeatedly reviewing what you already know well, focus your energy on improving your comprehension and ability to complete the more challenging problems.

I have identified what I do not know well enough for the test at least a week before the test. *Yes* ____ *No* ____

Memory Techniques

Memory techniques can be used for hard-to-remember rules, concepts, or problems. Memory techniques, which include repeating concepts or problems out loud, making associations, using mnemonic devices, and using acronyms, will improve your test-taking skills.

I have developed memory techniques for my test. *Yes* ____ *No* ____

Reviewing Concept Errors

One of the Six Types of Test-Taking Errors, which is discussed later in this chapter, is concept errors. Concept errors from previous tests need to be reviewed in order not to make the same mistakes again. Reviewing your concept errors can improve your understanding of mathematics.

Did you review your concept errors from previous tests? *Yes* ____ *No* ____
Did not record concept errors ____

Using Practice Tests

Practice tests help you find out what you don't know before the test instead of during the test. The best way to develop a practice test is with other students, because you can exchange questions. Developing practice tests can improve your ability to solve math problems on the real test.

I worked with other students to develop and take a practice test at lease two days before the test. *Yes* ____ *No* ____
Did not develop practice tests ____

Taking instructor-made practice tests can also help you to find out what problems you need to work on before, instead of during, the test. Using practice tests can help you find out what you need to study before the test.

I have worked the problems on the instructor's Practice test. *Yes* ____ *No* ____
There was no instructor practice test ____

Memory Data Dump

The information from a memory data dump can be used to help you during the test. Using a memory data dump on your test can improve your test scores. You can also make up memory techniques based on the problems that you missed on the practice tests.

I have developed memory devices to use during a data dump. *Yes* ____ *No* ____

Test-Taking Strategies

Some students use the "Ten Steps to Better Test-Taking" as a test-taking guide while others develop their own test-taking strategies. Either technique can improve your test-taking strategy.

I have developed and practiced my test-taking strategy. *Yes* ____ *No* ____

Are you wondering why we are asking you to complete the above items two days or more before the test instead of the night before the test? If you get stuck on a problem, find you don't understand a concept, or cannot develop one of the strategies, then you will still have at least one day to get help before the test. Remember, the night before the test you need to be reviewing material you already have learned—not learning new material. The most productive way to complete this checklist is to include these steps in your study time every day.

Copyright © Houghton Mifflin Company. All rights reserved.

The Ten Steps to Better Test Taking

You need to have a game plan to take a math test. This plan is different from plans for taking history, English, humanities, and some science tests. The game plan is to get the most points in the least amount of time. Many students lose test points because they use the wrong test-taking strategies for math. By following these ten steps you can demonstrate more knowledge on the test and get more problems right.

Step 1 *Use a memory data dump.* When you get your test, turn it over and write down the information that you might forget. Remember, this is your mental cheat sheet that you should have already made while preparing for the test. Your mental cheat sheet has now turned into a mental list, and writing down this information is not cheating. Do not put your name on the test, do not skim it, just turn it over and write down those facts, figures, and formulas from your mental cheat sheet or other information you might not remember during the test. This is called your *first memory data dump.* The data dump provides memory cues for test questions.

Example: It might take you a while to remember how to do a coin problem. However, if you had immediately turned your test over and written down different ways of solving coin problems, it would be easier to solve the coin problem.

Step 2 *Preview the test.* Put your name on the test and start previewing. Previewing the test requires you to look through the entire test to find different types of problems and their point values. Put a mark by each question that you can do without thinking. These are the questions that you will solve first.

Step 3 *Do a second memory data dump.* The second data dump is for writing down material that was jarred from your memory while previewing the test. Write this information on the back of the test.

Step 4 *Develop a test progress schedule.* When you begin setting up a test schedule, determine the point value for each question. Some test questions might be worth more points than others.

In some tests, word problems are worth 5 points and other questions might be worth 2 or 3 points. You must decide the best way to get the most points in the least amount of time. This might mean working the questions worth 2 or 3 points first and leaving the more difficult word problems for last.

Decide how many problems should be completed halfway though the test. You should have more than half the problems completed by that time.

Step 5 *Answer the easiest problems first.* Solve, in order, the problems you marked while previewing the test. Then review the answers to see if they make sense. Start working through the test as fast as you can while being accurate. Answers should be reasonable.

Example: The answer to a problem asking you to find the area of a rectangle cannot be negative, and the answer to a land-rate-distance problem cannot be 1000 miles per hour.

Clearly write down each step to get partial credit. Even if you wind up with an incorrect answer, you might get some credit. In most math tests, the easier problems are near the beginning of the first page;

Copyright © Houghton Mifflin Company. All rights reserved.

you need to answer them efficiently and quickly. This will give you both more time for the harder problems and time to review.

Step 6 *Skip difficult problems.* If you find a problem that you do not know how to work, read it twice and automatically skip it. Reading it twice will help you understand the problem and put it into your working memory. While you are solving other problems, your mind will still be working on that problem. A difficult problem could be a type of problem you have never seen before or a problem in which you get stuck on the second or third step. In either case, skip the problem and go on to the next one.

Step 7 *Review the skipped problems.* When working the skipped problems, think how you have solved other similar problems. Also try to remember how the instructor solved that type of problem on the board.

While reviewing skipped problems, or at any other time, you may have the "Aha!" response. The "Aha!" response is your remembering how to do a skipped problem. Do not wait to finish your current problem. Go to the problem on which you had the "Aha!" and finish that problem. If you wait to finish your current problem, your "Aha!" response could turn into an "Oh, no!" response.

Step 8 *Guess at the remaining problems.* Do as much work as you can on each problem, even if it is just writing down the first step. If you cannot write down the first step, rewrite the problem. Sometimes rewriting the problem can jar your memory enough to do the first step or the entire problem. This is particularly true for tactile/concrete learners, for whom writing can trigger the memory process of solving the problem. Remember, you did not learn how to solve math problems with your hands tied behind your back. If you leave the problem blank, you will get a zero. Do not waste too much time on guessing or trying to work the problems you cannot do.

Step 9 *Review the test.* Look for careless errors or other errors you may have made. Students usually lose 2 to 5 test points on errors that could have been caught in review. Do not talk yourself out of an answer just because it may not look right. This often happens when an answer does not come out even. It is possible for the answer to be a fraction or a decimal.

Remember

Research reveals that the odds of changing a right answer to a wrong answer are greater than the odds of changing a wrong answer to a right one.

Step 10 *Use all the allowed test time.* Review each problem by substituting the answer back into the equation or doing the opposite function required to answer the question. If you cannot check the problem in either of these two ways, rework the problem on a separate sheet of paper and compare the answers. Do not leave the test room until you have reviewed each problem two times or until the bell rings.

Even though we encourage students to work until the end of the test period, most students leave the classroom before the end of the period. These students state that even though they know they should use all

Copyright © Houghton Mifflin Company. All rights reserved.

the test time, they cannot stay in the room until the end of the test time. These students also know that their grades would probably improve if they kept checking their answers or kept working the problems they were having difficulty with. After talking to hundreds of these students, I discovered two different themes for leaving the classroom early. First, test anxiety gets so overwhelming that they cannot stay in the room. The relief from the test anxiety (leaving the room) is worth more than getting a better grade. If you are one of these students, you must learn how to decrease your test anxiety by following the suggestions in Chapter 3 or by using the *How to Reduce Test Anxiety* CD. Don't let test anxiety control your grades!

The other reason for leaving the test early is that they do not want to be the last student or one of the last few students to turn in their tests. They still believe that students who turn their tests in last are "dumb and stupid." These students also believe that students who turn their tests in first make As and Bs and students who turn their tests in last make Ds and Fs. If you are one of these students, you don't need to care about what other students think about you (it's usually wrong anyway). YOU need to fight the urge to leave early and use all the test time. Remember, passing mathematics is the best way to get a high-paying job and support yourself or your family.

Remember

There is no prize for handing your test in first, and some students who turn their papers in last make As.

Handing in your scratch paper with your math test has several advantages:

- If you miscopied an answer from the scratch paper, you will probably get credit for the problem.
- If you get the answer incorrect due to a careless error, your work on the scratch paper could give you a few points.
- If you do get the problem wrong, it will be easier to locate the errors when the instructor reviews the test. This will prevent you from making the same mistakes on the next math test.

Remember

Handing in your scratch paper may get you extra points or improve your next test score.

Section Review

1. List and explain the Ten Steps to Better Test Taking.

First Step: ____________________

____

Second Step: ____________________

____

Third Step: ____________________

____

Copyright © Houghton Mifflin Company. All rights reserved.

Fourth Step: ______________________________

____

Fifth Step: ______________________________

____

Sixth Step: ______________________________

____

Seventh Step: ______________________________

____

Eighth Step: ______________________________

____

Ninth Step: ______________________________

____

Tenth Step: ______________________________

____

2. After trying the Ten Steps to Better Test Taking, develop your own personalized test-taking steps.

First Step: ______________________________

Second Step: ______________________________

Third Step: ______________________________

Fourth Step: ______________________________

Fifth Step: ______________________________

Sixth Step: ______________________________

Seventh Step: ______________________________

Eighth Step: ______________________________

Ninth Step: ______________________________

Tenth Step: ______________________________

Additional steps: ______________________________

____

____

____

____

____

Copyright © Houghton Mifflin Company. All rights reserved.

The Six Types of Test-Taking Errors

To improve future test scores, you must conduct a test analysis of previous tests. In analyzing your tests, you should look for the following kinds of errors:

1. Misread-directions errors
2. Careless errors
3. Concept errors
4. Application errors
5. Test-taking errors
6. Study errors

Students who conduct math test analyses will improve their total test scores.

Misread-directions errors occur when you skip directions or misunderstand directions, but do the problem anyway.

> **Examples:** Suppose you have this type of problem to solve:
>
> $$(x + 1)(x + 1)$$
>
> Some students will try to solve for x, but the problem only calls for multiplication. You would solve for x only if you have an equation such as $(x + 1)(x + 1) = 0$.
>
> Another common mistake is not reading the directions before doing several word problems or statistical problems. All too often, when a test is returned, you find only three out of the five problems had to be completed. Even if you did get all five of them correct, it cost you valuable time that could have been used obtaining additional test points.

To avoid misread-directions errors, carefully read and interpret all the directions. Look for anything that is unusual, or if the directions have two parts. If you do not understand the directions, ask the instructor for clarification. If you feel uneasy about asking the instructor for interpretation of the question, remember the instructor in most cases does not want to test you on your interpretation of the question but how you answer it. Also, you don't want to make the mistake of assuming that the instructor will not interpret the question. Let the instructor make the decision to interpret the question, not you.

Careless errors are mistakes that you can catch automatically upon reviewing the test. Both good and poor math students make careless errors. Such errors can cost a student a higher letter grade on a test.

> **Examples:** *Dropping the sign:* $-3(2x) = 6x$, instead of $-6x$ which is the correct answer.
>
> *Not simplifying your answer:* Leaving $(3x - 12)/3$ as your answer instead of simplifying it to $x - 4$.
>
> *Adding fractions:* $1/2 + 1/3 = 2/5$, instead of $5/6$, which is the correct answer.
>
> *Word problems:* $x = 15$ instead of "The student had 15 tickets."

However, many students want all their errors to be careless errors. This means that the students did know the math, but simply made silly mistakes. In such cases, I ask the student to solve the problem immediately, while I watch.

If the student can solve the problem or point out his or her mistake in a few seconds, it is a careless error. If the student cannot find an error immediately, it is not a careless error and is probably a concept error.

When working with students who make careless errors, I ask them two questions. First, I ask, "How many points did you lose due to careless errors?" Then I follow with, "How much time was left in the class period when you handed in your test?" Students who lose test points due to careless errors are giving away points if they hand in their test papers before the test period ends.

To reduce careless errors, you must realize the types of careless errors that students make and recognize them when reviewing your test. If you cannot solve a missed problem immediately, it is not a careless error. If your major error is not simplifying answers, review each answer as if it were a new problem and try to reduce it.

Copyright © Houghton Mifflin Company. All rights reserved.

Concept errors are mistakes made when you do not understand the properties or principles required to work math problems. Concept errors, if not corrected, will follow you from test to test, causing a loss of test points.

> **Examples:** Some common concept errors are not knowing:
> - $(-)(-)x = x$, *not* $-x$
> - $1\ (2) > x(-1) = 2 < x$, *not* $2 > x$
> - $5/0$ is undefined, *not* 0
> - $(a + x)/x$ is *not* reduced to a
> - the order of operations

Concept errors must be corrected to improve your next math test score. Students who make numerous concept errors will fail the next test and the course if concepts are not understood. Just going back to rework a concept error problem is not good enough. You must go back to your textbook or notes and learn why you missed that type of problem, not just the one problem itself.

The best way to learn how to work the types of problems on which you tend to make concept errors is to set up a concept error problem page in the back of your notebook. Label the first page "Test One Concept Errors." Write down all your concept errors and how to solve the problems. Then, work five more problems that involve the same concept. Now, in your own words, write the concepts that you are using to solve these problems.

If you cannot write a concept in your own words, you do not understand it. Get assistance from your instructor if you need help finding similar problems using the same concept or if you cannot understand the concept. Do this for every test.

Application errors occur when you know a concept but cannot apply it to a problem. Application errors usually are found in word problems, deducing formulas (such as the Quadratic Formula), and graphing. Even some better students become frustrated with application errors; they understand the material but cannot apply it to problems.

To reduce application errors, you must predict the types of application problems that will be on the test. You must then think through and practice solving those types of problems using the appropriate concepts.

> **Example:** If you must derive the Quadratic Formula, you should practice doing it backwards and forwards while telling yourself the concept used to move from one step to the next.

Application errors are common with word problems. After completing a word problem, reread the question to make sure you have properly applied the answer to the intended question. Application errors can be avoided by appropriate practice and insight.

Test-taking errors apply to the specific way you take tests. Some students consistently make the same types of test-taking errors. Through recognition, these bad test-taking habits can be replaced by good test-taking habits. The result will be higher test scores. The list that follows includes the test-taking errors that can cause you to lose many points on an exam:

1. *Missing more questions in the first third, second third, or last third of a test* is considered a test-taking error.

   Missing more questions in the first third of a test can be due to carelessness when doing easy problems or due to test anxiety.

   Missing questions in the last third of the test can result from the fact that the last problems are more difficult than the earlier questions or from increasing your test speed to finish the test.

   If you consistently miss more questions in a certain part of the test, use your remaining test time to review that section of the test first. This means you may review the last part of your test first.

2. *Not completing a problem to its last step* is another test-taking error. If you have this bad habit, review the last step of each test problem first, before doing an in-depth test review.

3. *Changing test answers from correct ones to incorrect ones* is a problem for some students. Find out if you are a good or bad

Copyright © Houghton Mifflin Company. All rights reserved.

answer changer by comparing the numbers of answers you change to correct and to incorrect answers. If you are a bad answer changer, write on your test, "Don't change answers." Change answers only if you can prove to yourself or the instructor that the changed answer is correct.

4. *Getting stuck on one problem and spending too much time on it* is another test-taking error. You need to set a time limit on each problem before moving to the next problem. Working too long on a problem without success will increase your test anxiety and waste valuable time that could be used in solving other problems or in reviewing your test.

5. *Rushing through the easiest part of the test and making careless errors* is a common test-taking error for the better student. If you have the bad habit of getting more points taken off for the easy problems than for the hard problems, review the easy problems first, and the hard problems later.

6. *Miscopying an answer from your scratch paper to the test* is an uncommon test-taking error, but it does cost some students points. To avoid this kind of error, systematically compare your last problem step on scratch paper with the answer written on the test. In addition, always hand in your scratch paper with your test.

7. *Leaving answers blank* will get you zero points. If you look at a problem and cannot figure out how to solve it, do not leave it blank. Write down some information about the problem, rewrite the problem, or try to do at least the first step.

Remember

Writing down the first step of a problem is the key to solving the problem and obtaining partial credit.

8. *Solving only the first step of a two-step problem* causes some students to lose points. These students get so excited when answering the first step of the problem that they forget about the second step. This is especially true on two-step word problems. To correct this test-taking error, write "two" in the margin of the problem. That will remind you that there are two steps or two answers to this problem.

9. *Not understanding all the functions of your calculator* can cause major testing problems. Some students only barely learn how to use the critical calculator functions. They then forget or have to relearn how to use their calculators, which costs test points and test time. Do not wait to learn how to use your calculator during the test. Overlearn the use of your calculator before the test.

10. *Leaving the test early without checking all your answers* is a costly habit. Do not worry about the first person who finishes the test and leaves. Many students start to get nervous when students start to leave after finishing the test. This can lead to test anxiety, mental blocks, and loss of recall.

    According to research, the first students finishing the test do not always get the best grades. It sometimes is the exact opposite. Ignore the exiting students, and always use the full time allowed.

Make sure you follow the Ten Steps to Better Test Taking. Review your test taking procedures for discrepancies in following the ten steps. Deviating from these proven ten steps will cost you points.

Study errors, the last type of mistake to look for in test analysis, occur when you study the wrong type of material or do not spend enough time on pertinent material. Review your test to find out if you missed problems because you did not practice those types of problems or because you did practice them but forgot how to do them during the test. Study errors will take some time to track

Copyright © Houghton Mifflin Company. All rights reserved.

Figure 17 Math Test for Prealgebra

The answers are in boldface. The correct answers to missed questions are shaded. Identify the type of error based on the Six Types of Test-Taking Errors. The student's test score is 70.

1. Write in words: 32.685

   Thirty-two and six hundred eighty-five thousandths

2. Write as a fraction and simplify: 0.078

   $\mathbf{\frac{78}{1000}}$ $\quad$ $\mathbf{\frac{39}{500}}$ $\quad$ -2

3. Round to the nearest hundredth: 64.8653

   64.865 $\quad$ **64.87** $\quad$ -4

4. Combine like terms: $6.78x - 3.21 + 7.23x - 6.19$

   $\mathbf{= 6.78x + 7.23x + (-3.21) + (-6.19)}$

   $\mathbf{= 14.01x - 9.4}$

5. Divide and round to the nearest hundredth: $68.1357 \div 2.1$

   32.4454 → 32.45

6. Write as a decimal: $\frac{5}{16}$

   0.3125

7. Insert < or > to make a true statement:

   $\frac{3}{8} \quad < \quad \frac{6}{13}$

8. Solve: $\frac{3}{x} = \frac{9}{12}$ $\quad$ -2

   $9x = 3(12)$

   $\frac{x}{9} = \frac{36}{9}$

   $\mathbf{x = 5}$ $\quad$ $\mathbf{x = 4}$

9. What number is 35% of 60? $\quad$ -4

   2100 $\quad$ **21.00**

10. 20.8 is 40% of what number? $\quad$ -8

    52

11. 567 is what percent of 756?

    $\frac{756}{567} = \frac{9}{100}$ $\quad$ -8

    = 133.3% $\quad$ **75%**

12. Multiply: $\quad$ -2

    $(-6.03)(-2.31) = 13.9$ $\quad$ **13.9293**

down, but correcting study errors will help you on future tests.

If you are like most students, after analyzing one or several tests, you will recognize at least one major, common test-taking error. Understanding the effects of this test-taking error should change your study techniques or test-taking strategy.

> **Example:** If there are seven minutes left in the test, should you review for careless errors or try to answer those two problems you could not totally solve? This is a trick question. The real question is, do you miss more points due to careless errors or concept errors, or are the missed points about even? The answer to this question should determine how you will spend the final minutes of the test. If you miss more points due to careless errors or miss about the same number of points due to careless errors and concept errors, review for careless errors.

Careless errors are easier to correct than concept errors. However, if you make very few or no careless errors, you should be working on those last two problems to get the greatest number of test points. Knowing your test-taking errors can add more points to your test by changing your test-taking procedure.

Copyright © Houghton Mifflin Company. All rights reserved.

Answer Key for Prealgebra Test (Figure 17)

1. Correct
2. *Misread-directions error*—Forgot to simplify by reducing the fraction.
3. *Concept error*—Did not know that hundredths is two places to the right of the decimal.
4. Correct
5. Correct
6. Correct
7. Correct
8. Careless error—Divided incorrectly in the last step.
9. *Test-taking error*—Did not follow step 5 in test-taking steps: reviewing answers to see if they make sense. The number that equals 35% of 60 can't be larger than 60.
10. *Test-taking error*—Did not follow steps 7 and 8 in test-taking steps: don't leave an answer blank.
11. *Application error*—Solved the equation correctly but the equation setup was wrong.
12. *Concept error*—Did not know that when you multiply with one number in the hundredths, the answer must include the hundredths column.

Section Review

1. List the six types of test-taking errors.

   Type One: ____________________

   Type Two: ____________________

   Type Three: ____________________

   Type Four: ____________________

   Type Five: ____________________

   Type Six: ____________________

2. Which of these types of errors have you made in the past?

   ____

   ____

3. How can you avoid these types of errors on the next test?

   ____

   ____

4. Review the Math Test for Prealgebra (Figure 17) if you are in a prealgebra course. For each error, list the type of error, the points lost for the error, and a different example of that type of error.

   Error Type: ____________________ Points Lost for Error: ____________________

   Example of Error: ____________________

   Error Type: ____________________ Points Lost for Error: ____________________

   Example of Error: ____________________

Copyright © Houghton Mifflin Company. All rights reserved.

Error Type: ______________________ Points Lost for Error: ______________

Example of Error: ____

Error Type: ______________________ Points Lost for Error: ______________

Example of Error: ____

Error Type: ______________________ Points Lost for Error: ______________

Example of Error: ____

Error Type: ______________________ Points Lost for Error: ______________

Example of Error: ____

Error Type: ______________________ Points Lost for Error: ______________

Example of Error: ____

5. Review your last test and list the types of errors you made, the points lost for each error, and examples of the errors. You may have more errors than allowed for in the list below. Use a separate sheet of paper if you need to list more. (Remember: careless errors are problems you can solve immediately.)

Error Type: ______________________ Points Lost for Error: ______________

Problem With the Error in It: ____

Error Type: ______________________ Points Lost for Error: ______________

Problem With the Error in It: ____

Error Type: ______________________ Points Lost for Error: ______________

Problem With the Error in It: ____

Error Type: ______________________ Points Lost for Error: ______________

Problem With the Error in It: ____

Using the pages in the back of your math notebook, rework the problems on which you made concept errors and do five math problems just like each one. For each concept error, write why you could not solve the problem on the test and what new information you learned that allowed you to solve the problem. Do this for every major test. Give an example of one of your concept errors and the reasons why you can now solve the problem.

Concept Error: ____

Reasons Why I Can Now Solve the Problem: ______________________________

____

____

Copyright © Houghton Mifflin Company. All rights reserved.

How to Prepare for the Final Exam

The first day of class is when you start preparing for the final exam. Look at the syllabus or ask the instructor if the final exam is cumulative. A cumulative exam covers everything from the first chapter to the last chapter. Most math final exams are cumulative.

The second question you should ask is if the final exam is a departmental exam or if it is made up by your instructor. In most cases, departmental exams are more difficult and need a little different preparation. If you have a departmental final, you need to ask for last year's test and ask other students what their instructors say will be on the test.

The third question is how much the final exam will count. Does it carry the same weight as a regular test or, as in some cases, will it count as a third of your grade? If the latter is true, the final exam will usually make a letter grade difference in your final grade. The final exam could also determine if you pass or fail the course. Knowing this information before the final exam will help you prepare for it.

Preparing for the final exam is similar to preparing for each chapter test. You must create a pretest to discover what you have forgotten. You can use questions from the textbook chapter tests or questions from your study group.

Review the concept errors that you recorded in the back of your notebook labeled "Test One," "Test Two," and so on. Review your problem log for questions you consistently miss. Even review material that you knew for the first and second tests but that was not used on any other tests. Students forget how to work some of these problems.

If you do not have a concept error page for each chapter and did not keep a problem log, you need to develop a pretest before taking the final exam. If you are preparing for the final individually, then copy each chapter test and do every fourth problem to see what errors you may make. However, it is better to have a study group where each of the four members brings in ten problems with the answers worked out on a separate page. Then each group member can take a 30-question test made up from the problems brought in by the other group members to find out what they need to study. You can refer to the answers to help you solve the problems that you miss. Remember, that you want to find out what you don't know before the test, not during the test. Developing and using these methods before each test will improve your grades.

Make sure to use the Ten Steps to Better Test Taking and the information gained from your test analysis. Use all the time on the final exam, because you could improve your final grade by a full letter if you make an A on the final.

Section Review

What are the three questions you need to ask about your final exam?

First Question: ______________________________

Second Question: ______________________________

Third Question: ______________________________

Copyright © Houghton Mifflin Company. All rights reserved.

Dan's Take

The moment the professor hands out a math test, everyone dives in, frantically jotting down answers as fast as they can. The first few questions are easy, giving the test takers a false sense of security heading into the second page. At this point, those who know what they are doing begin to surge ahead, panicking their neighbors and pressuring them to hurry through their tests to keep up.

Then the first person finishes, and one by one, those taking their time watch their classmates leave. The few students that remain are left with a sense of failure before they even turn in their tests.

I don't understand why college students believe that a test is a race. Everyone knows that those who finish first don't always score the highest. But for some reason, we still feel the need to avoid the dreaded "last person to finish" label.

Math and speed do not mix well together. In fact, trying to finish a test quickly often causes mistakes. Even if you know the steps, a small error can make you get a question wrong. It might be that you just carried a number incorrectly. These mistakes happen when you rush through a test.

In high school I often fell into this trap. I would study and prepare for a test, and then be shocked when I got a C. Everything changed when I realized that I didn't need to be the first person out the door after a test. By taking my time, I was able to catch all the little mistakes that were making me lose points.

It is very important that you not feel pressured during a math test. When people finish before you, ignore them. What's the big deal? It's not fair to measure yourself by how quickly those around you work. Instead of worrying about getting things done quickly, worry about getting things done correctly.

Copyright © Houghton Mifflin Company. All rights reserved.

Name: ______________________________ Date: ______________

Chapter 7 Review

1. You should start studying for a test at least ______________ days ahead of time.
2. You should be reviewing only the material you have ______________ the night before the test.
3. When previewing a test, put a ______________ by each question you can solve without thinking, and do those problems ______________.
4. When taking a test, you must decide the best way to get the ______________ points in the ______________ amount of time.
5. Halfway through the test, you should have ______________ than half of the problems completed.
6. If you cannot write down the first step of a problem, you should ______________ the problem to help you remember how to solve it.
7. Do not leave the test room until you have reviewed each problem ______________ times or until the bell rings.
8. In reviewing your test, if you cannot find an error immediately (within a few seconds), it is not a ______________ error and is probably a ______________ error.
9. Students who make numerous ______________ errors will fail the next test and the course if the ______________ are not understood.
10. The ______________ day of class is when you start preparing for the final exam.

What is the most important information you learned from this chapter?

____

____

____

How can you immediately use it?

____

____

____

Copyright © Houghton Mifflin Company. All rights reserved.

Appendix

Math Autobiography

The purpose of your math autobiography is to reflect on your past experiences when learning math, how they made you feel then, and how these experiences and feelings shape how you feel about your current math classes. It will close with solutions to help you improve your experiences in math classes.

The following writing process will simplify this task while improving the final paper.

1. Use the questions from Chapter 3 on types of math anxiety and causes of math anxiety to brainstorm ideas for your paper. Record these answers.
2. Next to each experience you record, write how the experience made you feel.
3. To further your brainstorming, complete the following sentences:

   My favorite math instructor was ______________________________

   because he/she ______________________________

   I always felt ______________________________

   One math instructor who bothered me was ______________________________

   because he/she ______________________________

   I always felt ______________________________

   When I hear the word *math*, I think of

   ____

   I did well in math until ______________________________

   The first time I experienced math anxiety was when ______________________________

   The first time I was anxious before or during a math test was when ______________________________

   The most recent time I was anxious about math class was when ______________________________

   ____

   The most recent time I was anxious before or during a test was when ______________________________

   ____

4. Since an autobiography is in chronological order, identify the important pieces of information in your brainstorming and place them into the correct time categories in the tables on the following pages. These tables will help create the outline for your paper.

5. You will write the introduction last, after you have thought through the meaning of your experiences. Then, when you write the final paper, you will place the introduction paragraph first.

Elementary School Main Paragraph One	
Experiences	Feelings
As a result of these experiences, now when I am in math class, studying math, or taking a math test, I ...	

Middle School Main Paragraph Two	
Experiences	Feelings
As a result of these experiences, now when I am in math class, studying math, or taking a math test, I ...	

Copyright © Houghton Mifflin Company. All rights reserved.

High School Main Paragraph Three	
Experiences	Feelings
As a result of these experiences, now when I am in math class, studying math, or taking a math test, I ...	

College and/or Work Experience Main Paragraph Four (If this applies)	
Experiences	Feelings
As a result of these experiences, now when I am in math class, studying math, or taking a math test, I ...	

Copyright © Houghton Mifflin Company. All rights reserved.

Conclusion Paragraph

When I look back on my experiences learning or using math, I understand why I have developed attitudes like

____

____

____

____

To develop a more positive perspective toward math, I need to improve certain behaviors.

Behaviors	**Solutions for Change**
1.	
2.	
3.	
4.	

As a result, I will...

____

____

____

Introduction Paragraph

(When you write your final paper, this paragraph will be first. This paragraph should introduce the main lesson you have learned through this activity. Look at what you have written for your conclusion paragraph for some ideas.)

____

____

____

____

____

____

6. Now, using the tables as your outline, complete the final paper to be turned in to your instructor.

Copyright © Houghton Mifflin Company. All rights reserved.

Key Words/Rules	Examples	Explanations

Copyright © Houghton Mifflin Company. All rights reserved.

Key Words/Rules	Examples	Explanations

Copyright © Houghton Mifflin Company. All rights reserved.

Careers and Mathematics

What are your reasons for attending college? I asked this question to math students and what do you think was the most common response? You're right! Most students said they are going to college to make more money. So does taking more math mean you can get a higher-paying career? Look at the graph below, which lists the most in-demand careers and the highest mathematics requirement for that major—and use your number sense!

Best Jobs Requiring a Bachelor's Degree*

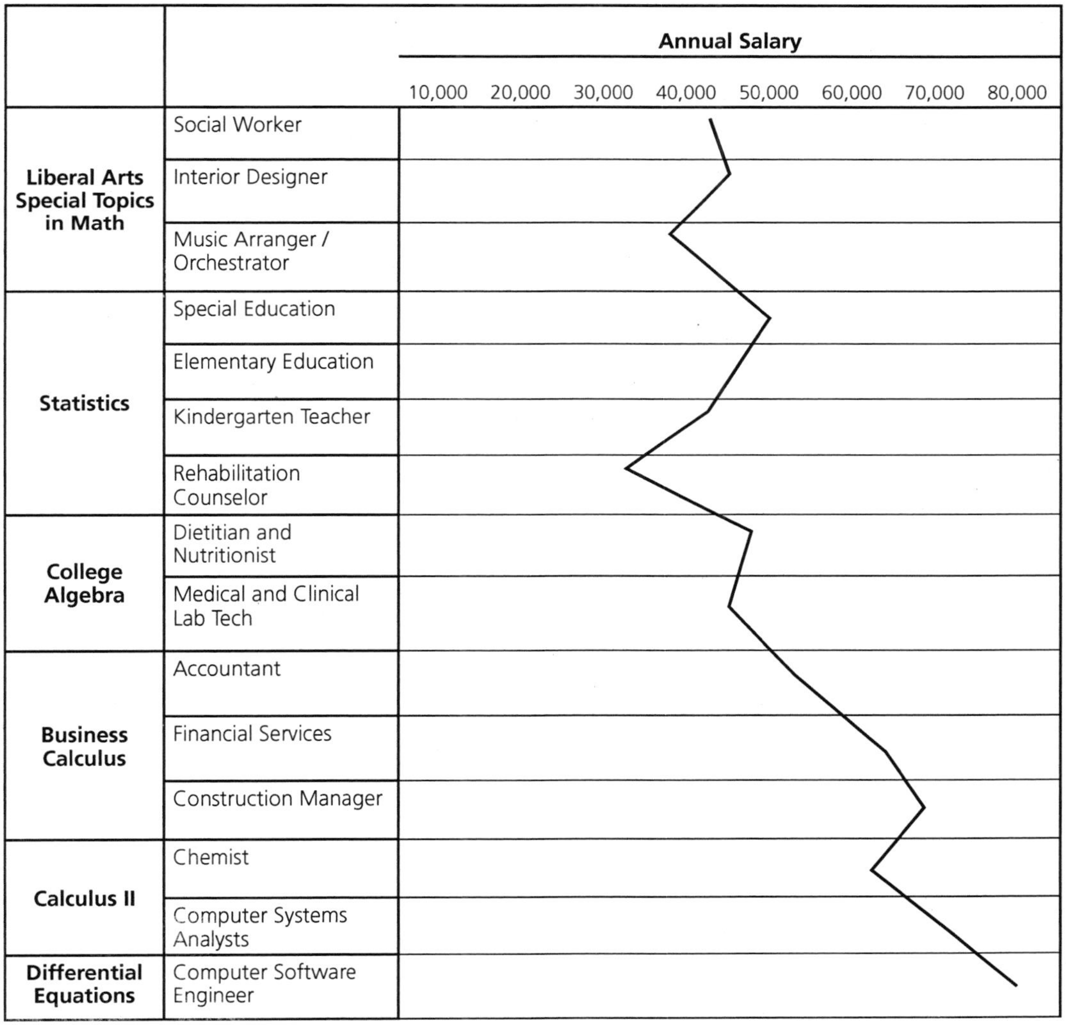

*Best Jobs for the 21st Century, Third Edition © JIST Works, 2004.

Copyright © Houghton Mifflin Company. All rights reserved.

Bibliography

Bloom, B. (1976). *Human characteristics and school learning.* New York: McGraw-Hill Book Company.

Cattell, R. B. (1966). The screen test for the number of factors. *Multivariate behavioral research*, *1*, 245–276.

Ellis, D. (2006). *Becoming a master student* (11th ed.). Boston: Houghton Mifflin Company, 309.

Farr, F. & Ludden, L. (2004). *Best jobs for the 21st century*. Indianapolis: JIST Publishing, Inc.

Fox, L. H. (1977). *Women and mathematics: Research perspective for change.* Washington D.C.: National Institute of Education.

Jessee D. (1997). In *Winning at math: Your guide to learning mathematics through successful study skills*. Bradenton, FL: Academic Success Press, Inc.

McCarthy, B. (1981). *The 4-Mat system: Teaching to learning styles with right/left mode techniques.* Barrington, IL: Excel.

Nolting, P. D. (1987). *How to reduce test anxiety* [cassette]. Bradentown, FL: Academic Success Press.

Richardson, F. C. & Suinn, R.M. (1973). A comparison of traditional systematic desensitization, accelerated mass desensitization, and math anxiety. *Behavior Therapy, 4*, 212–218.

Suinn, R.M. (1988). Mathematics anxiety rating scale (MARS). Fort Collins, CO: RMBSI, Inc.

Tobias, S. (1976). Why is a smart girl like you counting on your fingers? *Ms., 5*, 76–79.

Tobias, S. (1978). Who's afraid of math and why? *Atlantic Monthly*, September, 63–65.

Wolpe, J. (1958). *Psychotherapy by reciprocal inhibition.* Stanford, CA: Stanford University Press.

About the Author

Dr. Paul D. Nolting

Over the past twenty years, Learning Specialist Paul Nolting has helped thousands of students improve their math learning and obtain better grades. As a national expert, Dr. Nolting is a consultant for numerous universities and colleges, helping students and faculty improve learning experiences in math. He is also a consultant for many universities on math and learning disabilities, and is a former consultant for state education agencies such as the Texas Higher Education Coordinating Board. Dr. Nolting has presented national video conferences on PBS on topics such as math study skills and learning styles.

Dr. Nolting holds a Ph.D. in education from the University of South Florida. His dissertation was "The Effects of Counseling and Study Skills Training on Mathematics Academic Achievement." He is an adjunct instructor for the University of South Florida, teaching assessment and appraisal courses at the graduate level.

Dr. Nolting has been a workshop presenter for Houghton Mifflin faculty development programs for many years, and he is a frequent presenter and guest speaker at regional and national conferences, workshops, and conventions. He has been widely acclaimed for his focus on math success and ability to communicate with both faculty and students.

The National Association of Independent Publishers selected his book, *Winning at Math: Your Guide to Learning Mathematics Through Successful Study Skills,* as Book of the Year. "The strength of the book is the way the writer leads a reluctant student through a course, from choosing a teacher to preparing for the final examination," says *Mathematics Teacher,* a publication of the National Council of Teachers of Mathematics. *Winning at Math* and Dr. Nolting's other titles are available at http://www.academicsuccess.com.

Dr. Nolting's two audiocassettes, *How to Reduce Test Anxiety* and *How to Ace Tests* were also award winners in the National Association of Independent Publishers competition. "Dr. Nolting," says *Publisher's Report,* "is an innovative and outstanding educator and learning specialist."

Major Contributors

Kimberly Nolting

Over the past ten years, Kimberly Nolting has worked with many students to develop productive learning behaviors that improve their college experiences. She is a consultant for Retention Management Planning; is an experienced workshop presenter at conferences and universities, focusing on student engagement, teaching, and learning in Developmental Education; and is currently completing her Ph.D. dissertation in psycho-social factors and math course completion. Kimberly is also an editor for Academic Success Press, Inc., and the author of *Navigating College: Strategy Manual for a Successful Journey.*

Daniel Crown

Dan is a recent college graduate from Oklahoma Christian University. As a gifted writer and journalism major, Dan was the sports editor for his college newspaper. In this new edition of the *Math Study Skills Workbook,* Dan provides real student experiences and perspectives in each chapter. Dan also assisted with the editing of Dr. Nolting's *Winning at Math.*

Copyright © Houghton Mifflin Company. All rights reserved.

Research on Mathematics Learning

Dr. Paul Nolting and Kimberly Nolting present their research and other research articles on successful practices to improve math success at www.academicsuccess.com. The research is on math study skills, learning styles, student engagement, test anxiety, and instruction. The research articles are a more in-depth look at how math study skills, learning styles, and student engagement can influence math success. Students and faculty alike can benefit from visiting this site.

Books and Materials by Academic Success Press, Kimberly Nolting and Dr. Paul Nolting

How to Ace Tests. Academic Success Press, 1987.

How to Reduce Test Anxiety. Academic Success Press, 1987. (audiocassette)

How to Develop Your Own Math Study Skills Workshop and Course. Academic Success Press, 1991.

Math and the Learning Disabled Student: A Practical Guide for Accommodations. Academic Success Press, 1991.

Math and Students with Learning Disabilities: A Practical Guide to Course Substitutions. Academic Success Press, 1993.

Navigating College: Strategy Manual for a Successful Journey. Kimberly Nolting. Academic Success Press, 2006.

Strategy Cards for Higher Grades. Academic Success Press, 1989. (card deck)

Winning at Math — Computer Evaluation Software. Academic Success Press.

Winning at Math: Your Guide to Learning Mathematics Through Successful Study Skills. Academic Success Press, 1997.

Ordering Information

For ordering information on *Winning at Math* and other books and learning materials listed above or additional downloadable study and tutor aids, call toll free: 1-800-247-6553 or visit www.academicsuccess.com. Credit card, checks, and purchase orders are accepted. For a free catalog, call (941) 359-2819.

Copyright © Houghton Mifflin Company. All rights reserved.

Index

Copyright © Houghton Mifflin Company. All rights reserved.

Copyright © Houghton Mifflin Company. All rights reserved.